The Chemistry

of

Synthetic Dyes and Pigments

Edited by

H. A. Lubs

Organic Chemicals Department

E. I. DuPont de Nemours & Company

American Chemical Society
Monograph Series

BOOK DIVISION

REINHOLD PUBLISHING CORPORATION

430 Park Avenue, New York

1955

Copyright 1955 by

REINHOLD PUBLISHING CORPORATION

———

Library of Congress Catalog Card Number 54–12433

Printed in U.S.A.
by WAVERLY PRESS, INC.
BALTIMORE, MARYLAND

GENERAL INTRODUCTION

American Chemical Society's Series of Chemical Monographs

By arrangement with the Interallied Conference of Pure and Applied Chemistry, which met in London and Brussels in July, 1919, the American Chemical Society was to undertake the production and publication of Scientific and Technologic Monographs on chemical subjects. At the same time it was agreed that the National Research Council, in cooperation with the American Chemical Society and the American Physical Society, should undertake the production and publication of Critical Tables of Chemical and Physical Constants. The American Chemical Society and the National Research Council mutually agreed to care for these two fields of chemical progress. The American Chemical Society named as Trustees, to make the necessary arrangements of the publication of the Monographs, Charles L. Parsons, secretary of the Society, Washington, D. C.; the late John E. Teeple, then treasurer of the Society, New York; and the late Professor Gellert Alleman of Swarthmore College. The trustees arranged for the publication of the ACS Series of (a) Scientific and (b) Technological Monographs by the Chemical Catalog Company, Inc. (Reinhold Publishing Corporation, successor) of New York.

The Council of the American Chemical Society, acting through its Committee on National Policy, appointed editors (the present list of whom appears at the close of this sketch) to select authors of competent authority in their respective fields and to consider critically the manuscripts submitted.

The first Monograph of the Series appeared in 1921. After twenty-three years of experience certain modifications of general policy were indicated. In the beginning there still remained from the preceding five decades a distinct though arbitrary differentiation between so-called "pure science" publications and technologic or applied science literature. By 1944 this differentiation was fast becoming nebulous. Research in private enterprise had grown apace and not a little of it was pursued on the frontiers of knowledge. Furthermore, most workers in the sciences were coming to see the artificiality of the separation. The methods of both groups of workers are the same. They employ the same instrumentalities, and frankly recognize that their objectives are common, namely, the search for new knowledge for the service of man. The officers of the Society therefore combined the two editorial Boards in a single Board of twelve representative members.

Also in the beginning of the Series, it seemed expedient to construe rather broadly the definition of a Monograph. Needs of workers had to be recognized. Consequently among the first hundred Monographs appeared works in the form of treatises covering in some instances rather broad areas. Because such necessary works do not now want for publishers, it is considered advisable to hew more strictly to the line of the Monograph character, which means more complete and critical treatment of relatively restricted areas, and, where a broader field needs coverage, to subdivide it into logical subareas. The prodigious expansion of new knowledge makes such a change desirable.

These Monographs are intended to serve two principal purposes: first, to make available to chemists a thorough treatment of a selected area in form usable by persons working in more or less unrelated fields to the end that they may correlate their own work with a larger area of physical science discipline; second, to stimulate further research in the specific field treated. To implement this purpose the authors of Monographs are expected to give extended references to the literature. Where the literature is of such volume that a complete bibliography is impracticable, the authors are expected to append a list of references critically selected on the basis of their relative importance and significance.

PREFACE

When Mauve, the first man-made dye, was discovered in England by William Perkin in 1856, followed by the erection in 1857 of a factory for its production, no one dreamed of the far-reaching influence of these events on world history during the next century. The dye industry catalyzed the development of the general synthetic organic chemical industry in England, France, and Germany, and more recently in the United States. Had Germany not lost its leadership in the field and had not England and America grown strong since 1914, the course of world history would have been entirely different.

This book was born as a result of two world wars. World War I brought about the cessation of dye imports from Germany, and thus there came a near-paralysis of the textile and other important industries. As a result, there was established an American dye industry with the consequent development of a large number of chemists and engineers thoroughly versed in the chemistry and technology of this difficult and complicated field. From this situation came the Jackson Laboratory of the Du Pont Company—today one of the world's largest laboratories of industrial chemical research.

All nineteen of the contributors to this Monograph have been on the staff of this laboratory. Each contributor has spent the major portion of his scientific life in the field of dyes or intermediates, and each has had from twelve to forty years' experience in his chosen field. It is this broad background that makes possible the selectivity we have striven for. These authoritative specialists have illustrated their discussions of dye and pigment chemistry with examples chosen for historical or chemical interest, or because of their usefulness in the American economy. In many cases, a single dye is cited to typify a class or group of related products, since the accent is on chemistry rather than complete tabulation. No attempt whatsoever is made to treat the subject in an encyclopedic manner. For those who wish more detailed or comprehensive information, the abundant and carefully selected literature references will be of great value.

Prior to World War II, the processes and practices of the dye and organic chemical manufacturers were, for the most part, closely guarded secrets. After the Allied occupation of Germany, various governmental missions collected and published for general information virtually all of the important processes developed by the German chemical industry. The availability of this information was an important factor in facilitating the preparation of this Monograph. We have drawn heavily on the FIAT and

BIOS reports. The disclosures in these reports are spread through many documents and are often difficult to find and interpret without the proper background and experience. The editor believes the various contributors have rendered an invaluable service to other investigators by a judicious selection from these reports and by the inclusion of abundant references on important processes and products.

The discovery and development of the phthalocyanine pigments is perhaps the greatest advance in the dye field during the past generation. The outstandingly bright and fast blue and green phthalocyanine pigments have already found extensive use in industry, particularly in paints, paper, textiles, and plastics, and their use is constantly growing. For these reasons we have tried to discuss all the important chemistry and include all pertinent literature references bearing on this relatively new and highly important development.

Just as we saw in 1914 the development of the very important alkyd resin field from an old dye intermediate, phthalic anhydride, we some years later witnessed the production of two remarkable new products—Dacron polyester fiber and Mylar polyester film—from terephthalic acid. Today we are just beginning to develop wide uses for isocyanates based on well-known and old aromatic diamines previously used only for dye syntheses. The possibilities for the production of new plastics, elastomers, finishes, textile treating agents, and pharmaceuticals from the isocyanates almost stagger the imagination.

These few examples are cited to illustrate how important it is to maintain a strong dye industry so that there will continue to be a full reservoir of organic chemical products as a basis for future important developments. It should be abundantly clear both to the layman and the scientist that this is indispensable to the nation's further growth, prosperity, health, and security. The impact of the chemical industry on our academic life is strikingly shown by the fact that in 1914 there were only 71 Ph.D.'s in chemistry granted in the United States, whereas in 1953 there were 1,164, and the demand is ever increasing.

Those of us who participated in the preparation of this Monograph were largely motivated by a desire to contribute something to lighten the task of training the scientists and technical men of tomorrow, and to repay in part our debt to those who in years gone by, at home and abroad, developed the fundamental scientific information on which the modern chemical industry is based. Perhaps this book will serve to stimulate greater activity in the field and encourage the maintenance of a strong and dynamic organic chemical industry, which is so essential to the welfare of America.

H. A. Lubs

Wilmington, Delaware
January 15, 1955

ACKNOWLEDGMENT

To Professor A. H. Corwin, of the Johns Hopkins University, and to Dr. L. G. S. Brooker, of the Eastman Kodak Company, I am greatly indebted for the painstaking and critical review of several chapters. To my past and present associates at the Jackson Laboratory, I am grateful for the hearty cooperation and the care and thoroughness with which they have prepared their various sections and chapters. Especial thanks are due Dr. Otto Stallmann and Dr. C. W. Maynard, Jr., for they, in addition to the preparation of their respective chapters, have given me invaluable assistance in editorial detail. Without their help, this Monograph would have been much longer in preparation.

This acknowledgment would be incomplete indeed without recognition of the sympathetic encouragement of the management of the Organic Chemicals Department of the Du Pont Company. Were it not for the department's broad publication policy and its desire to aid education, a volume such as this would not have been possible.

H. A. Lubs

CONTENTS

	Page
PREFACE	v
1. BENZENE INTERMEDIATES	1
The Benzene Aromatic System	1
Sulfonation	3
Nitration	12
Halogenation	17
Alkylation	30
Introduction of Formyl and Carboxy Groups	33
Hydroxylation	37
Reactions with Ammonia	38
Oxidation	42
Reduction	46
Heterocyclic Intermediates	51
2. NAPHTHALENE INTERMEDIATES	65
Sulfonation	67
Nitration	71
Halogenation	73
Hydroxylation	75
Amination	76
Naphthalenesulfonic Acids	77
Naphthols	79
Naphthylamines	82
Aminonaphthols	82
Aminonaphthalenesulfonic Acids	83
Aminonaphtholsulfonic Acids	88
3-Hydroxy-2-naphthoic Acid	90
3. AZO DYES	96
Mechanisms of the Diazotization and the Azo Coupling Reactions	97
The Diazotization Reaction	97
The Azo Coupling Reaction	101
Conclusion	109
Azo Dyes for Cotton	111
Theory of Cotton Dyeing	112
Early Cotton Dyes	113
Benzidine Dyes	114

Page

Stilbene Dyes.. 119
After-treated Dyes.................................. 121
Dyes from Aminonaphtholsulfonic Acids.............. 123
Dyes from Heterocyclic and Acyclic Intermediates..... 133
Dyes Discovered Since 1915......................... 134
Azo Dyes for Wool.................................. 143
Early Wool Dyes 143
Acid Dyes.. 144
Neutral-dyeing or Milling Dyes..................... 151
Chrome Dyes..................................... 153
Premetallized Dyes............................... 161
Disperse Azo Dyes.................................. 167
Monoazo Dyes.................................... 168
Disazo Dyes...................................... 171
Water-soluble Dyes............................... 172
Developed Dyes................................... 172
Solvent-soluble Dyes............................... 174
Oil-soluble Dyes.................................. 174
Spirit-soluble Dyes............................... 177
Food Dyes....................................... 178
4. AZOIC DYES... 181
Dyeing by Impregnation............................ 182
Coupling Components.............................. 182
Diazotizable Amines (Azoic Bases).................. 193
Relation of Properties to Structure.................. 194
Stable Diazonium Salts............................ 208
Printing Compositions.............................. 208
Diazotates....................................... 208
Triazenes.. 217
Diazosulfonates.................................. 221
Temporarily Solubilized Pigments.................. 224
5. MISCELLANEOUS DYES................................ 228
Acridine Dyes..................................... 231
Azine Dyes.. 235
Ketone Imine Dyes................................. 245
Metallized Azomethine Dyes........................ 247
Methine Dyes...................................... 248
Nitro Dyes.. 254
Nitroso Dyes...................................... 258
Oxazine Dyes...................................... 259
Quinoline Dyes.................................... 261

Page

p-Quinone Imine Dyes................................. 263
Thiazine Dyes....................................... 266
Thiazole Dyes....................................... 269
Triarylmethane Dyes................................. 272
Triphenodioxazine Dyes.............................. 288
Xanthene Dyes...................................... 291
6. SULFUR DYES... **302**
Structure... 303
Manufacture.. 305
The Sulfur Bake................................... 305
The Polysulfide Bake.............................. 306
Solvent Thionation................................ 307
After-treatments.................................. 308
Properties.. 308
Physical Properties................................ 308
Chemical Properties............................... 309
Applications.. 312
Commercial Products................................ 312
Dyes from Aliphatic Compounds.................... 312
Dyes from Aromatic Hydrocarbons................. 313
Dyes from Phenols................................ 313
Dyes from Aromatic Amines........................ 316
Dyes from Aminophenols.......................... 317
Dyes from Indophenols............................ 321
Dyes from Heterocyclic Compounds................. 327
7. ANTHRAQUINONE DYES AND INTERMEDIATES.................. **335**
Anthraquinone Intermediates......................... 337
Reactivity.. 337
Routes to Anthraquinone Compounds................ 338
Haloanthraquinones............................... 345
Nitroanthraquinones.............................. 350
Anthraquinonesulfonic Acids....................... 352
Anthraquinonecarbo Derivatives.................... 356
Aminoanthraquinones............................. 359
Hydroxyanthraquinones........................... 367
Anthraquinone Ethers............................. 369
Anthraquinonethiols and Thioethers................ 372
Leuco Intermediates............................... 372
Benzanthrones.................................... 377
Anthraquinone Acid Dyes............................ 390
Sulfonic Acids.................................... 393

Page

Dihydroxy Compounds. 397
Diamino Compounds. 400
Aminohydroxy Compounds. 406
Heterocyclic Dyes. 408
Anthrimides and Naphthocarbazoles. 409
Bromamine Acid Derivatives. 412
Disperse Dyes. 417
Yellow to Orange Structures. 419
Red Structures. 419
Violet Structures. 420
Blue to Green Structures. 421
Fused Ring Derivatives. 421
Water-soluble Dyes. 423
Commercial Products. 424
Metallizable Dyes. 426
Vat Dyes. 431
Carbocyclic Dyes. 432
Benzoquinones and Naphthoquinones. 432
Acylaminoanthraquinones. 434
Benzanthraquinones and Pyrenediones. 442
Anthanthrones. 444
Dibenzopyrenediones. 446
Pyranthrones. 450
Dibenzanthrones. 453
Other Related Dyes. 457
Five-membered Heterocyclic Dyes. 460
Anthraquinonecarbazoles. 460
Anthrapyrazolones. 468
Anthraquinoneoxazoles, Thiazoles, Imidazoles. 472
Other Related Dyes. 478
Six-membered Heterocyclic Dyes. 481
Pyridines and Pyridones. 481
Benzanthroneacridines. 483
Flavanthrone. 486
Anthraquinoneacridones. 487
Anthrapyrimidines. 508
Pyrazines. 511
Anthraquinoneazines. 512
Thiapyrans and Thiaxanthones. 524
Other Related Dyes. 529
Solubilized Vat Dyes. 534
Other Vat Dyes. 548

Page

8. INDIGOID DYES.. **551**
    2,2'-Bisindole Dyes................................... 553
    2,3'-Bisindole Dyes................................... 561
    2,2'-Bisthianaphthene Dyes........................... 562
    2'-Indole-2-thianaphthene Dyes....................... 569
    3'-Indole-2-thianaphthene Dyes....................... 572
    1'-Acenaphthene-2-indole Dyes........................ 572
    1'-Acenaphthene-2-thianaphthene Dyes................. 573
    2'-Arene-2-indole Dyes............................... 573
    2'-Arene-2-thianaphthene Dyes........................ 575
9. PHTHALOCYANINE PIGMENTS............................... **577**
    Structure.. 579
    Properties... 581
    Synthesis.. 584
    Application.. 587
    Unsubstituted Phthalocyanines........................ 590
    Substituted Phthalocyanines.......................... 596
10. PHTHALOCYANINE DYES.................................. **607**
    Phthalocyanine Direct Dyes........................... 608
        Sulfonic Acids................................... 609
        Sulfonic Acid Derivatives........................ 611
        Carboxylic Acids................................. 612
        Other Direct Dyes............................... 616
    Aminophthalocyanines................................. 618
    Phthalocyanine Vat Dyes.............................. 619
    Phthalocyanine Sulfur Dyes........................... 622
    Phthalocyanine Formation in the Fiber................ 622
11. ORGANIC PIGMENTS.................................... **625**
    Chemically Quasi-neutral Compounds................... 631
        Nitro Compounds.................................. 631
        Azo Compounds.................................... 632
        Polynuclear Compounds............................ 637
    Chemically Reactive Compounds........................ 638
        Cationic Derivatives............................. 638
        Anionic Derivatives.............................. 642
            Nitroso Compounds............................ 643
            Nitro Compounds.............................. 645
            Azo Compounds............................... 645
            Triarylmethane Derivatives................... 652
            Quinoline Derivatives........................ 654
            Xanthene Derivatives......................... 654

Page

     Anthraquinone Derivatives........................ 655
     Phthalocyanines................................. 657
12. COLOR AND CHEMICAL CONSTITUTION OF DYES.............. **662**
     Basic Concepts.................................. 662
     Conjugation of Chromophores....................... 663
     Auxochromes.................................... 670
     Steric Hindrance................................ 674
     Effects of Environment........................... 675
     The Colors of Azo Dyes........................... 677
     The Colors of Quinonoid Dyes...................... 680
     Dyes Containing Metal Atoms....................... 685
     Summary....................................... 686
13. COMMON NAMES OF DYE INTERMEDIATES.................... **689**
14. CRITICAL BIBLIOGRAPHY................................ **692**
     BIOS and FIAT Reports............................ 692
     References in Chapter Sequence..................... 693
     General References............................... 700
DYE INDEX... **703**
SUBJECT INDEX... **711**

1. BENZENE INTERMEDIATES

A. C. Stevenson

THE BENZENE AROMATIC SYSTEM

There are three types of reactions involving substitution of the hydrogen atoms of the benzene nucleus which differ in the nature of the attacking reagent. The three types of attacking reagents are: (1) electrophilic (electron accepting), (2) nucleophilic (electron donating) and (3) free radical. A number of familiar reagents belonging in these respective classes are as follows: (R = alkyl or H).

Electrophilic	Nucleophilic	Free Radical
Cl^+		$F\cdot$
	^-OH	$Cl\cdot$
Br^+	$^-OCH_3$	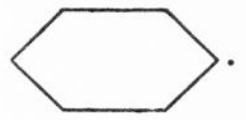
NO_2^+	$^-NR_2$	
SO_3H^+	^-SR	
RN^+ $\overset{\|\|\|}{N}$	^-CN	

The electrophilic reagent is deficient in electrons. It reacts with the aromatic nucleus at a point of high electron density and establishes a bond by sharing an electron pair, both the electrons making up the bond having been contributed by the aromatic nucleus. After the initial fusion of the attacking group to the activated aromatic nucleus, the reaction is completed by the discharge of a proton and a return of the molecule from an unstable intermediate compound to a stable state.

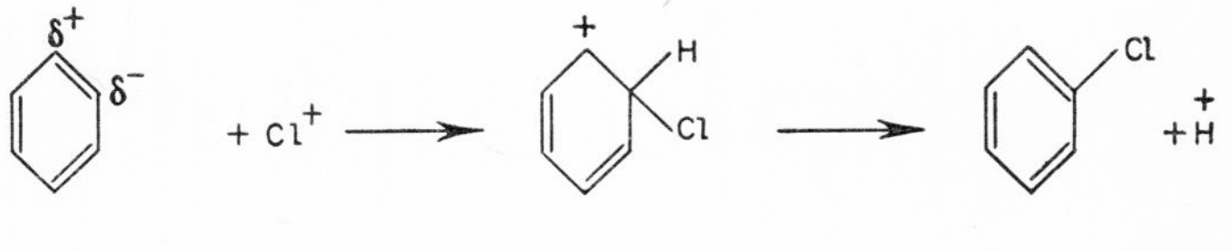

1

The greater majority of the familiar reactions involving direct substitution on the aromatic hydrocarbon fall into this category.

Nucleophilic substitution is concerned usually with the reaction of a substituted aromatic nucleus with a reagent possessing an unshared electron pair. In nucleophilic substitution hydrogen is seldom replaced. The replaced groups are ordinarily halogen atoms or other groups possessing reasonable stability as anions. Most practical applications involve replacement of groups which are activated through other substituents in the aromatic nucleus. The reaction is completed by withdrawal of the anion from the unstable intermediate compound. When hydrogen is replaced, the use of oxidizing agents facilitates the change through reaction with the liberated proton and excess electrons. The nucleophilic reagent attacks the aromatic system at a point of low electron density corresponding to positions which are unreactive to the more familiar electrophilic reagents. The familiar meta-directing groups for the electrophilic substitution are ortho- and para-directing in the case of nucleophilic substitution. Conversely the ortho- and para-directing groups of the electrophilic reagents become meta-directing for nucleophilic substitution. Thus the nitro group in the following example directs the attacking nucleophilic group (:OH) to the ortho position.

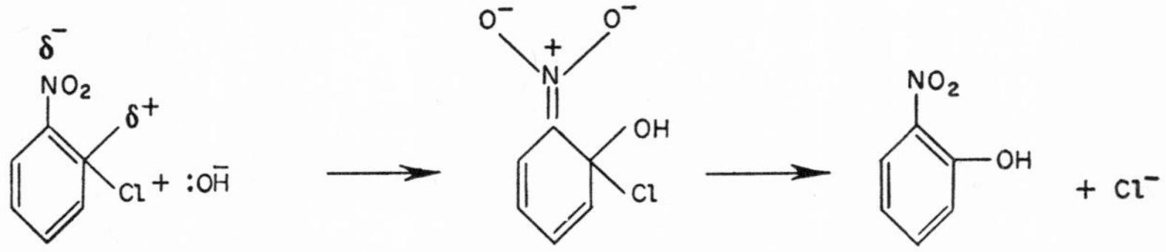

The nucleophilic reagent may be either a charged particle or a neutral molecule, e.g., ammonia; its distinguishing characteristic is its unshared electron pair. Nucleophilic substitution is involved in many common substitution reactions, e.g., replacement of halogen with ammonia, amines, alkoxides, hydroxy ions, and thiolates. Likewise, under proper conditions, nitro, sulfo, alkoxy, and hydroxy groups are replaced with nucleophilic reagents.

The free radical type of reaction may be illustrated with the reaction of the free phenyl radical (resulting from the decomposition of benzoyl peroxide) with nitrobenzene to give a mixture of 2- and 4-nitrobiphenyl[44].

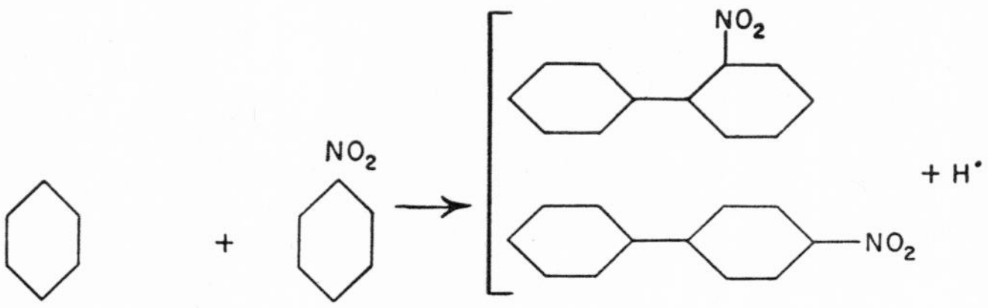

Orientation Effects

Unquestionably orientation effects stem from relative reactivities (electron availability) of the different positions of the substituted aromatic nucleus.

Meta-directing groups for the electrophilic reagent are electron seeking in nature. They tend to decrease the electron density in the aromatic nucleus, making it less susceptible to attack by electron seeking reagents. While there is a general deadening through this inductive effect, there is a localization of this deactivation at the ortho and para positions through mesomeric effects (resonance). As a result, the meta position is relatively more reactive. It is pointed out that while this is the more reactive position, it is appreciably less reactive than the parent nucleus, e.g., the nitration of nitrobenzene requires more vigorous reaction conditions than are required for nitrating benzene.

Ortho- and para-directing groups, with the exception of the halogens, tend to release electrons in the direction of the aromatic nucleus. This tends to increase the electron density in the nucleus with the result that it is more susceptible to attack by electron seeking reagents. In addition to this general activation by induction, the ortho and para positions are activated further by mesomeric effects, hence they become the preferred positions for the attacking cation. In this case, the nucleus is more reactive than the parent substance.

The nucleophilic reagent attacks the substituted aromatic nucleus in a manner exactly opposite from the electrophilic reagent. Negative groups, e.g., nitro groups, direct the nucleophilic reagent ortho and para while the positive groups orient the nucleophilic reagent meta.

Whereas the ortho and para positions are relatively the more reactive positions in a positively substituted aromatic nucleus, the meta position is more reactive also than the unsubstituted aromatic nucleus. Thus, the meta position in toluene is more reactive to an electrophilic reagent than is the unsubstituted aromatic nucleus (benzene).

The halogens offer an exception to this general rule, for although they are ortho and para directing for electrophilic reagents, they render the nucleus less reactive.

A complete treatment of the nature of aromatic character and orientation effects is beyond the scope of this work. The reader is referred to a number of excellent references[22a, 310, 330] on these phases of the problem.

SULFONATION

Aromatic sulfonic acids of the benzene series are of interest in the chemistry of dyes chiefly as intermediates for a number of azo colors and for conversion to the corresponding phenols through alkali fusion.

The more familiar procedures for sulfonation of the aromatic nucleus

involve treatment of the starting compound with the following reagents:

(1) strong sulfuric acid

(2) a combination of sulfuric acid and sulfur trioxide (oleum)

(3) sulfur trioxide in an inert solvent, e.g., sulfur dioxide or 1,2-dichloro-ethane

(4) an addition compound of sulfur trioxide with an ether or an organic base, e.g., bis(chloromethyl) ether or pyridine

(5) chlorosulfonic acid.

The procedure employed in a given instance is dependent to a large extent on the reactivity of the compound. In some cases boron trifluoride functions as a catalyst for sulfonation of the benzene system[43].

Starting materials for the benzene sulfonic acids are principally aromatic hydrocarbons, aromatic nitro compounds, amines, halogen derivatives and carboxylic acids.

The reaction of sulfuric acid with an aromatic nucleus is reversible. The reaction of benzene and sulfuric acid at 100 to 200°C reaches equilibrium when the concentration of sulfuric acid reaches 73 to 78 per cent[35, 332]. The equilibrium can be shifted to favor higher conversion to benzenesulfonic acid by removing the products of the reaction, i.e., either the water formed during the reaction or the aromatic sulfonic acid. The addition of any water to the reaction mass tends to reverse the equilibrium and regenerate the starting material. This property of aromatic sulfonic acids to undergo desulfonation is made use of in the separation of the isomeric xylenes through the stepwise desulfonation of the mixture of the respective sulfonic acids[25].

It is often the practice to use sufficient excess sulfuric acid or SO_3 dissolved in sulfuric acid (oleum) to assure a minimum concentration of acid as a means of shifting the equilibrium and maintaining the attacking power of the reagent to favor sulfonation. Water in this system acts as a base to neutralize sulfuric acid and thus diminishes its reactivity toward the aromatic nucleus. For this reason removal of the by-product water aids the reaction. Other commercial techniques[302] demonstrate this and show that it is possible to avoid the use of much of the excess acid and use essentially stoichiometric amounts of sulfuric acid and benzene in an inert high-boiling solvent by removing the by-product water through azeotropic distillation as the reaction proceeds. The Tyrer Process[285, 328] for the manufacture of benzenesulfonic acid accomplishes the same result by using excess benzene which upon being distilled from the reaction mass during the course of the reaction effects the removal of the water resulting from the reaction and retains the acidity necessary for sulfonation. This technique has been applied, likewise, to the manufacture of the monosulfonic acids of toluene[20] and aniline[275].

The use of SO_3 as a direct sulfonation agent avoids the adverse effects due to by-product water. The reaction may be carried out in the liquid or vapor phase. This technique has been judged by some[305], [306] to be the basis of the most economically attractive process for the manufacture of benzene-sulfonic acid. Equilibrium is reached much more quickly than when using sulfuric acid. For example, equal volumes of benzene and sulfuric acid react at the reflux temperature to the extent of 80 per cent of theory at equilibrium which is reached after 20 to 30 hours[295], whereas with sulfur trioxide the reaction is essentially instantaneous at 0 to 10°C with a yield of 90 per cent of the theoretical[34]. This reaction of SO_3 and benzene may be effected also in liquid SO_2 at approximately 15°C.

Mechanism

A number of mechanisms have been postulated for the sulfonation of aromatic hydrocarbons. The more modern theories[2], [16], [308] regard the cation $^+SO_3H$ as the actual sulfonating agent. The mechanism involves an attack on the intermediate activated complex by the electrophilic reagent, $^+SO_3H$, at a point of high electron density. The reaction is completed with the displacement of a proton and a return of the molecule to the stable state. Sulfur trioxide serves as a sulfonation reagent by virtue of a relatively positive sulfur atom.

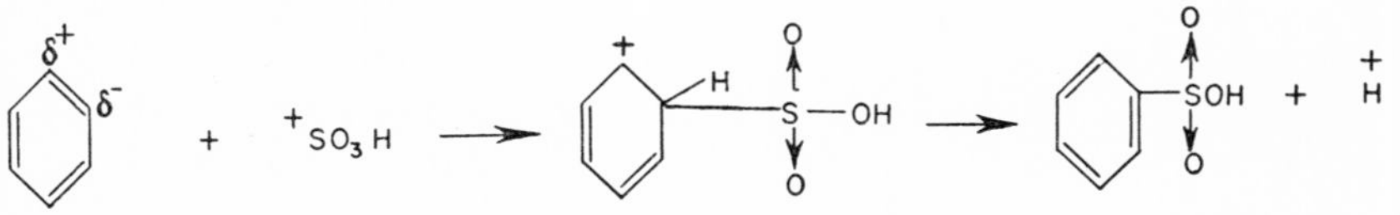

A mechanism suggested for the formation of the sulfonation reagent visualizes the formation of an intermediate compound involving a molecule of sulfuric acid and a proton. This has been demonstrated to exist in 100 per cent sulfuric acid. Subsequent decomposition of this compound leads to the cationic reagent.

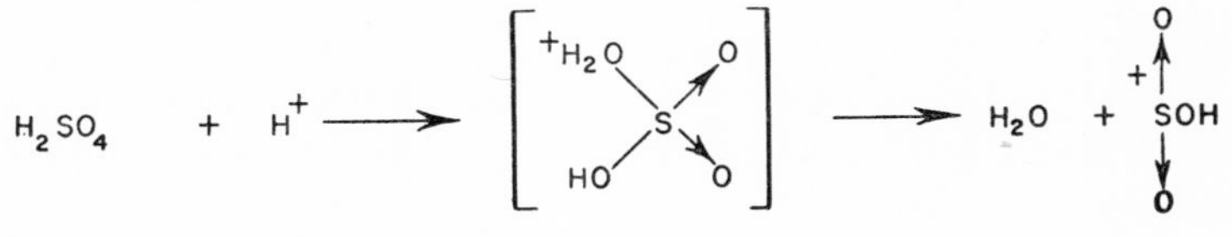

Sulfonation of Amines

Aromatic aminosulfonic acids constitute an important class of dye intermediates particularly for azo dye chemistry. Amines are sulfonated by two general procedures: (1) direct and (2) indirect or baking procedure. Generally speaking, the direct procedure is carried out at a comparatively low temperature with strong sulfuric acid or a combination of sulfuric acid and

TABLE 1. SULFONATION OF AMINES
(Direct Procedure)

Starting Material	Reaction Temp. (°C)	Reagent % Oleum (1) or H₂SO₄ (2)	Product	% Yield	Ref.
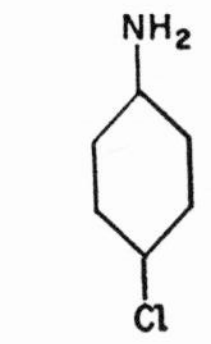 (structure: NH_2–ring–Cl)	100–125	65 (1)	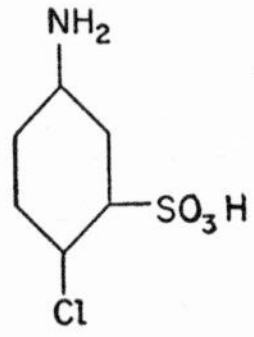 (structure: NH_2, SO_3H, Cl)	80	175
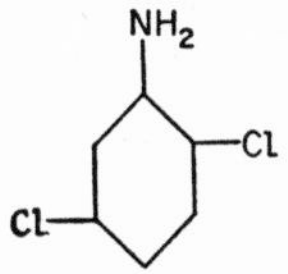 (structure: NH_2, Cl, Cl)	80	65 (1)	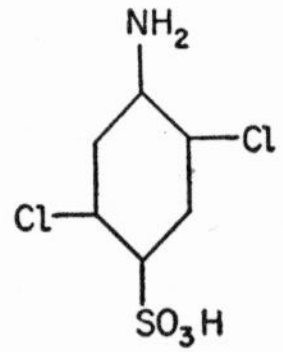 (structure: NH_2, Cl, Cl, SO_3H)	84	176
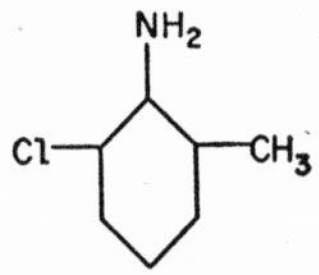 (structure: NH_2, CH_3, Cl)		100 (2)*	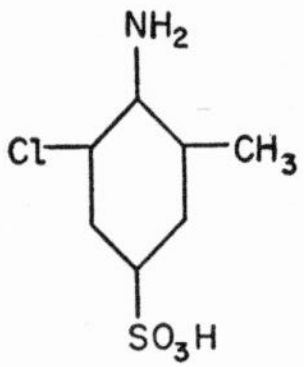 (structure: NH_2, CH_3, Cl, SO_3H)	97	77
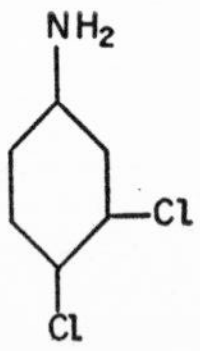 (structure: NH_2, Cl, Cl)			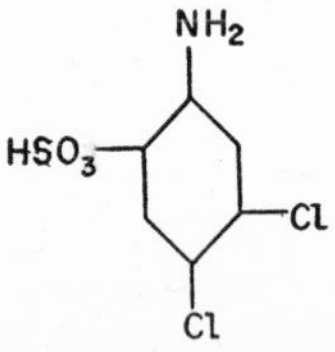 (structure: NH_2, Cl, Cl, HSO_3)	84	142

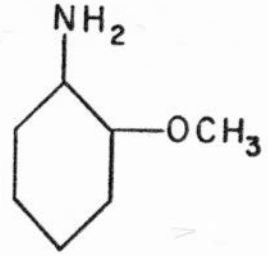

171   92

172   89

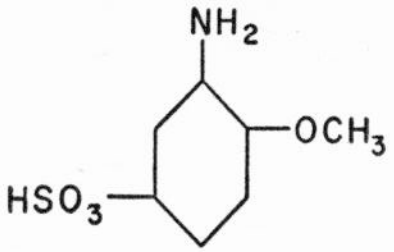

212   80

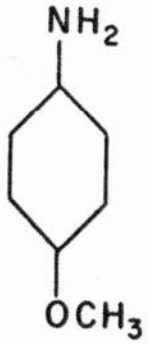

221   90

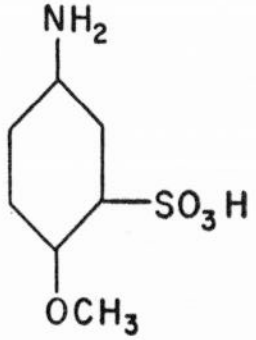

168   90

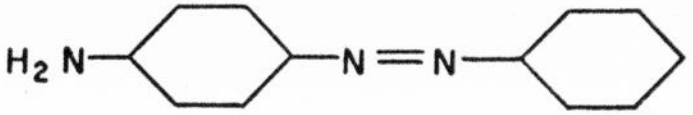

98 (2)   50–55

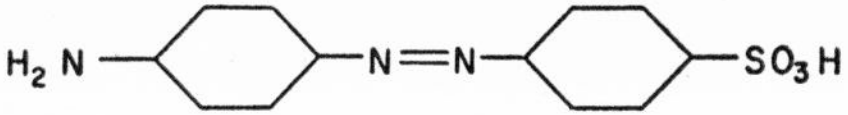

65 (1)   30–40

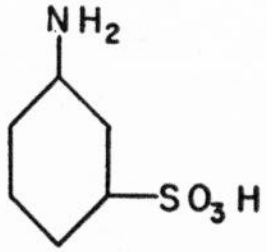

65 (1)   0–20

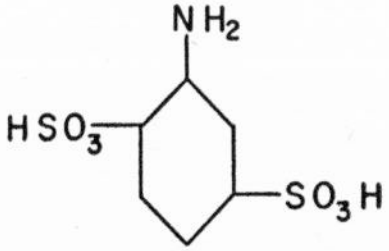

65 (1)   160

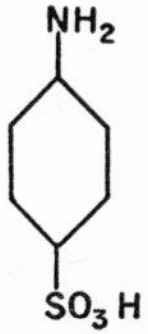

20 (1)   130

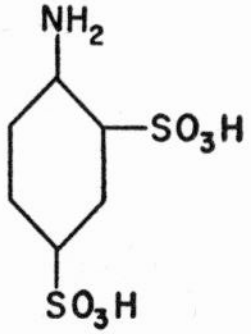

* *o*-dichlorobenzene is used as solvent.

dissolved sulfur trioxide. The indirect or baking procedure involves a high temperature baking of the amine acid sulfate.

The indirect procedure offers the advantage of giving products more nearly free of isomers and also it favors substitution in the para position when both ortho and para positions are available in the aromatic nucleus.

The general applicability of the direct procedure is illustrated with the examples which have been included in Table 1. It is of interest to note the orientation of the sulfo group relative to the amino group. In general, there is a strong tendency for the sulfo group to go para to the amino group, but this is modified by the basicity of the amine, and directive influences of other substituents in the ring. The more basic amines, e.g., o- and p-anisidine and p-chloraniline, lead to meta substitution while the less basic ones lead to ortho or para substitution. One may reason that the stronger bases react with the acid to form a more stable —NH_3^+ group which directs the cationic reagent SO_3H^+ to the meta position.

Sulfonation by the baking process is accomplished through formation of the amine acid sulfate by a pretreatment of the amine with strong sulfuric acid. The resulting thick paste of amine acid sulfate is then charged into a suitable reactor and heated to temperatures ranging from 100 to 300°C. Under these conditions the compound undergoes an intramolecular rearrangement resulting in an aminosulfonic acid. Table 2 lists a number of examples of this procedure.

Other Direct Sulfonations of the Substituted Aromatic Nucleus

Sulfonations involving aromatic nitro, chloro and phenolic compounds are effected under similar conditions. Temperatures in the range of 85 to 125°C are used with acid concentrations varying from 98 per cent sulfuric acid to 65 per cent oleum. For example, nitrobenzene is sulfonated with 65 per cent oleum at 80 to 105°C to m-nitrobenzenesulfonic acid[252]. Chlorobenzene under similar conditions yields p-chlorobenzenesulfonic acid[244]. Similarly, 1-chloro-4-nitrobenzene yields 2-chloro-5-nitrobenzenesulfonic acid[152]. Salicylic acid undergoes sulfonation with 98 per cent sulfuric acid to form 2-hydroxy-5-sulfobenzoic acid (5-sulfosalicylic acid)[206].

Sulfonation by Substitution

The less direct means of introduction of the sulfonic acid group involves substitution of the nucleophilic sodium bisulfite reagent for a labile functional group already attached to the aromatic nucleus. This reaction is characteristic of negatively substituted aromatic bromo, chloro, hydroxy, nitro, and nitroso compounds.

o-Chlorobenzoic acid and aqueous sodium bisulfite in the presence of copper catalyst react to form o-sulfobenzoic acid[324].

TABLE 2. SULFONATION OF AMINES
(Indirect Procedure)

Starting Material	Reaction Temp. (°C)	Product	% Yield	Ref.
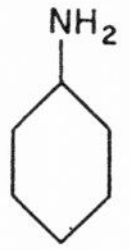 NH$_2$ (cyclohexyl)	260–280	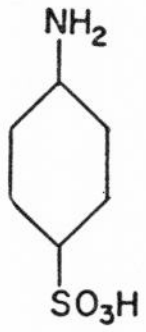 NH$_2$ ... SO$_3$H	94.5	147 267
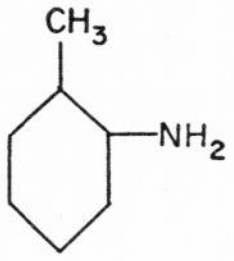 CH$_3$ / NH$_2$	235–255	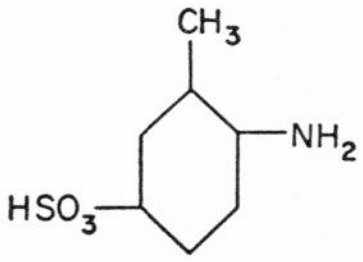 CH$_3$ / HSO$_3$ / NH$_2$	97.0	148
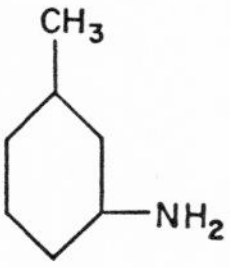 CH$_3$ / NH$_2$	255	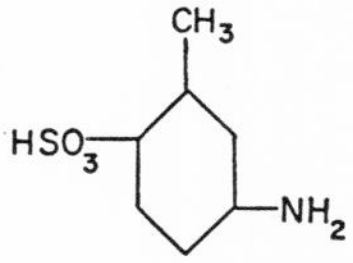 CH$_3$ / HSO$_3$ / NH$_2$	93.0	139
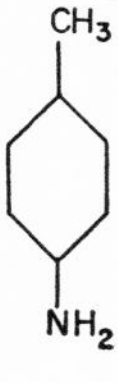 CH$_3$ / NH$_2$	160–195	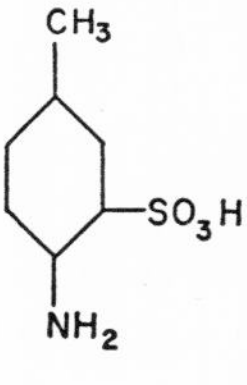 CH$_3$ / SO$_3$H / NH$_2$	91.4	149
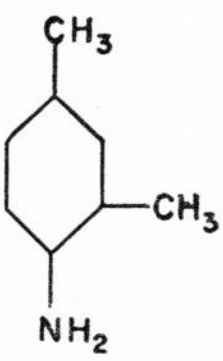 CH$_3$ / CH$_3$ / NH$_2$	300	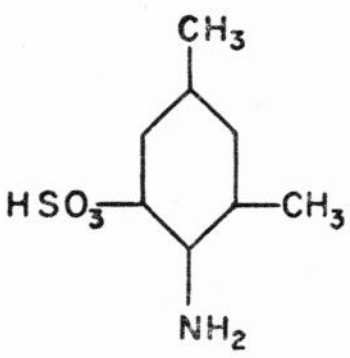 CH$_3$ / HSO$_3$ / CH$_3$ / NH$_2$	85.0	170

TABLE 2—*Cont.*

Starting Material	Reaction Temp. (°C)	Product	% Yield	Ref.
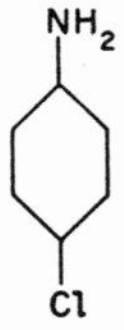 NH_2 ... Cl (aniline with Cl)	230	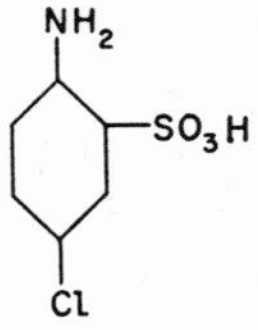 NH_2 ... SO_3H ... Cl	91.0	174
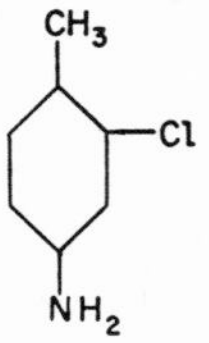 CH_3 ... Cl ... NH_2	100	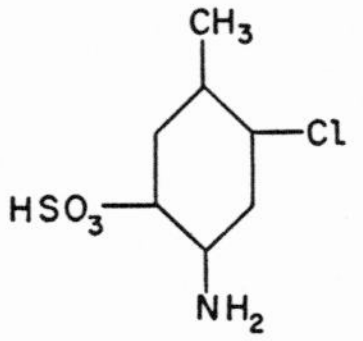 CH_3 ... Cl ... HSO_3 ... NH_2	91.0	177
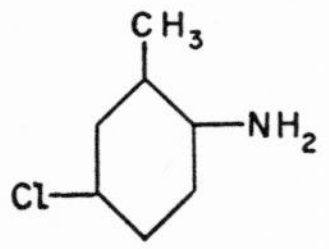 CH_3 ... NH_2 ... Cl	300	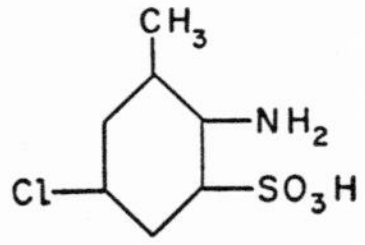 CH_3 ... NH_2 ... SO_3H ... Cl	93.0	229
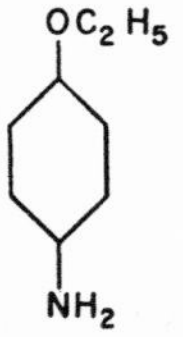 OC_2H_5 ... NH_2	175	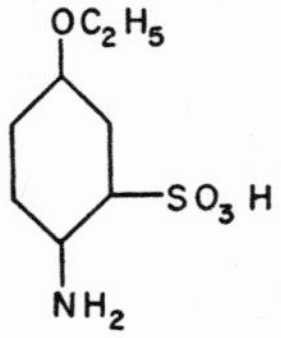 OC_2H_5 ... SO_3H ... NH_2	93.0	173

Replacement of a labile chlorine in *o*-chlorobenzaldehyde is readily effected with sodium bisulfite in the presence of sodium carbonate at 190 to 195°C. The corresponding benzaldehyde-*o*-sulfonic acid (*o*-formylbenzenesulfonic acid) is formed in 83 per cent yield[192, 224].

In an analogous manner *m*-nitrotoluene and sodium bisulfite react to form the sodium salt of *m*-tolylsulfamic acid with some by-product sodium salt of 6-sulfo-*m*-tolylsulfamic acid (2-sulfamino-*p*-toluenesulfonic acid)[12]. Nitrobenzene undergoes a similar reaction[326].

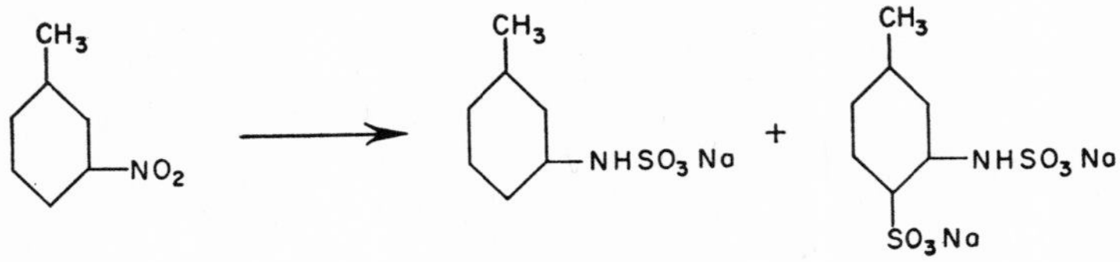

CH_3 ... NO_2 $\longrightarrow$ CH_3 ... $NHSO_3Na$ + CH_3 ... $NHSO_3Na$ ... SO_3Na

Hydrolysis of phenylsulfamic acids leads to migration of the sulfo group to the ring. Similarly, *m*-dinitrobenzene yields the sodium salt of 4-amino-2-nitrobenzenesulfonic acid (2-nitrosulfanilic acid)[296].

Chlorosulfonation

Chlorosulfonic acid, $HOSO_2Cl$, is occasionally used as a sulfonation agent, but is more frequently employed for introduction of the chlorosulfonyl group in the aromatic nucleus. Where it is used as a sulfonation agent, it is necessary to employ solvent systems and avoid any excess reagent, otherwise a mixture of the sulfonic acid and sulfonyl chloride is obtained. In this manner, resorcinol treated with chlorosulfonic acid in nitrobenzene solution at 15 to 75°C results in an essentially quantitative yield of 2,4-dihydroxybenzenesulfonic acid[304].

Chlorosulfonations are effected in much the same manner as the related sulfonation reactions. Considerable excess chlorosulfonic acid is required for best results in preparing aromatic sulfonyl chlorides, otherwise the product is contaminated with some free sulfonic acid. 1-Chloro-2-nitrobenzene and 2 to 6 moles of chlorosulfonic acid react at 100 to 135°C to give an 88 per cent yield of 4-chloro-3-nitrobenzenesulfonyl chloride[18].

Chlorosulfonation of toluene yields approximately 40 per cent ortho- and 60 per cent para-toluenesulfonyl chlorides. By keeping excess toluene to a minimum during the reaction the product comprises largely the para isomer[36b]. Salicyclic acid reacts with excess chlorosulfonic acid at 45°C to give 5-(chlorosulfonyl)salicyclic acid[227] in 76 to 78 per cent yields.

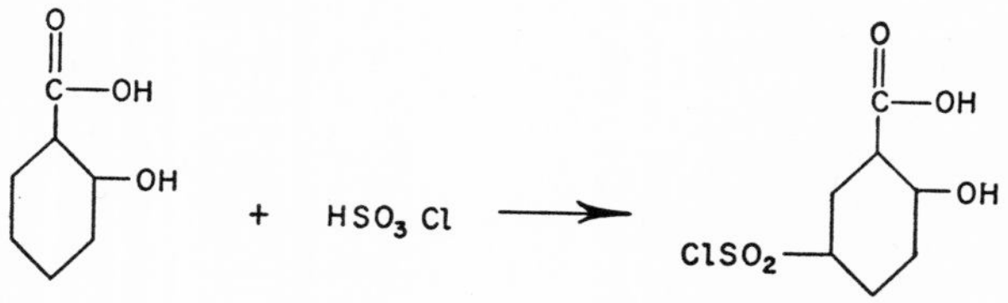

Similarly, *o*-acetanisidide gives 3-acetamido-4-methoxybenzenesulfonyl chloride in 84 to 86 per cent yield[211].

Nitrobenzene is converted to *m*-nitrobenzenesulfonyl chloride in 79 per cent yield by treatment with 4 moles of chlorosulfonic acid at a maximum temperature of 105°C[153].

NITRATION

The process of nitrating the benzene nucleus is an important one since the resulting nitro compounds are readily reduced to the corresponding amines, which have broad application in dye chemistry. Nitrations are carried out on a diversity of starting materials. These include, in addition to aromatic hydrocarbons, aromatic sulfonic acids, amines, phenols, halogenated derivatives, carboxylic acids and ethers as well as combinations of these functional groups within the same molecule.

Nitric acid in both aqueous and organic solvent systems is used for nitrating more reactive compounds, whereas more difficultly soluble and less reactive materials require a combination of nitric and sulfuric acid, "mixed acids." The compositions of these "mixed acids" vary from 35 per cent nitric-65 per cent sulfuric acid to 83 per cent nitric-12 per cent sulfuric acid.

The sulfuric acid serves as a solvent for carrying out the reaction and, in addition, it is effective in reacting with the nitric acid molecule to form the nitronium ion NO_2^+ which is the actual nitrating agent. In many cases, additional sulfuric acid is used for dissolving the material to be nitrated prior to addition of the "mixed acids." Procedures have been devised also for carrying out nitration of the aromatic nucleus with aqueous nitric acid in the vapor phase in such a manner that the water resulting from the reaction is continuously distilled from the reaction. In this way, the concentration of nitric acid is maintained sufficiently high throughout the course of the reaction to function as an effective nitrating agent. Using this system, benzene is nitrated with 61 per cent aqueous nitric acid at approximately 80°C[301].

Mechanism

Many of the earlier workers concerned with the mechanism studies of the nitration of aromatic compounds considered the role of sulfuric acid in the reaction mixture as being that of a dehydrating agent for withdrawing water formed in the reaction, and in this manner shifting the equilibrium to the right. Newer theories concerning the mechanism of the reaction regard the part played by sulfuric acid as one of effecting an ionization of nitric acid to form the positively charged nitronium ion (NO_2^+) according to the following equilibrium[31, 50, 323]:

$$HNO_3 + 2H_2SO_4 \rightleftarrows NO_2^+ + 2HSO_4^- + H_3^+O$$

When nitric acid is used in the absence of sulfuric acid, the nitronium ion results from an interaction of two molecules of nitric acid[50].

$$2HNO_3 \rightleftarrows H_2^+NO_3 + NO_3^-$$

$$H_2^+NO_3 \rightleftarrows H_2O + NO_2^+$$

Nitrations occurring with dilute aqueous nitric acid, e.g., 25 per cent, do not involve the nitronium ion. The nitracidium ion, $H_2NO_3^+$, has been suggested as the effective reagent under this condition. The more electron rich the aromatic nucleus is, the more readily will the nitronium ion or other nitrating agents react with it, and the milder are the nitrating reagents and reaction conditions which will be sufficient for the reaction. For example, 2-chloro-1,4-dimethoxybenzene is nitrated with 25 per cent aqueous nitric acid at 70°C[69], while toluene requires a mixed acid corresponding to 30 per cent HNO_3, 57.6 per cent H_2SO_4 and 12.4 per cent water[46].

Practical Applications

Benzene is readily nitrated at 45°C with a mixed acid comprising 35.5 per cent nitric acid, 52.5 per cent sulfuric acid and 12 per cent water to give a 99 per cent yield of nitrobenzene[179b]. The nitration of toluene employs a mixed acid within the following compositions: 28 to 32 per cent nitric acid, 52 to 56 per cent sulfuric acid and 12 to 20 per cent water. The product obtained in the case of toluene comprises 62 to 63 per cent ortho-, 33 to 34 per cent para- and 3 to 4 per cent meta-nitrotoluene[179c]. The isomers are separated by fractional distillation and crystallization. Subsequent nitration of *p*-nitrotoluene yields 2,4-dinitrotoluene in relatively pure form. Alternatively *o*-nitrotoluene or the mixture of isomers may be used for making dinitrotoluene but in this case a mixture of isomers is obtained[179d].

In order to illustrate the scope of the reaction, a number of different chemical types have been included in Tables 3, 4 and 5 with a minimum amount of data concerning reaction conditions and yields. These examples fall into three groups of compounds: (1) arylamines, (2) benzenesulfonic acids, and (3) a miscellaneous group which includes chloro, nitro, alkoxy and carboxy substituents on the benzene nucleus.

Nitration of Aromatic Amines. In the nitration of aromatic amines, it is usually necessary to protect the reactive amino groups to avoid oxidative attack by the strong nitric acid. This is accomplished by acylating the amine to the corresponding amide by treatment with acetic anhydride or acetic acid or other suitable acylating agents such as *p*-toluenesulfonyl chloride. Phosgene is used also for this purpose. When nitrating with concentrated acid or mixed acids, acylated derivatives are employed also for orienting the attacking nitronium ion in the para position.

Acylation of *o*-aminophenols with phosgene or acetic anhydride results in the formation of the benzoxazolone and benzoxazole ring systems, respectively. In this manner, both the reactive phenolic and amino groups are protected during the nitration[226].

An interesting orientation effect is observed by comparing the products of nitration of *p*-toluidine and *N*-ethyl-*p*-toluidine, as illustrated in Table 3. In view of the high yield of *N*-methyl-4-nitroacetanilide obtained under

TABLE 3. NITRATION OF MISCELLANEOUS ACYLATED ARYLAMINES

Starting Material	Composition of Nitrating Agent (%)			Conc. of Solvent H₂SO₄ (%)	Acyl Derivative	Temp. (°C)	Product	% Yield	Ref.
	HNO₃	H₂SO₄	H₂O						
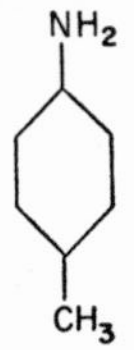	37.5	40.5	22	96	Acetyl	28–30	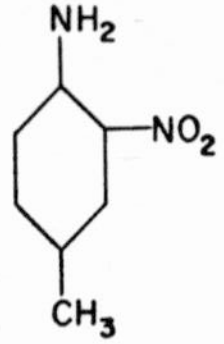	68.0	255
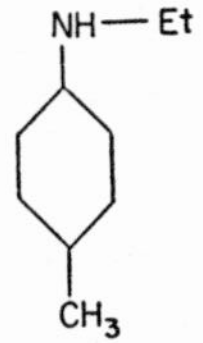	40.0	48.0	12	98	Acetyl	0	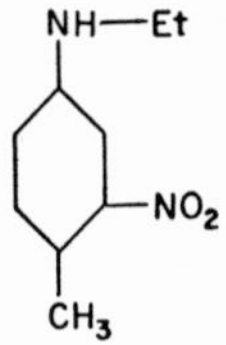	88.6	163
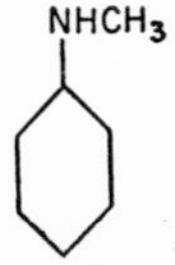	40.0	48.0	12	98	Acetyl	0	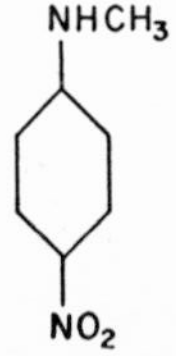	85.0	259

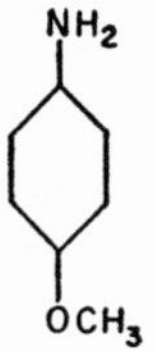	61.0	—	39	(Chloro-benzene)	Acetyl	20–30	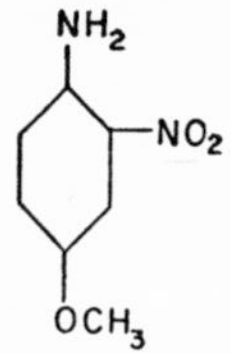	88.0	109
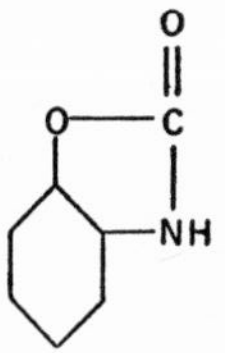	30.0	—	70	100	Carbonyl (from phosgene)	0–10	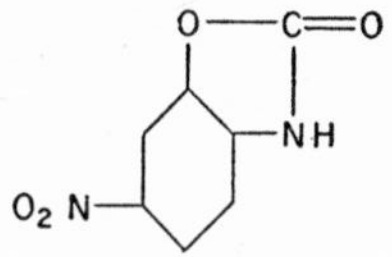	96.0	257
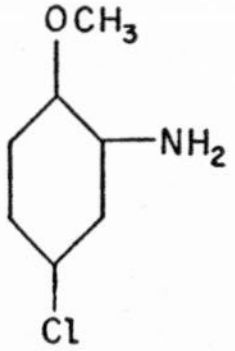	40.0	48.0	12	98	Formyl	0	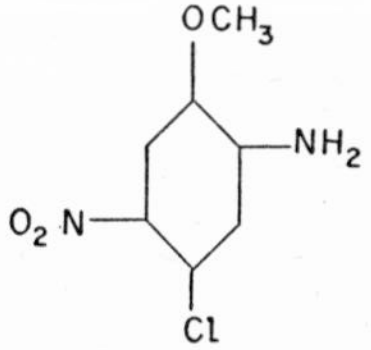	87.0	164
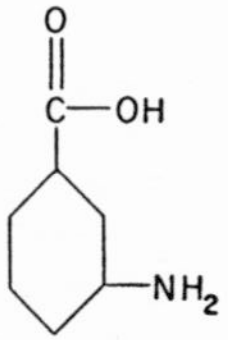	33.0	67.9	—	98	Acetyl	0	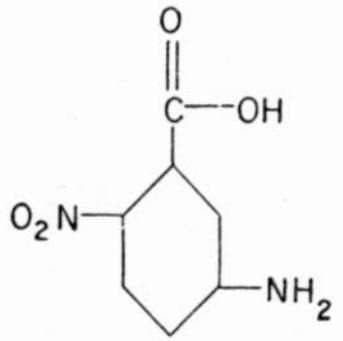	90.0	191

the same conditions, steric factors may be responsible for orienting the attacking nitronium ion meta in the case of *N*-ethyl-*p*-toluidine.

Nitration of Aromatic Sulfonic Acids. The nitration of sulfonic acids is very conveniently carried out by adding the nitrating agent to the crude sulfonation mass; thus, both the nitration and the sulfonation can be effected in what is essentially a one-step operation. In like manner, nitration may be followed by sulfonation in the same reaction mass. In certain cases, the sulfo group is simultaneously replaced with a nitro group during nitration. Thus, 4-chloro-1-phenol-2-sulfonic acid yields 4-chloro-2,6-dinitrophenol[231] and 2-chloro-1-phenol-4-sulfonic acid correspondingly gives 2-chloro-4,6-dinitrophenol[232].

A number of applications of the nitration of aromatic sulfonic acids have been summarized in Table 4. In the case of 3-chloro-*p*-toluenesulfonic acid, one would expect the nitronium ion to be oriented in the 5 position by both the sulfo and methyl groups, but apparently the resonance effect involving the chlorine atom dominates the orientation effects of the other two groups and the cationic attack falls in the 6 position.

TABLE 4. NITRATION OF SUBSTITUTED BENZENESULFONIC ACIDS

| Starting Material | Composition of Nitrating Agent (%) | | | Conc. of Solvent H$_2$SO$_4$ (%) | Temp. (°C.) | Product | % Yield | Ref. |
	HNO$_3$	H$_2$SO$_4$	H$_2$O					
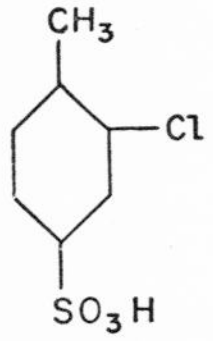 (structure)	74	—	26	ca. 95	30	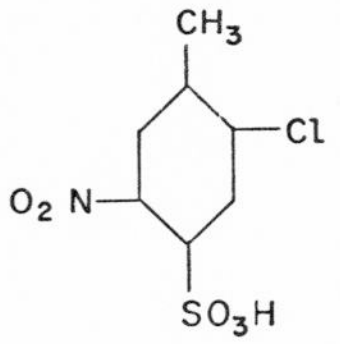 (structure)	—	78
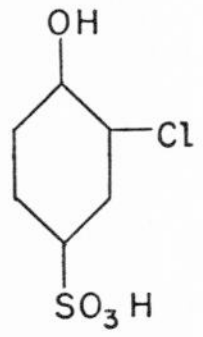 (structure)	77	—	23	95	30–80	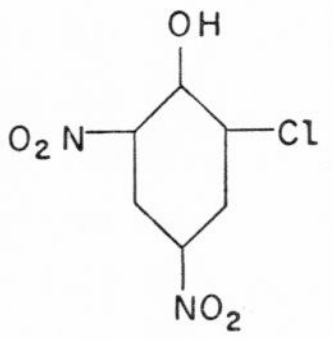 (structure)	90	232
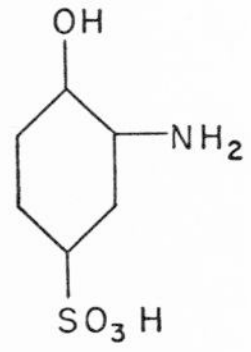 (structure)	33	67	—	5*	—	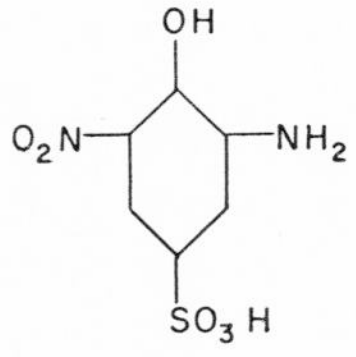 (structure)	81	183

TABLE 4—*Cont.*

Starting Material	Composition of Nitrating Agent (%) HNO₃	H₂SO₄	H₂O	Conc. of Solvent (%) H₂SO₄	Temp. (°C.)	Product	% Yield	Ref.
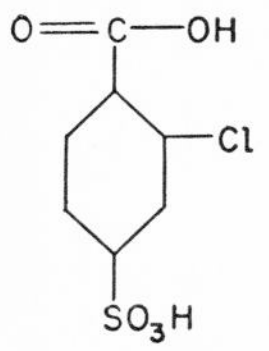 (O=C—OH; —Cl; SO₃H)	74	—	26	100	40	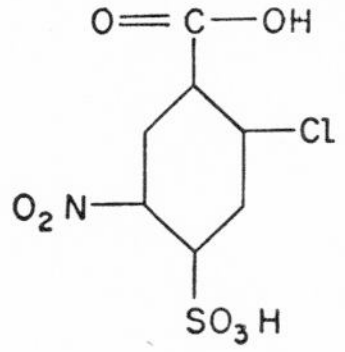 (O=C—OH; —Cl; O₂N—; SO₃H)	79.3	237
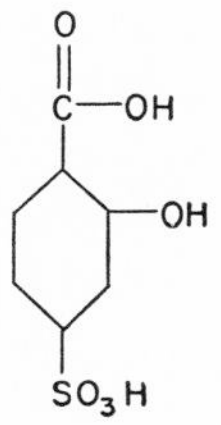 (C(=O)—OH; —OH; SO₃H)	78	—	22	ca. 95	18–22	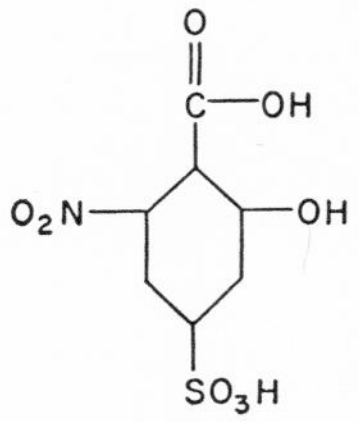 (C(=O)—OH; —OH; O₂N—; SO₃H)	95–97	206
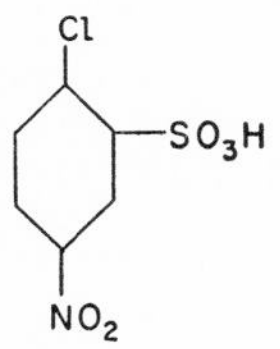 (Cl; —SO₃H; NO₂)	98	—	—	ca. 95	70–105	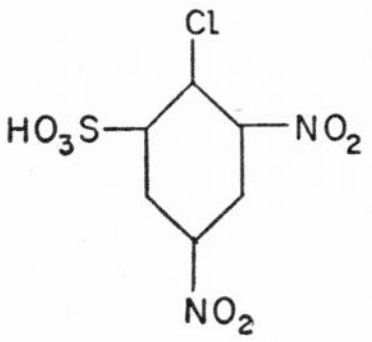 (Cl; HO₃S—; —NO₂; NO₂)	80	182

* Oleum.

A commercial innovation[327] in connection with the nitration of benzene is found in the effect of mercuric salts on the nature of the reaction. This procedure leads to the formation of nitrophenols in a single operation, e.g., nitration of benzene with 50 per cent nitric acid containing 7 per cent mercuric nitrate leads to a mixture of mono-, di- and trinitrophenols.

A number of additional examples of nitrations involving the aromatic nucleus containing other familiar functional groups have been included in Table 5 for the purpose of indicating the range of application to the manufacture of intermediates.

HALOGENATION

The chloro derivatives constitute the most important class of halogen substituted intermediates of the benzene series. While in many cases, bromination and iodination may be effected by essentially the same proce-

TABLE 5. NITRATION OF THE BENZENE NUCLEUS CONTAINING MISCELLANEOUS SUBSTITUENTS

Starting Material	Composition of Nitrating Agent (%)			Conc. of Solvent H_2SO_4 (%)	Temp. (°C)	Product	% Yield	Ref.
	HNO_3	H_2SO_4	H_2O					
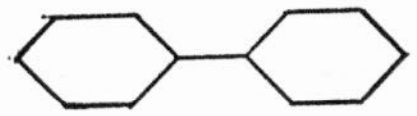	33	48.5	18.5	64	68–70	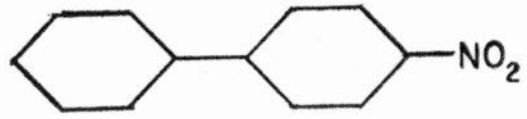	52–55*	258
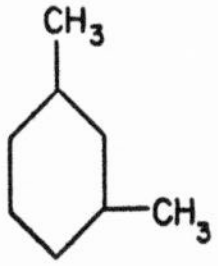	28	56.5	15.5	78	50	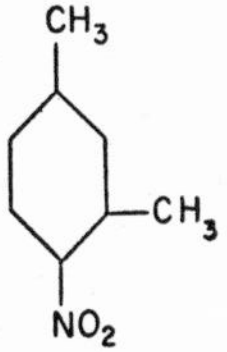	70	263
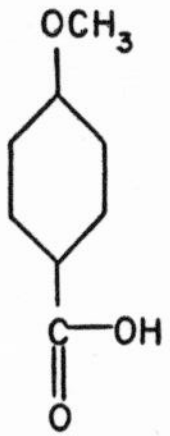	33	48.0	19.0	98	0	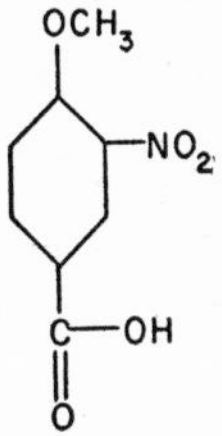	82	256
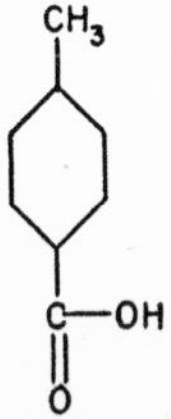	40	48.0	12.0	98	50	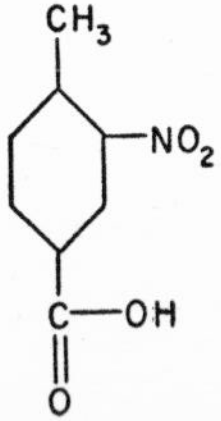	94.8	261

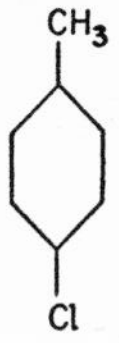

72

116

113

68

(a)56.7
(b)30.6

87.0

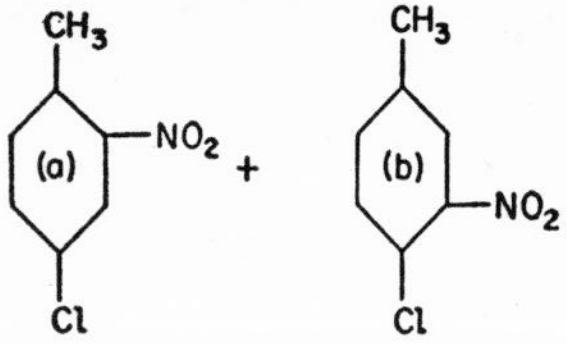

91.0

(a)34
(b)66

CH₃ (b) NO₂ Cl

CH₃ (a) NO₂ + Cl

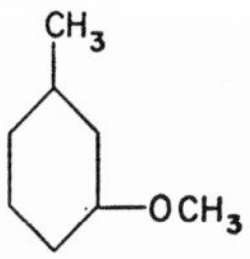

CH₃ OCH₃ O₂N

OCH₃ NO₂ OCH₃

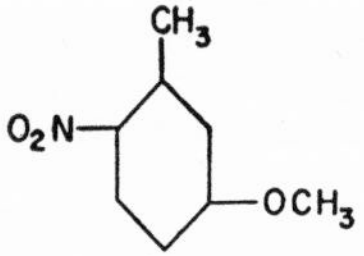

Cl (b) NO₂

Cl (a) NO₂ +

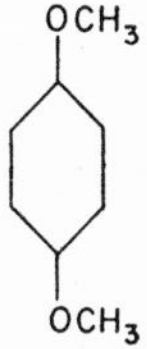

15–20

0–30

85

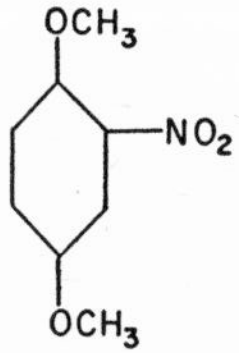

70–80

—

CCl₄

—

—

5

25

66

14

60

—

—

56

35

75

34

30

CH₃ Cl

CH₃ OCH₃

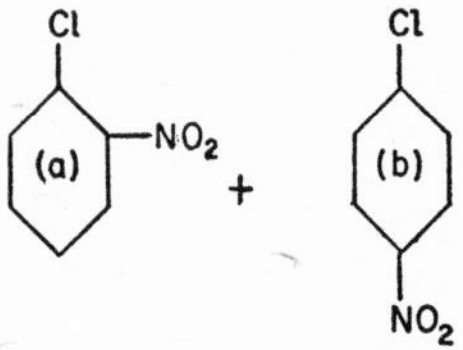

OCH₃ OCH₃

Cl

TABLE 5—Cont.

Starting Material	Composition of Nitrating Agent (%)			Conc. of Solvent H_2SO_4 (%)	Temp. (°C)	Product	% Yield	Ref.
	HNO₃	H₂SO₄	H₂O					
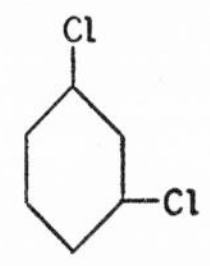 (1,3-dichlorobenzene)	35	60	5	—	20	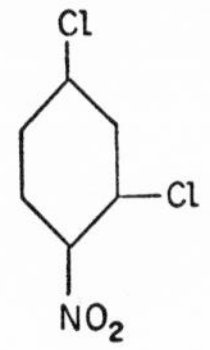 (2,4-dichloro-1-nitrobenzene)	52.0	89
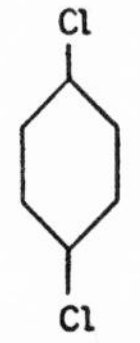 (1,4-dichlorobenzene)	35	60	5	—	65	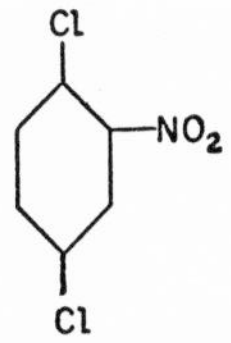 (1,4-dichloro-2-nitrobenzene)	97.0	90

* The 2-nitrobiphenyl occurring in the crude product is separated by alcohol recrystallization.

dures employed for chlorination, these compounds have not experienced broad application. A growing interest in fluorine chemistry has led to a number of intermediates containing fluorine. Because of the extreme reactivity of fluorine, quite different techniques are necessary in bringing about substitution of the aromatic hydrogen with fluorine.

Chlorination

Chlorination of the aromatic nucleus can be effected by several different techniques, the most common of which involves direct chlorination, generally in the presence of a catalyst ($FeCl_3$) which functions by inducing polarization of the chlorine molecule.

$$RH + Cl_2 + FeCl_3 \rightarrow RH \cdot \cdot Cl^+ + (FeCl_6)^=$$

In the absence of such a catalyst but under exposure to actinic rays, the chlorine attacks, through a radical mechanism, any alkyl group which is attached to the aromatic nucleus.

$$Cl_2 \xrightarrow{h\nu} 2Cl \cdot$$

In the complete absence of iron, other inorganic chlorides, e.g., phosphorus trichloride, function as catalysts for side chain chlorination.

A second technique makes use of active nascent chlorine generated in situ from a chlorine-containing compound, e.g., hydrochloric acid, and an appropriate oxidizing agent.

Hypochlorites are used as chlorination agents in alkaline solution.

A fourth type of chlorination reaction makes use of active chlorine containing compounds such as phosphorus oxychloride, phosphorus pentachloride, sulfuryl chloride, and thionyl chloride. With the exception of sulfuryl chloride, the use of these reagents is practically limited to replacement of active functional groups with chlorine as illustrated in the making of acid chlorides and alkyl chlorides from the corresponding carboxy or hydroxy compounds.

Mechanism. There is much evidence[279, 309] which indicates that the mechanism of the direct chlorination reaction involves a cationic attack of the aromatic nucleus by the cation Cl^+. This reacts with an activated aromatic nucleus by forming a covalent bond through accepting an electron pair from the aromatic nucleus. Subsequent loss of a proton, probably through reaction with Cl^-, completes the reaction:

A simple bimolecular reaction mechanism has been shown to apply when carrying out the reaction in acetic acid solution[13, 276]. Under these conditions, the aromatic nucleus is attacked directly by the bromine molecule $ArH + Br_2 \rightarrow ArHBr^+ + Br^-$.

Technical Applications. An example of direct chlorination is found in the chlorination of toluene, which results in approximately an equimolar mixture of o- and p-chlorotoluene. A 3°C difference in boiling point of the two isomers permits fractionation of the crude mixture into the two isomers of approximately 90 per cent purity. The ortho isomer is purified by distillation while the para isomer is purified by fractional crystallization. Further chlorination of p-chlorotoluene leads to a mixture of 2,4- and 3,4-dichlorotoluene, which upon separation by fractional distillation results in yields of 64.4 per cent of theory of 2,4-dichlorotoluene and 19.8 per cent of theory of 3,4-dichlorotoluene[91].

A similar mixture[73] of isomers is obtained in the chlorination of p-nitrotoluene. The crude product is purified by fractional crystallization with a resulting yield of 72.4 per cent of 2-chloro-4-nitrotoluene based on the starting p-nitrotoluene.

Chlorination of o-nitrotoluene at 35 to 40°C in the presence of ferric chloride results in a crude reaction mixture which contains approximately 49 per cent 2-chloro-6-nitrotoluene and 21 per cent 4-chloro-2-nitrotoluene. Purification by fractionation and crystallization (sweating) results in a recovery of 80 per cent of the 2-chloro-6-nitrotoluene and 53 per cent of the 4-chloro-2-nitrotoluene as pure materials[71].

2-Chloro-p-xylene results from the direct chlorination of p-xylene at 10 to 15°C. The crude product is purified by fractional distillation. The over-all conversion to distilled 2-chloro-p-xylene is approximately 64 per cent of the theoretical[80]. Additional product and unreacted p-xylene are recoverable from the fore-shots and tail fractions.

Chlorination of the alkyl side chain is illustrated with the direct chlorination of several chlorotoluenes to the corresponding chlorobenzotrichlorides. The reaction is carried out in the absence of iron but in the presence of catalytic amounts of phosphorus trichloride[87].

o-, *m*-, and *p*-Chlorotoluenes are chlorinated by similar procedures at 80 to 165°C to the corresponding *o*-, *m*- and *p*-chlorobenzotrichlorides. The yields are approximately 88 per cent of the theoretical based on the starting chlorotoluenes[61].

Direct chlorination of *p*-xylene in carbon tetrachloride solution in the presence of light leads to a 46 per cent yield of α-chloro-*p*-xylene and approximately the same yield of α,α'-dichloro-*p*-xylene[300].

Chlorinations involving nascent chlorine are illustrated by the chlorination of *p*-nitroaniline and *p*-nitrophenol with hydrochloric acid and sodium chlorate to form 2,6-dichloro-4-nitroaniline[88] and 2,6-dichloro-4-nitrophenol[47]. An 81 per cent yield is obtained in the former case.

Nascent chlorine has been applied successfully to the continuous vapor phase chlorination of benzene using a mixture of hydrochloric acid and air over a copper-alumina catalyst at 210°C. The procedure employs a large excess of benzene. A yield of 90 per cent of theory is obtained with a 10 per cent conversion of benzene[27].

Sulfuryl chloride, SO_2Cl_2, is used as the reagent in the chlorination of *p*-dimethoxybenzene. A yield of 53.5 per cent of the theoretical is obtained[65].

Resorcinol reacts similarly[239].

Less direct methods of introduction of the halogen atom in the aromatic nucleus, particularly when the position is important and normal directive influences are complicated by the presence of other groups, involve the replacement of functional groups with the desired halogen.

The well-known Sandmeyer reaction is employed in the manufacture of 3,4,5-trichloroaniline from 2,6-dichloro-4-nitroaniline[271]. In like manner, 2-chloro-5-nitrophenol is made from 2-amino-5-nitrophenol[236].

An interesting[85] reaction involving replacement of functional groups is found in the chlorination of *m*-dinitrobenzene with the result that both nitro groups are replaced with chlorine giving a 79.3 per cent yield of *m*-dichlorobenzene; nitrosyl chloride (NO_2Cl) is formed as a by-product.

The crude product contains 1-chloro-3-nitrobenzene, trichlorobenzene and a small amount of unreacted dinitrobenzene. The reaction is carried out at 220°C in a tube with dry chlorine and molten dinitrobenzene.

Fluorination

During the past several years, considerable interest has developed in fluorine-containing compounds as intermediates in dye chemistry, principally because dyes containing fluorine atoms, usually as the trifluoromethyl group, show enhanced brightness of shade.

Because of the unusual reactivity of elemental fluorine, it is difficult to control the reaction of fluorine with organic compounds or arrest the reaction at intermediate stages, and consequently these compounds are not usually prepared from elemental fluorine in a manner analogous to that used for the corresponding bromine or chlorine compounds. The techniques usually used involve replacement of chlorine by treatment with hydrofluoric acid or conversion of an amino group to the corresponding fluoro derivative through application of the Sandmeyer reaction.

In contrast to bromination and chlorination, the mechanism by which fluorine reacts with aromatic compounds probably involves free radicals. Because of the strong electronegativity of the element, ionization comparable to that occurring with chlorine and bromine, i.e., $F_2 \rightarrow F^+ + F^-$, is unlikely. The mechanism is more probably free radical in nature and involves the following equilibrium:

$$F_2 \rightleftarrows 2F \cdot$$

Such a mechanism is supported by observation of side chain reactions in connection with fluorination, e.g., fragmentation, dimerization and polymerization which in all probability are initiated by a free radical mechanism[318]. Also, the tremendous energy release explains some peculiarities.

It is not usually possible to arrest direct fluorination reactions involving elemental fluorine at intermediate stages.

Introduction of fluorine in the side chain of an alkyl aromatic system is effected by replacing a chlorine atom or atoms of a chloroalkyl group by treatment with hydrofluoric acid. In one notable case involving the fluorination of acetophenone, hydrogen is replaced directly by treatment with fluorine in hydrofluoric acid solution in the presence of silver difluoride with the formation of α,α-difluoroacetophenone[317].

When the use of elevated temperatures and pressures is found ineffective in bringing about replacement of chlorine in less reactive systems, a number of metallic fluorides or combinations of fluorides and chlorides may be used separately, or in conjunction with HF, as catalyst and/or fluorinating agents, e.g., KF, KHF$_2$, ZnF$_2$, SbF$_3$, HgF$_2$, SbF$_3$Cl$_2$, CoF$_3$, SbF$_3$ + SbCl$_5$, SbF$_3$ + HF, SbF$_5$, HgO + HF, BrF$_3$ and IF$_4$[319].

In the replacement of the chlorine atoms of a trichloromethyl group with fluorine by treatment with HF, as a general rule the first two are more easily replaced than the third chlorine atom. Nevertheless, quite satisfactory yields of a number of substituted trifluoromethylbenzenes are obtained. *m*-Bis(trichloromethyl)benzene ($\alpha,\alpha,\alpha,\alpha',\alpha',\alpha'$-hexachloro-*m*-xylene) reacts with anhydrous (i.e., 99 to 100 per cent) HF at 125 to 130°C and 35 atmospheres of pressure to give a 74 to 78 per cent yield of bis(trifluoromethyl)benzene[274]. While the *m*- and *p*-bis(trichloromethyl)benzenes react under these conditions, the ortho isomer does not. Similarly, *m*-(trichloromethyl)benzoyl chloride reacts with HF at 30 to 90°C at 22 atmospheres of pressure to form the corresponding (trifluoromethyl)benzoyl fluoride[140].

As one moves up the series from the trichloromethyl group to perchloroethyl and propyl groups, the chlorine atoms attached to the more remote carbon atoms of the alkyl chain become more difficult to replace and it is necessary to use more reactive fluorinating agents. For example, SbCl$_5$[290] is required as a catalyst in conjunction with HF in the conversion of pentachloroethylbenzene to the corresponding fluorine compound.

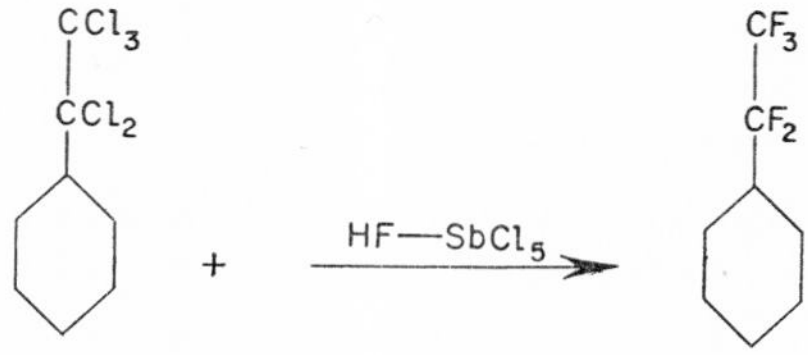

The corresponding heptachloroisopropylbenzene requires pressure in addition to SbCl$_5$ to effect the conversion[293].

McBee and Pierce[292] point out that *p*-(pentachloroethyl)benzotrichloride reacts with HF and SbF$_3$ + SbCl$_5$ at 110°C to form the partially fluorinated (trichlorodifluoroethyl)benzotrifluoride, and that higher temperatures are necessary for conversion to the (pentafluoroethyl)benzotrifluoride.

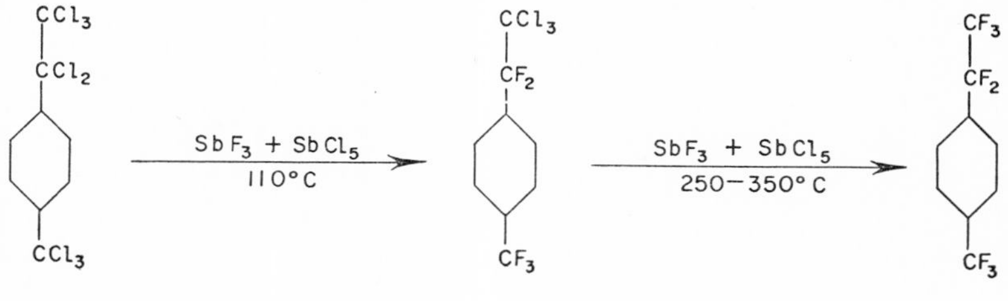

Even under these conditions, high yields are not obtained and much of the material is incompletely fluorinated in the side chain. Antimony pentafluoride, bromine trifluoride and iodine pentafluoride are examples of the more vigorous fluorine carriers used for the more difficult replacements of the halogen atoms. The dichloromethylene group, $-CCl_2-$, attached directly to the aromatic nucleus is labilized by the aromatic nucleus of the compound while a $-CCl_3$ group, isolated from the ring by a $-CF_2-$ group, offers considerable resistance to complete fluorination. This observation has an analogy in the aliphatic series where the $-CCl_3$ group attached to a $-CF_2-$ group undergoes the replacement reaction with difficulty[320]. The mechanism of this reaction probably involves an equilibrium of the type

$$\langle\!\!\!\!\!\!\!\!\!\rangle\!-Cl_2Cl_3 \rightleftarrows + \langle\!\!\!\!\!\!\!\!\!\rangle\!=\!\overset{\displaystyle Cl}{\underset{\displaystyle |}{C}}\!-CCl_3 + Cl^-$$

After replacement of the chlorine atoms of the methylene group, the CF_2- group will oppose any tendency for the terminal $-CCl_3$ to ionize.

The completely fluorinated side chain is relatively unreactive, chemically. It resists hydrolysis in boiling sodium carbonate solution. It remains intact under drastic oxidation as demonstrated by the fact that m-aminobenzotrifluoride yields trifluoroacetic acid upon vigorous oxidation. However, the trifluoromethyl group does react with aluminum chloride, and reverts to the $-CCl_3$ group. The $-CF_3$ group in the aromatic nucleus is strongly electron attracting and consequently directs entering groups largely to the meta position. In the presence of a chloro substituent in the aromatic nucleus, the chlorine dominates the trifluoromethyl group in orienting additional substituents.

For the purpose of this discussion, fluorine-containing intermediates have been divided into several natural subdivisions according to their functional groups and method of manufacture. The principal fluorine-containing intermediates have been included even though much of the chemistry in their manufacture, as presented, does not involve fluorine chemistry.

Intermediates Containing the Fluoroalkoxy Group. A substituted 2,2,2-trifluoroethyl phenyl ether is prepared by reacting potassium 2,2,2-trifluoroethoxide with a compound containing a labile aromatic chlorine atom, e.g., 1-chloro-4-nitrobenzene[207].

Conversely, sodium phenolate reacts with 2,2,2-trifluoroethyl benzene-sulfonate to form 2,2,2-trifluoroethyl phenyl ether[208].

$$C_6H_5-ONa \; + \; CF_3CH_2OSO_2-C_6H_5 \; \longrightarrow \; C_6H_5-O-CH_2CF_3$$

Tetrafluoroethyl and (beta-dichlorodifluoroethyl) phenyl ethers are prepared from tetrafluoroethylene and 1,1-dichloro-2,2-difluoroethylene, respectively, by condensation with phenol in the presence of catalytic amounts of sodium hydroxide[210].

$$C_6H_5-OH \; + \; CF_2{=}CCl_2 \; \xrightarrow{\text{NaOH}} \; C_6H_5-O-CF_2CCl_2H$$

Using typical Friedel-Crafts reaction conditions with $FeCl_3$ as catalyst, α,α,α-trifluoroacetophenone is prepared from benzene and trifluoroacetyl chloride[209].

$$C_6H_6 \; + \; ClC(O)-CF_3 \; \xrightarrow{\text{FeCl}_3} \; C_6H_5-C(O)-CF_3$$

Intermediates Containing the Perfluoroalkyl Group. Because of the inertness of the $-CF_3$ group to sulfonation, nitration, reduction, etc., trifluoromethylbenzene and chlorotrifluoromethylbenzene have been used as starting materials for aromatic dye intermediates.

The isomeric chloro(trifluoromethyl)benzenes are prepared commercially from the corresponding chloro(trichloromethyl)benzenes by treatment with 98 per cent hydrofluoric acid at 100 to 110°C and 25 atmospheres of pressure[62]. The by-product, hydrochloric acid, is bled off during the reaction. Any HF escaping with the HCl is condensed and returned for reuse. This method is applicable to all three isomeric chloro(trifluoromethyl)benzenes. The yields are in the range of 80 to 90 per cent of theory.

4-Chloro-3-trifluoromethylphenol is prepared from 4-chloro-3-trifluoro-methylaniline through diazotization and subsequent hydrolysis of the diazonium compound in dilute sulfuric acid[281].

Bromination of trifluoromethylbenzene may be effected in the vapor phase at 700 to 900°C[280].

Alkyl or phenyl trifluoromethyl ethers are readily prepared from the corresponding chloro- or bromotrifluoromethane by treatment with alkali metal alkoxides[289], or phenoxides[287].

Aromatic Amines Containing the Trifluoromethyl Group. The activated chlorine atom in 2-chloro-3,5-dinitrobenzotrifluoride undergoes ammonolysis under the very mild condition of 25 to 28°C at atmospheric pressure[29].

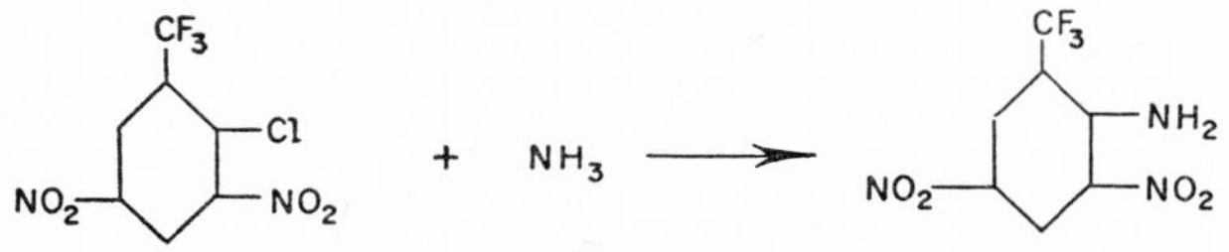

The use of catalytic amounts of cuprous oxide with aqueous ammonia is effective in converting 2-chloro-3(and 5)-nitrobenzotrifluoride to the corresponding amino compounds[28].

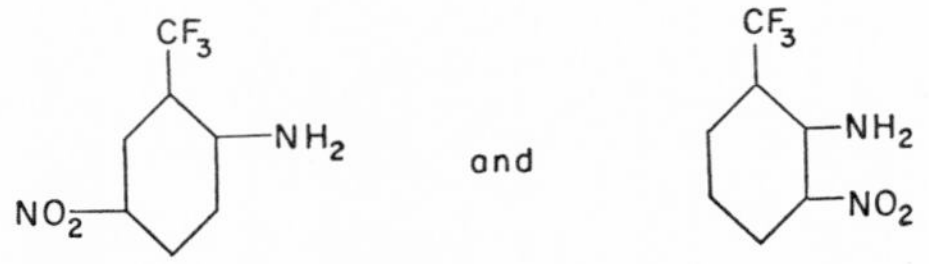

4-Chloro-3-nitrobenzotrifluoride reacts with ammonia at 105 to 120°C under autogenous pressure to form 4-amino-3-nitrobenzotrifluoride in yields of 93 per cent[273] of theory.

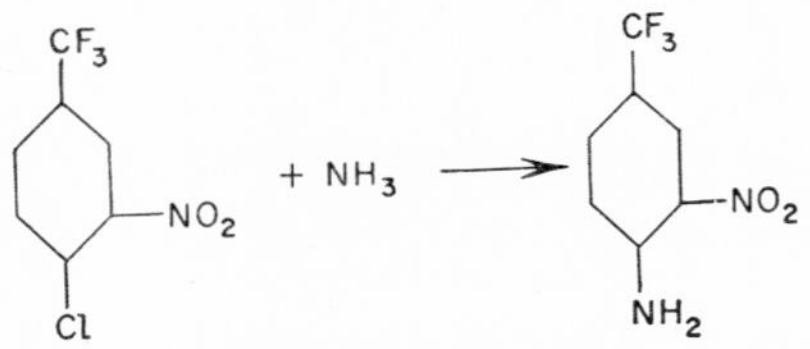

Amino(trifluoromethyl)benzene can be sulfonated with chlorosulfonic acid to yield amino(trifluoromethyl)benzenesulfonic acid[283]. It is stated that sulfonation cannot be effected with sulfuric acid or oleum. Treatment of benzotrifluoride with chlorosulfonic acid yields benzotrichloride.

The reactive chlorine atom in 4-chloro-3-nitrobenzotrifluoride reacts with sodium ethanesulfinate[112] to form 4-ethylsulfonyl-3-nitrobenzotrifluoride (intermediate for Golden Orange GR Base) in 92 to 93.5 per cent yields based on 4-chloro-3-nitrobenzotrifluoride[262].

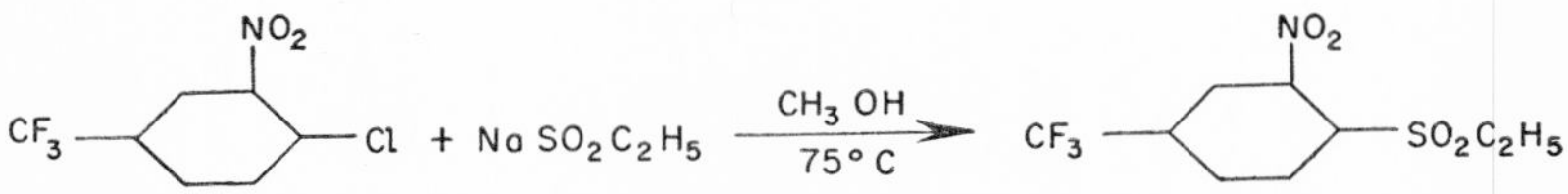

The nitro(trifluoromethyl)benzenes readily undergo reduction to yield the corresponding amines. In industrial practice, these reductions have been effected with iron and dilute acid; however, catalytic techniques can be used. The reactions go without difficulty and the products are obtained in good yield. In this manner 3-amino-4-chlorobenzotrifluoride (6-chloro-α,α,α-trifluoro-*m*-toluidine)[79], 5-amino-1,3-bis(trifluoromethyl)benzene ($\alpha,\alpha,\alpha,\alpha',\alpha',\alpha'$-hexafluoro-3,5-xylidine)[220], and 2-ethylsulfonyl-5-trifluoromethylaniline (6-ethylsulfonyl-α,α,α-trifluoro-*m*-toluidine)[99] are prepared from the corresponding nitro compounds.

Substituted Nitro(trifluoromethyl)benzenes. *m*- and *p*-Chlorobenzotrifluoride are nitrated in 100 per cent sulfuric acid with a nitrating acid composed of 30 per cent nitric and 70 per cent sulfuric acid. Yields are 81 per cent and 97 per cent of the theoretical, respectively[74, 75].

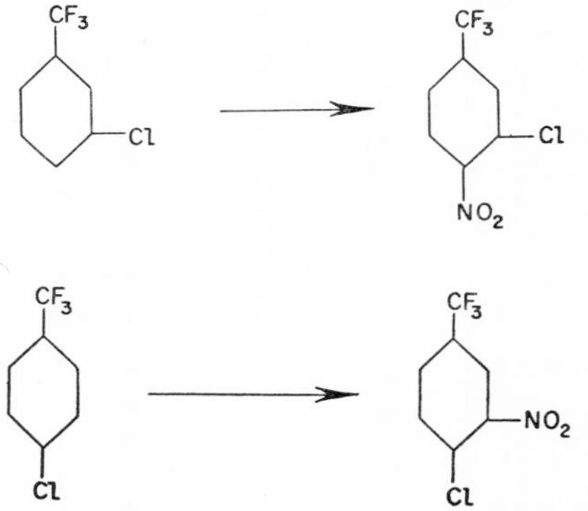

Likewise, *m*-bis(trifluoromethyl)benzene is nitrated to the corresponding 5-nitro-1,3-bis(trifluoromethyl)benzene in yields of 80 per cent of theory[264].

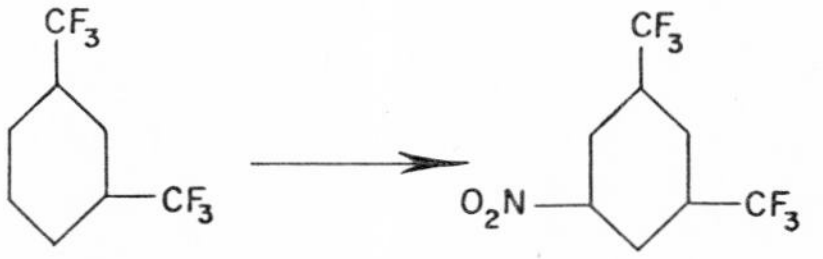

A synthesis of 2-amino-4-(trifluoromethyl)benzoic acid involves 4-amino-3-nitrobenzotrifluoride, described above, as a starting material. Conversion to the 4-cyano-3-nitrobenzotrifluoride is effected by diazotization in dilute sulfuric acid solution and subsequent treatment of the diazonium salt with sodium cuprous cyanide. The resulting nitrile is hydrolyzed to the corresponding acid by a stepwise treatment with 80 per cent sulfuric acid and sodium nitrite. The resulting 2-nitro-4-(trifluoromethyl)benzoic acid is reduced to 2-amino-4-(trifluoromethyl)benzoic acid.

Fluorination of the Aromatic Nucleus. In order to effect fluorination of the aromatic nucleus, it is necessary to employ indirect procedures similar to those used in the alkyl series. In the preparation of hexafluorobenzene from hexachlorobenzene, the reaction is carried out in a stepwise manner through the completely saturated cyclohexane derivative. The several stages are illustrated as follows:

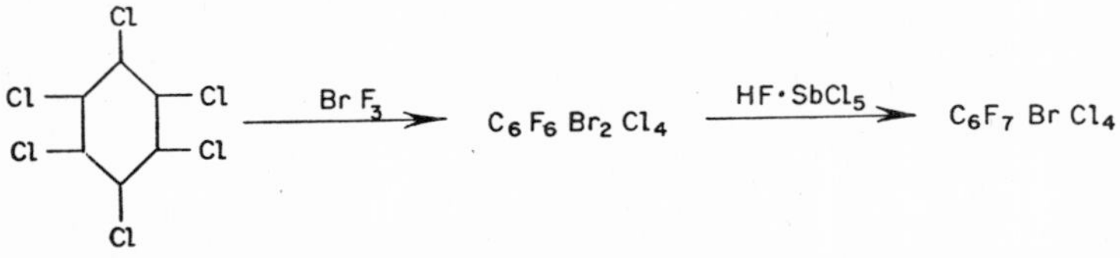

Dehalogenation of the compound, $C_6F_7BrCl_4$, with zinc removes the chlorine, bromine and excess fluorine and hexafluorobenzene results[321]. Perfluorotoluene may be made in the same manner[291].

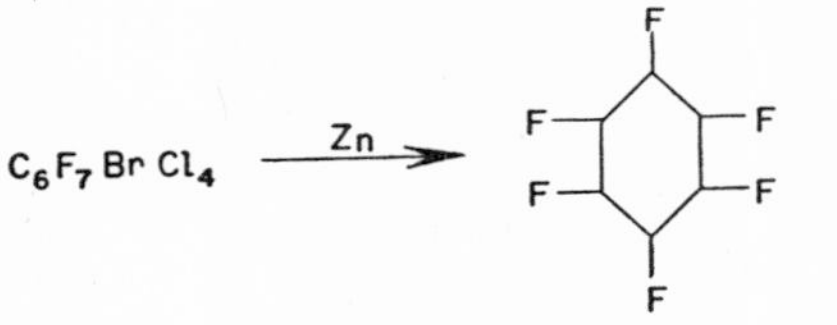

Hexafluorobenzene

This procedure is obviously not applicable to the preparation of intermediates where substitution in the aromatic nucleus is limited and position of the fluorine atom is important. For these cases, it is necessary to resort to the well known procedure involving an intermediate, diazonium fluoride. Subsequent decomposition of this compound yields the corresponding fluoride[4, 101]. A newer procedure known as the Schiemann reaction[7] substitutes diazonium fluoborate for diazonium fluoride.

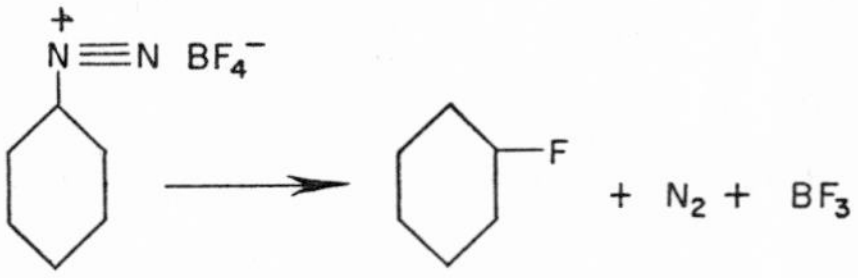

Using this technique, mono-, di-(o-, m-, and p-) and 1,2,4-trifluorobenzene have been prepared[322]. The reaction is broadly applicable to a wide variety of aromatic systems[3].

While the aromatic fluorine atom is very unreactive when present as the only substituent, the presence of an activating group, for example, a nitro group in the ortho or para position, renders fluorine the most labile of all the halogens to nucleophilic substitution[325].

ALKYLATION

Methods of introduction of the alkoxy group into the benzene nucleus through the direct reaction of an alcohol and phenol are known[17], for example, ethyl alcohol reacts with phenol at 175 to 225°C in the presence of an alumina catalyst to form phenetole, but industrial practice is essentially limited to two general methods. The first is based on alkylating a phenolic group by treatment with a dialkyl sulfate, an alkyl arenesulfonate, or an alkyl halide, while the second involves replacement of a labile aromatic halogen with the nucleophilic reagent prepared from an alkali metal alkoxide. In either case the reaction is base catalyzed and the reaction mass must be kept alkaline. With the use of dimethyl or diethyl sulfate, it is customary to carry out the reaction in a manner that will minimize exposure of the alkyl sulfate to strongly alkaline conditions, otherwise much of the alkylating agent is sacrificed due to hydrolysis. While the first alkyl group of the dialkyl sulfate is readily reacted, it is usually necessary to resort to more vigorous conditions and an anhydrous system to force the second to react.

The stepwise nature of the reaction is illustrated by the methylation of phenol[45]. With the use of one mole of dimethyl sulfate per mole of phenol at 10 to 80°C an 85 to 92 per cent yield of anisole is obtained. When the dimethyl sulfate is reduced to essentially 0.5 mole per mole of phenol, it is necessary to reflux the reaction mass for 15 hours and the yield of anisole falls to 72 to 75 per cent.

The general scope of the reaction is illustrated by the methylation of *p*-hydroxybenzoic acid to anisic acid[222], the conversion of vanillin to veratraldehyde (3,4-dimethoxybenzaldehyde)[22] and the methylation of 3-hydroxydiphenylamine (*m*-anilinophenol) to 3-methoxydiphenylamine[253]. Yields fall in the range of 80 to 90 per cent.

Alkylation with Alkyl Halides

The reaction of an alkyl halide with alkali phenoxides to form alkyl aryl ethers is carried out in aqueous caustic under the comparatively low pressures of 200 to 300 psi[2]. Temperatures range from 80 to 125°C. While the yields, based on the starting phenolic compounds, are good, one disadvantage of the system is the inherent material losses in dealing with alkyl halides which have high vapor pressures under the working conditions. Usual practice requires a substantial excess of the alkyl chloride compared to a slight excess in the case of the dialkyl sulfate procedure. The reaction is practically limited to straight-chain alkyl halides since with secondary and tertiary alkyl chlorides, the reaction is complicated by dehydrohalogenation of the alkylating agent. A number of applications of alkylations of this type are found in Table 6.

Alkoxylation with Metal Alkoxides

There are numerous instances of direct replacement of a labile aromatic halogen by a nucleophilic alkoxide reagent. This reaction is best carried out

TABLE 6. ALKYLATION WITH ALKYL HALIDES

Starting Material	Alkylating Agent	Temp. (°C)	Initial Pressure	Product	% Yield	Ref.
			psi			
Phenol.............	Methyl chloride	125	240	Anisole	93.7	57
m-Cresol...........	Methyl chloride	125	240	*m*-Methylanisole	94.1	107
Hydroquinone.......	Methyl chloride	120–125	300	*p*-Dimethoxybenzene	87.2	103
Hydroquinone.......	Ethyl chloride	120	250	*p*-Diethoxybenzene	92.1	102
3-Hydroxy-4'-methyldiphenylamine (*m*-[*p*-Toluidino]-phenol)...........	Ethyl chloride	60–100	30–60	3-Ethoxy-4'-methyldiphenylamine (*N*-[*p*-Tolyl]-*m*-phenetidine)	73.6	161

TABLE 7. ALKOXYLATION OF AROMATIC HALOGEN COMPOUNDS

Starting Material	Alcohol	Temp. (°C)	Product	Yield % Th.	Ref.
1-Chloro-2-nitrobenzene	Methanol	70–95	*o*-Nitroanisole	94.3	110
1-Chloro-4-nitrobenzene	Methanol	40–50	*p*-Nitroanisole	96.0	111
1,3-Dichloro-4-nitrobenzene	Methanol	90	1,3-Dimethoxy-4-nitrobenzene	—	112
1,4-Dichloro-2-nitrobenzene	Methanol	70–90	4-Chloro-2-nitroanisole	94.0	67
1,2,4-Trichloro-5-nitrobenzene	Methanol	90	1-Chloro-2,4-dimethoxy-5-nitrobenzene	85.5	70
4-Chloro-3-nitrotoluene	Methanol	100	4-Methyl-2-nitroanisole	85.6	115

in an alcohol medium, where the nucleophilic reagent —OR is made in situ by the addition of sodium or potassium hydroxide. Reaction temperatures range from 70 to 100°C with corresponding pressures up to 300 psi. Table 7 summarizes a number of applications of this technique.

Caution should be exercised in application of this reaction on a large scale, particularly when the reactants are nitro compounds. There is danger of violent side reactions which become explosive in nature.

In applying this technique to compounds containing reducible groups, e.g., nitro compounds, precaution must be taken since caustic and alcohol constitute a reducing system which tends to reduce the nitro compounds to azo and azoxy compounds. This can be largely eliminated[1] by charging a small amount of air into the reaction vessel at the start of the reaction. This undesirable side reaction can be controlled also by rigidly controlling the amount of sodium hydroxide used in the reaction. In the manufacture of *o*- and *p*-nitrophenetoles, a procedure[1, 151] has been devised for controlling the amount of sodium hydroxide in the reaction mass by carrying out the reaction under reflux and diverting the reflux over solid sodium hydroxide before it is returned to the reaction mass. By controlling the temperature and rate of reflux, the amount of caustic in the charge can be controlled within comparatively narrow limits.

Because of a side reaction leading to hydroxylation, ethoxylation does not give as high yields as the corresponding methoxylation. The by-product phenolic compound can be converted to the desired product by treating the crude reaction mixture with ethyl chloride at the end of the reaction. In this manner, yields of 95 per cent of theory of *p*- and 92 per cent of *o*-nitrophenetole are attained[1, 151].

An analogous reaction involving replacement of a labile chlorine atom with the phenoxy group is found in the preparation of 4-chloro-2-nitrophenyl phenyl ether from 1,4-dichloro-2-nitrobenzene[150].

INTRODUCTION OF THE FORMYL AND CARBOXY GROUPS

Newer techniques for introducing the formyl and carboxy groups in the benzene nucleus involve direct oxidation of alkylbenzenes with air and a suitable catalyst or, in some cases, with nitric acid. These procedures, which are discussed under another section, are limited essentially to the preparation of unsubstituted simple aromatic aldehydes and carboxylic acids.

A number of less direct procedures are employed for introducing these groups in the benzene nucleus which already contains functional substituents.

Carboxylation

Procedures for introduction of the carboxy group involve oxidation of alkyl and acyl side chains, the use of phosgene and cyanogen chloride and the hydrolysis of the trichloromethyl group. A practical procedure for the manufacture of 2,5-dichlorobenzoic acid is found in the reaction of phosgene with *p*-dichlorobenzene in tetrachloroethane solution.

The intermediate acid chloride is hydrolyzed with dilute sodium hydroxide. A yield of 81.8 per cent based on the starting *p*-dichlorobenzene is obtained[154].

A similar procedure involves the reaction of a carbamyl chloride/aluminum chloride addition compound with the benzene nucleus to form the carboxamide. Subsequent hydrolysis yields the carboxylic acid. The addition compound is prepared by reacting ammonia and phosgene at 400 to 450°C in a hot tube and quickly condensing the products in a neutral solvent, e.g., benzene, in which aluminum chloride is suspended[48]. This reaction is illustrated with the conversion of biphenyl to 4-biphenylcarboxamide.

Aromatic carboxylic acids are prepared also through acylation of the aromatic ring and subsequent oxidation to the corresponding acid. An application of this procedure is found in the reaction of acetyl chloride and biphenyl in the presence of anhydrous aluminum chloride to form *p*-phenylacetophenone. Oxidation of the acetyl group with alkaline sodium hypochlorite yields the corresponding acid in 80 per cent over-all yield based on the starting biphenyl[155].

Cyanogen chloride, and bromide, may be used in the presence of $AlCl_3$ for the direct introduction of the cyano group which yields the corresponding carboxylic acid upon hydrolysis. This reaction is most successful in cases where the ring is somewhat activated by the presence of alkoxy groups[315]. The halogen in arylhalides can be replaced in many cases by the cyano group by treatment with copper or zinc cyanide and pyridine[274b].

Carboxylation of Phenols. Hydroxybenzoic acids are made in good yield by application of the well-known Kolbe-Schmitt reaction. The alkali salt of the starting phenolic compound is heated under pressure in the presence of carbon dioxide. The potassium salt orients the carboxy group largely in the para position while the sodium salt orients ortho. The reaction is carried out in steps in which the charge is alternately subjected to carbon dioxide under pressure and vacuum distillation to remove unreacted phenol.

In this manner phenol yields largely salicylic acid when the carboxylation is carried out at 150 to 160°C with sodium phenoxide[1]. If the temperature is controlled in the range of 205 to 220°C, and potassium phenoxide is used, the product is largely *p*-hydroxybenzoic acid[104]. The yield based on the phenol consumed is approximately 90 per cent in the first case and 85 per cent in the latter.

This reaction has been applied also to the preparation of 2-hydroxy-3-carbazolecarboxylic acid[331].

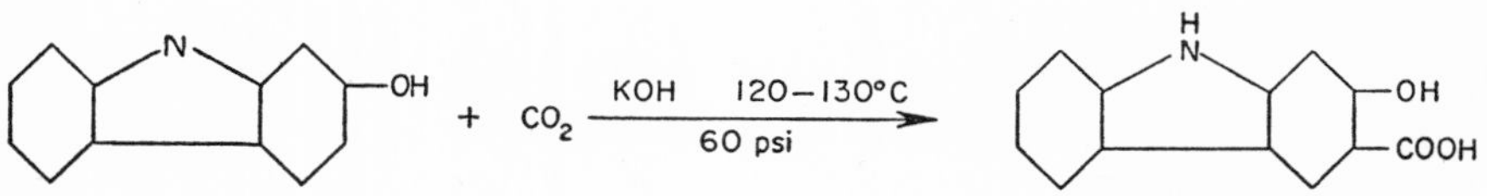

Yields fall in the range 82 to 85 per cent of theory, based on the 2-hydroxycarbazole consumed. Likewise, *o*-phenylphenol yields the corresponding 2-hydroxy-3-biphenylcarboxylic acid.

Carboxylation Through Hydrolysis. In the preparation of 2,4-dichlorobenzoic acid, the trichloromethyl group of 2,4-dichlorobenzotrichloride is hydrolyzed in 78 per cent sulfuric acid to the corresponding carboxylic acid.

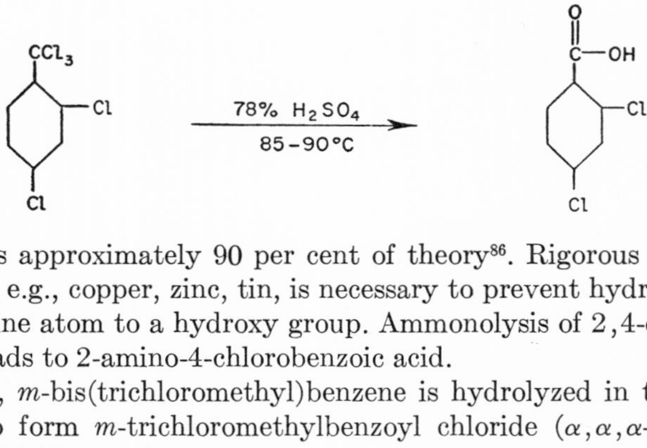

The yield is approximately 90 per cent of theory[86]. Rigorous exclusion of metal salts, e.g., copper, zinc, tin, is necessary to prevent hydrolysis of the ortho chlorine atom to a hydroxy group. Ammonolysis of 2,4-dichlorobenzoic acid leads to 2-amino-4-chlorobenzoic acid.

Similarly, *m*-bis(trichloromethyl)benzene is hydrolyzed in the presence of FeCl₃ to form *m*-trichloromethylbenzoyl chloride (α,α,α-trichloro-*m*-toluyl chloride)[272].

Introduction of the Formyl Group (Aldehydes)

Procedures have been devised for introduction of the aldehyde group by controlled direct oxidation of alkylated hydrocarbons but they are practically limited to the simpler unsubstituted compounds. The most familiar procedure for introduction of the aldehyde group involves the hydrolysis of a dichloromethyl group, e.g., *o*-chlorobenzaldehyde results from *o*-chloro-toluene through the following sequence of reactions[230].

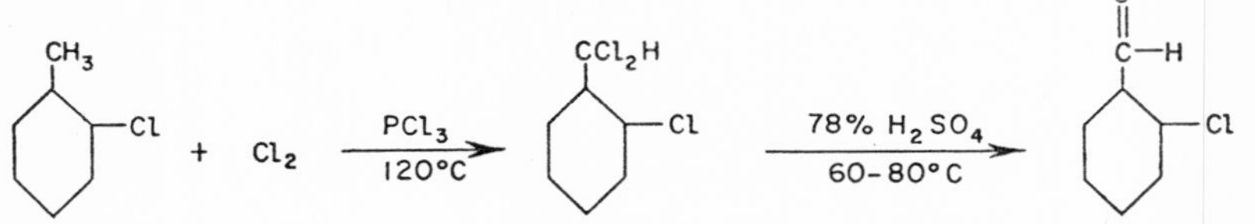

The same conditions are used for the preparation of the para isomer. Less generalized techniques are illustrated with the novel preparation of *p*-dimethylaminobenzaldehyde by reacting N,N-dimethylaniline and formaldehyde in the presence of N,N-dimethyl-*p*-nitrosoaniline according to the following scheme[193].

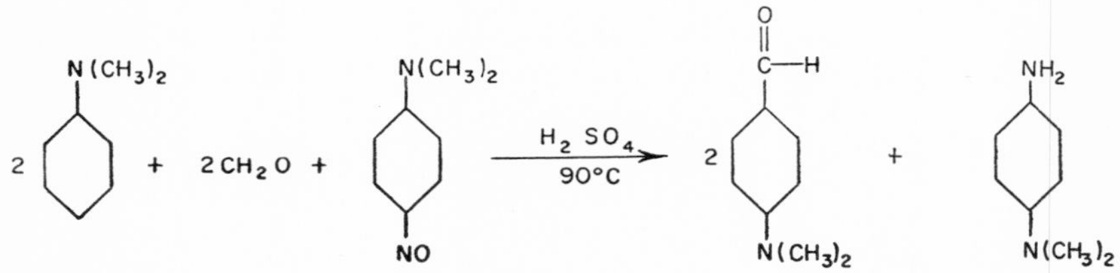

The reaction is almost quantitative based on the formaldehyde. *p*-Diethylaminobenzaldehyde is prepared in a similar manner[242].

p-Aminobenzaldehyde is made from *p*-nitrotoluene by an intramolecular oxidation-reduction in the presence of sulfur and caustic soda. A 72 per cent yield is obtained[213].

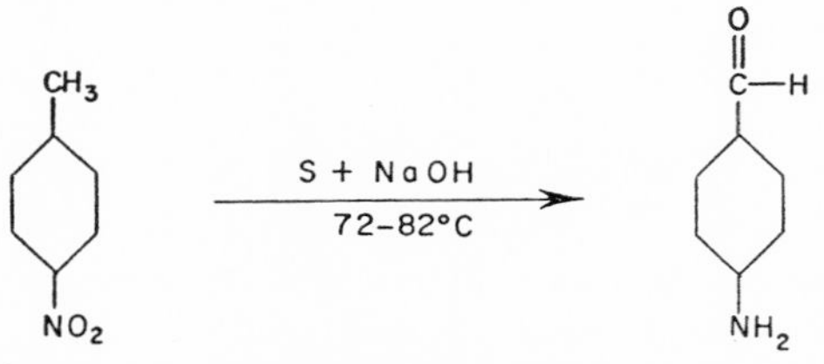

p-(*N*-Methyl-*p*-phenetidino)benzaldehyde results from the reaction of *N*-methylformanilide with *N*-methyl-*N*-phenyl-*p*-phenetidine in the presence of $POCl_3$[194].

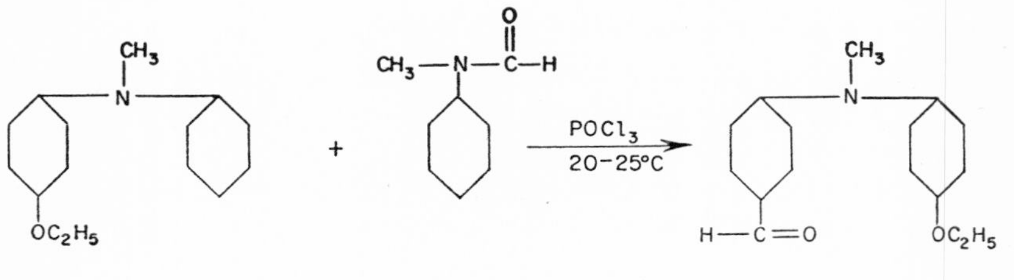

AROMATIC HYDROXYLATION

Introduction of the hydroxy group in the aromatic nucleus is accomplished through a variety of procedures which range from alkali fusion of the corresponding aromatic halide or sulfonic acid to the direct oxidation of the aromatic hydrocarbon. The diversity of routes to phenolic compounds is illustrated with procedures for the three isomeric dihydroxybenzenes. Pyrocatechol, *o*-dihydroxybenzene, is made commercially by a high temperature hydrolysis of *o*-chlorophenol or *o*-dichlorobenzene with strong sodium hydroxide in the presence of barium chloride which forms an insoluble metal salt with the product and protects it from decomposition. Hydroquinone, *p*-dihydroxybenzene, is prepared by the oxidation of aniline with manganese dioxide in dilute sulfuric acid to *p*-quinone which is then reduced to the final product[274a]. Resorcinol, *m*-dihydroxybenzene, is prepared by fusing sodium *m*-benzenedisulfonate with sodium hydroxide at 330°C[136].

Recent developments in the manufacture of phenols have resulted in novel routes of considerable technical importance. *p*-Cresol is made commercially from toluene by bubbling toluene vapors through a mixture of sulfuric acid and a boron catalyst. A complex compound of toluene and boron is formed which is hydrolyzed to the corresponding hydroxylated compound[24]. This procedure is adaptable to other phenolic compounds, e.g., phenol and resorcinol. A new commercial process for phenol[23] involves alkylation of benzene with propene to cumene[277] which is oxidized to cumene hydroperoxide[26, 36]. The latter is decomposed into phenol and acetone:

Starting with toluene, *p*-cresol can be made by a similar route.

A familiar procedure for introduction of the aromatic hydroxy group, which is employed when more direct methods are not adaptable, involves diazotization of a corresponding amine and subsequent decomposition. Application of this technique is illustrated by the manufacture of *m*-cresol with a yield of 79 per cent of theory[81] and *p*-cresol in 87 per cent of theory[82] from the corresponding amines, and of 3-nitro-4-methylphenol (3-nitro-*p*-cresol) via *p*-toluidine and 3-nitro-4-methylaniline (3-nitro-*p*-toluidine). The over-all yield in the latter case is 69 per cent of theory based on the starting *p*-toluidine[260].

Substituted phenols are frequently made through nucleophilic substitution of hydroxy for a labilized halogen. For example, 1-chloro-4-nitrobenzene is hydrolyzed in 30 per cent sodium hydroxide at 95 to 100°C to p-nitrophenol[114], and 1-chloro-2,4-dinitrobenzene undergoes hydrolysis in sodium hydroxide solution at 95 to 100°C to form 2,4-dinitrophenol[97]. Likewise 4-chloro-3-nitrobenzenesulfonamide undergoes hydrolysis in boiling sodium hydroxide solution with 92 per cent yields of 2-nitro-1-phenol-4-sulfonamide[181].

The well-known Dow process for the manufacture of phenol involves the direct reaction of chlorobenzene with sodium hydroxide under the vigorous reaction conditions of 360°C and 4,000 psi pressure[6, 33, 294].

REACTIONS WITH AMMONIA

An alternative procedure for manufacturing aromatic amines involves nucleophilic attack of a substituted aromatic nucleus by ammonia or amines. Best results are obtained in cases where the group to be replaced is ortho to a negative group, and thus in a position for nucleophilic attack. This general type of reaction can be extended to include reactions of alkyl and arylamines with negatively substituted aromatic halides. Other reactions involving ammonia include the preparation of nitriles. These reactions of commercial interest in the field of benzene intermediates have been classified as follows:

(1) Amination of aromatic halides
(2) Reactions of ammonia with aromatic carboxylic acids or anhydrides
(3) Arylation of aromatic amines with (a) phenols (b) aryl halides
(4) Alkylation of aromatic amines

Amination of Aromatic Halides

A number of aromatic amines are manufactured by direct ammonolysis of the corresponding halogen compounds. Success of this route depends upon the labilizing effect (to attack by nucleophilic reagents) of electron-attracting groups attached to the aromatic nucleus in an ortho or para position relative to the chloro group. Copper is frequently used as a catalyst. A typical application of this reaction is found in the process for the manufacture of p-nitroaniline[179e, 254]. The reaction may be effected continuously with 40 per cent aqueous ammonia at 200 atmospheres pressure and at 237 to 240°C. The reactants are pumped continuously through a coil which serves as the reactor. The yield is nearly quantitative.

4-Chloro-2-nitroaniline is manufactured by direct amination of the readily obtainable 1,4-dichloro-2-nitrobenzene. The yield is 99 per cent of theory[66, 234]. Strong aqueous ammonia is used at 150 to 175°C.

Similarly, *o*-chlorobenzoic acid reacts with isobutylamine resulting in a 72 per cent yield of *N*-isobutylanthranilic acid[250].

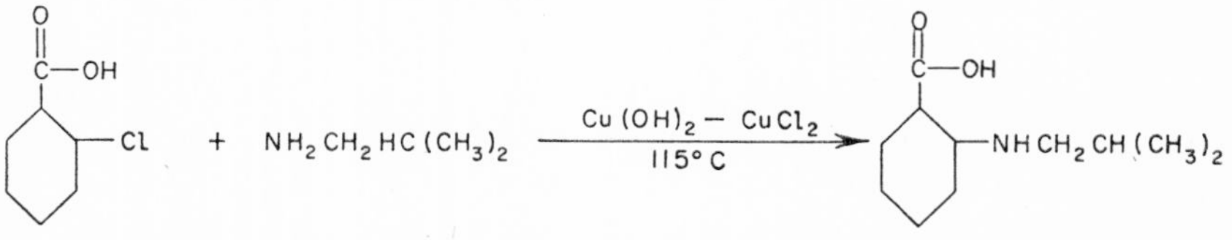

Nearly quantitative yields of *o*-nitroaniline are obtained by reacting 1-chloro-2-nitrobenzene with 27 per cent aqueous ammonia at 185°C and 450 psi pressure[108]. Likewise, 1-chloro-2,4-dinitrobenzene reacts with ammonia to form 2,4-dinitroaniline[162].

Excellent yields of 2-amino-5-nitrobenzenesulfonic acid are obtained by reacting 2-chloro-5-nitrobenzenesulfonic acid and 27 per cent aqueous ammonia at 120°C at approximately 100 psi pressure[178].

Nitriles from Aromatic Carboxylic Acids

The reaction of ammonia with organic compounds to form nitriles cannot be classified as ammonolysis in the narrow sense, nevertheless, this reaction has been included in this group of industrial reactions which involve ammonia and lead to dye intermediates.

Practical commercial processes for the manufacture of nitriles involve the vapor phase reaction of ammonia and an acid or acid anhydride over an alumina catalyst at high temperatures. Best results are obtained with the use of a large excess of ammonia. The contact times of the reacting gases with the catalyst are relatively short, e.g., 2 to 5 seconds. In this manner, benzonitrile[141] and phthalonitrile[134] are prepared commercially in very satisfactory yields from benzoic acid and phthalic anhydride, respectively.

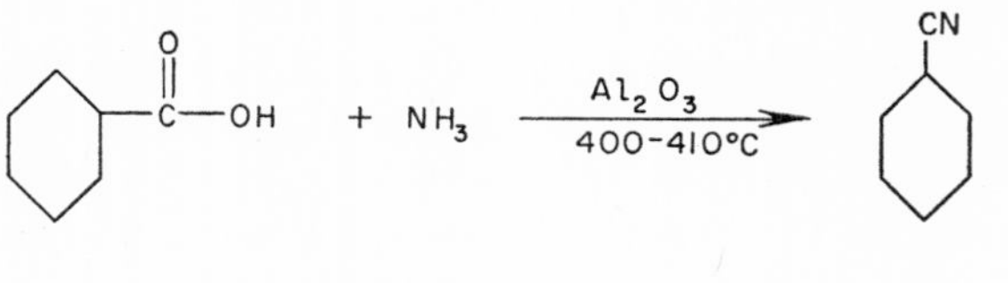

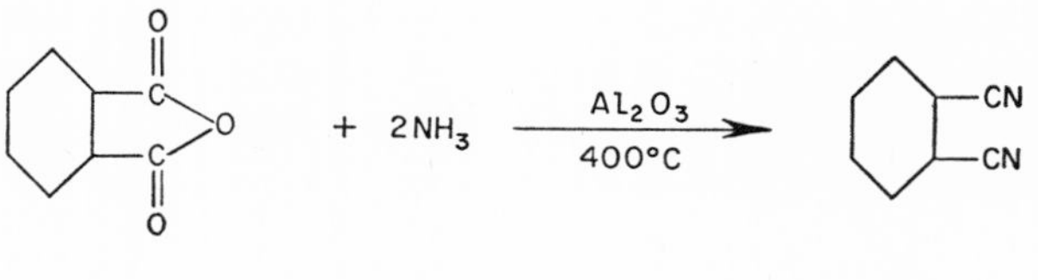

A recent innovation[286] in the manufacture of nitriles concerns the reaction of toluene and xylene directly with ammonia. The reaction occurs at high temperatures in contact with catalysts consisting of the oxides of molybdenum, phosphorus and aluminum. While conversions per pass are relatively low, e.g., 10 per cent, practical yields are obtained by recycling unreacted material.

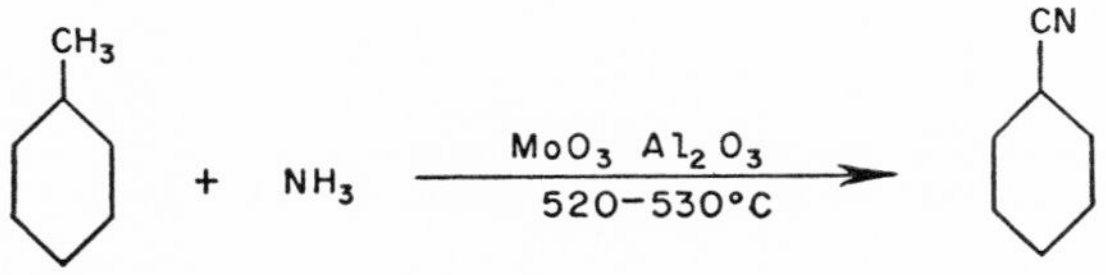

Arylation of Aromatic Amines

A number of important intermediates result from arylation of aromatic amines by treatment with phenols, aryl halides or other arylamines. These reactions are usually carried out at comparatively high temperatures often in an excess of one of the reactants which serves as a solvent. In the reaction of aryl halides and amines, the reaction is facilitated with the use of bases or base-forming materials which neutralize the by-product acid.

Acidic materials, for example, $FeCl_3$, $AlCl_3$ and sulfanilic acid, are effective catalysts for the alkylation of aromatic amines with phenols.

Thus, aniline and hydroquinone react at 200°C in the presence of excess aniline and catalytic amounts of sulfanilic acid or aluminum chloride to form 4-hydroxydiphenylamine (*p*-anilinophenol) in 79 per cent yields[247].

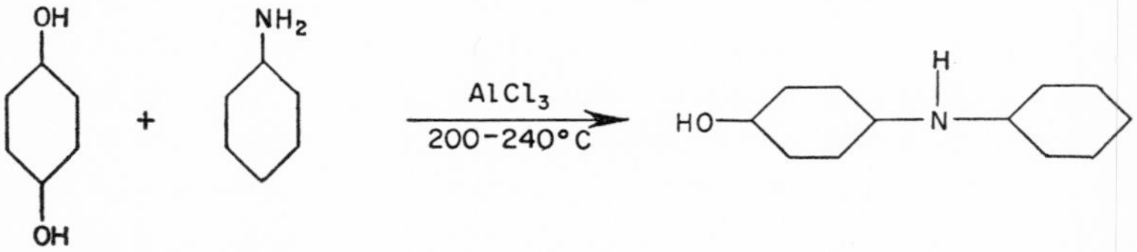

Water is distilled from the reaction mixture as it is formed during the course of the reaction. Aniline which distills with the water is continuously recycled to the system. The course of the reaction is readily followed by measuring the amount of water collected. 3-Hydroxydiphenylamine (*m*-anilinophenol) is made in a similar manner from resorcinol and aniline. A 73.4 per cent yield based on resorcinol is obtained[145].

3-Hydroxy-4'-methyldiphenylamine (*m*-[*p*-toluidino]phenol) is made by the same technique from resorcinol and *p*-toluidine in 88 per cent yields[106].

A number of applications of the general reaction of aryl halides with arylamines are included in Table 8. The yields are based on the aromatic chloro derivatives unless otherwise indicated.

TABLE 8. REACTIONS OF AROMATIC AMINES WITH ARYL HALIDES

Starting Material	Catalyst	Acid Acceptor	Reaction Temp. (°C)	Product	% Yield	Ref.
(a) o-Chlorobenzoic acid	Cu	KOH	150	N-Phenylanthranilic acid	92.8	98
(b) Aniline						
(a) 2-Chloro-5-nitrobenzene-sulfonic acid	None	MgO	175	2-(p-Chloroanilino)-5-nitro-benzenesulfonic acid	>83.8†	228
(b) p-Chloroaniline						
(a) 1-Chloro-2,4-dinitroben-zene	None	CaCO₃	Boil	p-(2,4-Dinitroanilino)-phenol	99.0*	96
(b) p-Aminophenol						
(a) 2-Chloro-5-nitrobenzene-sulfonic acid	None	MgO	160–165	2-(p-Methoxyanilino)-5-nitrobenzenesulfonic acid	92.0†	53
(b) p-Anisidine						
(a) 2-Chloro-5-nitrobenzene-sulfonic acid	—	MgO	143	2-(o-Methoxyanilino)-5-nitrobenzenesulfonic acid	75.5†	219
(b) o-Anisidine						

* Based on p-aminophenol. Nitro compound not isolated but reduced to corresponding amine in over-all yield.
† Based on amine from subsequent reduction.

Alkylation of Aromatic Amines

N-Alkylation of aromatic amines is very readily carried out in good yields. Alkylation agents may vary from alcohols and alkyl halides to ethylene oxide and alkyl ethers. A number of applications of this reaction are listed in Table 9. The yields are based on the aromatic amines.

TABLE 9. ALKYLATION OF AROMATIC AMINES

Starting Material	Alkylation Agent	Temp. (°C)	Product	% Yield	Ref.
o-Aminophenol	Ethylene oxide	98	2-o-Hydroxyanilinoethanol	71.0	248
N-Ethylaniline	Ethylene oxide	125–135	2-N-Ethylanilinoethanol	99.0	249
Sulfanilic acid	Methyl chloride	70–75	N,N-Dimethylsulfanilic acid	83.0	243
Metanilic acid	Ethyl chloride	120–125	N,N-Diethylmetanilic acid	87.0	93
o-Anisidine	Formaldehyde/sodium bisulfite	70–80	o-Methoxyanilinomethanesulfonic acid	95.0	223
Aniline	Methanol (PCl₃)	270–280	N,N-Dimethylaniline	—	95
Carbazole	Ethyl chloride	215	9-Ethylcarbazole	98.0	100
Aniline	n-Butanol (PCl₃)	270	N-Butylaniline	58.0	158
o-Toluidine	Dimethyl ether (Al₂O₃)	Vapor phase	N,N-Dimethyl-o-toluidine	89.0	143
N-Ethyl-m-toluidine	Ethylene oxide	112–130	2-(N-Ethyl-m-toluidino)ethanol	100.0	144
o-Toluidine	Diethyl ether (Al₂O₃)	250–255	N,N-Diethyl-o-toluidine	30.0	157
			o-Toluidine	10.0	
			N-Ethyl-o-toluidine	60.0	
Aniline	Ethylene oxide	65–70	2-Anilinoethanol	86.0	159
Aniline	Ethylene oxide	95	2,2'-Phenyliminodiethanol	88.0	160

OXIDATION

The alternative procedures for carrying out oxidation reactions in the manufacture of benzene intermediates include the familiar techniques making use of chemical oxidizing agents, e.g., manganese dioxide, potassium permanganate, chromic acid, lead oxide and chlorine. While these agents are still the basis of many going processes, particularly with the more complex starting materials, more recently developed practical techniques are based upon catalytic air oxidation in both liquid and vapor phases. Nitric acid and nitrogen oxides are economically attractive oxidizing agents, but in many cases the oxidation reaction is complicated by the tendency toward nitration. Alkylaromatic nitro compounds show less tendency toward this property and, consequently, can be oxidized to the corresponding nitroaromatic carboxylic acids with facility. These procedures avoid the use of the older chemical oxidizing agents which are generally more expensive and which are frequently less easily adapted to continuous processes and systems making use of automatic process controls.

Liquid Phase Catalytic Air Oxidation

The liquid phase catalytic air oxidation of alkyl aromatics involves the formation of an intermediate hydroperoxide which upon decomposition results in an oxidized form of the parent hydrocarbon material. The end product of the oxidation is largely determined by the reaction conditions and to some extent by the catalyst used.

The reaction proceeds through successive steps via a chain mechanism[329]. It is generally believed that the reactions are initiated through attack of a free radical by the oxygen molecule, Eq. (1). The resulting peroxide free radical attacks a molecule of the hydrocarbon material with the formation of a second hydrocarbon free radical and a hydroperoxide molecule, Eq. (2). Subsequent decomposition of the hydroperoxide leads to an oxidized form of the parent hydrocarbon.

(1) $\diagdown CH\cdot + O_2 \rightarrow \diagdown CH\cdot O\cdot O\cdot$

(2) $\diagdown CH\cdot O\cdot O\cdot + \diagdown CH_2 \rightarrow \diagdown CH\cdot O\cdot OH + \diagdown CH\cdot$

Robertson and Waters[311] have visualized the mechanism of the decomposition of a hydroperoxide, in the presence of a metal ion serving as a catalyst, to proceed according to the following scheme. The chain-starting mechanism is represented by Eq. (3).

(3) $\diagdown CH\cdot O\cdot OH + M^+ \rightarrow \diagdown CH\cdot O{:}^- + \cdot OH + M^{++}$

This step is then followed by Eq. (4).

$$(4) \quad \diagdown\!\!\diagup\!\!\mathrm{CH\cdot O\cdot OH} + \cdot\mathrm{OH} \rightarrow \mathrm{H_2O} + \diagdown\!\!\diagup\!\!\overset{\cdot}{\mathrm{C}}\cdot\mathrm{O\cdot OH} \rightarrow \diagdown\!\!\diagup\!\!\mathrm{C\!:\!O} + \cdot\mathrm{OH}$$

The metal ion M^{++} returns to its lower valence state by picking up an electron from a peroxide anion.

$$(5) \quad\quad\quad M^{++} + \mathrm{R\cdot O\cdot O\!:^-} \rightarrow \mathrm{R\cdot O\cdot O\cdot} + M^+$$

It should be noted that this mechanism provides an $\cdot$OH radical, which in taking up a proton from a molecule of hydrocarbon or from a hydroperoxide molecule, e.g.

$$\diagdown\!\!\diagup\!\!\mathrm{CH\cdot O\cdot OH} + \cdot\,\mathrm{OH} \rightarrow \mathrm{H_2O} + \diagdown\!\!\diagup\!\!\mathrm{CH\cdot O\cdot O\cdot}$$

produces a new free radical which effects perpetuation of the chain mechanism.

The catalyst, i.e., cobalt, iron, lead, zinc or manganese, usually in the form of an oil-soluble naphthenate salt, is effective by virtue of its acceleration of the decomposition of the hydroperoxide.

In practical application liquid phase oxidations are carried out by passing air through the warm agitated liquid material which is to be oxidized. The reaction generally requires several hours to reach equilibrium. There is usually considerable unchanged starting material at the end which must be separated from the product and recycled.

An application of this technique is found in a German process for the manufacture of benzoic acid from toluene. Some by-product, benzyl benzoate, is obtained. The reaction is effected at 130 to 135°C at approximately 30 psi pressure. Cobalt naphthenate is used as the catalyst[51].

Benzoic acid is also prepared from an alkylbenzene through catalytic air oxidation in acetic acid solution in the presence of a cobalt salt at approximately 200°C[40].

Similarly, acetophenone results from the liquid phase oxidation of ethylbenzene at 115°C in the presence of a catalyst comprising manganese, zinc and lead naphthenates[204]. The product consists of 65 per cent acetophenone, 26 per cent unchanged ethylbenzene and 9 per cent benzoic acid.

Terephthalic acid is made from p-xylene by passing air through a system consisting of p-xylene and lead acetate at approximately 200°C and at 700 to 900 psi pressure[32].

Vapor Phase Catalytic Air Oxidation

Catalytic vapor phase oxidation reactions are typified by the classic procedure for the manufacture of phthalic anhydride by the catalytic air oxidation of naphthalene over a vanadium pentoxide catalyst at 450°C. Manufacturing facilities for this product have undergone continual expansion since 1920. Present plant capacity in the United States exceeds 224 million lb. annually. Recent developments[282] in this connection have been concerned with the use of o-xylene, which has become available through the petroleum industry, as a starting material for the manufacture of phthalic anhydride. With the exception of a higher temperature, i.e., 540°C instead of 450°C, the conditions used for the oxidation of o-xylene are essentially those of the naphthalene oxidation. Raney nickel has been suggested also as a catalyst for this reaction[312].

Benzoic acid is readily obtained by passing crude phthalic anhydride and water vapors over an alumina/zinc oxide catalyst at 340°C. Under these conditions, the phthalic anhydride undergoes hydration and decarboxylation and benzoic acid is obtained in yields, based on naphthalene, in the range of 87 to 91 per cent of theory[225].

The use of a vanadium pentoxide catalyst modified with potassium sulfate arrests the vapor phase oxidation of naphthalene at the 1,4-naphthoquinone stage[30].

1,2,4,5-Tetramethylbenzene (durene) is oxidized over a vanadium pentoxide/potassium sulfate catalyst at 450°C to 1,2,4,5-benzenetetracarboxylic acid (pyromellitic acid)[8].

Hydrobromic acid is claimed to be effective in controlling by-product formation and the explosive nature of the reaction in the oxidation of benzene and alkylated benzenes in the vapor phase using air or oxygen as the oxidizing agents[314]. It has been used advantageously in the oxidation of toluene and ethylbenzene to benzyl alcohol and acetophenone, respectively[313].

The vapor phase air oxidation of benzene under properly controlled conditions results in a 50 per cent yield of phenol. The conversions per pass fall in the range of 4 to 8 per cent[298]. Boric oxide is used as a catalyst for this reaction[297].

Nitric Acid Oxidation

The use of nitric acid as an oxidizing agent for organic compounds is well known but it has not been widely used industrially. While nitric acid is readily available and economically attractive as an oxidizing agent, its use at elevated temperature requires special corrosion-resistant alloys and the oxidation reaction is accompanied by nitration of some starting materials. Where this tendency can be overcome with the use of low nitric acid concentrations and sufficiently low reaction temperatures, nitric acid is an excellent candidate for an oxidizing agent.

A number of patents describe processes involving the use of nitric acid in oxidizing alkyl side chains to the corresponding carboxylic acids. The mechanism of this oxidation reaction is generally believed to involve an initial side chain nitration followed by oxidative attack at the point of nitration, as expressed by the following scheme:

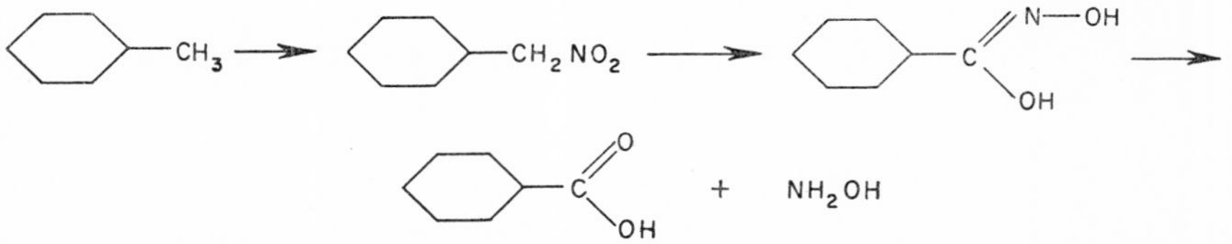

$$C_6H_5{-}CH_3 \longrightarrow C_6H_5{-}CH_2NO_2 \longrightarrow C_6H_5{-}C{\Big\langle}^{N{-}OH}_{OH} \longrightarrow$$

$$C_6H_5{-}C{\Big\langle}^{O}_{OH} \quad + \quad NH_2OH$$

The concentration of nitric acid is kept sufficiently low to prevent appreciable ring nitration. The by-product hydroxylamine reacts with a second mole of nitric acid. This leads to the formation of 2 moles of nitric oxide according to the following equation:

$$NH_2OH + HNO_3 \rightarrow 2NO + 2H_2O$$

The use of air or oxygen in conjunction with nitric acid is effective in regenerating, in situ, part of this by-product, nitric oxide, and in this manner reduces correspondingly the amount of nitric acid required for the reaction.

Some practical applications of this type of oxidation are found in the oxidation of alkyl aromatics. Nitrotoluene is readily oxidized to nitrobenzoic acid by treatment with 65 per cent nitric acid at atmospheric pressure[284] at the boiling point or with 20 to 40 per cent nitric acid at temperatures in the range of 120 to 190°C[9, 10]. Nitric acid of 30 or 40 per cent concentration with pressures of 40 to 80 psi and temperatures of 80 to 90°C has been used with manganese dioxide as a catalyst[316].

p-Xylene is oxidized to terephthalic acid with 30 per cent nitric acid at approximately 180°C and 200 psi pressure. The product is composed of 90 per cent terephthalic acid and approximately 10 per cent p-toluic acid. The combined over-all yield is 93 per cent of theory based on p-xylene[19].

Nitric acid has been used in oxidizing 2-picoline to picolinic acid. The reaction is carried out by treating 2-picoline in 93 per cent sulfuric acid solution[299] with 70 per cent nitric acid in the presence of selenous acid and potassium bromide catalyst. The reaction is effected at 250°C. Similarly 3-picoline in 96 per cent sulfuric acid is oxidized with nitrogen tetroxide in the presence of catalytic amounts of selenium dioxide at 315 to 330°C. Approximately 50 per cent of the picoline is attacked with a resulting yield of nicotinic acid of 75 per cent[307].

It has been reported[278] that 2-chloro-4-nitrotoluene is oxidized with 60 per cent HNO_3 at atmospheric pressure to the corresponding carboxylic acid in 75 per cent yields.

Chemical Oxidations

For the purpose of comparison, a few examples of chemical oxidations of a number of chemical types have been included in Table 10. While these reactions are of a specific nature, they have been included by way of illustrating actual working procedures for the manufacture of benzene intermediates involving oxidation.

TABLE 10. CHEMICAL OXIDATIONS

Starting Material	Oxidizing Agent	Product	% Yield	Ref.
Bis(p-nitrophenyl) sulfide	Cl_2	Bis(p-nitrophenyl) sulfone	80–90	245
Aniline sulfate	MnO_2-H_2SO_4	p-Quinone	88–91	246
2-Chloro-4-nitrotoluene	$Na_2Cr_2O_7$-H_2SO_4	2-Chloro-4-nitrobenzoic acid	64	235
m-Xylene	$Na_2Cr_2O_7$-H_2SO_4	Isophthalic acid	78	251
3-Chloro-p-toluenesulfonic acid	$KMnO_4$-Alkaline	2-Chloro-4-sulfobenzoic acid	88	240
2,4,5-Trimethylbenzenesulfonic acid	$KMnO_4$-Alkaline	5-Sulfotrimellitic acid	91	156
p,p'-Methylenebis-(N,N-dimethylaniline)	PbO_2-H_2SO_4	4,4'-Bis(dimethylamino)benzhydrol	87	268

REDUCTION

The most general application of reduction in the field of benzene intermediates involves reduction of the aromatic nitro group. Without special precautions these reductions result in the corresponding amine as is illustrated in the reduction of nitrobenzene to aniline.

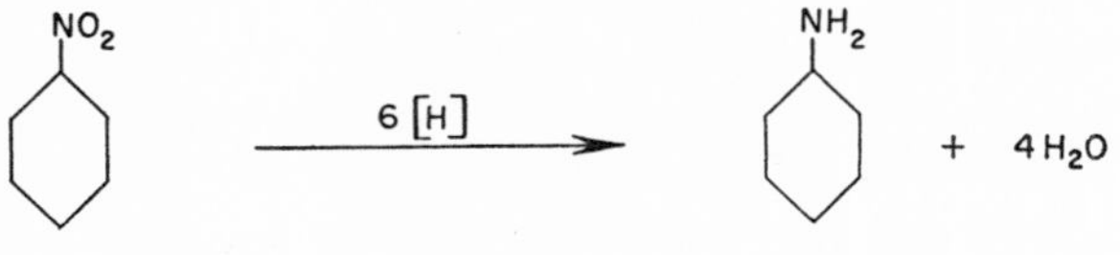

With the use of proper conditions and/or specific reducing agents, it is possible to arrest this reduction at intermediate stages, and in this manner azo and hydrazo compounds are obtained. The reaction passes through several stages which are illustrated in the reduction of nitrobenzene to hydrazobenzene.

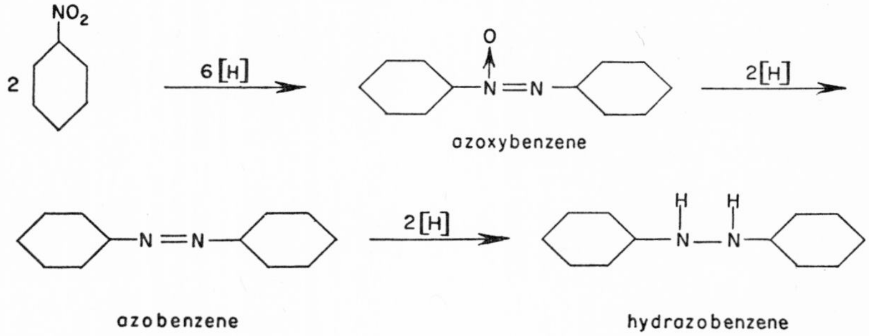

Brand and Mahr have proposed that the azoxybenzene structure results from a condensation of primary reduction products of nitrobenzene, e.g., nitrosobenzene and N-phenylhydroxylamine according to the following scheme[15]:

$$\begin{matrix} \text{aryl—NO} \\ \text{aryl—NH(OH)} \end{matrix} \rightarrow \begin{matrix} \text{aryl—N—O}^- \\ \text{aryl—N}^+\text{—OH} \\ \quad\quad | \\ \quad\quad\text{H} \end{matrix} \rightarrow \begin{matrix} \text{aryl—N—O}^- + \text{H}^+ \\ \text{aryl—N—OH} \end{matrix} \rightarrow$$

$$\begin{matrix} \text{aryl—N}^+\text{—O}^- \\ \quad\quad\| \\ \text{aryl—N} \end{matrix} + \text{OH}^-$$

Reductions involving the aromatic nitro group usually fall into one of four main categories depending upon the type of reducing agent or system used: (1) catalytic hydrogenation, (2) the Béchamp or iron reduction, (3) sodium sulfide reduction and (4) zinc reduction in the presence of caustic soda.

The trend in the development of new processes for the reduction of nitro compounds is toward replacement of chemical reducing agents with catalytic hydrogenation. The advantage in the catalytic procedure rests in the ease of process control, its adaptability to continuous procedures and the generally high quality of the crude which simplifies workup and isolation of the product.

From the economic viewpoint, there are numerous cases where chemical reduction proves more economical than catalytic reduction procedures, particularly where the production is small and the isolation of the products offers no problem.

Catalytic Hydrogenation

Most of the comparatively small-scale catalytic hydrogenations are carried out in the liquid phase in aqueous or solvent systems. Isopropyl alcohol has been found an effective solvent in many cases. Reaction temperatures usually range from 70 to 100°C with pressures ranging up to 500 psi. Nickel, cobalt, copper, palladium, and platinum are some of the more common catalysts. These metals are usually carried on a support.

Continuous liquid and vapor phase techniques for effecting catalytic hydrogen reduction are more adaptable to large scale operation. During the war, there was a great deal of interest in large quantities of xylidines. A number of patents dealing with this subject reveal continuous liquid phase processes making use of catalysts containing the sulfides of one or more of the following elements; molybdenum, tungsten, nickel and zinc, preferably on a support[21, 288]. Reaction temperatures in this type of system range up to 300°C with corresponding pressures of 1000 to 4000 psi. A reduced nickel catalyst is suitable also for this reduction[49].

Aniline has been made on a large scale by a continuous vapor phase process in which the reaction is carried out at 350 to 460°C at essentially atmospheric pressure[205]. Yields of 98 to 99 per cent of theory are obtained. The catalyst is composed of copper/copper oxide supported on silica.

Practical liquid phase catalytic hydrogenation procedures have been developed for the manufacture of benzidine, o-tolidine, o-toluidine, p-toluidine and the xylidines. A typical case is illustrated with the procedure for converting nitrobenzene to benzidine. The reaction is effected in isopropyl alcohol in the presence of nickel or palladium catalyst and a small amount of sodium hydroxide[38]. Hydrogen pressures of 100 to 200 psi and temperatures of 80 to 85°C are used. The charge absorbs hydrogen rapidly and it is necessary to apply external cooling to dissipate the heat of reaction. While the principal product is hydrazobenzene under these conditions, a minor portion of the nitrobenzene is reduced directly to aniline which is obtained as a by-product. Upon treatment with strong cold hydrochloric acid, the hydrazobenzene undergoes the well-known inversion reaction forming benzidine which is isolated as its hydrochloride or sulfate. Yields of isolated benzidine, based on the starting nitrobenzene, fall in the range of 60 to 70 per cent[41]. Some of this yield loss is due to partially inverted material, semidine (N-phenyl-p-phenylenediamine), which is lost in the mother liquors.

With essentially the same conditions, the catalytic reduction of o-nitrotoluene leads to o-tolidine in 60 to 70 per cent yields with 15 to 20 per cent of o-toluidine being obtained as a by-product[39].

o-Tolidine

Likewise, o-nitroanisole yields o-dianisidine (3,3'-dimethoxybenzidine).

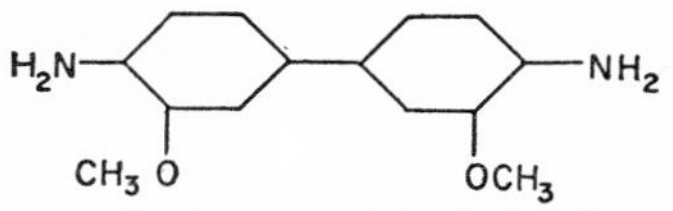

*o-*Dianisidine

The catalytic hydrogen reduction of *o*-nitrotoluene, *p*-nitrotoluene, and nitroxylene at 80 to 100°C and 400 to 500 psi over a catalyst consisting of nickel supported on kieselguhr leads to the corresponding amines in yields of 96 to 99 per cent of theory[37]. A small amount of sodium hydroxide in the reaction mixture is essential in controlling the reaction.

The catalytic hydrogenation of nitrobenzene in an acid medium, e.g., 20 per cent sulfuric acid with a noble metal catalyst (platinum), at 100 to 110°C and 500 psi pressure, results in a 57 per cent yield of *p*-aminophenol[42]. The formation of this compound results from a simultaneous rearrangement of the intermediate, *N*-phenylhydroxylamine, according to the following scheme:

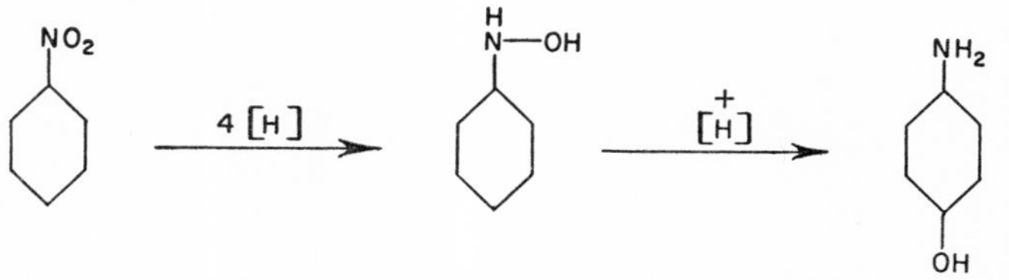

This reduction can likewise be effected with nascent hydrogen resulting from the action of acid on metal. Nitrobenzene can be reduced with metallic aluminum in dilute organic acid solution at 80 to 100°C. The yield of *N*-phenylhydroxylamine is 73 per cent of theory based on the starting nitrobenzene[11].

Béchamp Reduction

The Béchamp or iron reduction still occupies a prominent place in the manufacture of dye intermediates after having been in use for over fifty years. The effective reducing agent is nascent hydrogen generated by the reaction of gray iron and water. While iron and hot water react under essentially neutral conditions, the reaction rate is greatly accelerated by the hydrogen ion which is supplied in the form of acids, e.g., formic, acetic, or hydrochloric, or by salts of strong acids which produce acids upon hydrolysis. The effective amount of hydrogen ion used is but a fraction of the theoretical amount needed to liberate the molar quantity of the reducing agent. The over-all reaction is illustrated with the following equation:

$$2RNO_2 + 5Fe + 4H_2O \xrightarrow{[H]^+} 2Fe(OH)_2 + Fe_3O_4 + 2RNH_2$$

The disadvantages of this type of reduction are usually associated with the isolation of the product after the reduction is complete. The reaction mass comprises the product amine, water, a small amount of acid, soluble iron salts and the iron oxide sludge.

Despite this disadvantage, the iron reduction procedure is generally adaptable and economically competitive with other types of reduction and it is still widely applied in industry. A number of examples of the application of this reaction are listed in Table 11. While this list is by no means complete, it will serve to indicate the various chemical types which may be reduced by this procedure.

TABLE 11. APPLICATION OF IRON REDUCTION

Starting Material	Product	Acid Used	% Yield	Ref.
m-Nitrotoluene	m-Toluidine	Formic	87	138
4-Nitrobiphenyl	Xenylamine	Formic	95	216
1-Chloro-3-nitrobenzene	m-Chloroaniline	Formic	95	59
2-Chloro-6-nitrotoluene	3-Chloro-o-toluidine	Formic	ca. 100	76
p-Nitroaniline	p-Phenylenediamine	FeCl₃	93	265
p-Nitrophenol	p-Aminophenol	HOAc	97	54
2-Nitro-p-cresol	2-Amino-p-cresol	HCl	81–83	215
4-Methyl-2-nitroanisole	5-Methyl-o-anisidine	Formic	91	55
1,4-Dimethoxy-2-nitrobenzene	2,5-Dimethoxyaniline	Formic	91.8	92
p-Nitrobenzoic acid	p-Aminobenzoic acid	HCl	97	165
2-Chloro-5-nitrobenzoic acid	5-Amino-2-chlorobenzoic acid	HCl	90–91	166
m-Nitrobenzenesulfonic acid	Metanilic acid	HCl	89*	167
3-Nitro-5-sulfosalicylic acid	3-Amino-5-sulfosalicylic acid	—	ca. 76	206
5-Nitro-o-toluenesulfonic acid	5-Amino-o-toluenesulfonic acid	HCl	93–95	169
1,3-Dichloro-4-nitrobenzene	2,4-Dichloroaniline	HCl	95.5	84
4-Chloro-2-nitroanisole	5-Chloro-o-anisidine	Formic	79.5†	60
1-Chloro-2,5-dimethoxy-4-nitrobenzene	4-Chloro-2,5-dimethoxy-aniline	—	89.8*	63
2-Chloro-4-nitroaniline	2-Chloro-p-phenylenediamine	FeCl₃	92.0	238
Bis(p-nitrophenyl) sulfone	p,p'-Sulfonyldianiline	Formic	60.0	241

* Over-all yield based on nitrobenzene.
† Purified (crude yield 93 per cent).

Zinc Reduction

While catalytic hydrogen reductions are gradually replacing zinc reductions in the preparation of benzidine and its derivatives, zinc reductions are still used extensively in this field. The reaction is illustrated with the following equation:

$$10NaOH + 5Zn + 2RNO_2 \rightarrow R\!-\!\underset{H}{\overset{|}{N}}\!-\!\underset{H}{\overset{|}{N}}\!-\!R + 5Na_2ZnO_2 + 4H_2O$$

Subsequent hydrolysis of the sodium zincate results in the formation of zinc hydroxide, and sodium hydroxide is regenerated. Consequently, only a fraction of the theoretical amount of sodium hydroxide is required. The reduction is generally carried out in an aqueous system. In some instances alcohol or even nonpolar solvents have been used to advantage. The reaction between zinc and the nitro compound is vigorous and it must be controlled by adding one or more of the reactants gradually throughout the reduction. The reaction proceeds through several stages in the manner described with the catalytic procedure, the end product being the hydrazo compound which is subsequently inverted to the corresponding 4,4'-diamino derivative. Table 12 summarizes a number of applications of this technique in the manufacture of the benzidine types from the parent nitro compounds. The yields refer to isolated diamine. They are based on the starting nitro compound.

TABLE 12. ZINC-CAUSTIC REDUCTION OF NITROBENZENE DERIVATIVES

Starting Material	Product	Solvent	% Yield Including Inversion	Ref.
Nitrobenzene	Benzidine	Naphtha	83.5	58
o-Nitrotoluene	*o*-Tolidine	Naphtha	83	137
o-Nitroanisole	*o*-Dianisidine (3,3'-Dimethoxybenzidine)	Naphtha	76	83
o-Nitrobenzoic acid	4,4'-Diamino-3,3'-biphenyl-dicarboxylic acid	—	77	190
m-Nitrobenzenesulfonic acid	4,4'-Diamino-3,3'-biphenyl-disulfonic acid	—	75–76	188
3-Nitro-*p*-toluenesulfonic acid	4,4'-Diamino-5,5'-di-methyl-2,2'-biphenyldi-sulfonic acid	—	75–76	189
4-Chloro-2-nitroanisole	2,2'-Dichloro-5,5'-di-methoxybenzidine	—	55	187
1-Chloro-2-nitrobenzene	3,3'-Dichlorobenzidine	—	78	186

Sulfide Reduction

Sodium sulfide, sodium hydrosulfide, and sodium polysulfide have been used with facility in carrying out reductions of nitro compounds to the corresponding amines. One of its unique features is its adaptability to effecting partial reductions, e.g., the classical example of reduction of *m*-dinitrobenzene to *m*-nitroaniline. The reactions are carried out in the range of 50 to 100°C in an aqueous system.

Table 13 includes a number of applications of this technique.

TABLE 13. SULFIDE REDUCTION

Starting Materials	Product	Reducing Agent	Temp. (°C)	% Yield	Ref.
o-Nitroaniline	o-Phenylenediamine	Na₂S	50–105	83.5	185
p-Nitroanisole	p-Anisidine	Na₂S	85–115	94.3	56
1,4-Dimethoxy-2-nitrobenzene	2,5-Dimethoxyaniline	NaSH	70	84.5	94
1-Chloro-2,4-dimethoxy-5-nitrobenzene	5-Chloro-2,4-dimethoxyaniline	NaSH	100	83.0	64
2,4,6-Trinitrophenol	2-Amino-4,6-dinitrophenol	NaSH	45	75–80	266
3,5-Dinitro-p-toluenesulfonic acid	3-Amino-5-nitro-p-toluenesulfonic acid	NaSH-MgO	35	65.0	179
5-Phenylazosalicylic acid	5-Aminosalicylic acid	Na₂Sₓ	100	83.4	184
3-Methoxy-4-nitrosodiphenylamine	2-Methoxy-N⁴-phenyl-p-phenylenediamine	Na₂Sₓ	40–80	ca. 74.0	218
4,4′-Dinitro-2,2′-stilbenedisulfonic acid	4-Amino-4′-nitro-2,2′-stilbenedisulfonic acid	NaSH	38–40	90.0	180
5-(p-Nitrobenzamido)-salicylic acid	5-(p-Aminobenzamido)-salicylic acid	NaSH	80	83.0	214

HETEROCYCLIC INTERMEDIATES

While the following structures as such are of little interest as dye intermediates, a number of their derivatives have found broad application, particularly in the chemistry of azo dyes.

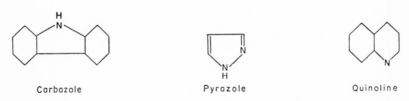

Carbazole   Pyrazole   Quinoline

Carbazoles

In the preparation of intermediates involving heterocyclic ring systems containing functional groups, it is usually necessary to build the heterocyclic nucleus from fragments which already contain the desired substituents rather than attempt direct substitution on the heterocyclic ring. An exception to this is found in reactions in which carbazole can be nitrated and the resulting product subsequently reduced to yield the corresponding amine according to the following scheme[198].

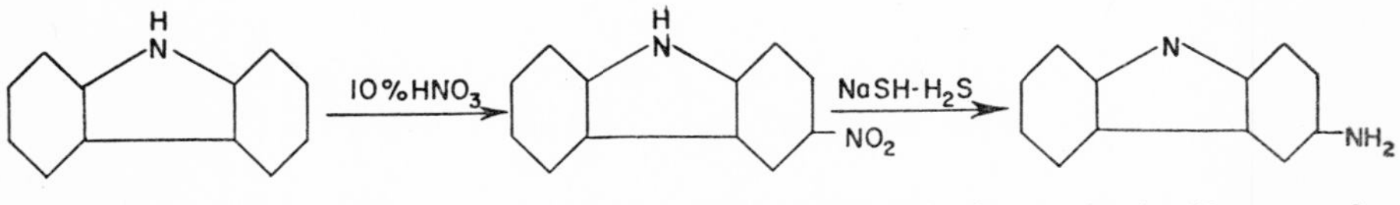

The more usual procedure for intermediates of this type is illustrated with the following steps for the manufacture of the more highly substituted 10-methyl-11H-benzo[a]carbazol-4-ol from 1,5-naphthalenediol and o-tolylhydrazine[105].

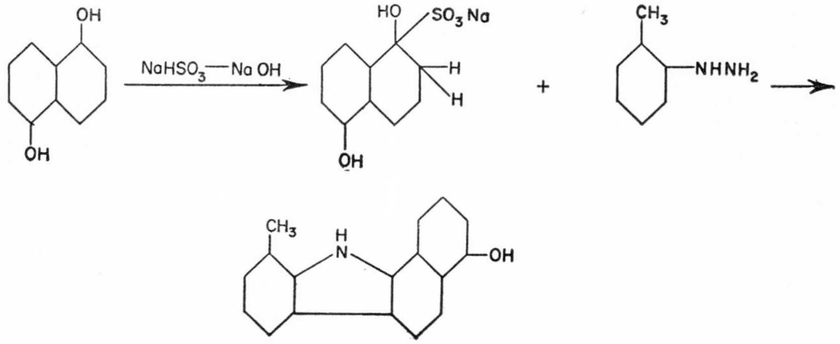

The yield based on 1,5-naphthalenediol is 68 per cent of theory.

Quinoline Derivatives

Anthranilic acid serves as a starting material for a number of substituted quinolones. Treatment of *N*-methylanthranilic acid with acetic anhydride gives 75 to 77 per cent yields of 4-hydroxy-1-methyl-2(1H)-quinolone (4-hydroxy-1-methylcarbostyril)[146, 196].

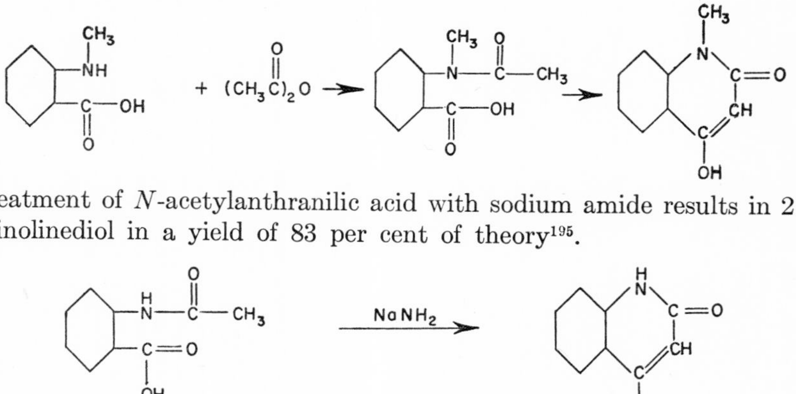

Treatment of *N*-acetylanthranilic acid with sodium amide results in 2,4-quinolinediol in a yield of 83 per cent of theory[195].

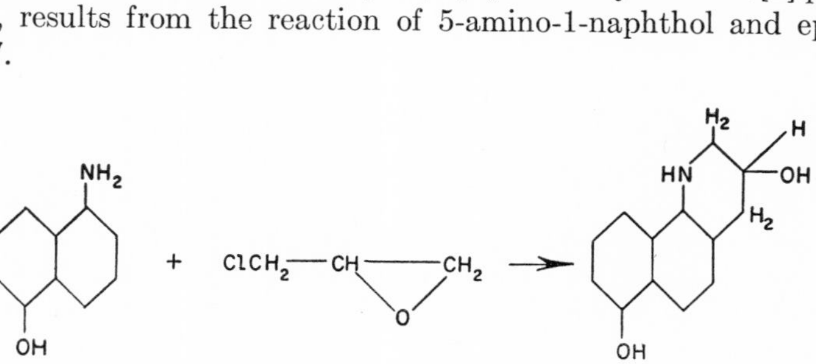

A related quinoline derivative, 1,2,3,4-tetrahydrobenzo[h]quinoline-3,7-diol, results from the reaction of 5-amino-1-naphthol and epichlorohydrin[197].

Quinaldine is made by heating aniline and crotonaldehyde, in the presence of a small amount of ammonium vanadate, with *m*-nitrobenzenesulfonic acid which serves as the oxidizing agent[135].

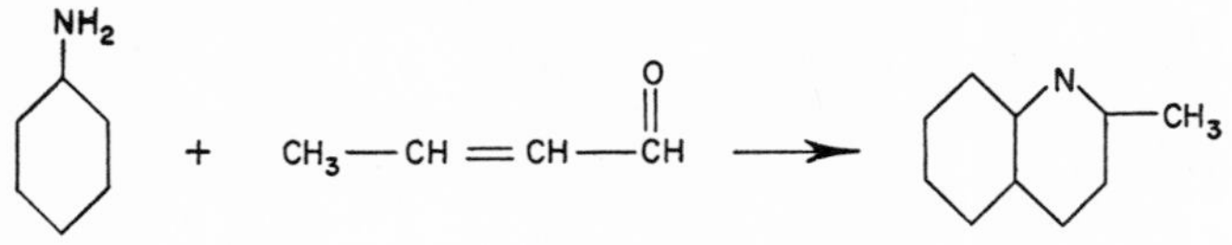

Pyrazolones

The substituted pyrazolones have found wide application in the field of azo colors. Over 200 tons was manufactured annually in Germany prior to the war. All of these pyrazolones are derived from aromatic amines and consequently they contain the phenyl group as a common substituent. They vary in the functional groups attached to the aromatic portion of the molecule as well as in the other substituents attached to the heterocyclic ring.

The general preparation procedure involves diazotization of an aromatic amine, reduction to the hydrazine, condensing the hydrazine with an acylacetic acid ester, and finally ring-closure of the condensation product to the pyrazolone. The reactions are illustrated as follows:

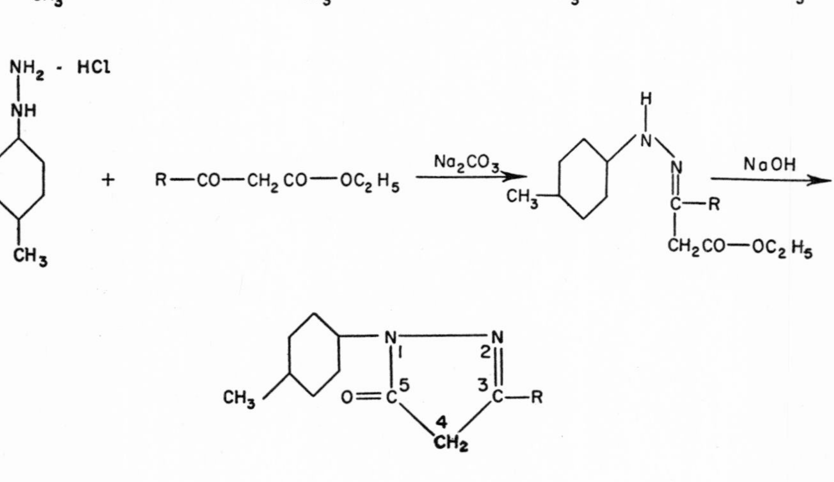

The preparation of the intermediate hydrazine is straight-forward in most cases and the yields are generally good. The diazotization is carried out in cold strong hydrochloric or sulfuric acid. The reduction is accomplished by running the diazotized amine into alkaline sodium sulfite. After reduction is complete, the disulfonate is hydrolyzed to the hydrazine sulfate or hydrochloride by boiling under weakly acidic conditions.

A number of hydrazines are listed in Table 14 with the yields in which they are obtained. While this list is by no means complete, a number of typical chemical types have been included to illustrate the range of application.

TABLE 14. HYDRAZINES

	% Yield	Ref.
p-Hydrazinobenzenesulfonic acid	94.0	118
2-Hydrazino-*p*-benzenedisulfonic acid	93.5	119
3-Chloro-4-hydrazinobenzenesulfonic acid	92.0	120
5-Chloro-4-hydrazino-*m*-toluenesulfonic acid	90.0	120
2,5-Dichloro-4-hydrazinobenzenesulfonic acid	93.4	121
6-Hydrazinotoluene-3,4-disulfonic acid	78.0	121
2,4,5-Trichloro-3-hydrazinobenzenesulfonic acid	95.0	122
m-Hydrazinobenzoic acid	85.0	123
3-Hydrazino-5-sulfosalicylic acid	90.0	124
p-Nitrophenylhydrazine	89.0	125
p-Tolylhydrazine	93.0	269

Treatment of the hydrazine with an acylacetic acid ester under slightly alkaline conditions results in the condensation product which upon boiling under strongly alkaline conditions ring-closes to form the pyrazolone. In a few cases, the condensation is found to work better under slightly acid conditions. While it has been the usual practice to use sodium carbonate, triethanolamine (2,2',2''-nitrilotriethanol) has been found very effective in promoting condensation of the hydrazine and the acylacetic acid ester[52].

A number of typical pyrazolones have been included in Table 15 in order to illustrate the different chemical types.

Conversion of ethyl 5-oxo-1-phenyl-2-pyrazoline-3-carboxylate to the corresponding carboxamide is readily accomplished by treatment with aqueous ammonia. The yield approximates 90 per cent of theory[200].

TABLE 15. PYRAZOLONES

Hydrazine	Ester	Product*	% Yield (Based on Hydrazine)	Ref.
Phenylhydrazine	Diethyl oxalacetate	5-Oxo-1-phenyl-2-pyrazoline-3-carboxylic acid	80	132
Phenylhydrazine	Ethyl acetoacetate	3-Methyl-1-phenyl-5-pyrazolone	93	117
m-Hydrazinobenzoic acid	Ethyl p-nitrobenzoyl-acetate	1-(m-Carboxyphenyl)-3-(p-nitrophenyl)-5-pyrazolone	ca. 60	203
p-Nitrophenylhydrazine	Ethyl acetoacetate	3-Methyl-1-(p-nitrophenyl)-5-pyrazolone	75	130 261
p-Tolylhydrazine	Ethyl acetoacetate	3-Methyl-1-p-tolyl-5-pyrazolone	—	270
5-Chloro-4-hydrazino-m-toluenesulfonic acid	Ethyl acetoacetate	1-(6-Chloro-4-sulfo-o-tolyl)-3-methyl-5-pyrazolone	81	133 233
3-Hydrazino-5-nitro-p-toluenesulfonic acid	Ethyl acetoacetate	3-Methyl-1-(3-nitro-5-sulfo-o-tolyl)-5-pyrazolone	ca. 58	199
p-Hydrazinobenzenesulfonic acid	Diethyl oxalacetate	5-Oxo-1-(p-sulfophenyl)-2-pyrazoline-3-carboxylic acid	90	131
3-Chloro-4-hydrazinobenzenesulfonic acid	Diethyl oxalacetate	1-(2-Chloro-4-sulfophenyl)-5-oxo-2-pyrazoline-3-carboxylic acid	83.5	126
2,5-Dichloro-4-hydrazinobenzenesulfonic acid	Diethyl oxalacetate	1-(2,5-Dichloro-4-sulfophenyl)-5-oxo-2-pyrazoline-3-carboxylic acid	92	127
2,4,5-Trichloro-3-hydrazinobenzenesulfonic acid	Diethyl oxalacetate	5-Oxo-1-(2,3,6-trichloro-5-sulfophenyl)-2-pyrazoline-3-carboxylic acid	92.5	128
4-Hydrazino-m-toluenesulfonic acid	Diethyl oxalacetate	5-Oxo-1-(4-sulfo-o-tolyl)-2-pyrazoline-3-carboxylic acid	77	128
3-Hydrazino-5-sulfosalicylic acid	Ethyl acetoacetate	1-(3-Carboxy-2-hydroxy-5-sulfophenyl)-3-methyl-5-pyrazolone	85	129

* In this table all products are named as derivatives of pyrazoline, even though the 1-sulfo(or carboxy)phenyl-3-methylpyrazolones are indexed by C. A. under the aromatic acid.

Miscellaneous Heterocyclic Intermediates

p-Phenetidine sulfate reacts with ammonium thiocyanate in an *o*-dichlorobenzene solution to give 1-*p*-phenetyl-2-thiourea which is then ring-closed with sulfur monochloride forming 2-amino-6-ethoxybenzothiazole in 90 per cent yield[217].

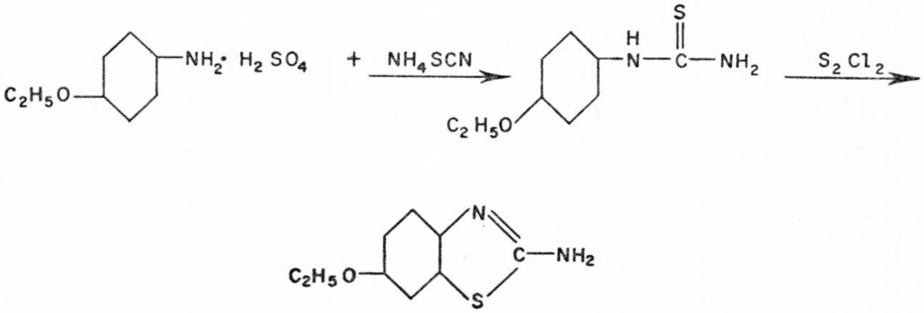

This same heterocyclic ring system is found in dehydrothio-*p*-toluidine, (2-(*p*-aminophenyl)-6-methylbenzothiazole),

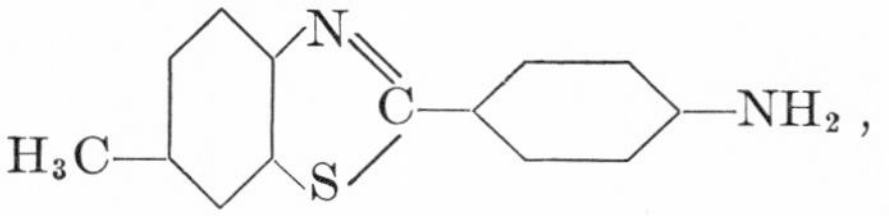

which is made by fusing sulfur and *p*-toluidine. This reaction may be extended to cover starting materials with other substituents, e.g., sulfo groups, in the aromatic ring[202].

An example of the formation of the triazole system is found in the reaction of cyanamide and hydrazine to form the intermediate aminoguanidine, which upon treatment with oxalic acid yields 5-amino-1,2,4-triazole-3-carboxylic acid.

$$NH_2CN + NH_2{-}NH_2 \rightarrow H_2N{-}\underset{\underset{NH}{\|}}{C}{-}\overset{H}{N}{-}NH_2 \xrightarrow{(COOH)_2}$$

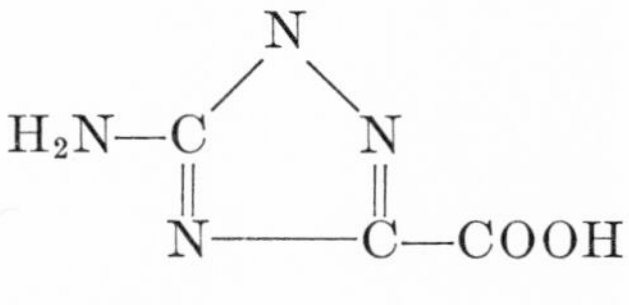

Yields for both steps fall in the range of 90 per cent[201].

Literature Cited

1. Adams, D. A. W., *Ann. Repts. Soc. Chem. Ind. on Progr. Appl. Chem.*, **32**, 52 (1947).

2. Adams, R., ed., "Organic Reactions," New York, John Wiley & Sons, Inc., III, 142, (1946).
3. ——, *ibid.*, V, 193 (1949).
4. Aelony, *J. Am. Chem. Soc.*, **56**, 2063 (1934).
6. Aylsworth, U.S. Patent 1,213,143 (1917).
7. Balz and Schiemann, *Ber.*, **60**, 1186 (1927).
8. Beach, U.S. Patent 2,509,855 (1950).
9. Beal and Bradner, U.S. Patent 1,488,730 (1924).
10. —— and ——, U.S. Patent 1,546,191 (1925).
11. Bean, U.S. Patent 2,525,515 (1950).
12. Bogdanov, *J. Gen. Chem. (U.S.S.R.)*, **13**, 797–800 (1943); *C.A.*, **39**, 918 (1945).
13. Bradfield and Jones, *Trans. Faraday Soc.*, **37**, 726 (1941).
14. Bradley and Robinson, *J. Chem. Soc.*, **1932**, 1254.
15. Brand and Mahr, *J. prakt. Chem.*, **131**, 119 (1931).
16. Braude, *Ann. Repts. on Progr. Chem. (Chem. Soc. London)*, **46**, 135 (1949).
17. British Patent 600,837 (1948).
18. British Patent 625,757 (1949).
19. British Patent 655,074 (1951).
20. Brown, U.S. Patent 2,362,612 (1944).
21. ——, U.S. Patent 2,432,087 (1947).
22. Buck, *Org. Syntheses*, Coll. Vol. **2**, 619 (1943).
22a. Bunnett and Zahler, *Chem. Revs.*, **29**, 273 (1951).
23. *Chem. Week*, **68**, 5 (1951), No. 21, June 9.
24. ——, **68**, 16 (1951), No. 20, June 2.
25. Cole and Burtt, U.S. Patent 2,348,329 (1944).
26. Corson and Kutz, U.S. Patent 2,572,701 (1951).
27. Crawford, *Chem. Eng. Progr.*, **46**, 483 (1950).
28. Daudt, U.S. Patent 2,194,926 (1940).
29. —— and Woodward, U.S. Patent 2,194,925 (1940).
30. Fierz-David, Blangey and Krannichfeldt, *Helv. Chim. Acta*, **30**, 237 (1947).
31. Gillespie and Millen, *Quart. Rev. (Chem. Soc. London)*, **2**, 277 (1948).
32. Gresham, U.S. Patent 2,479,067 (1949).
33. Griswold, U.S. Patent 1,602,766 (1926).
34. Grob and Adams, U.S. Patent 1,422,564 (1922).
35. Guyot, *Chimie & industrie*, **2**, 879 (1919).
36a. Hall and Quin, U.S. Patent 2,547,938 (1951).
36b. Harding, *J. Chem. Soc.*, **119**, 1261 (1921).
37. Henke and Benner, U.S. Patent 2,131,734 (1938).
38. —— and ——, U.S. Patent 2,194,938 (1940).
39. —— and ——, U.S. Patent 2,233,129 (1941).
40. —— and ——, U.S. Patent 2,276,774 (1942).
41. —— and Jones, U.S. Patent 2,233,128 (1941).
42. —— and Vaughen, U.S. Patent 2,198,249 (1940).
43. Hennion, U.S. Patent 2,365,638 (1944).
44. Hey, *J. Chem. Soc.*, **1934**, 1966.
45. Hiers and Hager, *Org. Syntheses*, Coll. Vol. **1**, 2nd ed., 58 (1941).
46. Holleman, *Proc. Acad. Sci. Amsterdam*, **II**, 248–256 (1908).
47. ——, *Rec. Trav. Chim.*, **37**, 99 (1918).
48. Hopff and Ohlinger, *Angew. Chem.*, **61**, 183 (1949).
49. Houghton and Lowdermilk, U.S. Patent 2,489,886 (1949).
50. Hughes, Ingold and Reed, *J. Chem. Soc.*, **1950**, 2400.

51. I. G. Farbenindustrie, BIOS 666, pp. 6–7 (PB 49207).
52. ——, BIOS 986, Vol. I, p. 17 (PB 77764).
53. ——, *ibid.*, p. 39.
54. ——, *ibid.*, p. 45.
55. ——, *ibid.*, p. 46.
56. ——, *ibid.*, p. 51.
57. ——, *ibid.*, p. 52.
58. ——, *ibid.*, p. 57.
59. ——, *ibid.*, p. 66.
60. ——, *ibid.*, p. 69.
61. ——, *ibid.*, p. 73.
62. ——, *ibid.*, p. 74.
63. ——, *ibid.*, p. 79.
64. ——, *ibid.*, p. 81.
65. ——, *ibid.*, p. 87.
66. ——, *ibid.*, p. 96.
67. ——, *ibid.*, p. 98.
68. ——, *ibid.*, p. 100.
69. ——, *ibid.*, p. 105.
70. ——, *ibid.*, p. 106.
71. ——, *ibid.*, p. 107.
72. ——, *ibid.*, p. 111.
73. ——, *ibid.*, p. 114.
74. ——, *ibid.*, p. 115.
75. ——, *ibid.*, p. 116.
76. ——, *ibid.*, p. 127.
77. ——, *ibid.*, p. 128.
78. ——, *ibid.*, p. 130.
79. ——, *ibid.*, p. 134.
80. ——, *ibid.*, p. 136.
81. ——, *ibid.*, p. 137.
82. ——, *ibid.*, p. 139.
83. ——, *ibid.*, p. 144.
84. ——, *ibid.*, p. 148.
85. ——, *ibid.*, p. 151.
86. ——, *ibid.*, p. 152.
87. ——, *ibid.*, p. 155.
88. ——, *ibid.*, p. 159.
89. ——, *ibid.*, p. 161.
90. ——, *ibid.*, p. 162.
91. ——, *ibid.*, p. 163.
92. ——, *ibid.*, p. 166.
93. ——, *ibid.*, p. 169.
94. ——, *ibid.*, p. 172.
95. ——, *ibid.*, p. 174.
96. ——, *ibid.*, p. 181.
97. ——, *ibid.*, p. 183.
98. ——, *ibid.*, p. 185.
99. ——, *ibid.*, p. 194.
100. ——, *ibid.*, p. 197.
101. ——, *ibid.*, p. 203.

102. ——, *ibid.*, p. 216.
103. ——, *ibid.*, p. 217.
104. ——, *ibid.*, p. 219.
105. ——, *ibid.*, p. 229.
106. ——, *ibid.*, p. 231.
107. ——, *ibid.*, p. 252.
108. ——, *ibid.*, p. 263.
109. ——, *ibid.*, p. 285.
110. ——, *ibid.*, p. 290.
111. ——, *ibid.*, p. 291.
112. ——, BIOS 986, Vol. II, p. 293 (PB 77764).
113. ——, *ibid.*, p. 295.
114. ——, *ibid.*, p. 296.
115. ——, *ibid.*, p. 306.
116. ——, *ibid.*, p. 307.
117. ——, *ibid.*, p. 316.
118. ——, *ibid.*, p. 330.
119. ——, *ibid.*, p. 331.
120. ——, *ibid.*, p. 332.
121. ——, *ibid.*, p. 333.
122. ——, *ibid.*, p. 334.
123. ——, *ibid.*, p. 335.
124. ——, *ibid.*, p. 336.
125. ——, *ibid.*, p. 342.
126. ——, *ibid.*, p. 347.
127. ——, *ibid.*, p. 348.
128. ——, *ibid.*, p. 349.
129. ——, *ibid.*, p. 350.
130. ——, *ibid.*, p. 355.
131. ——, *ibid.*, p. 356.
132. ——, *ibid.*, p. 358.
133. ——, *ibid.*, p. 362.
134. ——, *ibid.*, p. 377.
135. ——, *ibid.*, p. 382.
136. ——, *ibid.*, p. 385.
137. ——, *ibid.*, p. 395.
138. ——, *ibid.*, p. 397.
139. ——, *ibid.*, p. 399.
140. ——, *ibid.*, p. 408.
141. ——, *ibid.*, p. 417.
142. ——, *ibid.*, p. 424.
143. ——, *ibid.*, p. 427.
144. ——, *ibid.*, p. 431.
145. ——, *ibid.*, p. 432.
146. ——, *ibid.*, p. 433.
147. ——, *lbid.*, p. 440.
148. ——, *ibid.*, p. 441.
149. ——, *ibid.*, p. 442.
150. ——, BIOS 1149, p. 34 (PB 80376).
151. ——, BIOS 1153, p. 16 (PB 85687).
152. ——, *ibid.*, p. 31.

153. ——, *ibid.*, p. 38.
154. ——, *ibid.*, pp. 56–62.
155. ——, *ibid.*, p. 63.
156. ——, *ibid.*, p. 65.
157. ——, *ibid.*, p. 71.
158. ——, *ibid.*, p. 72.
159. ——, *ibid.*, p. 75.
160. ——, *ibid.*, p. 76.
161. ——, *ibid.*, p. 95.
162. ——, *ibid.*, p. 98.
163. ——, *ibid.*, p. 128.
164. ——, *ibid.*, p. 139.
165. ——, *ibid.*, p. 153.
166. ——, *ibid.*, p. 155.
167. ——, *ibid.*, p. 165.
168. ——, *ibid.*, p. 171.
169. ——, *ibid.*, p. 174.
170. ——, *ibid.*, p. 177.
171. ——, *ibid.*, p. 179.
172. ——, *ibid.*, p. 180.
173. ——, *ibid.*, p. 181.
174. ——, *ibid.*, p. 182.
175. ——, *ibid.*, p. 184.
176. ——, *ibid.*, p. 185.
177. ——, *ibid.*, p. 188.
178. ——, *ibid.*, p. 189.
179a. ——, *ibid.*, p. 191.
179b. ——, BIOS 1144, p. 2 (PB 77729).
179c. ——, *ibid.*, p. 9.
179d. ——, *ibid.*, p. 13.
179e. ——, BIOS 1147 (PB 87879).
180. ——, BIOS 1153, p. 197 (PB 85687).
181. ——, *ibid.*, p. 217.
182. ——, *ibid.*, p. 225.
183. ——, *ibid.*, p. 232.
184. ——, *ibid.*, p. 244.
185. ——, *ibid.*, p. 261.
186. ——, *ibid.*, p. 269.
187. ——, *ibid.*, p. 273.
188. ——, *ibid.*, p. 280.
189. ——, *ibid.*, p. 283.
190. ——, *ibid.*, p. 285.
191. ——, *ibid.*, p. 304.
192. ——, *ibid.*, p. 314.
193. ——, *ibid.*, p. 317.
194. ——, *ibid.*, p. 319.
195. ——, *ibid.*, p. 323.
196. ——, *ibid.*, p. 326.
197. ——, *ibid.*, p. 329.
198. ——, *ibid.*, p. 330.
199. ——, *ibid.*, p. 340.

200. ——, *ibid.*, p. 346.
201. ——, *ibid.*, p. 348.
202. ——, *ibid.*, p. 349.
203. ——, BIOS 1355, p. 76 (PB 79236).
204. ——, BIOS 1652, p. 51 (PB 91689).
205. ——, FIAT 649 (PB 81279).
206. ——, FIAT 1016, p. 15 (PB 67569).
207. ——, FIAT 1114, p. 47 (PB 80338).
208. ——, *ibid.*, p. 48.
209. ——, *ibid.*, p. 51.
210. ——, *ibid.*, p. 53.
211. ——, FIAT 1313, Vol. I, p. 18 (PB 85172).
212. ——, *ibid.*, p. 19.
213. ——, *ibid.*, p. 20.
214. ——, *ibid.*, p. 22.
215. ——, *ibid.*, p. 27.
216. ——, *ibid.*, p. 31.
217. ——, *ibid.*, p. 33.
218. ——, *ibid.*, p. 39.
219. ——, *ibid.*, p. 43.
220. ——, *ibid.*, p. 53.
221. ——, *ibid.*, p. 54.
222. ——, *ibid.*, p. 55.
223. ——, *ibid.*, p. 56.
224. ——, *ibid.*, p. 57.
225. ——, *ibid.*, p. 61.
226. ——, *ibid.*, p. 69.
227. ——, *ibid.*, p. 77.
228. ——, *ibid.*, p. 90.
229. ——, *ibid.*, p. 96.
230. ——, *ibid.*, p. 97.
231. ——, *ibid.*, p. 98.
232. ——, *ibid.*, p. 100.
233. ——, *ibid.*, p. 106.
234. ——, *ibid.*, p. 108.
235. ——, *ibid.*, p. 110.
236. ——, *ibid.*, p. 113.
237. ——, *ibid.*, p. 115.
238. ——, *ibid.*, p. 118.
239. ——, *ibid.*, p. 119.
240. ——, *ibid.*, p. 121.
241. ——, *ibid.*, p. 133.
242. ——, *ibid.*, p. 136.
243. ——, *ibid.*, p. 146.
244. ——, *ibid.*, p. 149.
245. ——, *ibid.*, p. 158.
246. ——, *ibid.*, p. 164.
247. ——, *ibid.*, p. 175.
248. ——, *ibid.*, p. 178.
249. ——, *ibid.*, p. 181.
250. ——, *ibid.*, p. 182.

251. ——, *ibid.*, p. 185.
252. ——, *ibid.*, p. 187.
253. ——, *ibid.*, p. 193.
254. ——, *ibid.*, p. 195.
255. ——, *ibid.*, p. 205.
256. ——, *ibid.*, p. 206.
257. ——, *ibid.*, p. 209.
258. ——, *ibid.*, p. 213.
259. ——, *ibid.*, p. 218.
260. ——, *ibid.*, p. 219.
261. ——, *ibid.*, p. 221.
262. ——, *ibid.*, p. 223.
263. ——, *ibid.*, p. 225.
264. ——, *ibid.*, p. 226.
265. ——, *ibid.*, p. 231.
266. ——, *ibid.*, p. 242.
267. ——, *ibid.*, p. 255.
268. ——, *ibid.*, p. 256.
269. ——, *ibid.*, p. 258.
270. ——, *ibid.*, p. 260.
271. ——, *ibid.*, p. 263.
272. ——, *ibid.*, p. 265.
273. ——, *ibid.*, p. 267.
274. ——, *ibid.*, p. 268.
274a. ——, PB 532.
274b. ——, PB 626.
275. Jacobs, Othmer and Hokanson, *Ind. Eng. Chem.*, **35**, 321–3 (1943).
276. Jones, *J. Chem. Soc.*, **1942**, 418.
277. Joris, U.S. Patent 2,577,768 (1951).
278. Justoni, Terruzzi and Pirola, *Farm Sci. e tec.* (*Pavia*), **3**, 509–525 (1944); *C.A.*, **43**, 2189 (1949).
279. Karasch, White and Mayo, *J. Org. Chem.*, **3**, 33 (1938).
280. Kohl, U.S. Patent 2,494,817 (1950).
281. Lawson and Suter, U.S. Patent 2,489,423 (1949).
282. Levine, U.S. Patent 2,438,369 (1948).
283. Lisk, *Ind. Eng. Chem.*, **41**, 1926 (1949).
284. Lloyd and Gershon, U.S. Patent 1,458,715 (1923).
285. Maguire and Gould, U.S. Patent 2,379,585 (1945).
286. Marisic, Denton and Bishop, U.S. Patent 2,450,677 (1948).
287. Markarian and Peck, U.S. Patent 2,464,877 (1949).
288. McArdle, U.S. Patent 2,454,468 (1948).
289. McBee, Bolt and Teffe, U.S. Patent 2,471,829 (1949).
290. ——, Hass, Rothrock, Newcomer, Clipp, Welch and Gochenour, *Ind. Eng. Chem.*, **39**, 384 (1947).
291. ——, Lindgren and Ligett, *Ibid.*, **39**, 378 (1947).
292. —— and Pierce, *Ibid.*, **39**, 397 (1947).
293. —— and ——, *ibid.*, **39**, 399 (1947).
294. Meyer and Bergius, *Ber.*, **47**, 3155 (1914).
295. Michael and Adair, *Ber.*, **10**, 585 (1877).
296. Miller, Mosher, Gray and Whitmore, *J. Am. Chem. Soc.*, **71**, 3559–60 (1949).
297. Moyer, U.S. Patent 2,328,920 (1943).

298. —— and Klingelhoefer, U.S. Patent 2,223,383 (1940).
299. Mueller, U.S. Patent 2,449,906 (1948).
300. Norton, U.S. Patent 2,446,430 (1948).
301. Othmer, *Ind. Eng. Chem.*, **34**, 286 (1942).
302. —— and Leyes, *Ibid.*, **33**, 158 (1941).
304. Peterson, U.S. Patent 2,487,586 (1949).
305. Planovskii and Kagan, *Khim. Prom.*, **1944** No. 9, 5–10; *C.A.*, **40**, 2123 (1946).
306. —— and ——, *Org. Chem. Ind. (U.S.S.R.)*, **7**, 296–304 (1940); *C.A.*, **35**, 3985 (1941).
307. Porter and Bumpus, U.S. Patent 2,513,251 (1950).
308. Price, *Chem. Revs.*, **29**, 37 (1941).
309. —— and Arntzen, *J. Am. Chem. Soc.*, **60**, 2835 (1938).
310. Remick, "Electronic Interpretations of Organic Chemistry," 2nd ed., New York, John Wiley & Sons, Inc., 1949.
311. Robertson and Waters, *Trans. Faraday Soc.*, **42**, 201 (1946).
312. Rollman, U.S. Patent 2,416,350 (1947).
313. Rust and Vaughan, U.S. Patent 2,415,800 (1947).
314. ——, Raley and Vaughan, U.S. Patent 2,421,392 (1947).
315. Scholl and Noerr, *Ber.*, **33**, 1052 (1900).
316. Seydel, U.S. Patent 1,576,999 (1926).
317. Simons and Herman, *J. Am. Chem. Soc.*, **65**, 2064 (1943).
318. Smith, *Ann. Repts. on Progress Chem. (Chem. Soc. London)*, **44**, 92 (1947).
319. ——, *ibid.*, **44**, 98 (1947).
320. ——, *ibid.*, **44**, 100 (1947).
321. ——, *ibid.*, **44**, 102 (1947).
322. ——, *ibid.*, **44**, 107 (1947).
323. Spasokukotskii, *Uspekhi Khim.*, **17**, 55–73 (1948); *C.A.*, **42**, 5435 (1938).
324. Stammbach, U.S. Patent 2,407,351 (1946).
325. Suckling, *Chemistry and Industry*, **68**, 907 (1949).
326. Suter, "Organic Chemistry of Sulfur," p. 359, New York, John Wiley & Sons, Inc., 1944.
327. Teeters and Mueller, U.S. Patent 2,455,322 (1948).
328. Tyrer, U.S. Patent 1,210,725 (1917).
329. Waters, *Ann. Repts. on Progr. Chem. (Chem. Soc. London)*, **42**, 138 (1945).
330. Wheland, "The Theory of Resonance," New York, John Wiley & Sons, Inc., 1944.
331. Wolthuis and Shafer, U.S. Patent 2,453,105 (1948).
332. Zakharov, *J. Chem. Ind. (U.S.S.R.)*, **6**, 1648 (1929); *C.A.* **25**, 5154 (1931).

2. NAPHTHALENE INTERMEDIATES

H. M. Parmelee

By naphthalene intermediates we mean those derivatives of naphthalene which are used in the manufacture of dyes. Over 58 million pounds of these compounds was manufactured in the United States in 1951 and the reader of this Monograph will meet with many references to them within its covers. This chapter is devoted to a discussion of the more important of them and to their chemistry and manufacture.

Naphthalene is a colorless, crystalline material, freezing at 80.0 to 80.1°C and boiling at 217.9°C. It sublimes readily. It is found in coal and petroleum tars and is formed along with other products in the pyrolyses of many organic compounds.

The principal commercial source is the "middle oil" fraction obtained in the distillation of coal tar. The naphthalene crystallizes from this fraction when it is cooled, and is removed by means of a centrifuge. The crude naphthalene is hot-pressed to remove the remaining oil. After hot-pressing it is washed with sulfuric acid, with alkali solution, and then with water. It is finally distilled. It may be vacuum distilled over metallic sodium[193] for additional purification.

German commercial processes for the recovery of naphthalene have been described[64] by the Allied Investigating Teams.

Naphthalene was first isolated by Garden in 1820[30] from the products resulting when coal tar is passed through a red-hot tube. Its composition was determined as $C_{10}H_8$ by Faraday in 1826[25]. Erlenmeyer in 1866[23] proposed the bicylic structure,

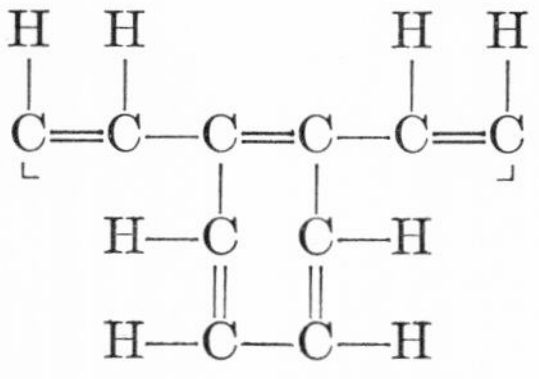

$$
\begin{array}{cccccc}
\text{H} & \text{H} & & & \text{H} & \text{H} \\
| & | & & & | & | \\
\text{C}=\text{C}-\text{C}=\text{C}-\text{C}=\text{C} \\
& & | & | & \\
& & \text{H}-\text{C} & \text{C}-\text{H} \\
& & || & || & \\
& & \text{H}-\text{C}-\text{C}-\text{H} \\
\end{array}
$$

in a footnote to an article on organic acids.

This structure was proved by Graebe[34], who showed that naphthalene consists of two groups of four carbon atoms which are joined together by two more carbon atoms common to both, forming two benzene rings. Graebe wrote the formula

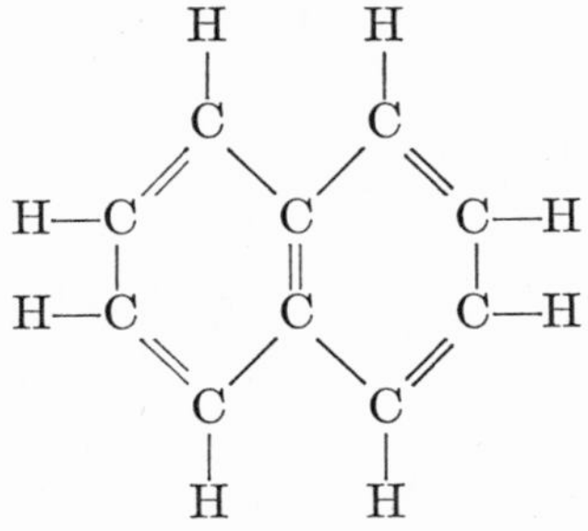

$$
\begin{array}{ccc}
\text{H} & & \text{H} \\
| & & | \\
\text{C} & & \text{C} \\
\end{array}
$$

Much later, Pauling and Wheland[166] considered the 42 possible arrangements of the bonds in this formula from the standpoint of quantum mechanics and calculated the resonance energies for several of the contributing structures. They noted that the "unexcited" structures,

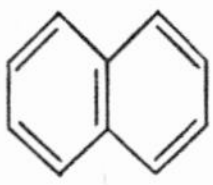

(I) 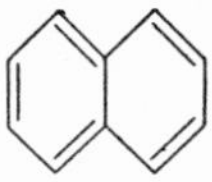   (II)    (III)

contribute a major part of the total resonance energy. Sherman[172] calculated that structure (I) contributes 50 per cent more than either (II) or (III). This conclusion was corroborated by Hunsberger[38] from infrared spectra. Naphthalene is usually written

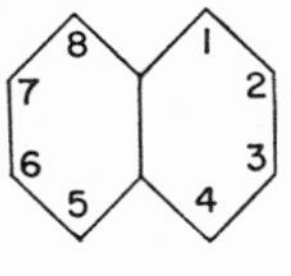

The numerals are those commonly used to designate the positions of substituents, although in mono-substituted compounds the 1,4,5 and 8 positions are often called the alpha positions, while the 2,3,6 and 7 positions are called the beta positions.

The manufacture of naphthalene intermediates is one of the older branches of synthetic organic chemistry. The more important of these compounds have been manufactured for decades, and while the processes and equipment have been improved in detail, they have experienced little, if any, change in their essential nature.

The primary reactions employed in the manufacture of naphthalene intermediates are sulfonation, nitration and halogenation. Secondary reactions of great importance are the replacement of sulfo groups with hydroxy, the reduction of nitro groups and the interchange between amino and hydroxy groups in the presence of a bisulfite. These general reactions are worthy of separate discussion. Other reactions will be described in connection with particular compounds.

Sulfonation of Naphthalene

Naphthalene reacts with sulfuric acid to give principally mono- and disulfonic acids. Trisulfonic acids are known[181] to occur in small amounts when naphthalene is treated with 100 per cent sulfuric acid at room temperature for a long time. For practical purposes, however, sulfuric acid containing dissolved sulfur trioxide is used for the preparation of naphthalene polysulfonic acids. The orientation follows the rule of Armstrong

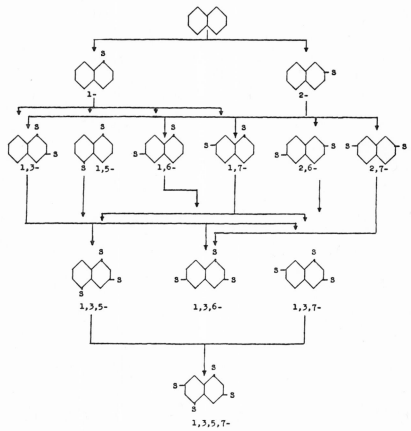

Fig. 1. Sulfonation of Naphthalene

and Wynne[3] that two sulfo groups never occupy positions ortho, para or peri to each other. This limits the number of isomers that can be formed by direct sulfonation of naphthalene to two monosulfonic acids, six disulfonic acids, three trisulfonic acids and one tetrasulfonic acid. Figure 1 shows the relationship of these compounds as it is often presented.

Monosulfonation. When naphthalene is treated with sulfuric acid at 80 to 100°C the principal product is 1-naphthalenesulfonic acid[24]. If the reaction is carried out at 160 to 165°C the principal product is 2-naphthalenesulfonic acid[203]. The more concentrated the sulfuric acid, or—in the case of fuming sulfuric acid—the more concentrated the sulfur trioxide, the more rapid and complete is the sulfonation. Increasing the temperature increases the rate of both sulfonation and desulfonation[2]. Despite much study, little is known about the nature and kinetics of the reaction.

Early work[19, 37, 169] indicated that the sulfonation of naphthalene was an equilibrium reaction, but the various workers chose different experimental conditions and their data are not readily correlated.

More recently, both Lantz and Spryskov have studied the sulfonation of naphthalene[148, 177]. Their work indicates that the monosulfonation of naphthalene involves two simultaneous equilibrium reactions:

(1) $C_{10}H_8 + H_2SO_4 \rightleftarrows 1\text{-}C_{10}H_7SO_3H + H_2O$

(2) $C_{10}H_8 + H_2SO_4 \rightleftarrows 2\text{-}C_{10}H_7SO_3H + H_2O$

These workers both found that reaction (1) reached equilibrium much more rapidly than reaction (2). Spryskov[178, 179, 182] found that after a few hours at 100°C the monosulfonic acid produced by the reaction between naphthalene and sulfuric acid is predominantly the 1 isomer. If the reaction is allowed to proceed for a period of 57 days at 100°C the monosulfonic acid is predominantly the 2 isomer.

Spryskov found that, although higher temperatures favor desulfonation, the effect is rather small, and equimolecular reactant quantities give a high yield of naphthalenemonosulfonic acids. He attributed this, in part at least, to the tendency of the sulfonic acids as well as of sulfuric acid to form hydrates. He determined the heat of hydration of 1-naphthalenesulfonic acid[180] to be 5.7 kcal per mole and the heat of formation of the monosulfonic acids, predominantly the 1 isomer, to be 5.07 kcal per mole.

An explanation of the behavior of naphthalene in sulfonation and desulfonation is offered by Hodgson and Hathaway[46]. They suggest that in the three dominant contributing resonance forms of naphthalene, the α carbon atoms may be considered the terminal carbon atoms of a butadiene system, with a relatively high electron density, and hence are more subject to substitution by the electrophilic sulfonating agent than are the β carbon atoms. In 1-naphthalenesulfonic acid, the C—S bond is subject to electron withdrawal due both to the sulfo group and to the adjoining benzene nucleus, which weakens the bond and favors ready hydrolysis. The β position in naphthalene is not affected by the adjoining nucleus, hence 2-naphthalenesulfonic acid desulfonates less readily. Moreover, these authors consider that 2-naphthalenesulfonic acid is related predominantly to the contributing resonance forms

and that this accounts for the resistance of 2-naphthalenesulfonic acid to hydrolysis.

The nature of the attacking electrophilic agent has not been definitely fixed. Where excess sulfur trioxide is present it may well be the sulfur trioxide itself, with its unfilled valence shell. Baumgartner[6] has offered evidence of the existence of free sulfur trioxide in concentrated aqueous sulfuric acid. Baddeley, Holt and Kenner[4] concluded that, in sulfonation, sulfuric acid must be considered as $H_2O \cdot SO_3$ and that the rate of desulfonation is proportional to the proton concentration. Price[167] gives the equation $HO \cdot SO_2OH \rightleftarrows H\bar{O} + \overset{+}{S}O_2OH$. Suter and Weston[184] suggest a possible mechanism for this arrangement, which involves the donation of a proton by the strong acid with subsequent loss of a molecule of water.

$$O_2S(OH)_2 + H^+ \rightarrow [O_2S(OH)_2 \cdot H]^+ \rightarrow H_2O + \overset{+}{S}O_2OH$$

Lantz[152] has set up the sulfonation and desulfonation thus:

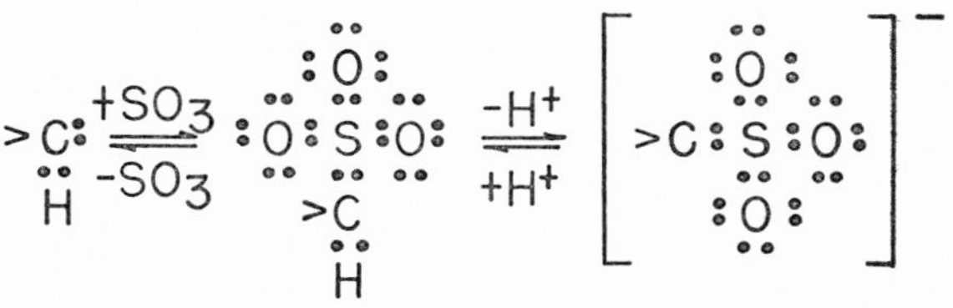

stating that the equilibrium depends on the concentrations of the sulfur trioxide and the proton donor and on the tendency of the intermediate compound,

$$:\overset{\cdot\cdot}{O}:$$
$$:\overset{\cdot\cdot}{O}:\overset{\cdot\cdot}{S}:\overset{\cdot\cdot}{O}:$$
$$>\overset{\cdot\cdot}{C}$$
$$H$$

to lose either SO_3 or a proton.

Disulfonation. All of the six possible naphthalenedisulfonic acids have been found among the products of the sulfonation of naphthalene but the 1,3 isomer occurs only in very small amounts. The second sulfo group enters the naphthalene molecule with more difficulty than the first, and the reaction is less exothermic[27]. Lantz[150] found that the hydrolysis of an alpha or beta sulfo group in a naphthalenedisulfonic acid is slower than that for the corresponding group in a naphthalenemonosulfonic acid, and that 2,6- and 2,7-naphthalenedisulfonic acids are desulfonated more slowly than are 1,5- and 1,6-naphthalenedisulfonic acids. In general, the entrance of the second sulfo group proceeds in a manner similar to that for the first. Low temperatures favor sulfonation in the alpha position. High temperatures favor sulfonation in the beta position, probably by a desulfonation-resulfonation mechanism similar to that described for monosulfonation.

At low temperatures, sulfonation of 1-naphthalenesulfonic acid gives a mixture of 1,5- and 1,6-naphthalenedisulfonic acids, while 2-naphthalenesulfonic acid gives a mixture of 1,6- and 1,7-naphthalenedisulfonic acids[26, 151]. The 1,5 isomer is gradually converted to 1,6 and 1,7 isomers by heating with strong aqueous sulfuric acid. At 130°C, the 1,5-naphthalenedisulfonic acid disappears and the 2,7 isomer appears, and above 140°C the 2,6-naphthalenedisulfonic acid is found. The conversion of the 1,6 and 1,7 isomers to 2,6- and 2,7-naphthalenedisulfonic acids is practically complete at 170°C[27]. These last two compounds reach a state of equilibrium with each other at 170°C[39, 155].

While investigators have not always agreed on the amounts of each isomer present at equilibrium, it appears that the sulfo groups tend to arrive eventually in the beta position whenever the temperature and concentration will permit.

Trisulfonation and Tetrasulfonation. The trisulfonation of naphthalene is of particular interest because it is the first step in the manufacture of 8-amino-1-naphthol-3,6-disulfonic acid (H acid), one of the most important naphthalene intermediates. In this case the 1,3,6-naphthalenetrisulfonic acid is desired.

The sulfonation of 1,6- and 2,7-naphthalenedisulfonic acids gives 1,3,6-

naphthalenetrisulfonic acid, which does not sulfonate further. 1,5-Naphthalenedisulfonic acid leads to 1,3,5-naphthalenetrisulfonic acid, while 1,7-naphthalenedisulfonic acid gives 1,3,5- and probably some 1,3,7-naphthalenetrisulfonic acids. 2,6-Naphthalenedisulfonic acid progresses to 1,3,7-naphthalenetrisulfonic acid. The 1,3,5 and 1,3,7 isomers can receive one more sulfo group to give 1,3,5,7-naphthalenetetrasulfonic acid. The chemistry has been studied by Russian workers[191], who concluded that the maximum attainable yield of 1,3,6-naphthalenetrisulfonic acid in the sulfonation of naphthalene is about 65 per cent. This is not an equilibrium yield, however. Lantz[153, 154] studied the equilibrium relationships between the three trisulfonic acids and the tetrasulfonic acid and found that equilibrium is reached with difficulty and that only about 10 per cent of the 1,3,6 isomer is present.

The study of the kinetics of naphthalene sulfonation is hampered by the lack of easy, rapid and accurate methods of determining the various naphthalenesulfonic acids in the mixtures. Methods are available but they are relatively difficult and inaccurate.

Nitration of Naphthalene

Naphthalene reacts readily with mixed nitric and sulfuric acid at moderate temperatures (50 to 60°C) to give almost entirely 1-nitronaphthalene. Further nitration gives first a mixture of 1,5- and 1,8-dinitronaphthalene, next principally 1,4,5- and 1,3,8-trinitronaphthalene, and finally 1,4,5,7- and 1,3,6,8-tetranitronaphthalene with perhaps a trace of the 1,4,5,8 isomer[50]. Other isomers must be made indirectly. In general, in the nitration of naphthalene,

(1) The nitro group tends to enter in an alpha position.

(2) If one of the alpha positions is already occupied by a nitro or a sulfo group, the entering nitro group preferentially takes a position peri to the first group, with the 5 position as second choice.

(3) A nitro or sulfo group inhibits the entry of a nitro group on a carbon atom adjacent to that bearing the first group.

The third rule generally dominates the first two where conflict arises between them.

The nitration of naphthalene shows both similarities to and differences from the sulfonation of naphthalene. Hodgson and Ward[50] have summarized these relationships:

(1) The maximum number of nitro and/or sulfo groups which can be introduced into a naphthalene molecule is four.

(2) Nitro and sulfo groups alone or in combination exert a similar influence in their effect on further nitration.

(3) The sulfonation and the nitration of nitronaphthalenes and of naphthalenesulfonic acids, with respect to the position of the entering group, are similar *at low temperatures.*

(4) At higher temperatures, the migratory tendencies of the sulfo group cause divergent results.

(5) Entering nitro groups show a strong preference for the peri position, while on the other hand entering sulfo groups always avoid the peri position.

Hodgson might have added the fact that, whereas each sulfo group on a naphthalene nucleus makes the entry of another sulfo group more difficult, the presence of a nitro group on a naphthalene nucleus renders the entry of a succeeding nitro group easier. Thus naphthalene is more difficult to nitrate than is 1-nitronaphthalene, and 2-nitronaphthalene is more easily nitrated than either. Except for naphthalene itself, the more unoccupied alpha positions there are available, the easier is the nitration. 2,6- and 2,7-Dinitronaphthalene are especially easily nitrated. Hodgson and Ward[49] could not mononitrate 2,6-dinitronaphthalene directly to give a trinitronaphthalene. Instead, the product was a tetranitronaphthalene.

Hodgson and co-workers have made an extensive study of the nitronaphthalene compounds, and have set forth an explanation of the reactions[44, 45, 48, 49, 50], which amplifies the theory of Vasely and Jakěs[192], in terms of resonance. Hodgson considers that the first group enters in the 1 position because that position is the terminal carbon atom of a butadiene chain in the dominant contributing resonance structures. If the first substituent in naphthalene is in the 1 position and is ortho-, para-directing, i.e., electrophobic, it will tend to contribute electrons to the pool of the nucleus with an increase in electron density in the 2, 4, 5 and 7 positions, which will activate those positions towards further substitution by an electrophilic reagent. If the first substituent is ortho-, para-directing and is in the 2 position, the 1, 3, 6 and 8 positions will be activated. With meta-directing or electrophilic groups, such as nitro or sulfo, which tend to withdraw electrons from the pool of the nucleus, the effect is just the opposite. A nitro group in the 1 position tends to deactivate the 2, 4, 5 and 7 positions, which leaves only the 3, 6 and 8 positions for substitution by a second group. The nitro group tends to deactivate the ring to which it is attached much more strongly than the other ring of the nucleus, so that the 5 and 7 postions are deactivated by a 1-nitro group to a lesser degree than are the 2 and 4 positions, and to an even lesser degree than is the 3 position.

The nitration of 1-nitronaphthalene thus produces principally 1,8-dinitronaphthalene with a smaller amount of the 1,5 isomer. The lack of the 1,6- and 1,7-dinitronaphthalenes is explained by the preference of the nitro group for the alpha position. In a similar fashion the formation of the 1,6- and 1,7-dinitro derivatives from 2-nitronaphthalene can be explained.

Hodgson and his fellow-workers have extended this theory to the tri- and tetranitrations. It is a useful tool, but the picture is not complete. For example, many of the substitution products must be explained on the basis of the preference of the nitro group for the alpha position, without understanding the cause of this preference.

The fact that the migration of nitro groups has not been observed may be related to the use of low nitrating temperatures. Nitric acid is a strong oxidizer, especially at higher temperatures. The polynitro compounds often undergo oxidative decomposition (sometimes violently) when overheated. For this reason nitration temperatures seldom exceed 100°C and are generally lower. The migration of the sulfo group from the alpha to the beta position requires temperatures above 165°C to occur in a reasonable time, but it is unlikely that a nitration mass could be heated to 165°C without severe oxidation. Perhaps a nitration at lower temperatures, for a long time, would show some migratory tendencies on the part of the nitro group, just as Spryskov[177] found that 1-naphthalenesulfonic acid is slowly converted to 2-naphthalenesulfonic acid at 100°C.

The kinetics of the nitration of naphthalene have not been thoroughly studied. Lantz[149] stated that the maximum rate of nitration of naphthalenedi- and trisulfonic acids is obtained using sulfuric acid of about 90 per cent strength with respect to water.

It is generally considered that the active nitrating agent in the nitration of aromatic compounds is the "nitronium" ion, NO_2^+. Nitric acid acts as a base in concentrated acid solution in that it accepts a proton from the strong acid medium, for example, from sulfuric acid or from nitric acid itself.

$$HNO_3 + H_2SO_4 \rightleftarrows H_2NO_3^+ + HSO_4^-$$

$$H_2NO_3^+ \rightleftarrows NO_2^+ + H_2O$$

The kinetics of nitration in the benzene series have been studied rather thoroughly by Bennet, Brand, Williams *et al.*[8, 9, 10, 11, 14, 156, 161, 200] and by Ingold and his co-workers[7, 142, 143, 144, 145, 146] in England, as well as by Westheimer and Kharasch[196] and by Tomlinson and Groggins[189] in the United States. The kinetics are not simple, the reactions being of the zero, first or second order depending on the substance nitrated and on the medium.

Halogenation of Naphthalene

Direct halogenation of naphthalene is seldom if ever used in the preparation of naphthalene intermediates for dyes. It is worth mention here, however, in connection with the general problem of substitution in the naphthalene nucleus, as an example of the shift of a substituent from the alpha to the beta position with increasing temperature.

Naphthalene can be chlorinated and brominated easily at moderate temperatures, the halogens entering predominantly in the alpha positions. Normally mixtures are obtained and, in the case of chlorine, addition as well as substitution takes place. Suyvers and Wibaut[185] treated molten naphthalene with bromine at various temperatures and found that the percentage of 2-bromonaphthalene increases from 3 to 6.8 per cent as the temperature rises from 85 to 215°C. In the vapor phase the proportion of 2-bromonaphthalene increases from 1.7 to 47 per cent as the temperature is increased from 250 to 500°C. Above 500°C the amount of 2 isomer increases slowly to 50 per cent at 600 to 650°C. With ferric bromide as catalyst, the proportion of 2-bromonaphthalene increases greatly, and Wibaut, Sixma and Suyver[199] claim as high as 60.4 per cent 2 isomer from catalyzed bromination in the liquid phase at 200°C. Either 1-bromonaphthalene or 2-bromonaphthalene gives the same equilibrium mixture, about 40 per cent 1 isomer and 60 per cent 2 isomer, when heated at 150°C with ferric bromide[198].

The chlorination of naphthalene is similar to its bromination. Wibaut and Bloem[197] describe the chlorination of molten naphthalene with iodine as a catalyst and state that in the liquid phase the proportion of 2-chloronaphthalene is about 8 per cent. In the vapor phase the proportion of the 2 isomer rises from 8.9 per cent at 232°C to 46.8 per cent at 246°C, then slowly to 49.3 per cent at 527°C.

Sixma[173] and Sixma and Wibaut[174] offer an explanation of the bromination of naphthalene based on quantum mechanical considerations. They consider that the vapor phase bromination is an electrophilic substitution at lower temperatures while at high temperatures it is a true gas reaction with radical substitution.

The kinetics of naphthalene halogenation in acetic acid have been studied by de la Mere and Robertson[20], who found reaction orders up to the fourth, depending on the acetic acid concentration and the temperature.

While much work has been done on the general problem of substitution in the naphthalene nucleus, and much empirical knowledge gained, the theoretical explanation of the mechanics and kinetics of this substitution is not complete, although recent studies from the standpoint of resonance and quantum mechanics appear helpful.

In addition to the common reactions which introduce a substituent group directly into the naphthalene nucleus, there are three indirect types of reaction which are so frequently used in the manufacture of naphthalene intermediates that they deserve brief comment at this point. These reactions are hydroxylation by the alkaline hydrolysis of sulfo groups (alkali fusion), amination by the reduction of nitro groups, and the reversible interchange of hydroxy groups and amino groups in the presence of a bisulfite (Bucherer reaction).

Hydroxylation of Naphthalene

Naphthols are frequently produced by heating the corresponding sulfonic acids with sodium and/or potassium hydroxide, often in strong aqueous solution. In general, an alpha-sulfo group is more readily replaced by hydroxy than is a beta-sulfo group; the alpha sulfonic acid will usually require lower temperatures and/or less concentrated alkali than the corresponding beta compound. The conditions of hydrolysis vary widely with the particular compounds involved. Naturally the method is not suitable for compounds containing other groups which are sensitive to alkali, such as nitro or halo substituents. Compounds containing amino groups are generally stable to alkaline hydrolysis.

The reaction may be simply stated

$$\text{RSO}_3\text{Na} + 2\text{NaOH} \rightarrow \text{RONa} + \text{Na}_2\text{SO}_3 + \text{H}_2\text{O}$$

Actually it is much more complex than the foregoing equation indicates, although little has been published concerning the mechanism and kinetics of the reaction. Vorozhtzov[195] suggested a mechanism whereby the sodium hydroxide adds to the double bond adjacent to the sulfo group, with subsequent elimination of sodium bisulfite

The evidence offered for this mechanism is not conclusive, especially in view of the unorthodox behavior postulated for the sodium hydroxide. Makolkin[157] fused sodium 2-naphthalenesulfonate with sodium hydroxide which had been labeled with the oxygen isotope of mass 18 (O^{18}) and found O^{18} in the water formed in the reaction. He reduced the naphthol and found O^{18} in the water formed in the reduction, but this indicates only that the oxygen in the naphthol comes from the sodium hydroxide.

It seems plausible that in a mixture containing large numbers of OH⁻ ions, these ions would be attracted to the electron-poor carbon atom attached to the sulfo group to form a transition complex. The complex is then stabilized by the elimination of a bisulfite ion. Furthermore, the formation of the necessary transition complex, in which a sulfo group and a hydroxy group are both attached to the same carbon atom, however briefly, has an analogy in the complex formed between naphthols and sodium bisulfite in the Bucherer reaction (below). Some of these Bucherer complexes have been isolated and studied. It is clear that more experimental work is needed to elucidate the mechanism of the alkali fusion.

Amination of Naphthalene

A great many naphthalene intermediates bear an amino group. This group and the hydroxy group are the two substituents which are the most characteristic of this class of intermediates. These groups largely owe their importance to the property of "coupling" with diazo compounds which they confer upon aromatic intermediates. The amino group is also diazotized and coupled with other coupling components. One of the most important ways of obtaining an aminonaphthalene is the reduction of a nitro group. This may be accomplished in several ways but not all are of commercial importance. The most important methods are iron reduction, catalytic hydrogenation, and reduction with alkali metal sulfides in alkali solution. A discussion of these methods in detail along with others of less importance is given by Groggins[36], and examples will be encountered in the discussion of the manufacture of individual intermediates later in this chapter.

Naphthalene intermediates containing amino groups can also be prepared by the replacement of an hydroxy group with an amino group (Bucherer reaction). In this reaction the naphthol is heated with ammonium sulfite or ammonia and alkali metal bisulfite. The reaction is considered to take place by the addition of the bisulfite to the keto form of the naphthol. In the case of some of the compounds, the intermediate bisulfite addition complexes have been isolated, especially those of the dihydroxy compounds[28, 29]. Vorozhtzov[194] claimed the isolation of the addition compound of sodium 2-naphthol-1-sulfonate. The reaction is considered to take place thus:

Amines may sometimes be used in place of ammonia to give N-substituted naphthylamines.

The reaction is reversible, and amino groups may be replaced by hydroxy groups. A thorough discussion of the Bucherer reaction is given by Drake[22].

THE MANUFACTURE OF NAPHTHALENE INTERMEDIATES

Of the thousands of naphthalene compounds, a relatively small number are of sufficient value to be manufactured as intermediates for dyes, although a truly appalling number have been made in the laboratory, tested and sometimes patented. The 1950 U.S. Tariff Commission report on Synthetic Organic Chemicals lists the production figures on forty-five naphthalene intermediates and it is largely these compounds which will be discussed, more or less briefly, in the remaining part of this chapter. The reports of the American and British investigating teams which studied German industry after the second world war are valuable in a study such as this, because they frequently present complete, integrated processes on a plant scale. These processes are often similar to those used in the United States. They are not necessarily better nor worse than their American counterparts, and in fact they may not always be as economical, because of the different industrial systems in the two countries. They are in general sound processes, however, and frequent references will be made to them in this work.

Naphthalenesulfonic Acids

Neither of the two naphthalenemonosulfonic acids is consumed directly in the manufacture of dyes, but both are the first steps in the preparation of other intermediates. In some cases the formation of the monosulfonic acid is the first step, but frequently this is followed by further sulfonation or nitration *in situ*. In such cases the process will be considered under the name of the final intermediates produced.

1-Naphthalenesulfonic Acid. 1-Naphthalenesulfonic acid is manufactured by adding finely ground naphthalene to sulfuric acid at temperatures below 57°C, often below 30°C. The product is isolated as the free acid[59] or as the sodium salt[83, 109]. Several variations of the sulfonation process have been developed, but none is believed to be in wide use for the manufacture of 1-naphthalenesulfonic acid. Grob and Adams[35] and Suter[183] obtained patents describing the sulfonation of hydrocarbons such as naphthalene using solutions of sulfur trioxide in sulfur dioxide. Nawiasky and Springer[162] used the adduct of sulfur trioxide and dioxane as a sulfonating agent. Hennion and Schmiddle[42] describe the use of BF_3 as a catalyst, and Hennion received a patent covering this feature[41].

2-Naphthalenesulfonic Acid. 2-Naphthalenesulfonic acid is produced in much larger quantities than is the 1 isomer. A large part of this production is consumed in the manufacture of 2-naphthol. 2-Naphthalenesulfonic acid is made by sulfonating naphthalene with 96 per cent sulfuric acid at about 160°C for about 2 hours. The sulfonation mass is diluted and treated with steam to hydrolyze the 1-naphthalenesulfonic acid and to distill out the resulting naphthalene. (Sometimes the charge is partly neutralized with sodium sulfite, in which case the sulfur dioxide is also removed with the steam.) The 2-naphthalenesulfonic acid is precipitated as the sodium salt by the addition of sodium chloride solution.

There are numerous variations of this general method. Shreve[170] describes the process in which no sodium sulfite is used. Othmer, Jacobs and Bushman[163] propose to reduce the consumption of sulfuric acid by removing the water in an azeotropic distillation with kerosene, and Downs[21] patented the removal of water by placing the sulfonation mass under vacuum. Spryskov[176] proposed to save sulfuric acid by using excess naphthalene. Unfortunately this also favors sulfone formation.

Several German processes are known. Many of these are complete processes for 2-naphthol from naphthalene, and describe the preparation of sodium 2-naphthalenesulfonate ("beta salt") as a part of the process. Reference 62 is a complete description of a process in English. A process for preparing a solution of the free acid is also given[105]. A continuous process for the sulfonation of naphthalene was also examined by the German chemists[78] but was considered to have no advantage over the batch sulfonation.

Some of the beta salt was dried and converted to 2-naphthalenesulfonyl chloride, which was then reduced to 2-naphthalenethiol and condensed with chloroacetic acid to give (2-naphthylmercapto)acetic acid[114], an important dye intermediate.

Naphthalenedisulfonic Acids

The members of this class of compounds which are most important from a commercial standpoint are 1,5-naphthalenedisulfonic acid and 2,7-naphthalenedisulfonic acid. 2,6-Naphthalenedisulfonic acid is produced as a by-product but is not recovered.

The 1,5 isomer is made by disulfonating naphthalene at a relatively low temperature, generally below 55°C, using a large excess of sulfuric acid containing free sulfur trioxide. It is usually isolated as the sodium salt with a yield of 50 to 53 per cent[102], and most of the production is used to make 1,5-naphthalenediol.

The 2,6- and 2,7-naphthalenedisulfonic acids are produced together by the hot sulfonation of naphthalene using 3.5 to 4 moles of 100 per cent H_2SO_4 to one mole of naphthalene at a maximum temperature of 175°C[107]. The charge is then diluted and salt is added at 90 to 100°C to precipitate the sodium salt of the 2,6-naphthalenedisulfonic acid. After filtration the 2,7 isomer is precipitated from the filtrate by cooling. The process specifies yields of 43.6 per cent of theory of 2,7-naphthalenedisulfonic acid and 21.3 per cent of theory of 2,6-naphthalenedisulfonic acid. A continuous sulfonation process is described by Ambler, Lynch and Haller[1], in which naphthalene vapor is passed up a column counter current to 85 to 90 per cent sulfuric acid at 220 to 245°C. Using weight ratios of sulfuric acid to naphthalene of 2.5–3.8/1, the authors claim a 77 to 80 per cent yield of disulfonic acids containing 78 to 85 per cent of the desired 2,7-naphthalenedisulfonic acid.

Naphthalenetrisulfonic and -tetrasulfonic Acids

1,3,6-Naphthalenetrisulfonic acid is the only commercially important member of this group. It is made in large quantities as an intermediate for 8-amino-1-naphthol-3,6-disulfonic acid (H acid) but is not isolated and will be discussed under that intermediate.

Naphthols

Both 1-naphthol and 2-naphthol are important intermediates. The latter, however, is manufactured in far greater quantities. Over 31 million pounds of 2-naphthol was produced in the United States in 1950. This is more than any other naphthalene intermediate produced in that year, with the exception of naphthalene itself.

1-Naphthol is manufactured by the hydrolysis of 1-naphthylamine with dilute sulfuric acid[61, 99]. A better quality product is made by the acid hydrolysis of 5-amino-1-naphthalenesulfonic acid (Laurent's acid)[100]. 1-Naphthol may also be made by the alkaline fusion of 1-naphthalenesulfonic acid. A continuous vapor phase conversion of 1-naphthylamine to 1-naphthol by reaction with steam over an alumina catalyst has been patented[15].

2-Naphthol is manufactured by the alkaline fusion of 2-naphthalenesulfonic acid[62]. This fusion is not adaptable to continuous operation, due to the long time cycles and the viscous reaction mass. Nevertheless a patent[158] discloses a continuous alkaline fusion for the conversion of aromatic sulfonates to hydroxy compounds, including 2-naphthol. Another type of alkaline hydrolysis has been patented[190] in which sodium 2-naphthalenesulfonate is treated with steam at about 460°C in the presence of calcium hydroxide.

Naphthalenediols. Several isomers have received attention as intermediates in dyes but only 1,5-naphthalenediol is manufactured in important commercial quantities. This isomer is commonly prepared by the alkaline fusion of 1,5-naphthalenedisulfonic acid and is precipitated by acidification[101].

Naphtholsulfonic Acids. Naphtholsulfonic acids can be made by the sulfonation of naphthols, by the alkaline fusion of naphthalenedisulfonic acids, or by the replacement of the amino group in an aminonaphthalenesulfonic acid with a hydroxy group. The sulfonation of naphthols is a common method. By adjusting the conditions of temperature and concentration various isomers are produced[47]. Sulfonation of 1-naphthol under mild conditions gives 1-naphthol-2-sulfonic acid and 1-naphthol-4-sulfonic acid. Under more severe conditions 1-naphthol-2,4-disulfonic acid results, and finally 1-naphthol-2,4,7-trisulfonic is formed. 1-Naphthol-2,3,4,6-tetrasulfonic acid has been described by Blangey and Fierz-David[13] but they did not prepare it by the sulfonation of 1-naphthol. Sulfonation of

2-naphthol at low temperatures gives 2-naphthol-1-sulfonic acid. Increasing the temperature gives increasing amounts of 2-naphthol-8-sulfonic acid (Crocein acid), while at higher temperatures 2-naphthol-6-sulfonic acid predominates. Increasing the acid concentration produces 2-naphthol-3,6-disulfonic acid (R acid), 2-naphthol-6,8-disulfonic acid (G acid) and finally 2-naphthol-3,6,8-trisulfonic acid[36a].

The naphtholmonosulfonic acids which are of greatest commercial importance are 1-naphthol-4-sulfonic acid, 1-naphthol-8-sulfonic acid, 2-naphthol-1-sulfonic acid and 2-naphthol-6-sulfonic acid[191a]. The first two compounds are made by replacement of an amino group with an hydroxy group. 1-Naphthol-4-sulfonic acid is manufactured from naphthionic acid by boiling with sodium bisulfite[131]. 1-Naphthol-8-sulfonic acid is made from 8-amino-1-naphthalenesulfonic acid by diazotization and decomposition of the diazo compound[127]. It readily forms a cyclic sultone and is isolated and used as such.

H_2N SO_3H $\xrightarrow[H_2SO_4]{HNO_2}$ HO SO_3H $\longrightarrow$ $O\text{---}SO_2$

2-Naphthol-1-sulfonic acid was made in Germany by sulfonating 2-naphthol with sulfuric acid at low temperatures, and salting out the product as the sodium salt with sodium chloride[54, 106]. The product of this process tends to contain appreciable amounts of the 2,6 and 2,8 isomers, as well as unreacted 2-naphthol. A modification of the process was patented by Cotton[18] whereby the product crystallizes as it is formed, thus removing it from the reaction and preventing its transformation into the undesired isomers. The formation of the undesired isomers is diminished by sulfonating in a solvent at low temperatures, using sulfur trioxide or chlorosulfonic acid as a sulfonating agent. The sulfonation is thus carried out under anhydrous conditions, and hydrolysis of the 2,1 isomer with resulfonation to the 2,6 or 2,8 form is prevented. A. E. Parmelee[164, 165] describes the sulfonation of 2-naphthol in nitrobenzene using SO_3 as a sulfonating agent, or in o-nitrotoluene using $ClSO_3H$ as a sulfonating agent. Tinker and Hansen[187] describe the use of tetrachloroethane as a solvent and SO_3 as a sulfonating agent. The production of 2-naphthol-1-sulfonic acid is large, and almost all of it is converted to 2-amino-1-naphthalenesulfonic acid (Tobias acid) (see p. 83). 2-Naphthol-6-sulfonic acid (Schaeffer's acid) is made by sulfonating 2-naphthol to give a mixture of 2-naphtholmonosulfonic acids. This mixture is converted to 2-naphthol-6-sulfonic acid by a dry baking process[72].

German processes are also known for some of the less important naphtholmonosulfonic acids. 1-Naphthol-3-sulfonic acid can be manufactured by the hydrolysis of the amino group in 4-amino-2-naphthalenesulfonic acid[98], while 1-naphthol-5-sulfonic acid can be made by the alkaline fusion of 1,5-naphthalenedisulfonic acid[71, 132]. In the preparation of 2-naphthol-4-sulfonic acid, a sulfo group is removed by acid hydrolysis from 2-naphthol-4,8-disulfonic acid[79]. Another route is the elimination of the diazo group in 1-diazo-2-naphthol-4-sulfonic acid (naphth [1,2] oxadiazole-5-sulfonic acid). This was carried out by Morgan and Jones[159] using alcohol and later by German chemists using glucose[80]. 2-Naphthol-7-sulfonic acid (F acid) can be made by the alkaline fusion of 2,7-naphthalenedisulfonic acid[110]. 2-Naphthol-6- and 2-naphthol-8-sulfonic acids are formed together in the sulfonation of 2-naphthol. A process giving 15 per cent of the 2,6 isomer and 85 per cent of the 2,8 isomer is described[73]. According to Ref. 121, the isomers are produced in the ratio of 35 per cent 2,6 and 55 per cent 2,8 while Ref. 140 describes a process for 2-naphthol-6-sulfonic acid free from the 2-naphthol-3,6-disulfonic acid.

The naphtholdisulfonic acids of greatest commercial importance are 2-naphthol-6,8-disulfonic acid (G acid) and 2-naphthol-3,6-disulfonic acid (R acid). These compounds are produced together when 2-naphthol is sulfonated first with sulfuric acid and finally with 20 per cent oleum. The temperature is raised in controlled steps from 15 to 80°C. The 2-naphthol-6,8-disulfonic acid is isolated as the potassium salt and the 2-naphthol-3,6-disulfonic acid as the sodium salt by appropriate salting[66, 123]. 2-Naphthol-3,6-disulfonic acid can be produced along with 2-naphthol-6-sulfonic acid (Schaeffer's acid) by sulfonation with sulfuric acid alone at higher temperatures. German processes for the manufacture of R acid by this route are given[136, 137, 138] in which various methods of purification to reduce the Schaeffer's acid content are described.

Of somewhat less importance is 1-naphthol-4,8-disulfonic acid. It is produced by the sulfonation of 1-naphthol-8-sulfonic acid sultone[129] and is converted to 4,5-dihydroxy-1-naphthalenesulfonic acid (Dioxy S acid)[122] by alkaline fusion. Another dihydroxynaphthalenesulfonic acid, of minor importance, is 6,7-dihydroxy-2-naphthalenesulfonic acid which is manufactured by the alkaline fusion of 2-naphthol-3,6-disulfonic acid[63]. Derivatives of 1-naphthol-3,8-disulfonic acid (Epsilon acid) are of considerable value as naphthalene intermediates and are discussed in the section on aminonaphthalenesulfonic acids.

The dihydroxynaphthalenedisulfonic acids are not of much commercial importance, although 4,5-dihydroxy-2,7-naphthalenedisulfonic acid (Chromotropic acid) is used in some azo dyes. It can be made by the alkaline fusion of 1-naphthol-3,6,8-trisulfonic acid[119] or of 8-amino-1,3,6-naphthalenetrisulfonic acid (Koch acid)[120] under severe conditions.

Naphthylamines

The two isomeric naphthylamines are important dye intermediates. 1-Naphthylamine has been manufactured for many years by the reduction of 1-nitronaphthalene with iron[1]. A catalytic process for the reduction of 1-nitronaphthalene using hydrogen in the presence of nickel catalyst is also known[40]. Another route to this compound is the ammonolysis of 1-chloronaphthalene in the presence of cuprous oxide. Slagh improved this process by adding a little calcium oxide[175]. Several *N*-substituted derivatives of 1-naphthylamine have been made, but only the *N*-phenyl-1-naphthylamine is of commercial importance. It is manufactured by heating 1-naphthylamine with aniline in the presence of a small amount of an acid catalyst[55, 104].

2-Naphthylamine is usually manufactured by the treatment of 2-naphthol with concentrated ammonia and sulfur dioxide (Bucherer reaction)[88]. German chemists also developed a process for the vapor phase reaction between 2-naphthol and ammonia over an aluminum oxide catalyst. They reported a yield of about 95 per cent for each of the two processes[74]. The use of 2-naphthol as the starting compound for 2-naphthylamine is made necessary by the highly selective mononitration of naphthalene in the 1 position. *N*-Phenyl-2-naphthylamine is produced in considerable quantities by the reaction of 2-naphthol with aniline. A little sulfuric acid serves as a catalyst[56].

2-Naphthylamine is a useful intermediate for dyes and offers a convenient route to two other important intermediates, 6-amino-1,3-naphthalenedisulfonic acid (Amino J acid) and 7-amino-1,3-naphthalenedisulfonic acid (Amino G acid).* It is a hazardous chemical, however, and must be handled with great care, because it can cause severe toxic effects which may not appear until many years after exposure to the chemical[33].

Naphthalenediamines are not used widely as dye intermediates. 1,8-Naphthalenediamine has been used to some extent and a process is disclosed for its manufacture by the reduction of 1,8-dinitronaphthalene with iron[84, 103]. A process for the purification of the product by vacuum distillation is given[81].

Aminonaphthols

Two members of this class of compounds, 5-amino-1-naphthol and 8-amino-2-naphthol, have some value as dye intermediates. In a German

---

* The name Amino G acid correctly implies a functional relation to G acid (2-naphthol-6,8-disulfonic acid). The name Amino J acid is derived, quite differently, from its role as a precursor to J acid (6-amino-1-naphthol-3-sulfonic acid). Both trivial names are well established in industrial usage in describing the products of the oleum sulfonation of 2-naphthylamine (see p. 85).

process, 5-amino-1-naphthol is made from 5-amino-1-naphthalenesulfonic acid by alkaline fusion[51, 115]. No recent, complete process for 8-amino-2-naphthol was found in the literature, although several tons of this intermediate was imported into the U. S. in 1950 and 1951. Its manufacture was patented in Germany in 1890[32] but Brown, Hebdon and Withrow reported the process as unsatisfactory and described improved reaction conditions[16].

Aminonaphthalenesulfonic Acids

The aminonaphthalenesulfonic acids, sometimes called naphthylamine-sulfonic acids, are important dye intermediates. The monosulfonic acids are seldom made by direct sulfonation of the corresponding amines because the resulting mixtures are frequently difficult to resolve, or give an unduly large proportion of unwanted isomers. In the following discussion the amino-1-naphthalenesulfonic acids will be considered as one group and the amino-2-naphthalenesulfonic acids as another.

Among the most important members of the first group is 2-amino-1-naphthalenesulfonic acid (Tobias acid). Over 3.5 million pounds was produced in the United States in 1950. Tobias acid is manufactured by aminating 2-naphthol-1-sulfonic acid with ammonium sulfite[57]. This product can be purified by extraction of an aqueous solution of the sodium or ammonium salt with organic solvents[168]. This should remove 2-naphthylamine if any were present. Tobias acid can be produced directly by the sulfonation of 2-naphthylamine at moderate temperatures using sulfur trioxide in an inert solvent such as tetrachloroethane[188].

4-Amino-1-naphthalenesulfonic acid (naphthionic acid) is another important intermediate. This compound is usually made by heating 1-naphthylamine sulfate either as a dry baking operation or suspended in a solvent such as o-dichlorobenzene[128]. Naphthionic acid can be made directly by sulfonating 1-naphthylamine[82] but the product contains 20 to 25 per cent isomers.

5-Amino-1-naphthalenesulfonic acid (Laurent's acid) and 8-amino-1-naphthalenesulfonic acid (Peri acid) are formed together and must be separated. Peri acid is the more important commercially. Naphthalene is sulfonated at low temperatures to give predominantly 1-naphthalenesulfonic acid, which is then nitrated *in situ* to a mixture of 5- and 8-nitro-1-naphthalenesulfonic acids. This mixture is then reduced with iron to the corresponding aminonaphthalenesulfonic acids. These acids can be separated by controlling the acidity of the solution. If a solution of the sodium salts of the two isomers is acidified to pH 4.0 to 4.6, the 1,8 isomer precipitates and can be removed by filtering. The filtrate can then be made acid to Congo Red papers, to precipitate the 1,5 isomer[43]. The 1,8 isomer can also be precipitated by buffering the solution, for example with sodium bisulfite[186], or by acidifying the mass with sodium bisulfite[160]. In a German process[133] for Peri and Laurent's acid, part of the 1,8 isomer is precipitated hot at pH 4.6 and the rest of it is precipitated with the 1,5 isomer. The 1,5 isomer is then purified by crystallization as the magnesium salt. Another German process[96] utilizes a reverse method of manufacture, in which 1-nitronaphthalene is sulfonated and reduced with iron. This process has the advantage that it produces no Peri acid.

The N-phenyl[135] and N-p-tolyl[141] derivatives of 8-amino-1-naphthalenesulfonic acid are also of commercial importance. They are manufactured by heating Peri acid with aniline or p-toluidine, respectively, in the presence of a small amount of acid such as hydrochloric acid as a catalyst.

8-Amino-1-naphthalenesulfonic acid is also converted to the inner amide, called 1,8-naphthosultam. The conversion can be accomplished by heating with strong dehydrating agents. In a German process the Peri acid is mixed with salt in o-dichlorobenzene and the o-dichlorobenzene is distilled away under vacuum. The mixture is then heated with phosphoryl chloride (POCl$_3$) to complete the conversion[60]. A sultam is also formed when Peri acid is further sulfonated with sulfuric acid containing free sulfur trioxide[126].

6-Amino-1-naphthalenesulfonic acid (D acid) is much less important. It can be made by the sulfonation of 2-amino-1-naphthalenesulfonic acid to give 2-amino-1,5-naphthalenedisulfonic acid. This material can then be subjected to hydrolysis in strong acid to remove the 1-sulfo group[76]. Sulfonation of 2-naphthylamine under moderate conditions gives a mixture of 6-amino-1-naphthalenesulfonic acid and 7-amino-1-naphthalenesulfonic acid. This mixture has been made as a dye intermediate[58].

The first member of the amino-2-naphthalenesulfonic acid group, 1-amino-2-naphthalenesulfonic acid, is not widely used as a dye intermediate, but it can be made from 4-amino-1-naphthalenesulfonic acid by a dry bake method[201] and in a solvent[17].

The most important of the amino-2-naphthalenesulfonic acids are 5-amino-2-naphthalenesulfonic acid and 8-amino-2-naphthalenesulfonic acid. These two acids are commonly called 1-naphthylamine-6-sulfonic and 1-naphthylamine-7-sulfonic acids, or 1,6 and 1,7 Cleve's acids. In their manufacture[69] naphthalene is sulfonated to give predominantly 2-naphthalenesulfonic acid, which is then nitrated without isolation to produce a mixture of 5- and 8-nitro-2-naphthalenesulfonic acids containing a little 8-nitro-1-naphthalenesulfonic acid. The mixture is reduced to the corresponding amines, which may then be separated. The 5-amino-2-naphthalenesulfonic acid (1,6 Cleve's acid) is first precipitated and isolated as the magnesium salt. The filtrate is partially acidified to remove the 8,1 isomer as a solid. The 8-amino-2-naphthalenesulfonic acid is finally precipitated from a hot filtrate upon further acidification. The 5- and 8-amino-2-naphthalenesulfonic acids are generally purified further. For some purposes the three isomeric acids are used, without separation, as mixed Cleve's acids.

6-Amino-2-naphthalenesulfonic acid (Broenner's acid) is used in small quantities only. It can be made by the action of ammonia and ammonium sulfite on 2-naphthol-6-sulfonic acid[171].

Diaminonaphthalenesulfonic acids are not generally of commercial importance but one derivative of such an acid is used. This compound is 6,8-dianilino-1-naphthalenesulfonic acid (Diphenyl Epsilon acid). It is prepared by a reaction in which 8-amino-1,6-naphthalenedisulfonic acid (Amino Epsilon acid) is heated for a long time with aniline and an acid catalyst[70, 92]. The reaction is unusual in that not only is the amino group replaced by anilino but one sulfo group is also replaced. This fact helps to account for the otherwise irrelevant trivial name of the product.

Aminonaphthalenedisulfonic Acids

The most important of this group of intermediates is 6-amino-1,3-naphthalenedisulfonic acid (Amino J acid). This is produced with 7-amino-1,3-naphthalenedisulfonic acid (Amino G acid), another important intermediate, by sulfonating 2-naphthylamine (see also p. 82). The direct products of the sulfonation are 7-amino-1,3-naphthalenedisulfonic acid and 6-amino-1,3,5-naphthalenetrisulfonic acid. The sulfonation mass is diluted with water and the insoluble 7-amino derivative is removed by filtering. The filtrate is then heated, whereby the sulfo group ortho to the amino group is hydrolyzed, leaving 6-amino-1,3-naphthalenedisulfonic acid. After removal of the sulfuric acid by adding calcium carbonate and sodium sulfate and filtering, the solution of 6-amino-1,3-naphthalenedisulfonic acid, disodium salt, is used without isolation.

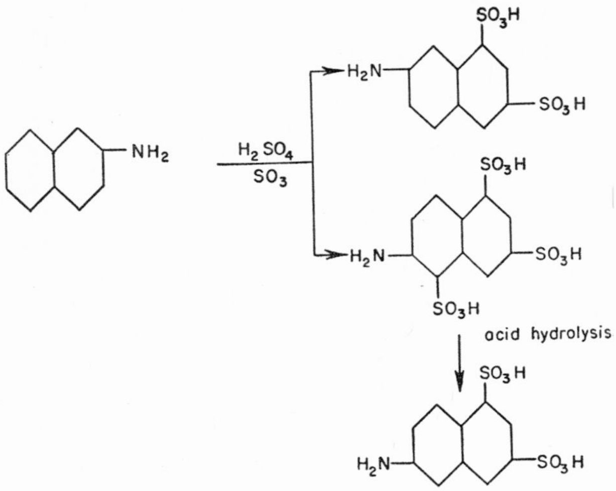

Practically all of the Amino J acid is consumed in the manufacture of 6-amino-1-naphthol-3-sulfonic acid (J acid) (see p. 89), while the 7-amino-1,3-naphthalenedisulfonic acid is converted to 7-amino-1-naphthol-3-sulfonic acid (Gamma acid)[116, 124] (see p. 89).

Because of the great care necessary in handling 2-naphthylamine, some manufacturers have used other routes to make Amino G and J acids. Amino J acid can be made by sulfonating 2-amino-1-naphthalenesulfonic acid (Tobias acid; see p. 83). This reaction produces almost entirely 6-amino-1,3,5-naphthalenetrisulfonic acid, which can be hydrolyzed as noted above to give amino J acid[93, 117]. Amino G acid may be made by amination of G acid in the form of its sodium or potassium salt with ammonia or ammonium sulfite[94]. Of much less importance is 3-amino-2,7-naphthalenedisulfonic acid (Amino R acid), which can be made by the amination of 2-naphthol-3,6-disulfonic acid (R acid). It also is formed in small amounts in the manufacture of Amino G and Amino J acids, but is not recovered.

Another group of aminonaphthalenedisulfonic acids arises from the disulfonation of naphthalene at low temperatures, which gives predominantly the 1,5-disulfonic acid. This is nitrated *in situ* to give a mixture of 3-nitro-1,5-naphthalenedisulfonic acid, 4-nitro-1,5-naphthalenedisulfonic acid and 8-nitro-1,6-naphthalenedisulfonic acid. The 3,1,5 isomer is isolated as the magnesium salt and reduced with iron to 3-amino-1,5-naphthalenedisulfonic acid (C acid). The filtrate from the isolation of the magnesium salt of 3-nitro-1,5-naphthalenedisulfonic acid is reduced with iron to a mixture of 4-amino-1,5-naphthalenedisulfonic acid and 8-amino-1,6-naphthalenedisulfonic acid (Amino Epsilon acid). The two amino acids are separated by means of their differing solubilities in different concentrations of hydrochloric acid[90].

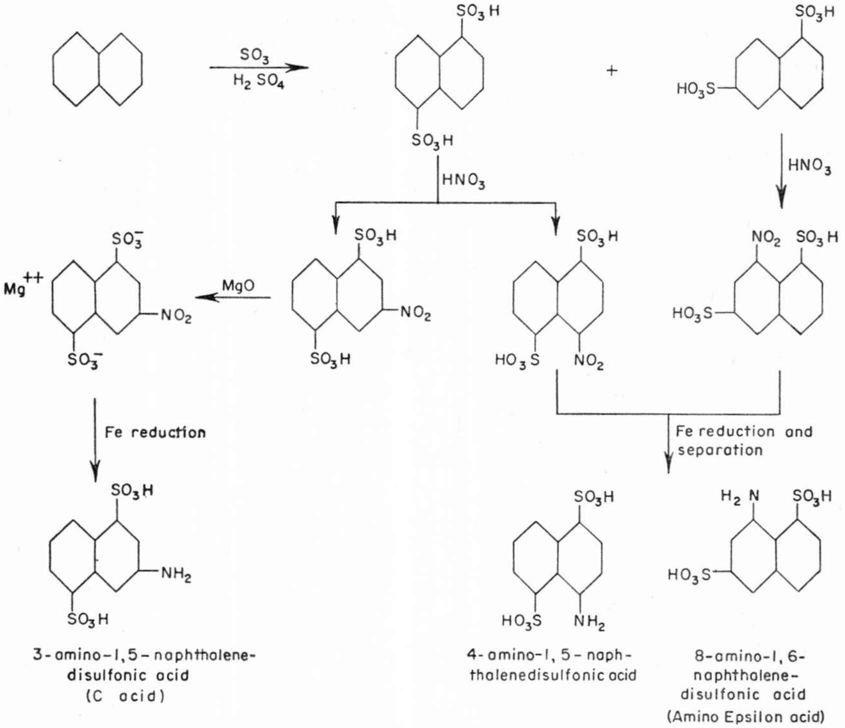

3- amino-1,5-naphthalene-
disulfonic acid
(C acid)

4-amino-1,5-naph-
thalenedisulfonic acid

8-amino-1,6-
naphthalene-
disulfonic acid
(Amino Epsilon acid)

After isolation and purification of these products the yields are low, the predominating compound, 4-amino-1,5-naphthalenedisulfonic acid, comprising only about 30 per cent of the theory from naphthalene. The C and Amino Epsilon acids are produced at yields of about 8 and 5 per cent, respectively. Variant methods of manufacture which produce larger yields of industrial products are known. 8-Amino-1-naphthalenesulfonic acid (Peri acid) can be sulfonated to produce an 82 per cent yield of 4-amino-1,5-naphthalenedisulfonic acid[130]. C acid is produced in 47.5 per cent yield by modification of the sulfonation and nitration operations[91]. By sulfonation at higher temperatures followed by nitration and reduction, Amino Epsilon acid may be produced in 32.6 per cent yield[75].

Aminonaphthalenetrisulfonic Acids

Two aminonaphthalenetrisulfonic acids are of commercial significance. The most important of these is 8-amino-1,3,6-naphthalenetrisulfonic acid (Koch acid). It is seldom isolated but is an intermediate for 8-amino-1-naphthol-3,6-disulfonic acid (H acid), which is produced in large tonnages annually. Koch acid is manufactured by sulfonating naphthalene with sulfuric acid at high temperatures to produce predominantly the 2 isomer, followed by further sulfonation with 65 per cent oleum in a step-wise manner. Temperature and acid concentrations are critical in this operation. The sulfonation mass is diluted and nitrated and the nitro compounds are reduced with iron[68]. The resulting mixture comprises mainly 8-amino-1,3,6-naphthalenetrisulfonic acid. After removal of excess sulfuric acid with lime, the solution may be used as it is or the Koch acid may be isolated by salting. 8-Nitro-1,3,6-naphthalenetrisulfonic acid may also be isolated before reduction if desired.

The second aminonaphthalenetrisulfonic acid is of less but still considerable importance. This is 4-amino-1,3,5-naphthalenetrisulfonic acid, which is made in the form of its inner amide or 4,5-sultam by sulfonation of 8-amino-1-naphthalenesulfonic acid[126]. The sultam is

converted to 8-amino-1-naphthol-5,7-disulfonic acid (Chicago acid), which is the dye intermediate.

Aminonaphtholsulfonic Acids

The aminonaphtholsulfonic acids are perhaps the most useful of all the naphthalene intermediates. Most of these compounds are produced by the alkaline fusion of the corresponding aminonaphthalenedi- or trisulfonic acids bearing one sulfo group in an alpha position. The fusion conditions are regulated so that only the alpha sulfo group is replaced by an hydroxy group. Possessing both amino and hydroxy groups, they behave both as diazo components and as coupling components. The member of the group which has the widest usage is 8-amino-1-naphthol-3,6-disulfonic acid (H acid). According to the U.S. Tariff Commission nearly 5 million pounds of H acid was produced in the United States in 1950. More H acid is produced than any other naphthalene intermediate except naphthalene itself and 2-naphthol. H acid is made by the alkaline fusion of 8-amino-1,3,6-naphthalenetrisulfonic acid (Koch acid) under moderate pressures in an autoclave[67]. The temperature used is generally about 180°C and the concentration of sodium hydroxide with respect to water is about 25 per cent. German chemists state that this concentration can be varied between 20 and 30 per cent without affecting the yield or quality of the product[108]. They also tried to operate the process as a continuous fusion but found that the precipitated sodium sulfite clogs the reaction tubes at temperatures low enough to yield H acid. Higher temperatures in this process produce 4,5-dihydroxy-2,7-naphthalenedisulfonic acid (Chromotropic acid)[86].

6-Amino-1-naphthol-3-sulfonic acid (J acid) and its *N*-substituted derivatives are also important. J acid is manufactured by the alkaline fusion of 6-amino-1,3-naphthalenedisulfonic acid (Amino J acid) with concentrated alkali at atmospheric pressure[125]. Several derivatives of J acid are also manufactured. 6-Anilino-1-naphthol-3-sulfonic acid (Phenyl J acid) is made by refluxing aniline and J acid with sodium bisulfite solution[87]. 6-(*m*-Aminobenzamido)-1-naphthol-3-sulfonic acid (*m*-Aminobenzoyl J acid) is manufactured by condensing *m*-nitrobenzoyl chloride with J acid in weakly alkaline solution to give 6-(*m*-nitrobenzamido)-1-naphthol-3-sulfonic acid (*m*-Nitrobenzoyl J acid), which is then reduced with iron and weak acid[12].

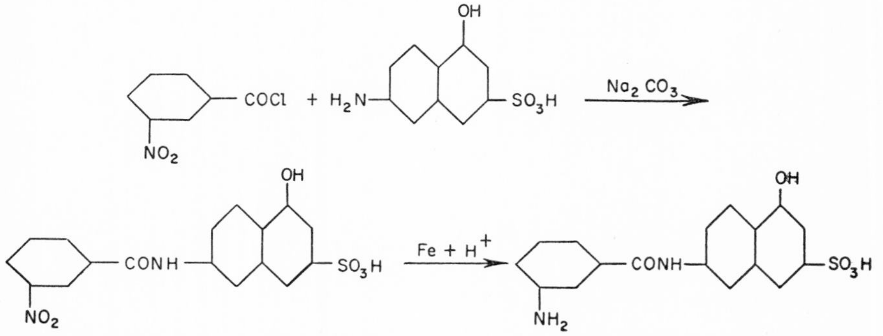

6-(*p*-Aminobenzamido)-1-naphthol-3-sulfonic acid (*p*-Aminobenzoyl J acid)[95] and 6-(4-nitro-*m*-toluamido)-1-naphthol-3-sulfonic acid[77] are made by similar procedures. 6,6'-Iminobis-1-naphthol-3-sulfonic acid (Rhoduline acid) can be made by heating a solution of the sodium salt of J acid with sodium bisulfite[5]. The addition of ammonium salts facilitates the reaction[202]. 6,6'-Ureylenebis-1-naphthol-3-sulfonic acid (Urea J acid) is made by the condensation of two molecules of J acid with phosgene[147].

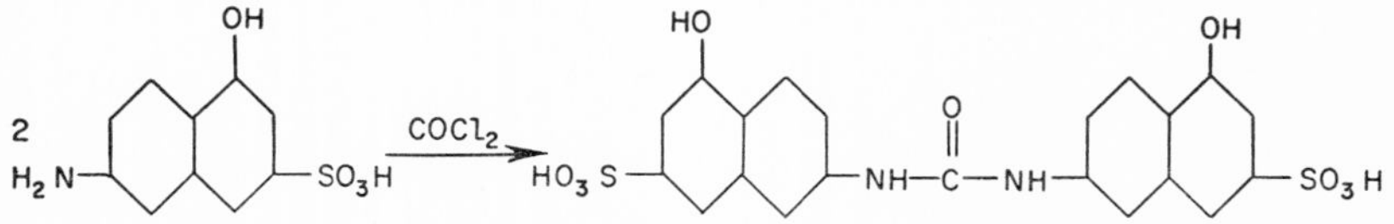

7-Amino-1-naphthol-3-sulfonic acid (Gamma acid) differs in structure from J acid only in the position of the amino group, and is made by the alkaline fusion of 7-amino-1,3-naphthalenedisulfonic acid (Amino G acid)[89]. Its *N*-phenyl derivative, 7-anilino-1-naphthol-3-sulfonic acid (Phenyl Gamma acid) is made by heating aniline and Gamma acid with sodium bisulfite solution[134].

The only one of the important aminonaphtholsulfonic acids which is not made by alkaline fusion is 1-amino-2-naphthol-4-sulfonic acid (1,2,4 acid).

This compound is made by nitrosation of 2-naphthol, followed by addition of sodium bisulfite and rearrangement, with one sulfo group entering the ring[52].

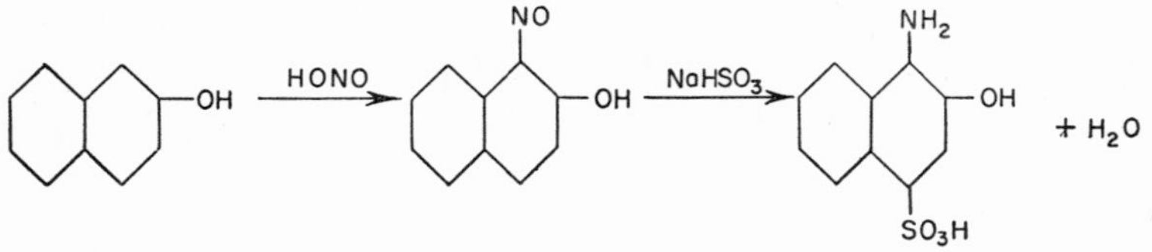

1-Amino-2-naphthol-4-sulfonic acid can be diazotized in the presence of copper sulfate to give a stable diazo oxide, naphth[1,2]oxadiazole-5-sulfonic acid, which may be isolated and dried and which is a valuable dye intermediate[97].

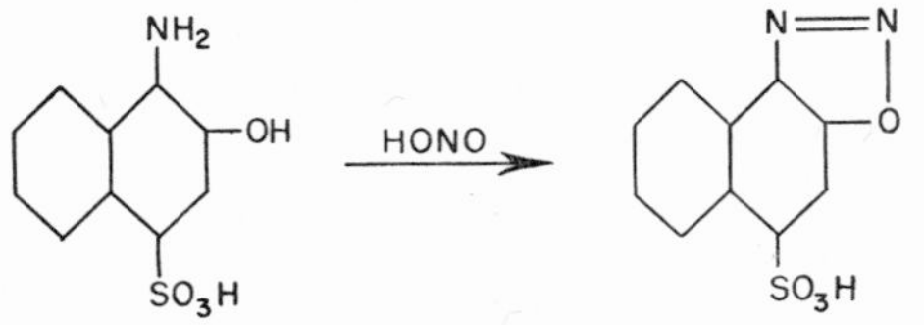

8-Amino-1-naphthol-5,7-disulfonic acid (Chicago acid) is made by the alkaline fusion of 4-amino-1,3,5-naphthalenetrisulfonic acid. Actually the 4,5-sultam is used, but the strong alkali hydrolyzes it to the amino acid in the reaction vessel[118].

The following three aminonaphtholsulfonic acids are made in smaller quantities than those above. 8-Amino-1-naphthol-5-sulfonic acid (S acid) is made by the alkaline fusion of 4-amino-1,5-naphthalenedisulfonic acid[85]. 5-Amino-1-naphthol-3-sulfonic acid (M acid)[65] and 7-amino-1-naphthol-3,6-disulfonic acid (RR acid)[139] are made in a similar fashion from 5-amino-1,3-naphthalenedisulfonic acid and 7-amino-1,3,6-naphthalenetrisulfonic acid, respectively.

3-Hydroxy-2-naphthoic Acid

3-Hydroxy-2-naphthoic acid is the only one of the naphthoic acids which is of commercial importance as a dye intermediate. About two and a half million pounds was produced in 1950. It is made by treating sodium 2-naphtholate with carbon dioxide under pressure at elevated temperatures[53].

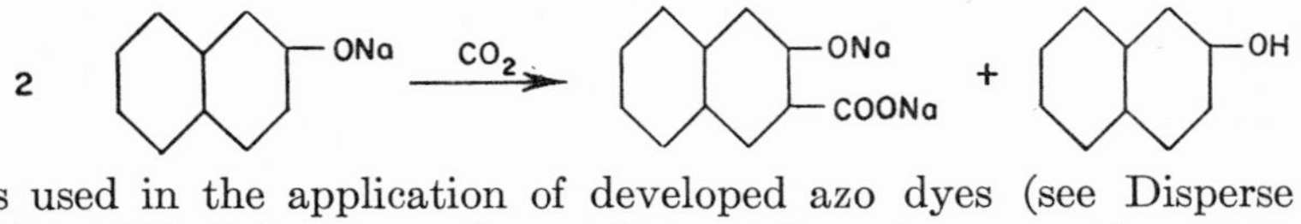

It is used in the application of developed azo dyes (see Disperse Azo Dyes, p. 172). It is also used as an intermediate for conversion to various arylamide derivatives which are commonly called Naphtol AS products (see Azoic Dyes, p. 182). These amides are manufactured by heating 3-hydroxy-2-naphthoic acid with the arylamine in toluene solution, with phosphorus trichloride as a condensing agent[111]. The reaction may be simply stated:

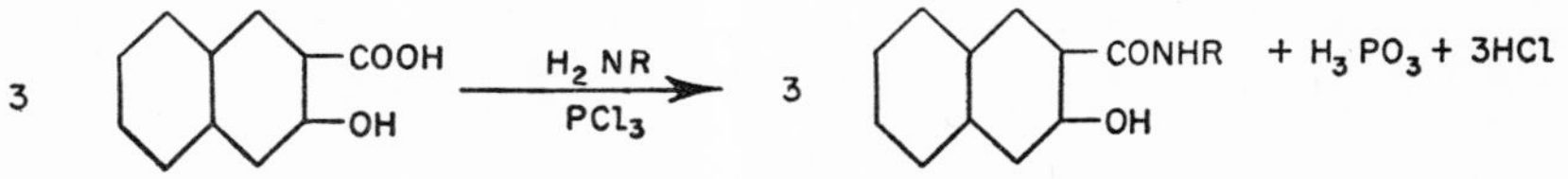

It is probably more complex. German chemists[112] postulate an intermediate compound between the arylamine and the phosphorus trichloride as part of the mechanism. The principal amines used are aniline, 1-naphthylamine, the toluidines, xylidines, anisidines and phenetidines. A method for purification of the Naphtol AS compounds is given in Ref. 113.

Literature Cited

1. Ambler, Linch and Haller, *Ind. Eng. Chem.*, **16**, 1264 (1924).
2. —— and Scanlon, *ibid.*, **19**, 417–21 (1927).
3. Armstrong and Wynne, *Chem. News*, **62**, 174 (1890).
4. Baddeley, Holt, and Kenner, *Nature*, **154**, 361 (1944).
5. Bammon and Forster, U.S. Patent 649,714 (1900).
6. Baumgartner, *Angew. Chem.*, **55**, 115–8 (1942).
7. Benford and Ingold, *J. Chem. Soc.*, **1938**, 929.
8. Bennett, Brand, James, Saunders and Williams, *ibid.*, **1947**, 474.
9. ——, ——, ——, —— and ——, *ibid.*, **1947**, 1185–90.
10. ——, —— and Williams, *ibid.*, **1946**, 869.
11. ——, —— and ——, *ibid.*, **1947**, 875.
12. Bertschmann, U.S. Patent 724,078 (1903).
13. Blangey, Fierz-David, Ulrich and Bretscher, *Helv. Chim. Acta*, **34**, 501–21 (1951).
14. Brand, *J. Chem. Soc.*, **1946**, 880.
15. British Patent 584,241 (1947).
16. Brown, Hebdon, and Withrow, *J. Am. Chem. Soc.*, **51**, 1786 (1939).
17. Conn and Weiss, U.S. Patent 2,471,400 (1949).
18. Cotton, U.S. Patent 1,913,748 (1933).
19. Courtot, *Rev. gen. mat. color.*, **33**, 177 (1929).
20. de la Mere and Robertson, *J. Chem. Soc.*, **1948**, 100–6.
21. Downs, U.S. Patents 1,279,295 and 1,279,296 (1918).
22. Drake, *Organic Reactions*, New York, John Wiley & Sons, Inc., **1**, 105 (1942).
23. Erlenmeyer, *Ann.*, **137**, 346 (1866).
24. Euwes, *Rec. trav. chim.*, **28**, 298 (1909).
25. Faraday, *Ann. chim. et phys.* [2] **34**, 104 (1827).
26. Fierz-David and Hasler, *Helv. Chim. Acta*, **6**, 1134 (1923).
27. —— and Richter, *ibid.*, **28**, 257–74 (1945).
28. Fuchs and Pirac, *Ber.*, **59**, 2458–61 (1926).
29. —— and Stix, *ibid.*, **55**, 658–670 (1922).
30. Garden, *Ann. of Philosophy*, **15**, 74 (1820).
31. German Patent 27,378 (1883).
32. German Patent 69,458 (1890).

33. Goldblatt, *Brit. J. Ind. Med.*, **6**, 65–81 (1949).
34. Graebe, *Ann.*, **149**, 1 (1869).
35. Grob and Adams, U.S. Patent 1,422,564 (1922).
36. Groggins, "Unit Processes in Organic Synthesis," 4th ed., p. 84, New York, McGraw-Hill Book Co., Inc., 1952.
36a. ——, *ibid.*, pp. 276–7.
37. Guyot, *Chimie & industrie*, **2**, 879 (1919).
38. Hunsberger, *J. Am. Chem. Soc.*, **72**, 5626 (1950).
39. Heid, *ibid.*, **49**, 844 (1937).
40. Henke and Benner, U.S. Patent 2,105,321 (1938).
41. Hennion, U.S. Patent 2,365,638 (1944).
42. —— and Schmiddle, *J. Am. Chem. Soc.*, **65**, 2468–9 (1943).
43. Hitch and Black, U.S. Patent 1,912,639 (1933).
44. Hodgson and Hathaway, *J. Soc. Dyers Colourists*, **61**, 283–5 (1945).
45. —— and ——, *ibid.*, **62**, 241–2 (1946).
46. —— and ——, *ibid.*, **63**, 46–48 (1947).
47. —— and ——, *ibid.*, **63**, 109–11 (1947).
48. —— and Turner, *ibid.*, **59**, 218 (1943).
49. —— and Ward, *ibid.*, **63**, 141–4 (1947).
50. —— and ——, *ibid.*, **63**, 177 (1947).
51. I. G. Farbenindustrie, BIOS 986, p. 41 (PB 77764).
52. ——, *ibid.*, p. 44.
53. ——, *ibid.*, p. 234.
54. ——, *ibid.*, p. 259.
55. ——, *ibid.*, p. 363.
56. ——, *ibid.*, p. 368.
57. ——, *ibid.*, p. 393.
58. —— *ibid.*, p. 423.
59. ——, *ibid.*, p. 435.
60. ——, BIOS 987, p. 125 (PB 75860).
61. ——, BIOS 1143, pp. 17–27 (PB 77720).
62. ——, BIOS 1152, p. 8 (PB 81027).
63. ——, *ibid.*, p. 23.
64. ——, FIAT 729 (PB 33270); U.S. Bur. Mines Inf. Circ. 7409 (1947).
65. ——, FIAT 1016, p. 40 (PB 67569).
66. ——, *ibid.*, p. 19.
67. ——, *ibid.*, p. 32.
68. ——, *ibid.*, p. 37.
69. ——, *ibid.*, pp. 25–27.
70. ——, FIAT 1313-I, p. 281 (PB 85172).
71. ——, *ibid.*, pp. 285–9.
72. ——, *ibid.*, p. 290.
73. ——, *ibid.*, p. 292.
74. ——, *ibid.*, p. 295.
75. ——, *ibid.*, p. 300.
76. ——, *ibid.*, p. 302.
77. ——, *ibid.*, p. 305.
78. ——, PB 14998, frames 142–4.
79. ——, PB 17657, frames 1717–8.
80. ——, PB 17679, frames 3823–7.
81. ——, PB 25602, frames 106–8.

82. ——, *ibid.*, frames 448–51.
83. ——, *ibid.*, frames 452–9.
84. ——, *ibid.*, frames 882–90.
85. ——, PB 25623, frame 176.
86. ——, *ibid.*, frames 203–4.
87. ——, *ibid.*, frames 476–81.
88. ——, *ibid.*, frame 488.
89. ——, *ibid.*, frame 493.
90. ——, *ibid.*, frames 497–508.
91. ——, *ibid.*, frame 511.
92. ——, *ibid.*, frames 513–7.
93. ——, *ibid.*, frame 525.
94. ——, *ibid.*, frame 526.
95. ——, *ibid.*, frame 529.
96. ——, *ibid.*, frame 549.
97. ——, *ibid.*, frame 574.
98. ——, PB 25624, frame 741.
99. ——, *ibid.*, frames 742–70.
100. ——, *ibid.*, frame 790.
101. ——, *ibid.*, frames 840–1.
102. ——, *ibid.*, frames 843–4.
103. ——, PB 70057, frames 8382–7.
104. ——, PB 70058, frames 8710–6.
105. ——, *ibid.*, frames 8972–3.
106. ——, *ibid.*, frame 9029.
107. ——, PB 70150, frames 464–6.
108. ——, PB 70361, frames 6671–3.
109. ——, *ibid.*, frames 6677–8.
110. ——, *ibid.*, frames 6919–20.
111. ——, PB 70421, frames 1316–1484.
112. ——, PB 70426, frames 5694–5702.
113. ——, *ibid.*, frames 5846–9.
114. ——, PB 73485, frames 1729–34.
115. ——, PB 74181, frames 2513–21.
116. ——, PB 74197, frames 766–8.
117. ——, *ibid.*, frame 769.
118. ——, *ibid.*, frame 772.
119. ——, *ibid.*, frames 773–4.
120. ——, *ibid.*, frames 775–6.
121. ——, *ibid.*, frames 780–1.
122. ——, *ibid.*, frames 787–8.
123. ——, *ibid.*, frames 793–4.
124. ——, *ibid.*, frames 795–7.
125. ——, *ibid.*, frames 805–6.
126. ——, *ibid.*, frame 811.
127. ——, *ibid.*, frame 817.
128. ——, *ibid.*, frames 820–7.
129. ——, *ibid.*, frames 828–9.
130. ——, *ibid.*, frame 838.
131. ——, *ibid.*, frames 842–4.
132. ——, *ibid.*, frames 847–9.

133. ——, *ibid.*, frames 851–2.
134. ——, *ibid.*, frames 853–4.
135. ——, *ibid.*, frame 855.
136. ——, *ibid.*, frame 856.
137. ——, *ibid.*, frames 857–8.
138. ——, *ibid.*, frame 859.
139. ——, *ibid.*, frames 862–3.
140. ——, *ibid.*, frames 864–5.
141. ——, *ibid.*, frame 866.
142. Ingold *et al.*, *J. Chem. Soc.*, **1950**, 2400–40.
143. ——, *ibid.*, **1950**, 2441–52.
144. ——, *ibid.*, **1950**, 2452–67.
145. ——, *ibid.*, **1950**, 2628–56.
146. ——, *ibid.*, **1950**, 2657–84.
147. Israel and Kothe, U.S. Patent 656,646 (1900).
148. Lantz, *Bull. soc. chim. France*, **2**, 2092–2109 (1935).
149. ——, *ibid.*, **6**, 280–302 (1939).
150. ——, *ibid.*, **12**, 253–62 (1945).
151. ——, *ibid.*, **12**, 262–74 (1945).
152. ——, *ibid.*, **12**, 1004–10 (1945).
153. ——, *ibid.*, **14**, 95–101 (1947).
154. ——, *Compt. rend.*, **222**, 1111 (1946).
155. ——, *ibid.*, **222**, 1239–40 (1946).
156. Lowen, Murray and Williams, *J. Chem. Soc.*, **1950**, 3318–22.
157. Makolkin, *Acta Physicochim. (URSS)*, **16**, 88–96 (1942); *C.A.*, **37**, 2355 (1943).
158. Miller, U.S. Patent 2,378,314 (1945).
159. Morgan and Jones, *J. Soc. Chem. Ind. (London)*, **42**, 97T (1923).
160. Mow, U.S. Patent 1,996,822 (1935).
161. Murray and Williams, *J. Chem. Soc.*, **1950**, 3328.
162. Nawiasky and Springer, U.S. Patent 2,219,748 (1940).
163. Othmer, Jacob and Bushman, *Ind. Eng. Chem.*, **35**, 326–9 (1943).
164. Parmelee, A. E., U.S. Patent 1,662,396 (1928).
165. ——, U.S. Patent 1,716,082 (1929).
166. Pauling and Wheland, *J. Chem. Phys.*, **1**, 362 (1933).
167. Price, *Chem. Revs.*, **29**, 37 (1941).
168. Rapp, U.S. Patent 2,058,911 (1936).
169. Renault, *Ann. chim. et phys.*, [2] **65**, 87 (1837).
170. Schreve, *Color Trade J. and Textile Chemist*, **14**, 42 (1924).
171. Schultz, "Die Chemie des Steinkohlenteers," p. 368, Braunschweig, Vieweg, 1926.
172. Sherman, *J. Chem. Phys.*, **2**, 488 (1934).
173. Sixma, *Rec. trav. chim.*, **68**, 915–20 (1949).
174. —— and Wibaut, *ibid.*, **69**, 577 (1950).
175. Slagh, U.S. Patent 2,391,848 (1945).
176. Spryskov, *J. Gen. Chem. (USSR)*, **16**, 1060–4 (1946).
177. ——, *ibid.*, **16**, 2126–31 (1946).
178. ——, *ibid.*, **17**, 591–600 (1947).
179. ——, *ibid.*, **17**, 1309–15 (1947).
180. ——, *ibid.*, **18**, 98–102 (1948).
181. ——, *ibid.*, **18**, 941–7 (1948).
182. —— and Ovsyankin, *ibid.*, **16**, 1057–9 (1946).

183. Suter, U.S. Patent 2,098,114 (1937).
184. —— and Weston, *Organic Reactions*, New York, John Wiley & Sons, Inc., **3**, 142 (1946).
185. Suyver and Wibaut, *Rec. trav. chim.*, **64**, 65 (1945).
186. Tinker, U.S. Patent 2,036,661 (1936).
187. —— and Hansen, U.S. Patent 1,934,216 (1933).
188. —— and ——, U.S. Patent 1,969,189 (1934).
189. Tomlinson and Groggins, *Chem. Eng.*, **57**, 131 (1950).
190. Tyrer, U.S. Patent 2,407,044 (1946).
191. Ufimzev and Krivoshluikova, *J. prakt. Chem.*, **141**, 172 (1934); also *Org. Chem. Ind. (USSR)*, **2**, 144–51 (1936).
191a. U.S. Tariff Commission, "Synthetic Organic Chemicals, U.S. Production and Sales, 1950."
192. Vasely and Jakěs, *Bull. soc. chim. France*, **33**, 952–62 (1923).
193. von Steiger, *Ber.*, **55**, 1872 (1922).
194. Vorozhtzov, *ibid.*, **62**, 57 (1929).
195. ——, *Org. Chem. Ind. (USSR)*, **6**, 293–300 (1939).
196. Westheimer and Kharasch, *J. Am. Chem. Soc.*, **68**, 1871 (1946).
197. Wibaut and Bloem, *Rec. trav. chim.*, **69**, 586–92 (1950).
198. ——, Sixma, Suyver and Hijland, *C. A.*, **43**, 2851 (1949); abs. from *Koninkl. Ned. Akad. Wetenschap. Proc.*, **51**, 776–86 (1948).
199. ——, —— and Suyver, *Rec. trav. chim.*, **68**, 525–46 (1949).
200. Williams and Lowen, *J. Chem. Soc.*, **1950**, 3312–18.
201. Wintringham, Moffatt and Conn, U.S. Patent 2,479,990 (1949).
202. Wirth, U.S. Patent 2,120,660 (1938).
203. Witt, *Ber.*, **48**, 743 (1915).

3. AZO DYES

Introductory Comments

Azo dyes make up the largest chemical class, and are usually considered the group with the fullest shade range and the most diverse uses. Their common structural characteristic is the azo chromophore ($-N{=}N-$) connecting two carbon systems, at least one of which is aromatic.

The relative ease and economy of preparation of azo dyes by the classic diazotization and azo coupling reactions has led to the synthesis and evaluation of uncounted thousands of examples. From these have been selected for commercial use, by both empirical and systematic technical efforts, the several hundred individual azo dyes which comprised, in 1951, 36 per cent of the total United States output of synthetic organic dyes. In the same year, for comparison, anthraquinone vat dyes accounted for 22 per cent, indigoid dyes for 13 per cent, and sulfur dyes for 11 per cent.

In this Monograph many of the dyes of importance in the American market are named and identified. In doing this, reliance is placed in many different sources of information. Since scientific missions to the I. G. Farbenindustrie uncovered many of the identifications involved (as well as processes), German trade names have been widely used here. In most cases there are American-made counterparts of the German dyes. For correlations of American trade names and dye manufacturers with German trade names and with dye structures, the reader is referred to the "Technical Manual and Year Book" of the American Association of Textile Chemists and Colorists and to the "Colour Index" of the Society of Dyers and Colourists (see General References, p. 700).

The fastness of azo dyes varies widely with structure and environment, but in general it tends to be less than that of anthraquinone vat dyes and indigoid dyes, and greater than that of sulfur dyes.

This chapter will open with a discussion of the mechanisms of the diazotization and the azo coupling reactions, following which the chemistry of azo dyes will be reviewed in sections on the basis of use fields—dyes for cotton, dyes for wool, disperse dyes, and solvent-soluble dyes.

MECHANISMS OF THE DIAZOTIZATION AND THE AZO COUPLING REACTIONS

S. N. Boyd

Introduction

The reaction of an aromatic amine with nitrous acid to yield a diazo compound and the combination of the diazo compound with a suitable component to yield an azo derivative are two of the older reactions in organic chemistry. The former was discovered by Griess[29] in 1858, while the latter was discovered by Kekulé and Hidegh[56] in 1870. In the years that followed, many investigators attempted to elucidate the mechanisms by which these two reactions occur. Only within the past few years, however, have we had available the theoretical background necessary for the understanding of these phenomena.

Unfortunately, even now we cannot say that the picture is complete. Both of these reactions occur in systems characterized by the existence of several independent equilibria. It is the understanding of these equilibria that must be achieved before we can chart unambiguously the course of the two reactions.

The Diazotization Reaction

There are many methods recorded for the preparation of diazo compounds[70]. The only method which will be considered here is the technically important one involving the reaction of an aromatic primary amine with nitrous acid in the presence of a mineral acid, usually in an aqueous medium. In such a system there are at least two equilibria which potentially are important in a consideration of the diazotization mechanism:

$$HNO_2 \rightleftharpoons H^+ + NO_2^-$$

$$ArNH_2 + H^+ \rightleftharpoons ArNH_3^+$$

Nitrous acid is a weak acid, having $k = 4 \times 10^{-4}$ at $18°$ C; accordingly, it has been agreed almost universally that diazotization involves nitrous acid rather than nitrite ion. The second equilibrium, on the other hand, has separated investigators into two schools: those who favor the amine salt and those who favor the free amine as the active entity in the reaction.

The modern electronic concept of organic reactions renders untenable any diazotization mechanism involving amine salt. The amine-salt hypothesis, however, was accepted widely until the beginning of the past decade. In order that the reasons for the rejection of this hypothesis may be quite explicit, the following discussion will be developed in a semi-chronological manner.

The first recorded investigation of the kinetics of the diazotization reaction was that of Hantzsch and Schuemann[35]. These authors studied the diazotization of several amines in aqueous hydrochloric acid and reported that the reaction followed second-order kinetics. The rate was *increased* by the presence of excess hydrochloric acid, although more than one molar excess had little additional effect. From this dependence of the rate on acid concentration it was proposed, quite logically, that diazotization involved reaction of nitrous acid with the amine salt, the concentration of which would increase with increasing acid concentration.

Reilley and Drumm[66] examined the necessary consequences of the amine-salt hypothesis and postulated that in the presence of insufficient acid to prevent hydrolysis of the amine salt, the rate at which the amine undergoes diazotization should be a direct function of the basicity of the amine. Moreover, the rate should not be altered appreciably by the presence of a greater amount of acid than that necessary for the prevention of hydrolysis of the amine salt. Data obtained for the diazotization of three amines of different basicities substantiated these postulates.

Böeseken and Schoutissen[6, 74], while purporting to strengthen the amine-salt hypothesis, actually introduced evidence inconsistent with this hypothesis. In an investigation of the diazotization of a wide variety of amines it was found that the rate of reaction is generally an *inverse* function of the basicity of the amine. The rate increased with increasing concentration of acid, but the effect of excess acid was greater than could be accounted for on the basis of decreased hydrolysis of the amine salt.

An increasing rate of diazotization with decreasing basicity of the amine was observed also by Ueno and Suzuki[81]. These authors report, moreover, that the speed of diazotization is a function of the *kind* and *concentration* of the acid employed rather than of the hydrogen-ion concentration. For the acids studied, diazotization proceeded least rapidly in nitric, sulfuric, or 1,5-naphthalenedisulfonic acid, more rapidly in hydrochloric acid, and most rapidly in hydrobromic acid. Diazotization was observed to be catalyzed by chloride ions, e.g., by added sodium chloride, but the effect was less than that produced by an equivalent amount of hydrochloric acid.

The validity of second-order kinetics for the diazotization reaction was questioned in 1928. Taylor[78] observed that a $0.05N$ solution of methylammonium nitrite, either as such or when $0.05N$ in sulfuric acid, did not undergo measurable decomposition over a period of two and one-half hours. When an equivalent amount of nitrous acid or nitrite ion was added, however, the methylammonium nitrite disappeared at a fairly rapid rate. Taylor[79] proposed that the reaction occurred between the ammonium ion, nitrite ion and undissociated nitrous acid.

Adamson and Kenner[2] provided an alternative interpretation of Taylor's results. Since an amine salt has no point of attack by an electrophilic agent, these authors suggested that the free amine was undergoing reaction. The following mechanism was proposed:

$$\text{HONO} \xrightarrow{\text{H}^+} \text{HO}-\text{N}\!\!=\!\!\overset{+}{\text{O}}\text{H} \xrightarrow{\text{RNH}_2} \underset{\underset{+}{\overset{|}{\text{RNH}_2}}}{\text{HO}-\text{N}-\text{OH}} \xrightarrow{-\text{H}_2\text{O}} \underset{\overset{|}{\text{NO}}}{\overset{+}{\text{RNH}_2}} \xrightarrow{\text{NO}_2^-}$$

$$\text{HNO}_2 + \text{RNH}-\text{NO} \rightarrow \text{RN}\!\!=\!\!\text{N}-\text{OH}$$

The reaction of primary and secondary aliphatic and aromatic amines with nitrous acid was studied extensively by Earl[16] and co-workers over a period of several years. Evidence that reaction occurred between free amine and nitrous acid resulted from a study of the reaction in mixed solvents. Thus, the formation of ammonium and nitrite ions should occur to a lesser extent as the dielectric constant of the solvent is decreased. In water-dioxane mixtures, the rate of the reaction increased as the dioxane content increased[17].

Schmid and Muhr[71] investigated the kinetics of the diazotization of aniline. The rate observed in aqueous sulfuric acid can be expressed by the equation

$$V = k_1(\text{C}_6\text{H}_5\text{NH}_2)(\text{HNO}_2)^2$$

In aqueous hydrochloric acid ($0.04N$), however, chloride-ion catalysis was observed, and the above equation must be modified as follows:

$$V = (\text{C}_6\text{H}_5\text{NH}_2)[k_1(\text{HNO}_2)^2 + k_2(\text{HNO}_2)(\text{H}^+)(\text{Cl}^-)]$$

Hammett[30] has shown that these kinetics can be explained satisfactorily if the rate-determining step involves the free amine and N_2O_3 or NOCl formed by the mobile equilibria

$$2\text{HNO}_2 \rightleftharpoons \text{N}_2\text{O}_3 + \text{H}_2\text{O}$$

$$\text{HNO}_2 + \text{H}^+ + \text{Cl}^- \rightleftharpoons \text{NOCl} + \text{H}_2\text{O}$$

All derivatives of nitrous acid can be represented by a limiting structure in which the nitrogen atom possesses a sextet of electrons, i.e., is electrophilic in character.

$$\text{X}-\overset{..}{\underset{..}{\text{N}}}\!:\!:\!\overset{..}{\text{O}} \leftrightarrow \text{X}-\overset{\overset{.\!+}{}}{\text{N}}\!:\!\overset{..}{\text{O}}\!:^-_{..} \qquad \text{(where } X \text{ represents OH, Cl, ONO, etc.)}$$

Hence, Hammett represents diazotization as a reaction between the amine and the electrophilic nitrous acid derivative, followed by elimination of the X^- anion and a molecule of water.

$$\underset{\text{X}-\overset{+}{\underset{..}{\text{N}}}-\overset{..}{\text{O}}\!:^-_{..}}{\text{C}_6\text{H}_5\text{NH}_2} \rightarrow \underset{\text{X}-\overset{|}{\text{N}}-\overset{..}{\text{O}}\!:^-}{\overset{+}{\text{C}_6\text{H}_5\overset{+}{\text{N}}\text{H}_2}} \rightarrow \text{C}_6\text{H}_5\overset{+}{\text{N}}\!\!=\!\!\text{N} + \text{H}_2\text{O} + \text{X}^-$$

Convincing support for the Hammett mechanism has been advanced recently by Hughes, Ingold and Ridd[45]. The diazotization of aniline in aqueous perchloric acid was studied. At acidities above 0.05N third-order kinetics were observed; at acidities below 0.002N, however, the reaction rate was proportional to the square of the nitrous acid concentration and *independent* of the amine concentration. Schmid and Woppmann[72] have observed the same dependence of kinetic order on acid concentration in aqueous nitric acid media. These observations are shown to be consistent with Hammett's conception of N_2O_3 as an active agent in diazotization. At the lower acidities the concentration of free amine is large enough to destroy the N_2O_3 as rapidly as it is formed, and the formation of this agent becomes rate-determining. At the higher acidities the amine concentration is much smaller, and the N_2O_3 is able to approach more closely its equilibrium concentration. Ingold[53] has reported that at low nitrous acid concentrations the kinetic expression may assume the form:

$$V = k \text{ (amine)} (HNO_2) (H^+)$$

This he attributes to the attack of the amine by protonated nitrous acid, in much the manner suggested by Adamson and Kenner[2]. This representation by Ingold provides an attractive alternative to the more complex mechanism advanced by Abel[1] to account for the above kinetics.

Hammett's and Ingold's mechanisms appear to offer a more generally satisfactory explanation of the observed experimental facts than do any of the other hypotheses proposed thus far. The increased rate with increasing hydrochloric acid concentration, and the chloride-ion catalysis observed by Ueno and Suzuki become understandable. This hypothesis explains also why diazotization proceeds more rapidly in hydrochloric than in sulfuric acid. A further test of the value of this hypothesis might be obtained by a consideration of the equilibrium

$$HNO_2 + HBr \rightleftharpoons NOBr + H_2O$$

The hypothesis that the free amine rather than the amine salt undergoes diazotization would appear to complicate any attempt to correlate speed of diazotization with base strength of amines. In media of low acid concentration we might expect the rate to be independent of base strength of the amine, except possibly for the very weakly basic amines. In any reaction kinetics proposed for the reaction in media of moderate-to-high acidity, the specific rate constant will include both the ammonium ion-amine equilibrium constant and the energy of activation for diazotization. Both of these values undoubtedly are related to the base strength of the amine. Increased base strength would be expected to lower the activation energy of the reaction by increasing the nucleophilic character of the amino nitrogen atom. On the other hand, increased base strength would result in a lower equilibrium concentration of the amine. The former effect would accelerate the reaction, while the latter would retard it.

The Azo Coupling Reaction

Diazo compounds react with a large number of "coupling components" to form azo derivatives. These coupling components may be classified under the following headings:

(1) Aromatic hydroxy compounds, e.g., phenols, naphthols, etc.
(2) Aromatic amines
(3) Substances containing reactive methylene groups
(4) Phenol and naphthol ethers
(5) Hydrocarbons

Of these classes, only the first three are of technical importance, but an acceptable mechanism for the coupling reaction should embrace all five types.

The rate at which an azo coupling proceeds in an aqueous medium at a given temperature is a function of the nature of the diazo compound, the nature of the coupling component, and the pH of the medium. The dye chemist has classified the diazo compounds as *weak* or *strong*, depending on the ease with which they react. Quite generally, the strong diazo components contain electron-attracting substituents in the aromatic nucleus, while the weak ones contain electron-donating substituents. Schoutissen[73, 75] has shown that for a given coupling component increasingly strong diazo components are able to couple in media of increasing acid strength.

The role played by the coupling component is somewhat more complex. Phenols couple very readily in an alkaline medium to give an *ortho-* or *para*-azo derivative. If a sufficient excess of the diazo compound is used a 2,4,6-trisazophenol may be obtained[4, 9, 37, 38]. Aniline, on the other hand, gives as the only azo product the monoazo derivative resulting from substitution in the *para* position. With both the phenols and amines coupling is impeded by electron-attracting substituents and facilitated by electron-donating substituents. When aminophenols or aminonaphthols undergo coupling in an alkaline medium the azo group enters in a position *ortho* or *para* to the hydroxy group; when the coupling occurs in an acid medium it is the amino group which orients the incoming azo group. The region in which amino-orientation gives way to hydroxy-orientation with increasing alkalinity will vary with the structure of the coupling component.

Reactive methylene compounds undergo the coupling reaction quite rapidly in alkaline media. Many compounds of this class, e.g., acetoacetanilides, dimethyldihydroresorcinol, etc., might have been considered along with the compounds of Class 1 as enol-hydroxy derivatives. There are, however, other methylene compounds, e.g., nitroparaffins[5, 18, 52, 61], which couple quite readily and which require that the active methylene compounds be considered as a distinct class.

The phenol and naphthol ethers usually couple much less readily than do the compounds of the first three classes. The rate of coupling is most rapid for strong diazo compounds and for coupling components containing several alkoxy groups[59]. The most striking feature of this reaction, however, is the fact that the alkyl portion of the ether may be eliminated partially or completely to form the corresponding hydroxyazo compound[54, 59]. Since the alkoxyazo compounds are quite stable under the coupling conditions employed, the "dealkylation" must occur at the moment of coupling[82].

Strong diazo compounds will couple with most conjugated dienes[58, 80] and with some highly substituted ethylene derivatives[7, 20]. The coupling of aromatic hydrocarbons, however, appears to be more specific. Diazotized picramide will couple with mesitylene, isodurene and pentamethylbenzene, but the closely related durene and *m*-xylene will not couple[60, 76].

The effect of the pH of the medium on the rate of coupling has been elucidated only for the coupling components of the first three classes. The low water-solubility of the hydrocarbons and the phenol and naphthol ethers usually makes it necessary to utilize organic media for couplings with these compounds. The rate at which the phenols, naphthols and active methylene compounds undergo the coupling reaction increases directly with the pH of the medium until, at a certain pH, the rate attains a maximum value. At pH values higher than this critical value, the rate decreases. It has been suggested that this decrease in coupling rate is due to the conversion of the diazo compound to the non-coupling isodiazotate[43, 86]. The rate at which an amine couples also increases with increasing pH of the medium. Couplings of this type are usually carried out in weakly acid media, however, to suppress the formation of triazene compounds[15, 22, 57, 68], i.e.,

$$ArN_2X + Ar'NH_2 \rightleftharpoons ArN{=}N{-}NHAr' + H^+ + X^-$$

A reaction mechanism which will account for the above facts must consider both the identity of the reacting entities and the manner in which the interaction occurs. The question of the identity of the reacting entities is complicated by the existence of several chemical individuals in the coupling system as a result of more or less complex equilibria. The diazo compounds exist in different forms in different pH ranges. In acid media they exist as diazonium salts (I). As the pH is raised to higher values this form is converted successively to the diazo hydroxide (II) and the non-coupling isodiazotate (see Azoic Dyes).

$$ArN_2{}^+X^- \underset{H^+}{\overset{OH^-}{\rightleftharpoons}} Ar{-}N{=}N{-}OH \underset{H^+}{\overset{OH^-}{\rightleftharpoons}} \text{isodiazotate}$$

$$\text{(I)} \qquad\qquad\qquad \text{(II)}$$

Each of the coupling components in the first three classes can give rise to two chemical individuals:

(1) $$ArOH \rightleftharpoons ArO^- + H^+$$

(2) $$ArNH_2 + H^+ \rightleftharpoons ArNH_3^+$$

(3) $$X—CH_2—Y \rightleftharpoons X—\bar{C}H—Y + H^+$$

(where X—CH$_2$—Y represents a reactive

methylene compound).

The phenol-ether* and hydrocarbon coupling components do not undergo facile transformations of this type under the coupling conditions employed, and in these cases we need concern ourselves only with the form in which the diazo compound reacts.

Conant and Peterson[10] have studied the coupling of several diazotized amines with phenol- and naphtholsulfonic acids in buffered solutions. Over a wide range of concentrations, the reaction rate closely followed the usual bimolecular equation. Up to a pH of about 9.15, the rate was found to be a simple function of the hydrogen-ion activity in the medium. These results parallel generally the less precise results obtained earlier by Goldschmidt and his co-workers[25, 26, 27, 28].

Conant and Peterson repeated the suggestion of Goldschmidt that coupling occurred by a *direct* attack of the diazo hydroxide at the coupling position of the phenol derivative, via the following scheme:

$$ArN_2X + OH^- \rightleftharpoons ArN=N—OH + X^-$$

$$ArN=N—OH + Phenol \rightarrow Ar—N=N—Phenol + H_2O$$

In the thirty years that separated these two sets of investigations, the direct-attack hypothesis met with but limited acceptance. Most of the workers in the field preferred a mechanism involving an initial attachment of the azo group to the hydroxy or amino group of the coupling component, followed by a rearrangement of the azo group to the final coupling position[11, 12, 13, 14, 32, 33, 34, 55].

Hodgson and Marsden[40, 41, 42, 43] have advanced a mechanism involving the attack of polarized diazo hydroxide on polarized phenol. This mechanism, however, is essentially a restatement of the Conant-Peterson mechanism with an explicit consideration of the role of bond polarizations.

The participation of a diazo hydroxide in the coupling reaction has been questioned seriously by the more recent investigators. Wistar and Bartlett[85]

---

* Zollinger[97] reports, however, that unpublished investigations by Puetter indicate that the rate of coupling of phenol ethers in water is not independent of the acidity of the medium.

pointed out that there are only four possible routes which the azo coupling reaction could follow, viz.,

Route 1. The diazo hydroxide couples with the ammonium ion.
Route 2. The diazonium ion couples with the free amine.
Route 3. The diazonium ion couples with the ammonium ion.
Route 4. The diazo hydroxide couples with the free amine.

The investigators then adopted two model equilibria,

$$R—NH_3^+ \rightleftharpoons RNH_2 + H^+ \qquad k = 1 \times 10^{-4}$$

$$ArN_2OH \rightleftharpoons ArN_2^+ + OH^- \qquad k = 1 \times 10^{-3}$$

and calculated the amount of each individual present in the equilibrium mixtures as a function of pH. These quantities then were inserted in the bimolecular rate equation, and the variation of the rate constant with change in pH was calculated for the above four reaction routes. An investigation of the coupling velocity for actual examples revealed that the observed pH dependence of the second order rate constant corresponded only to that calculated for either Route 1 or Route 2. Since aromatic ammonium ions undergo electrophilic substitution reactions only with difficulty, and since such substitution occurs in the position *meta* to the ammonium group, Route 2 was selected as the scheme which best explained the experimental observations. Thus the reaction involves coupling of the *diazonium ion* with the *free amine*. A reexamination of the results obtained by Conant and Peterson revealed that the coupling of phenols could be formulated equally well as a reaction between the diazonium ion and the phenolate ion.

This interpretation of the coupling reaction has been advanced also by Hammett[31] and by Puetter[64, 65]. The latter investigator has shown that the rate of coupling of several naphtholsulfonic acids is proportional to the dissociation constant of the hydroxy group. Zollinger and Buechler[98] have shown that in the coupling of dihydroxynaphthalenesulfonic acids the entering diazonium cation is oriented by the more acidic hydroxy group. On the basis of the above interpretation, Zollinger and Wittmer[99] have developed a general kinetic expression for the coupling of aminonaphthols in aqueous media at various acidities.

It has been pointed out that the diazonium ion is a hybrid of the two limiting structures (III) and (IV)[36, 69]:

$$Ar—\overset{+}{N}{\equiv}N: \leftrightarrow Ar—\overset{..}{N}{=}\overset{..}{N}{}^+$$

$$\text{(III)} \qquad\qquad \text{(IV)}$$

Structure (III) is the most important contributor to the hybrid, but the importance of (IV) is increased by proximity of a negative pole, i.e., at the moment of coupling. Hauser and Breslow[36] propose the following reaction mechanism:

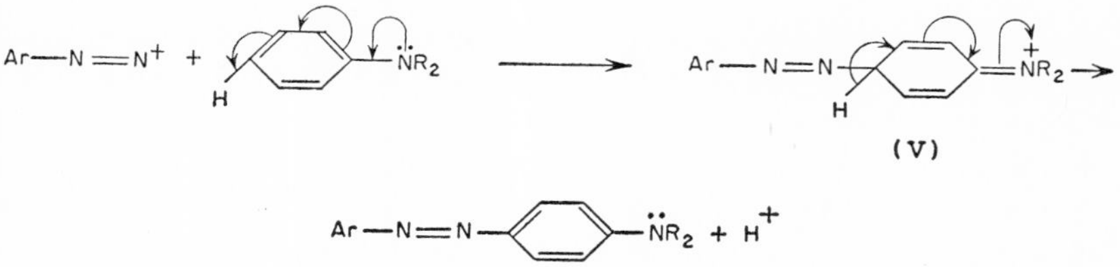

This scheme accounts for the fact that electron-attracting groups in the diazonium ion favor the coupling, since such groups cause Structure (IV) to contribute relatively more to the hybrid. The increase in coupling velocity with increase of pH of the medium is due to the relatively larger concentration of free amine (or phenoxide ion, etc.) available for reaction.

Hughes and Ingold[44] have discussed the effect of electron-releasing groups in the coupling component on the resonance stabilization of the transition state (V).

The above reaction scheme represents a special case of the general theory of electrophilic, or cationoid, aromatic substitution reactions[63, 67]. In view of this agreement with the general theory we shall probably be on relatively safe ground if we attempt to extend the above reaction scheme to other classes of coupling components. The ease with which a coupling component undergoes reaction thus will be related directly to the "electron density at the coupling position."* This assumption explains why the phenolate and naphtholate ions, rather than the corresponding unionized derivatives, are active in coupling. In the ions, the electron density at the coupling position is increased by the contributions of the resonance structures (VII) and (IX), respectively.

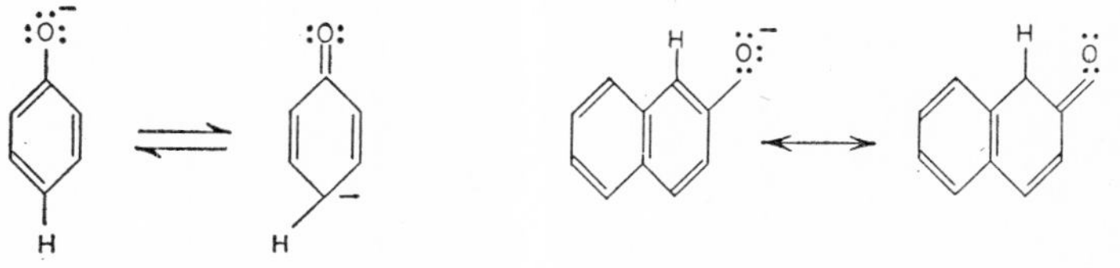

Analogous resonance structures for the unionized derivatives would require charge separation, would represent higher energy structures, and would be less effective in increasing the electron density at the coupling position.

The fact that phenol ethers couple with strong diazo compounds would suggest that certain *unionized* phenols or naphthols should be able to do

---

* This terminology is not intended to imply a static electronic situation. Rather it has been selected as a "shorthand" representation of the stabilization afforded the transition complex by an electron-donating substituent, in the manner considered by Hughes and Ingold[44].

likewise. Indeed, Allan[3] has reported recently that 2,4-dinitrobenzene-diazonium chloride will couple with selected phenols and naphthols in 83 per cent sulfuric acid. These reactions, of course, are much slower than the corresponding reactions in alkaline media.

The fact that one must formulate resonance structures with charges separated explains why the aromatic amines, unionized phenols, phenol ethers, and the hydrocarbons couple relatively slowly. It is probable that the coupling of active methylene compounds involves first the formation of the corresponding anion, which then reacts directly with the diazonium ion.

$$X—CH_2—Y \xrightarrow{OH^-} X—\bar{C}H—Y \xrightarrow{ArN_2^+} Ar—N{=}N—\underset{\underset{Y}{\diagdown}}{\overset{\overset{X}{\diagup}}{CH}}$$

The elimination of the alkyl group during the coupling of phenol ethers might be rationalized by the following scheme:

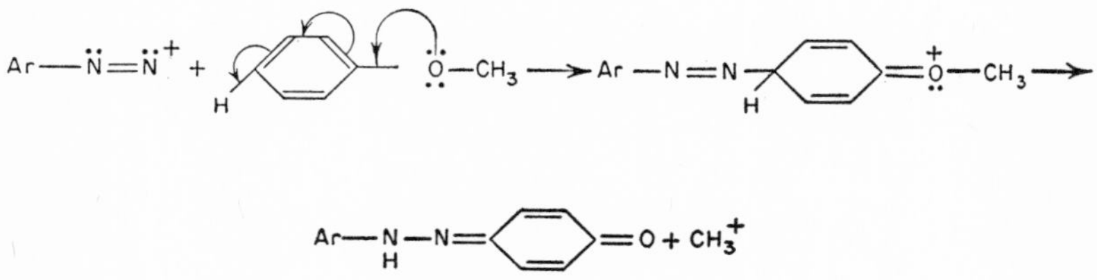

Such a rationalization, however, is purely hypothetical. Since the form in which the alkyl group appears in the reaction products has not been reported, it is conceivable even that this "dealkylation" reaction actually involves direct replacement of the *alkoxy* by a hydroxy group.

The ionic coupling mechanism can be applied also to the coupling of aromatic hydrocarbons.* It is seen that mesitylene (X), isodurene (XI) and pentamethylbenzene (XII) each have three methyl groups which by hyperconjugation can increase the electron density at the starred carbon atoms.

---

* Huisgen[46, 47, 48, 49, 50, 51] has observed that benzenediazo acetate couples with 2-naphthol at an immeasurably rapid rate in benzene solution. Huisgen's investigations suggest that azo coupling occurs by a different mechanism in nonaqueous solvents where the diazonium cation is not stabilized by solvation. While a detailed consideration of reactions in such media is beyond the scope of the present treatment, it is conceivable that some of the coupling reactions of phenol ethers and hydrocarbons discussed above occur via the nonaqueous mechanism.

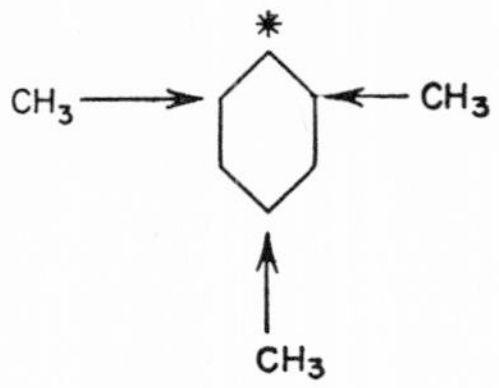

(X)

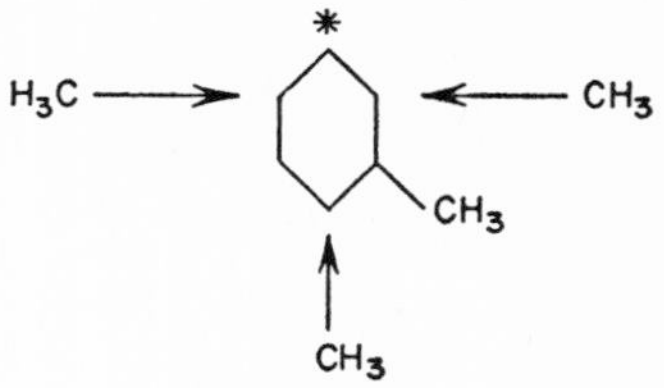

(XI)

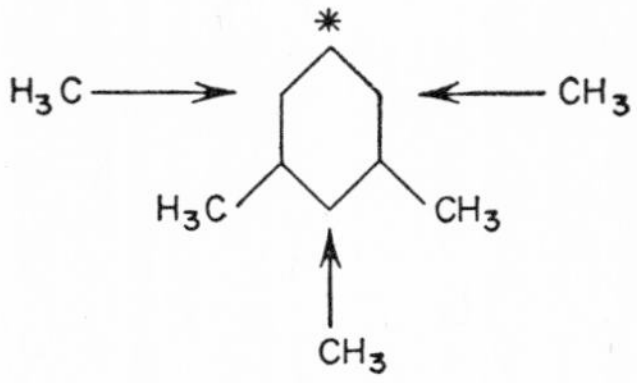

(XII)

This appears to afford "border-line" activation for coupling with strong diazo components. Durene and *m*-xylene have only two "activating methyl groups," and coupling does not occur.

Steric hindrance of two types has been observed in azo coupling. 2-Naphthol-3,6-disulfonic acid (XIII) will couple much more readily than will the isomeric 6,8-disulfonic acid (XIV). The bulky sulfo group in the 8 position of the latter apparently lowers the number of effective collisions between the diazonium ion and the 1 position.

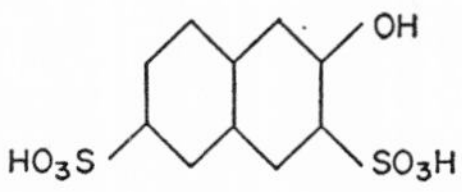

(XIII)

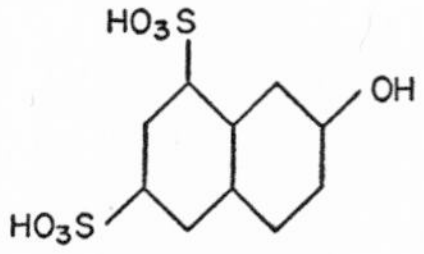

(XIV)

The second type of hindrance lends direct support to the ionic coupling mechanism. *N,N*-Dimethyl-*o*-toluidine (XV) couples very slowly and incompletely, while *N*-methyl-*o*-toluidine (XVI) couples readily[21, 55]. Brown, Kharasch and Sprowls[8] have suggested that steric interference of the *o*-methyl group with one of the *N*-methyl groups in XV prevents the molecule from assuming the planar form required by resonance structures such as XVII—the structure necessary to increase the electron density at the coupling position.

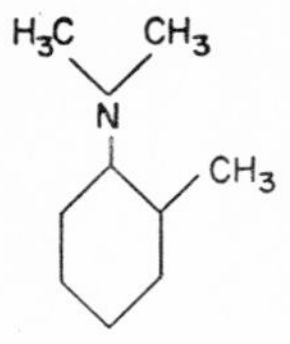

(XV) 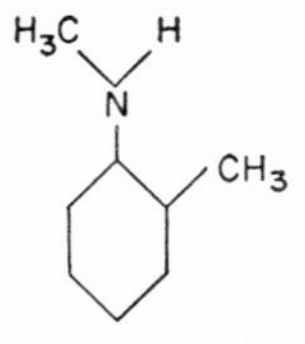   (XVI)

The mono-N-methyl amine does not suffer this restriction, since the repulsion exerted between the amino hydrogen atom and the nuclear methyl group is much less (XVIII).

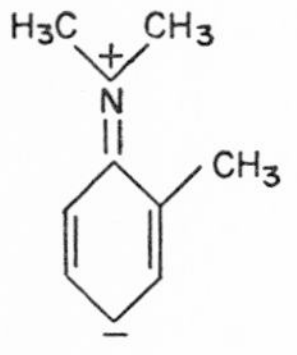

(XVII) 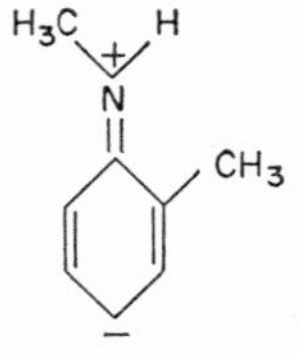   (XVIII) 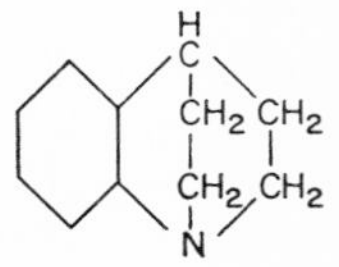   (XIX)

Likewise, the rigid pyramidal configuration of the nitrogen atom in benzoquinuclidine (3,4-dihydro-1(2H),4-ethanoquinoline) (XIX) prevents azo coupling[84].

The tendency of a diazonium ion to couple with phenols and naphthols is so great that a substituent occupying the normal coupling position may be expelled in favor of the entering azo group. Such behavior is noted frequently in 1-substituted-2-naphthols when the 1-substituent is a chlorine, bromine or iodine atom[39, 62], an arylmethyl group[77], or a sulfo group[23, 24, 83]. Ziegler and co-workers[87, 88, 89, 90, 91, 92, 93, 94, 95, 96] recently have studied a large number of substituted phenols which undergo coupling with elimination of a substituent, while Filippuichev and Chekalin[19] have reported that under certain conditions a diazonium ion can expel an azo group from an azo dye. These phenomena would appear to require a reaction scheme of the following nature:

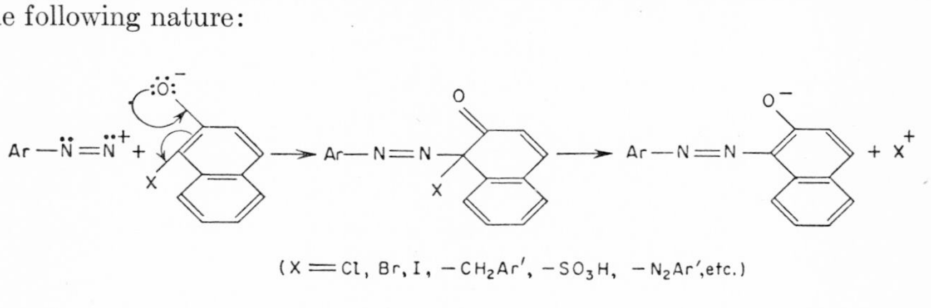

(X = Cl, Br, I, −CH₂Ar′, −SO₃H, −N₂Ar′,etc.)

Conclusion

The development of general ionic mechanisms for organic reactions has afforded criteria by which the earlier work on the diazotization and the azo coupling reactions could be evaluated. The application of these criteria has led to most of the recent progress in the understanding of azo chemistry and undoubtedly will determine the direction of future investigations in the field. A more complete development of the general theory of organic reactions should shed still more light on the phenomena discussed in the preceding pages.

On the basis of the present state of our knowledge the mechanisms of the diazotization and the azo coupling reactions may be summarized as follows:

The diazotization reaction proceeds by direct attack of an electrophilic derivative of nitrous acid, e.g.,

$$N_2O_3 , \; NOCl, \; NOBr, \; (HONOH)^+$$

with a "free" amine. The identity of the electrophilic agent and the kinetic order of the reaction are determined by the nature and concentration of the reagents present in the reaction medium.

In aqueous media the azo coupling reaction occurs between a diazonium cation and a nucleophilic coupling component. As a first approximation, the ease with which the coupling component undergoes reaction can be related directly to the electron density at the coupling position.

Literature Cited

1. Abel, *Monatsh.*, **83**, 1103 (1952).
2. Adamson and Kenner, *J. Chem. Soc.*, **1934**, 838.
3. Allan, *Collection Czechoslov. Chem. Commun.*, **16**, 620 (1953).
4. Bamberger, *Ber.*, **33**, 3188 (1900).
5. —— and Frei, *ibid.*, **36**, 3833 (1903).
6. Böeseken and Schoutissen, *Rec. trav. chim.*, **54**, 956 (1935).
7. British Patent 435,449 (1935).
8. Brown, Kharasch and Sprowls, *J. Org. Chem.*, **4**, 442 (1939).
9. Chattaway and Hill, *J. Chem. Soc.*, **121**, 2756 (1922).
10. Conant and Peterson, *J. Am. Chem. Soc.*, **52**, 1220 (1930).
11. Dimroth, *Ber.*, **40**, 2404 (1907).
12. —— and Hartmann, *ibid.*, **40**, 4460 (1907).
13. —— and ——, *ibid.*, **41**, 4012 (1908).
14. ——, Leichtlin and Friedmann, *ibid.*, **50**, 1534 (1917).
15. Earl, *ibid.*, **63**, 1666 (1930).
16. ——, *Research*, **3**, 120 (1950).
17. —— and Hills, *J. Chem. Soc.*, **1942**, 275.
18. Feasely and Degering, *J. Org. Chem.*, **8**, 12 (1943).
19. Filippuichev and Chekalin, *Anilinokrasochnaya Prom.*, **5**, 76 (1935); *C. A.*, **29**, 5087 (1935).
20. French Patent 769,113 (1934).

21. Friedlaender, *Monatsh.*, **19**, 627 (1898).
22. Friswell and Green, *J. Chem. Soc.*, **47**, 917 (1885).
23. German Patent 204,702 (1907).
24. German Patent 238,841 (1910).
25. Goldschmidt and Buss, *Ber.*, **30**, 2075 (1897).
26. —— and Keller, *ibid.*, **35**, 3534 (1902).
27. —— and Keppler, *ibid.*, **33**, 893 (1900).
28. —— and Merz, *ibid.*, **30**, 670 (1897).
29. Griess, *Ann.*, **106**, 123 (1858).
30. Hammett, "Physical Organic Chemistry," p. 294, New York, McGraw-Hill Book Co., 1940.
31. ——, *ibid.*, p. 314.
32. Hantzsch, *Ber.*, **41**, 3532 (1908).
33. ——, *ibid.*, **42**, 394 (1909).
34. ——, *ibid.*, **42**, 2137 (1909).
35. —— and Schuemann, *ibid.*, **32**, 1691 (1899).
36. Hauser and Breslow, *J. Am. Chem. Soc.*, **63**, 418 (1941).
37. Heller, *J. prakt. Chem.*, **77**, 189 (1908).
38. —— and Noetzel, *ibid.*, **76**, 58 (1907).
39. Hewitt and Mitchell, *J. Chem. Soc.*, **89**, 1167 (1906).
40. Hodgson, *J. Soc. Dyers Colourists*, **58**, 228 (1942).
41. —— and Marsden, *ibid.*, **60**, 16 (1944).
42. —— and ——, *ibid.*, **60**, 120 (1944).
43. —— and ——, *ibid.*, **61**, 20 (1945).
44. Hughes and Ingold, *J. Chem. Soc.*, **1941**, 608.
45. ——, —— and Ridd, *Nature*, **166**, 642 (1950).
46. Huisgen, *Angew. Chem.*, **61**, 450 (1949).
47. ——, *Ann.*, **573**, 163 (1951).
48. ——, *ibid.*, **574**, 184 (1951).
49. —— and Horeld, *ibid.*, **562**, 137 (1949).
50. —— and Krause, *ibid.*, **574**, 157 (1951).
51. —— and Nakaten, *ibid.*, **573**, 181 (1951).
52. Huenig, *Angew. Chem.*, **64**, 621 (1952).
53. Ingold, *Bull. soc. chim. France*, **1952**, 667.
54. Jambuserwala and Mason, *J. Soc. Dyers Colourists*, **46**, 339 (1930).
55. Karrer, *Ber.*, **48**, 1398 (1915).
56. Kekulé and Hidegh, *ibid.*, **3**, 233 (1870).
57. Kidd, *J. Org. Chem.*, **2**, 198 (1937).
58. Meyer, K. H., *Ber.*, **52**, 1468 (1919).
59. ——, Irschick and Schlosser, *ibid.*, **47**, 1741 (1914).
60. —— and Tochtermann, *ibid.*, **54**, 2283 (1921).
61. Meyer, V., and Ambuehl, *ibid.*, **8**, 751 (1875).
62. Pollack and Gebauer-Fuelnegg, *Monatsh.*, **50**, 310 (1928).
63. Price, *Chem. Revs.*, **29**, 37 (1941).
64. Puetter, *Angew. Chem.*, **61**, 449 (1949).
65. ——, *ibid.*, **63**, 188 (1951).
66. Reilley and Drumm, *J. Chem. Soc.*, **1935**, 871.
67. Remick, "Electronic Interpretations of Organic Chemistry," 2nd ed., pp. 342–374, New York, John Wiley & Sons, Inc., 1949.
68. Rosenhauer, *Ber.*, **64**, 1438 (1931).

69. Sarkar, *J. Indian Chem. Soc.*, **13**, 19 (1936).
70. Saunders, "The Aromatic Diazo-Compounds and Their Technical Applications," 2nd ed., London, Edward Arnold & Co., 1949.
71. Schmid and Muhr, *Ber.*, **70B**, 421 (1937).
72. —— and Woppmann, *Monatsh.*, **83**, 346 (1952).
73. Schoutissen, *J. Am. Chem. Soc.*, **55**, 4541 (1933).
74. ——, *ibid.*, **58**, 259 (1936).
75. ——, *Chem. Weekblad*, **34**, 506 (1937).
76. Smith and Paden, *J. Am. Chem. Soc.*, **56**, 2169 (1934).
77. Strohbach, *Ber.*, **34**, 4162 (1901).
78. Taylor, *J. Chem. Soc.*, **1928**, 1099.
79. —— and Price, *ibid.*, **1929**, 2052.
80. Thiele, *Ber.*, **33**, 666 (1900).
81. Ueno and Suzuki, *J. Soc. Chem. Ind. Japan*, **36**, 615B (1933); *Chem. Zentr.*, **1934**, I, 849.
82. Van Alphen and Drost, *Rec. trav. chim.*, **68**, 54 (1949).
83. Wahl and Lantz, *Bull. soc. chim. France*, [4] **33**, 93 (1923).
84. Wepster, *Rec. trav. chim.*, **71**, 1159 (1952).
85. Wistar and Bartlett, *J. Am. Chem. Soc.*, **63**, 413 (1941).
86. Woodward, in Groggins, "Unit Processes in Organic Synthesis," 3rd ed., p. 161, New York, McGraw-Hill Book Co., 1947.
87. Ziegler, *Österr. Chem. Ztg.*, **53**, 31 (1952).
88. ——, *ibid.*, **54**, 155 (1953).
89. ——, Kaufmann and Kreisel, *Monatsh.*, **83**, 1274 (1952).
90. —— and Snatzke, *ibid.*, **84**, 278 (1953).
91. —— and Zigeuner, *ibid.*, **79**, 363 (1948).
92. —— and ——, *ibid.*, **79**, 371 (1948).
93. —— and ——, *ibid.*, **80**, 295 (1949).
94. —— and ——, *ibid.*, **80**, 313 (1949).
95. —— and ——, *ibid.*, **80**, 359 (1949).
96. —— and ——, *ibid.*, **82**, 238 (1951).
97. Zollinger, *Chem Revs.*, **51**, 347 (1952).
98. —— and Buechler, *Helv. Chim. Acta*, **34**, 591 (1951).
99. —— and Wittwer, *ibid.*, **35**, 1209 (1952).

AZO DYES FOR COTTON

H. E. Woodward

Cotton is the most commonly used textile fiber. In the years 1946–50 the annual United States production of direct dyes for cotton (mainly azo) was over 20,000 tons or 22 per cent of the total production of synthetic dyes. The average unit selling price of azo dyes is about the same as the average for all dyes. Azo dyes for cotton therefore cost more than the low priced sulfur dyes but less than the expensive vat dyes.

Theory of Cotton Dyeing

The physical chemistry of dyeing has been thoroughly discussed by Valko[67] and by Vickerstaff[68] and the following is a summary of our present information.

Cotton, flax and other vegetable fibers, and regenerated cellulose, such as viscose rayon and cuprammonium rayon, consist mainly of cellulose fibers. These fibers, in the case of cotton, consist of chains of at least 100 and probably about 500 cellobiose units. (Fig. 1)

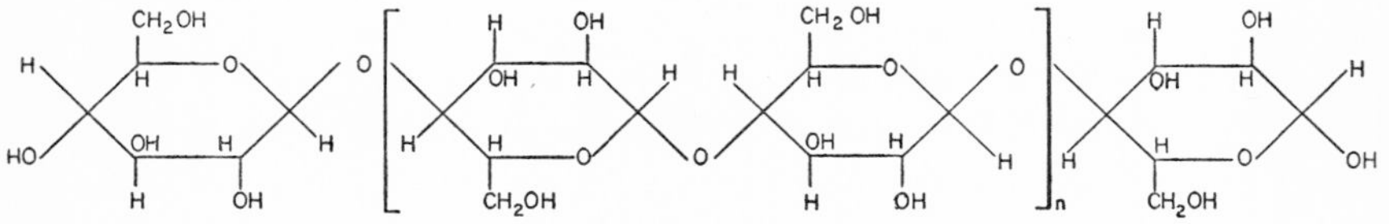

FIGURE 1. Cellulose Structure

In parts of the cellulose fiber, these chains are oriented into crystallites or micelles, where the chains are closely packed in parallel arrangement. In the remaining parts of the fiber, the chains are in an amorphous or uncrystallized form.

In a dye bath, water penetrates the amorphous portions, forming pores within the fiber. These pores are no larger than 10 mμ in size and probably are about 5 mμ. This limits the size of the dye molecule which can penetrate the fiber.

The physical properties of the dye bath are influenced by the concentration of the dye, the amount of electrolyte present and by the temperature. In a typical dye bath, the concentration of dye (assuming the commercial dye as sold contains about 50 per cent of diluents) may vary from 0.02 to 0.3 per cent and the concentration of electrolyte (usually NaCl) is from 0.5 to 5.0 per cent. In the dye bath, a dye suitable for dyeing cellulose is present as aggregates of a few molecules which are in equilibrium with single ions. The single anions of azo cotton dyes are approximately 2 to 3 mμ in length, which allows them to penetrate the pores of the cellulose fiber. The concentration of salt in the dye bath is not sufficient to flocculate the dye but is sufficient to prevent the cellulose fiber from becoming negatively charged. In the absence of salt, the direct dyes do not dye cotton.

In the process of dyeing, anions of the dye become attached to the surface of the fiber and migrate into the pores of the fiber. This migration or diffusion is a rather slow process and accounts for the need of approximately one hour for the dyeing operation. The rate of migration depends on the temperature and so the dye bath is kept at the boiling point. Within the fiber, the dye becomes attached to the cellulose molecule by the weak forces of hydrogen bonding. The dyeing process is reversible and the dye on the fiber is in equilibrium with the dye in solution under given conditions of concentration of dye, concentration of electrolyte, pH and temperature. Since this equilibrium favors the dye on the fiber at lower temperatures, the dye bath is allowed to cool before removing the dyed fiber.

The amount of dye which can be taken up by cellulose is approximately that which gives a monomolecular layer of dye on the surfaces of the micelles. This amount is less than 10 per cent for most natural fibers, but is more for cellulose degraded by chemical treatment such as mercerizing or regeneration from viscose or cuprammonium solutions. Ordinarily cotton is dyed with no more than about 1 per cent of its weight of dye.

Examination of the structure of cellulose, and of dyes known to have affinity for cotton, indicates that hydrogen bonding and van der Waals' forces are the probable cause of the attraction between the fiber and the dyes. The cellobiose unit has a length of 1.03 mμ and therefore similar hydroxy groups are repeated at this distance along the cellulose chain. Among the structural conditions in the dye molecule which probably affect the ability to become attached to the cellulose molecule are conjugation, planar configuration and spacing of approximately 1.03 mμ between groups which can donate or receive electrons to form the hydrogen bond. Pairs of groups with approximately this spacing are the azo groups of benzidine dyes, and the azo and amino groups in J acid dyes. The carboxamide group may owe its attractive force to the formation of a resonating hydrogen bridge structure:

$$R—C—N—R' \qquad \qquad R—C{=}N—R'$$
$$\underset{\underset{\underset{H—O—Cellulose}{\uparrow}}{\downarrow}}{\overset{\|}{O}} \; \overset{|}{\underset{H}{}} \qquad \leftrightarrow \qquad \underset{\underset{H{\leftarrow}O—Cellulose}{|}}{\overset{|}{O}} \; \overset{\downarrow}{\underset{H}{}}$$

Early Cotton Dyes

Before the advent of synthetic dyes, cotton was dyed with natural dyes of animal and plant origin. Some of these (such as Safflower, CI 1244, and Annato) dye cotton directly. Others (Indigo, CI 1249) are vat dyes (i.e., the reduced colorless form dyes cotton and is then oxidized), and others (such as Logwood, CI 1246, and Sanderswood) only dye cotton which has been treated with a tin salt or some other mordant. The first synthetic dyes were basic and could be dyed on cotton by the use of mordants such as tannic acid or salts of aluminum or other metals.

The first azo dyes to be manufactured were basic, since the amine used for making the diazo compound could also be used as a coupling component. The first of these, p-(phenylazo)aniline, introduced in England as Aniline

Yellow in 1863, had little value for dyeing any textile fiber, but it is still manufactured for other purposes, especially for use as a diazo component for disazo dyes.

In 1865 Martius discovered Bismarck Brown and manufactured it at the Berlin Plant of the Aktiengesellschaft für Anilinfabrikation (AGFA) of which he was one of the founders. This dye is made by adding two moles of sodium nitrite to three moles of *m*-phenylenediamine in a solution containing an excess of hydrochloric acid. This process gives a mixture of aminoazo compounds, but the main constituent is

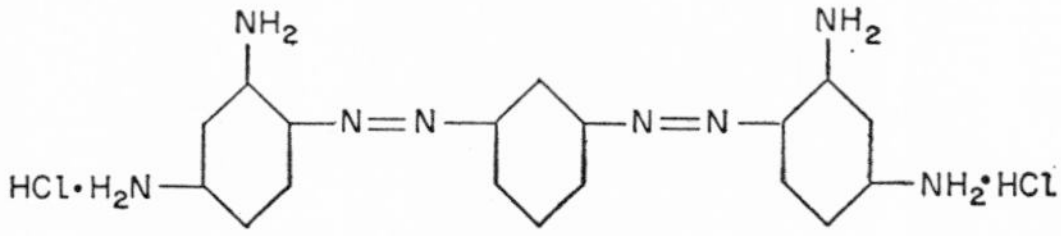

Bismarck Brown, CI 331

This product dyes mordanted cotton brown. A redder brown is obtained from toluene-2,4-diamine.

In 1875 Caro in Mannheim and later Witt in London independently discovered the basic yellow brown dye[69]

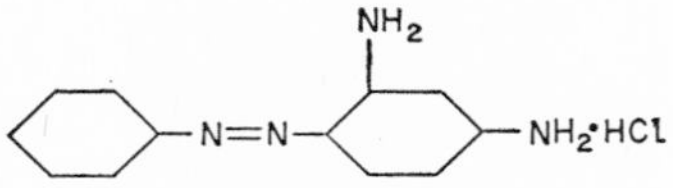

Chrysoidine, CI 20

This was the first dye to be manufactured by the now common process of diazotizing an amino compound (aniline) and coupling the resulting diazo compound with a different component (*m*-phenylenediamine). It was manufactured in April 1876 at the Star Chemical Works of Williams, Thomas and Dower, at Brenthouse near London. This marked the beginning of important commercial developments in azo dyes.*

Although Bismarck Brown and Chrysoidine are no longer important cotton dyes, their production in the United States is nearly 2 million pounds per year. They are used mainly for dyeing paper and leather.

Benzidine Dyes

Griess, Schultz, Caro and Witt, between 1867 and 1883, had made azo compounds using benzidine and other diamines as diazo components, and in some cases had noted the direct dyeing of cotton[19, 52]. Furthermore, the

---

* Detailed methods of diazotization and coupling may be found in the general references on page 695.

Bayer Company in 1881 patented the disazo dye made from tetrazotized benzidine and two moles of 2-naphthol-8-sulfonic acid and sold it as a wool dye, Bordeaux Extra, CI 385. In later years it was sold as a cotton dye by AGFA under the name Congo Violet.

However, the commercial production of direct dyes for cotton started with the discovery by Professor Paul Boettiger in 1884 of the red disazo dye from tetrazotized benzidine and 2 moles of naphthionic acid. A sample of this dye was submitted to a German dye manufacturer who found it of no interest for dyeing wool in comparison with available red dyes for wool because it became blue or black in an acid dye bath. Boettiger then sent a sample to AGFA where it was observed that this dye could be used for a simple direct dyeing of cotton from a neutral dye bath. It was realized that such a dyeing procedure for cotton, which could be carried out at home, would be of special value in countries such as India and China in comparison with the more complicated dyeing procedures with alizarin or with mordant dyes[60]. AGFA therefore manufactured this dye in the year of its discovery, and named it "Congo" on account of the political sensation of the year, the Congo Conference called in connection with the recognition of the Congo Free State.

Congo Red, CI 370

Congo Red is still manufactured in large amounts (nearly 2 million pounds a year in the United States). Red dyes having better fastness properties on cotton are now available, but they are mostly more expensive than Congo Red. Paper dyed with this dye is turned blue by solutions having a pH below 4.0 and for this reason Congo Red is a useful indicator for mineral acids.

Further work by AGFA and by the Bayer Company showed that other disazo derivatives of benzidine, o-tolidine, and o-dianisidine (3,3'-dimethoxybenzidine) dyed cotton. The dyes obtained were yellow, orange, red and blue. It was found that substituents ortho to the bond connecting the two phenyl radicals lessen the affinity for cotton, but if these substituents are part of a ring, as in "benzidine sulfone" (3,7-dibenzothiophenediamine, 5,5-dioxide), diaminocarbazole, or dibenzofurandiamine, then the dyes obtained are substantive for cotton. The present explanation of these properties is that the substituents prevent a planar structure of the dye, but the ring formation again makes the planar structure probable.

The benzidine dyes gave Germany a lead in the field of cotton dyes which was maintained for several decades. By 1887 Congo Red and the following benzidine type dyes were being manufactured in large amounts and they are still of commercial importance.

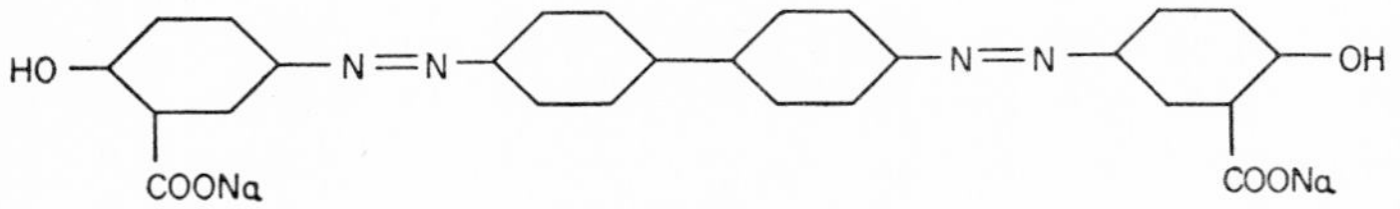

Chrysamine, CI 410

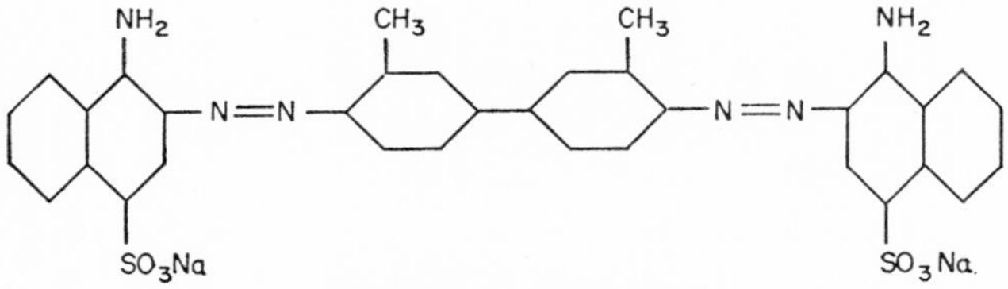

Benzopurpurin 4B, CI 448

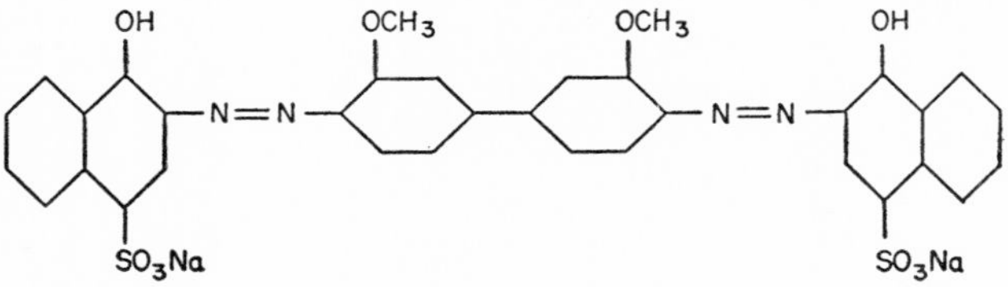

Benzazurin, CI 502

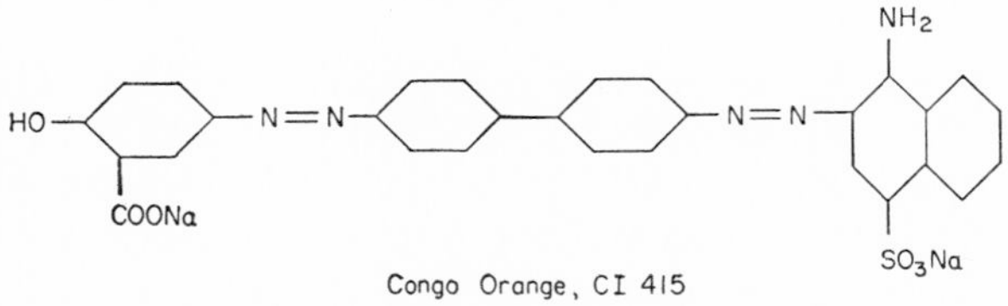

Congo Orange, CI 415

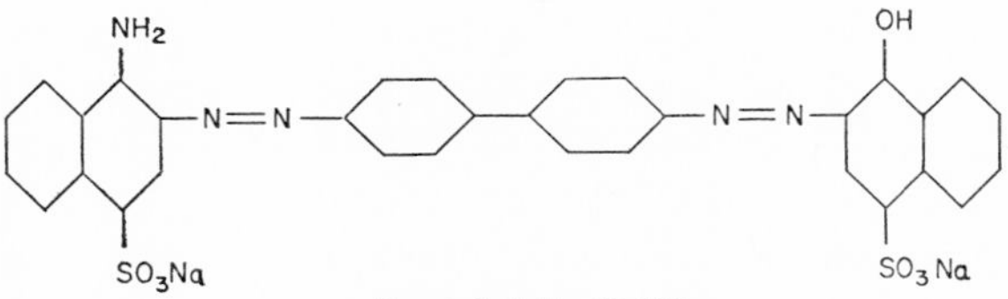

Congo Corinth, CI 375

The first dyes manufactured were those in which one mole of the tetrazotized diamine is coupled to two moles of a single coupling component. The unsymmetrical dyes, in which the tetrazo compound is coupled consecutively with two different coupling components, were made three years later. These unsymmetrical dyes are possible because the initial reaction of the tetrazo compound with the first coupling component produces a 4'-aryl-azo-4-biphenyldiazonium ion whose activity is sufficiently less than that of the tetrazo compound that the second coupling can be delayed until the first coupling is complete.

Tetrazo Compound   4'—arylazo—4—biphenyldiazonium ion

Schoutissen offered this explanation for the difference in activity of the two diazo groups in tetrazotized *p*-phenylenediamine[63]. The same explanation probably applies in this case, but the first coupling with tetrazotized benzidine requires a higher pH than with tetrazotized *p*-phenylenediamine.

In the years 1886-1887 more than 60 per cent of all patent applications and patents issued in Germany related directly or indirectly to the manufacture of azo dyes for cotton[6].

In 1895 Badische Anilin- u. Soda-Fabrik (BASF) patented a process of making disazo benzidine dyes by oxidation of monoazo dyes. For example, the monoazo compound aniline→naphthionic acid (3-(phenylazo)naphthionic acid, the arrow signifying a diazotization and coupling procedure) was treated with manganese dioxide in sulfuric acid to give Congo Red[12]. The process of electrolytic oxidation was also patented[12]. These newer methods encouraged reductions in the prices of benzidine dyes made by disazo couplings, so that these new oxidation processes were not used for large scale production[7].

Two trisazo dyes which are still manufactured in large amounts appeared in 1888. Benzo Brown D3G is made by coupling tetrazotized benzidine with one mole of salicylic acid and then with one mole of the monoazo compound sulfanilic acid→*m*-phenylenediamine.

Benzo Brown D3G, CI 596

* The above formula shows an unsymmetrical disazo coupling to *m*-phenylenediamine. This structure, according to Fierz-David and Blangey[4], explains the fact that a different dye is obtained if the order of coupling the *m*-phenylenediamine is reversed. Schmidt and Hajenbocker[62] showed that the second coupling to *m*-phenylenediamine (with benzenediazonium chloride) goes about equally to the symmetrical (4,6-) and unsymmetrical (2,4-) positions.

Congo Brown R, CI 598, is the similar dye using resorcinol in place of m-phenylenediamine. Numerous other combinations using homologs of each of the four components have been made, but the Brown D3G is the most useful. Like most benzidine dyes, it has poor lightfastness but is otherwise a good dye.

A few years later, a tetrakisazo dye of this general type was made by Boeniger of the Sandoz Company. This dye, Trisulfon Brown BT, still of commercial importance, is usually made by the following series of reactions, carried out without isolation of any of the intermediate diazo or azo compounds: Naphthionic acid is diazotized and coupled with 7-amino-1-naphthol-3,6-disulfonic acid in alkaline solution. This product is diazotized and coupled with toluene-2,4-diamine. This disazo compound is then coupled with the azo-diazo compound obtained from tetrazotized benzidine and salicylic acid.

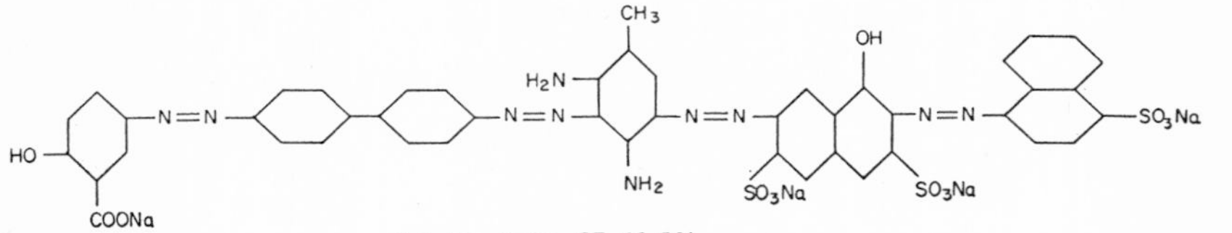

Trisulfon Brown BT, CI 561

It was soon found that diamines other than those of the biphenyl series would give cotton dyes. Among the discoveries in the period 1886–88 were dyes from 4,4'-diamino-2,2'-stilbenedisulfonic acid by Bender of the Leonhardt Company and from 4,4'-diaminocarbanilide by Mueller of BASF. Of the former, Brilliant Yellow and Chrysophenine are still of importance.

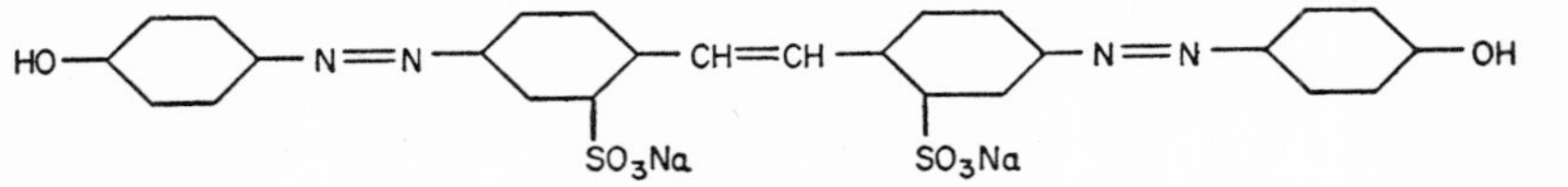

Brilliant Yellow, CI 364

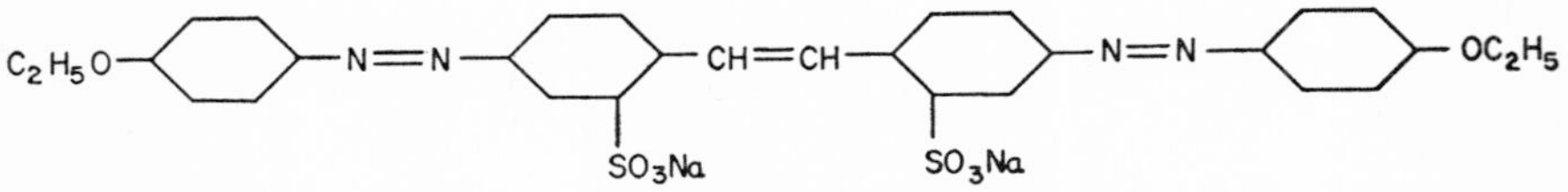

Chrysophenine, CI 365

Brilliant Yellow is not useful for dyeing cotton because it turns redder with the mild alkalies used in laundering, but it is used for dyeing paper. Paper dyed with Brilliant Yellow is an important indicator for testing alkalinity in the region of pH 8.0. In Chrysophenine, the hydroxy groups are protected by etherification with chloroethane, and this dye has good properties on cotton except for washing fastness.

The urea dye which appeared at this time is Benzo Fast Yellow 5GL. Although it may be made from 4,4'-diaminocarbanilide and salicylic acid, it is usually manufactured by coupling diazotized *p*-nitroaniline with salicylic acid, reducing the nitro group with sodium sulfide, and condensing the resulting amine with phosgene in slightly alkaline solution.

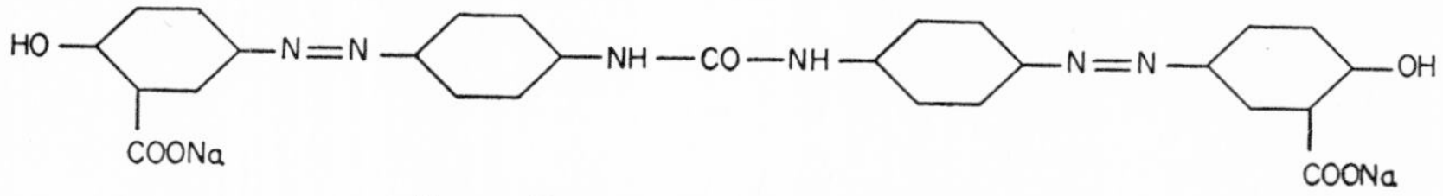

Benzo Fast Yellow 5GL, CI 346

The process of phosgenating amino-azo dyes has also been applied in many cases to make dyes which can not be obtained from diaminocarbanilide. Benzo Fast Yellow 4GL was made in 1908 by Guenther and Hesse by diazotizing *m*-aminobenzoic acid, coupling with *o*-anisidine, and condensing with phosgene.

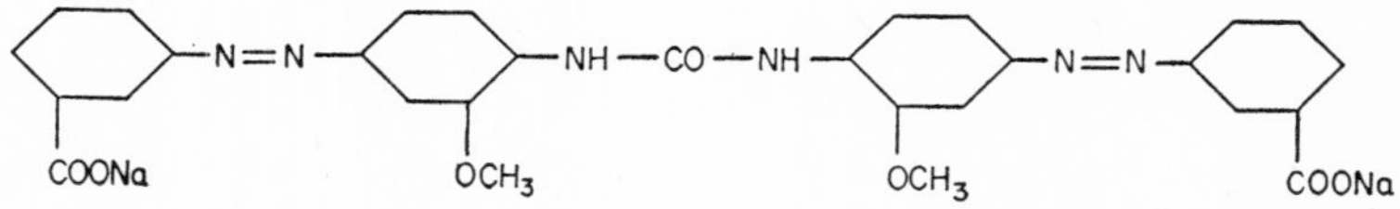

Benzo Fast Yellow 4GL, CI 349

Stilbene Dyes

In 1883 Walter discovered and Geigy manufactured Sun Yellow, CI 620, the first of a class of stilbene dyes which dye cotton. These dyes are mixtures of azo or azoxy compounds that are not made by the usual methods for azo dyes, but result from the action of aqueous sodium hydroxide on 5-nitro-*o*-toluenesulfonic acid (para acid). A few years later, Bender found that mild oxidation of Sun Yellow gives a greener yellow and mild reduction gives a redder yellow. Based on this discovery Leonhart manufactured Mikado Yellow, CI 622, and Mikado Orange, CI 621.

According to Green and Crossland[15] para acid in alkaline solution first condenses to form 4,4'-dinitroso-2,2'-stilbenedisulfonic acid.

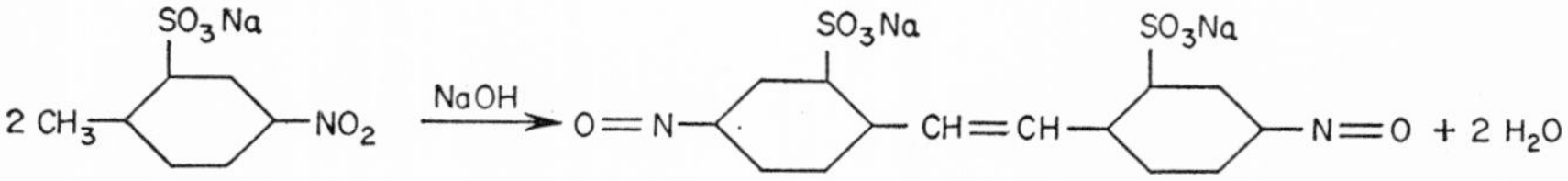

This then condenses further to give a mixture of dyes of doubtful constitution. 4,4″-Azobis(4′-nitro-2,2′-stilbenedisulfonic acid), below, is believed to be a major constituent of this reaction mixture:

$$O_2N-\langle\ \rangle-CH=CH-\langle\ \rangle-N=N-\langle\ \rangle-CH=CH-\langle\ \rangle-NO_2$$
$$\quad\ \ SO_3Na \qquad\quad SO_3Na \qquad\qquad SO_3Na \qquad\quad SO_3Na$$

The final product dyes cotton a greenish yellow and its sulfuric acid solution is orange colored. Partial reduction converts this dye to a mixture of azoxy compounds, which gives a red solution in sulfuric acid and dyes cotton a reddish yellow. Complete reduction with mild reducing agents such as glucose produces a mixture of azo compounds which dyes cotton an orange color and dissolves in sulfuric acid with a blue color. For some of these dyes ring structures were suggested by Green and were adopted in CI 620 and 621, 1st ed. These structures have been rejected by chemists of the I. G. Farbenindustrie[50]. These chemists have suggested other structures that are not adequately supported by published experimental data.

If the condensation of para acid in sodium hydroxide is carried out with sodium hypochlorite, either dinitrobibenzyldisulfonic acid or dinitrostilbenedisulfonic acid is obtained, depending on the temperature, pH and amount of available chlorine. Dinitrostilbenedisulfonic acid may be reduced in alkaline solution with mild reducing agents such as glucose or glycerol to give a series of dyes which are similar in properties to the products obtained directly from para acid but without the azomethine impurities present in dyes from para acid.

The stilbene yellows and oranges made directly from para acid and indirectly through dinitrostilbenedisulfonic acid are still of commercial importance on account of their low price and good affinity for cotton. They are inferior to other dyes for cotton in the discharge process. The light fastness of these dyes is poor but their production in the United States amounts to over a million pounds a year.

A number of dyes have also been made by reacting the primary condensation product from para acid with aromatic amines. In 1908, Alfred Gressly[16] of the Cassella Company made new dyes of improved fastness to light by condensing dinitrostilbenedisulfonic acid with sulfonated amino-azo compounds. Diamine Fast Orange EG[22] is made by boiling for several hours a strongly alkaline solution containing equivalent amounts of 4,4′-dinitro-2,2′-stilbenedisulfonic acid and the azo dye made by coupling diazotized sulfanilic acid to m-toluidine. The reaction product probably is a mixture of azo and azoxy compounds.

Diamine Fast Orange EG has good fastness properties but it does not give a white discharge on cotton. Gressly later (1934) showed that reduction of the dye with glucose gives a dye which is brighter and faster to light[17].

Other amino compounds, including dehydrothio-*p*-toluidine, have been used in place of the above mentioned amino-azo dyes for the condensation with dinitrostilbenedisulfonic acid. The dyes thus obtained are of little present importance.

After-treated Dyes

Not long after the discovery of the direct cotton dyes, methods of improving the properties of the dyes by after-treatment of the dyed fiber were found. The first of these methods was discovered by Green in 1887[14]. It consisted of treating a fiber dyed with an amino compound with nitrous acid to form a diazo compound, followed by developing with a solution of a coupling component (such as 2-naphthol) to give an azo dye which usually had fairly good washing fastness. The improved washing fastness is a result of the higher molecular weight and lower solubility of the new azo compound produced in the fiber. The amino compound used by Green was not an azo dye until after the coupling had occurred on the fiber. However, it was soon found that if amino-azo compounds were diazotized and coupled with suitable coupling components on the fiber, much better results were obtained[59]. Green's new dye, known as Primuline, CI 812, is made by fusing *p*-toluidine with sulfur, followed by sulfonation. The principal component is:

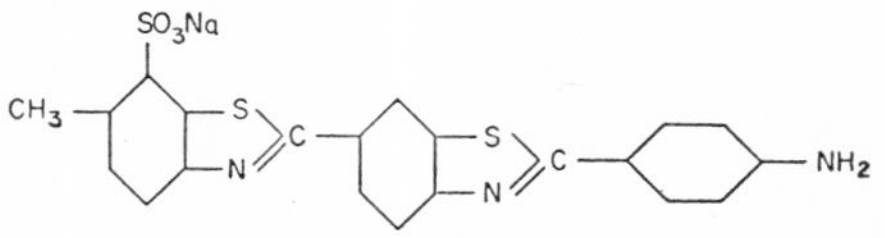

Primuline, CI 812

The position of the sulfo group is different from that shown in the Colour Index, 1st ed. The above structure is considered more likely in view of the work of Schubert[64].

This compound dyes cotton a yellow of little value, but when diazotized on the fiber and developed with 2-naphthol, it gives a red azo dye. The developed dyes from Primuline are not fast to light and when discharged they are reduced to the original yellow Primuline. However, Primuline still finds some use. Green named this type of dye an "ingrain" dye. It is now generally called a "diazo" or "developed" dye.

Azo dyes suitable for diazotization on the fiber and development are an important part of the total production of azo dyes for cotton. They include the whole range of colors, and they are mostly made from intermediates not known at the time Primuline was discovered. Suitable examples are shown later in connection with the different types of direct colors. The diazo blues and blacks are generally completely conjugated compounds after development. The diazo yellows, oranges, reds, violets and greens contain a blocking group which has adjacent single bonds separating two conjugated parts of the molecule of the developed dye. Diazo dyes containing two diazotizable amino groups often give developed dyeings of very good washing fastness.

Another method of after-treatment of direct dyes used to some extent around 1890 was treatment with copper salts[2]. This method was especially applicable to dyes containing salicylic acid as a coupling component or to some *o*-hydroxy-azo dyes such as Benzazurin.* In this type of dye the methoxy group and the hydroxy group ortho to the same azo group form a complex with the copper which is faster to light than the uncoppered dye, but this improvement in lightfastness is sometimes lost after a mild washing[48]. In the case of dyes containing salicylic acid, copper reacts with the hydroxy and carboxy groups ortho to each other to form a complex which is faster to washing and sometimes faster to light. The development of a line of after-coppered dyes was rather slow, and after about 1915, it appeared that they would be replaced by copper-containing or pre-coppered dyes. The latter have the same improved lightfastness, without the necessity of the dyer performing the after-treatment. Such dyes are discussed later. However, the development of after-coppered dyes continued and this class of dyes now comprises a wide range which has not only good lightfastness but good washfastness. The Coprantine dyes of Ciba and the Benzo Fast Copper dyes of I. G. Farbenindustrie are dyes of this class, some of which are shown below:

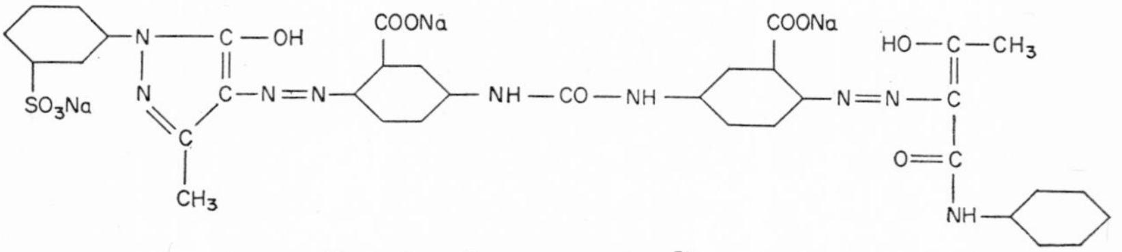

Benzo Fast Copper Yellow RLN[51]

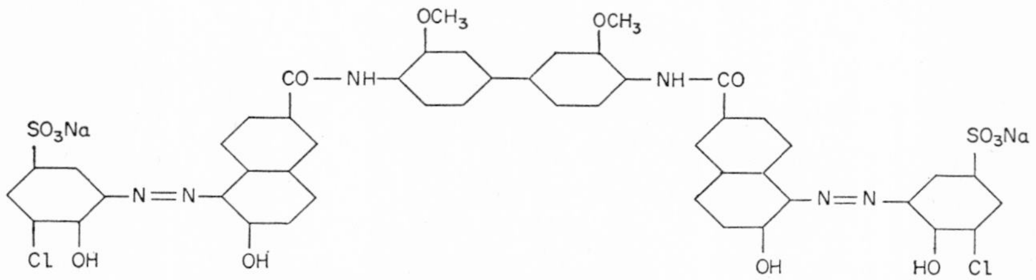

Benzo Fast Copper Rubine RL[24]

* Formula on page 116.

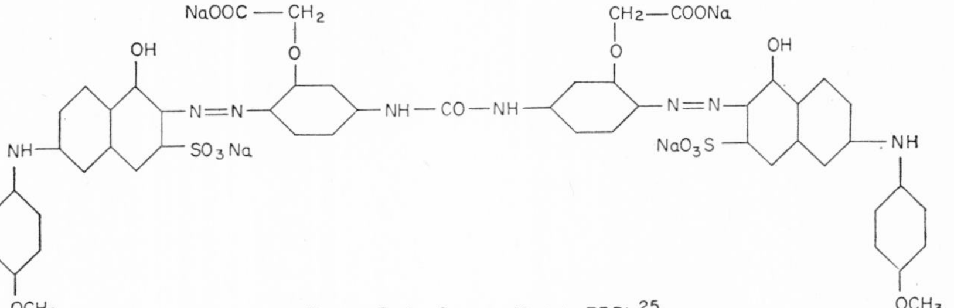

Benzo Fast Copper Violet F3BL[25]

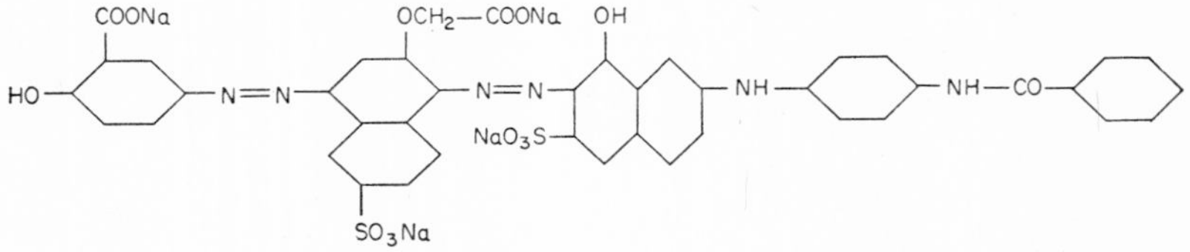

Benzo Fast Copper Blue F3GL[51]

The other method of after-treatment which was applied in the early days of direct cotton dyes was treatment with formaldehyde in the case of dyes containing resorcinol or *m*-phenylenediamine as end coupling components. Although this treatment was known around 1890, it was much later before special dyes designed for this method of dyeing were manufactured. The after-treatment with formaldehyde probably ties together two or more molecules of dye in the fiber, forming aggregates which are not so easily removed by washing. It is especially used in black dyes. Dyeings which can be after-treated with formaldehyde may instead be after-treated with a solution of a diazo compound to cause a similar improvement in washing fastness, but such after-treatment is more complicated and the improvement in fastness is no better.

Cotton Dyes from Aminonaphtholsulfonic Acids

In 1889 Gans discovered[11] and Cassella manufactured the first dyes from aminonaphtholsulfonic acids. The most important aminonaphtholsulfonic acids are 1-naphthols. Gamma acid (7-amino-1-naphthol-3-sulfonic acid) was the first of these new intermediates. It was found that acid and alkaline couplings to Gamma acid gave different products due to different positions of coupling. Coupling with tetrazotized benzidine in alkaline solution gave Diamine Black B, while coupling in acid solution gave Diamine Violet N.

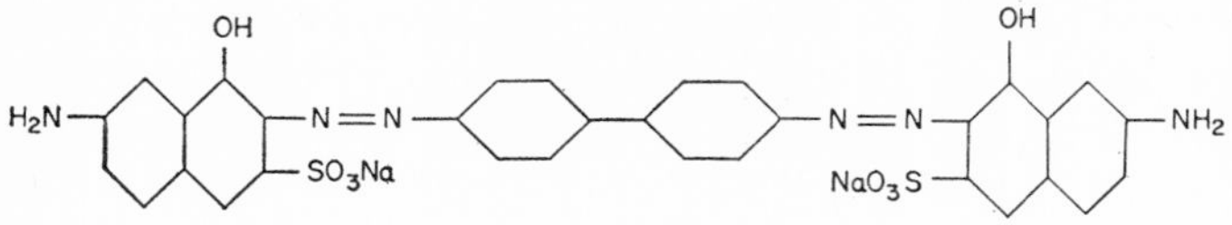

Diamine Black B, CI 395

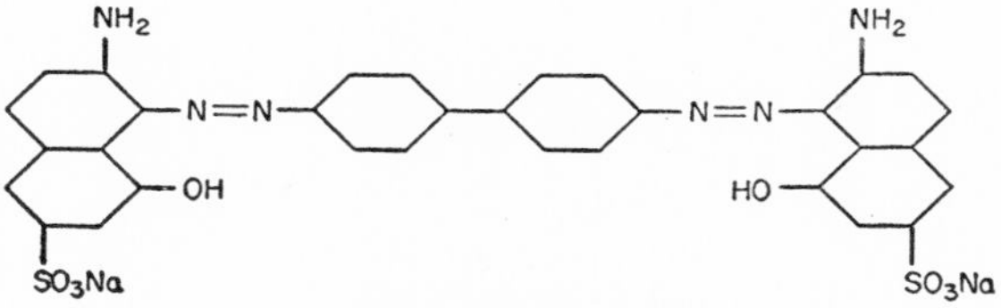

Diamine Violet N, CI 394

The latter dye is still manufactured in the United States in amounts of about 100,000 pounds a year. The former can be diazotized on the fiber and coupled with 2-naphthol to improve the intensity and fastness of the dyeing[59]. It was the first developed azo dye.

Two more dyes introduced in 1889 and still of considerable importance were Diamine Fast Red F

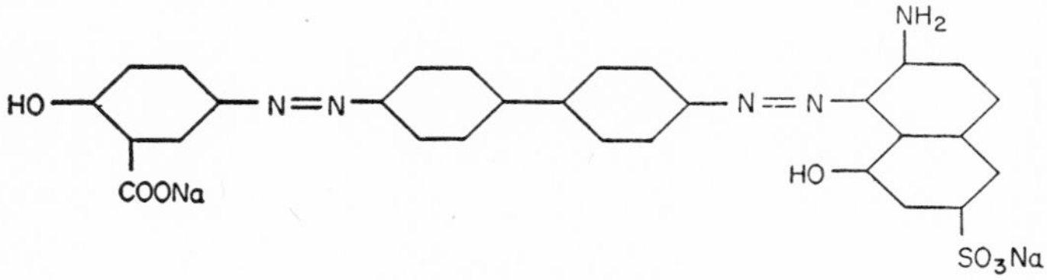

Diamine Fast Red F, CI 419

and the isomeric Diamine Brown M

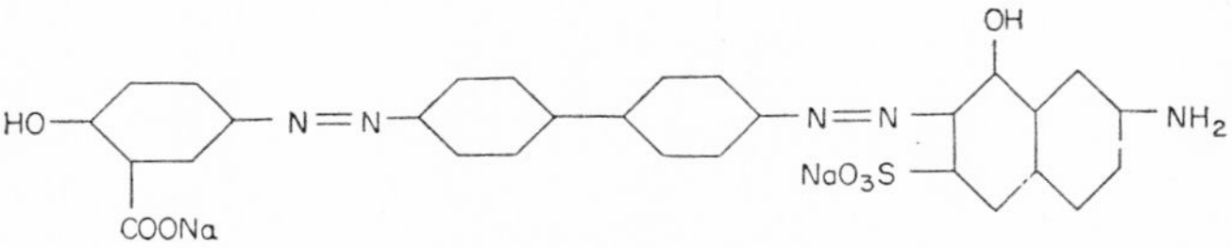

Diamine Brown M, CI 420

Another Gamma acid dye introduced in 1900 by Bayer was Benzo Fast Pink 2BL.

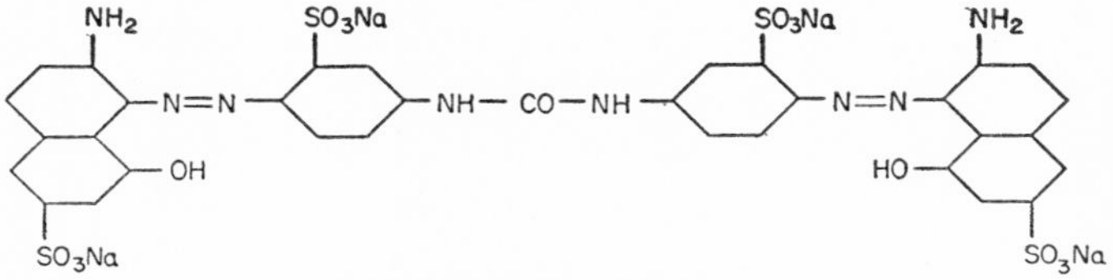

Benzo Fast Pink 2BL, CI 353

This is made by diazotizing 2-amino-5-nitrobenzenesulfonic acid, coupling with Gamma acid in acid solution, reducing the nitro group with sodium sulfide, and treating with phosgene to form the urea. The above dyes from Gamma acid have good fastness properties on cotton except for fastness to severe washing.

In the next few years, many aminonaphthol mono- and disulfonic acids were made, mainly by the Bayer and Cassella Companies.

The following dyes from H acid (8-amino-1-naphthol-3,6-disulfonic acid) were introduced in 1890 and are still produced in large amounts.

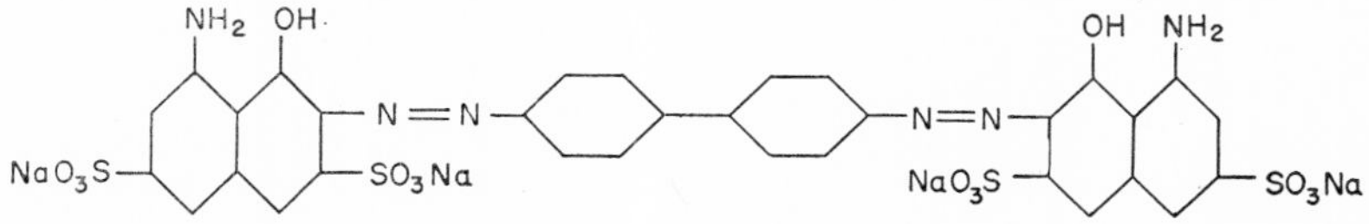

Diamine Blue 2B, CI 406

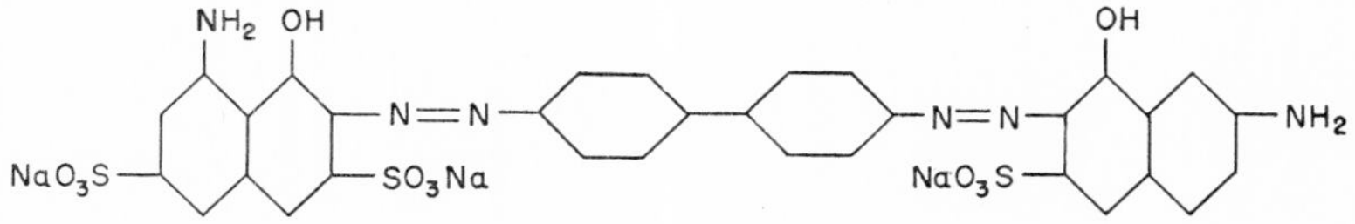

Developed Black BH, CI 401

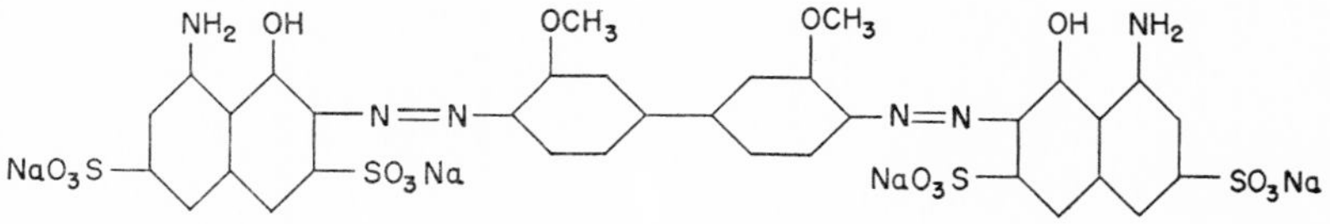

Benzo Sky Blue 5B, CI 520

About a year later, Chicago acid (8-amino-1-naphthol-5,7-disulfonic acid) was discovered[54]. It gave greener and brighter dyes than H acid. Chicago Blue 6B, also known as Brilliant Benzo Blue 6B or Sky Blue 6B, was introduced about the time of the Columbian Exposition in Chicago. Annual production in the United States is over 700,000 pounds, although dyes from 8-amino-1-naphtholsulfonic acids have poor lightfastness.

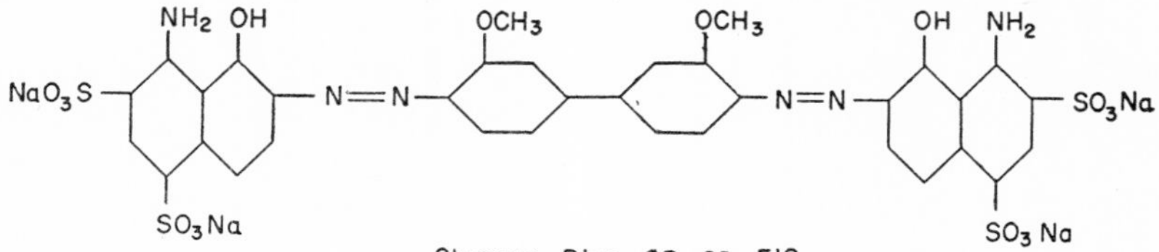

Chicago Blue 6B, CI 518

The first direct green dyes for cotton were discovered by Hoffmann and Daimler of the Cassella Company in 1891. One of these, Diamine Green B, is made by coupling H acid first in acid solution with diazotized p-nitroaniline, then in alkaline solution with a molecular equivalent of tetrazotized benzidine, followed by a final coupling with phenol. This dye is still made in amounts of over a million pounds a year in the United States.

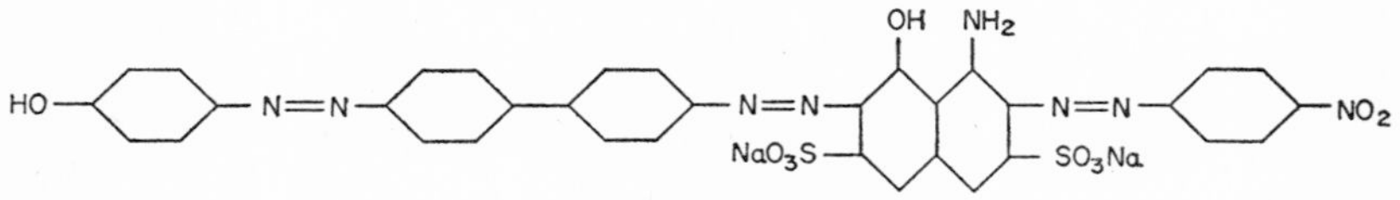

Diamine Green B, CI 593

Other greens are also made in smaller amounts using salicylic acid in place of phenol, or o-tolidine in place of benzidine, or various amines in place of p-nitroaniline.

About 1896 three black dyes for cotton appeared. Two were direct blacks and one was a developed black. They were the first satisfactory azo blacks for cotton and they are still of commercial importance. None of them is of the benzidine type but all contain Gamma acid. The first, Benzo Fast Black L, is made by diazotizing 5-aminosalicylic acid, coupling with 1-naphthylamine, diazotizing this amino-azo compound, and coupling in alkaline solution with Gamma acid.

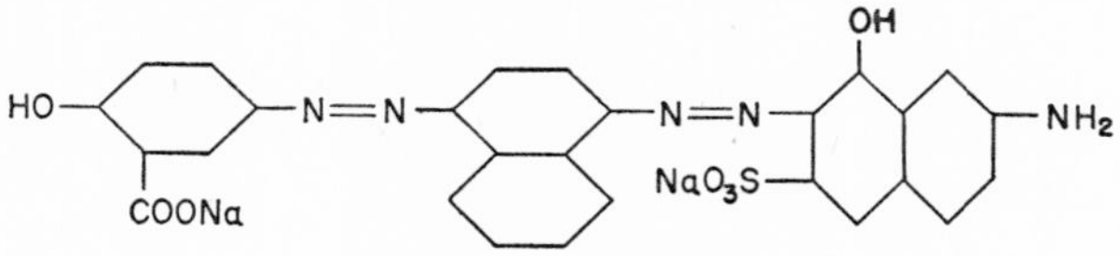

Benzo Fast Black L[47](Pr.24)

The first component, usually made by nitration of salicylic acid and reduction of the nitro group, contains some 3-aminosalicylic acid. This dye was patented by the Bayer Company as early as 1892, but its value as a cotton dye was not recognized for several years. In weak dyeings it is a neutral gray and its fastness to light is good.

Columbia Black FF, discovered by Clausius (1896) and manufactured by AGFA, is a trisazo dye. It is made by coupling diazotized p-nitroaniline with 5(or 8)-amino-2-naphthalenesulfonic acid, reducing the nitro group, monodiazotizing the diamino-azo compound (by using only one molar equivalent of sodium nitrite) and coupling with Gamma acid in alkaline solution, then monodiazotizing this disazo compound and coupling with m-phenylenediamine.

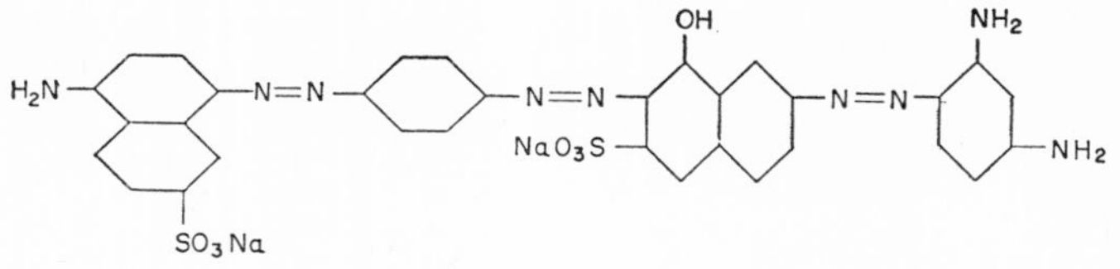

Columbia Black FF, CI 539

An alternate method is to couple diazotized *p*-aminoacetanilide with Gamma acid, remove the acetyl group by hydrolysis, tetrazotize the mono-azo compound, and couple with one mole of 5(or 8)-amino-2-naphthalene-sulfonic acid and with one mole of *m*-phenylenediamine. The products obtained by these two methods may contain different impurities in small amounts, and therefore the selection of the method to use will depend on the dyeing properties and the costs, which will vary in different manufacturing plants. This dye is a neutral black, but it is not as fast to light as Benzo Fast Black L. When after-treated with formaldehyde, it has good washing fastness.

Columbia Black FF was improved in 1907 by Dressel and Kothe of the Bayer Company, who found that the use of *N*-(*m*-aminophenyl)glycine in place of *m*-phenylenediamine improved the affinity for cotton and reduced the affinity for wool. In 1911 Blank and Heidenreich further modified this dye to make Plutoform Black.

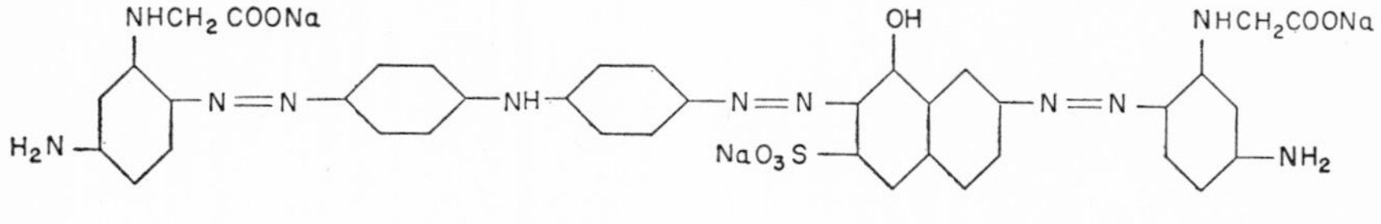

Plutoform Black, CI 545

Another important black dye to appear in 1896 was Zambesi Black D (AGFA). This is made by successive diazotization and coupling of *p*-nitro-aniline, cresidine (5-methyl-*o*-anisidine) and Gamma acid, with final reduction of the nitro group by means of sodium sulfide. It was the first good developed or diazo black. The dyeing is diazotized and developed with toluene-2,4-diamine or with 2-naphthol.

This developed dye has been largely replaced by Zambesi Black V introduced by AGFA in 1902. Black V is made from the same diamino-monoazo compound used in making Columbia Black FF, but the mono-diazo compound obtained from it is coupled with the monoazo compound made by an acid coupling of diazotized *p*-nitroaniline with 8-amino-1-naphthol-5-sulfonic acid. The nitro group is finally reduced.

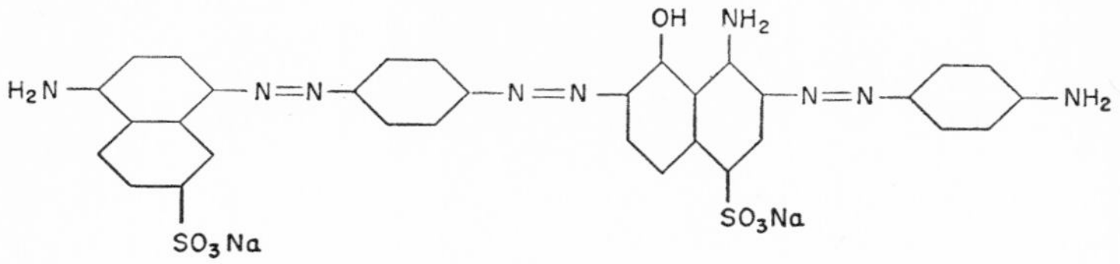

Zambesi Black V*

A developed black of good lightfastness was introduced in 1906 by Cassella, as Oxydiaminogen OB[39]. It differs from Columbia Black FF only in having Gamma acid as the final coupling component in place of *m*-phenylenediamine.

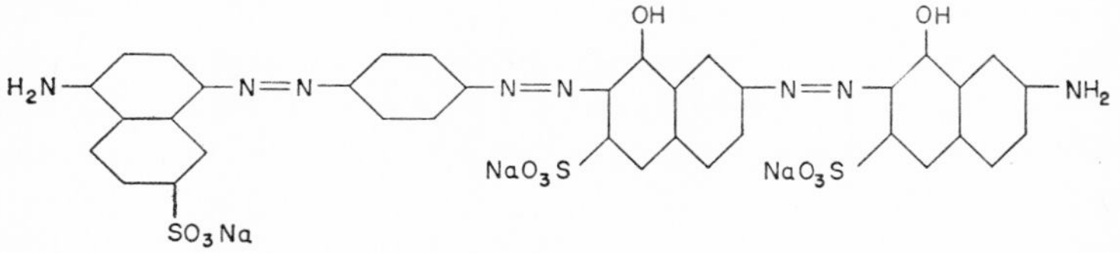

Oxy Diaminogen OB (Pr. 147)

At the close of the 19th century Friedlaender[3] stated in regard to cotton dyes that "the number of components available for technical use is even now sufficient to make the possibilities of combination appear almost unlimited. Today, the elaboration of this field has by no means been completed, even though economic considerations are causing continuously increasing limitations and excluding the manufacture of many dyes which are intrinsically useful."

A study of the U. S. Tariff Commission reports on United States production of coal tar dyes for the years 1946–50 shows that, of the twelve azo cotton dyes produced in largest amount, all but one were known in the 19th century, and the twelfth one is made from intermediates known at that time.

The dye which now accounts for over 25 per cent of American direct cotton dye production and over 14 per cent of azo dye production was discovered by Oscar Mueller of the Schoellkopf, Hartford and Hanna Company in Buffalo, New York in 1901[56]. It is Erie Direct Black EW.

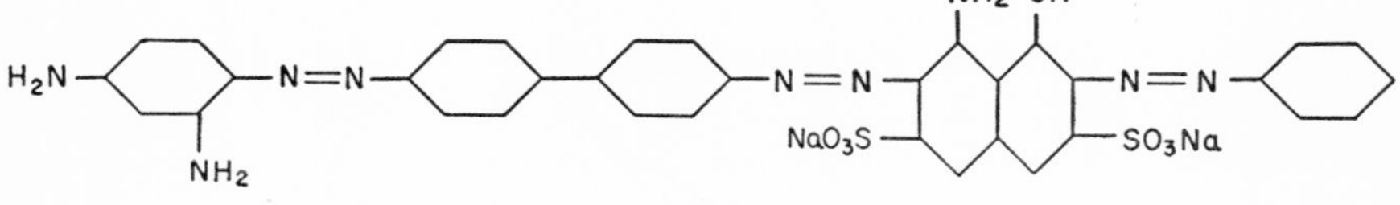

Erie Direct Black EW, CI 481

* Schultz[65] gives a slightly different formula for this dye but its structure should correspond with that for Columbia Black FF.

This dye is made by coupling tetrazotized benzidine with one mole of H acid in acid solution, making this combination alkaline and adding diazotized aniline, and—when this second coupling is complete—finally adding m-phenylenediamine to accomplish the third coupling. The homologous dye using toluene-2,4-diamine in place of m-phenylenediamine is a redder black, Direct Black RX, CI 582. If phenol is used for the last coupling in place of the diamine, Erie Direct Green ET, CI 583, is obtained.

The black of Mueller proved to be very useful not only for cotton and rayon, but also for paper, leather and tin-weighted silk. The dyeing on cotton has poor fastness to light and washing, but after-treatment with formaldehyde improves the washing fastness. The intermediates used were all relatively inexpensive since they were also used in other dyes, and the low cost was, and still is, the reason for its popularity. It is manufactured by several companies in the United States, many of which supply it in different brands containing varying amounts of by-products or impurities, or different standardizing agents.

J acid (6-amino-1-naphthol-3-sulfonic acid) was made soon after the other important aminonaphtholsulfonic acids, but it was not used commercially until the first decade of the twentieth century. It is an isomer of Gamma acid, but is not so easily obtained, and on account of its higher cost it is not used in the benzidine type of dyes. It was observed that even monoazo dyes from J acid dye cotton. This is especially noticeable with N-acyl derivatives such as Acetyl J acid or Benzoyl J acid. The urea and thiourea derivatives of J acid contribute even greater affinity for cotton[9]. The dyes made from J acid are more expensive than the previously known dyes from benzidine, but on account of better dyeing and fastness properties they are very important, especially for the brighter colors such as red, violet, blue and green.

The first important J acid dyes were those from J acid urea. They were discovered by Israel and Kothe and manufactured by the Bayer Company. Representative dyes of this type are:

Benzo Fast Orange S, CI 326

Benzo Fast Scarlet 4 BS, CI 327

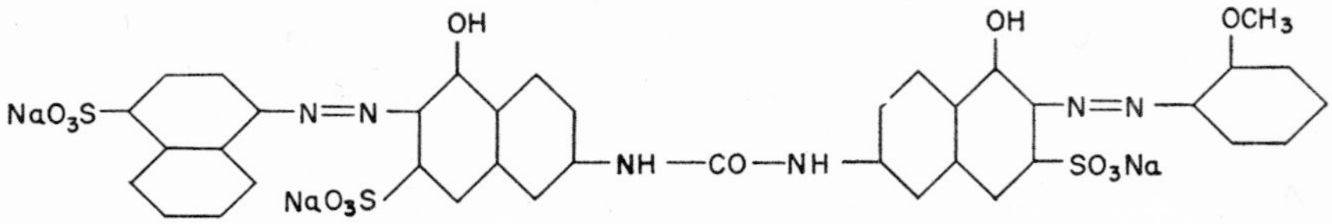

Benzo Fast Scarlet 8BS[23]

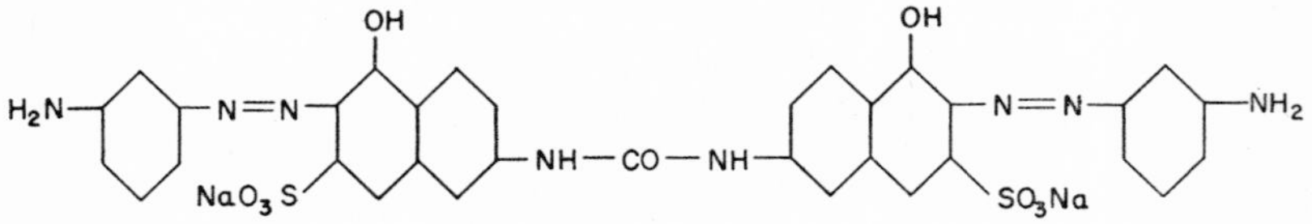

Diazo Brilliant Scarlet 2BL[34] (Pr. 79)

A few years later Bertschmann discovered and Ciba manufactured a series of monoazo dyes from *p*(or *m*)-Aminobenzoyl J acid. These dye cotton orange and red, and the dyeing is diazotized and developed with 2-naphthol to give a color not much different in shade from the original dyeing but stronger and faster to washing.

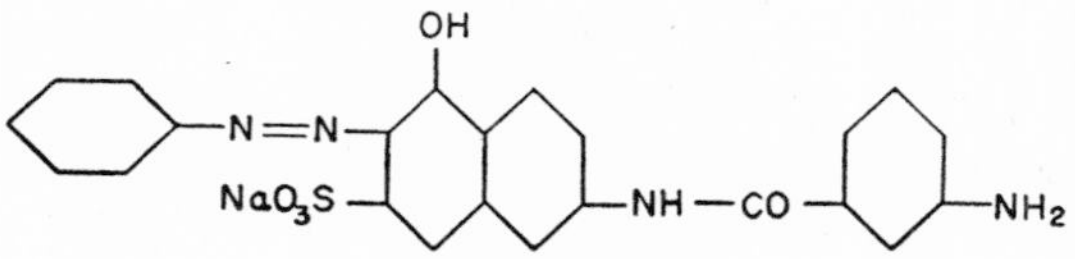

Direct Dye

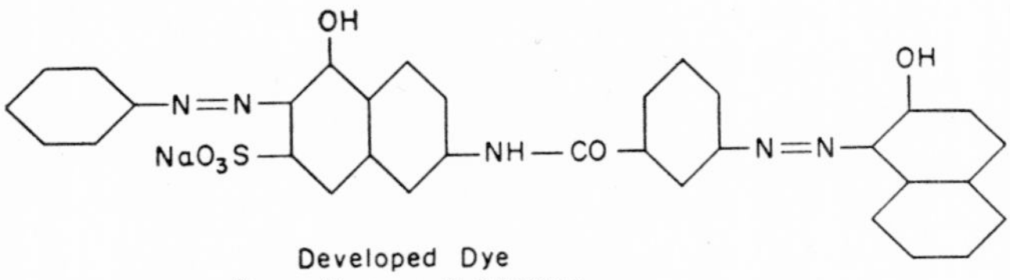

Developed Dye
Rosanthrene O, C I 324A

The fact that development to a disazo compound does not cause a marked change from the shade of the monoazo compound is due to the fact that the conjugated system is (more or less completely) broken or blocked at the —NH—CO— group by three single bonds. The developed dye, therefore, owes its shade to two unconjugated monoazo colors each of which is orange to red.

Beginning in 1907, the Bayer Company introduced several red, violet and blue disazo dyes made by coupling J acid derivatives with diazotized aminoazo compounds. These dyes were discovered by Guenther, Hesse and Zart, who also found that the best lightfastness in this type of dye is obtained when the first component is an *o*-aminoarenesulfonic acid or an

8-amino-1-naphtholsulfonic acid[18]. Some of the commercially important dyes of this type are:

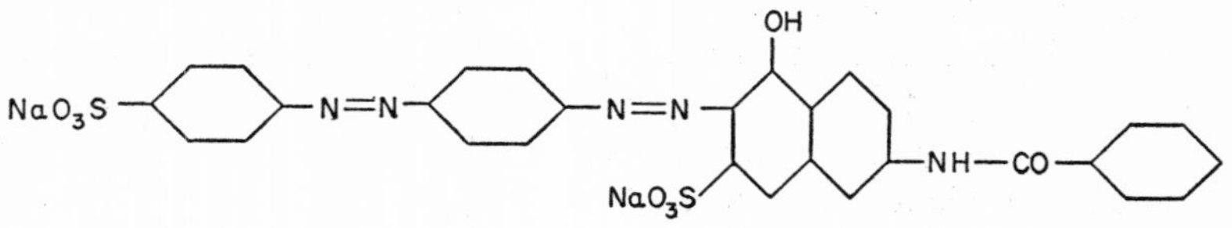

Benzo Fast Red 8BL, CI 278

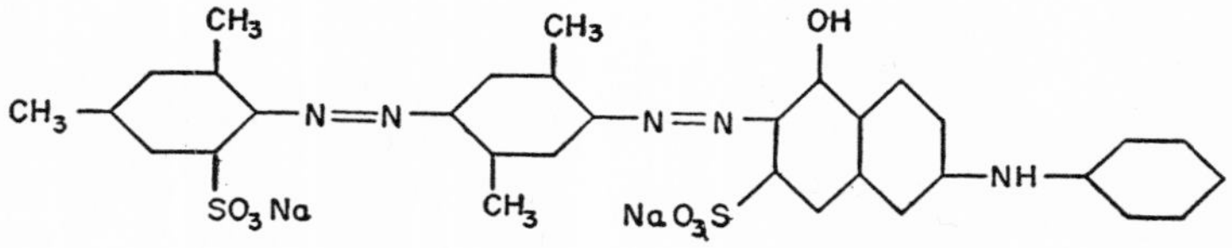

Brilliant Benzo Fast Violet 2RL[40]

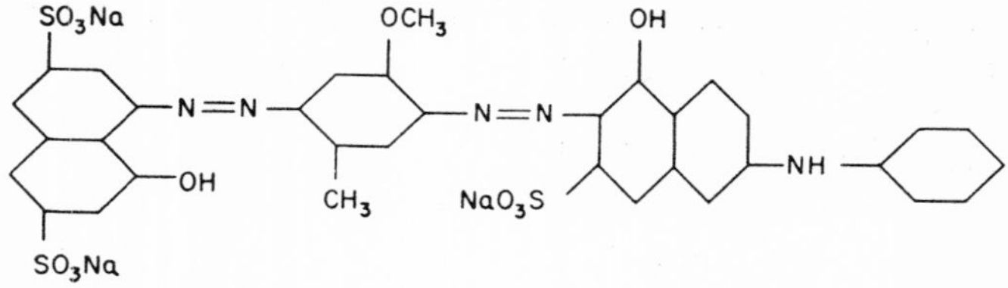

Brilliant Benzo Fast Blue BL, CI 319

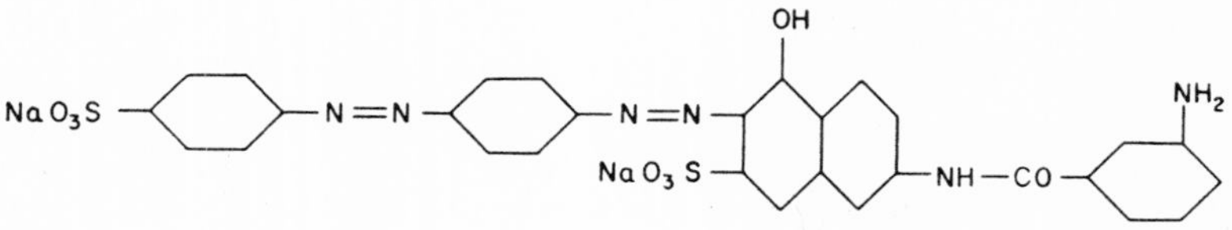

Diazo Light Red 7BL[37] (Pr. 85)

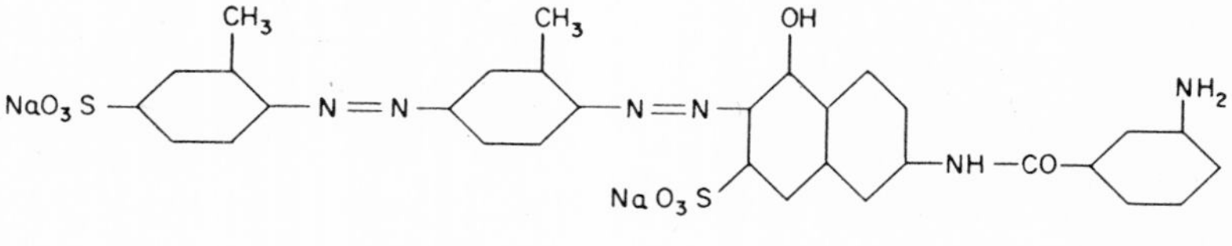

Diazo Fast Bordeaux 2BL[35] (Pr. 172)

Developed dyes of this type did not extend beyond the bordeaux range, because the color of the unconjugated monoazo part of the molecule formed by development with 2-naphthol can not be changed much from an orange (maximum absorption band in the blue part of the visible spectrum).

The shade range of developed dyes was extended in 1914 by Guenther of the Bayer Company, who showed that a diazo green of this type results from making a disazo blue and developing it with a yellow-producing coupling component.

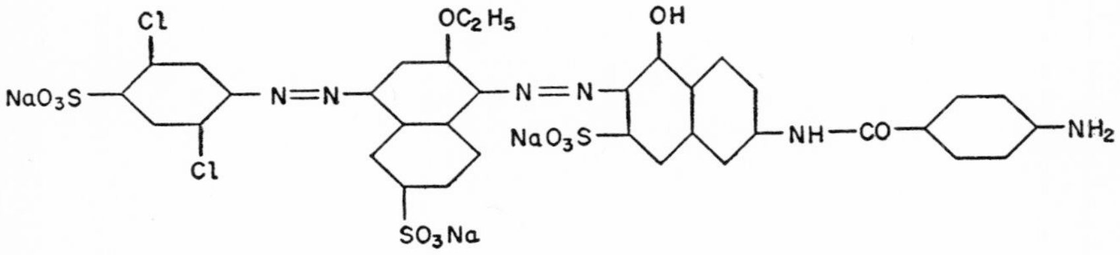

Diazo Brilliant Green 3G[33] (Pr. 78)

This product dyes cotton blue (main absorption peak at 604 mμ). When it is diazotized and developed with 3-methyl-1-phenyl-5-pyrazolone, it becomes green due to an additional absorption band at about 400 mμ. The developed dye has the constitution:

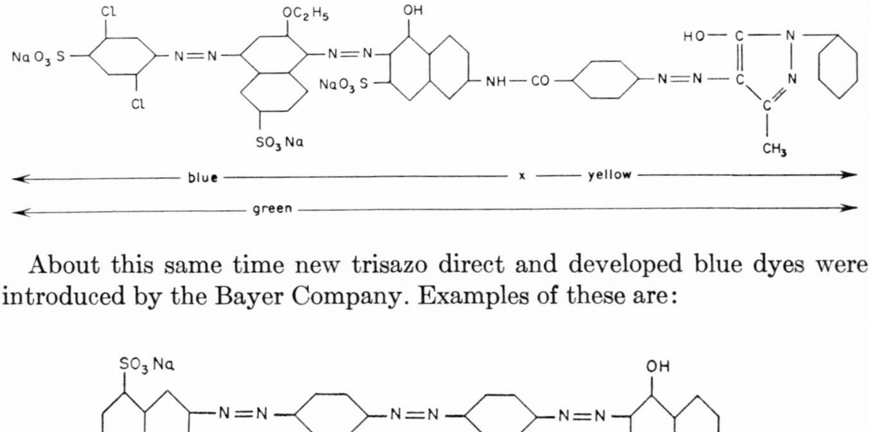

About this same time new trisazo direct and developed blue dyes were introduced by the Bayer Company. Examples of these are:

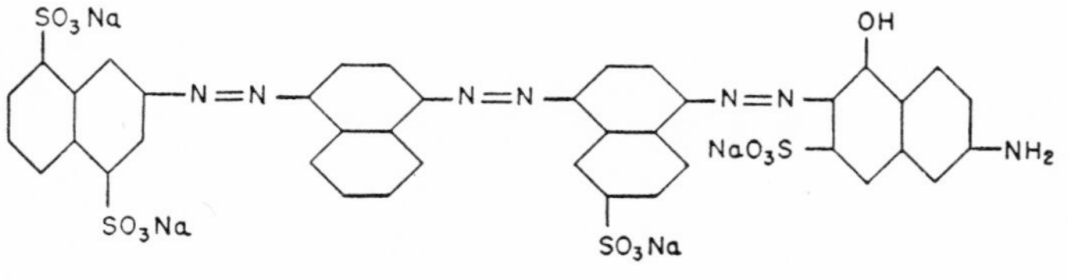

Diamine Fast Blue FFB[32] (Pr. 71)

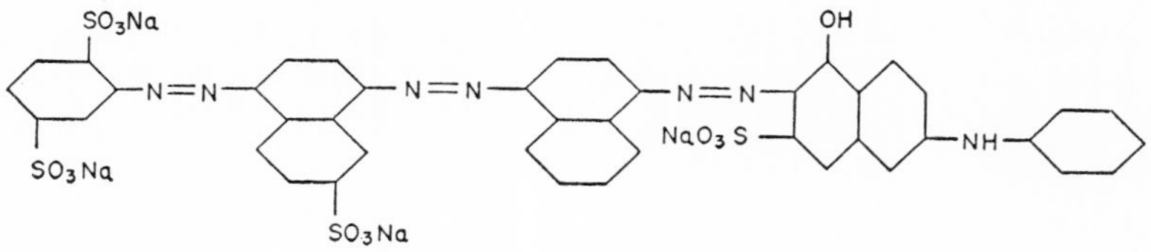

Benzo Light Blue 4GL[28] (Pr. 26)

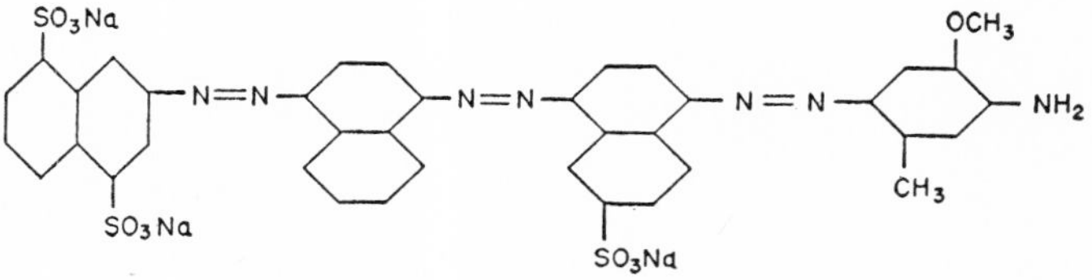

Diazo Indigo Blue 2RL[36]

Diazo blues of this type are developed with 2-naphthol. There is no blocking group in these diazo dyes and the developed dye is therefore completely conjugated.

Dyes from Heterocyclic and Acyclic Intermediates

Shortly after the discovery of Primuline, the first developed dye, other cotton azo dyes from benzothiazoles were found. These are covered in the chapter on Miscellaneous Dyes in the section on Thiazoles.

Sometime later, 3-methyl-1-phenyl-5-pyrazolone and its derivatives came into use as yellow-producing coupling components in place of salicylic acid for cotton dyes. While the pyrazolones are more expensive intermediates, they confer improved qualities such as brightness and fastness to light. Acetoacetanilide is also used for the same purpose. Examples of dyes of this class which were introduced in the early part of the 20th century are:

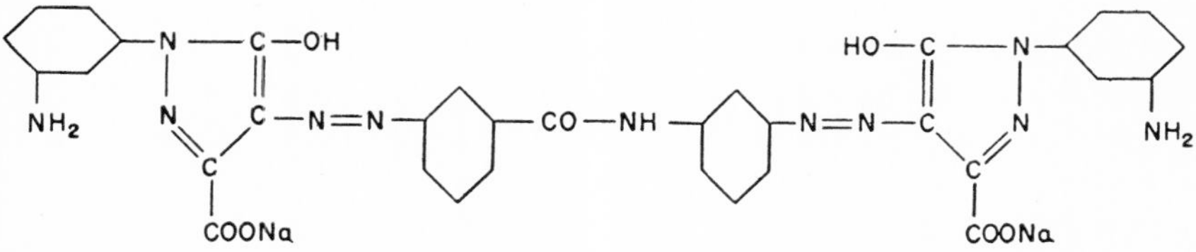

Rosanthrene Orange R[26] (Pr. 173)

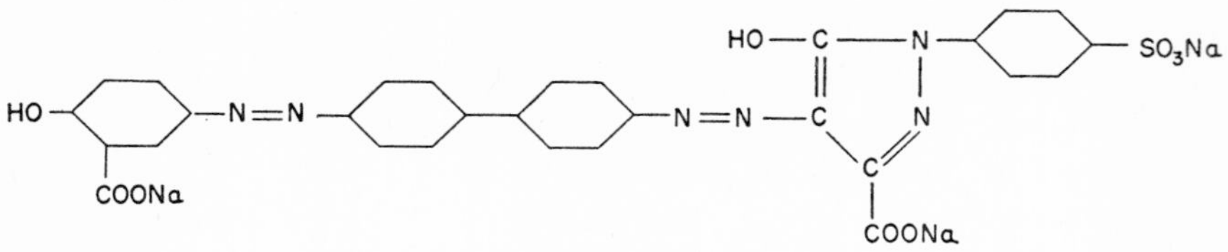

Pyrazol Orange, CI 653

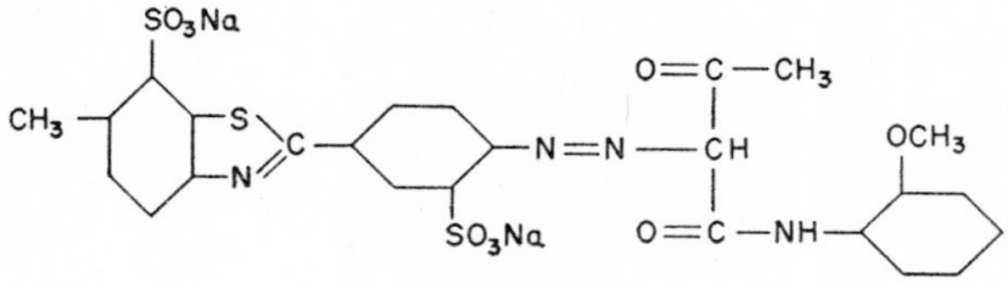

Brilliant Benzo Fast Yellow GL[41]

An unusual dye made in 1910 by Holste is Diazo Yellow 2GL, which is colorless until diazotized and developed on the fiber with 3-methyl-1-phenyl-5-pyrazolone. A similar dye has been made from 4,4'-diamino-2,2'-stilbenedisulfonic acid.

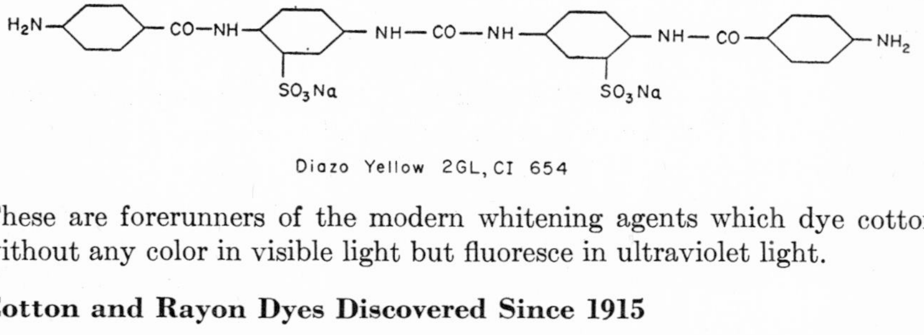

Diazo Yellow 2GL, CI 654

These are forerunners of the modern whitening agents which dye cotton without any color in visible light but fluoresce in ultraviolet light.

Cotton and Rayon Dyes Discovered Since 1915

At the time of the first World War, azo dyes for cotton were practically all of German (or Swiss) origin and manufacture. New dyes discovered since then have come from several countries. In addition to the development of new dyes and a shift of much of the production away from Germany there have been some other interesting developments.

The rapid increase in rayon production in the third decade of the twentieth century brought problems in connection with its dyeing. Although rayon is a regenerated cellulose fiber, its dyeing properties are slightly different from those of cotton and it has been necessary to modify some old dyes and dyeing methods in order to obtain level dyeings. This has been done mainly by reducing the dye-fiber affinity and the rate of dyeing, especially through replacement of J acid by other aminonaphtholsulfonic acids.

The use of cellulose acetate as a fiber to produce white effects in dyed goods required improvement in the quality of most cotton dyes to remove impurities which stain cellulose acetate. These impurities are mainly amino-azo compounds of only slight solubility in water.

The development of the method of printing white or colored patterns on dyed cotton and rayon by the use of discharge pastes, which reduce (or "discharge") azo dyes to colorless amino compounds which can be washed out of the fiber, required an improvement in the quality of most azo cotton dyes, so that they would leave a pure white "discharge" (undyed area).

The better quality of dyes for leaving cellulose acetate effect-fibers white and for giving white discharge patterns is partly due to the use of purer intermediates and partly due to improvements in processes such as charcoal filtration of solutions and pH control. These quality improvements are often accompanied by a higher yield of dye.

It was found possible by Schweitzer in 1924 to obtain greener blues of the type of Benzo Light Blue 4GL by using 5-amino-6-ethoxy-2-naphthalenesulfonic acid as the third component and by making the last coupling in a water-pyridine solution of the coupling component. Without the pyridine no coupling is obtained[66].

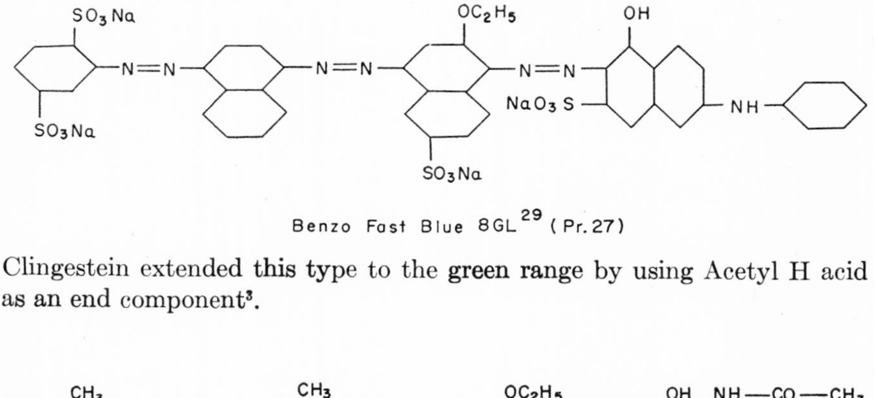

Benzo Fast Blue 8GL[29] (Pr. 27)

Clingestein extended this type to the green range by using Acetyl H acid as an end component[3].

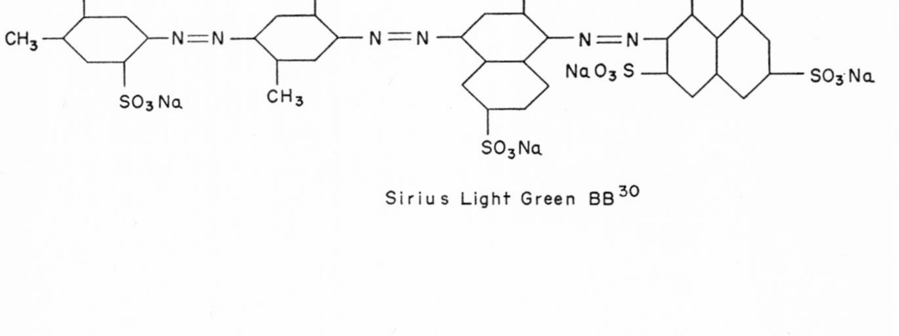

Sirius Light Green BB[30]

New tetrakisazo dyes from J acid urea were found by Penny[58] to have good washing fastness and some of them are now manufactured, for example:

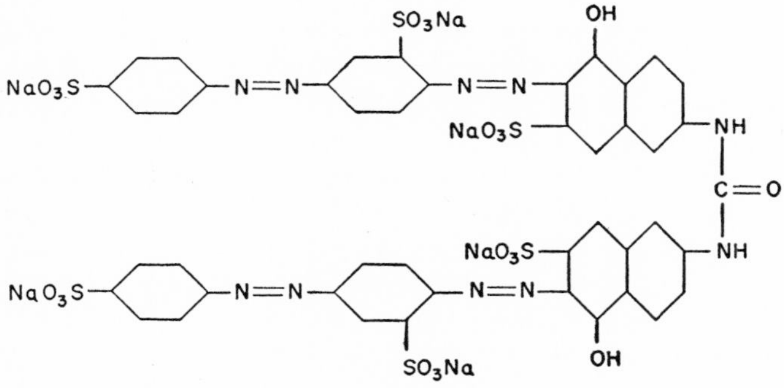

Solantine Fast Red 8BNL[27]

Richard in 1929[61] discovered a tetrakisazo type of direct green by using in place of the end component in the Benzo Fast Blues a monoazo compound made by coupling a diazo component with J acid in acid solution.

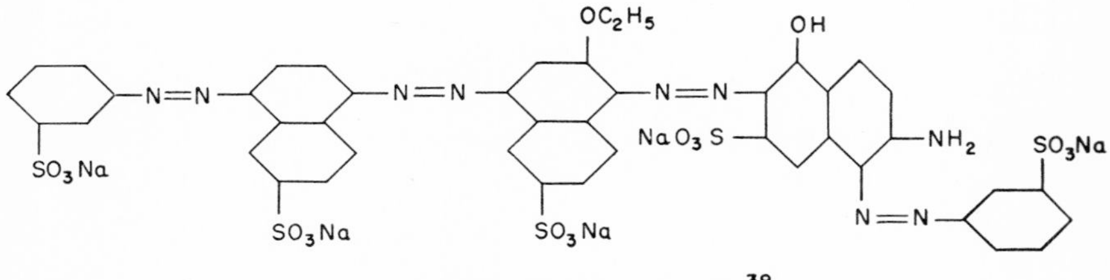

Diphenyl Fast Blue Green BL[38]

In 1928 Fritzsche disclosed the use of cyanuric chloride to tie together different amino compounds[10]. Its use to join together a blue and a yellow compound through an unconjugated group to give a green dye is shown in the following two examples:

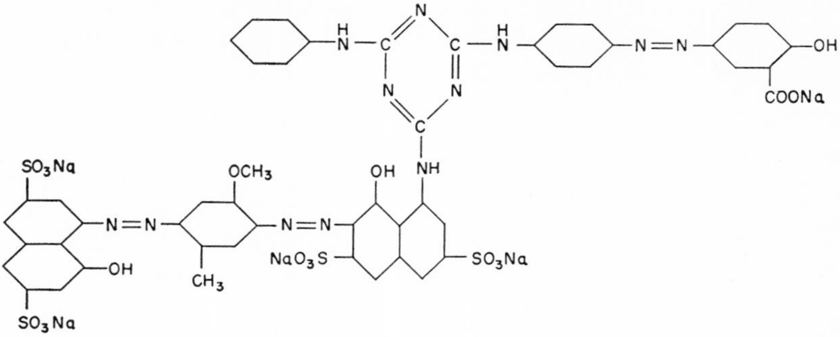

Chlorantine Fast Green BLL* (Pr. 425)

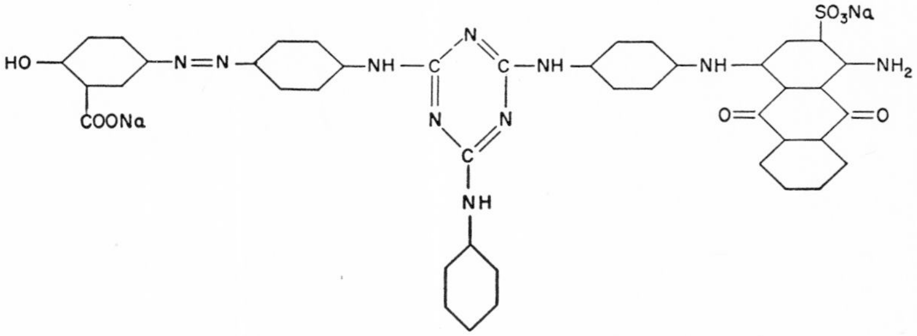

Chlorantine Fast Green 5GLL[45]

Chlorantine Fast Red 6BLL, introduced by Ciba[55] in 1928, has very good lightfastness.

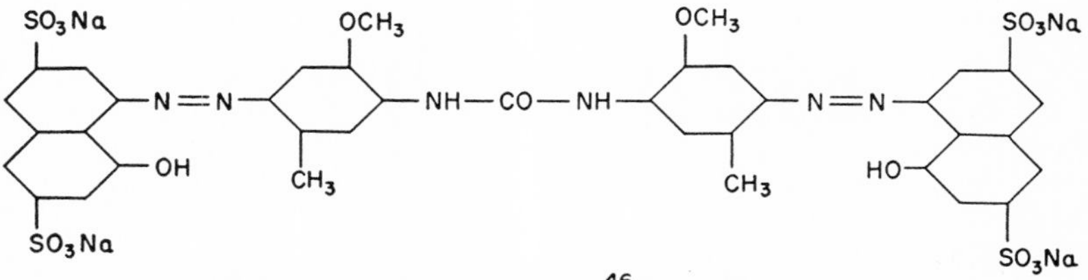

Chlorantine Fast Red 6BLL[46] (Pr. 428)

It is made by diazotizing the H acid ester of *p*-toluenesulfonic acid, coupling with cresidine, and treating the amino-azo compound with phosgene, after which the sulfonic acid ester group is hydrolyzed to form a peri hydroxy-azo configuration.

* Fierz-David and Mather[5] identified this product, but according to I. G. Farbenindustrie information the above formula corresponds to Chlorantine Light Green BL[43], and Chlorantine Light Green BLL[44] differs from it in having a methyl group in place of the anilino group on the triazine ring.

A number of direct and developed dyes, with good cellulose affinity due to benzamido groups, appeared around 1929 as the result of discoveries by Hitch, Jordan and Bradley. Some examples of these are:

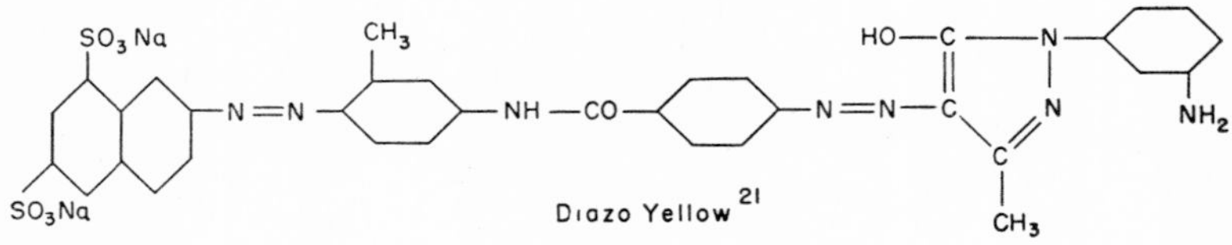

Diazo Yellow [21]

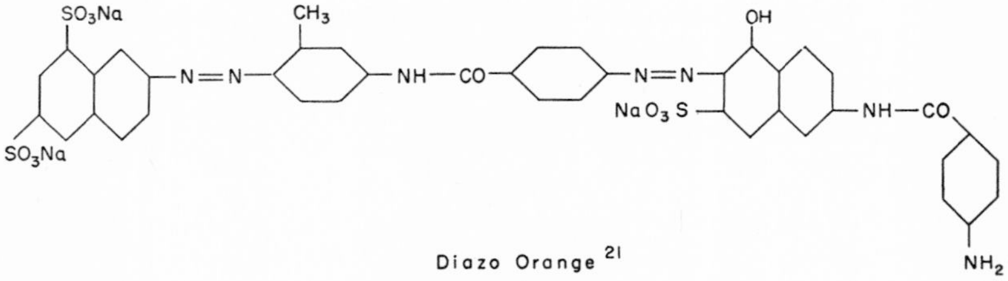

Diazo Orange [21]

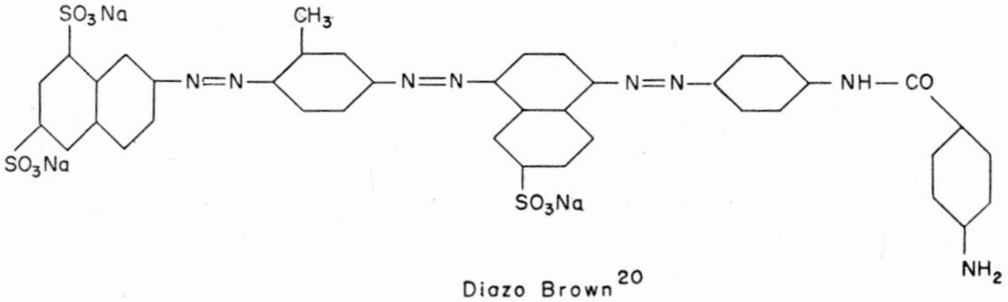

Diazo Brown [20]

The first satisfactory developed violet was discovered about this same time by Woodward. It has the constitution:

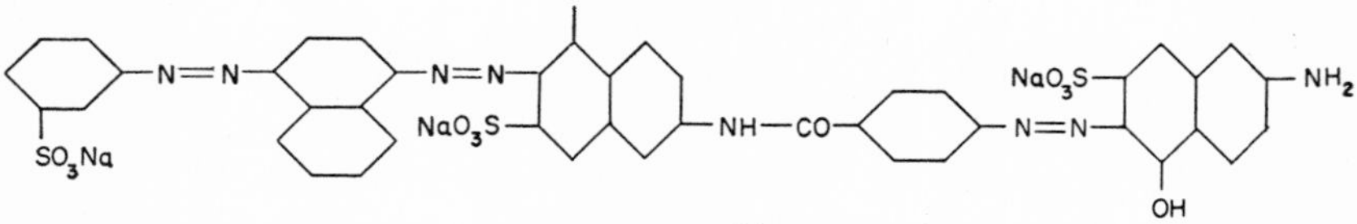

Diazo Violet [70]

When diazotized and developed on the fiber with 2-naphthol the resulting tetrakisazo dye has an amide blocking group in the middle with a violet disazo structure on each side of it.

Trisazo developed greens were found by Woodward[71] and Murphy[57] to have better lightfastness than the previously known disazo developed greens. An example is:

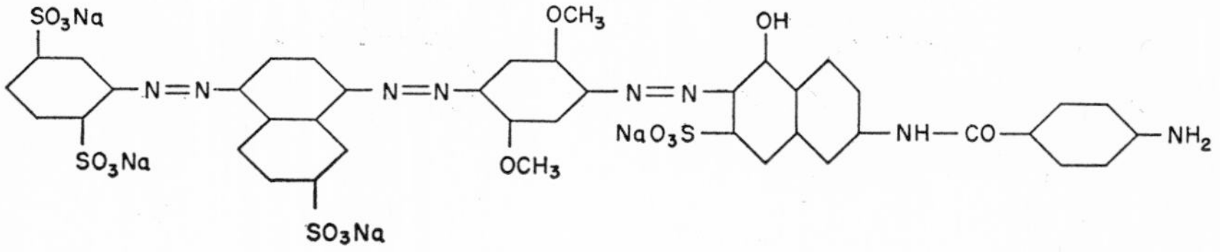

Diazo Green

Phosgenation of some amino-disazo dyes has been found by Zinner[72] to give very fast-to-light dyes such as

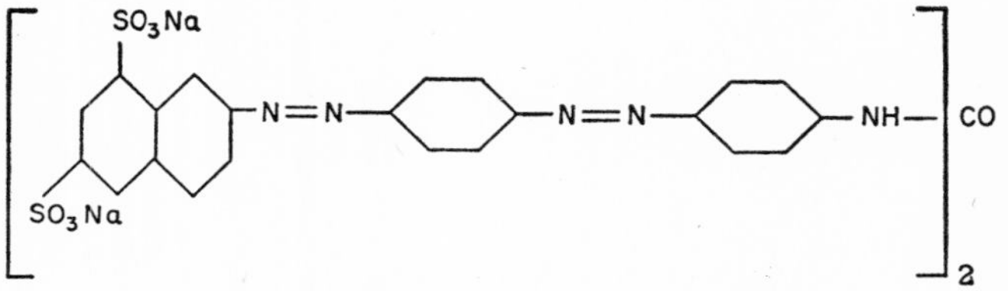

Direct Orange

Cotton dyes containing copper bound by coordinate and covalent bonds have been increasingly important since about 1920. Ciba was the pioneer in this field with dyes covered by the patent of Anderwert, Fritzsche and Schoebel[1]. Most of these dyes are made from coupling components in which the coupling position is ortho to an hydroxy group, as in J acid and its derivatives, and from diazo components containing in the position ortho to the amino group an hydroxy, methoxy, carboxy or carboxymethoxy group. Copper is bound to the azo group by a coordinate bond. Cotton dyeings made with such copper-containing dyes have good fastness to light but are rather dull in shade. Many of these dyes are not adversely affected by resin treatments designed to impart crease resistance to the dyed fabrics. A considerable number of these dyes are now on the market and a few representative ones are shown below.

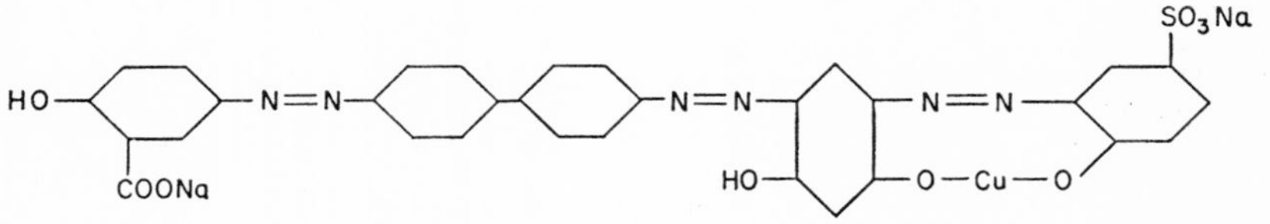

Chlorantine Light Brown BRL[42]

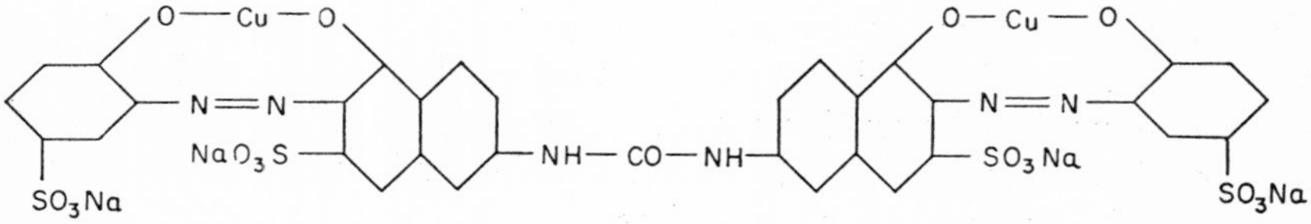

Sirius Supra Rubine BBL[49]

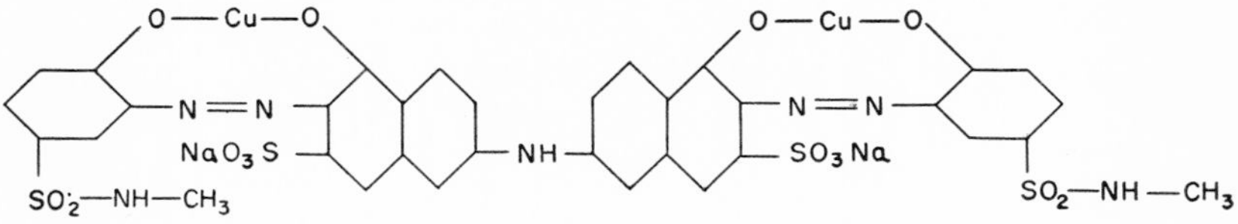

Sirius Supra Violet BL[48]

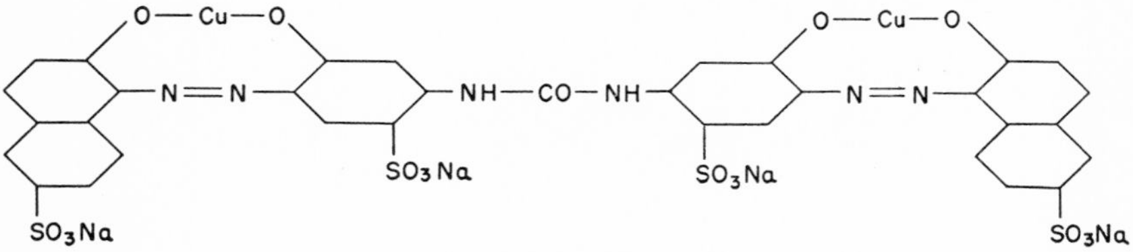

Sirius Red Violet RL[31] (Pr. 277)

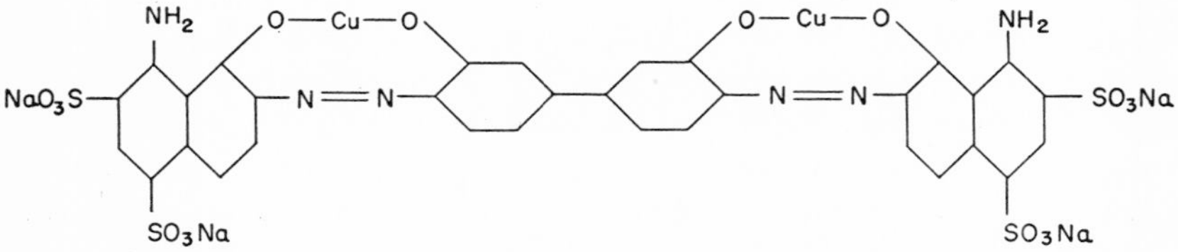

Greenish Blue [53]

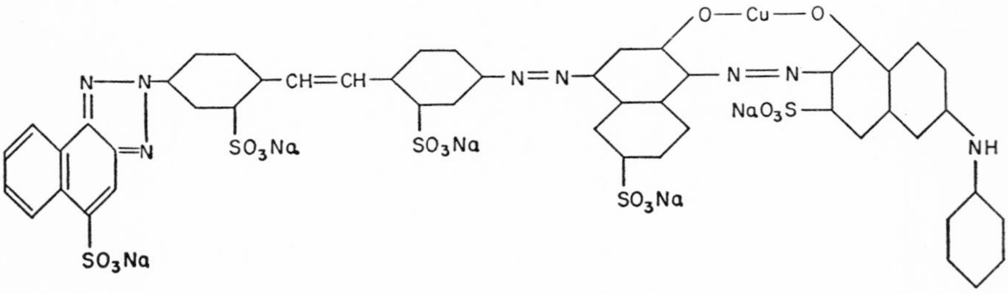

Sirius Supra Green BTL.[50]

Sirius Supra Green BTL is made by diazotizing 4-amino-4'-nitro-2,2'-stilbenedisulfonic acid, coupling with naphthionic acid, and oxidizing the o-amino-azo structure to a triazole. Then the nitro group is reduced with sodium sulfide, the resulting amino group is diazotized, and 5-amino-6-methoxy-2-naphthalenesulfonic acid is coupled with it. This compound is diazotized and coupled with Phenyl J acid, and finally the product is treated with copper ammonium sulfate.

Direct Dyes Produced in the Largest Amount in the United States

Average Annual Production (1946–1950)

(U. S. Tariff Commission Reports)

CI	Dye	1000 Pounds	First Manufacturer	Year Discovered	Discoverer
581	Direct Black EW	10,108	Schoelkopf	1901	Mueller
401	Developed Black BH	2,881	Cassella	1890	Gans and Hoffmann
406	Direct Blue 2B	2,035	Cassella	1890	Rudolf
370	Congo Red	1,803	AGFA	1884	Boettiger
593	Direct Green B	1,088	Cassella	1891	Hoffmann and Daimler
596	Direct Brown 3GO	996	Wulfing and Dahl	1888	
365	Chrysophenine G	975	Leonhart	1887	Bender
620	Direct Yellow R (Curcumine)	954	Geigy	1883	Walter
326	Direct Fast Scarlet	932	Bayer	1900	Israel and Kothe
518	Direct Sky Blue FF	742	Bayer	1891	Ulrich and Bammann
420	Direct Brown M	690	Cassella	1889	Gans
448	Benzo Purpurin 4B	674	AGFA	1885	Schultz
582	Direct Black RX	606	Schoelkopf	1901	Mueller
375	Congo Corinth G	541	AGFA	1886	Pfaff
545	Plutoform Black	456	Bayer	1911	Blanck and Heidenreith
419	Direct Fast Red F	403	Cassella	1889	Gans
Pr. 47	Chlorantine Fast Brown BRL	391	Ciba		
278	Direct Fast Red 8BL	365	Bayer	1907	Hesse, Guenther, and Zart
Pr. 202	Zambesi Black V	356	AGFA	1902	
Pr. 71	Diamine Fast Blue FFB	351	Bayer		
539	Columbia Fast Black FF	339	AGFA	1898	Clausius
561	Trisulfon Brown BT	307	Sandoz	1897	Boniger
583	Trisulfon Green ET	275	Schoelkopf	1901	Mueller
Pr. 53	Chlorantine Fast Yellow 4GL	272	Badische	1887	Mueller
364	Brilliant Yellow	270	Leonhart	1886	Bender
477	Benzo Blue 3B	268	Bayer	1890	Bammann and Ulrich
Pr. 24	Benzo Fast Black L	259	Bayer	1896	
502	Benzo Azurin G	252	Bayer	1885	Duisberg
327	Direct Fast Scarlet 4BA	244	Bayer	1900	Israel and Kothe
520	Direct Pure Blue	227	Cassella	1890	Bammann and Ulrich

Literature Cited

1. Anderwert, Fritzsche and Schoebel, U. S. Patent 1,292,385 (1919).
2. Bayer, U. S. Patent 418,153 (1889).
3. Clingestein, U. S. Patent 1,701,717 (1929).
4. Fierz-David and Blangey, "Fundamental Processes of Dye Chemistry," p. 287, New York, Interscience Publishers Inc., 1949.
5. —— and Mather, *J. Soc. Dyers Colourists*, **53**, 433 (1937).
6. Friedlaender, "Fortschritte der Teerfarbenfabrikation," Berlin, Julius Springer, **1**, 459 (1888).
7. ——, *ibid.*, **4**, 649 (1899).
8. ——, *ibid.*, **5**, 476 (1901).
9. ——, *ibid.*, **6**, 839 (1904).
10. Fritzsche, Krummenacher, Gubler, and Kaiser, U. S. Patent 1,667,312 (1928).
11. Gans, U. S. Patent 442,369 (1890).
12. German Patent 84,893 (1895).
13. German Patent 88,597 (1896).
14. Green, *J. Soc. Dyers Colourists*, **4**, 39 (1888).
15. —— and Crossland, *J. Chem. Soc.*, **89**, 1602 (1906).
16. Gressly, U. S. Patent 903,284 (1908).
17. ——, U. S. Patent 1,982,159 (1934).
18. Guenther, Hesse, and Zart, U. S. Patents 877,643; 897,529 (1908); 933,447; 933,562 (1909).
19. Heumann, "Die Anilinfarben und ihre Fabrikation," Braunschweig, Vieweg, **4**, 1093 (1906).
20. Hitch and Jordan, U. S. Patent 1,735,924 (1929).
21. ——, —— and Bradley, U. S. Patent 1,739,031 (1929).
22. I. G. Farbenindustrie, PB 25625, frame 235.
23. ——, PB 74025, frame 1268.
24. ——, PB 74026, frame 2277.
25. ——, *ibid.*, frame 2278.
26. ——, PB 74058, frame 7760.
27. ——, PB 74122, frame 2321.
28. ——, PB 74722, frame 1205.
29. ——, *ibid.*, frame 1215.
30. ——, *ibid.*, frame 1415.
31. ——, *ibid.*, frame 1964.
32. ——, PB 74747, frame 6610.
33. ——, *ibid.*, frame 7820.
34. ——, *ibid.*, frame 7860.
35. ——, *ibid.*, frame 7939.
36. ——, *ibid.*, frame 8004.
37. ——, *ibid.*, frame 8089.
38. ——, *ibid.*, frame 8369.
39. ——, PB 74753, frame 2161.
40. ——, PB 74767, frame 9338.
41. ——, *ibid.*, frame 9346.
42. ——, PB 74772, frame 2041.
43. ——, *ibid.*, frame 2080.
44. ——, *ibid.*, frame 2082.
45. ——, *ibid.*, frame 2087.
46. ——, *ibid.*, frame 2106.

47. Knight, *J. Soc. Dyers Colourists*, **66,** 412 (1950).
48. ——, *ibid.*, **66,** 413 (1950).
49. ——, *ibid.*, **66,** 414 (1950).
50. ——, *ibid.*, **66,** 417 (1950).
51. ——, *ibid.*, **66,** 419 (1950).
52. Levinstein, *ibid.*, **65,** 269, 272 (1949).
53. Mendoza, U. S. Patent 2,036,159 (1936).
54. Moeller, U. S. Patent 511,708 (1893).
55. Montmallin, Gubler and Spieler, U. S. Patent 1,846,546 (1932).
56. Mueller, U. S. Patent 688,478 (1901).
57. Murphy, U. S. Patent 1,965,201 (1934).
58. Penny, U. S. Patent 1,509,442 (1924).
59. Pfitzinger, U. S. Patent 501,160 (1893).
60. Pietsch, *Klepzig's Textil-Z.*, **12,** 204 (1939).
61. Richard, U. S. Patent 1,829,673 (1931).
62. Schmidt and Hajenbocker, *Ber.*, **54,** 2201 (1921).
63. Schoutissen, *J. Am. Chem. Soc.*, **55,** 4541 (1933).
64. Schubert, *Ann.*, **558,** 10 (1947).
65. Schultz, "Farbstofftabellen," 7th ed., Vol. 1, no. 621, Leipzig, Akad. Verlag, 1931.
66. Schweitzer, U. S. Patent 1,602,991 (1926).
67. Valko, *Colloid Chem.*, **6,** 594–619 (1946); *C. A.*, **40,** 2310 (1946).
68. Vickerstaff, "The Physical Chemistry of Dyeing," London, Imperial Chem. Ind., 1950.
69. Witt, *Ber.*, **10,** 350, 388 (1877).
70. Woodward, U. S. Patent 1,716,098 (1929).
71. ——, U. S. Patent 1,784,617 (1930).
72. Zinner, U. S. Patent 1,866,786 (1932).

AZO DYES FOR WOOL

H. E. Woodward

Early Wool Dyes

Before the establishment of the first synthetic dye plant in 1857 by William Perkin who had not reached his 20th birthday, wool was dyed with naturally occurring dyes. Among them were some which dyed wool from an acid bath, such as Archil, CI 1242, others which dyed wool from a reduced bath (or vat), such as Indigo, CI 1247, or Tyrian purple, CI 1248, and others which dyed wool mordanted with chromium, aluminum or tin salts, such as Fustic, CI 1232, Logwood, CI 1246, and Cochineal, CI 1239.

The first synthetic dye, Aniline Purple or Mauve, CI 862, discovered by Perkin in 1856, and other basic dyes discovered soon afterwards were used to some extent for wool. The first commercial azo dyes such as *p*-phenyl-azoaniline, CI 15, (1863), Bismarck Brown, CI 331, (1865) and Chrysoidin,

CI 20, (1875) were also basic dyes and found some use in dyeing wool. However, dyes having a colored anion have been found more useful for wool dyeing than those having a colored cation.

Wool is composed of the protein keratin which may be represented by the formula

$$\left(\begin{array}{c} -NH-CH-CO-NH-CH-CO-NH-CH-CO- \\ | \qquad\qquad | \qquad\qquad | \\ R_1 \qquad\qquad R_2 \qquad\qquad R_3 \end{array}\right)_n$$

where the R's represent amino acid residues such as glutamic acid, cystine, and arginine, and n is probably 100 or more. The fiber of wool is amorphous except in certain regions where the long polypeptide chains are closely packed to form crystallites or micelles.

The isoelectric point of wool is at a pH of about 4.65. At a lower pH it absorbs acid, one kilogram of wool absorbing about 0.82 gram moles of HCl or an equivalent amount of an acid dye. The dye anion is absorbed more slowly and at a lower concentration of hydrogen ion. This is because the diffusion rate of the large dye anion is slower and the affinity is greater.

Acid Dyes

The acid dyes are those which dye wool from a bath made acid with formic acid or sulfuric acid. They depend for their affinity on the positive charge taken by the wool in a dye bath of low pH (from 1.0 to 4.0). These dyes transfer from dyed wool to undyed wool and, therefore, give level dyeings but they do not have good wetfastness. However, they are bright and have fair to good lightfastness. Furthermore, they are relatively inexpensive as a class.

In 1876, the year which saw the first commercial production of an azo dye (Chrysoidin, CI 20) by the process in which a diazo compound is coupled with a coupling component, Peter Griess first used diazotized sulfanilic acid with different coupling components. The next year, Roussin, using sulfanilic acid as diazo component, manufactured the first acid dyes for wool at the Poirrier Color Works at St. Denis near Paris. The coupling components in these were 1-naphthol in Orange I, CI 150, 2-naphthol in Orange II, CI 151, N,N-dimethylaniline in Orange III, CI 142, and diphenylamine in Orange IV, CI 143. Orange II and Orange IV became important commercial dyes, but in 1887 Orange II was partly replaced by the redder homolog Orange R, and Orange IV was almost entirely superseded in 1879 by the faster-to-light isomer Metanil Yellow of the Bayer Company.

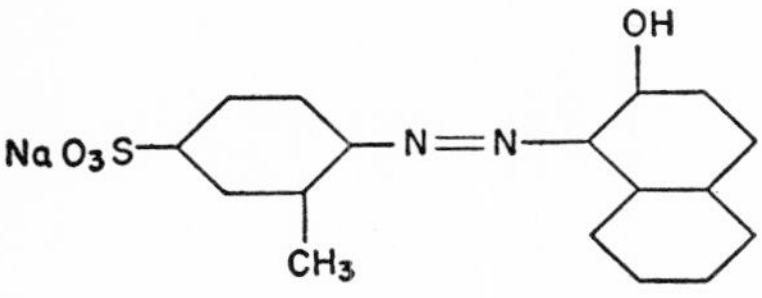

Orange R, CI 161 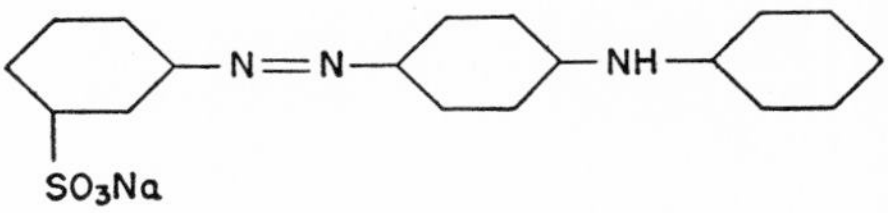   Metanil Yellow, CI 138

Nitro derivatives of Orange IV appeared in 1880 and later. They are Citronine, CI 145 and 146, made by Knecht, who nitrosated and nitrated Orange IV, and Azo Flavine FF, CI 147, of Noelting and Salis, made by condensing *p*-(*p*-aminophenylazo)benzenesulfonic acid with 1-chloro-2,4-dinitrobenzene.

In the same year in which the Oranges were first manufactured, Caro of Badische Anilin- und Soda-Fabrik (BASF) discovered the first red azo dye of technical value, Fast Red AV.

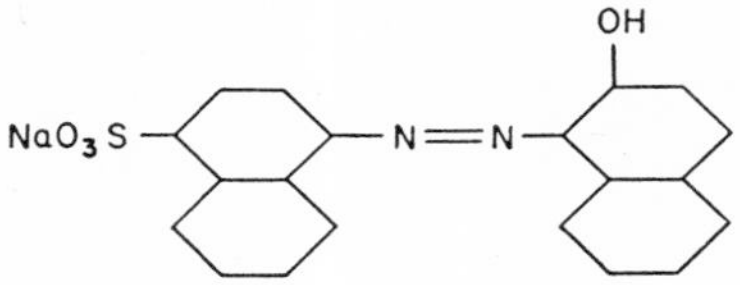

Fast Red AV, CI 176

The same dye was discovered independently by Roussin and manufactured as Roccelline. This was the first dye made from naphthalene intermediates only and it led to a more intensive study of this field. Fast Red AV is still manufactured in large amounts in the United States on account of its low cost and good dyeing and fastness properties.

Baum[2] in 1878 made an important discovery in separating the isomeric 2-naphtholdisulfonic acids, G salt (2-naphthol-6,8-disulfonic acid) and R salt (2-naphthol-3,6-disulfonic acid). The great difference in hue of dyes obtained from these two intermediates showed the importance of preparing pure isomers for the manufacture of azo dyes. From these intermediates Meister, Lucius and Bruening (MLB) made Orange G (aniline → G salt)*, Ponceau 2G (aniline → R salt), Cochineal Red A, CI 185, (naphthionic acid → G salt) and Amaranth, CI 184, (naphthionic acid → R salt) as well as several other different reds from all available diazo components. Three

* The arrow signifies diazotization and coupling.

of these dyes are now made in large amounts:

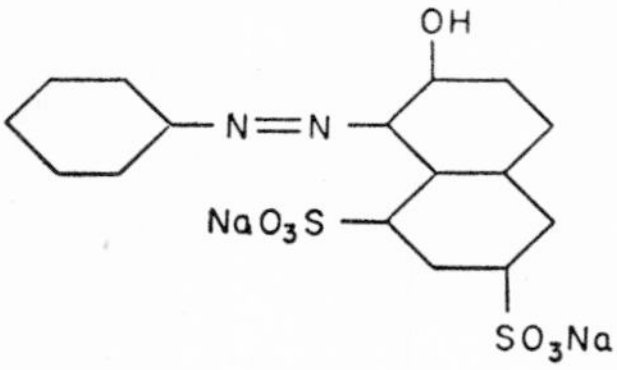

Orange G, CI 27

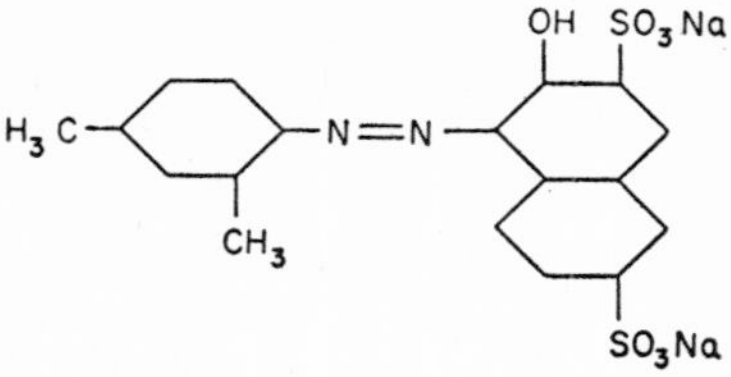

Ponceau R, CI 79

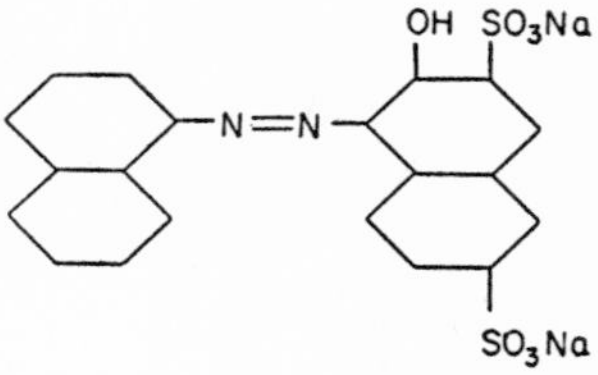

Fast Red B, CI 88

Other naphtholsulfonic acids were soon made and used as coupling components for other red dyes. These dyes ranged from yellow-reds to blue-reds in the order listed below.

Crocein acid	2-naphthol-8-sulfonic acid
G salt	2-naphthol-6,8-disulfonic acid
Schaeffer's salt	2-naphthol-6-sulfonic acid
R salt	2-naphthol-3,6-disulfonic salt
Nevile & Winther's acid	1-naphthol-4-sulfonic acid
L acid	1-naphthol-5-sulfonic acid

The red dyes obtained from these naphtholsulfonic acids soon displaced the natural red dye obtained from the cochineal insect. Two of these which are still made in large amounts are Carmoisine or Azo Rubine and Carmoisine L or Fast Red VR.

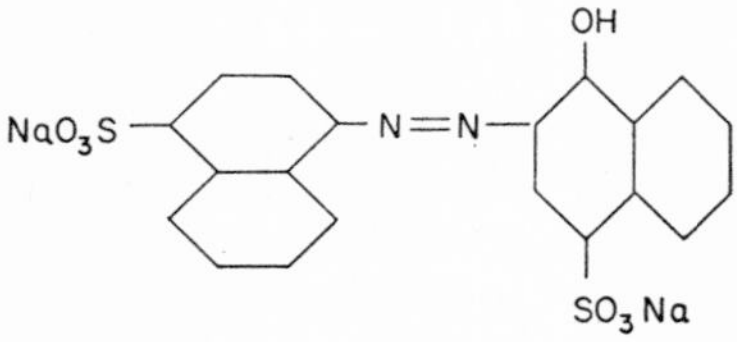

Carmoisine, CI 179

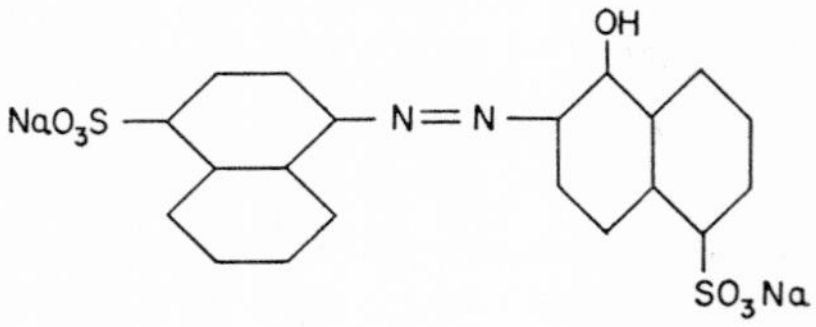

Carmoisine L, CI 180

In discussing the orange, scarlet and red wool dyes discovered before 1890, Friedlaender[8] stated, "They will probably not be superseded in the future as they satisfy all requirements in regard to ease of application and beauty of shade. Furthermore, the low cost of manufacture can not be surpassed." While dyes of better fastness properties have been discovered, the eight monoazo dyes whose formulas are shown above are among the sixteen azo acid dyes of largest production in the United States at present.

During the years 1877–1879, Caro and Schraube[3] had shown that amino azo compounds could be used as diazo components for azo dyes, Koehler had disulfonated *p*-phenylazoaniline to make Fast Acid Yellow, and Nietzke had used this product as a diazo component to make the first commercial disazo dye

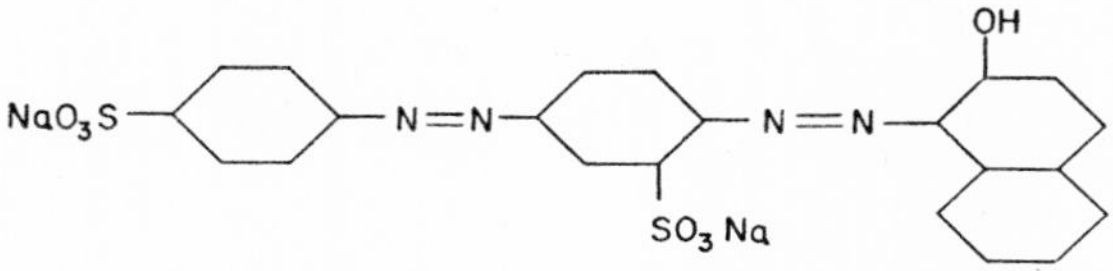

Biebrich Scarlet, CI 280

A few years later (1882) Glaser of BASF discovered the disazo dye Blue Black B, CI 312, 6(and 7)-amino-1-naphthalenesulfonic acid → 1-naphthylamine → R salt. Weinberg of Cassella improved this in 1885 by using Amino G acid as the first component

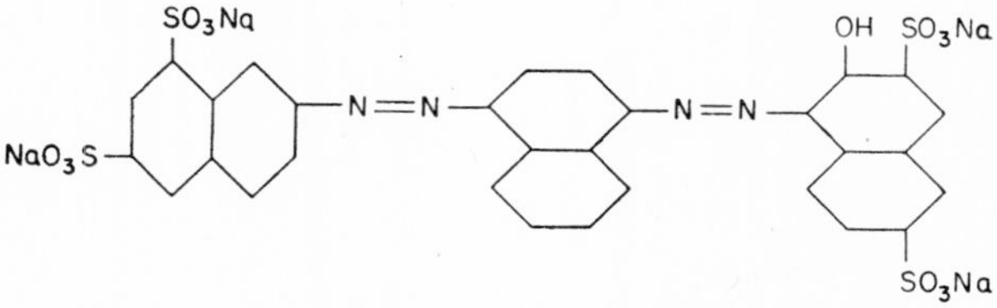

Naphthol Black B, CI 315

Another type of acid disazo dye was found by Wallach of Aktiengesellschaft für Anilinfabrikation (AGFA) in 1881. It is made by coupling resorcinol with two different diazo compounds and is represented by Resorcin Brown.

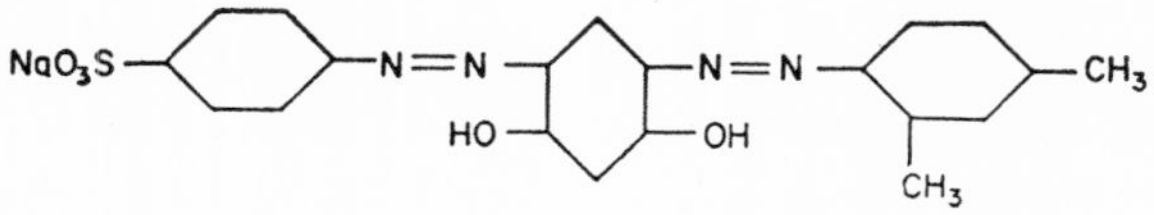

Resorcin Brown, CI 234

This dye has a present production rate in the United States of over half a million pounds a year, but it is used more for dyeing silk and leather than for wool. An analogous dye (naphthionic acid)$_2 \rightrightarrows$ resorcinol, Resorcin Dark Brown, CI 235, is also a high production acid dye.

An important type of acid yellow was discovered by Ziegler of BASF in 1884. He made the dye known as Tartrazine by condensing two moles of *p*-hydrazinobenzenesulfonic acid with one mole of dioxosuccinic acid.

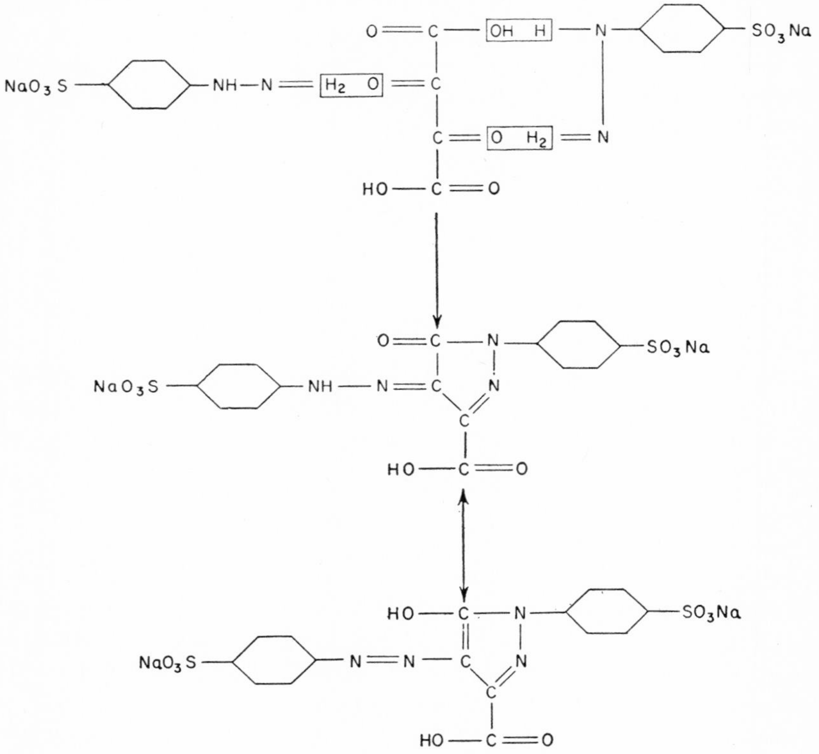

Tartrazine, CI 640

Ziegler also obtained the same dye by condensing *p*-hydrazinobenzene-sulfonic acid with diethyl oxalacetate to make 5-oxo-1-*p*-sulfophenyl-2-pyrazoline-3-carboxylic acid and coupling this with diazotized sulfanilic acid. This process made possible a variety of azo pyrazolone dyes. Tartrazine, the first, is still among the most important, ranking third among azo acid dyes.

Later, Knorr[30] made 3-methyl-1-phenyl-5-pyrazolone by condensing phenylhydrazine with ethyl acetoacetate. Mollenhoff[33] prepared the *p*-sulfo derivative of this intermediate and coupled it with diazotized aniline to make the dye Fast Light Yellow G.

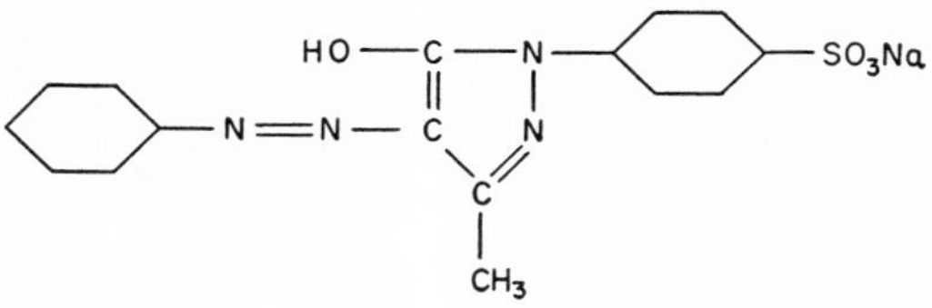

Fast Light Yellow G, CI 636

A later important addition to this line of dyes was made from the hydrazine derived from 2,5-dichlorosulfanilic acid by Boeniger of Sandoz in 1908.

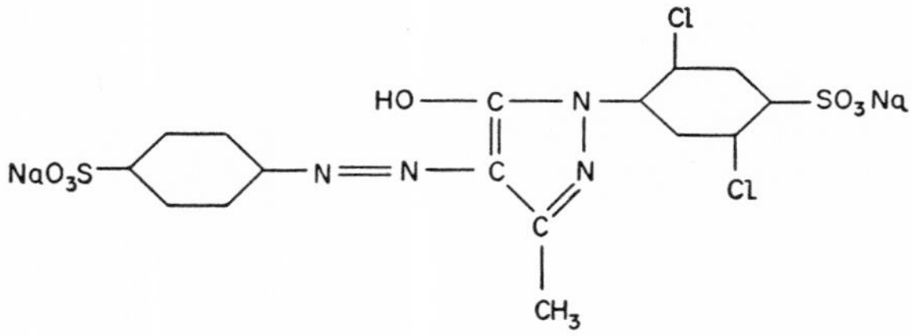

Xylene Light Yellow 2G, CI 639

The azo pyrazolone dyes cover a range of bright yellows, from greenish to reddish, with very good lightfastness. Tartrazine, Xylene Light Yellow 2G and Fast Light Yellow G are among the twenty azo acid dyes of highest production.

After 1890, newly discovered acid dyes for wool were mostly similar in type to the earlier dyes, but use was made of newly developed intermediates such as 8-anilino-1-naphthalenesulfonic acid, aminonaphtholsulfonic acids and (*p*-aminoanilino)benzenesulfonic acids.

Otto of MLB made Victoria Violet 4BS in 1891 by diazotizing *p*-nitroaniline (or *p*-aminoacetanilide), coupling with Chromotropic acid (4,5-dihydroxy-2,7-napthalenedisulfonic acid) and reducing the nitro group (or hydrolyzing the acetamido group).

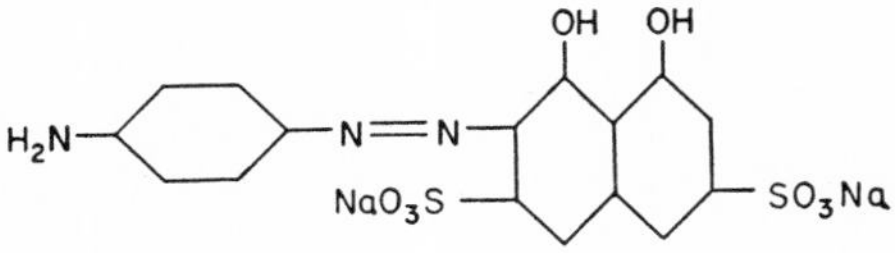

Victoria Violet 4BS, CI 53

Redder dyes are obtained when the substituent para to the azo group is less basic (e.g., acetamido or nitro). When the substituent is more basic (e.g., methylamino or dimethylamino), bluer dyes are obtained.

The acid dye of highest production in the United States (about two million pounds a year) is Naphthol Blue Black B, discovered by Hoffmann of Cassella in 1891. It is a disazo dye made by coupling H acid with diazotized *p*-nitroaniline in acid solution and then with diazotized aniline in alkaline solution.

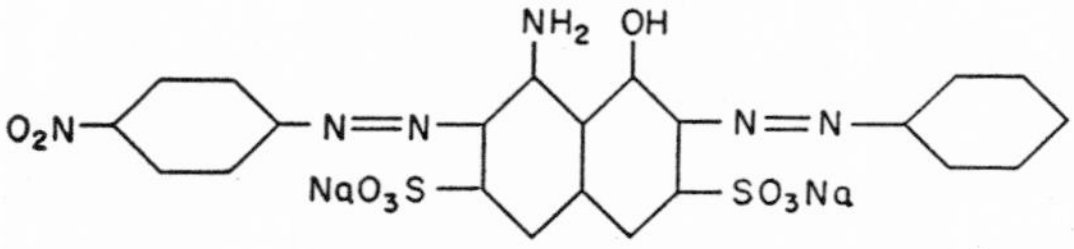

Naphthol Blue Black B, CI 246

Its popularity is based on the use of low cost intermediates and on its good lightfastness.

The blue monoazo dye Sulfon Acid Blue R, discovered in 1897 by Ulrich of the Bayer Company, has very good fastness to light.

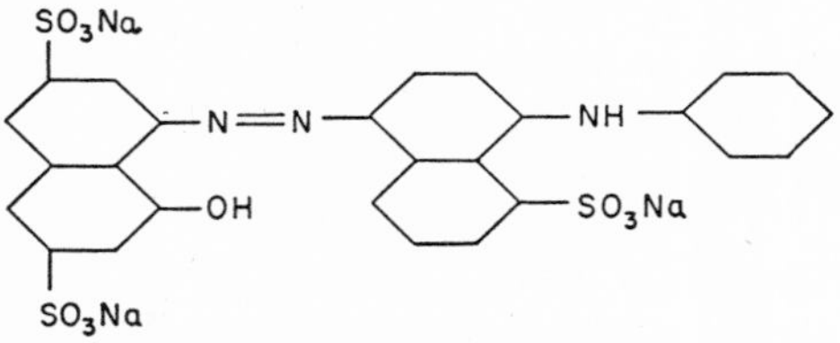

Sulfon Acid Blue R, CI 208

The aminonaphtholsulfonic acids as coupling components have not been used as much in wool dyes as in cotton dyes, but a few important dyes do make use of them. Good fastness-to-light is shown by the red to violet dyes of MLB made from 2-amino-5-nitrobenzenesulfonic acid diazotized and coupled to Gamma acid (7-amino-1-naphthol-3-sulfonic acid) in acid solution.

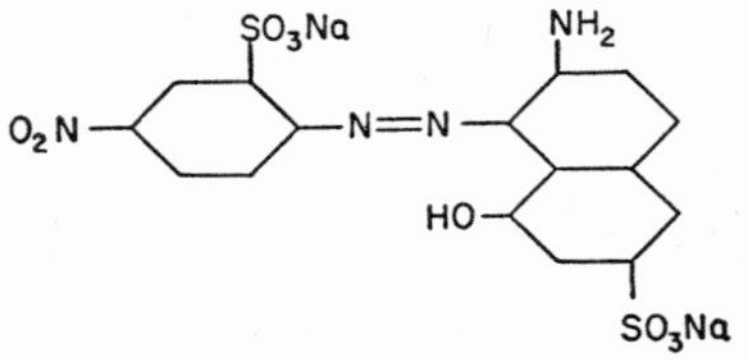

Victoria Fast Violet 2R[26] (Pr. 197)

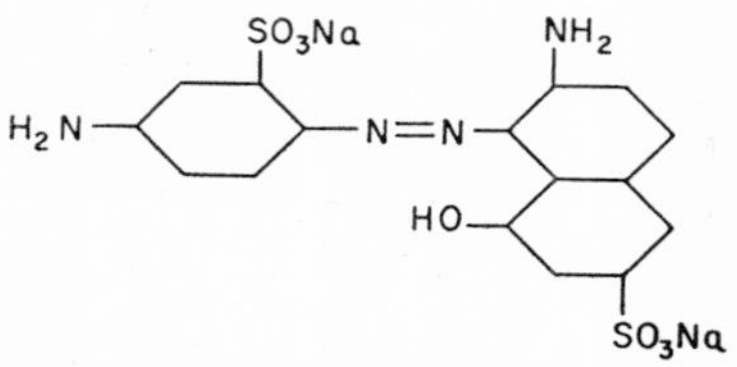

Azo Acid Carmine[25]

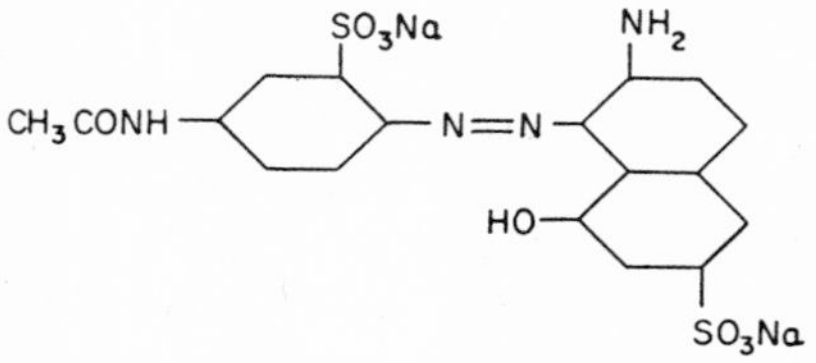

Guinea Fast Red BL[24] (Pr. 101)

Two level-dyeing reds, which now account for over a million pounds of production per year in the United States, were made from Acetyl H acid by MLB in 1902.

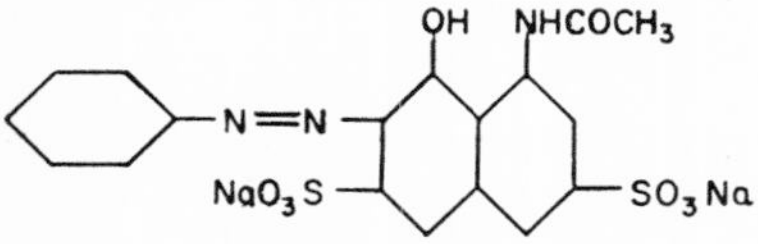

Amido Naphthol Red G, CI 31

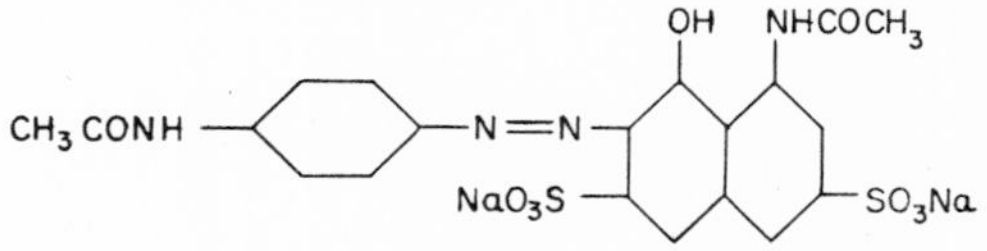

Amido Naphthol Red 6B, CI 57

Neutral-dyeing or Milling Dyes

There is no sharp line of demarcation between acid and neutral dyeing wool dyes, and some dyes which are usually dyed from a weakly acid dye bath may be dyed from a neutral bath containing sodium chloride or sodium sulfate. Usually an ammonium salt, such as ammonium acetate, is also added in order to develop gradually a slightly acid reaction in the boiling dye bath (pH 5 to 7). In solution, many neutral-dyeing dyes are aggregated more than level-dyeing acid dyes, especially at temperatures much below 100°C. They also have a lower rate of diffusion and better affinity. Some other dyes are strongly attracted to the fiber interface because they lower the surface tension of the dye bath[1]. On account of their better affinity and greater degree of aggregation, they have good fastness to wet treatment, especially alkaline fulling (or milling). Since the affinity does not depend on a positive charge on the wool fiber, it is probably based on hydrogen bonding and surface activity. It may be due partly to a hydrogen bridge system between a —CO—NH— group of the wool and a hydroxy or amino group of the dye[5, 42].

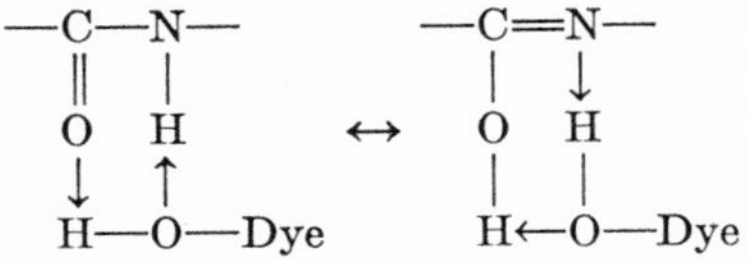

The blues and blacks in the neutral-dyeing line are mostly 19th century dyes while the others are mostly discoveries of the 20th century. Sulfon Cyanine Blue GR of Bayer (Ott 1892) has good fastness properties, and is produced in the United States in amounts of about 500,000 pounds a year.

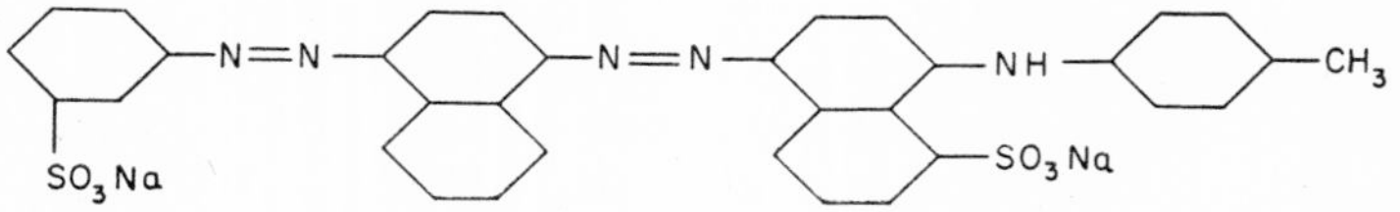

Sulfon Cyanine GR, CI 289

A number of analogous dyes are made using Phenyl Peri acid in place of Tolyl Peri acid, and other diazo components in place of metanilic acid. An important one of these is Sulfon Cyanine Black B of Bayer, introduced in 1902.

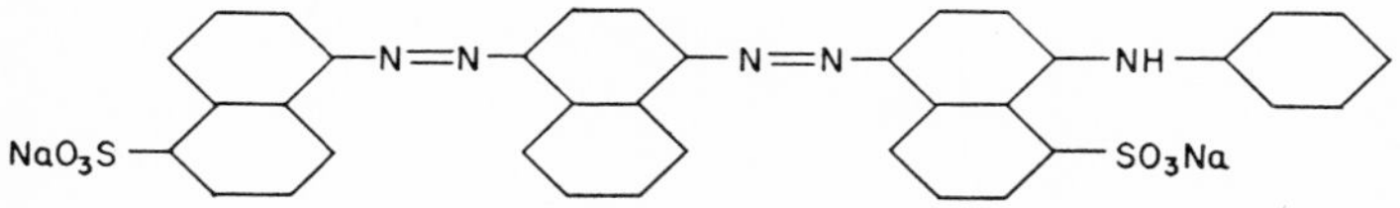

Sulfon Cyanine Black B, CI 307

The Nerols, discovered by Herzberg of AGFA in 1897, use 5-amino-2-arylaminobenzenesulfonic acids , made by reacting aniline or its homologs with 2-chloro-5-nitrobenzenesulfonic acid and reducing the nitro group.

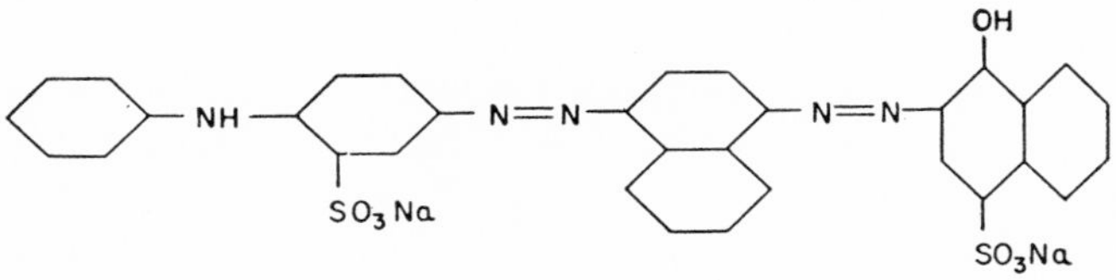

Nerol 2B, CI 304

Acid Anthracene Reds G and 3B, introduced by Bayer around 1904, had been known nearly 20 years earlier[9] before the advantages of the neutral-dyeing dyes were appreciated.

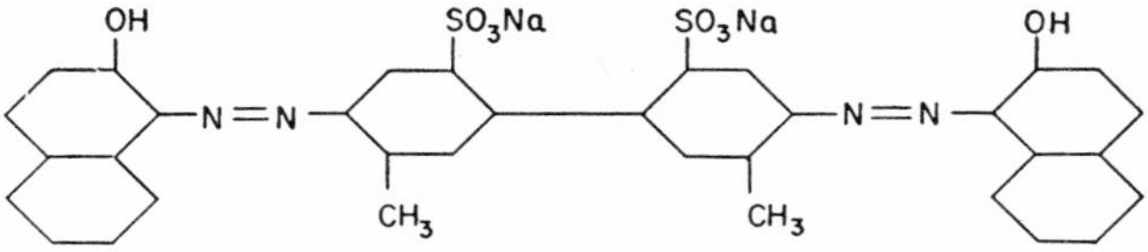

Acid Anthracene Red 3B, CI 487

Red 3B is produced in large amounts. Red G, the homolog of less importance, is made from benzidinedisulfonic acid (4,4'-diamino-2,2'-biphenyldisulfonic acid).

In 1912, Geigy added some yellow, orange and red milling dyes discovered by Richards. Some of these dyes are characterized by the presence of tosyl ester groups formed by the action of p-toluenesulfonyl chloride (tosyl chloride) on p-hydroxy azo dyes. Representative dyes of this group are

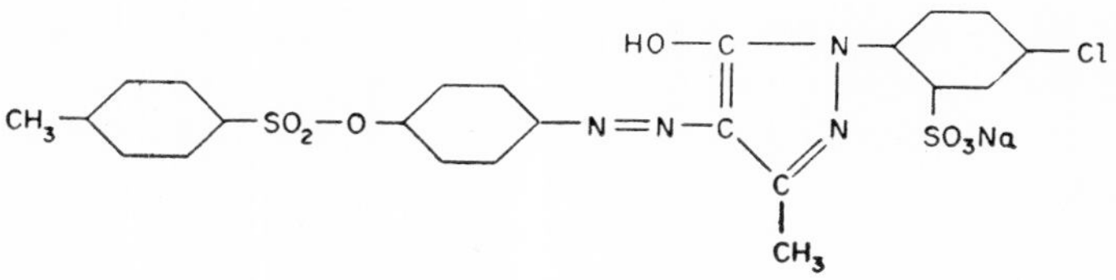

Polar Yellow 5G, CI 642 *

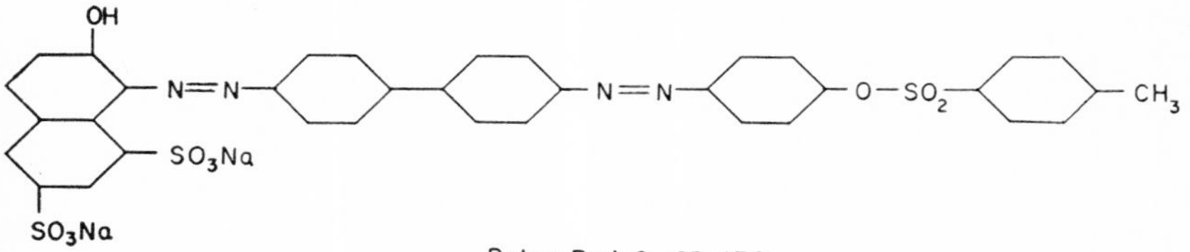

Polar Red G, CI 430

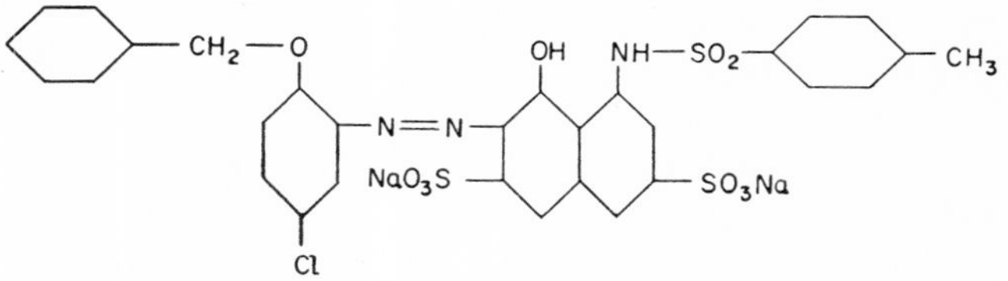

Polar Brilliant Red 3B[7]

Chrome Dyes

Inorganic salts, especially those of aluminum, chromium, iron, copper and tin, had been used as mordants for dyeing wool with natural dyes before synthetic dyes were known. These salts were also found to have desirable effects in dyeing wool with some synthetic dyes, especially azo dyes. With the great variety of azo dyes available, it was not necessary to use different metals to obtain different colors, and salts of chromium soon displaced those of the other metals, since "chromed" azo dyes give in general a combination of the best brightness with the best fastness to light and washing.

Chromium is generally used in the form of sodium dichromate or other salts of chromic acid but it combines with the wool and the azo dye only after reduction to $Cr(OH)_3$. The reducing agent is usually the wool fiber. In some cases the dye or an added organic acid such as formic or oxalic acid may serve as reducing agents. Chrome dyes are applied by three methods.

(1) *Bottom Chrome or Chrome Mordant.* In this method the wool is first

* Fierz-David and Blangey[6] place the sulfo group ortho to the chlorine atom in the pyrazolone, but German information[14] agrees with the Colour Index structure.

treated with an inorganic chromate and is then dyed. This method is used less than the others.

(2) *Top Chrome or After Chrome Method.* By this method, the wool is dyed with a suitable dye and is then treated with sodium dichromate in the same or in a fresh dye bath. Most chrome dyes can be applied by modifications of this method.

(3) *Metachrome or Chromate Method.* By this method, which is only applicable to a limited number of chrome dyes, the combination of chromium and dye with the wool and of chromium with the dye is carried out simultaneously in a single bath which contains dye, sodium dichromate and ammonium sulfate. It is advantageous for the dyer because it saves time and heat, but the dyes suitable for this method must have affinity for wool in a bath which is only slightly acid, must not be oxidized by the chromate, and must not be precipitated by chromium salts.

Schetty[40] has shown that the suitability of *o,o'*-dihydroxy azo dyes for application by the one-bath chroming method decreases with an increase in the number of groups which are capable of hydration. Such groups are hydroxy and sulfo groups which are not in a position to form hydrogen bonds within the molecule. For example, the two following dyes are suitable for metachrome dyeing,

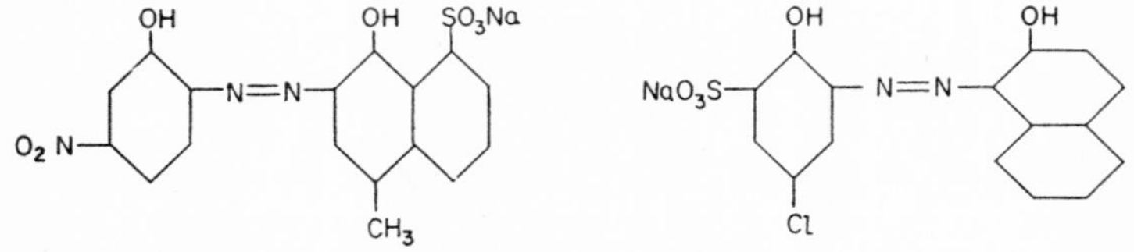

while the following dyes which are isomeric with the above are not suitable for metachrome dyeing.

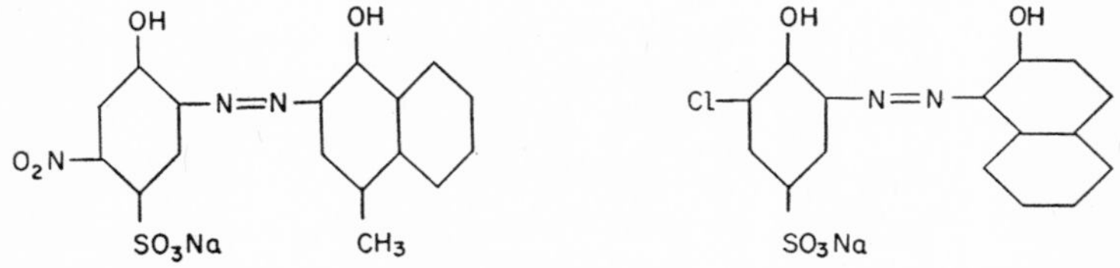

The chrome dyes with few exceptions are of no value when dyed without chromium. Most chromable dyes have *o,o'*-dihydroxy azo structures, but some have *o*-carboxy-*o'*-hydroxy azo, *o*-hydroxy carboxy (salicylic acid type) or peri dihydroxy structures. These characteristics were first recognized by Kostanecki[31] and later by Nietzke[36].

When wool, dye, and trivalent chromium react by one of the three methods shown above there is formed a complex compound of all three.

The exact structure of such compounds is not well known, but it is believed that the chromium forms electrovalent bonds with wool and with hydroxy groups of the dye and coordinate bonds with nearby oxygen or nitrogen atoms which can form five or six membered rings with it. Structures of some prechromed complexes are shown on p. 162. Race, Rowe and Speakman[37] showed that some o,o'-dihydroxy azo dyes form a complex compound on wool which contains one chromium atom to two dye molecules. The formation of a complex compound of chromium with wool and dye results in good washing fastness for this class of dyes. The chrome dyes in which the azo group can coordinate with the chromium atom have good lightfastness.

Chrome Dyes With *o*-Hydroxy Carboxy Structures. The oldest of the chrome azo dyes still in use is Alizarin Yellow R.

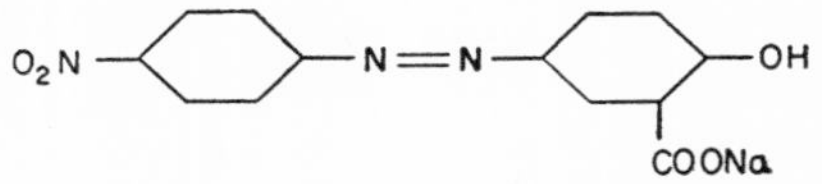

Alizarin Yellow R, CI 40

The "alizarin" in the name of this dye indicated that it could be dyed in the same manner as the mordant dye Alizarin. Alizarin Yellow R has good fastness to washing and fulling. The isomeric dye from *m*-nitroaniline, Alizarin Yellow GG, CI 36, first made by Nietzke in 1887, is produced in larger amounts. Several other monoazo dyes from salicylic acid are also used as chrome yellows. One of these which is among the best in fastness to light and fulling is the symmetrical Eriochrome Flavine A, which is made by coupling diazotized 5-amino-2-chlorobenzoic acid with salicylic acid and hydrolyzing the chloro substituent by heating in alkaline solution.

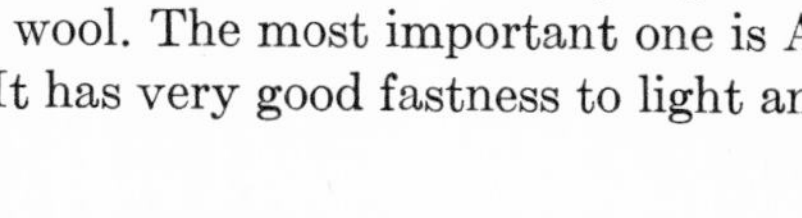

Eriochrome Flavine A, CI 219

Some disazo dyes with salicylic acid as coupling component are also useful chrome dyes for wool. The most important one is Anthracene Yellow C of Cassella (1891). It has very good fastness to light and to fulling.

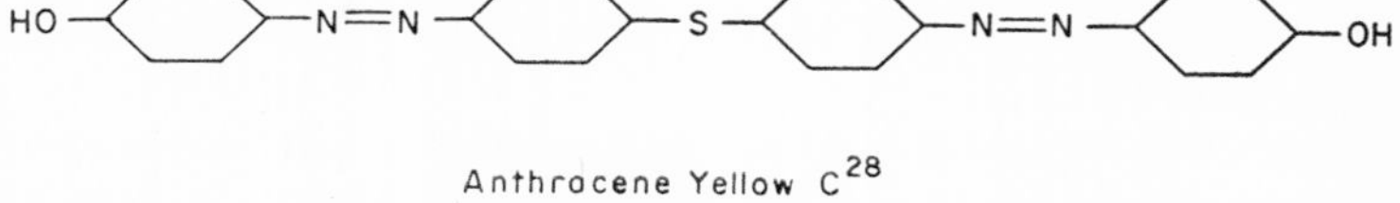

Anthracene Yellow C[28]

The cotton dye Diamine Fast Red F, CI 419, (see p. 124 in the section on Azo Dyes For Cotton) is sometimes used as a chrome dye on wool.

The *o*-hydroxy carboxy structure can also be introduced into dyes by using 5-aminosalicylic acid as a diazo component, as in Diamond Black F made in 1889 by Lauch and Krehaler.

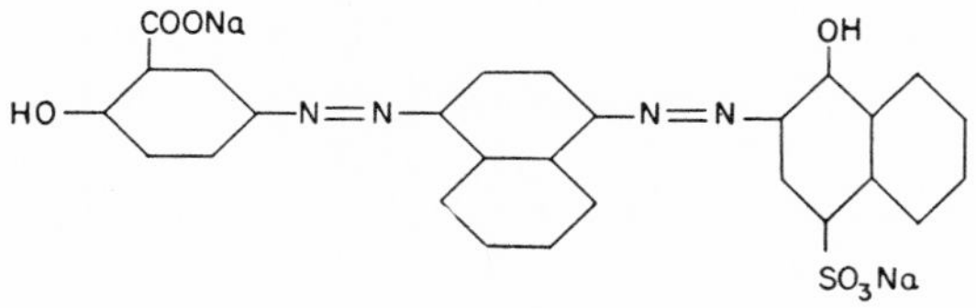

Diamond Black F, CI 299

In Diamond Red 3B[12] the *o*-hydroxy carboxy structure is introduced into the dye in such a way that chroming has very little effect on the hue of the dyeing. The dye, being similar to Victoria Fast Violet 2R, (see p. 150) has good lightfastness, and its washing fastness is good after it is chromed.

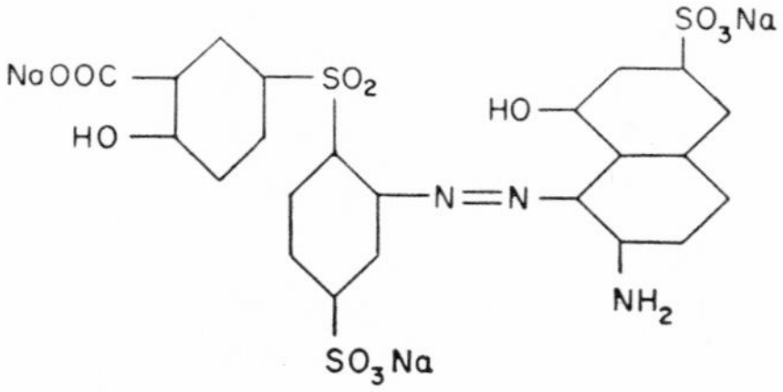

Diamond Red 3B

Chrome Dyes With Peri Dihydroxy Structures. In 1890 Kuzel of MLB discovered the chromotrope dyes, represented by Chromotrope 2R.

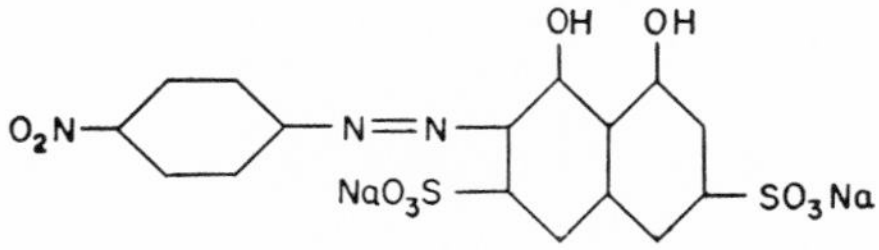

Chromotrope 2R, CI 29

In this type of dye, chromium reacts with the two peri hydroxy groups. There is no oxidation involved here since chromium fluoride (CrF_3) gives practically the same results as sodium dichromate. These dyes do not find much use now.

Chrome Dyes With *o*-Carboxy-*o'*-hydroxy Azo Structures. Few chrome dyes of this type are made. The principal example is Acid Alizarin Red B of MLB (discovered by Gullbransson in 1902).

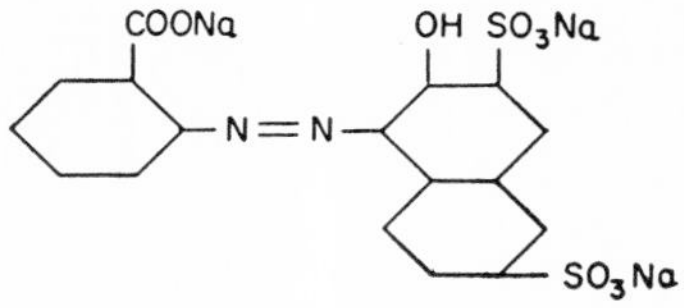

Acid Alizarin Red B, CI 216

This is a versatile dye, being used as an acid dye, a chrome dye and for the preparation of a pigment in the form of its barium salt on a substratum of aluminum hydroxide.

Another dye of this type having excellent fastness to light, washing and fulling is Bayer's Acid Anthracene Brown PG[10] (discovered by Guenther, Hesse, Zart and Schweitzer in 1911).

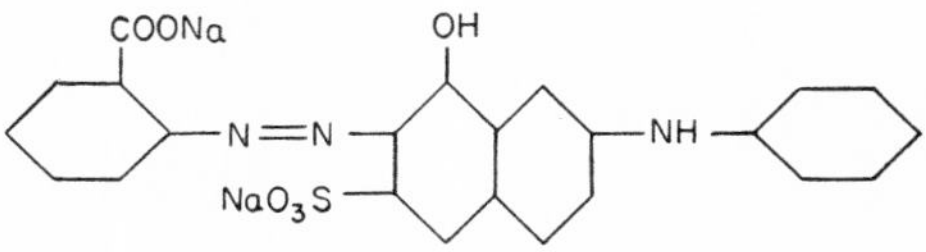

Acid Anthracene Brown PG,[13] (Pr. 4)

Chrome Dyes With *o,o'*-Dihydroxy Azo (or *o*-Amino-*o'*-hydroxy Azo) Structures. The greatest variety of chrome dyes is obtained from diazotized *o*-aminophenols (or naphthols) coupled ortho to an amino or hydroxy group of the coupling component. The earliest dyes of this type seemed to be of little practical importance. About 1900 the use of amino-nitrophenols caused enough improvement to change the former opinion on these dyes and many valuable products were developed.

Typical dyes include Anthracene Chrome Violet B (first made by Griess in 1877),

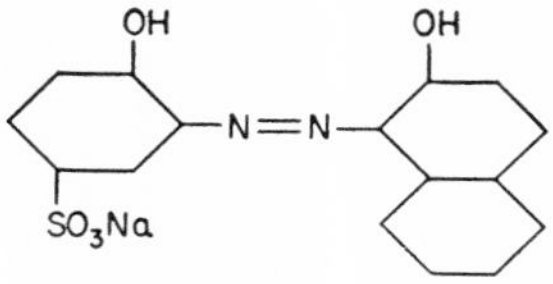

Anthracene Chrome Violet B, CI 169

Metachrome Brown B of AGFA (discovered by Herzberg and Hausmann in 1898) and Alizarin Black R of MLB (discovered by Ernst and Schirmacher in 1900).

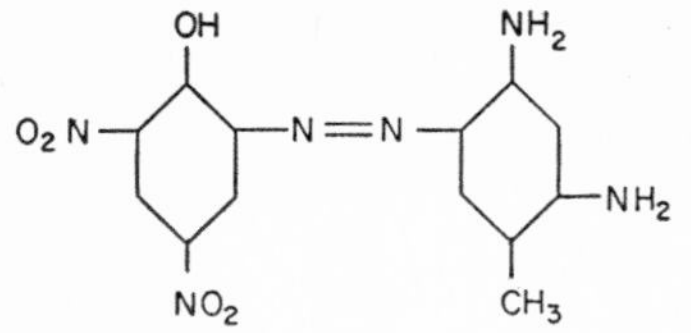

Metachrome Brown B, CI 101

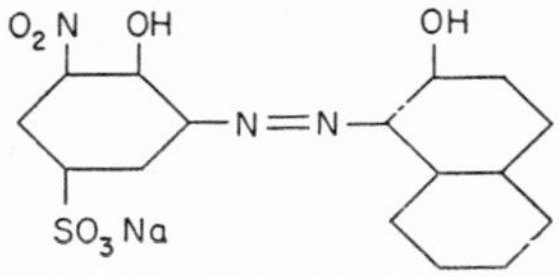

Acid Alizarin Black R, CI 172

A later modification of the brown was Acid Anthracene Brown RH, introduced by Bayer in 1911.

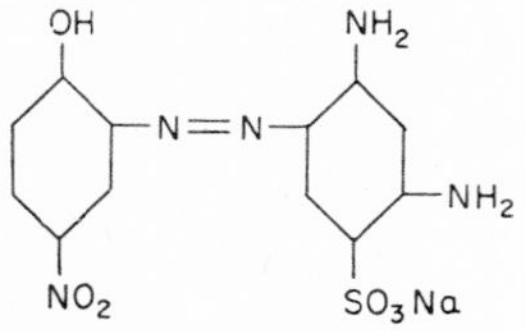

Acid Anthracene Brown RH, CI 98

On account of the low cost of this dye, its production in the United States is now the fourth largest of the azo chrome dyes.

Near the beginning of the twentieth century several discoveries brought about the development of some very important azo chrome dyes. The use of o-aminonaphthols as diazo components had been delayed because 1-amino-2-naphthol and 2-amino-1-naphthol are easily oxidized by nitrous acid during diazotization. It was known that some groups ortho to a diazonium group are easily hydrolyzed, especially if there are other negative groups favorably located in the ortho or para positions. However, if the hydrolyzed group is a sulfo group, the resulting sulfite prevents a good yield of azo coupling. In 1904 Julius, Reindel and Guenther of BASF[29] diazotized 4-amino-1,3-naphthalenedisulfonic acid and made it alkaline to produce 4-sulfonaphthalene-1-diazo-2-oxide (naphth[1,2]oxadiazole-5-sulfonic acid).

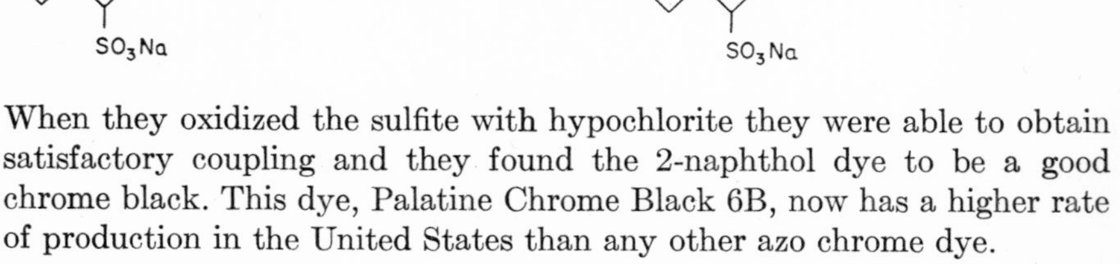

When they oxidized the sulfite with hypochlorite they were able to obtain satisfactory coupling and they found the 2-naphthol dye to be a good chrome black. This dye, Palatine Chrome Black 6B, now has a higher rate of production in the United States than any other azo chrome dye.

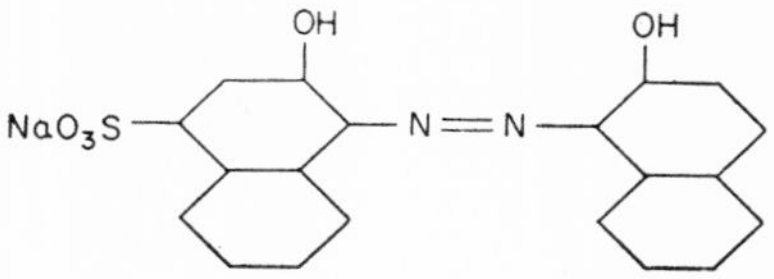

Palatine Chrome Black 6B, CI 202

In 1904 Sandmeyer[39] of the Geigy Company improved the process of making this dye when he discovered that 1-amino-2-naphthol-4-sulfonic acid can be diazotized directly in good yield without any added acid if a small amount of copper sulfate (approximately 0.05 equivalent) is added before the sodium nitrite. This was a more economical method of producing this diazo compound than the indirect method of Julius et al., since 1-amino-2-naphthol-4-sulfonic acid is easily made from 2-naphthol by nitrosation and treatment with sodium bisulfite. Geigy introduced the isomeric 1-naphthol dye as Eriochrome Blue Black B, CI 201. It is not nearly as important as the 2-naphthol isomer.

About the same time Hagenbach of Geigy found that 4-sulfonaphthalene-1-diazo-2-oxide can be nitrated[11], and the derived 1- and 2-naphthol dyes were introduced. The 1-naphthol dye, Eriochrome Black T, is second in importance among azo chrome dyes.

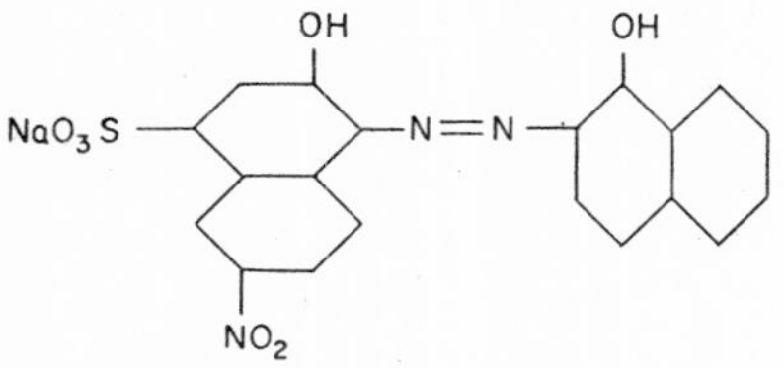

Eriochrome Black T, CI 203

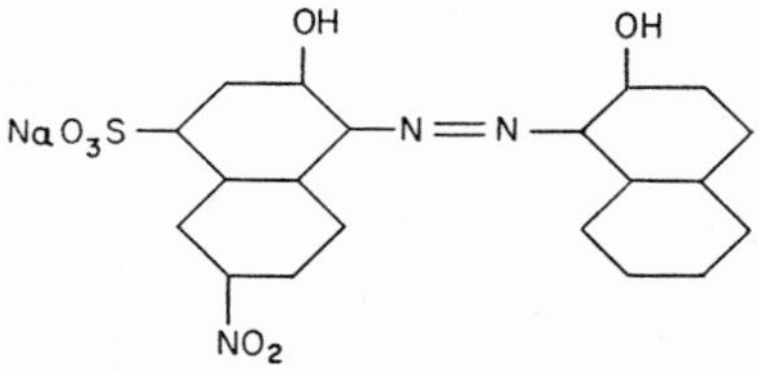

Eriochrome Black A, CI 204

Hagenbach also used 3-methyl-1-phenyl-5-pyrazolone as a coupling component and made Eriochrome Red B, the most important chrome red.

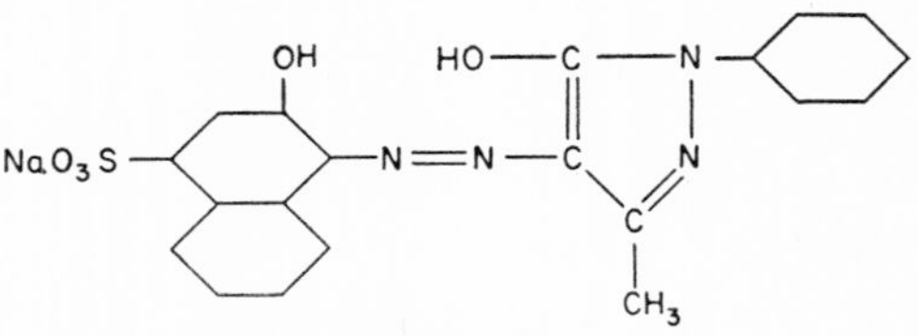

ERIOCHROME RED B, CI 652

Two new disazo chrome dyes were introduced in 1907, in each of which only one azo group is involved in the coordinate structure of the chromium compound.

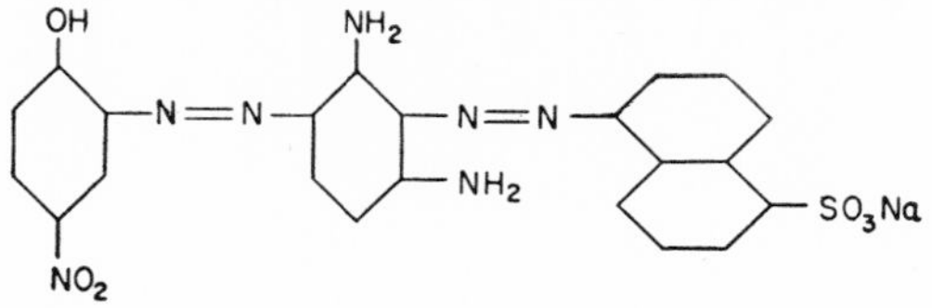

Anthracene Chromate Brown EB[27] (Pr. 14)

Cassella's Anthracene Chromate Brown EB is made from 2-amino-4-nitrophenol, *m*-phenylenediamine and 5-amino-1-naphthalenesulfonic acid.

Eriochrome Verdon A of Geigy (discovered by Richard) is made from sulfanilic acid, 2-amino-*p*-cresol and 2-naphthol.

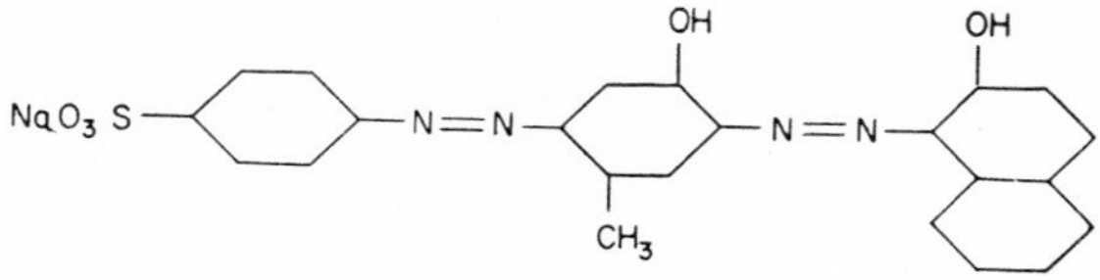

Eriochrome Verdon A, CI 292

It dyes wool a claret color which is changed to blue green when after-chromed.

Dyes Oxidized by Chromate. There are some azo chrome dyes which require sodium chromate instead of a chromic salt for after-treatment. One of these is the dye Carmoisine mentioned above as a red acid dye. In 1894 MLB introduced it as Chromotrope FB, for producing blue after-chromed dyeings. Since it does not form a blue chromium complex with chromium fluoride, and since with sodium chromate it gives the same blue complex that is obtained by treating 1-amino-2-naphthol-4-sulfonic acid → 1-naphthol-4-sulfonic acid with chrome alum, it appears that the dye is oxidized by treatment with sodium chromate[38].

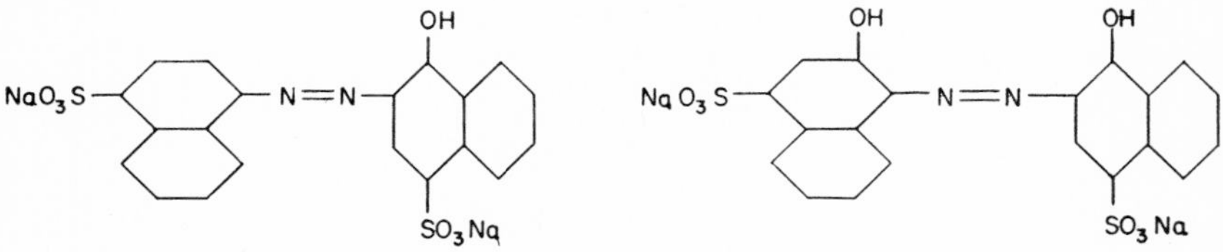

Chromotrope FB, CI 179

Acid dye (red)   Oxidized form (gives blue chromium complex)

Diamond Black PV of Bayer, discovered by Kahn in 1902, requires oxidation for development to a black chromium complex. The structure of the chromium complex of the oxidized form is not known, but Morgan and Smith[34] believe that the chromium is probably combined with the peri oxygen atoms on the naphthalene nucleus.

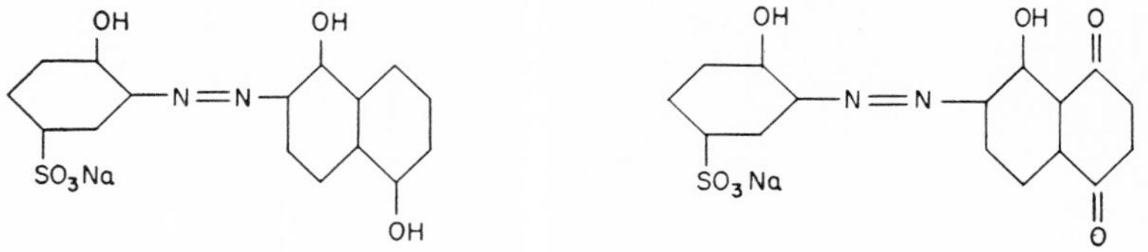

Diamond Black PV, CI 170

Acid dye   Oxidized form

In dyeing with the chrome dyes discussed in this section, an excess of sodium chromate or of chromic salt is used, and this forms a weakly colored chromium/wool complex which causes some dullness of the dyeing[37].

Premetallized Dyes

Many of the chrome dyes described above can be prechromed to form fairly pure metal complex dyes having a ratio of chromium atoms to moles of dye of 1 to 1 or 1 to 2. The structure of the dye and the conditions of metallization determine the ratio of metal to dye. The complexes with a 1 to 1 ratio (fully chromed dyes) are generally superior in fastness properties to the half-chromed dyes[43].

The use of such prechromed complexes instead of chroming the dye on the fiber is an advantage to the dyer for several reasons, such as: (1) the process of dyeing is simplified, (2) more uniform results are obtained, (3) no chromium/wool compound is formed to cause dullness and (4) no oxidative degradation of wool occurs.

The majority of commercial prechromed dyes are o,o'-dihydroxy azo dyes. Some authors[35] believe that the two hydroxy groups ortho to the azo group are not equivalent and that only one of them reacts with chromium. Schetty[40] has shown that only one of the hydroxy groups can react with aromatic sulfonyl chlorides. The simple o,o'-dihydroxy azo compound before metallization is probably in an unsymmetrical trans form[41]:

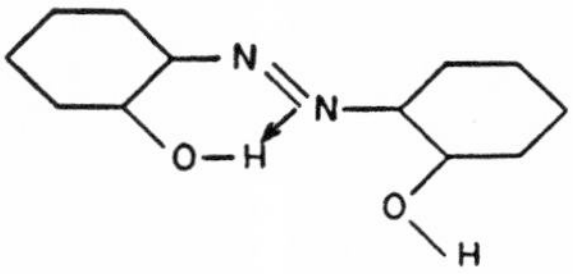

Other groups present in the molecule must determine which hydroxy group is hydrogen-bonded to the azo group. However, when there is only one hydroxy group ortho to the azo group and no complex-forming group in the other ortho position the dye does not form a chromium complex.

Schetty[41] suggests the following structure to explain the special chemical, physical and dyeing properties of chromium complexes of dyes containing a sulfo group ortho or peri to one of these hydroxy groups which is adjacent to the azo group.

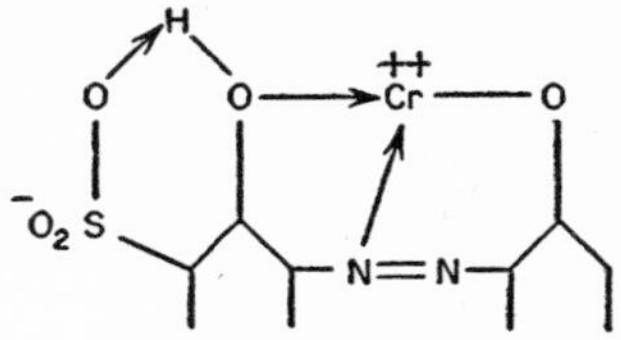

Other authors[4, 37] adhere to the older theory that both hydroxy groups react with chromium, and that coordination with the azo group results by formation of five and six membered rings. It is not clear which nitrogen of the azo group coordinates or whether the pair of electrons is donated by both nitrogens. It may be assumed that, when one of the components is a naphthalene and the other a benzene compound, the former probably is part of the *six* membered ring which contains the metal (as shown in the structure below), while the benzene component takes part in the formation of the *five* membered ring. Drew and Fairbairn propose the following formula for the chromium complex of Anthracene Chrome Violet B.

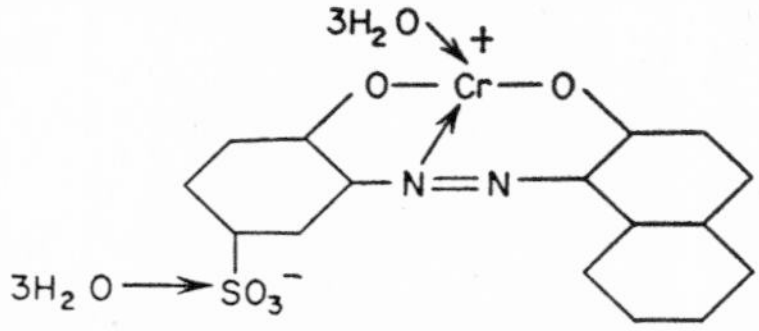

This complex is soluble in water, but after removal of 6 H_2O it is insoluble in all solvents. It is suggested that this is due to polymerization by bonding between the $=Cr^+$ and $-SO_3^-$ of several molecules. When the above chromic salt is treated with another molecule of dye a different chromium complex is formed in which the ratio of metal to dye is 1:2 as shown below.

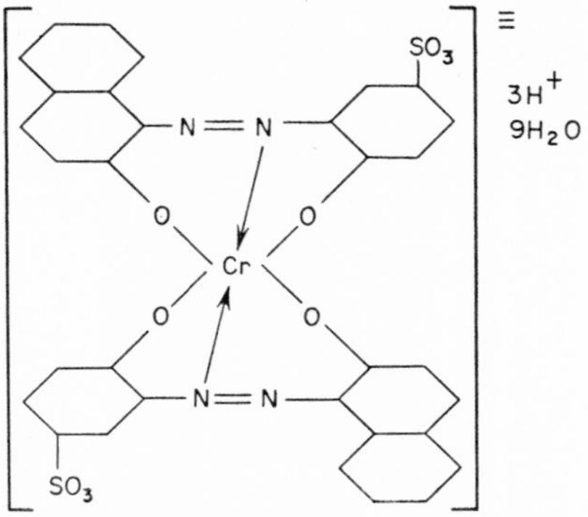

Formation of acids of this type (in which a negative charge is associated with the Cr) with two molecules of dye seems to be general whether or not sulfo groups are present. Chromium complexes of this type involving two unlike dye molecules can be made. They are soluble in alkaline solution.

About 1912 BASF began making chromium complexes of salicylic acid dyes. A few years later Ciba introduced chromium complexes of *o,o'*-dihydroxy azo dyes under the name of Neolan dyes. At about the same time

BASF made a similar line under the trade name Palatine Fast dyes. These dyes require a dye bath of low pH for successful dyeing. This appears to be due to the fact that the hydroxy groups are not available for hydrogen bonding with the wool fiber and the main attraction of the wool for the dye is by electrovalent bonds[32].

The chromium complex azo dyes for wool include the whole range of colors. They are somewhat duller but faster to light than the acid dyes. Some important ones are listed below in their unchromed forms:

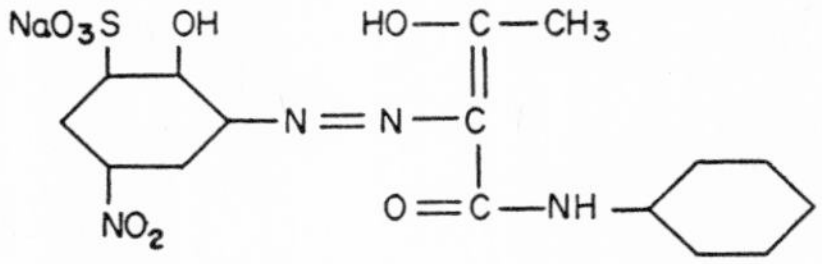

Neolan Yellow GR[21] (Pr. 316)

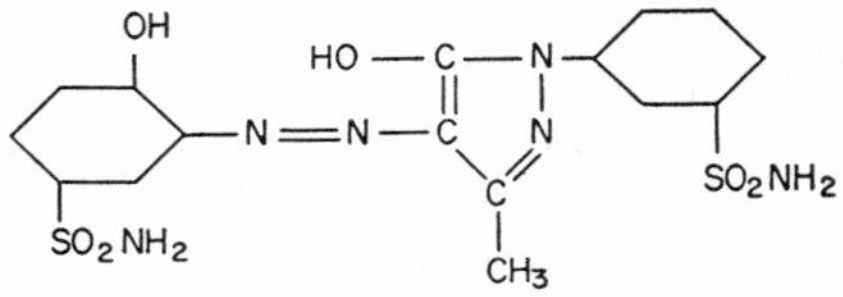

Neolan Orange R[23] (Pr. 146)

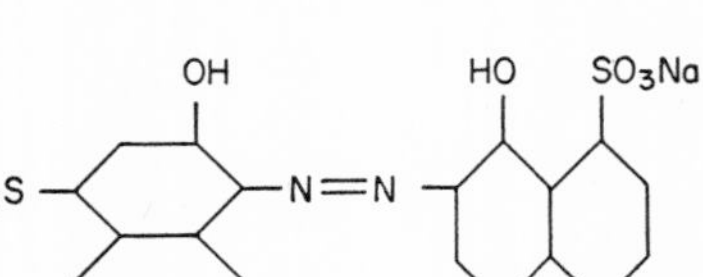

Neolan Bordeaux R[19] (Pr. 145)

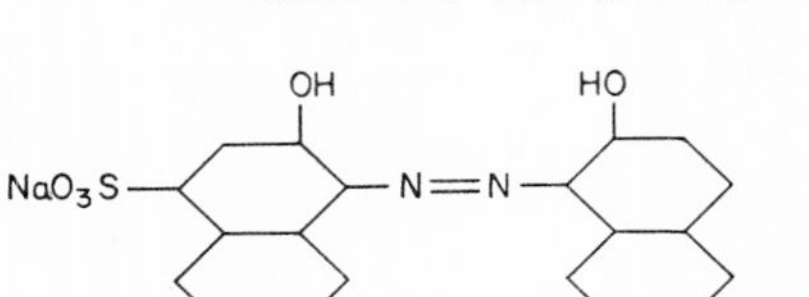

Neolan Blue 2G[18] (Pr. 144)

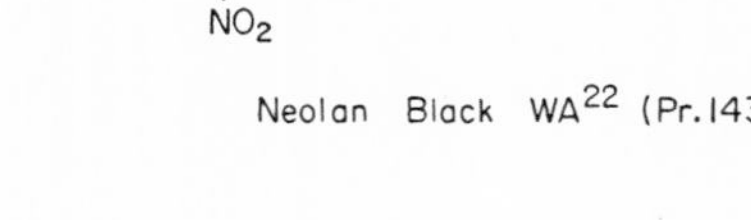

Neolan Black WA[22] (Pr. 143)

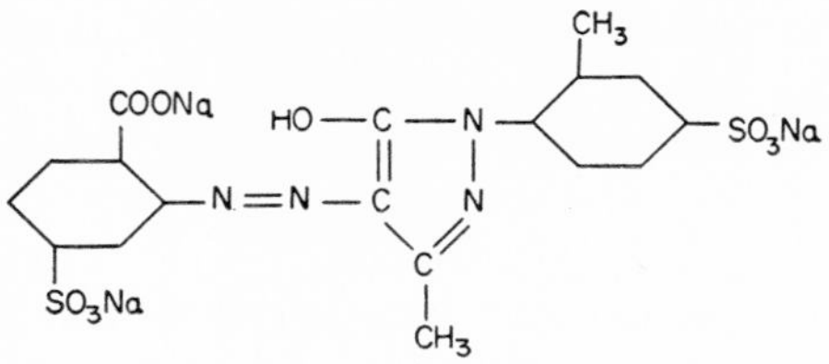

CH$_3$

COONa   HO—C—N

—N=N—C   N

C

SO$_3$Na

CH$_3$

SO$_3$Na

Neolan · Yellow BE[20] (Pr. 330)

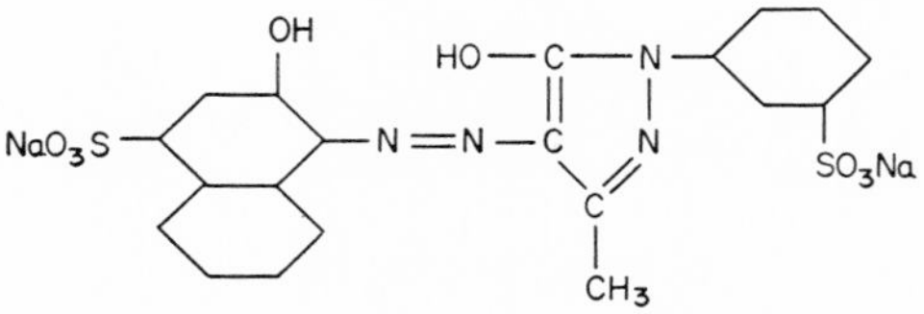

OH   HO—C—N

NaO$_3$S   —N=N—C   N

SO$_3$Na

C

CH$_3$

Palatine Fast Pink BN [16] (Pr. 326)

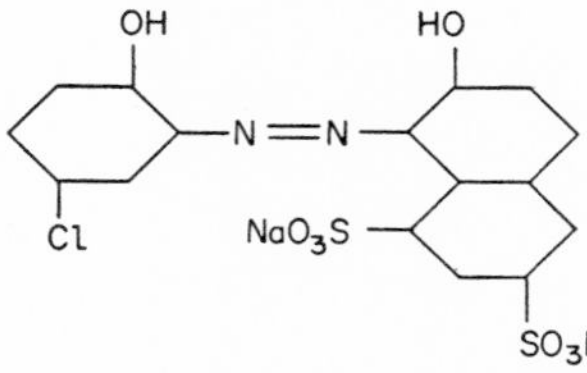

OH   HO

—N=N—

Cl   NaO$_3$S

SO$_3$Na

Palatine Fast Violet 5RN [17] (Pr. 329)

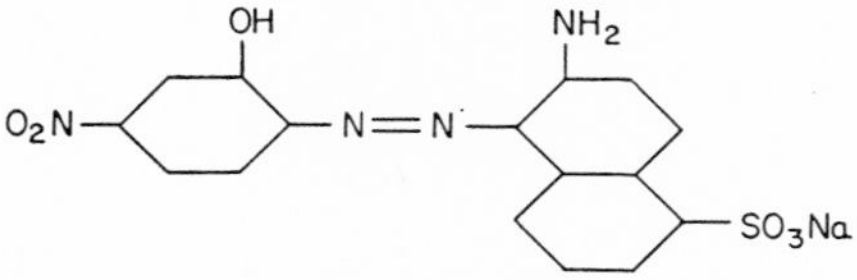

OH   NH$_2$

O$_2$N—   —N=N—

SO$_3$Na

Palatine Fast Green BL [15] (Pr. 321)

The ratio of chromium to dye in the above examples is 1 to 1 except for Neolan Orange R and Neolan Black WA, for which the references disclose a ratio of 2 atoms of chromium to 3 molecules of dye. This ratio probably represents a mixture of the 1 to 1 and 1 to 2 complexes.

ANNUAL U.S. PRODUCTION OF CERTAIN WOOL DYES—1946–50*

CI	Name of Dye	Production in 1,000 Pounds

I. Acid Dyes

CI	Name of Dye	Production in 1,000 Pounds
246	Naphthol Blue Black	1929
151	Orange II	1487
640	Tartrazine	704
31	Amido Naphthol Red G	690
234	Resorcin Brown	670
138	Metanil Yellow	507
639	Xylene Light Yellow	472
79	Ponceau R	445
57	Amido Naphthol Red 6B	380
27	Orange G	348
161	Orange R	345
235	Resorcin Dark Brown	256
176	Fast Red A	222
179	Azo Rubine	212
185	Cochineal Red A	160
88	Fast Red B	139
208	Sulfon Acid Blue R	130
Pr. 197	Victoria Fast Violet 2R	121
636	Fast Light Yellow G	110
53	Victoria Violet 4BS	107

II. Neutral Dyeing Dyes

CI	Name of Dye	Production in 1,000 Pounds
289	Sulfon Cyanine GR	473
430	Polar Red	310
307	Sulfon Cyanine Black B	208
487	Acid Anthracene Red 3B	111

III. Chrome Dyes

CI	Name of Dye	Production in 1,000 Pounds
202	Chrome Blue Black R	1337
203	Chrome Black T	968
Pr. 14	Anthracene Chromate Brown GB	281
98	Chrome Brown R	207
299	Diamond Black F	160
Pr. 4	Acid Anthracene Brown PG	160
652	Chrome Red B	156
204	Chrome Black A	153
36	Alizarin Yellow 2G	152
180	Diamond Blue 3B	136

IV. Prechromed Dyes

CI	Name of Dye	Production in 1,000 Pounds
Pr. 144	Neolan Blue GG	391
Pr. 330	Palatine Fast Yellow ELN	123

*U. S. Tariff Commission, Census of Dyes.

Literature Cited

1. Alexander and Charman, *Textile Research J.*, **20,** 11 (1950).
2. Baum, U. S. Patent 210,233 (1878).
3. Caro and Schraube, *Ber.*, **10,** 2230 (1877).
4. Drew and Fairbairn, *J. Chem. Soc.*, **1939,** 823.
5. Eistert, "Tautomerie und Mesomerie," Stuttgart, Enke, 1938.
6. Fierz-David and Blangey, "Fundamental Processes of Dye Chemistry," p. 266, New York, Interscience Publishers, Inc., 1949.
7. —— and ——, *ibid.*, p. 404.
8. Friedlaender, "Fortschritte der Teerfarbenfabrikation," Berlin, Julius Springer, **2,** 308 (1890).
9. German Patent 43,100 (1888).
10. Guenther, Hesse, Zart and Schweitzer, U. S. Patent 982,954 (1911).
11. Hagenbach, U. S. Patent 790,363 (1905).
12. I. G. Farbenindustrie, PB 74025, frame 1230.
13. ——, PB 74711, frame 8597.
14. ——, PB 74713, frame 5071.
15. ——, PB 74753, frame 2578.
16. ——, *ibid.*, frame 2615.
17. ——, *ibid.*, frame 2711.
18. ——, PB 74760, frame 9490.
19. ——, *ibid.*, frame 9509.
20. ——, *ibid.*, frame 9536.
21. ——, *ibid.*, frame 9540.
22. ——, *ibid.*, frame 9600.
23. ——, *ibid.*, frame 9614.
24. ——, PB 74762, frame 5528.
25. ——, *ibid.*, frame 5533.
26. ——, PB 74771, frame 7820.
27. ——, PB 82175, frame 5716.
28. ——, *ibid.*, frame 5844.
29. Julius, Reindel and Guenther, U. S. Patent 770,177 (1904).
30. Knorr, *Ber.*, **16,** 2597 (1883).
31. Kostanecki, *ibid.*, **20,** 3146 (1887).
32. Luttringhaus, *Am. Dyestuff Reptr.*, **39,** 152 (1950).
33. Mollenhoff, *Ber.*, **25,** 1945 (1892).
34. Morgan and Main Smith, *J. Chem. Soc.*, **121,** 2866 (1922).
35. —— and ——, *ibid.*, **125,** 1731 (1924).
36. Nietzke, *Farben-Ztg.*, **1,** 8 (1889).
37. Race, Rowe and Speakman, *J. Soc. Dyers Colourists*, **62,** 372 (1946).
38. Rosenhauer, Wirth and Koeniger, *Ber.*, **62,** 2717 (1929).
39. Sandmeyer, U. S. Patent 793,743 (1904).
40. Schetty, *Textil-Rundschau*, **5,** 399 (1950).
41. ——, *Helv. Chim. Acta*, **35,** 716 (1952).
42. Valko, *J. Soc. Dyers Colourists*, **55,** 173 (1939).
43. Widmer, *Chimia (Switz.)*, **5,** 77 (1951).

DISPERSE AZO DYES

J. F. Laucius

Definition

Disperse dyes are organic colors which are applied from near-colloidal aqueous dispersions to textile fibers in which the dyes literally dissolve[1, 54, 55] to produce the desired coloration.

The U. S. Tariff Commission refers to these products as acetate rayon dyes. Since the man-made fibers on which these colors are useful now include polyamides and polyesters as well as cellulose acetate, the general term disperse dyes has been adopted in American and British usage. It is planned to use the newer term in the second (1955) edition of the Colour Index, and in future editions of the Technical Manual and Year Book of the American Association of Textile Chemists and Colorists.

This discussion will deal with the azo dyes of the disperse application class.

Importance

Disperse dyes include colors of the azo, azomethine, nitroarene, and anthraquinone[3] chemical classes. The total sales of colors of this type in the United States in 1950 amounted to 8.5 million pounds (4.5 per cent of total dye sales) valued at 12.3 million dollars (6.4 per cent of total).

Disperse dyes account for almost all the dyeing of cellulose acetate and polyethylene terephthalate textile fibers. They are also used in dyeing nylon, where their uniform coloration of the fiber is of value (despite their moderate wash fastness) in masking the unevenness or barré effect often caused by more durable selected acid colors, which tend to accentuate the chemical differences in nylon continuous filament. Disperse dyes find some use in the surface coloration of plastics.

History

When cellulose acetate was introduced to the textile trade in the early 1920's, few of the available colors would dye the new fiber. Acid and direct colors do not normally dye cellulose acetate, while vat colors applied with strong alkali tender the fiber by saponification. New dyes were necessary, and the disperse color development dates from the discovery that certain azo and nitro compounds of low water-solubility will color the fiber[4, 5, 7, 12, 13, 14]. Some of the insoluble dyes for cellulose acetate were called SRA colors because they were dispersed with sulfo ricinoleic acid.

An early British shade range consisted of dyes called Ionamines[23, 25], which were temporarily solubilized by the *N*-sulfomethyl group. They were made as follows:

$$aryl—NH_2 + HCHO + NaHSO_3 \rightarrow aryl—NH—CH_2SO_3H$$

The arylaminomethanesulfonic acid was coupled with a diazonium compound to give a dye which would hydrolyze in the dyebath to the insoluble amino compound, which would then dye the cellulose acetate.

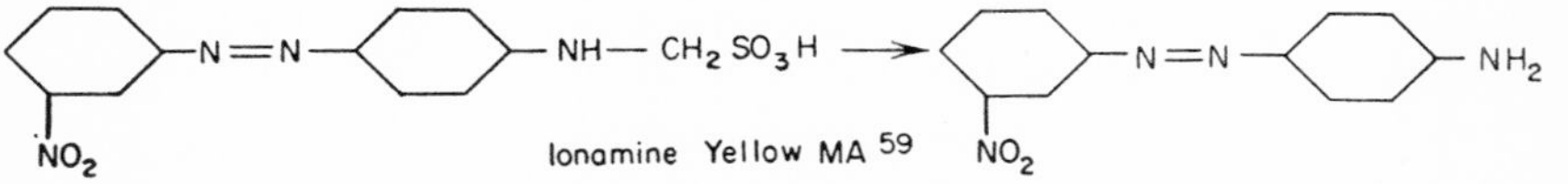

Ionamine Yellow MA [59]

Not only did the Ionamine dyes hydrolyze at different rates but their shade in solution was different from that in the fiber. Consequently, in dyeing with mixtures of colors, matching of shades was a tedious process.

The disperse dyes themselves were finally adopted commercially, and the finely divided colors showing little water solubility have become the most popular type for coloring the man-made fibers in which a solution dyeing mechanism is a major factor.

The insoluble colors must be finely divided, as they dye cellulose acetate by a mechanism involving a very dilute solution in water as an intermediate step, followed by solution in the fiber[1, 11, 52].

Chemistry

Monoazo Dyes. The most popular disperse yellow is Celliton Fast Yellow G (IG)[18, 30, 38], Pr. 242, produced by coupling diazotized p-aminoacetanilide to p-cresol:

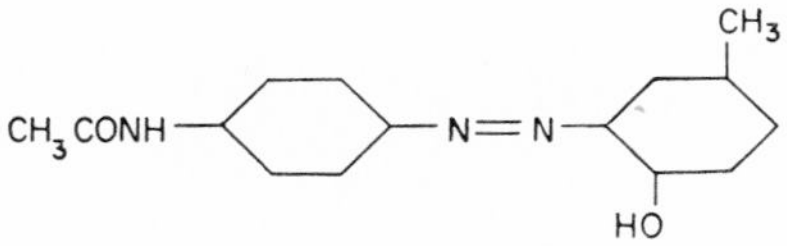

A greener shade yellow, less fast to light, is Celliton Yellow 5G[28, 29, 39], Pr. 245, derived from m-nitroaniline and 4-hydroxy-1-methylcarbostyril

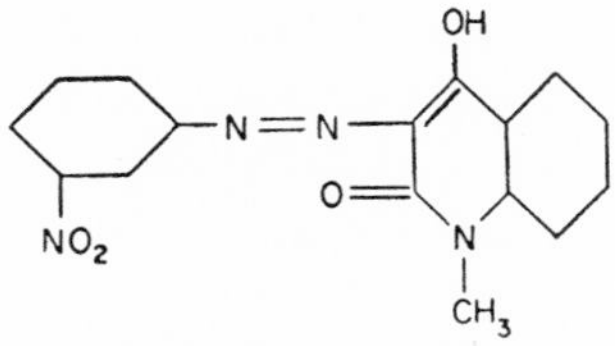

Its fastness to sublimation (ability to resist unwanted transfer from a colored area to other areas or articles when heated, as in ironing) is much superior to that of the methine dye Celliton Fast Yellow 7G (see Miscellaneous Dyes, p. 249).

Another green shade yellow[49], made from 5,5-dimethyl-1,3-cyclohexane-dione, is relatively fast to light, presumably due to hydrogen bonding in the *o*-nitrohydrazone structure (II):

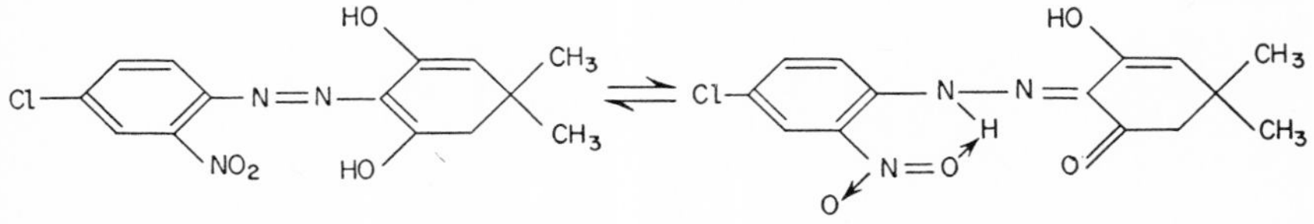

(I)   (II)

Disperse dyes containing the 2-nitrodiphenylamine structure, such as Fast Yellow GLF[17, 48, 51], have a similar make-up. Lightfastness in this case is excellent.

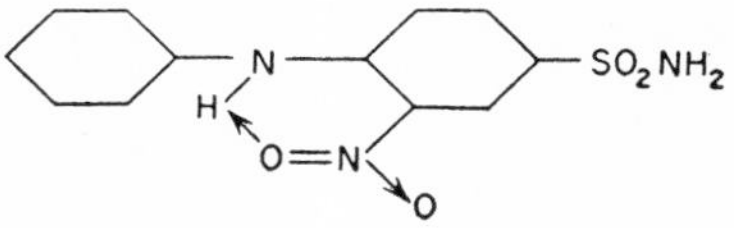

Fost Yellow GLF

The orange most widely used is Celliton Orange GR[31, 53], Pr. 43,

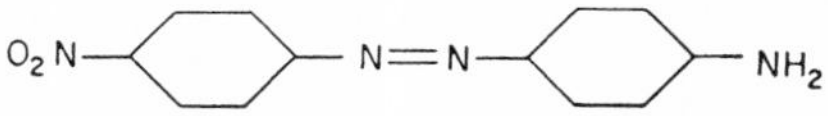

which is made by coupling *p*-nitrobenzenediazonium ion to anilinomethane-sulfonic acid, followed by hydrolysis to remove the sulfomethyl group[21]. This color is a fast-to-light orange on cellulose acetate, and a dull red of only fair lightfastness on nylon.

Celliton Discharge Pink BRF[41] has the structure

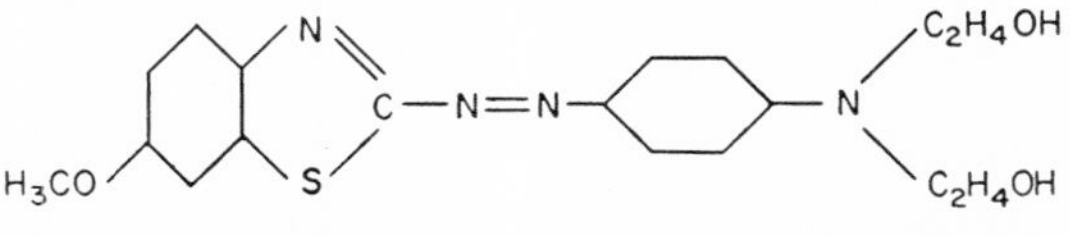

It dyes nylon and acetate much more nearly the same shade than does Celliton Scarlet B[32, 56], Pr. 244, which has the structure:

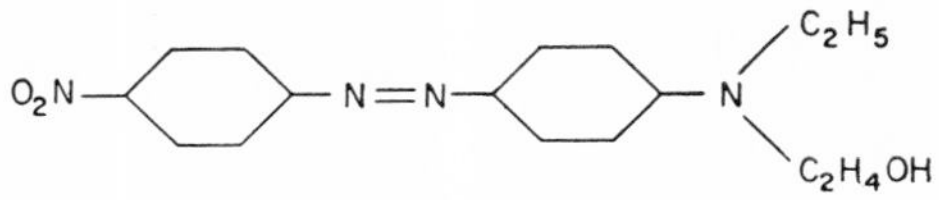

Both the shade and lightfastness differences shown on acetate vs. nylon by dyes like Cellitons Orange GR and Scarlet B are probably related to the effect of the *p*-nitro group on the strength of the forces which attract the dye molecule to active sites in the fiber, especially in nylon. Such dyes show corresponding color differences in different solvents, as in carbon tetrachloride (like acetate) compared with methanol (like nylon).

Use of the 2-hydroxyethyl group leads to better dispersibility[23].

Celliton Fast Red 2G[33], Pr. 236, has the structure

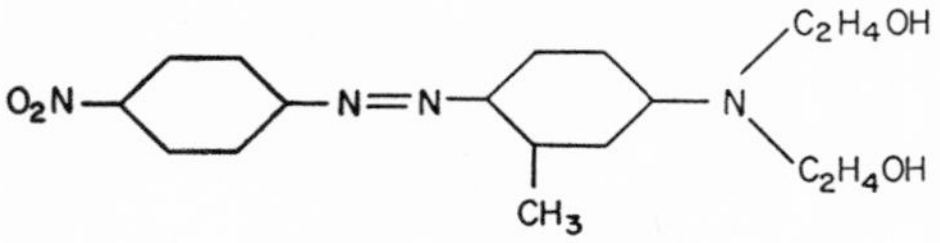

It is more easily dispersed than Celliton Scarlet B.

Dispersol Fast Red R[47] is

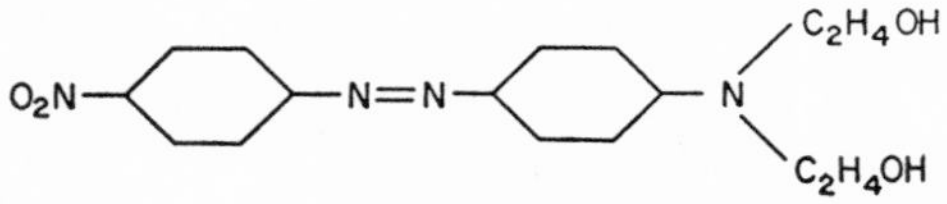

Introduction of an *o*-chlorine atom in the diazo component in Celliton Scarlet B gives Celliton Fast Rubine B[34, 57]. The bathochromic effect of the *o*-chlorine atom is characteristic and significant.

Celliton Violet R has the structure[42]

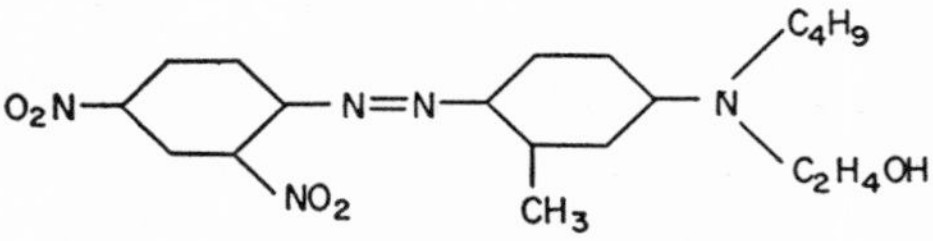

In the synthesis of this color, the dinitroaniline is diazotized in concentrated sulfuric acid in contrast to the aqueous diazotization of the amines used to make the dyes cited earlier.

Celliton Discharge Blue 5G shows poor fastness to light but good fastness to nitric oxide fumes in the atmosphere. This dye has the structure[27, 35, 40]

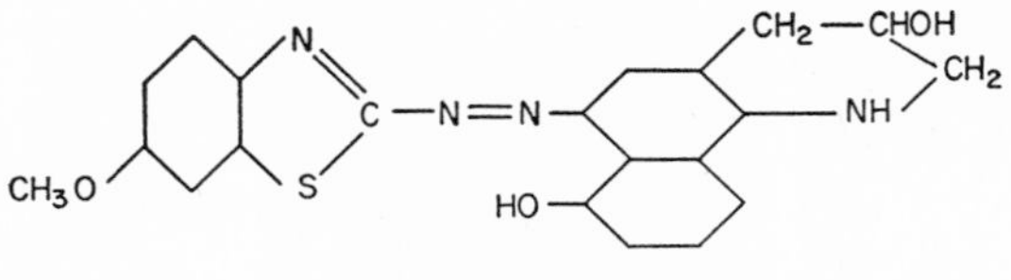

The following disperse blue[9, 50] has poor lightfastness but excellent gas fume fastness.

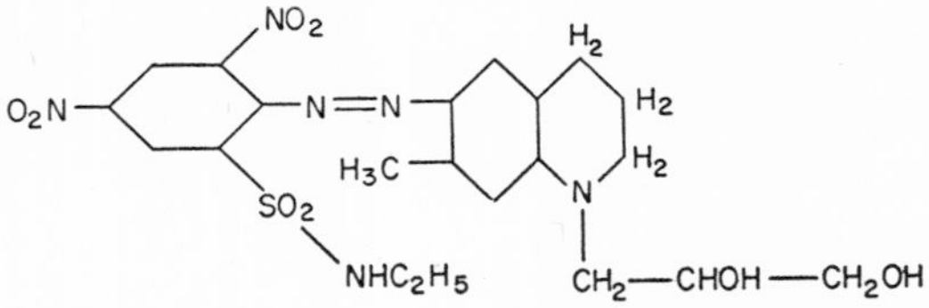

Celliton Fast Brown 3R, actually a dull orange, has the structure[36, 58]

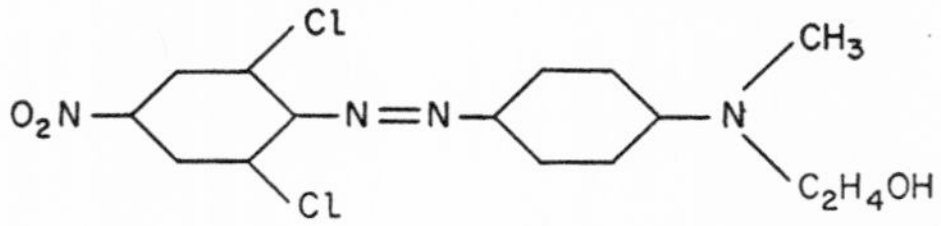

As in the case of Celliton Violet R, the 2,6-dichloro-4-nitroaniline is diazotized in concentrated sulfuric acid.

The lightfastness of the disperse monoazo yellows and oranges ranges from good to excellent, while with increasing depth of shade from red to violet to blue, it decreases markedly. The washing fastness is fair, and cellulose acetate fabrics colored with these dyes can be laundered only under very mild conditions. Such dyeings are, however, fast to dry cleaning. Generally the monoazo disperse dyes are dischargeable (i.e., can be reduced on the fabric to a pair of colorless primary amines, in order to produce a design or pattern) by means of formaldehyde sulfoxylates. Their sublimation fastness is dependent on the vapor pressure of the dye. For example, Celliton Scarlet B is faster to sublimation than Celliton Orange GR.

Disazo Dyes. A number of disazo colors are useful disperse dyes. The following structures illustrate two commercial products.

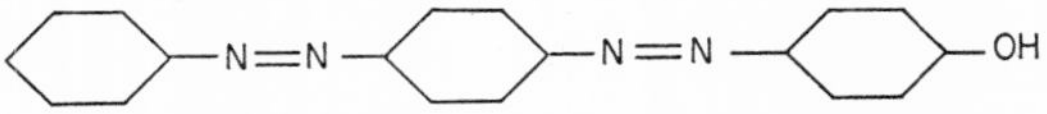

SRA Golden Yellow XIII [8, 10, 15, 44]

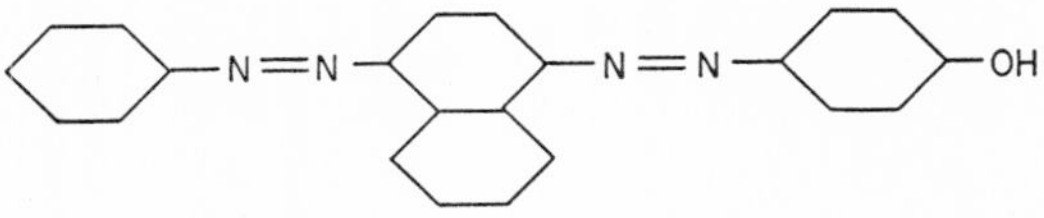

SRA Golden Orange I [13, 43]

Diluents for the disperse dyes include sugar, dextrin and inorganic salts, in addition to the necessary dispersing agents, examples of which are Dispersing Agent SS[37, 46] (prepared from cresol by condensation with formaldehyde and then with 2-naphthol-6-sulfonic acid) and salts of ligninsulfonic acids.

Soluble Dyes. The disperse dyes have been supplemented to a small extent in Europe by soluble colors of the type

$$R_1\!-\!N\!-\!C_2H_4OSO_3Na^{6,\ 24,\ 26}$$
$$\overset{\displaystyle R_2}{|}$$

A typical soluble color is Solacet Fast Scarlet BS[45]

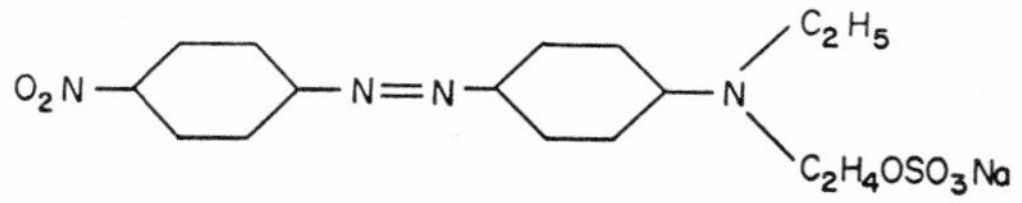

These products are applied to fibers such as cellulose acetate with salts like sodium chloride, in much the same manner that direct dyes are applied to cellulose fibers. The lightfastness of the soluble colors is comparable to that of disperse colors of similar constitution, and they are superior to disperse dyes in penetration and washfastness. They presumably dye by a direct color mechanism, involving hydrogen bonding to the —OH group of the cellulose acetate.

The use of soluble dyes is limited by their higher price and their less uniform dyeing rate in mixtures, compared with disperse dyes.

Developed Dyes. In the production of deep shades, such as navy blues and blacks, a diazotizable aromatic amine which in itself may be an azo color is applied to the acetate fiber, followed by diazotization with nitrous acid and development of the final shade by coupling with 3-hydroxy-2-naphthoic acid. The amine and the coupling component can be applied to the fiber together, followed by concurrent diazotization and coupling.

Cellitazol B[16] is *o*-dianisidine (3,3'-dimethoxybenzidine). The final disazo dye on the fiber is a navy blue. Cellitazol ST[19, 20, 22] is made by diazotizing *p*-nitroaniline, coupling to 1-naphthylamine, and reducing to yield the following structure.

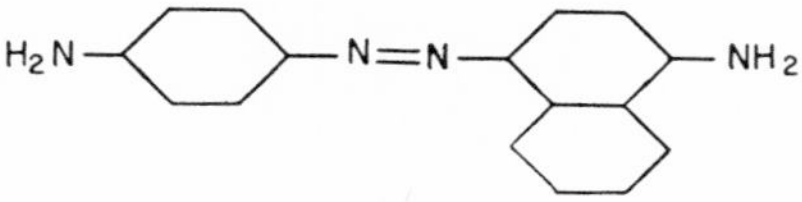

In this case the final trisazo color is a black. The product of the following structure[23],

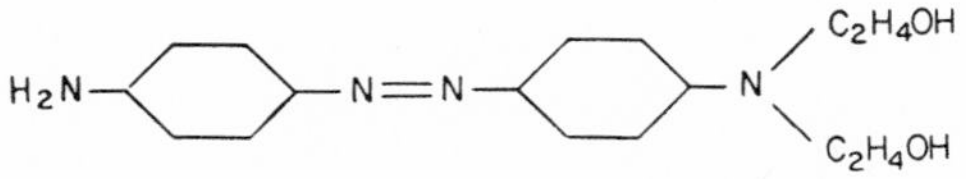

used as a developed dye, leads to a greener shade disazo black and has better dispersibility than Cellitazol ST. Other shades of good fastness properties are obtainable by application of selected base and coupling component combinations from the azoic dyes (see Chapter 4). Celliton Orange GR developed on acetate fiber with 3-hydroxy-2-naphthoic acid gives a wine color.

Literature Cited

1. Bird, Manchester, and Harris, *Discussions Faraday Soc.*, No. 16, p. 85 (1954).
2. Bommer *et al.*, U. S. Patent 1,828,592 (1931).
3. British Patent 211,720 (1924).
4. British Patent 222,001 (1924).
5. British Patent 224,925 (1924).
6. British Patent 237,739 (1925).
7. British Patent 273,819 (1927).
8. British Patent 398,842 (1932).
9. British Patent 548,903 (1942).
10. Caro and Schraube, *Ber.*, **10**, 2230 (1877).
11. Clavel, *Rev. gén. mat. color.*, **28**, 158 (1924).
12. ——, U. S. Patent 1,448,432 (1923).
13. Ellis, U. S Patent 1,618,413 (1927).
14. ——, U. S. Patent 1,840,572 (1932).
15. ——, U. S. Patent 2,072,252 (1937).
16. —— and Goldthorpe, U. S. Patent 1,630,481 (1928).
17. Fischer, *Ber.*, **24**, 3794 (1891).
18. —— and Mueller, U. S. Patent 1,706,484 (1929).
19. Fischesser and Pokorny, *Bull. soc. ind. Mulhouse*, **61**, 625 (1891).
20. French Patent 212,063 (1891).
21. German Patent 131,860 (1902).
22. German Patent 198,008 (1907).
23. Green and Saunders, *J. Soc. Dyers Colourists*, **39**, 10 (1923).
24. —— and ——, *ibid.*, **39**, 39 (1923).
25. —— and ——, *ibid.*, **40**, 138 (1924).
26. —— and ——, U. S. Patent 1,483,084 (1924).
27. Helberger and Taube, U. S. Patent 2,149,051 (1939).
28. Holzach and von Rosenberg, U. S. Patent 1,969,463 (1934).
29. I. G. Farbenindustrie, BIOS 1548, p. 197 (PB 85593).
30. ——, *ibid.*, p. 198.
31. ——, *ibid.*, p. 199.
32. ——, *ibid.*, p. 200.
33. ——, *ibid.*, p. 201.
34. ——, *ibid.*, p. 202.
35. ——, *ibid.*, p. 203.
36. ——, *ibid.*, p. 204.
37. ——, FIAT 1013 (PB 57500).
38. ——, PB 25625, frames 108–9.
39. ——, *ibid.*, frame 111.
40. ——, PB 73561, frame 614.
41. ——, PB 74706, frame 1212.
42. ——, *ibid.*, frame 1447.
43. ——, PB 74719, frame 5179.
44. ——, *ibid.*, frame 5186.
45. ——, PB 74722, frame 2202.

46. Kesseler and Eifflaender, U. S. Patent 1,892,280 (1932).
47. Knight, *J. Soc. Dyers Colourists*, **66**, 170 (1950).
48. Kopp and Gangueux, U. S. Patent 2,506,224 (1950).
49. McNally and Dickey, U. S. Patent 2,183,997 (1939).
50. —— and ——, U. S. Patent 2,261,176 (1941).
51. —— and ——, U. S. Patent 2,422,029 (1947).
52. Millson and Turl, *Textile Research J.*, **21**, 685 (1951).
53. Noelting and Binder, *Ber.*, **20**, 3015 (1887).
54. Remington, *Am. Dyestuff Reptr.*, **41**, 859 (1952).
55. Schuler and Remington, *Discussions Faraday Soc.*, No. 16, p. 201 (1954).
56. Swiss Patent 149,405 (1931).
57. Swiss Patent 151,868 (1932).
58. Swiss Patent 151,869 (1932).
59. Thorpe and Whiteley, eds., "Dictionary of Applied Chemistry," 4th ed., London, Longmans, Green & Co., **1**, 40, (1937).

SOLVENT-SOLUBLE DYES

H. E. Woodward

While most dyes are used for dyeing textiles and other fibrous materials by absorption from a water solution, some dyes are used for dyeing and staining materials from solvents other than water, and some are used for coloring material by simple solution of the dye in the material. Dyes for such purposes may be divided into three classes—oil-soluble, spirit-soluble and water-soluble. Materials colored by these dyes include oils, fats, waxes, lacquers, spirit inks, leather, wood, plastics and food.

Oil-soluble Dyes

These dyes are used for coloring motor fuel, waxes, food and plastics. The largest use of dyes dissolved in nonpolar solvents is in coloring motor fuel. Originally synthetic dyes were added to gasoline to neutralize or to mask objectionable color, or to save the cost of the refining necessary to obtain a colorless distillate, as well as to identify the product. Only small amounts of dye were needed to neutralize the yellow or brown tint of petroleum distillates. For actually coloring the product, the amount used is from 20 to 50 milligrams per liter (7 to 17 pounds per 1000 barrels). A considerable amount of motor fuel is colored to convey information. By U. S. Government order, any gasoline which contains tetraethyllead to increase the antiknock value must be colored for safety reasons. Different colors are used to identify aviation gasolines of different antiknock values (octane numbers).

Other uses of oil-soluble dyes are for decorative effects as in plastic articles, wax candles and shoe polish. A certain amount is used for coloring food products. The most important uses of this type are the coloration of butter, to make winter butter appear of the same quality as summer butter, and the coloring of oleomargarine.

Oil-soluble dyes are insoluble in water but are more or less soluble in organic solvents, including alcohol. Most of them are simple aromatic compounds with few amino, hydroxy or azo groups. Alkyl groups improve their oil-solubility.

Azo dyes have long been used for coloring oils, fats and waxes. *p*-Phenylazoaniline, discovered in 1859 by Peter Griess and manufactured as Aniline Yellow in 1863 by the British firm of Simpson, Manle and Nicholson by a process patented by Méne, was the first commercial azo dye. It and its homolog, aminoazotoluene (4-*o*-tolylazo-*o*-toluidine), first made in 1877 by Nietzke, were used for coloring a variety of substances including butter, margarine and cheese. They are still manufactured as oil-soluble dyes and for other purposes. Important oil-soluble azo dyes are *N*,*N*-dimethyl-*p*-phenylazoaniline or Oil Yellow, discovered by Witt in 1876, Sudan I or Oil Orange, discovered by Liebermann in 1883 and Sudan IV or Oil Red, first described in 1887 by Zincke and Lawson.

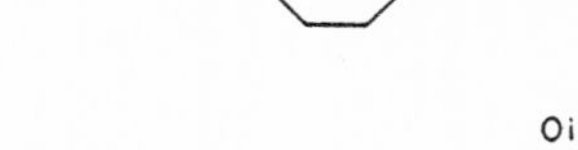

Oil Yellow, CI 19 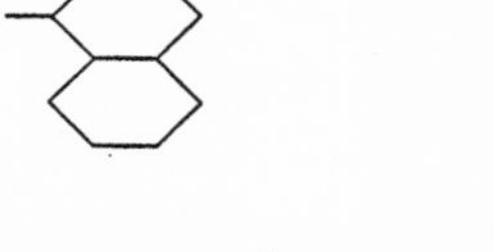   Oil Orange, CI 24

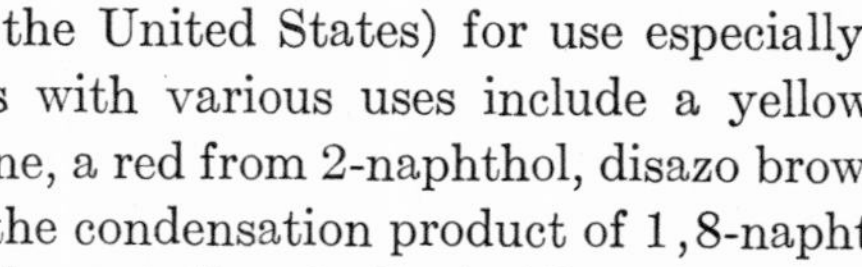

Oil Red, CI 258

The above azo dyes are produced in large amounts (nearly a million pounds a year in the United States) for use especially in gasoline. Other types of azo dyes with various uses include a yellow from 3-methyl-1-phenyl-5-pyrazolone, a red from 2-naphthol, disazo browns from 1-naphthol and a black from the condensation product of 1,8-naphthalenediamine and acetone (2,3-dihydro-2,2-dimethylperimidine). This black is used mainly for shoe polish and for the coloration of plastics.

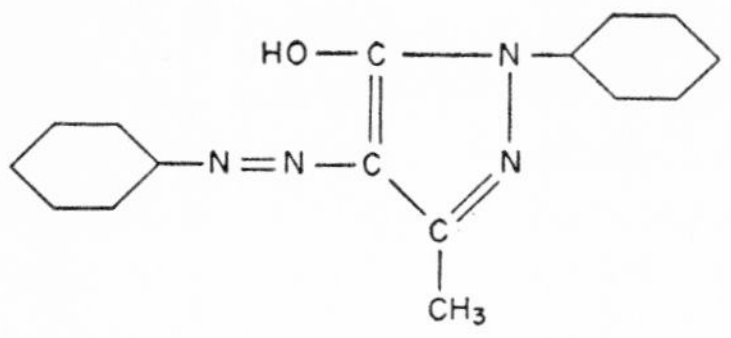

Sudan Yellow 3G[11]

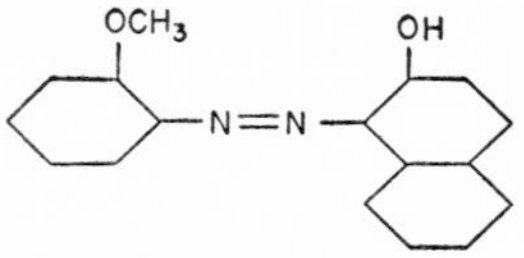

Sudan Red G, CI 113

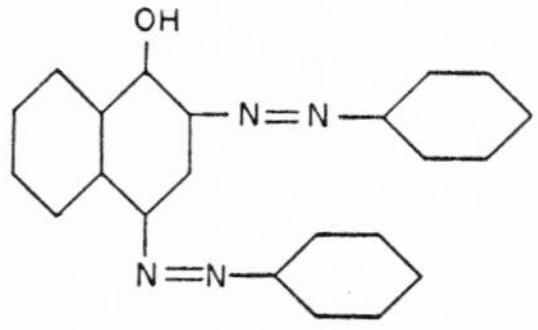

Sudan Brown 5B[10]

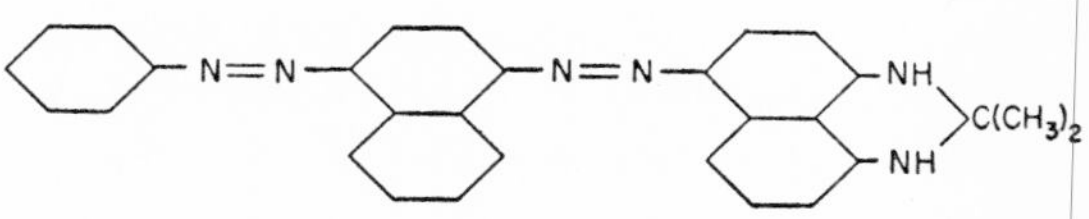

Sudan Black B[14]

A monoazo dye permitted by federal regulations for use in butter is FD&C Yellow No. 3 or Yellow AB

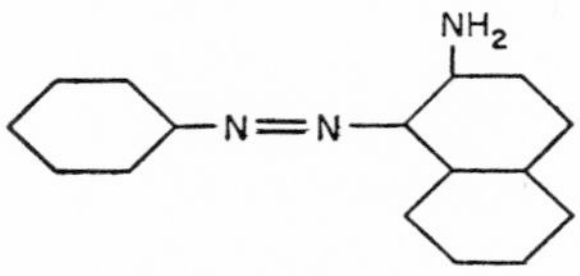

Yellow AB, CI 22

There are some disazo dyes of very good oil-solubility made from 4,4'-methylenedianiline or its homologs.

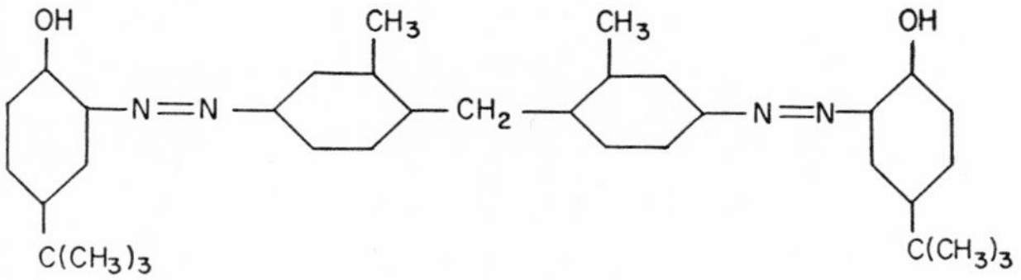

Sudan Yellow 3GN[12]

Anthraquinone dyes are used for coloring gasoline, oils and waxes in the blue range. They are more expensive than azo dyes, but the latter do not equal them in fastness properties. Examples of those in use are:

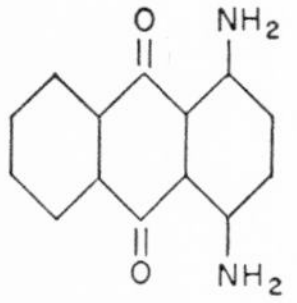

Sudan Violet R[15]

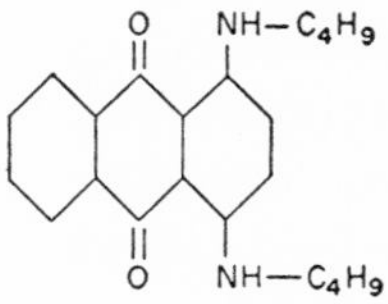

Sudan Blue GL[9]

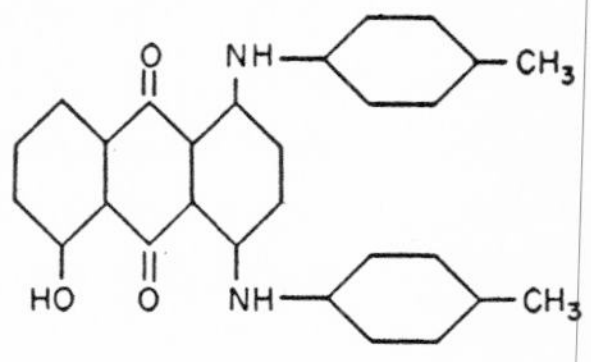

Sudan Green BB[13]

The most important black solvent-soluble dye is Nigrosine, CI 864, used especially in shoe polish. This color is produced in amounts of about 3 million pounds a year in the United States for use both as an oil-soluble and a spirit-soluble dye. It is a complex product which can be made by condensing crude nitrophenol, aniline and aniline hydrochloride at 180–200° C in the presence of iron.

Spirit-soluble Dyes

Dyes soluble in alcohols, ketones, esters and ethers are used for spirit printing inks, for ball point pen inks, for staining wood and leather, for the coloring of lacquers for aluminum foil, and for coloring some plastics. Four general classes of dyes are soluble in these solvents and are used commercially for the above purposes.

Salts of Organic Bases with Dyes Having Acid Groups. The dyes of this class are water-soluble as sodium salts and are usually selected from commercial cotton and wool dyes. The organic bases include among others diarylguanidine[19] (Du Pont Luxol dyes), mono- and dicyclohexylamine[17] (I.G. Zapon and Azosol colors), and diisoamylamine[18] (Calco Spirit dyes). For example, Zapon Fast Scarlet CG[6] is the dicyclohexylamine salt of Crocein Scarlet 3B, CI 252.

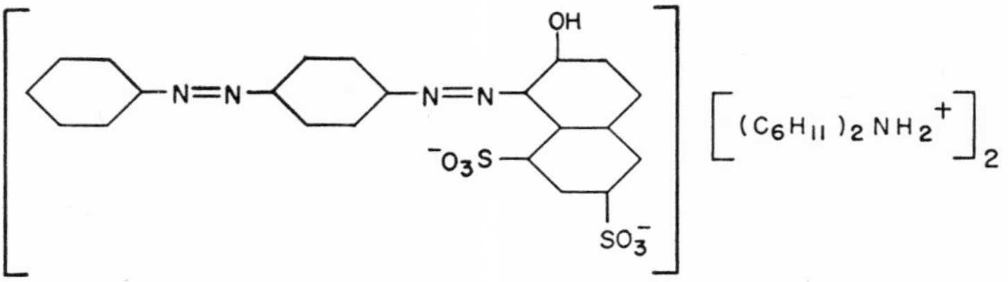

Zapon Fast Scarlet CG

Calco Fast Spirit Black R[1] is reported to be the diisoamylamine salt of a chromium complex compound

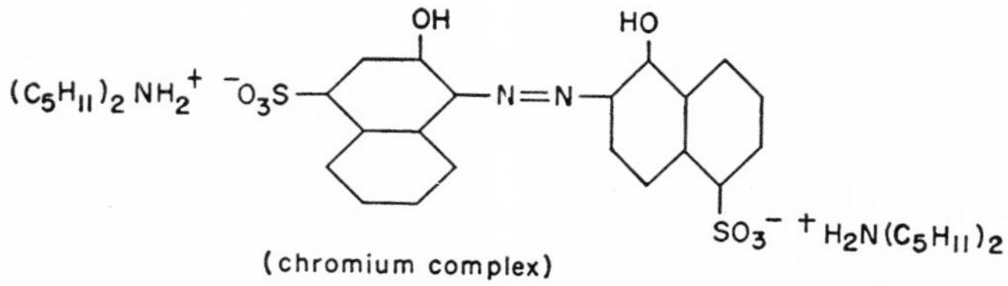

(chromium complex)
Calco Fast Spirit Black R

Metal Complex Compounds of Azo Dyes. Many metal complexes of o,o'-dihydroxy monoazo dyes, especially those devoid of sulfo groups, are more or less soluble in alcohol and similar solvents. Many of these dyes have very good lightfastness in nitrocellulose lacquers. The Ciba Co. and the I.G. Farbenindustrie were the principal manufacturers of this class of spirit-soluble colors. Some I.G. Zapon types are the free sulfonic acid forms of wool dyes and others contain no sulfo or carboxy groups. For a discussion of the structure of metal complexes of azo dyes, see Azo Dyes for Wool. Typical Zapon dyes are the following:

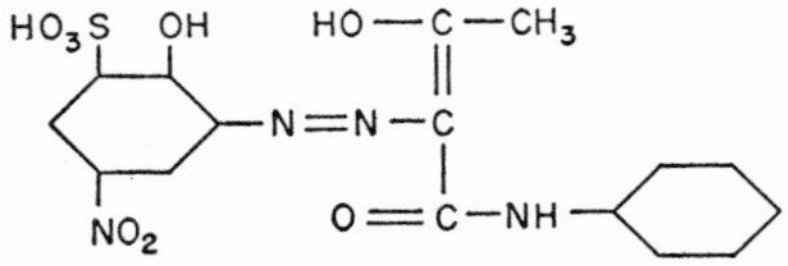

(chromium complex)
Zapon Fast Yellow GR[3]

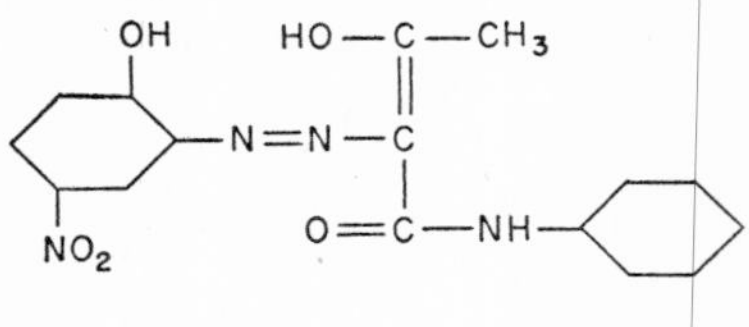

(cobalt complex)
Zapon Fast Orange GE[4]

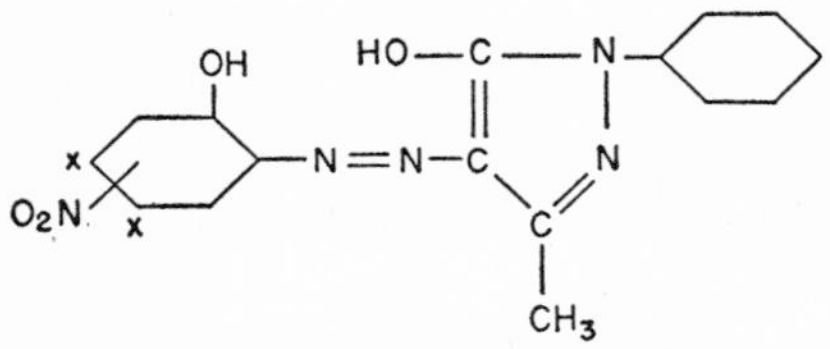

(chromium complex)
Zapon Fast Red RE[5]

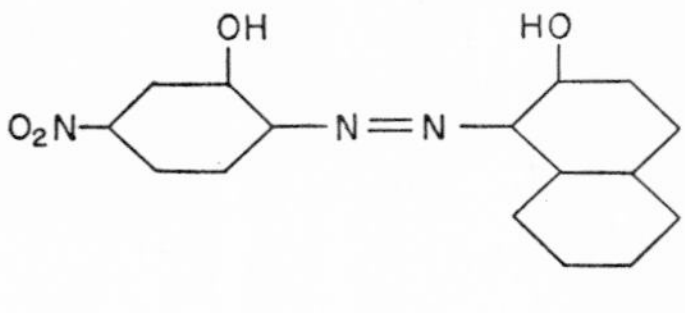

(cobalt complex)
Zapon Fast Violet BE[7]

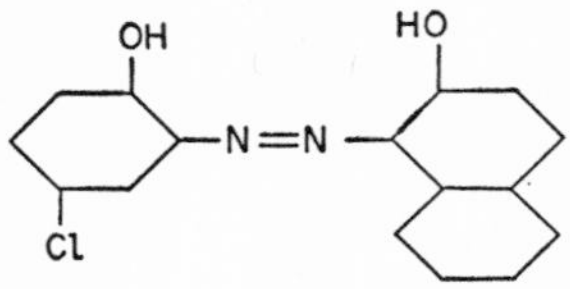

(Iron complex)
Zapon Black[8]

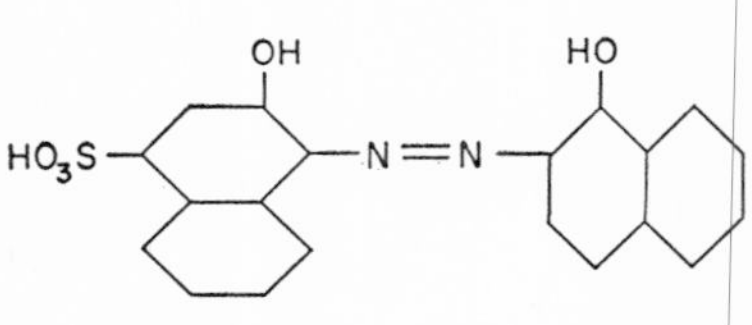

(chromium complex)
Zapon Fast Blue G[2]

Basic Dyes. Where lightfastness is not important, some basic dyes are used, for example, the triphenylmethane dye Spirit Blue, CI 689, and the xanthene dye Methyl Eosine, CI 769. More important are the azines, Spirit Induline, CI 860, and Nigrosine, CI 864. Basic dyes of the above types are discussed in Chapter 5 on Miscellaneous Dyes.

Oil-soluble Dyes. Many of the oil-soluble colors are used as spirit-soluble dyes where good spirit-solubility or lightfastness is not required.

Food Dyes

Food may be colored artificially if this fact is stated on the label and if the added color does not conceal inferiority or does not make the article appear of better quality or value than it is.* For most food coloring, water-soluble dyes are used, but such foods as butter, of course, require oil-soluble dyes. If foods are colored with coal tar dyes, the dye must be from a certi-fied batch of a permitted food dye. These batches are certified on the basis of complete analysis showing the amount of pure dye and of specified impurities present[16].

Eighteen different synthetic dyes (four being oil-soluble) are permitted in foods in the United States[20] and several more are permitted in drugs and cosmetics. The total production in the United States in 1948 was nearly a million pounds. The most used dyes are the following:

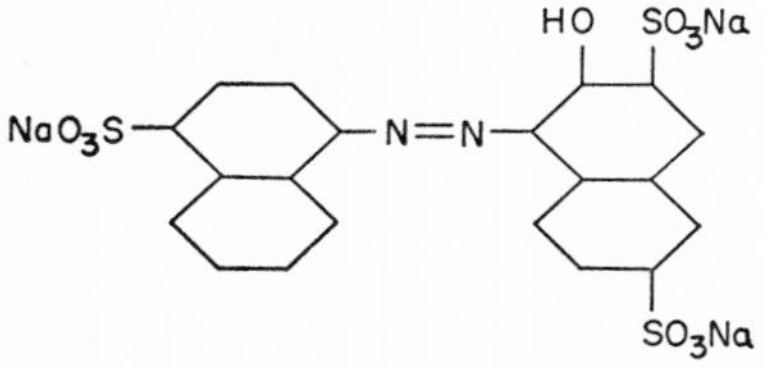

FD & C Red No.2
Amaranth, CI 184

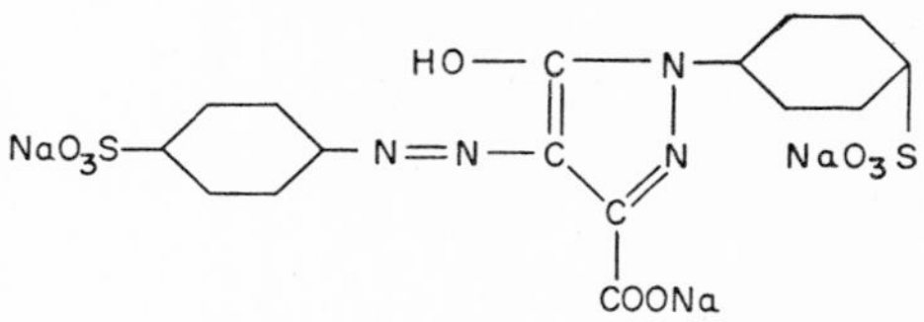

FD & C Yellow No.5
Tartrazine, CI 640

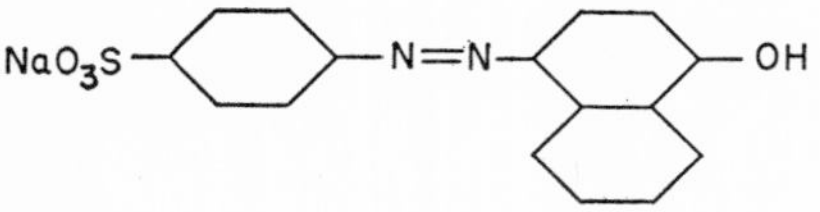

FD & C Orange No.1
Orange I, CI 150

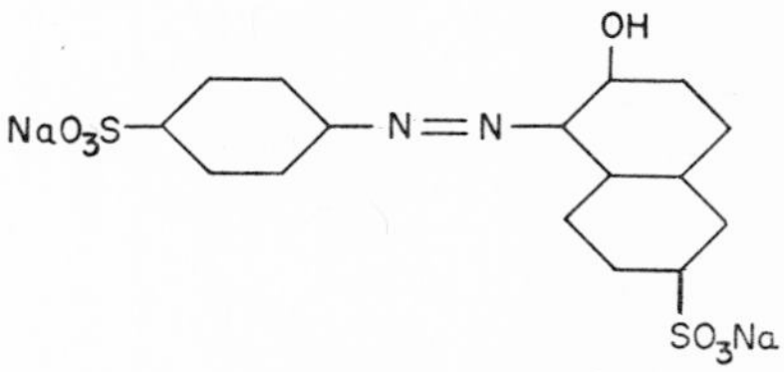

FD & C Yellow No.6

Literature Cited

1. I. G. Farbenindustrie, PB 74706, frame 381.
2. ——, PB 74725, frame 294.
3. ——, *ibid.*, frame 331.
4. ——, *ibid.*, frame 356.
5. ——, *ibid.*, frame 389.
6. ——, *ibid.*, frame 396.
7. ——, *ibid.*, frame 426.
8. ——, *ibid.*, frame 455.
9. ——, PB 74773, frame 3535.
10. ——, *ibid.*, frame 3559.
11. ——, *ibid.*, frame 3619.
12. ——, *ibid.*, frame 3621.
13. ——, *ibid.*, frame 3636.

* Some dairy products are exempt from this provision of the Food, Drug and Cosmetic Act.

14. ——, *ibid.*, frame 3691.
15. ——, *ibid.*, frame 3706.
16. Inskeep and Kretlow, *Ind. Eng. Chem.*, **44,** 12 (1952).
17. Kraenzlein, Hartman and Hardt, U. S. Patent 1,800,300 (1931).
18. Payne, U. S. Patent 2,095,077 (1937).
19. Rose, U. S. Patent 1,674,128 (1928).
20. U. S. Dept. Agric., Food and Drug Adm., Service and Regulatory Announcements, FD&C No. 3, "Coal-tar Color Regulations," 1940.

4. AZOIC DYES

C. W. Maynard, Jr.

Definition

Azoic dyes are insoluble azo colors which are formed on cellulosic fiber from selected diazo and coupling components.

Importance

The U. S. Tariff Commission reports that, of the total 1951 United States production of synthetic dyes of 186 million pounds, azo colors (including azoic dyes) comprised 36 per cent and azoic dyes and their components comprised 3.8 per cent. In economic terms, of the total 1951 United States sales of synthetic dyes of $174 million, azo colors (including azoic dyes) comprised 39 per cent and azoic dyes and their components comprised 7.0 per cent.

The role of azoic colors in the dye industry is primarily one of complementing the vat color range in the red and violet shade groups where the vat colors known to date are relatively dull. Generally speaking, in fastness properties on cellulose, the azoic colors are second only to the vat colors.

Origin

In 1880 the British firm of Read, Holliday and Sons discovered[34] the process of impregnating cotton with a water solution of the sodium salt of a phenol such as 2-naphthol followed by the development of a dye on the fiber by immersion in a solution of a diazotized aromatic amine such as p-nitroaniline. The dye from p-nitroaniline and 2-naphthol was known as Para Red.

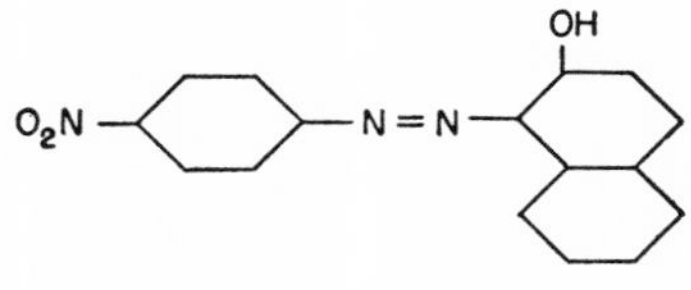

The name "ice colors" which is frequently applied to this class of dyes is derived from the use of ice in the diazotization of aromatic amines for carrying out this type of dyeing process. The term "azoic dyes," as distinguished from azo dyes in general, originated with the active German contributors to the synthetic dye field and is the term used most widely in current English and American practice.

A thorough discussion of azoic colors from the standpoints of their use and of the patent literature has been prepared by Louis Diserens[8]. D. A. W. Adams[1] has published a well-organized summary of the development of the azoic dye field from the dye manufacturer's point of view. K. Venkataraman[74] has written a review of the literature on azoic dyes, making full use of published data from I. G. Farbenindustrie.

Since the main identifying characteristic of azoic colors is the fact that they are first formed as colors on the fiber on which they are to be used, the chemistry of these dyes will be classified on the basis of two fundamental dyeing procedures, impregnation and composition printing.

Dyeing by Impregnation (Separate application of coupling component and diazo component to fiber)

The impregnation technique of synthesizing azoic dyes is based upon the application of coupling components to cellulose from water solutions of their alkali metal salts followed by contact of the treated fabric with a water solution of a diazonium salt. If the contact is through immersion, the resulting effect is that of an over-all dyeing. If the contact is with a thickened paste made from the diazo solution and applied from an engraved printing roller or through a stencil-like screen, the resulting effect is that of a pattern-dyeing, or a print. In the latter case, the unused coupling component in the unprinted areas of the fabric is washed off and discarded.

Coupling Components. The first practical azoic coupling component was 2-naphthol, which was used almost exclusively in this dye field until the introduction in 1911, by the German Griesheim-Elektron firm, of arylamides of 3-hydroxy-2-naphthoic acid as coupling components having definite cotton affinity and producing azoic dyeings of greatly improved brilliance and fastness. The group of azoic coupling components of this type is known as the Naphtol* AS series on the basis of the term "Anilid Säure."[12]

The first member of the 3-hydroxy-2-naphthoic arylamide class was the aniline derivative, which is known as Naphtol AS. Naphtol AS was first made by Schoepff[72] in 1892, and was first recommended for azoic dyeing by Kunert[50] in 1912. The Naphtol AS group has been extended by the systematic synthesis and evaluation of many hundred related compounds in the

---

* The spelling "Naphtol" is that of the trade-mark under which azoic coupling components are most widely known. It will be used here to afford a clear distinction over hydroxynaphthalenes in general.

interests of improvements in application behavior and in the shade and fastness properties of the resulting azoic dyes.

These coupling components are prepared generally by the condensation of 3-hydroxy-2-naphthoic acid with the appropriate arylamine in boiling toluene with phosphorus trichloride as a condensing agent[77]. Alternate Naphtol syntheses include the condensation of 3-hydroxy-2-naphthoyl chloride with the arylamine in refluxing nitrobenzene[3], the reaction between 3-hydroxy-2-naphthoic acid sodium salt (to increase yields over the free naphthoic acid process) and the arylamine in boiling toluene with phosphorus trichloride as a condensing agent[39, 44], and the interaction of 3-hydroxy-2-naphthoic acid with a phosphazo derivative of the arylamine made with phosphorus trichloride[25], such as C_6H_5—N$=$P—NH—C_6H_5.

The contribution of a coupling component made from 3-hydroxy-2-naphthoic acid to an azoic dye is, in general, more one of fiber affinity during the impregnation and of dye fastness than one of shade modification.

A second important group of azoic coupling components comprises arylamides of *o*-hydroxycarboxylic acids of nuclei other than naphthalene, notably anthracene[14], carbazole[67], benzocarbazole[68] and diphenylene oxide[61]. This type of Naphtol is usually prepared by condensation of the appropriate *o*-hydroxycarboxylic acid or its sodium salt with the desired arylamine in a boiling inert hydrocarbon solvent (toluene or xylene) with phosphorus trichloride as a condensing agent. The usefulness of the members of this group rests mainly in the shade of the dyes they produce, in that they permit the synthesis of useful monoazo green, brown, and black dyes which would otherwise be very difficult to achieve.

A third general class of coupling components comprises acylacetarylamides[53] for the production of dyes in the yellow shade range through diazo coupling to the active methylene groups in the manner of the Hansa yellow azo pigments. The synthesis of this class of coupling components involves either condensation of the acylacetic acid ethyl ester with the arylamine in a boiling solvent like xylene, or addition of ketene dimer to the arylamine in boiling acetone[5] or ethylene dichloride[6].

The most important members of these three groups of coupling components[40] are cited by name, AATCC Prototype number, structure, and color properties in Table 1. Coupling positions are marked by asterisks. Chemical Abstracts nomenclature is used.

The substantivity, or affinity for cellulose, of azoic coupling components for use in the impregnation dyeing procedure plays a large part in the usefulness of the individual compounds. The relation between cotton substantivity of azoic coupling components and their structure has been discussed from several standpoints[3, 4, 10, 59, 66] but little agreement has been reached. It appears most probable[73a] that cotton substantivity in this series is a func-

TABLE 1. AZOIC COUPLING COMPONENTS

Name	No.	Structure	M.P.[41] (°C)	Substantivity† (%)	Special Properties
Naphtol AS	Pr. 302	3-hydroxy-2-naphthanilide	243-4	11.6	Widely used for textile printing with diazos, due to low substantivity and ease of removal from unprinted areas
Naphtol AS-BG	Pr. 385	3-hydroxy-2',5'-dimethoxy-2-naphthanilide	180-1	16.0	Produces an inexpensive brown dye with Scarlet GG Base
Naphtol AS-BM		3,3''-dihydroxy-4',4'''-bi-2-naphtho-o-toluidide	327		

Naphtol AS-BO	Pr. 303	3-hydroxy-*N*-1-naphthyl-2-naphthamide 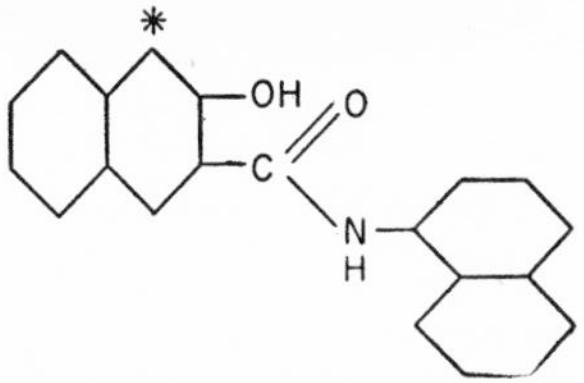		223	20.4	
Naphtol AS-BR	Pr. 304	3,3''-dihydroxy-4',4'''-bi-2-naphth-*o*-anisidide 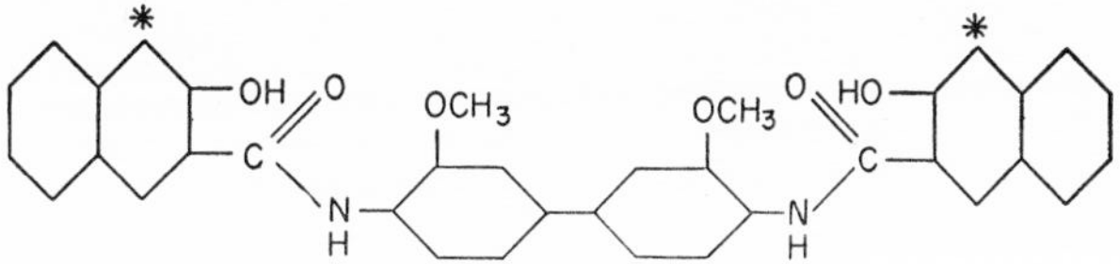		348	32.3	Mixed with Naphtol AS-SW (of similar substantivity) for dulling of shades
Naphtol AS-BS	Pr. 305	3-hydroxy-3'-nitro-2-naphthanilide 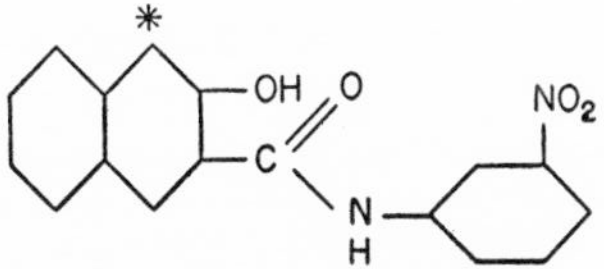		246-7	17.6	Used for maroons with Red G Base and 5-methyl-*o*-anisidine (cresidine)
Naphtol AS-BT	Pr. 307	2-hydroxy-2',5'-dimethoxy-3-dibenzofurancarboxanilide 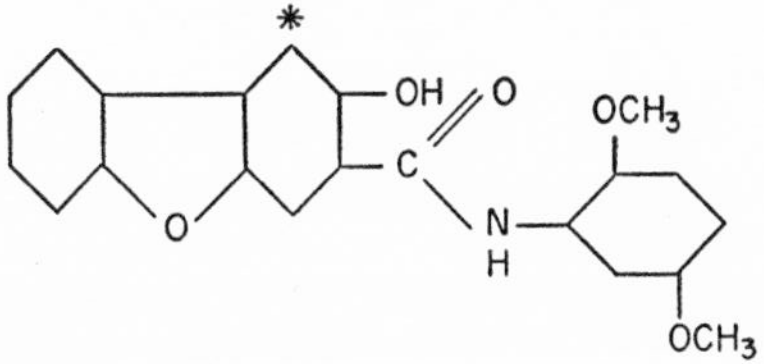			44.4	Used for light-fast deep browns

TABLE 1—Continued

Name	No.	Structure	M.P.[41] (°C)	Substantivity[‡] (%)	Special Properties
Naphtol AS-D	Pr. 306	3-hydroxy-2-naphtho-o-toluidide 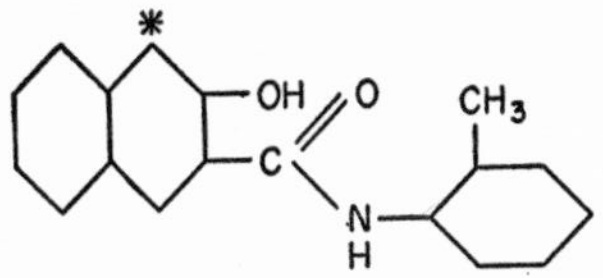	196–7	11.6	Used for deeper shades, with other properties like Naphtol AS
Naphtol AS-E	Pr. 308	4'-chloro-3-hydroxy-2-naphthanilide 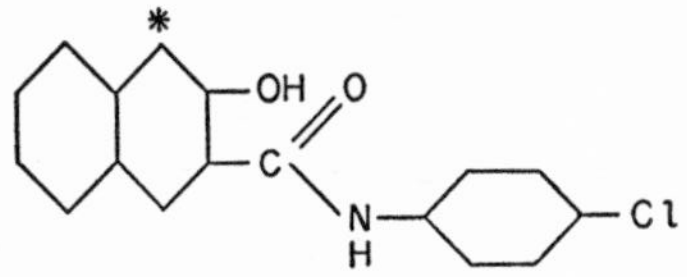	258–9	22.8	
Naphtol AS-G	Pr. 309	4,4'-bi-o-acetoacetotoluidide 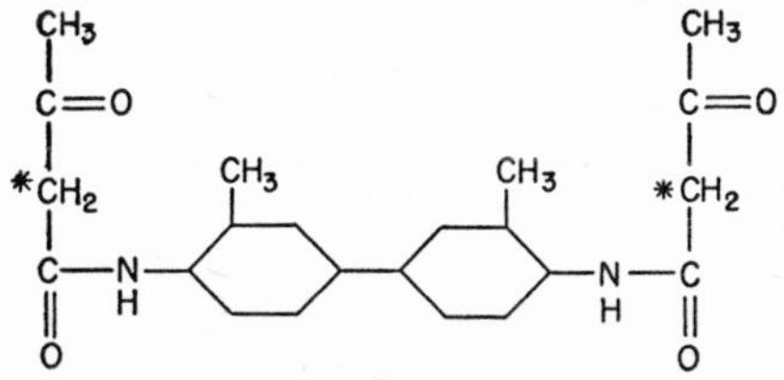	208	19.0[†]	Widely used for yellows of good general fastness

† Substantivity measured in presence of 30 g Na₂SO₄ per liter Naphtol solution.

Naphtol AS-GR	Pr. 386	3-hydroxy-2-o-anthrotoluidide		70.0

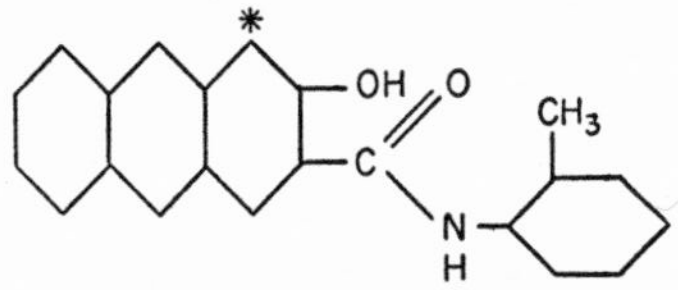

Used for a dull blue-green with Blue BB Base. Only azoic coupling component capable of yielding monoazo greens

| Naphtol AS-13GH | | 4-chloro-2,5-dimethoxyacetoacetanilide | 105–6 | |

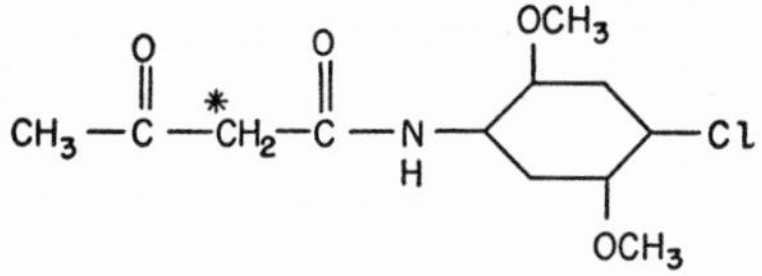

Used for light-fast green-yellows

| Naphtol AS-ITR | Pr. 310 | 5'-chloro-3-hydroxy-2',4'-dimethoxy-2-naphthanilide | 193–4 | 19.0 |

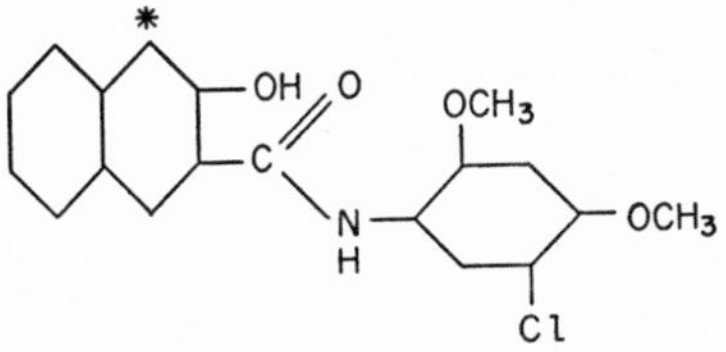

With Red ITR Base gives the only azoic red light-fast in weak dyeings (tints)

| Naphtol AS-LB | Pr. 387 | 4'-chloro-2-hydroxy-3-carbazolecarboxanilide | | 44.4 |

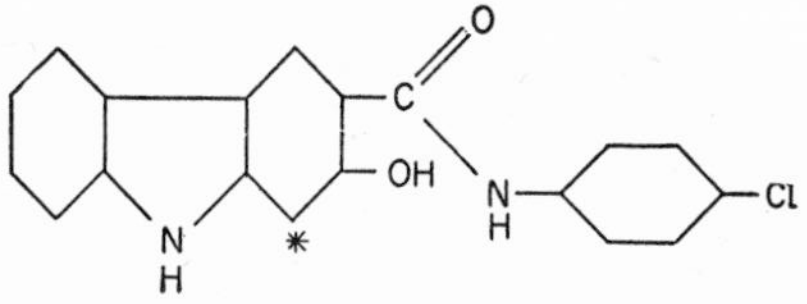

Gives fastest known yellow-brown cotton dyeings

TABLE 1—Continued

Name	No.	Structure	M.P.[41] (°C)	Substantivity‡ (%)	Special Properties
Naphtol AS-LC	Pr. 460	4'-chloro-3-hydroxy-2',5'-dimethoxy-2-naphthanilide 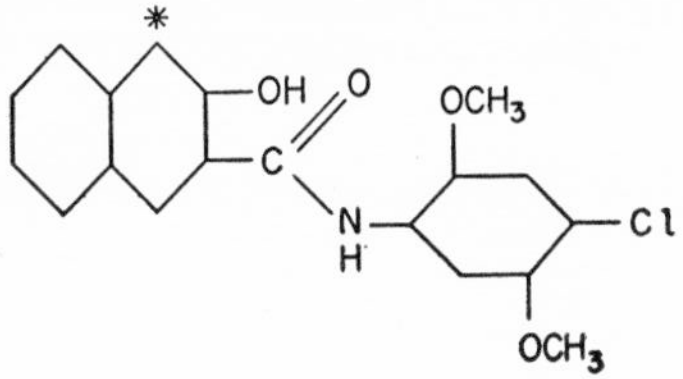	188-9	38	More substantive than AS-SW. Used for maximum lightfastness in machine-dyed reds and oranges with Golden Orange GR, Red FR, and Scarlet GG Bases
Naphtol AS-LG	Pr. 505	α,α'-terephthaloylbis(5-chloro-2,4-dimethoxyacetanilide) 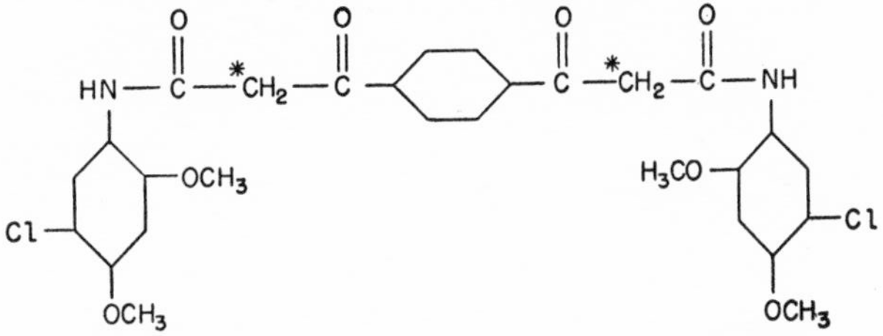	253-4	46.8	Used for yellows requiring high substantivity
Naphtol AS-L3G	Pr. 555	α,α'-terephthaloylbis(4-chloro-5-methyl-o-acetanisidide) 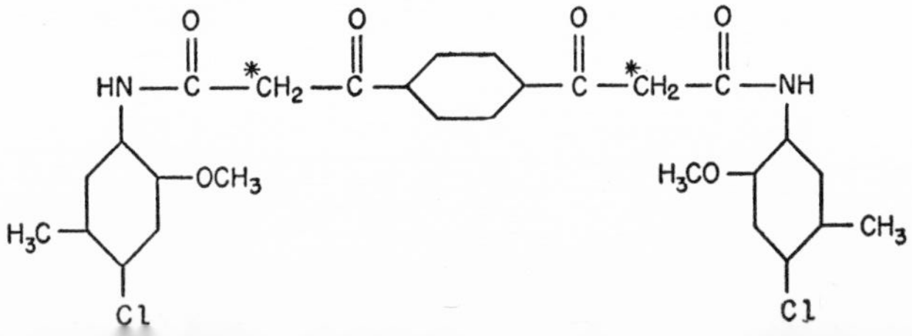	245-6	41.5	Used for green-yellows requiring high substantivity

Naphtol AS-L4G		2-α-acetylacetamido-6-ethoxybenzothiazole 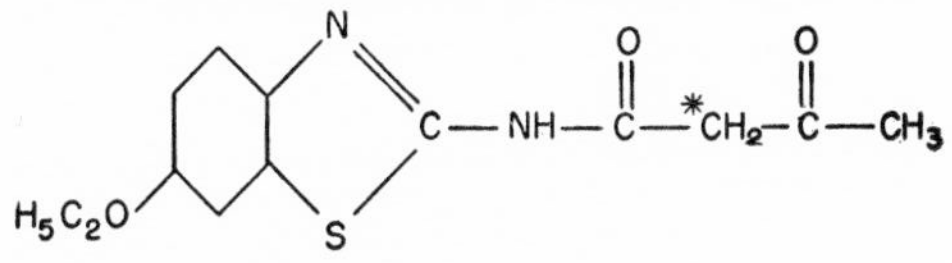		24.3†	Used for light-fast green-yellows
Naphtol AS-LT	Pr. 506	3-hydroxy-2′-methyl-2-naphth-*p*-anisidide 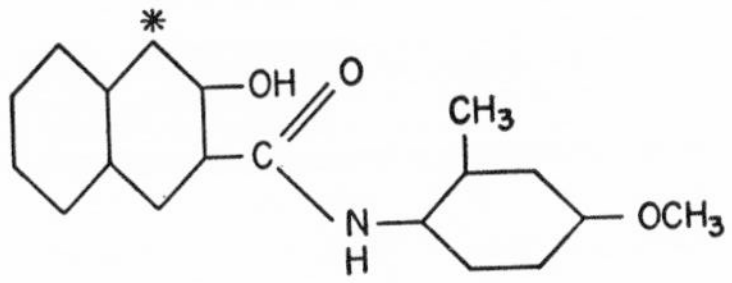		196–7	16.0
Naphtol AS-MX	Pr. 556	3-hydroxy-2-naphtho-2,4-xylidide 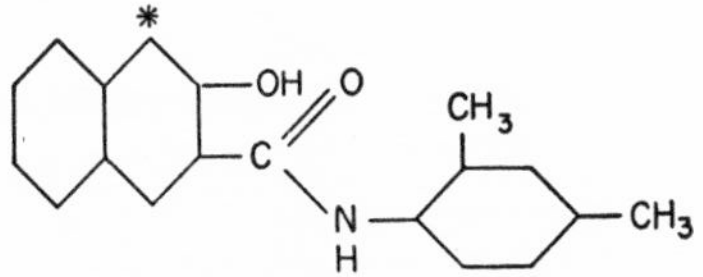		223–5	
Naphtol AS-OL	Pr. 311	3-hydroxy-2-naphth-*o*-anisidide 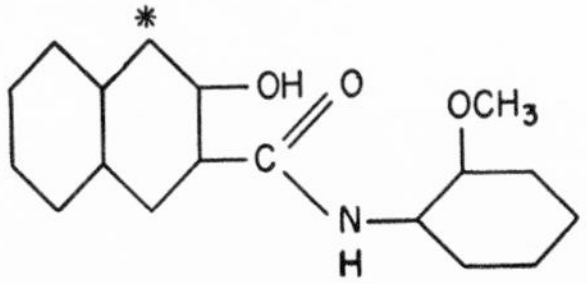		167–8	13.6	Used for light shades in Naphtol AS substantivity range

† Substantivity measured in presence of 25 g Na₂SO₄ per liter Naphtol solution.

TABLE 1—Continued

Name	No.	Structure	M.P.[41] °C	Substantivity[‡] (%)	Special Properties
Naphtol AS-PH	Pr. 557	3-hydroxy-2-naphtho-o-phenetidide 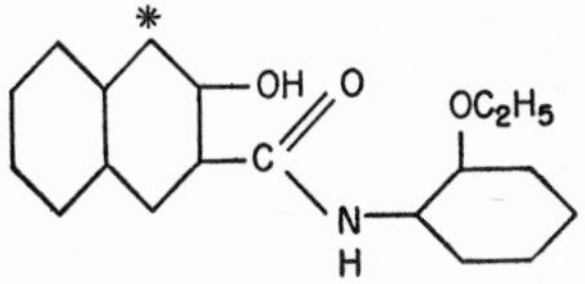	157–8		Used only in Rapidogen mixtures (see Table 5 p. 220)
Naphtol AS-RL	Pr. 312	3-hydroxy-2-naphth-p-anisidide 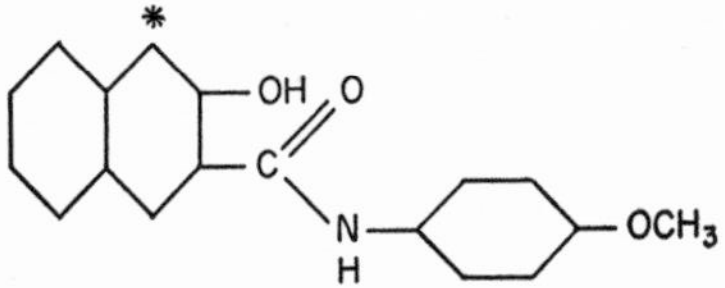	230	16.0	Used for good all-purpose red with Red RL Base
Naphtol AS-S		3-hydroxy-N-(2-methoxy-3-dibenzofuryl)-2-naphthamide 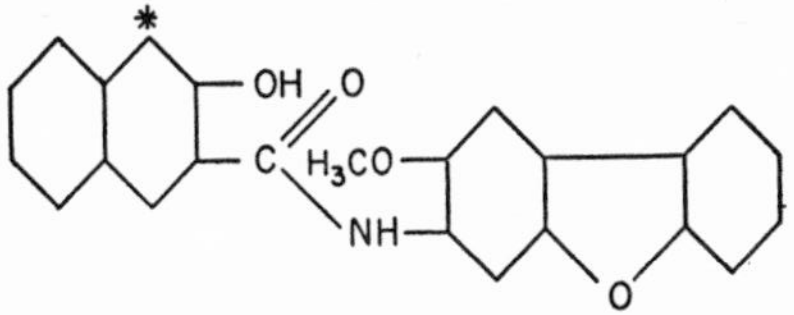	207–211		Intended to be a high substantivity complement to Naphtol AS
Naphtol AS-SG	Pr. 388	2-hydroxy-11H-benzo[a]carbazole-3-carbox-p-anisidide 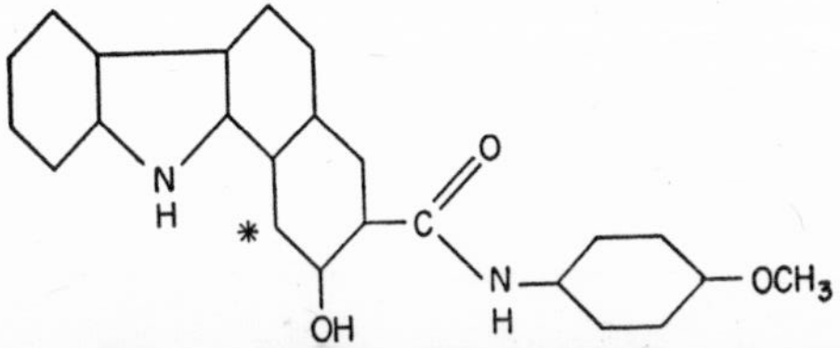		87	Used for good-quality green-blacks with Red B Base. Also mixed with Naphtol AS-SW for dulling of shades

Naphtol AS-SR	Pr. 558	2-hydroxy-2'-methyl-11H-benzo[a]carbazole-3-carbox-p-anisidide	87	Used for good-quality red-blacks with Red B Base
Naphtol AS-SW	Pr. 313	3-hydroxy-N-2-naphthyl-2-naphthamide	243-4	Widely used for machine dyeing of cotton yarn with Red KB Base or Red PC Base
Naphtol AS-TR	Pr. 314	4'-chloro-3-hydroxy-2-naphtho-o-toluidide	245	Used for "Turkey Red" shade with Red TR Base
Naphtol IFG		4'-α-benzoylacetamido-2',5'-dimethoxybenzanilide	166-7	Used for light-fast Rapidogen yellow mixes (see Table 5, p. 220)

TABLE 1—Continued

Name	No.	Structure	M.P.[41] (°C)	Substantivity[‡] (%)	Special Properties
Naphtol 30992		5'-chloro-3-hydroxy-2-naphtho-o-toluidide 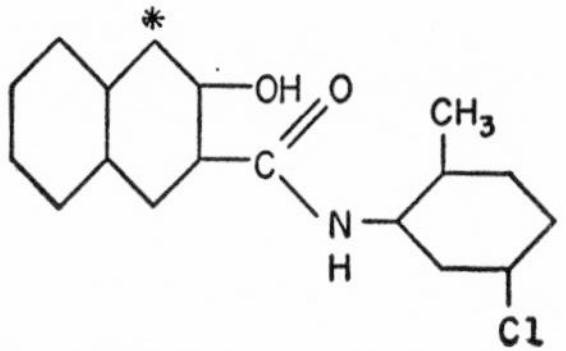	237		
Naphtol 31855		7-bromo-3-hydroxy-2-naphth-o-anisidide 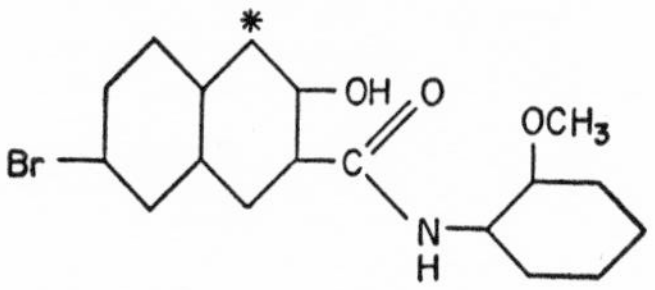	189–90		Used for a peroxide-bleach-fast bordeaux with Bordeaux OL Base (ref. 39, Vol. III, p. 138)
Cibanaphthol RT[9]		3-hydroxy-2-naphtho-p-toluidide 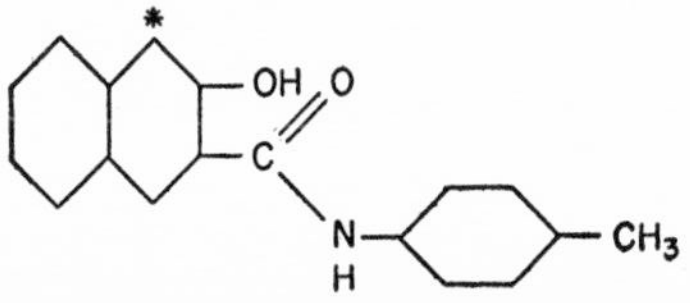	222		

‡ 5 g Naphtol per liter, as sodium salt in water, as initial concentration. Data from IG Farbenindustrie curves in azoic dyeing manual. Percentages cited represent proportion of total Naphtol in solution which is transferred by substantivity to cotton skeins immersed at 1 part cotton by weight for each 20 parts Naphtol solution by volume at equilibrium.

tion of the ease with which hydrogen bonding can be established between the cellulose fiber and the sodium salt of the coupling component in water solution, which, in turn, must be related to the proper spacing and stereo-positions of potential hydrogen bonding points in the coupling component molecule with relation to the repeating cellobiose units of cellulose. While the substantivity of a coupling component governs the conditions under which cotton fiber may be successfully impregnated by it, there is little evidence to indicate that the substantivity of the coupling component is directly related to the properties of the azoic dye finally formed on the fiber. Quantitative estimates of the substantivity of many of the individual azoic coupling components will be found in Table 1.

Diazotizable Amines (Azoic Bases). As indicated above, the first amine used for developing ice colors was *p*-nitroaniline. Again the expansions of this principle have been made primarily by German industry through the careful screening of hundreds of possible compounds on the basis of the useful properties of azoic dyes made from them. All useful azoic bases or diazotizable amines are free from water-solubilizing groups such as —OH, —SO$_3$H, or —COOH and are largely made up of anilines, toluidines, and anisidines substituted by groups such as chloro, nitro, cyano, trifluoromethyl, arylamino, and acylamino.

Beyond the general characteristics indicated above, it is difficult to cite properties common to useful azoic bases. It is, however, interesting to note that the largest structural group in this general class consists of aromatic amines of the following formula,

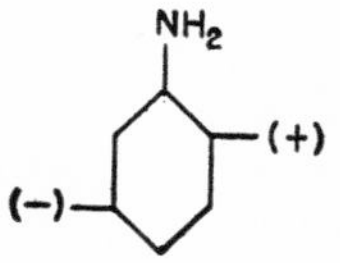

in which (+) indicates an electro-positive substituent and (−) indicates an electro-negative substituent. The principal examples of this class are the following ten bases:

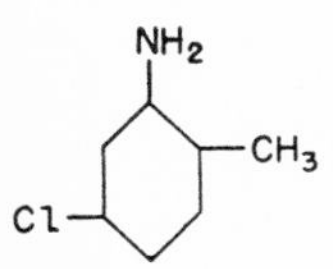

Red KB 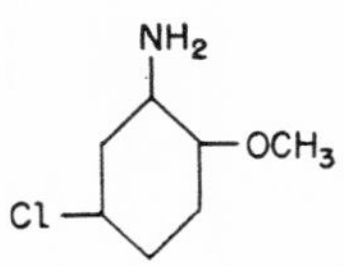   Red RC 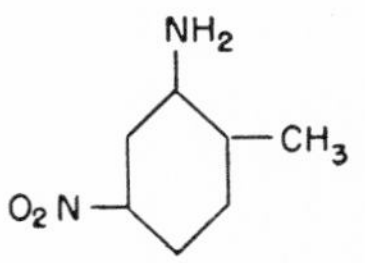   Scarlet G 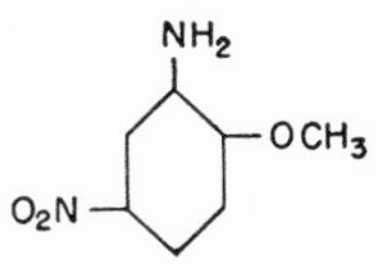   Scarlet R

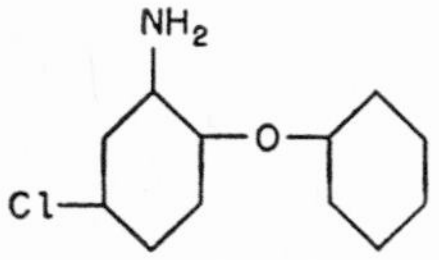

Red FG

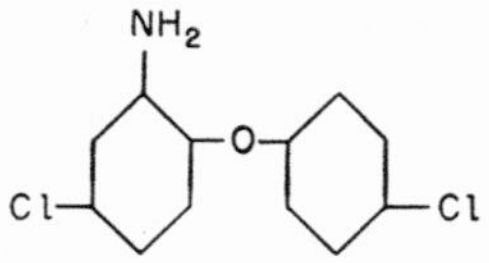

Red FR

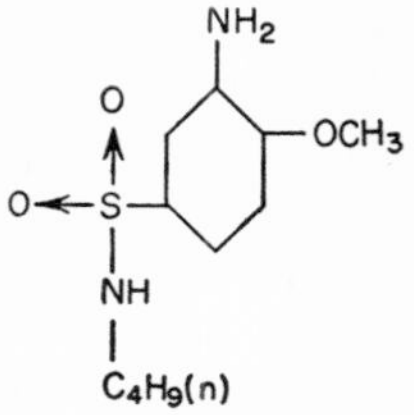

Red PC

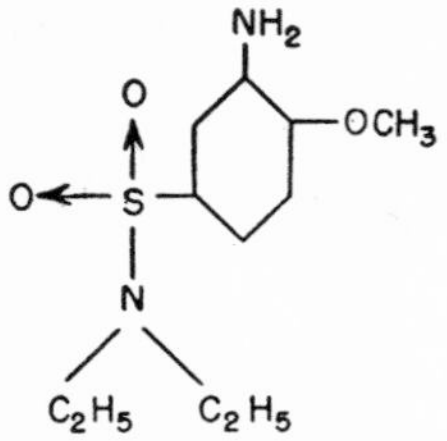

Red ITR

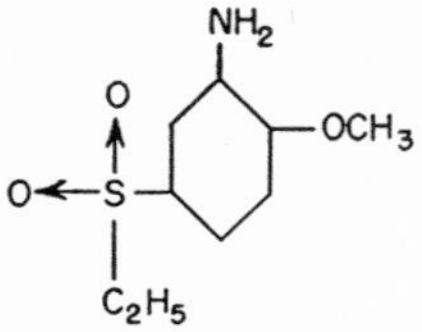

Red GTR

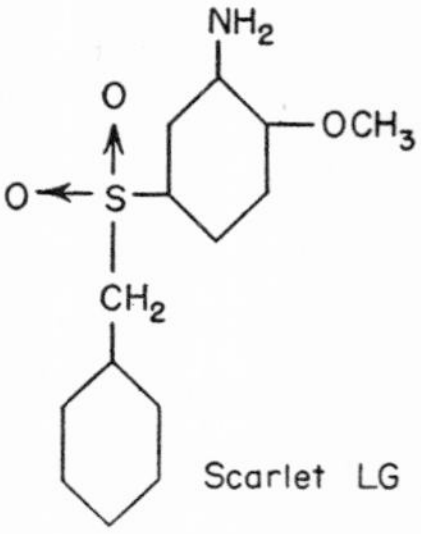

Scarlet LG

The above structure type appears to be particularly favorable for the synthesis of azoic dyes of brilliant shade and outstanding fastness, particularly to light, but it must be reemphasized that the basis for the choice of these compounds and of all other useful ones has been essentially empirical.

When the coupling component is of the 3-hydroxy-2-naphthoic arylamide type, the shade of the resulting azoic dye is controlled primarily by the structure of the diazotizable amine. This fact is probably due to the nearness of the diazotized amine nucleus to the azo chromophore, in comparison with the remote nonconjugated position of the arylamide nucleus.

The procedures useful for diazotizing azoic color bases vary widely with the type of amine involved and have been thoroughly discussed elsewhere[26, 49, 65, 74].

The names, Colour Index or AATCC Prototype numbers, structures, and color properties of the most important diazotizable amines[38, 40] in the azoic color class are included in Table 2. Chemical Abstracts nomenclature is used in single names of compounds and in the parenthetical part of twin names.

Relation of Dye Properties to Structure. All useful azoic dyes are empirically selected specific combinations of diazo and coupling components, so that assignments of relations between dye properties and structure must be essentially after-the-fact rationalizations. The general concepts cited below are the only ones known to apply with reasonable consistency.

Shade. A substituent which causes a dye to absorb light nearer the ultraviolet (thus causing the dye to appear yellower) is called *hypso*chromic (*higher* frequency light is absorbed). Conversely, a substituent which moves the spectral absorption peak of a dye nearer the infrared (thus making the dye appear bluer) is called *batho*chromic (*lower* frequency light is absorbed).

(1) Effect of Diazo Component. A single substituent in an aniline molecule follows the hypsochromic to bathochromic sequence of ortho to meta to para.

The common substituents follow the hypsochromic to bathochromic sequence of nitro to chloro to alkyl to alkoxy. The position of hydrogen in this series is variable, from before nitro to after chloro, depending on the remainder of the dye structure.

Nitro groups tend to dull the shade, while chloro and cyano groups tend to brighten it.

The 2-(+)-5-(−)-aniline structure (see p. 193) is generally favorable both for brilliance of shade and maximum fastness.

(2) Effect of Coupling Component. In the 3-hydroxy-2-naphthoic arylamide type, a single substituent in the arylamide nucleus tends to follow the hypsochromic to bathochromic sequence of ortho to meta to para, although many exceptions are known.

The common substituents in the above arylamide nucleus follow the hypsochromic to bathochromic sequence of alkoxy to hydrogen to alkyl to chloro to nitro.

The heterocyclic coupling components which undergo azo coupling on the heterocyclic nucleus lead to nonselective light absorption and thus to brown or black shades. The anthracene nucleus in a coupling component is bathochromic versus the naphthalene nucleus, and leads to the only known azoic green dyes.

Active methylene coupling positions, as in acylacetarylamides, lead to absorption of violet light and thus to yellow shades.

Fastness. The physical agglomeration of azoic dyes on cellulose fiber, which is encouraged by soaping treatments, is primarily responsible for the relatively high lightfastness of these colors.

Trifluoromethyl groups in the diazo component tend to give good lightfastness.

Tri-substitution in the 2, 4, and 5 positions in the arylamide nucleus of a 3-hydroxy-2-naphthoic arylamide tends to lead to good lightfastness.

The —C—NH— group in a coupling component gives lessened chlorine-
$\quad\;\;\|$
$\quad\;\;$O

fastness and good substantivity. The replacement of the —C—NH—
$\qquad\qquad\qquad\qquad\qquad\qquad\qquad\qquad\qquad\quad\;\;\|$
$\qquad\qquad\qquad\qquad\qquad\qquad\qquad\qquad\qquad\quad\;\;$O

group by a —C—N— group destroys substantivity. The substantivity of
$\qquad\qquad\;\;\|\;\;\;|$
$\qquad\qquad\;\;$O$\;\;\;$alkyl

TABLE 2. AZOIC BASES (DIAZOTIZABLE AMINES)

Name	No.	Structure	Special Properties
(Fast) Black B (Base)	Pr. 255	4,4'-diaminodiphenylamine 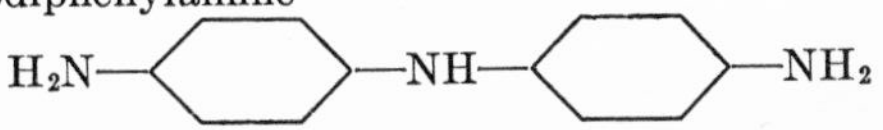 	
Black G		4-amino-4'-(4-amino-6-methyl-m-phenetylazo)diphenylamine (N-[p-(4-amino-6-methyl-m-phenetylazo)phenyl-p-phenylene-diamine) 	
Black K	Pr. 256	2,5-dimethoxy-4-(p-nitrophenylazo)aniline 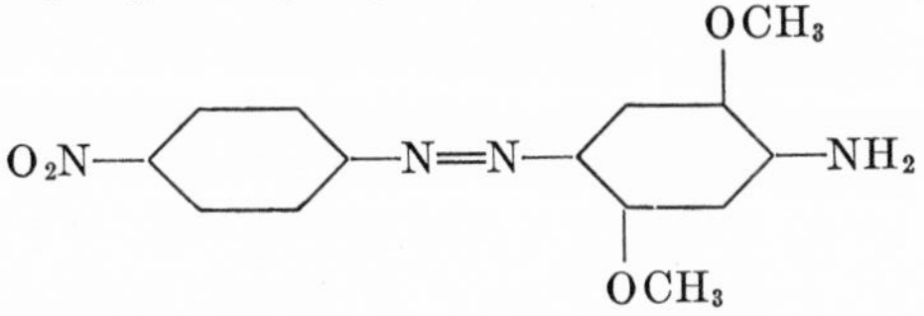 	
Blue B	CI 499	o-dianisidine (3,3'-dimethoxybenzidine) 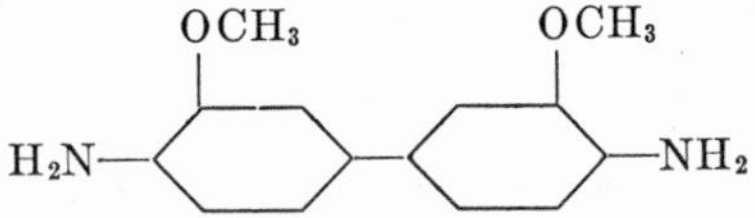 	Widely used for blues of moderate lightfastness

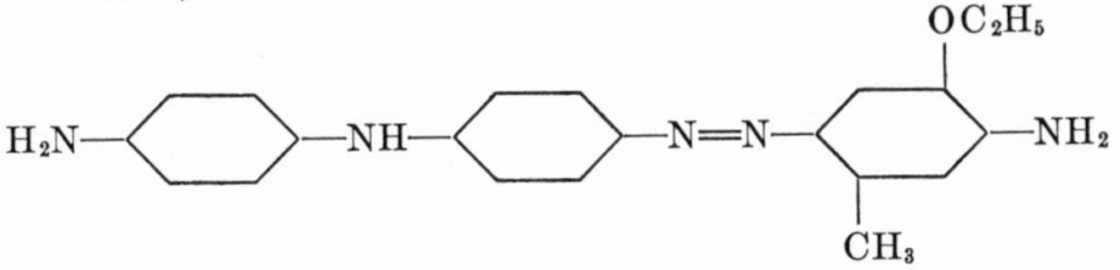

Name	Pr. No.	Chemical name	Structure	Notes
Variamine Blue B	Pr. 357	4-amino-4'-methoxydiphenylamine (*N*-[*p*-methoxyphenyl]-*p*-phenylenediamine) 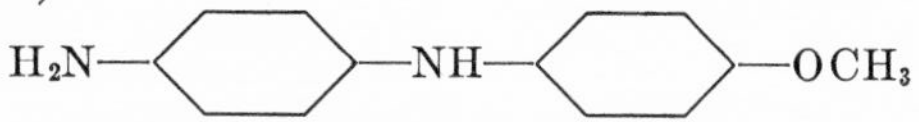		Gives blues of improved light-fastness vs. Blue B
Blue BB	Pr. 258	4'-amino-2',5'-diethoxybenzanilide 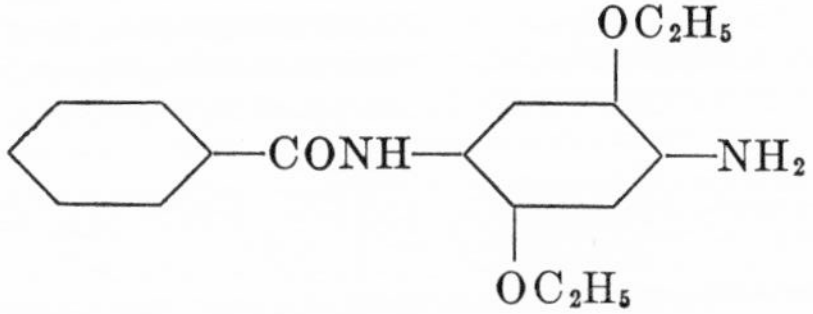		Gives maximum lightfastness in azoic blues. Gives a green with Naphtol AS-GR
Variamine Blue FG	Pr. 498	4-amino-3-methoxydiphenylamine (2-methoxy-*N*⁴-phenyl-*p*-phenylenediamine) 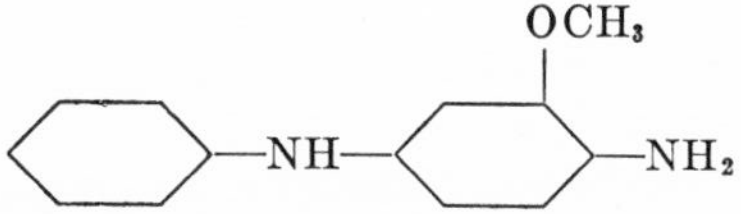		Redder shades vs. Variamine Blue B. Used for a green with Naphtol AS-GR
Blue RR		4'-amino-2',5'-dimethoxybenzanilide 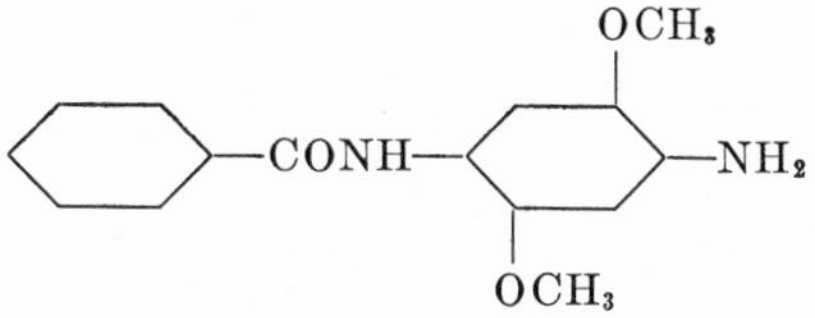		Redder shades vs. Blue BB
Variamine Blue RT	Pr. 358	4-aminodiphenylamine (*N*-phenyl-*p*-phenylenediamine) 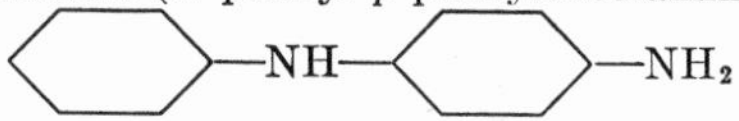		Redder shades vs. Variamine Blue FG

TABLE 2—*Continued*

Name	No.	Structure	Special Properties
Bordeaux BD	Pr. 259	4-amino-2,5-dimethoxybenzonitrile 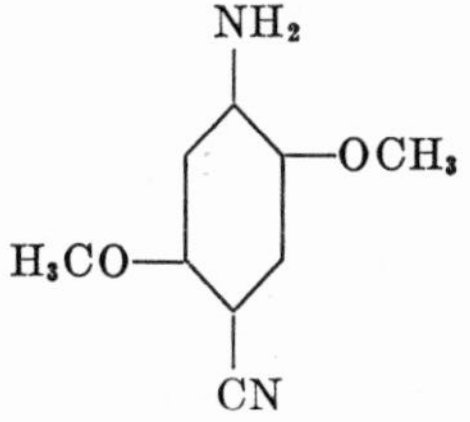	Used for maximum brightness in azoic bordeaux dyeings
Bordeaux GP	Pr. 260	3-nitro-4-aminoanisole (2-nitro-*p*-anisidine) 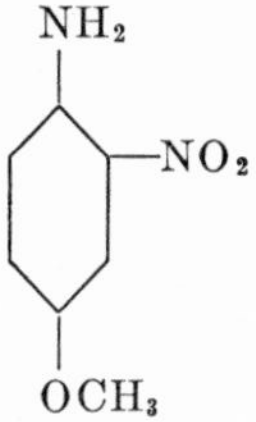	Used widely for azoic bordeaux dyeings
Brown V		6-(2-chloro-4-nitrophenylazo)-4-methyl-*m*-anisidine 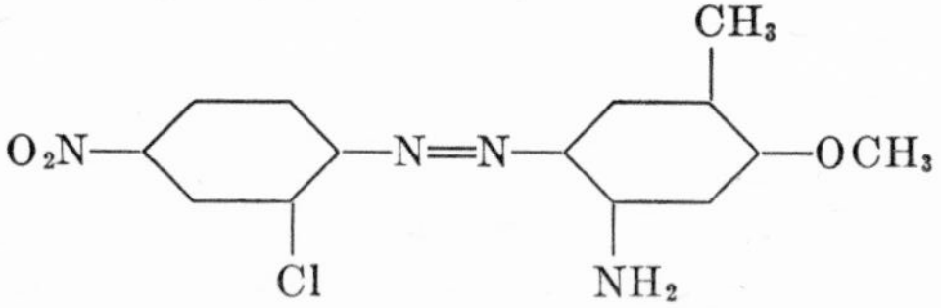	Used with Naphtols AS-RL or AS-LT to give best known browns in which shade is controlled by azoic base

Corinth LB   Pr. 499   4'-amino-5'-chloro-o-benzanisidide

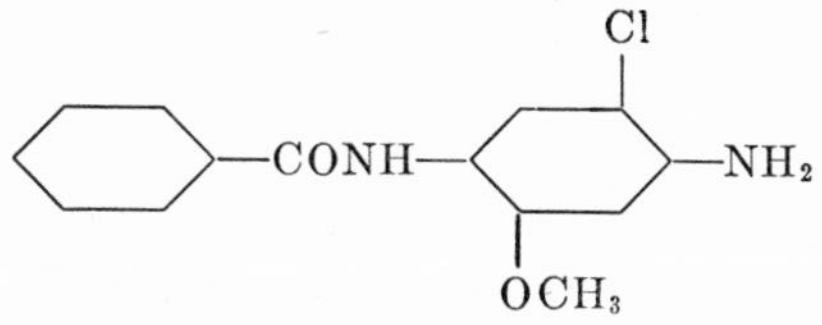

Corinth V   Pr. 261   5-methyl-4-(2-nitro-p-tolylazo)-o-anisidine

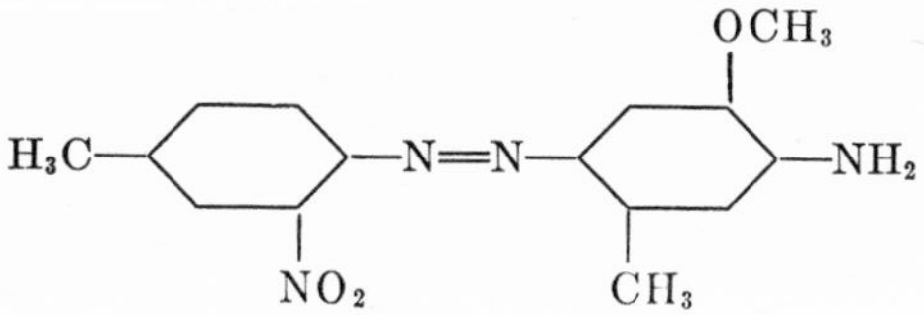

Garnet GBC   CI 17   o-aminoazotoluene (4-[o-tolylazo]-o-toluidine)

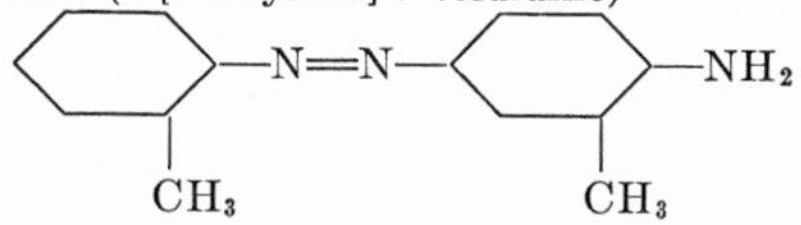

Orange GC   Pr. 264   m-chloroaniline

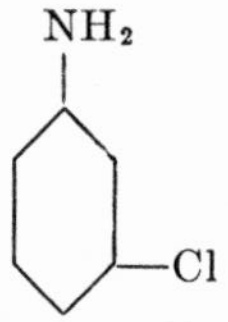

TABLE 2—*Continued*

Name	No.	Structure	Special Properties
Orange GGD		3,5-bis(trifluoromethyl)aniline ($\alpha,\alpha,\alpha,\alpha',\alpha',\alpha'$-hexafluoro-3,5-xylidine) 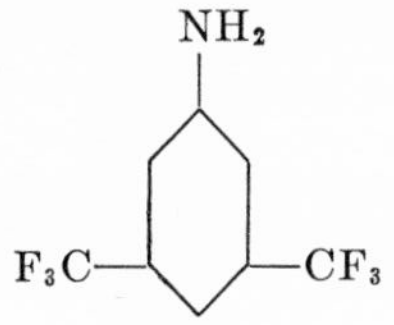	Used for light-fast yellow-oranges
Orange GR	Pr. 265	*o*-nitroaniline 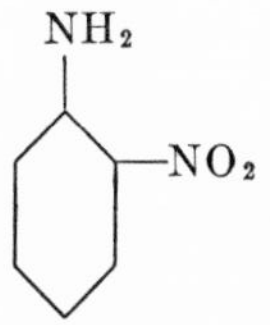	
Golden Orange GR		2-ethylsulfonyl-5-trifluoromethylaniline (6-ethylsulfonyl-α,α,α-trifluoro-*m*-toluidine) 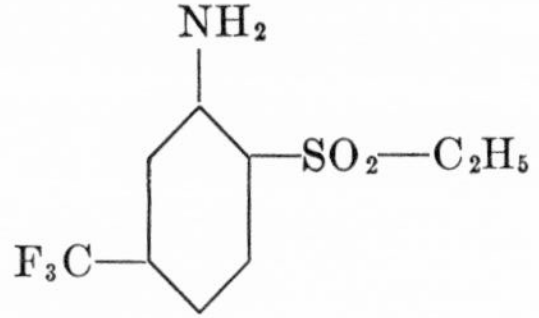	Gives red-oranges of high lightfastness
Orange LG		*o*-(phenylsulfonyl)aniline 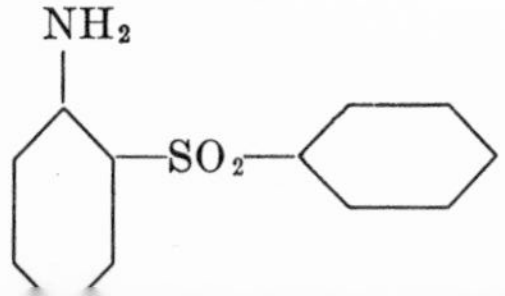	

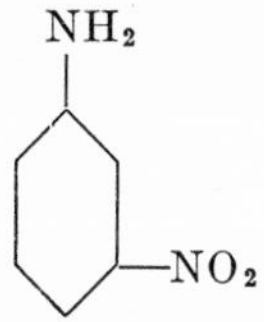

Orange RD   Pr. 266   2-chloro-5-trifluoromethylaniline (6-chloro-α,α,α-trifluoro-*m*-toluidine)   Used for high lightfastness in oranges

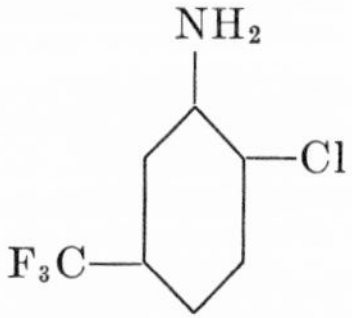

Red AL   Pr. 267   1-aminoanthraquinone   Used for high lightfastness in dull reds

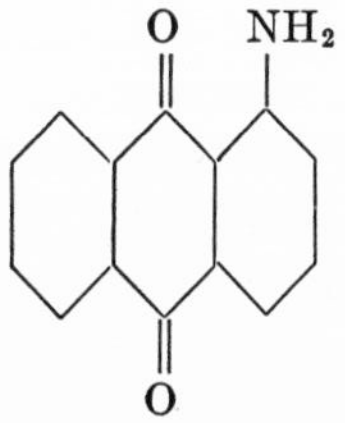

Red B   CI 117   5-nitro-2-aminoanisole (4-nitro-*o*-anisidine)

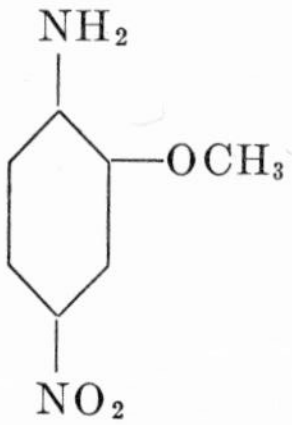

TABLE 2—*Continued*

Name	No.	Structure	Special Properties
Red FG		5-chloro-2-phenoxyaniline 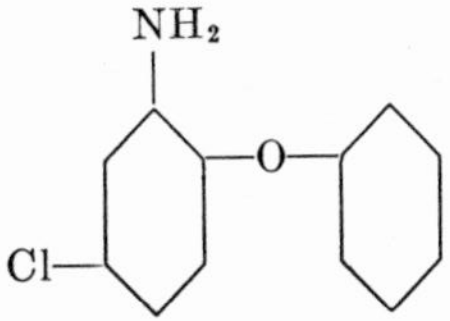	
Red FR	Pr. 500	5-chloro-2-(*p*-chlorophenoxy)aniline 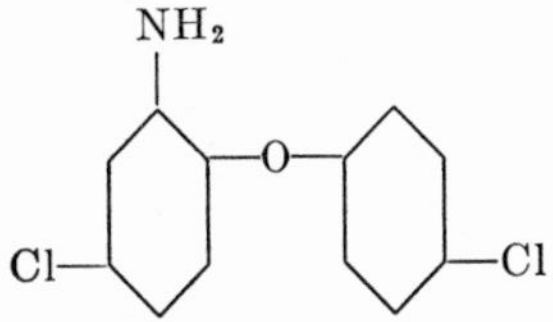	
Red G	CI 69	3-nitro-4-aminotoluene (2-nitro-*p*-toluidine) 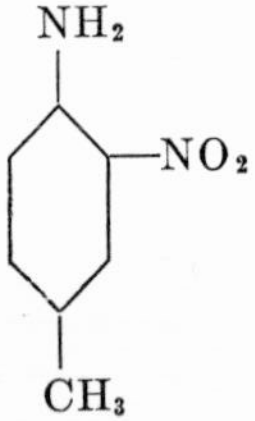	

Red GG	CI 44	*p*-nitroaniline 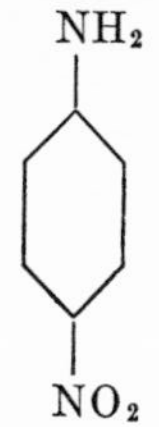	
Red 3G	Pr. 269	4-chloro-2-nitroaniline 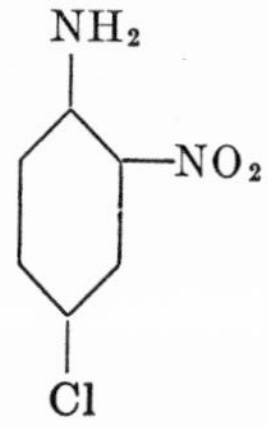	
Red GTR		4-ethylsulfonyl-2-aminoanisole (5-ethylsulfonyl-o-anisidine) 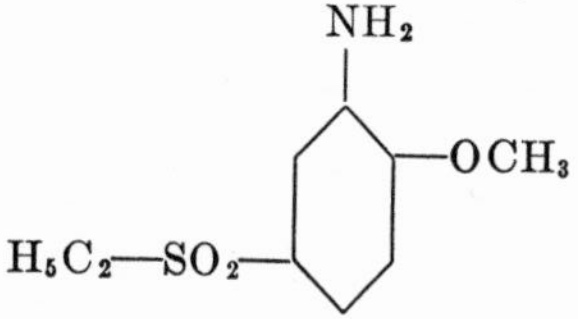	
Red ITR	Pr. 378	4-(diethylsulfamyl)-2-aminoanisole (N^1,N^1-diethyl-4-methoxymetanilamide) 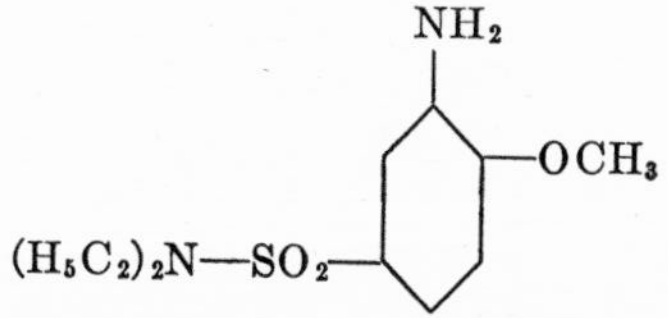	With Naphtol AS-ITR, gives the only azoic red light-fast in weak dyeings (tints)

TABLE 2—*Continued*

Name	No.	Structure	Special Properties
Red KB	Pr. 270	4-chloro-2-aminotoluene (5-chloro-o-toluidine) 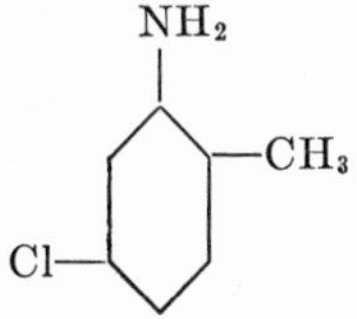	Widely used for machine dyeing of cotton yarn with Naphtol AS-SW
Red NC		2-aminobiphenyl (2-biphenylamine) 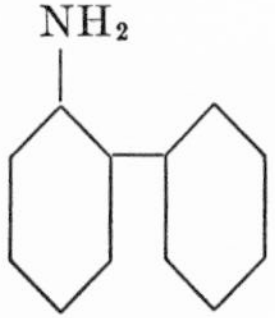	
Red PDC	Pr. 501	4-(n-butylsulfamyl)-2-aminoanisole (N¹-butyl-4-methoxymetanilamide) 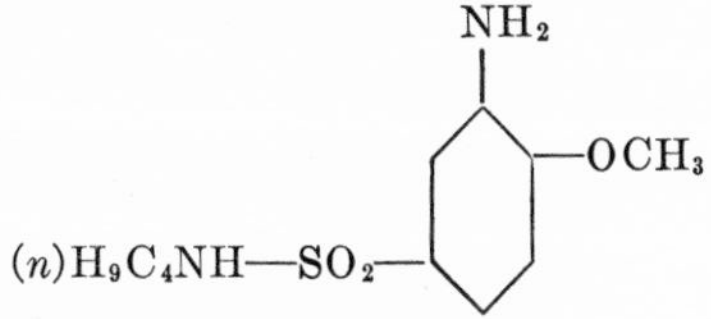	Widely used for fast-to-peroxide-bleaching machine dyeing with Naphtol AS-SW
Red RC	Pr. 271	4-chloro-2-aminoanisole (5-chloro-o-anisidine) 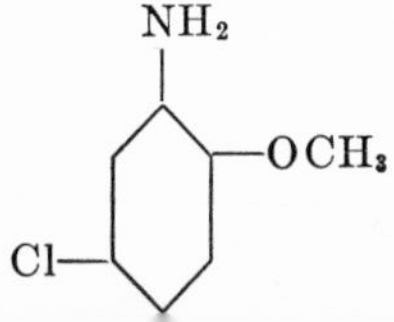	

Red RL	Pr. 272	5-nitro-2-aminotoluene (4-nitro-o-toluidine) 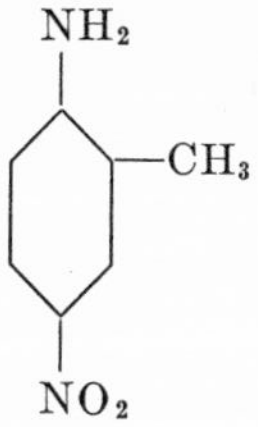		Used for good all-purpose red with Naphtol AS-RL
Red TR	Pr. 273	5-chloro-2-aminotoluene (4-chloro-o-toluidine) 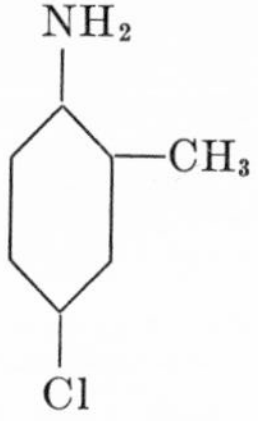		Used for "Turkey Red" shade with Naphtol AS-TR
Scarlet G	CI 68	4-nitro-2-aminotoluene (5-nitro-o-toluidine) 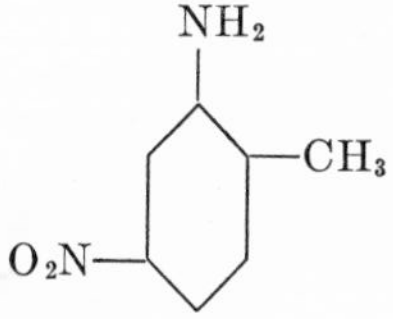		
Scarlet GG	Pr. 94	2,5-dichloroaniline 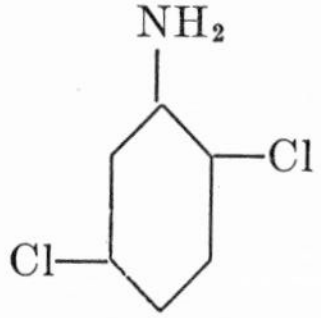		

TABLE 2—Continued

Name	No.	Structure	Special Properties
Scarlet LG		4-benzylsulfonyl-2-aminoanisole (5-benzylsulfonyl-o-anisidine) 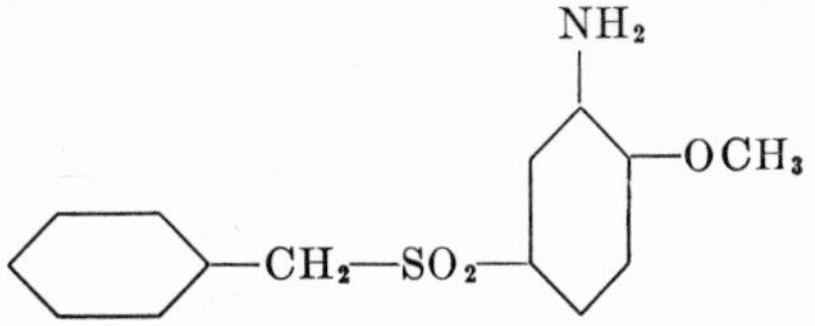	
Scarlet R	CI 118	4-nitro-2-aminoanisole (5-nitro-o-anisidine) 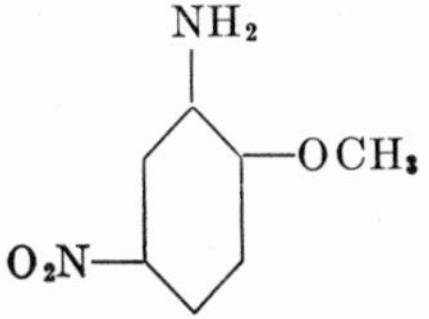	Widely used for brilliant scarlet with Naphtol AS-SW
Scarlet TR	Pr. 442	6-chloro-2-aminotoluene (3-chloro-o-toluidine) 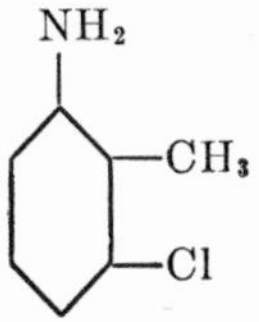	
Scarlet VD		4-chloro-2-trifluoromethylaniline (4-chloro-α,α,α-trifluoro-o-toluidine) 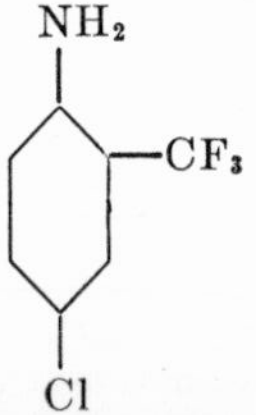	Used with Naphtol AS in World War II for weather-fast red in German flags

Violet B Pr. 274 4'-amino-6'-methyl-*m*-benzanisidide

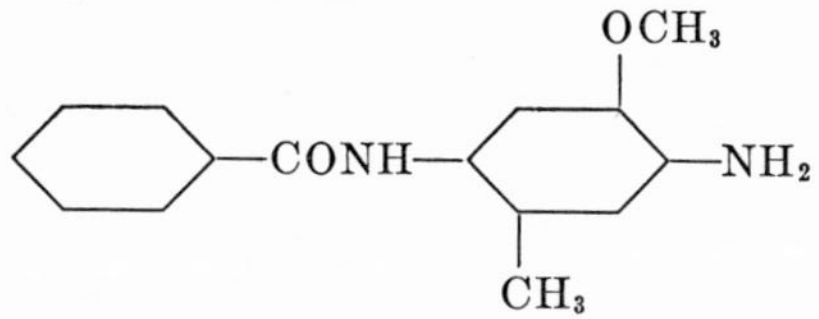

Used for bright fast violet with Naphtol AS

Yellow GC Pr. 275 o-chloroaniline

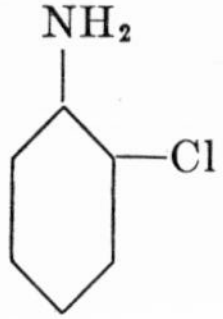

Most hypsochromic known azoic base

a coupling component is not directly related to the washfastness of the azoic dye. Washfastness in azoic colors is due primarily to the absence of water-solubilizing groups in the dye molecule.

Stable Diazonium Salts. The need for active, stable forms of diazos for dissolving in water and direct development of solid and pattern dyeings (prints) from Naphtol-impregnated cellulosic textiles became apparent early to the dye industry[13]. The period from 1898–1930 saw the development, primarily in Germany, of numerous dry compositions containing diazo compounds in the form of water-soluble salts, appropriately diluted for safety and stability on storage. Early preparations were made by low-temperature vacuum concentration of diazo solutions followed by dilution with inorganic salts. Later developments (now in wide commercial use) included precipitation of diazo salts from water solution as diazonium halides[46] or sulfates[71], as complexes with heavy metal halides (e.g., $ZnCl_2$)[27] or with nonmetallic fluorides (e.g., HBF_4)[15, 76], or as salts of aromatic sulfonic acids[47]. These products as marketed are generally known as "Fast Salts," in view of the fastness properties of the applied colors. These intermediates are stabilized and buffered by the use of selected organic and inorganic diluents as components of the marketed Fast Salts.

Table 3 includes the names, Colour Index or AATCC Prototype numbers, and structures of the most important stable diazonium salts[43] used in the azoic color field.

Printing Compositions (Simultaneous application of coupling component and diazo component to fiber)

Diazotates. The procedures mentioned above (pp. 182, 208) for producing azoic patterns, by printing a thickened, active diazo solution (made by diazotizing an azoic base or by dissolving a stable diazonium salt) on cloth impregnated with a coupling component, require the unused coupling component in the unprinted areas of the pattern to be washed away and discarded. The first successful commercial technique for avoiding this waste was developed by German chemists in 1914. This development consisted of mixing Naphtols with passive sodium aryldiazotates[51]. These mixtures are known as "Rapid Fast" colors. They are applied by printing the mixture, dissolved in a thickened aqueous paste, on cellulose fabric, followed by activation of the diazo component by steam and dilute acid to produce the desired color in the printed areas. This technique permits the printing of azoic colors in fast and brilliant shades by cheap and simple techniques without loss of unused coupling component.

The Rapid Fast colors are limited in their usefulness by the fact that positively substituted diazo components are not well adapted to the formation of passive sodium diazotates[63]. In addition, these colors tend to decompose gradually on standing.

TABLE 3. STABLE DIAZONIUM SALTS

Name	No.	Structure
(Fast) Black (Salt) B	Pr. 255	zinc chloride complex 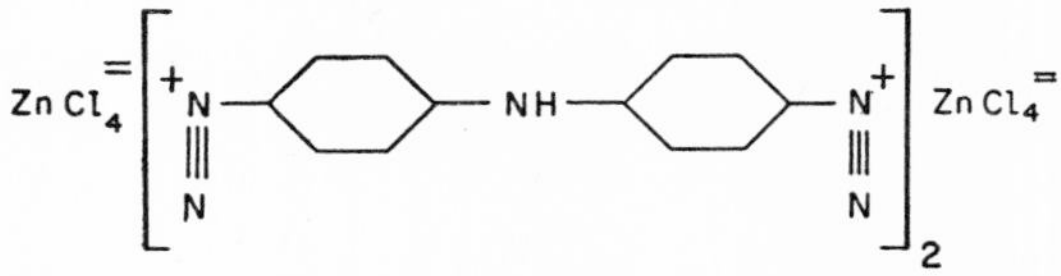

Black G   zinc chloride complex

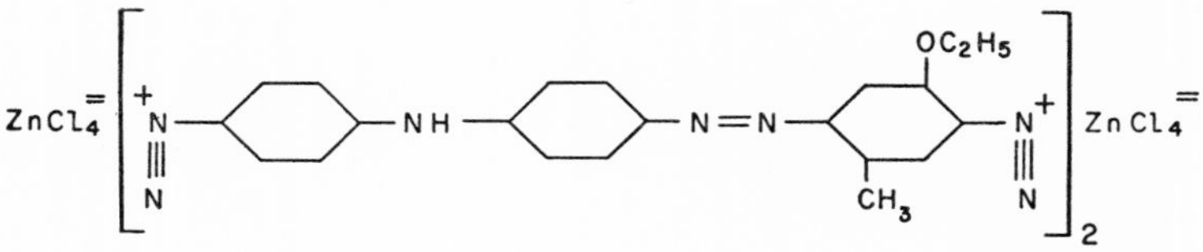

Black K   Pr. 256   zinc chloride complex

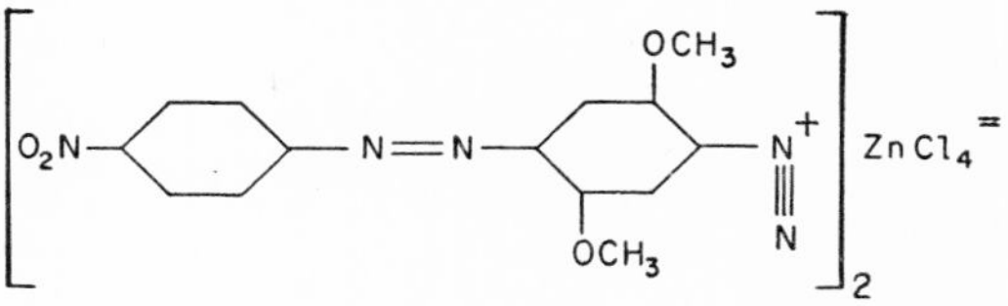

Blue B   CI 499   zinc chloride complex

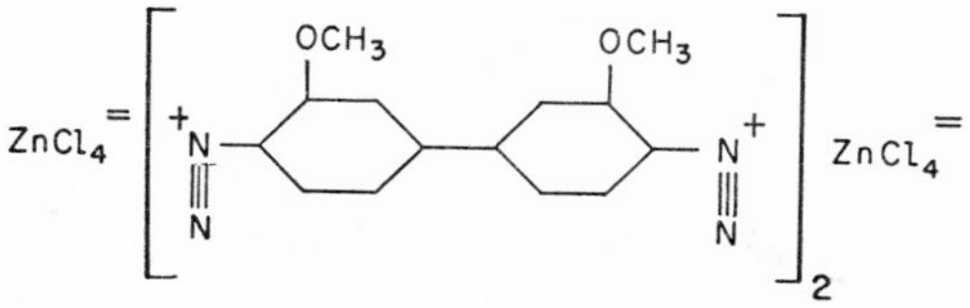

Variamine Blue B   Pr. 357   diazonium chloride

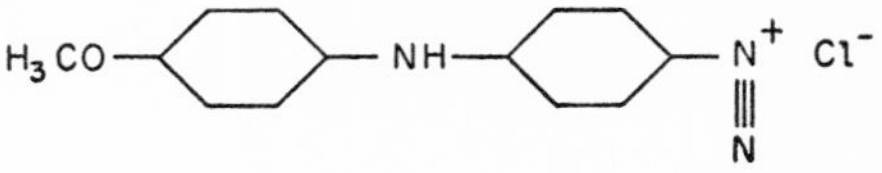

Blue BB   Pr. 258   zinc chloride complex

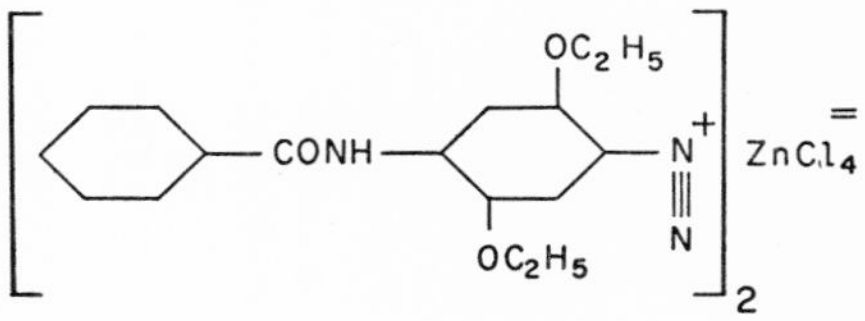

TABLE 3—*Continued*

Name	No.	Structure
Variamine Blue FG		diazonium chloride 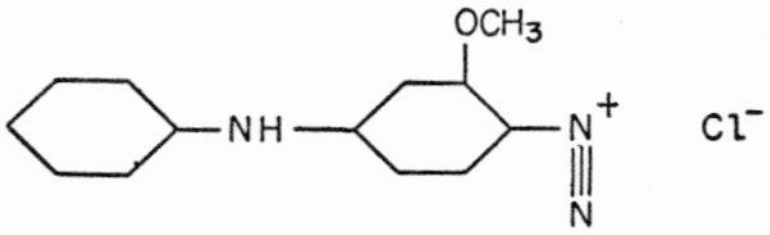
Blue RR	Pr. 498	zinc chloride complex 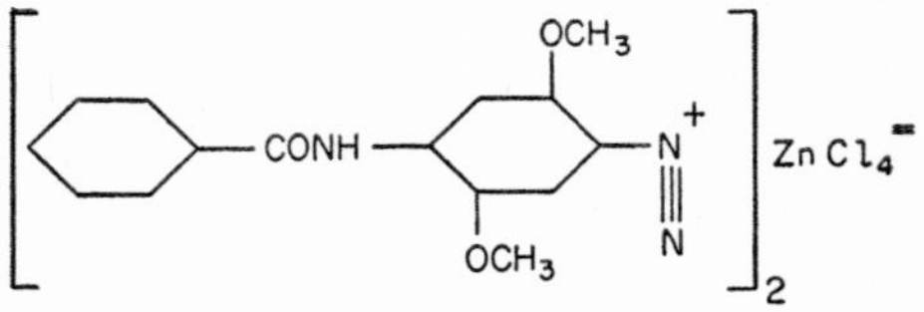
Variamine Blue RT	Pr. 358	diazonium chloride 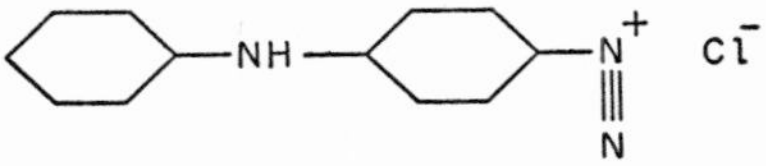
Bordeaux BD	Pr. 259	zinc chloride complex 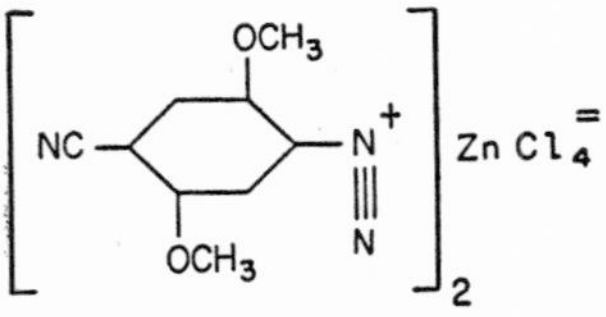
Bordeaux GP	Pr. 260	zinc chloride complex 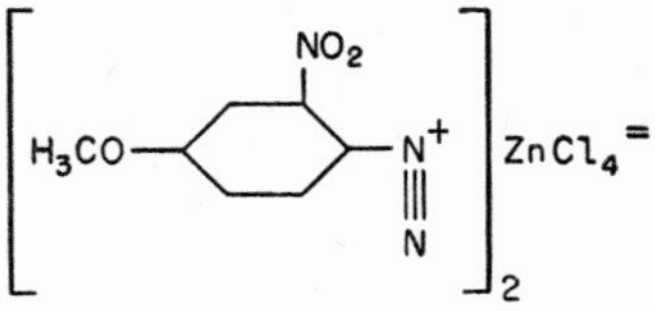
Corinth LB	Pr. 499	zinc chloride complex 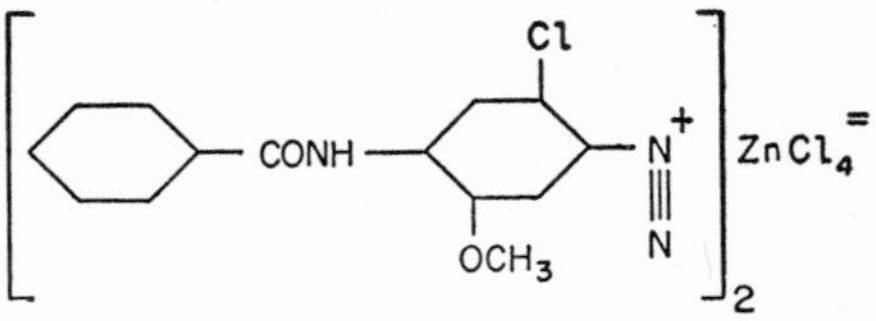

TABLE 3—*Continued*

Name	No.	Structure
Corinth V	Pr. 261	zinc chloride complex 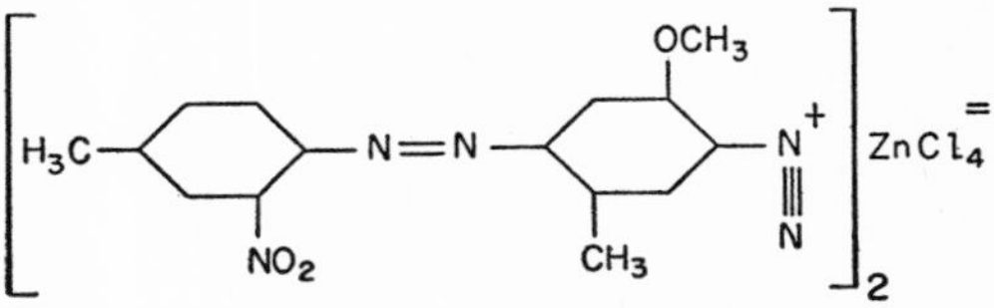

| Garnet GBC | CI 17 | diazonium acid sulfate 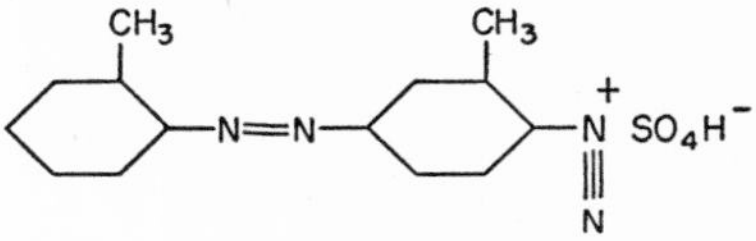 |

| Orange GC | Pr. 264 | diazonium fluoborate 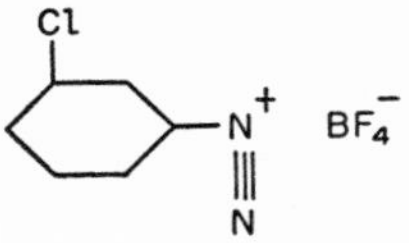 |

| Orange GGD | | zinc chloride complex 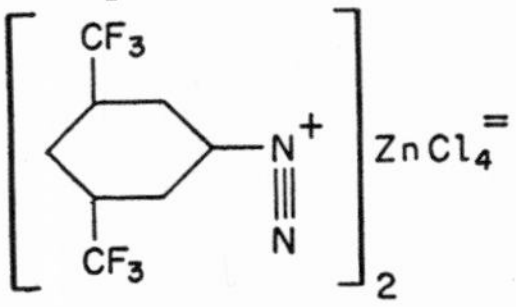 |

| Orange GR | Pr. 265 | zinc chloride complex 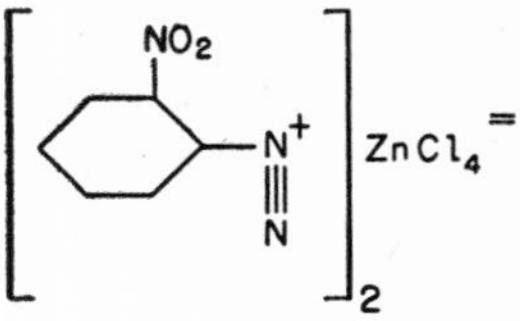 |

| Golden Orange GR | | zinc chloride complex 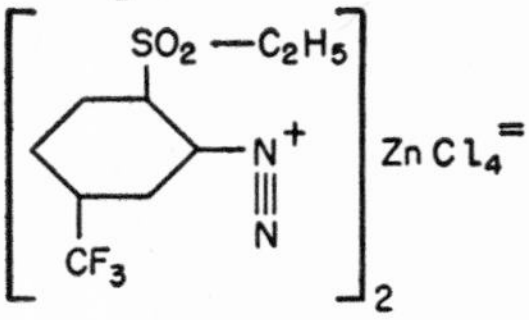 |

TABLE 3—*Continued*

Name	No.	Structure
Orange LG		zinc chloride complex

Orange R		acid 1,5-naphthalenedisulfonate

Orange RD	Pr. 266	zinc chloride complex

Red AL	Pr. 267	zinc chloride complex

Red B	CI 117	acid 1,5-naphthalenedisulfonate

Red FG		zinc chloride complex

TABLE 3—*Continued*

Name	No.	Structure
Red FR	Pr. 500	cobaltous chloride complex 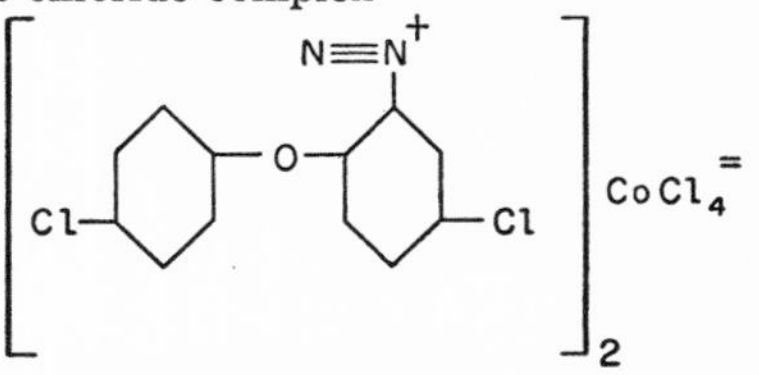

$$\left[\text{Cl}-\bigcirc-\text{O}-\bigcirc(\text{N}{\equiv}\text{N}^+)-\text{Cl} \right]_2 \text{CoCl}_4^=$$

| Red G | CI 69 | acid 1,5-naphthalenedisulfonate |

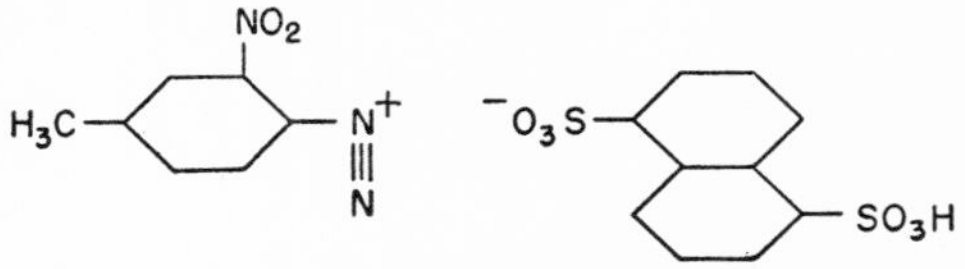

$$\text{H}_3\text{C}-\bigcirc(\text{NO}_2)-\underset{\text{N}}{\overset{+}{\text{N}}}\ \ ^-\text{O}_3\text{S}-\bigcirc\bigcirc-\text{SO}_3\text{H}$$

(zinc chloride complex is also used)

| Red GG | CI 44 | diazonium fluoborate |

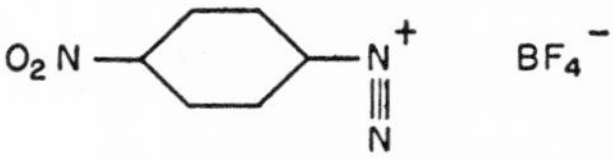

$$\text{O}_2\text{N}-\bigcirc-\underset{\text{N}}{\overset{+}{\text{N}}}\ \ \text{BF}_4^-$$

(*p*-chlorobenzenesulfonate is also used)

| Red 3G | Pr. 269 | zinc chloride complex 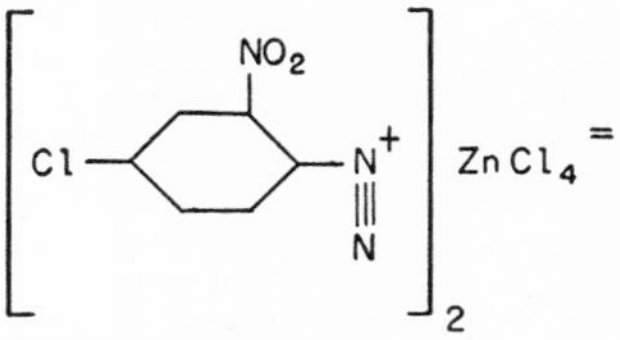 |

$$\left[\text{Cl}-\bigcirc(\text{NO}_2)-\underset{\text{N}}{\overset{+}{\text{N}}} \right]_2 \text{ZnCl}_4^=$$

| Red GTR | | zinc chloride complex 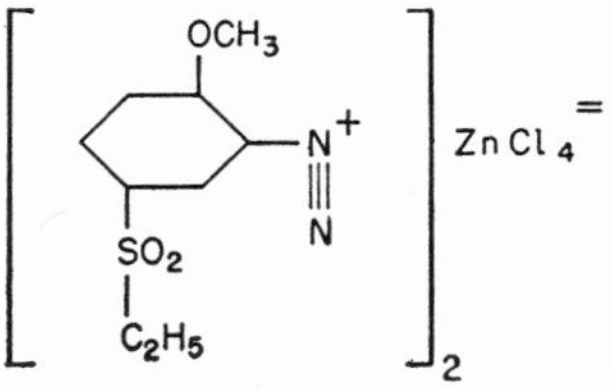 |

$$\left[\bigcirc(\text{OCH}_3)(\text{SO}_2{-}\text{C}_2\text{H}_5)-\underset{\text{N}}{\overset{+}{\text{N}}} \right]_2 \text{ZnCl}_4^=$$

| Red ITR | Pr. 378 | zinc chloride complex 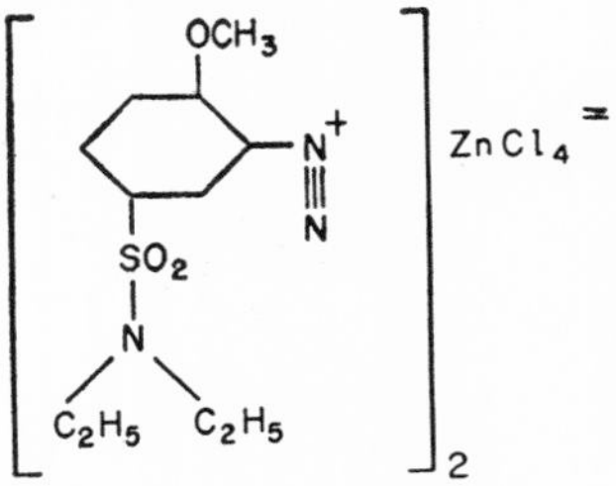 |

$$\left[\bigcirc(\text{OCH}_3)(\text{SO}_2{-}\text{N}(\text{C}_2\text{H}_5)(\text{C}_2\text{H}_5))-\underset{\text{N}}{\overset{+}{\text{N}}} \right]_2 \text{ZnCl}_4^=$$

213

TABLE 3—*Continued*

Name	No.	Structure

Red KB   Pr. 270   *N*-acetylsulfanilate

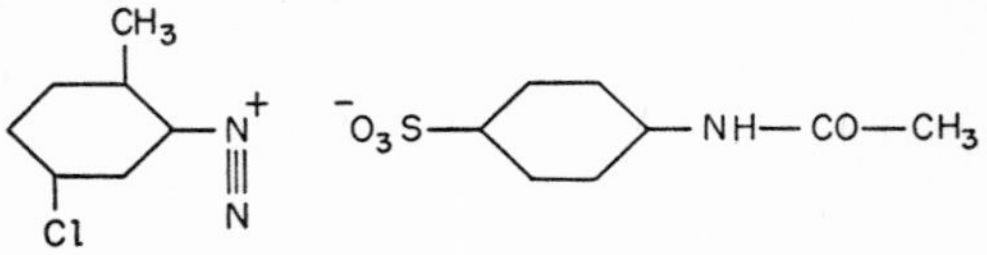

Red RC   Pr. 271   zinc chloride complex

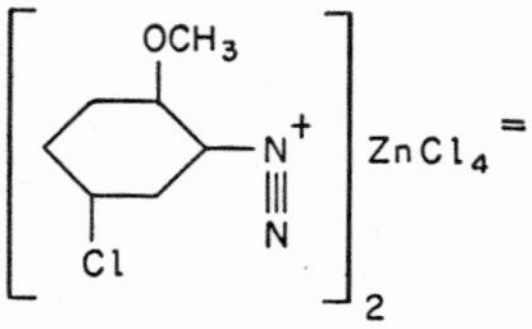

Red RL   Pr. 272   diazonium fluoborate

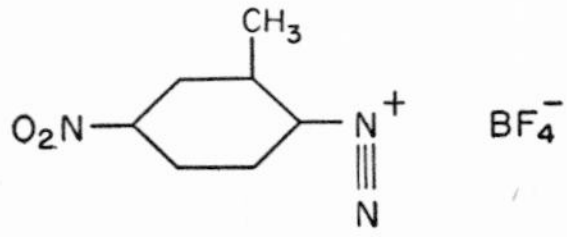

Red TR   Pr. 273   acid 1,5-naphthalenedisulfonate

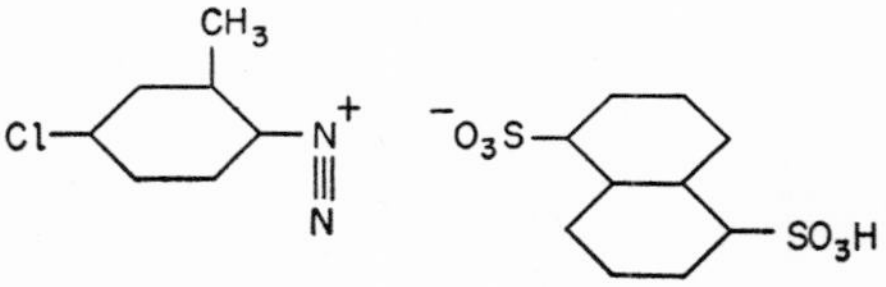

Scarlet G   CI 68   acid 1,5-naphthalenedisulfonate

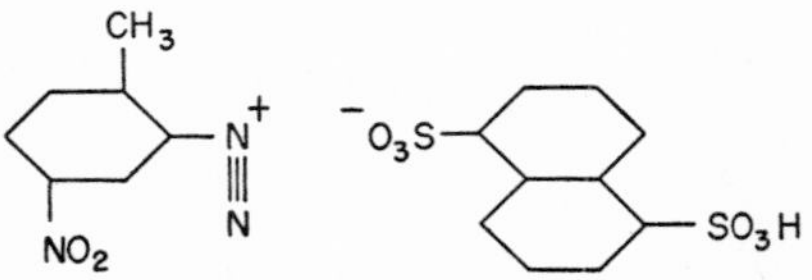

Scarlet GG   Pr. 94   zinc chloride complex

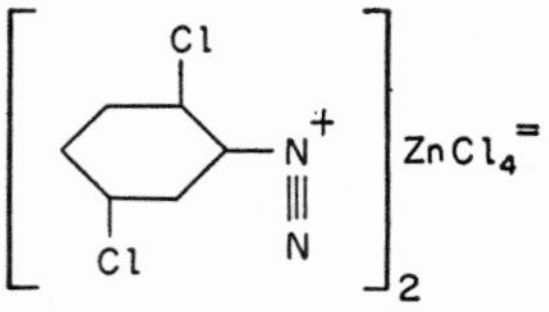

TABLE 3—*Continued*

Name	No.	Structure

Scarlet LG   zinc chloride complex

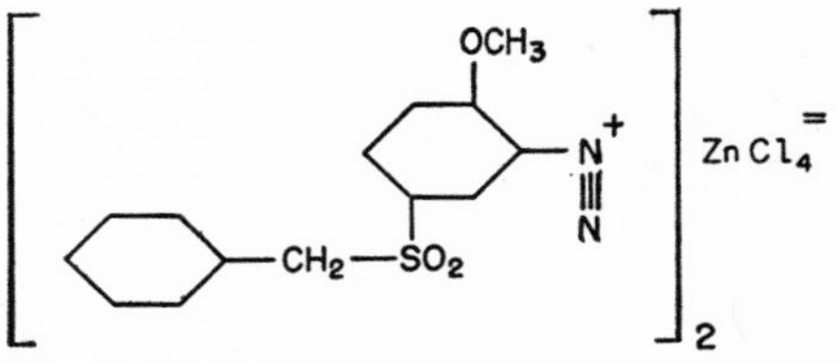

$$\left[\ \bigcirc-CH_2-SO_2- \overset{OCH_3}{\underset{}{\bigcirc}} -\overset{+}{N}\equiv N \right]_2 ZnCl_4^{=}$$

Scarlet R   CI 118   zinc chloride complex

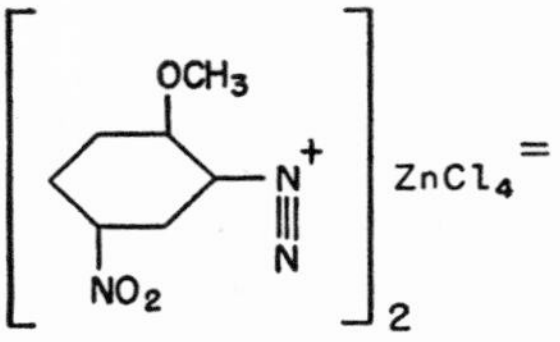

$$\left[\overset{OCH_3}{\underset{NO_2}{\bigcirc}} -\overset{+}{N}\equiv N \right]_2 ZnCl_4^{=}$$

Scarlet VD   acid 1,5-naphthalenedisulfonate

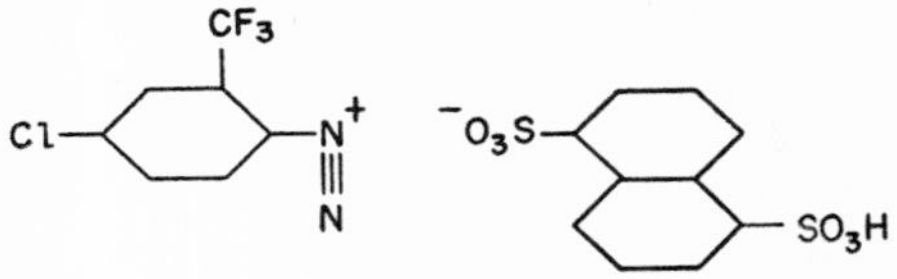

$$Cl-\overset{CF_3}{\underset{}{\bigcirc}}-\overset{+}{N}\equiv N \qquad {}^-O_3S-\bigcirc\bigcirc-SO_3H$$

Violet B   Pr. 274   zinc chloride complex

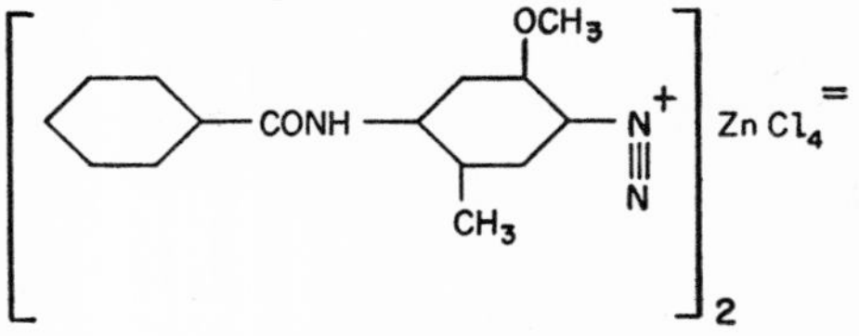

$$\left[\bigcirc-CONH-\overset{OCH_3}{\underset{CH_3}{\bigcirc}}-\overset{+}{N}\equiv N \right]_2 ZnCl_4^{=}$$

Yellow GC   Pr. 275   zinc chloride complex

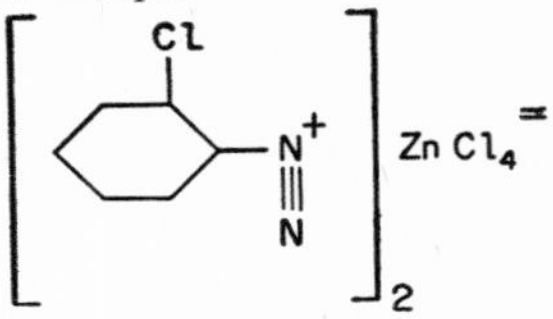

$$\left[\overset{Cl}{\underset{}{\bigcirc}}-\overset{+}{N}\equiv N \right]_2 ZnCl_4^{=}$$

Table 4 lists the names, AATCC Prototype numbers, and color components of the most important Rapid Fast colors[35].

The question of the structure of diazo compounds in general and of alkali metal diazotates in particular has been investigated actively since Griess's

TABLE 4. RAPID FAST COLORS

Color	No.	Base of Isodiazotate	Coupling Component
Blue B	Pr. 464	Blue B	Naphtol AS
Bordeaux IB	Pr. 465	Red B	Naphtol AS-BO
Bordeaux RH		Red RC	Naphtol AS-BS
Brown GGH		Scarlet GG	Naphtol AS-LB
Brown IBH		Red RC	Naphtol AS-LB
Brown IRH	Pr. 400	Scarlet GG	Naphtol AS-BG
Orange RG		Orange GR	Naphtol AS
Orange RH	Pr. 334	Scarlet GG	Naphtol AS-PH
Red B		Red B	Naphtol AS
Red BB		Red B	Naphtol AS-BS
Red FGH	Pr. 335	Red KB	Naphtol AS-D
Red GL		Red G	Naphtol AS
Red GZH		Scarlet GG	Naphtol AS
Red ILB		Red RL	Naphtol AS-RL
Red IRH		Red TR	Naphtol AS-LT
Red RH	Pr. 336	Red RC	Naphtol AS-OL
Scarlet ILH	Pr. 337	Scarlet GG	Naphtol AS-OL
Scarlet RH	Pr. 401	Red KB	Naphtol AS-PH
Yellow GGH	Pr. 338	Red RC	Naphtol AS-G
Yellow GH		Scarlet GG	Naphtol AS-G
Yellow I3GH		Red TR	Naphtol I3GH

original discovery[21]. The problem is still unsolved and much careful work with modern tools remains to be done before agreement on the structure question is reached.

A good general discussion of diazo structure is provided by Saunders[65].

Griess encountered the normal or active potassium benzenediazotate in 1866[23]. The iso- or passive diazotates, capable of inertness in contact with sodium 2-naphtholate, were discovered by Schraube and Schmidt, staff chemists of BASF, in 1894[73]. Their work with sodium p-nitrobenzenediazotate in its inactive or iso form is the basis for today's Rapid Fast colors. The term "nitrosamine," which is widely used in industrial laboratories in describing isodiazotates, was first used by Schraube and Schmidt. They observed that one of the tautomers in their diazotate from p-nitroaniline was

since it could be reacted with methyl iodide to yield N-methyl-p-nitro-N-nitrosoaniline.

The most far-reaching early studies on the structure of diazo compounds were carried out by Hantzsch[31] and his students. The formulas proposed by

Hantzsch, while not universally accepted, form the basis for most current use. Hantzsch proposed that the salt-forming organic base of acid diazo systems be represented by the pentavalent-nitrogen diazonium cation [benzene ring]—N+≡N. He further proposed that the labile normal diazotate which

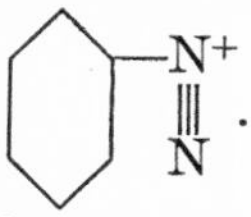

is the reactive isomer readily formed from positively substituted diazo compounds and aqueous sodium hydroxide be known as the "syn" form on the basis of its relatively high energy content: [benzene ring]—N=N—ONa (NaO—N). The stable

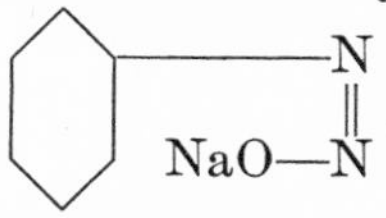

isodiazotate was described by Hantzsch as the "anti" form represented by: [benzene ring]—N, N—ONa. The passive isodiazotates are formed readily from

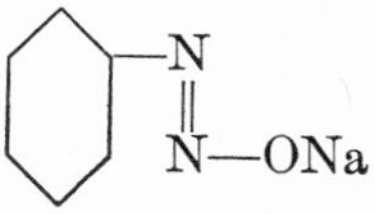

negatively substituted diazo compounds and aqueous sodium hydroxide. The labile normal diazotates may be converted to the passive iso form by heating[63].

The subject of diazo structure has been reattacked in recent years by the British. The discussions of Hodgson[32], Le Fevre[55], and Waters[75] on diazotates, diazocyanides, and the mechanisms of diazo decomposition are spirited if not in agreement with each other. Russian workers[62] also are active in the field.

Triazenes. Diazo compounds react with amines in weakly acid or alkaline solution to form triazenes. Negatively substituted diazo compounds frequently form triazenes with undiazotized portions of the starting aromatic amine during the diazotization process if insufficient nitrous acid is present.

Triazenes of practical usefulness result if the non-diazo amine, or stabilizer, is free from azo coupling positions and bears groups promoting solubility in water. Such triazenes are then water-soluble and yield the original diazo compound on treatment with volatile acids and steam.

Griess made the triazene from diazobenzene and *m*-aminobenzoic acid in 1864[22].

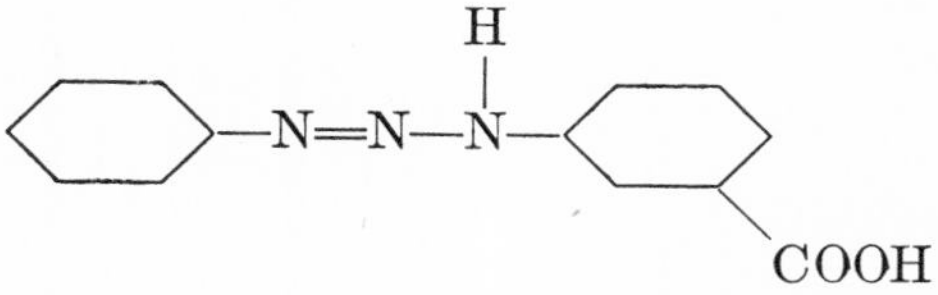

He reported the water-soluble triazene from diazobenzene and *m*-ethylaminobenzoic acid in 1877[24].

$$\text{} \quad \overset{\displaystyle C_2H_5}{\underset{|}{}}$$

The hydrolysis of water-soluble triazenes by acid to yield diazo compounds and the stabilizing amines was described by Mehner in 1901[58].

Mixtures of triazenes with Naphtols were first brought to commercial usefulness as Rapidogen colors by I. G. Farbenindustrie in the early 1930's[16]. These colors are used widely for printing bright, durable patterns on cellulosic textiles from thickened aqueous printing pastes. Development of the color on the fiber is achieved by passing the printed textile through steam containing vaporized acetic and formic acids. Trade names of related products include Arigens (Interchemical), Atcogens (Atlantic Chemical), Brentogens (Imperial Chemical Industries), Calconyls (American Cyanamid), Diagens (Du Pont), Naccogenes (Allied Chemical and Dye), Novagens (Nova Chemical), and Pharmols (Pharma Chemical).

The Rapidogen colors share with the Rapid Fast colors described above the advantage of clear white areas on printed patterns in comparison with prints made with Fast Salts on Naphtolated cloth. The Rapidogens also resemble the Rapid Fast colors in permitting the printing of patterns without discarding unused Naphtol from the unprinted areas. In addition, the triazene form of stabilized diazo compound yields brighter shades than the corresponding diazotate, since less diazo decomposition is encountered in the triazene synthesis and in the diazo regeneration on the fabric. The triazene principle can be applied to a wide range of color combinations. Rapidogen colors are appreciably more stable to storage than are the Rapid Fast colors.

One of the disadvantages of the triazene principle in azoic dye printing is the fact that the requirement for acid conditions in color development does not favor the use of Rapidogen colors in the same pattern with vat colors, since the acid liberates sulfur dioxide and formaldehyde from the vatting agents, resulting in chemical attack on the azoic color. An ingenious solution to this problem is provided by a recent German innovation[69] in Rapidogen printing, in which a steam-volatile water-soluble strong organic base (e.g., 2-diethylaminoethanol—Rapidogen Developer N) is substituted for sodium hydroxide in dissolving the Rapidogen mixture for printing, whereby appropriately constituted Rapidogens can be developed fully on the fiber by pH lowering through the action of steam alone. This technique makes it possible to print Rapidogen and vat colors in the same pattern without liberating sulfur dioxide or formaldehyde from the vat color reducing agents.

Table 5 lists the names, AATCC Prototype numbers, and constitutions of the most important Rapidogen colors[37].

The outstanding commercial success of the German-developed Rapidogen colors and the patent protection enjoyed by their originators created a competitive situation which led to the use of widely varied chemical types as stabilizing amines.

German usage[16] centers on methylaminoacetic acid (sarcosine), 2-methylaminoethanesulfonic acid (*N*-methyltaurine), and 2-ethylamino-5-sulfobenzoic acid. American developments have resulted in the use of *N*-methylglucamine[7], 2,2′-iminodiethanol[48], pipecolic acid[56], proline[56], (ethylenediimino)diacetic acid[57], and 3-guanylureasulfonic acid[54].

The stabilizer chosen for use with a given diazo compound is dictated by the structure of the diazo. A substantially constant strength must be maintained in the hydrolyzable N—N bond in the triazene in order to assure similar development behavior in all of the colors in the Rapidogen shade range. Negatively substituted diazo compounds thus require negatively substituted stabilizers in order that the triazene be sufficiently labile for complete color development on the fiber. Positively substituted diazo compounds in turn require positively substituted stabilizers in order that premature hydrolysis of the triazene component of the Rapidogen mixture will not occur during storage or in the textile printing paste. A schematic illustration of the effect of substituents on the hydrolyzable N—N bond in an azoic triazene follows.

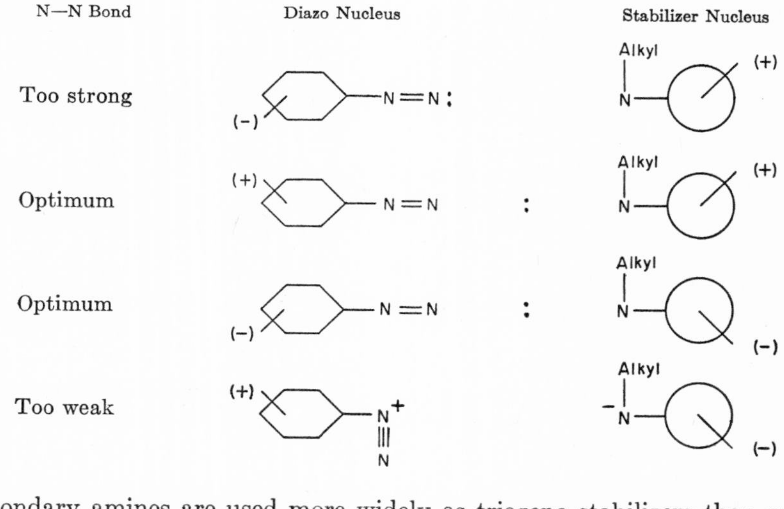

Secondary amines are used more widely as triazene stabilizers than are primary amines for two reasons. First, in the case of an aliphatic stabilizer, especially if it is a positively substituted type, there is a tendency for two

TABLE 5. RAPIDOGEN COLORS

Triazene

Color	No.	Base	Stabilizer*	Coupling Component
Black IT		Red B	MASB	Naphtol AS-SR (40%)
				Naphtol 44-S† (60%)
Blue B	Pr. 163	Blue BB	50:50 S:MT	Naphtol AS
Navy Blue B		Blue B	MT	Naphtol AS
Blue R	Pr. 342	Blue RR	MT	Naphtol AS
Navy Blue R		Blue BB (60%)	50:50 S:MT	Naphtol AS-BO
		Blue RR (40%)	MT	
Bordeaux IB		Red B	MASB	Naphtol AS-BO
Bordeaux RN	Pr. 165	Red RL	EASB	Naphtol AS-D
Brown IB	Pr. 343	Red RC	S	Naphtol AS-LB
Brown IBR	Pr. 344	p-Toluidine	S	Naphtol AS-LB
Brown IR	Pr. 466	Scarlet GG	EASB	Naphtol AS-BG
Brown IRRN		Red RL	EASB	Naphtol AS-LB
Black Brown ITR		Red ITR	EASB	Naphtol AS-BT
Black Brown T		Red RC	S	Naphtol AS-BT
Corinth IB	Pr. 511	Corinth LB	MASB	Naphtol AS-LT
Green B	Pr. 347	Blue BB	50:50 S:MT	Naphtol AS-GR
Orange G	Pr. 348	Orange GC	ASB	Naphtol AS-D
Golden Orange IGG		Golden Orange GR	(diazotate)	Naphtol AS-D
Orange IGN		Orange GGD	EASB	Naphtol AS-OL
Orange IRR		Orange RD	EASB	Naphtol AS-OL
Orange R	Pr. 349	Scarlet GG	EASB	Naphtol AS-PH
Red G	Pr. 168	Red KB	ASB	Naphtol AS-D
Red GS	Pr. 168	Red KB	S	Naphtol AS-D
Red IGG	Pr. 468	Red GR‡	MASB	Naphtol AS-LC
Red ITR	Pr. 402	Red ITR	EASB	Naphtol AS-ITR
Red R	Pr. 169	Red RC	S	Naphtol AS-OL
Scarlet IL	Pr. 403	Scarlet GG	EASB	Naphtol AS-OL
Scarlet R	Pr. 170	Red KB	ASB	Naphtol AS-PH
Scarlet RS	Pr. 170	Red KB	S	Naphtol AS-PH
Violet B	Pr. 351	Violet B	S	Naphtol AS
Red Violet RR	Pr. 350	Violet RR§	EASB	Naphtol AS-BO
Yellow G	Pr. 171	Red KB	ASB	Naphtol AS-G
Yellow GG	Pr. 353	Red RC	S	Naphtol AS-G
Yellow GS	Pr. 171	Red KB	S	Naphtol AS-G
Yellow I4G	Pr. 469	Red TR	MT	Naphtol AS-I3GH
Golden Yellow IFG	Pr. 467	Red RC	S	Naphtol IFG

* ASB, 2-amino-4-sulfobenzoic acid (4-sulfoanthranilic acid)
  EASB, 2-ethylamino-5-sulfobenzoic acid (N-ethyl-5-sulfoanthranilic acid)
  MASB, 2-methylamino-5-sulfobenzoic acid (N-methyl-5-sulfoanthranilic acid)
  MT, N-methyltaurine
  S, sarcosine
† 5,6,7,8-tetrahydro-3-hydroxy-N-1-naphthyl-2-naphthamide[42]
‡ 4-dimethylsulfamyl-2-aminotoluene (3-amino-N,N-dimethyl-p-toluenesulfonamide)
§ 2-methoxy-5-methyl-4-nitroaniline (5-methyl-4-nitro-o-anisidine)

molecules of diazo compound to react with one molecule of the primary amine stabilizer. This leads to low triazene solubility and to erratic diazo regeneration on the printed fiber. Secondly, in cases in which the stabilizer is a negatively substituted primary aromatic amine, the possibility of diazo interchange is presented:

$$
\begin{array}{ccc}
\overset{\displaystyle H}{\underset{\displaystyle |}{}} & & \overset{\displaystyle H}{\underset{\displaystyle |}{}} \\
-N{=}N{-}N{-} & \rightleftharpoons & -N{-}N{=}N{-}
\end{array}
$$

The diazo interchange tends to approach an equilibrium[11] in which the principal triazene component is the one whose acid hydrolysis would yield a diazo compound bearing the nucleus with the highest degree of negative substitution. The diazo interchange equilibrium causes an undesirable mixture of dyes when color is developed on the printed fabric.

Triazenes are prepared, in general, by slow addition of a cold (0 to 5°C) aqueous light-protected diazo solution to an agitated aqueous solution of a secondary amine kept alkaline to a pH of 8–9 (Brilliant Yellow test paper, e.g.) with sodium carbonate. The diazo is added no faster than the rate at which it is absorbed by the amine, as judged by external test on absorbent paper with a dilute (1 to 2 per cent) aqueous solution of an azo coupling component (such as H acid or R salt) in sodium carbonate. The triazene product is isolated by filtration or liquid phase separation, preceded by salting if necessary, and is dried at 50 to 90°C, preferably in vacuum. Highly soluble triazenes must sometimes be isolated by vacuum or spray drying of the entire solution. Positively substituted diazos frequently require upward adjustment of pH with sodium hydroxide toward the end of the reaction to permit complete condensation of the diazo with the amine. Negatively substituted diazos frequently require downward adjustment of pH (sodium acetate in place of sodium carbonate) to avoid formation of a sodium aryldiazotate instead of the desired triazene.

Diazosulfonates. Diazo compounds react with alkali metal sulfites in neutral water solution to form solid salt-like products variously known as diazosulfonates, diazosulfonic acids or diazosulfites. These products dissolve in water as inactive diazo compounds requiring carefully controlled neutral oxidation (as with sodium chromate) for activation.

The German commercial development of diazosulfonates used diazotized aminodiphenylamines[78], which were marketed as mixtures with azoic coupling components as Rapidazole colors[79] for printing blue and black shades on cotton fibers. The Rapidazole colors are applied by dissolving the mixture in a water solution of sodium hydroxide containing sodium chromate, followed by thickening, printing, and developing in neutral steam for 10 minutes.

This application of diazosulfonates is uniquely useful with aminodiphenylamine bases, since this type of base does not lend itself readily to the formation of diazotates (for use in Rapid Fast colors) or to the formation of triazenes (for use in Rapidogen colors) due to the tendency of diazos from aminodiphenylamines to revert in the presence of alkali to quinone diazides.*

Table 6 includes the names and constitutions of the German Rapidazole colors[36]. These products are standardized with precipitated sulfur and sodium sulfite.

TABLE 6. RAPIDAZOLE COLORS

Color	Base of Diazosulfonate	Coupling Component
Black B	4-amino-4'-methoxydiphenylamine	Naphtol AS-OL (88%) Naphtol AS-G (12%)
Navy Blue G	4-amino-4'-methoxydiphenylamine	Naphtol AS-D
Blue IB	4-amino-4'-methoxydiphenylamine	Naphtol AS
Navy Blue RR	4-aminodiphenylamine	Naphtol AS-D

The French offered mixtures of diazosulfonates derived from mono-nuclear bases with coupling components[52], designed to yield printed yellow, scarlet, red, and blue shades on cotton. The application of these "Photorapide" colors involves dissolving the mixture in aqueous sodium hydroxide, thickening, printing, and developing by a 5-minute exposure to a mercury vapor lamp in a steam atmosphere at a controlled temperature of 57 to 60°C measured at the surface of the goods. This application is not of commercial importance in the United States, due mainly to the long light exposure required for full color development.

The first diazosulfonate was prepared by Schmitt and Glutz from p-aminophenol[70]. Hantzsch[28] proposed that the two physical forms in which diazosulfonates occur be represented as syn and anti isomers by analogy with alkali diazotates.

---

* The water-insoluble explosive quinone diazides were discovered by Hantzsch[30] and were later studied by Morgan[60]. These workers assumed that quinone diazides existed in one or the other of two forms:

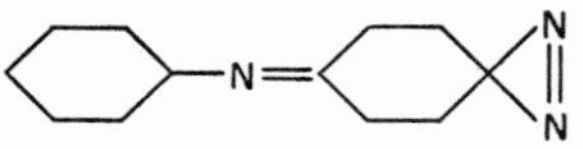

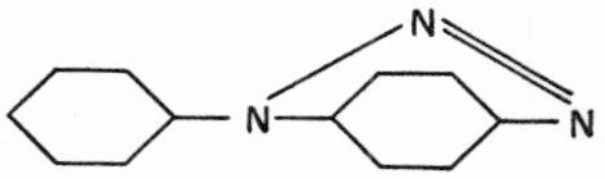

The quinone diazide from diazotized 4-aminodiphenylamine was referred to by Hantzsch as "phenylimidoquinone diazide," and was assumed to resemble a diazophenol. The structures proposed by Hantzsch are unlikely on a stereochemical basis, and it is probable that a salt form such as 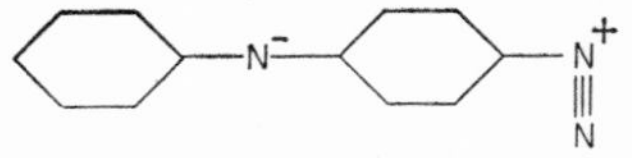 prevails.

These compounds can be reactivated in cold mineral acid to diazonium salts.

syn   anti

Bamberger[2] later suggested that Hantzsch's syn isomer could be better represented as an aryldiazosulfite and that the anti form of Hantzsch was probably an aryldiazosulfonate.

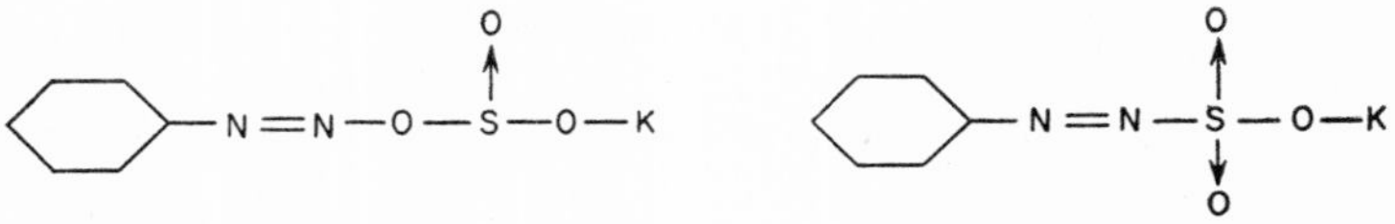

active diazosulfite   inactive diazosulfonate

Recent studies by Hodgson[33] appear to confirm Bamberger's structures·
The reactive diazosulfite isomer is formed readily from positively substituted diazos, is deeply colored, reacts with 2-naphthol, liberates nitrogen in contact with copper sulfate, reduces iodine, and liberates sulfur dioxide in contact with mineral acid. This isomer also absorbs diazotized p-nitroaniline as an inactive complex.

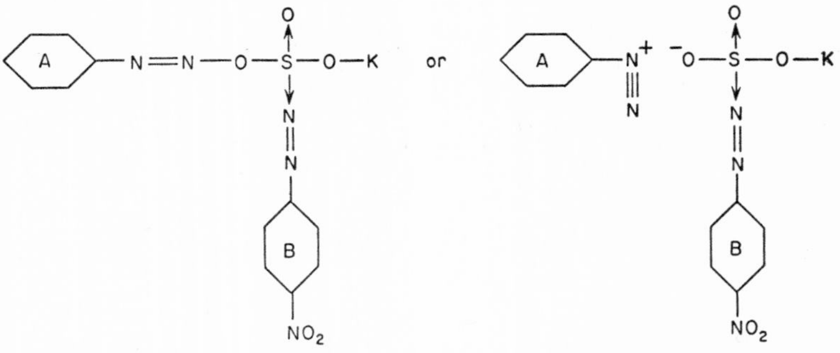

Thus diazo residue A is active (will couple with 2-naphthol, e.g.), while diazo residue B is inactive. The diazosulfite concept is consistent with the known instability of many diazo oxides.

The reactive diazosulfites are converted rapidly in the presence of water to the light colored unreactive diazosulfonates, which show no reaction with 2-naphthol, copper sulfate, or iodine, and which do not release sulfur dioxide in the presence of acids. The diazosulfonates react with diazotized p-nitroaniline to form an active complex.

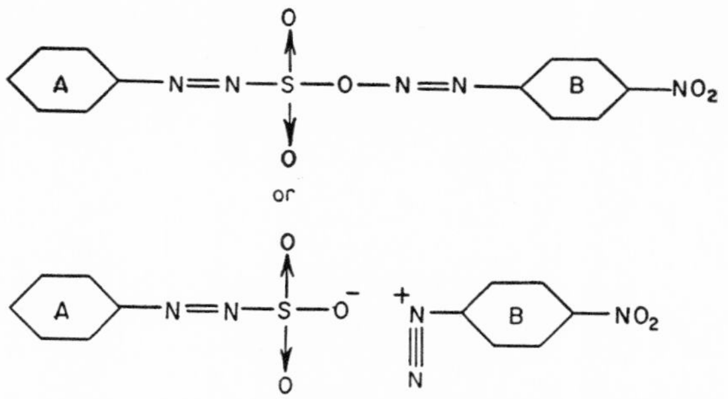

Thus in this case diazo residue A is inactive and diazo residue B is active. The diazosulfonate structure is substantiated further by the known general stability of the —N=N—S— link.

As indicated above, diazosulfonates are converted to active diazonium compounds under the influence of oxidation by chromates or by air. Negatively substituted diazo compounds go directly to the unreactive diazosulfonate form when reacted with alkali sulfites[29].

Temporarily Solubilized Pigments. In 1935 the Swiss developed a group of textile-printing colors known as Neocotones[17]. These products are largely preformed azoic pigments which have been reacted with m-(chlorosulfonyl)benzoic acid in pyridine to produce water-soluble derivatives. These derivatives can be printed from aqueous pastes onto cellulose fabric, steamed for penetration, and developed to insoluble pigment form in an aqueous solution of sodium hydroxide, barium chloride, and sodium chloride. The Neocotone colors have not enjoyed nearly as much use as the Rapidogen colors in the American textile printing industry.

The general structure of the Neocotones[18, 19, 20] is,

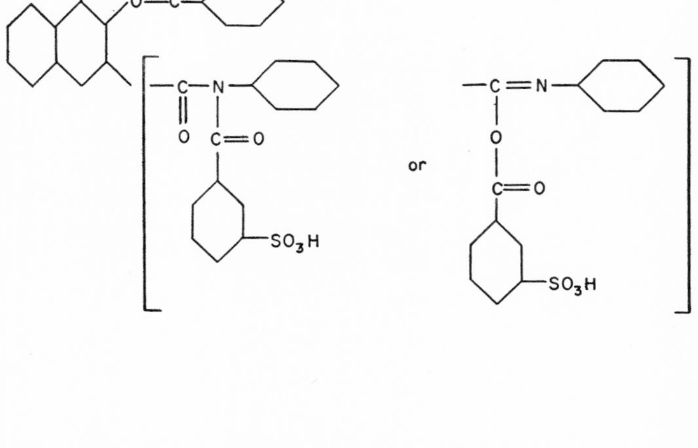

in which the lower sulfobenzoic acid residue may be bound either to the keto or the enol tautomer of the pigment.

Table 7 lists the names and structures of representative Neocotone colors[1, 45].

TABLE 7. NEOCOTONE COLORS

Color	Base	Coupling Component
Blue B	Blue BB	Naphtol AS
Bordeaux B	Bordeaux GP	Naphtol AS-OL
Bordeaux R	Red RL	Naphtol AS-D
Orange GR	Orange GC	Naphtol AS-OL
Red R	Red TR	Naphtol AS-TR
Red 2G	Red KB	Naphtol AS-D
Scarlet G	Scarlet GG	Naphtol AS-OL
Scarlet 27	Red KB	Naphtol AS-PH
Yellow G	Condensation production of 1 mole of cyanuric chloride with 2 moles of 2-aminoanthraquinone and 1 mole of aniline	

Ruggli and Gruen[64] have described the interesting behavior of *m*-(chlorosulfonyl)benzoic acid in the formation of amides and esters. With sodium hydroxide as acid acceptor, its reactions are normal. With pyridine as acid acceptor, it reacts as a carbonyl chloride, as illustrated on page 224. It is postulated that the anomalous behavior of *m*-(chlorosulfonyl)benzoic acid in pyridine is due to the formation of an addition complex with pyridine. This complex has been isolated in the cold and reacted with aniline to give 3-sulfobenzanilide. A similar reaction is known to take place when *p*-toluenesulfonyl chloride, benzoic acid, pyridine, and aniline are reacted together, the principal reaction product being benzanilide.

Literature Cited

1. Adams, *J. Soc. Dyers Colourists*, **67,** 223 (1951).
2. Bamberger, *Ber.*, **27,** 2586, 2930 (1894).
3. Bhat, Forster, and Venkataraman, *J. Soc. Dyers Colourists*, **56,** 166 (1940).
4. —— and Venkataraman, *ibid.*, **58,** 155 (1942).
5. Boese, U.S. Patent 2,152,786 (1939).
6. ——, *Ind. Eng. Chem.*, **32,** 16 (1940).
7. Dahlen and Zwilgmeyer, U.S. Patent 1,968,878 (1934).
8. Diserens, "The Chemical Technology of Dyeing and Printing," transl. from the 2nd German ed. by Wengraf and Baumann, Vol. I, pp. 212–409 (The Insoluble Azo Dyestuffs), New York, Reinhold Publishing Corp., 1948.
9. ——, *ibid.*, p. 354.
10. Eistert, *Ann.*, **556,** 91 (1944).
11. Ershov and Ioffe, *J. Gen. Chem. (USSR)*, **9,** 2211 (1939); *C.A.*, **34,** 5420 (1940).
12. Fieser and Fieser, "Organic Chemistry," 2nd ed., p. 938, Boston, D. C. Heath & Co., 1950.
13. Friedlaender, "Fortschritte der Teerfarbenfabrikation," Berlin, Julius Springer, **IV,** 644 (1894).
14. Gassner and Meiser, U.S. Patent 1,917,443 (1933).

15. German Patent 281,055 (1914).
16. Glietenberg, Neelmeier, Haller, and Hentrich, U.S. Patents 1,882,560–1–2 (1932).
17. Graenacher, Ackermann, and Bruengger, U.S. Patent 2,095,600 (1937).
18. ——, ——, and ——, U.S. Patent 2,199,048 (1940).
19. ——, ——, and ——, U.S. Patent 2,276,187 (1942).
20. ——, Bruengger, and Ackermann, *Helv. Chim. Acta*, **24**, 40E (1941).
21. Griess, *Ann.*, **106**, 123 (1858).
22. ——, *Phil. Trans.*, **154**, 680 (1864); *Chem. Zentr.*, **37**-I, 97 (1866).
23. ——, *Ann.*, **137**, 39 (1866).
24. ——, *Ber.*, **10**, 525 (1877).
25. Grimmel, Guenther, and Morgan, *J. Am. Chem. Soc.*, **68**, 539 (1946).
26. Groggins, "Unit Processes in Organic Synthesis," 4th ed., Chap. III by Woodward, New York, McGraw-Hill Book Co., 1952.
27. Guenther and Lange, U.S. Patent 1,572,715 (1926).
28. Hantzsch, *Ber.*, **27**, 1716, 1726 (1894).
29. ——, *ibid.*, **30**, 89 (1897).
30. ——, *ibid.*, **35**, 889, 895 (1902).
31. ——, *ibid.*, **45**, 3036 (1912); —— and Reddelien, "Die Diazoverbindungen," Berlin, Julius Springer, 1921. —— memorial lecture, *J. Chem. Soc.*, **1936**, 1051.
32. Hodgson, *J. Chem. Soc.*, **1944**, 395—diazocyanides; **1945**, 207—diazotates; **1948**, 348—diazo free radicals; **1948**, 1097—diazocyanides.
33. ——, *ibid.*, **1943**, 470; **1948**, 1183.
34. Holliday and Holliday, U.S. Patent 241,661 (1881); British Patent 2,757 (1880).
35. I. G. Farbenindustrie, BIOS 988, p. 12 (PB 60885).
36. ——, *ibid.*, pp. 12–13.
37. ——, *ibid.*, pp. 39–44.
38. ——, BIOS 1149, p. 141 (PB 80376).
39. ——, FIAT 1313, Vol. II, pp. 247–250 (PB 85172).
40. ——, "Economic Study," PB 548–561 (1945); *Bibl. Sci. Ind. Repts.*, **5**, 3 (1947).
41. ——, PB 70421, frame 1196; *Bibl. Sci. Ind. Repts.*, **7**, 571 (1947).
42. ——, *ibid.*, frame 1211.
43. ——, PB 74200; *Bibl. Sci. Ind. Repts.*, **6**, 471, 663 (1947).
44. ——, PB 74202; *Bibl. Sci. Ind. Repts.*, **6**, 471 (1947).
45. ——, PB 74760, frame 9445; *Bibl. Sci. Ind. Repts.*, **8**, 57 (1948).
46. Jacobson, Henrich, and Klein, *Ber.*, **26**, 693 (1893).
47. Keller and Schnitzspahn, U.S. Patent 1,717,453 (1929).
48. Kern, U.S. Patent 2,078,387 (1937).
49. Kirk and Othmer, eds., "Encyclopedia of Chemical Technology," New York, Interscience Publishers, Inc., article by Morse, Rottschaefer, Stanley, and West, **5**, 38–50 (1950).
50. Kunert, *Rev. gén. mat. color.*, **16**, 255 (1912); —— and Acker, *J. Soc. Dyers Colourists*, **30**, 128 (1914).
51. —— and Acker, U.S. Patent 1,127,027 (1915).
52. Lantz, U.S. Patent 2,206,611 (1940).
53. Laska and Zitscher, U.S. Patent 1,505,568 (1924).
54. Lecher and Parker, U.S. Patent 2,154,405 (1939).
55. Le Fevre, *J. Chem. Soc.*, **1938**, 431—diazocyanides; **1947**, 445, 457—diazocyanides.
56. Markush, U.S. Patent 1,982,681 (1934).
57. ——, Mayzner, and Miller, U.S. Patent 2,110,270 (1938).
58. Mehner, *J. prakt. Chem.*, **63**, 302 (1901).
59. Meyer, *Melliand Textilber.*, **9**, 573 (1928).

60. Morgan and Micklethwait, *J. Chem. Soc.*, **93**, 602 (1908).
61. Muth, U.S. Patent 2,026,908 (1936).
62. Porai-Koshits and Grachev, *J. Gen. Chem. (USSR)*, **16**, 571 (1946); *C.A.*, **41**, 1215 (1947).
63. Rozova, *Bull. acad. sci. (URSS), Classe sci. tech.*, 39 (1938) No. 6; *Chem. Zentr.*, **113**-I, 2708 (1942).
64. Ruggli and Gruen, *Helv. Chim. Acta*, **24**, 197 (1941).
65. Saunders, "The Aromatic Diazo-Compounds and Their Technical Applications," 2nd ed., London, Edward Arnold & Co., 1949.
66. Scheel, Thesis, Univ. of Frankfurt a/M., (1927); see Ruggli, *J. Soc. Dyers Colourists*, Jubilee Issue (after Vol. 50), 81 (1934).
67. Schmelzer, Ballauf, and Muth, U. S. Patent 1,919,573 (1933).
68. ——, ——, and Hefner, U.S. Patent 1,934,009 (1933).
69. ——, U.S. Patent 2,232,405 (1941).
70. Schmitt and Glutz, *Ber.*, **2**, 51 (1869).
71. Schnitzspahn and Jung, U.S. Patent 1,975,409 (1934).
72. Schoepff, *Ber.*, **25**, 2744 (1892).
73. Schraube and Schmidt, *Ber.*, **27**, 514 (1894); U.S. Patent 531,973 (1895).
73a. Spiegler, *J. Org. Chem.*, **18**, 1292 (1953).
74. Venkataraman, "The Chemistry of Synthetic Dyes," Vol. I, pp. 650–704, New York, Academic Press, Inc., 1952.
75. Waters, *J. Chem. Soc.*, **1946**, 1154—diazo free radicals; **1948**, 882—diazo free radicals.
76. Wilke-Doerfurt and Balz, *Ber.*, **60**, 115 (1927).
77. Zitscher, U.S. Patent 1,101,111 (1914).
78. —— and Seidenfaden, U.S. Patent 1,897,410 (1933).
79. ——, ——, and Jellinek, U.S. Patent 1,920,542 (1933).

5. MISCELLANEOUS DYES

S. E. Krahler

General Introduction

As the chapter heading implies, the group of dyes to be discussed is heterogeneous, involving all dyes which do not belong to the azo, anthraquinone, indigoid, sulfur or phthalocyanine classes.

No truly general statements can be made regarding the miscellaneous dyes, since they are extremely varied both chemically and in their dye character and properties. The dye classes to be discussed are:

(1) Acridine
(2) Azine and complex azine
(3) Ketone imine
(4) Metallized azomethine
(5) Methine, cyanine and polymethine
(6) Nitro
(7) Nitroso
(8) Oxazine
(9) Quinoline
(10) *p*-Quinone imine
(11) Thiazine
(12) Thiazole
(13) Triarylmethane
(14) Triphenodioxazine
(15) Xanthene

Historically, this dye group encompasses the oldest artificial organic dye, picric acid, which was used long before the time of Sir William Perkin for the dyeing of animal fibers. Mauve, the violet dye which Perkin isolated from the oxidation products of crude aniline in 1856 and which he exploited to start the coal-tar dye industry, belongs to this group. Other products include some of the tinctorially brightest dyes produced commercially, some of the newest colors for the new synthetic fibers of the polyamide, polyester, polyacrylonitrile, and cellulose acetate types, dyes formed during the development of color photographic emulsions and other equally varied items.

Since some of the earliest exploited synthetic dyes belong to the miscellaneous group, many of the dyes have had large production up to the present. Of these dyes, many are unlikely to attain increased consumption since newer dyes of more satisfactory lightfastness and other properties are being developed in other fields. Nonetheless, it is practically impossible to make any generalizations in this respect, since the tinctorial brightness and strength of many of the miscellaneous colors create demand for them for applications in which fastness requirements are not severe. Moreover, some of the dyes to be discussed possess extremely good fastness properties and are likely to be of great commercial importance.

In terms of current dye production, the miscellaneous group is not as important as the azo or anthraquinone groups, since the total miscellaneous color production does not exceed 10 per cent of the total United States synthetic dye manufacture. However, this group is extremely interesting, since the various individual types are chemically and synthetically very different.

Many of the dyes to be discussed have the dye chromophore as a cation. Bury[1] has observed that the intense absorption of light which characterizes these dyes is linked with resonance shifts in electrons within the cationic chromophore. For example, Crystal Violet, CI 681, is actually a resonance hybrid derived from the following and other possible electronic configurations.

The observation by Bury[1] that resonance shifts of electrons in the triphenylmethane and other dye chromophores are linked with the intense absorption of light that characterizes dyes has shown the inadequacy of such a representation. Crystal Violet is actually a resonance hybrid derived from the following and other possible electronic configurations:

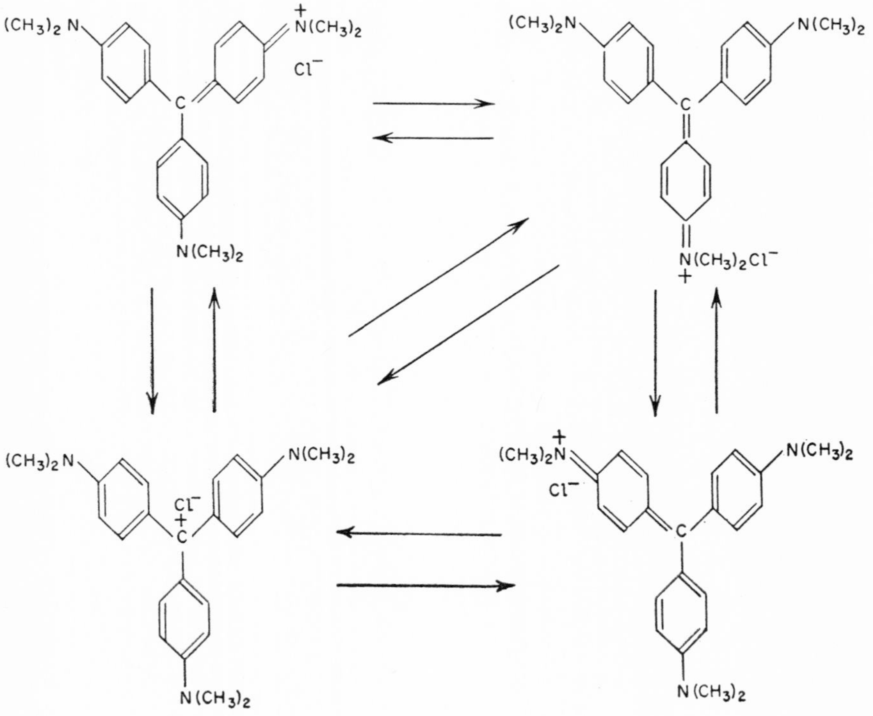

Since the actual location of the positive charge is not known, and since its location is unimportant in the representation of the dye, the cationic dyes generally will be represented in the text which follows by formulas such as:

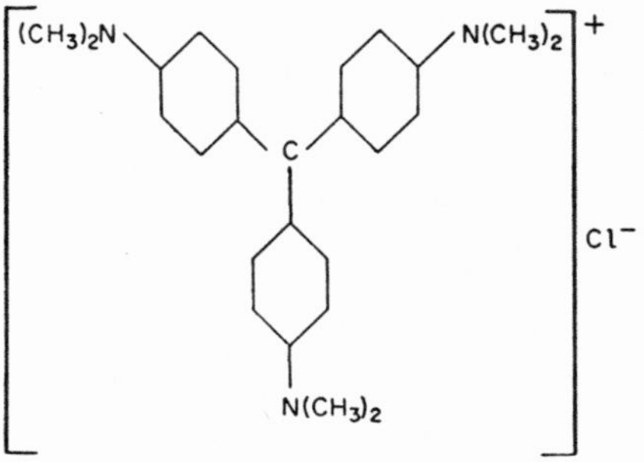

The cationic nature of many of the dyes of this group permits their precipitation as water-insoluble pigments by treatment with a phosphomolybdotungstic acid complex[2]. The complex salts or phosphomolybdotungstic lakes are much faster to light than the parent cationic dyes from which they are derived. They find use in printing inks, tinting of paper, in lacquers and in other pigment applications.

In the separate sections which follow, the history, chromophoric nature, synthesis, shade range and applications of the more important dye types are discussed in approximately that order. Actual manufacturing processes are cited wherever possible, so that the reader can obtain detailed information as to the methods involved in the commercial production of synthetic dyes.

Literature Cited

1. Bury, *J. Am. Chem. Soc.*, **57**, 2115 (1935).
2. I. G. Farbenindustrie, BIOS 1433, p. 110 (PB 81029).

Acridine Dyes

Commercial exploitation of dyes containing the acridine nucleus followed Fischer and Koerner's[4] identification of Chrysaniline as a derivative of 9-

phenylacridine. Chrysaniline (I), a yellow dye, is a by-product of the nitro-benzene oxidation of *p*-toluidine and aniline to give Fuchsine (see section on Triarylmethane Dyes, p. 272). Its isolation from the Fuchsine melt indicates that it is formed by partial ortho condensation as follows:

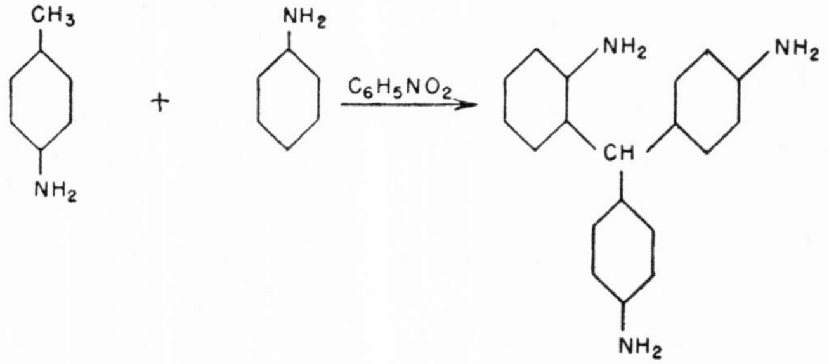

which on further oxidation is converted to:

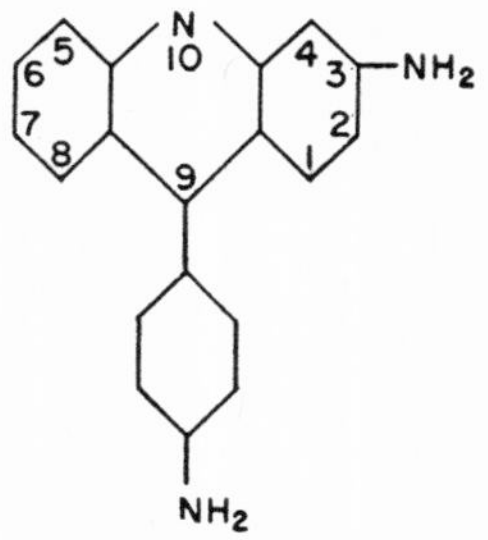

(I) Chrysaniline

Chrysaniline was isolated and named by Hofmann (1862)[12]; its nitrate was introduced to the dyeing trade as Phosphine, CI 793, by Nicholson.

The identification of Chrysaniline led to a group of basic colors containing the acridine nucleus as chromophore and having amino groups in the three and/or six positions as auxochromes. These yellow, red, orange and brown dyes are used chiefly for the coloring of leather, inasmuch as they give good shades on vegetable- and chrome-tanned leathers with an opaque effect which covers many imperfections.

Other products of this group have achieved much importance as pharmaceuticals. In 1910 Benda[3, 5] found that a 3,6-diaminoacridinium salt had strong action on the trypanosomes responsible for "sleeping sickness." This product was marketed as Trypaflavine, CI 790 (II).

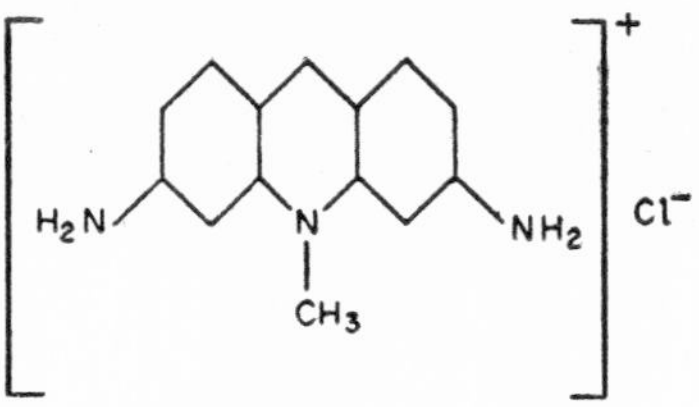

(II) Trypaflavine

It and other acridine derivatives of the same general type, in particular those of 9-aminoacridine (e.g., Rivanol, the lactate of 6,9-diamino-2-ethoxyacridine[2]), have been used to a considerable extent as antiseptics and as a means of combating streptococcal and staphylococcal infections.

During World War II, Atabrine (III), another acridine pharmaceutical, was used with great success in treating malaria.

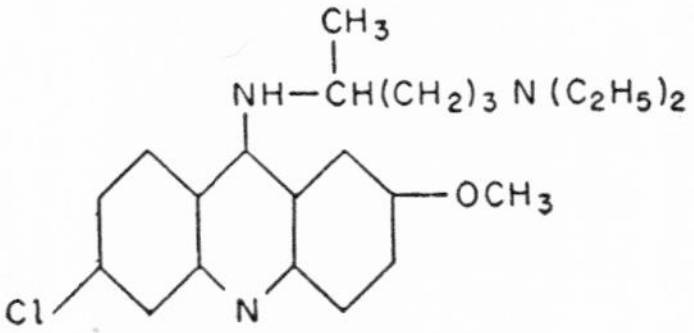

(III) Atabrine

The acridine dyes fall into two general groups—those based on acridine itself and those based on 9-phenylacridine.

Acridine Derivatives. The synthetic methods most commonly used for this group of colors are:

(1) *Acridine Yellow, CI 785 (IV), Synthesis[7]*. This involves the condensation of toluene-2,4-diamine and formaldehyde to the corresponding diphenylmethane derivative, ring closure under pressure to the dihydroacridine and air or ferric chloride oxidation to the dye.

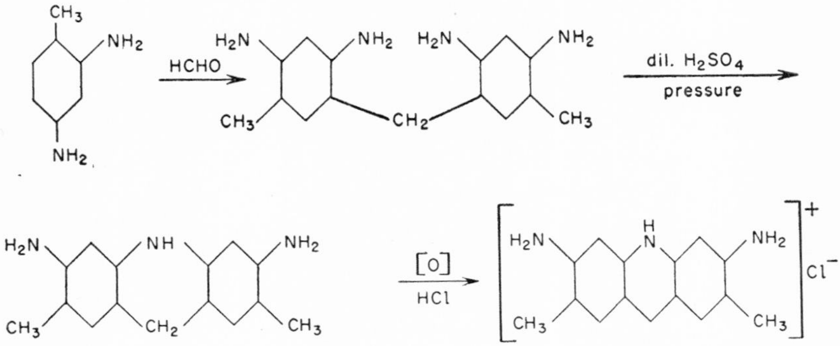

(IV) Acridine Yellow

(2) *Acridine Orange, CI 788 (V), Synthesis*[6]. In this synthesis, p,p'-methylenebis[N,N-dimethylaniline] is first nitrated and reduced; the remainder of the synthesis is similar to that for Acridine Yellow.

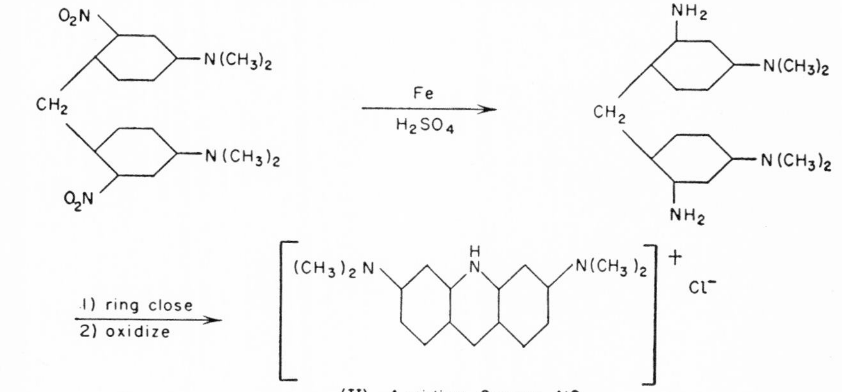

(V) Acridine Orange NO

(3) *Proflavine (VI) Synthesis*[1]. The Proflavine synthesis illustrates a one-step route for acridine dye preparation. It involves the action of formic acid (or oxalic acid) and glycerol on the appropriate amine in the presence of strong mineral acid.

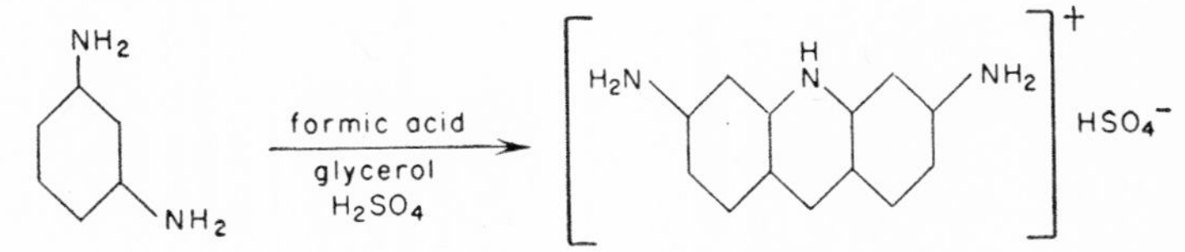

(VI) Proflavine

The observation by Ullmann[13] that the formation of acridinium salts is favored by methylation of Acridine Yellow with dimethyl sulfate in an inert solvent while methylation of the amino nitrogens predominates with alkyl halides has led to two groups of dyes, both of which are more soluble in water than the parent Acridine Yellow.

(a) *Acridinium salt formation*[9]:

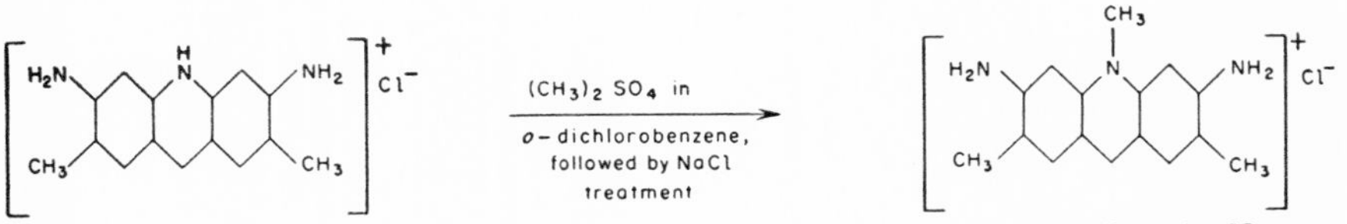

Diamond Phosphine GF

(b) *Alkylation of amino groups*[8]:

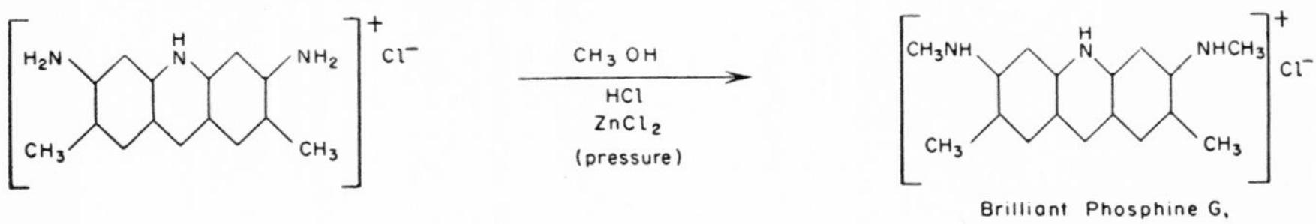

Brilliant Phosphine G,
CI 789

In the second method, the shade desired controls the degree of methylation—the greater the amount of methylation, the redder the shade of yellow obtained.

9-Phenylacridine Derivatives. The isolation of Chrysaniline from the Fuchsine melt was described earlier. Other processes for dyes of this group include:

(1) *Phosphine E (VII) Process*[11]. This method involves the condensation and ring closure of *p*-aminobenzaldehyde and 4-methyl-N^1-phenyl-*m*-phenylenediamine to a dihydroacridine, followed by oxidation with 2,4-dinitrotoluene and hydrochloric acid to the dye. Phosphine E is closely related to Chrysaniline.

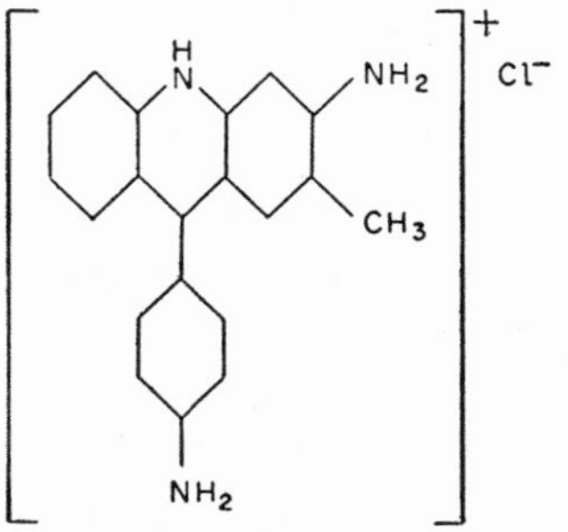

(VII) Phosphine E

(2) *Rheonine AL, CI 795 (VIII), Process*[10]. Rheonine AL is produced by condensation of 4,4'-bis(dimethylamino)benzophenone (Michler's ketone) and *m*-phenylenediamine to an auramine derivative, followed by oxidative ring closure to the dye in presence of zinc chloride.

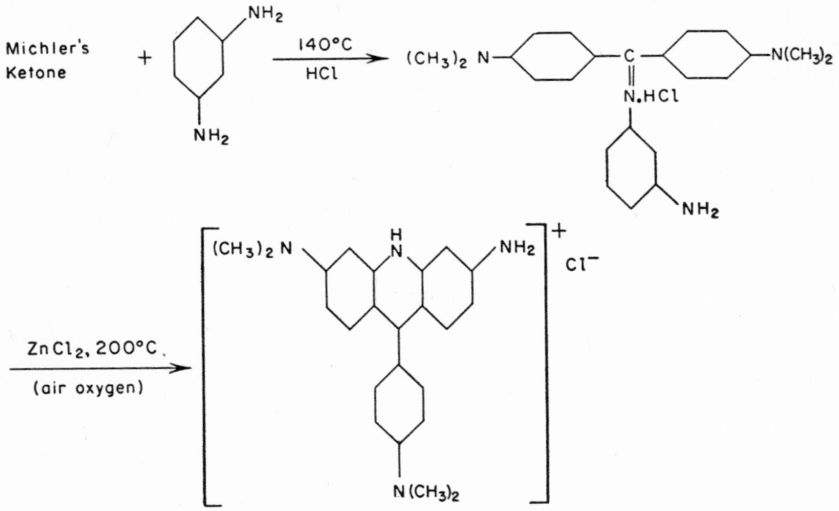

(VIII) Rheonine AL

Literature Cited

1. Albert, *J. Chem. Soc.*, **1947**, 244.
2. Albert and Gledhill, *J. Soc. Chem. Ind.*, **61**, 159 (1942).
3. Benda, *Ber.*, **45**, 1787 (1912).
4. Fischer and Koerner, *ibid.*, **17**, 203 (1884).
5. German Patent 243,085 (1912).
6. I. G. Farbenindustrie, BIOS 959, p. 42 (PB 63858).
7. ——, PB 25626, frame 1369.
8. ——, PB 70135, frame 852.
9. ——, *ibid.*, frame 861.
10. ——, *ibid.*, frame 1569.
11. ——, PB 74067, frame 23.
12. Hofmann, *Compt. rend.*, **55**, 817 (1862).
13. Ullmann and Marié, *Ber.*, **34**, 4307 (1901).

Azine and Complex Azine Dyes

In 1856, Perkin oxidized a dilute solution of crude aniline sulfate with potassium dichromate. By means of benzene and alcohol extraction of the black oxidation product, he isolated about 5 per cent of a violet dye which he patented and which was manufactured as Mauve (Mauveine), CI 846[1]. Perkin's discovery was of extreme importance, since it gave great impetus to the research on aniline as a basis for synthetic dyes. This research led ultimately to our present-day dye industry.

Research on Mauve and other dyes produced from oxidation of crude anilines (this study is well summarized in reference 9), showed that Mauve had the structure (I) and that its synthesis resulted from the presence of toluidines in the starting material.

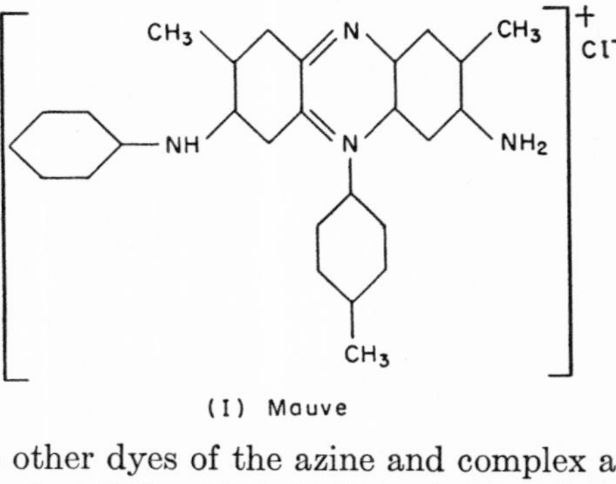

(I) Mauve

Mauve and the other dyes of the azine and complex azine group are derivatives of phenazine (II), which is their chromophore. Amino and hydroxy groups para to one of the ring nitrogens are the usual auxochromes. The strong color of these products is due to resonance stabilization related to several contributing structures[5].

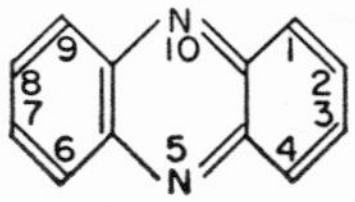

(II) Phenazine

Three possible structures for 3,7-diaminophenazine hydrochloride (IIIa, IIIb, and IIIc) illustrate the *o*- and *p*-quinonoid forms for the azine dyes:

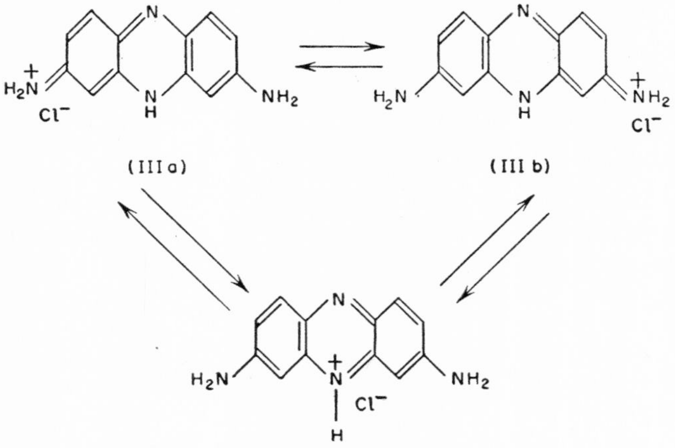

(IIIa)   (IIIb)

(IIIc)

The dyes of this section and their fields of application are discussed under the following headings:

(a) Non-auxochromic azines
(b) Eurhodines
(c) Aposafranines
(d) Safranines
(e) Complex azines

Non-auxochromic Azines. The general synthetic route to these products is the condensation of an *o*-quinone and an aromatic *o*-diamine. An example is Flavinduline O, CI 824 (IV), prepared by the condensation of *N*-phenyl-*o*-phenylenediamine and phenanthrenequinone[22]:

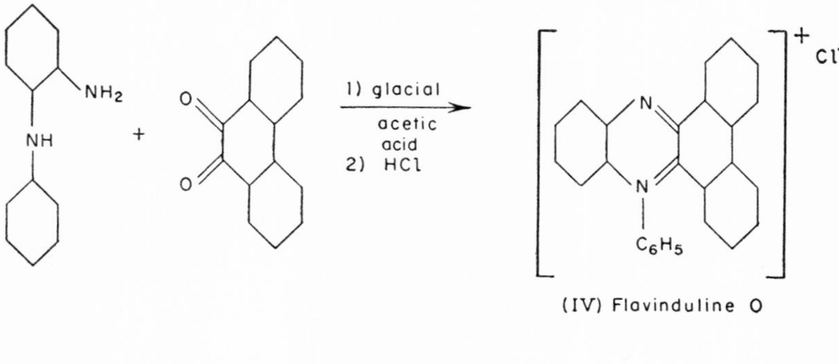

(IV) Flavinduline O

A second product of this type is the sulfonated form of (V), a compound prepared by the condensation of 1-aminocarbazole and isatin[20]:

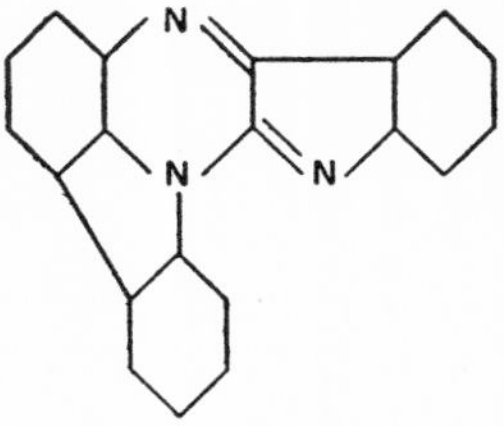

(V)

The dyes of this subclass range in shade from yellow to reddish-brown. They are not important commercially.

Eurhodines. The eurhodines, mono- and diaminophenazines, are of little technical interest. One, Neutral Red, CI 825 (VII), was produced in Germany as a dye for rubber and for use as a bacteriological stain.

The synthesis of Neutral Red by the reaction of toluene-2,4-diamine and N,N-dimethyl-p-nitrosoaniline hydrochloride[11] illustrates the general preparatory method, the formation of the intermediate indamine (VI) (see section on p-Quinone Imine Dyes, p. 263) being characteristic of azine dye syntheses:

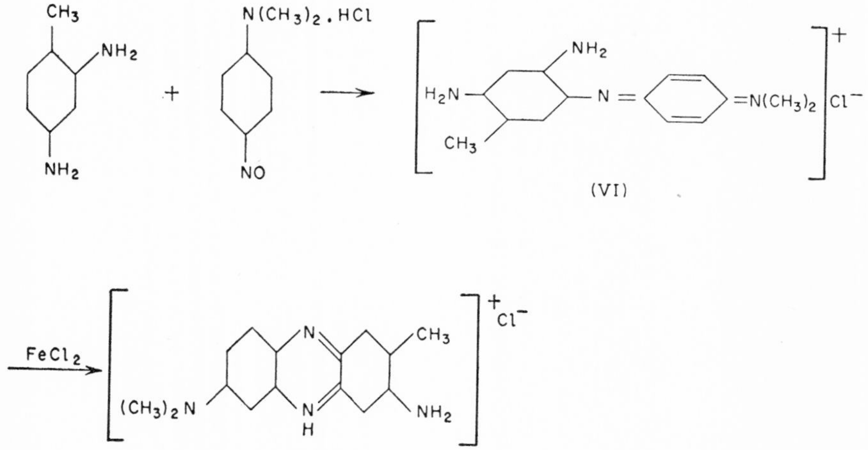

(VI)

(VII) Neutral Red

Aposafranines. The monoamino- or monohydroxy-N-phenylphen-azines are called aposafranines. Two syntheses for dyes of this subclass are given below:

(1) *Azocarmine Synthesis.* The fusion of 4-phenylazo-1-naphthylamine with aniline and aniline hydrochloride gives phenylrosinduline (VIII)[7] which is sulfonated to the disulfonic acid, Azocarmine G, CI 828[21].

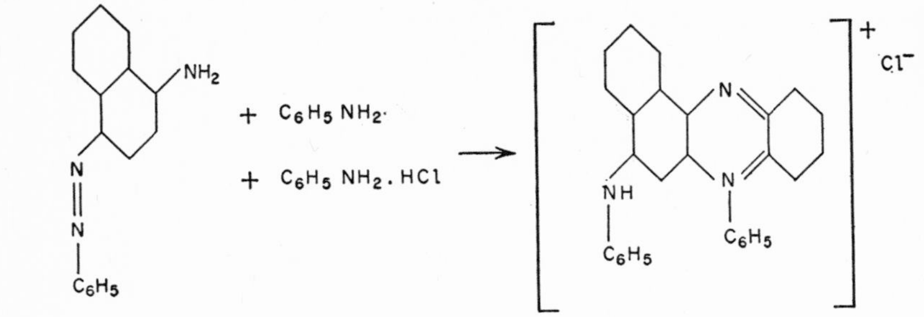

(VIII) Phenylrosinduline

(2) *Oxidative Synthesis.* The German dye intermediate known as Blue I (IX) is an aposafranine prepared by the following oxidative route[16]:

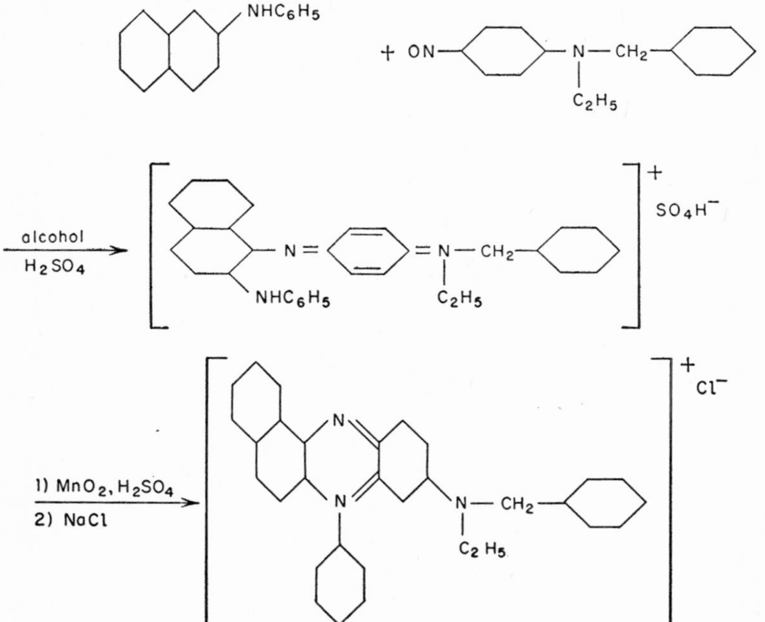

(IX) Blue I

The aposafranines generally are not important. Azocarmine G has been used to a slight extent as a biological stain and as a red dye for wool and silk. Blue I is an intermediate for Indocyanine B, an important wool dye which is discussed with the safranines.

Safranines. The safranines are diamino-*N*-phenylphenazines and are commercially more important than the other simple azines. The United States 1950 production of one of these colors, Safranine T, CI 841, was 326,000 pounds[23].

Dyes of this subclass are prepared by addition of an aromatic amine to the quinoid system of an indamine or aposafranine, followed by oxidation to the dye. Three examples of this synthesis are given below:

(1) *Safranine T* (X)[13]:

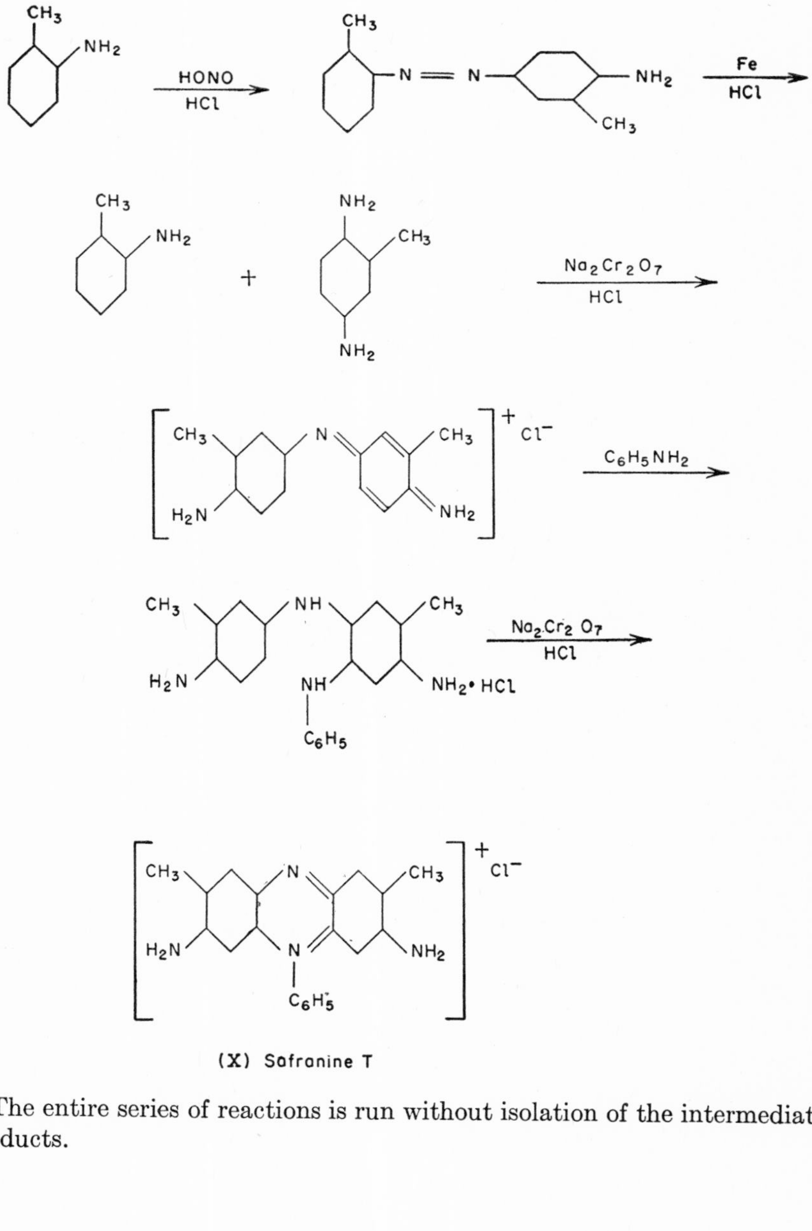

(X) Safranine T

The entire series of reactions is run without isolation of the intermediate products.

(2) *Wool Fast Blue BL, CI 833, (XI)*[15]:

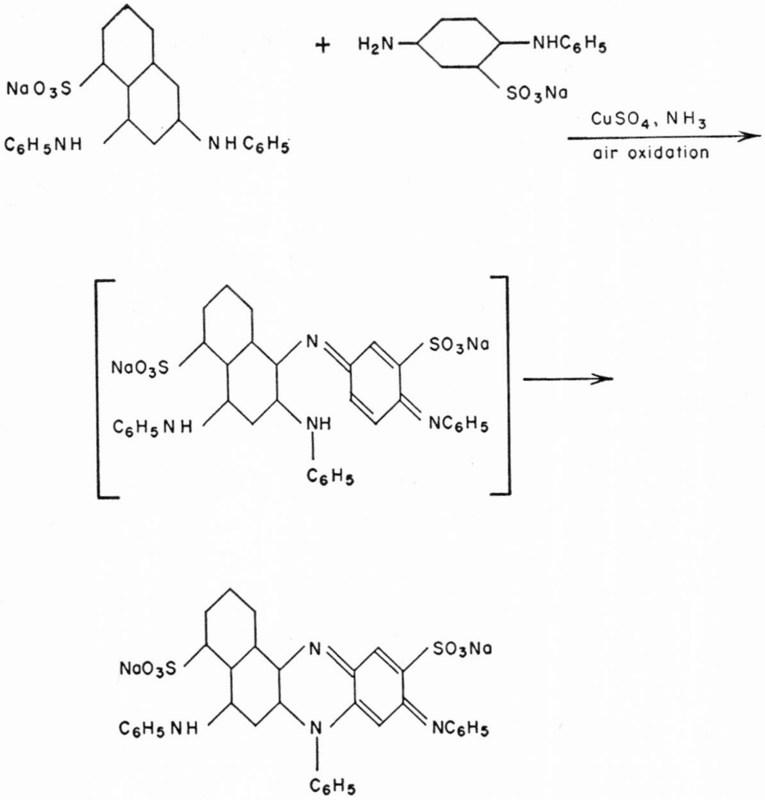

(XI) Wool Fast Blue BL

(3) *Indocyanine B, Pr 128*[17]:

In this process aposafranine Blue I (IX) is oxidized with N,N-diethyl-p-phenylenediamine to safranine Blue II (XII), which is disulfonated to give Indocyanine B.

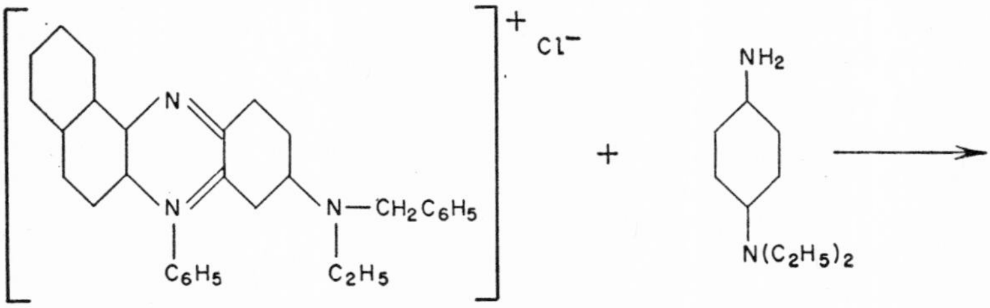

(IX) Blue I

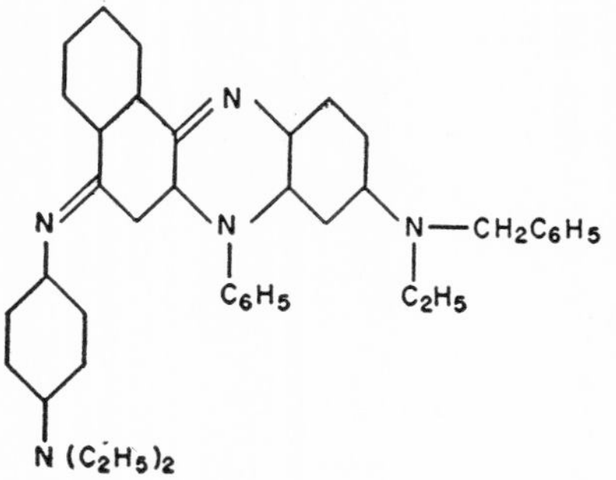

(XII) Blue II

The safranines range in shade from red to blue. Safranine T is used primarily as a red dye for paper. Wool Fast Blues BL and GL, CI 833 (XIII)[14], and Indocyanine B give bright blue shades on wool, the dyeings being only moderately fast to light.

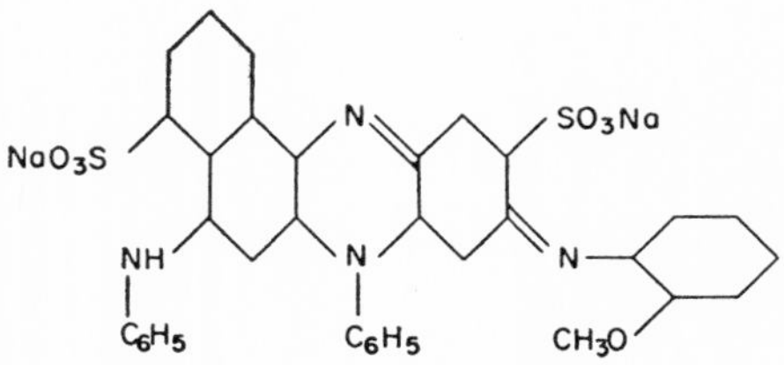

(XIII) Wool Fast Blue GL

Although 101,000 pounds of the Wool Fast Blues was manufactured in the United States in 1950[23], it appears likely that the azine wool blues will give way gradually to the more light-fast blues of the anthraquinone or metallized azo series.

 Complex Azines. Three groups of complex azines, the indulines, the nigrosines and the aniline colors, are of great technical importance. These products are inexpensive blues, violets, browns and blacks which have many applications.

Indulines. The first induline was prepared by Dale and Caro in 1863 by the fusion of aniline hydrochloride and sodium nitrite[3], the first reaction being formation of *p*-phenylazoaniline followed by its condensation with more aniline hydrochloride to give a blue dye. Later investigators showed that the induline melt gave phenylated safranines, two of which were Induline 3B, CI 860 (XIV), and Induline 6B, CI 860 (XV)[19].

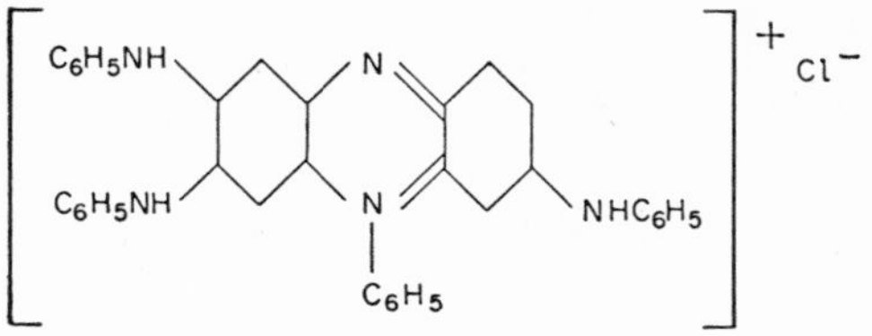

(XIV) Induline 3B

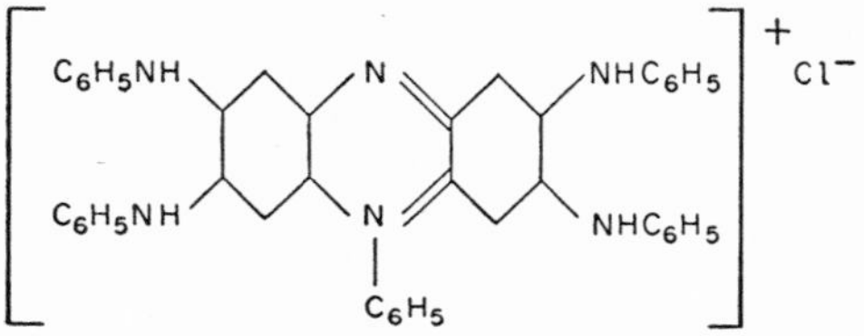

(XV) Induline 6B

The commercial induline process used today is substantially that of Dale and Caro. *p*-Phenylazoaniline is prepared first and it is then fused with aniline hydrochloride in the presence of ferrous chloride and nitrobenzene to give the dye[12]. The nature of the product depends on the fusion conditions, a shorter fusion giving a redder shade of blue and a longer fusion a greener blue.

Treatment of induline with caustic yields the free base; sulfonation of the base gives water-soluble induline (CI 861). The indulines themselves are alcohol-soluble and are used in spirit varnishes and lacquers. The fat-soluble bases are used for the coloring of fats and waxes. The water-soluble derivatives are used for the dyeing of paper and leather.

Nigrosines. The nigrosines (CI 864 and 865), discovered by Coupier[4], are bluish-black to black products produced by the oxidation of aniline and aniline hydrochloride with nitrobenzene in the presence of ferric chloride at 160 to 180°C[4]. As in the case of the indulines, the shade of the product is dependent on the fusion conditions.

The structure of the products obtained in the nigrosine fusion is not known definitely. In 1938, Rudolf[18], a German chemist, concluded that nigrosine is a mixture of triphenazineoxazines (XVI, XVII) and phenazineazines (XVIII, XIX) plus 5 per cent of Induline 6B (XV):

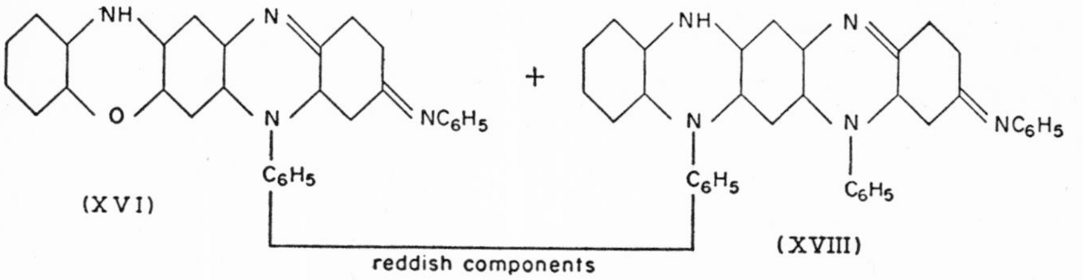

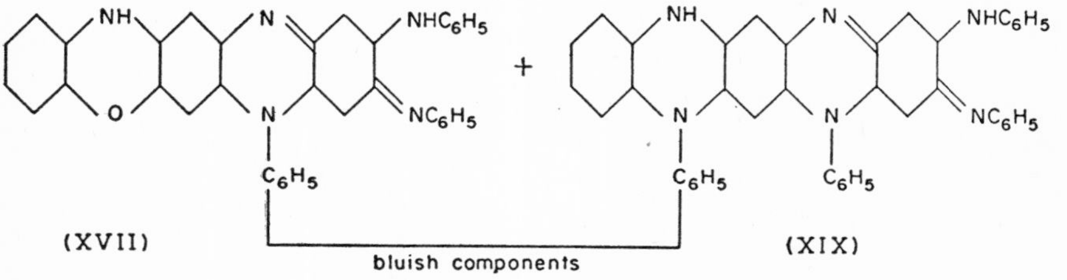

reddish components

(XVI) (XVIII)

bluish components

(XVII) (XIX)

Like the indulines, the nigrosines are marketed as the alcohol-soluble chlorides, the oil- and wax-soluble free bases and as their water-soluble sulfonates. The bases and chlorides are used in coloring lacquers, waxes and as wood stains while the water-soluble brands are used chiefly for the dyeing of leather and paper. Their cheapness combined with their high tinctorial strength makes them large volume colors for use wherever inexpensive black dyes of only fair lightfastness are required. The nigrosines alone constituted 2.2 per cent of the total poundage of the synthetic dye out-put in the United States for 1950[24].

Aniline Colors. Although Fritsche had shown as early as 1840 that aniline could be oxidized with chromic acid to give dark-green to blue-black insoluble compounds[8], the use of Aniline Black, CI 870, as a textile dye was not exploited until much later. Lightfoot successfully produced Aniline Black on cotton fiber by immersing the fiber in a solution of aniline hydrochloride, potassium chlorate and copper chloride and aging it in warm, moist air[2], leading to the industrial application of the color.

The Aniline Black process has changed little since Lightfoot's time. Catalyst modifications have been made, such as the substitution of lead chromate or vanadium chloride for the copper chloride[6].

Investigations of Aniline Black by Willstaetter and Green and their collaborators showed that intermediate p-quinone imines (XX, XXI) are involved and that these further react with aniline to give azine type compounds (XXII)[10].

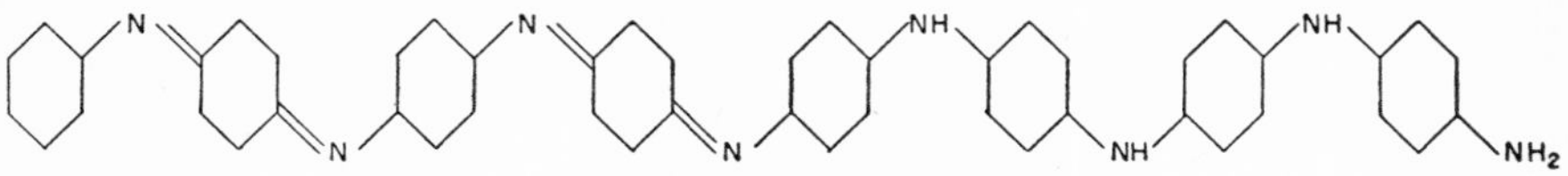

(XX) Emeraldine

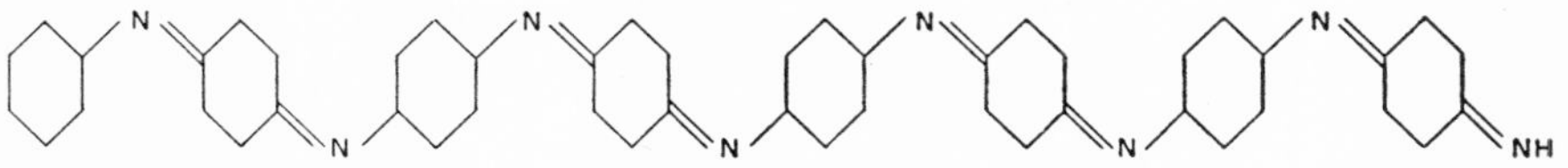

(XXI) Pernigraniline

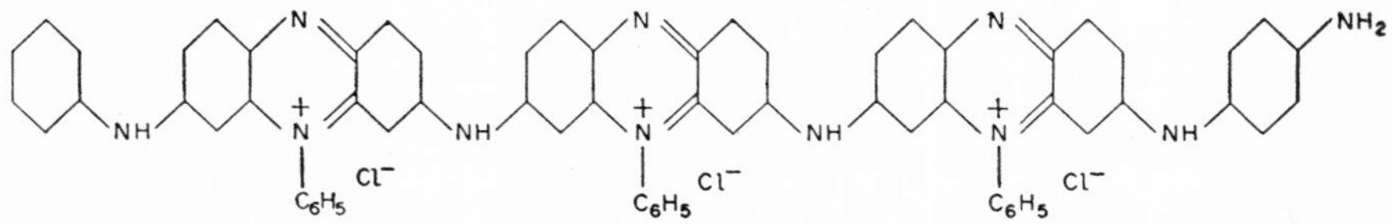

(XXII) "Ungreenable." Aniline Black

In practice, the desired color is the "ungreenable" form, since it is very fast to light and stable to acids and reducing agents. The intermediate products are not fast to acids, as would be expected from their quinone imine structure.

Other black and brown aniline colors are prepared by analogous procedures, using *N*-phenyl-*p*-phenylenediamine (CI 871), *p*-aminophenol or *p*-phenylenediamine (CI 875) in place of aniline.

The aniline colors are used widely in textile printing and in the dyeing of fur and hair.

Literature Cited

1. British Patent 1984 (1856).
2. British Patent 2327 (1865).
3. British Patent 3307 (1863).
4. British Patent 3657 (1867).
5. Bury, *J. Am. Chem. Soc.*, **57**, 2115 (1935).
6. Fierz-David, "Kuenstliche Organische Farbstoffe," pp. 342, 343, Berlin, Julius Springer, 1926.
7. Fischer and Hepp, *Ann.*, **256**, 233 (1890).
8. Fritsche, *J. prakt. Chem.*, **20**, 454 (1840).
9. Georgievics and Grandmougin, "A Text-book of Dye Chemistry," pp. 346–362, London, Scott, Greenwood & Son, 1920.
10. Green and Wolff, *J. Soc. Dyers Colourists*, **29**, 105 (1913).

11. I. G. Farbenindustrie, BIOS 1433, pp. 29, 30 (PB 81029).
12. ——, *ibid.*, pp. 93–98.
13. ——, FIAT 1313, Vol. II, pp. 377, 378 (PB 85172).
14. ——, *ibid.*, pp. 379, 381.
15. ——, *ibid.*, pp. 380, 381.
16. ——, *ibid.*, p. 382.
17. ——, *ibid.*, pp. 383, 384.
18. ——, PB 70336, frames 7956–7967.
19. Kehrmann and Klopfenstein, *Ber.*, **56**, 2394 (1923).
20. Schepss and Bayer, U.S. Patent 2,215,859 (1940).
21. Schraube, U.S. Patent 430,975 (1890).
22. ——, U.S. Patent 543,784 (1895).
23. U.S. Tariff Commission Report No. 173, "Synthetic Organic Chemicals, U.S. Production and Sales, 1950," p. 17.
24. ——, *ibid.*, p. 22.

Ketone Imine Dyes

The ketone imine dyes are derivatives of diphenylmethane, the simplest and best known being Auramine, CI 655 (II). This product was synthesized by Caro and Kern in 1883, by reacting Michler's ketone [4,4′-bis(dimethylamino)benzophenone] (I) and ammonium chloride in the presence of zinc chloride[1].

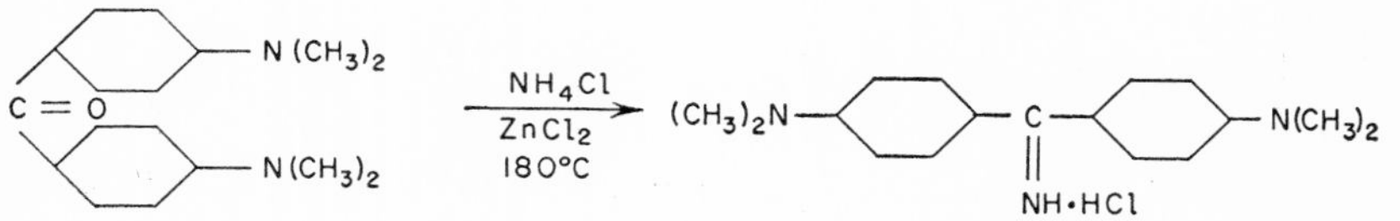

(I)　　　　　　　　(II) Auramine

Auramine, a tinctorially strong yellow dye for paper and tannin mordanted cotton, met with immediate and continued commercial success. In 1950 its United States production constituted about 0.5 per cent of the total synthetic dye output[6].

The fact that the ketone imine colors range in shade from yellow to brown has led Hodgson[4] to postulate the ketimine hydrochloride shown for Auramine as the predominant resonance form. Acetylauramine (III), which has a nonbasic nitrogen on the center carbon, gives blue salts due to the electron distribution along a conjugate system of 11 atoms.

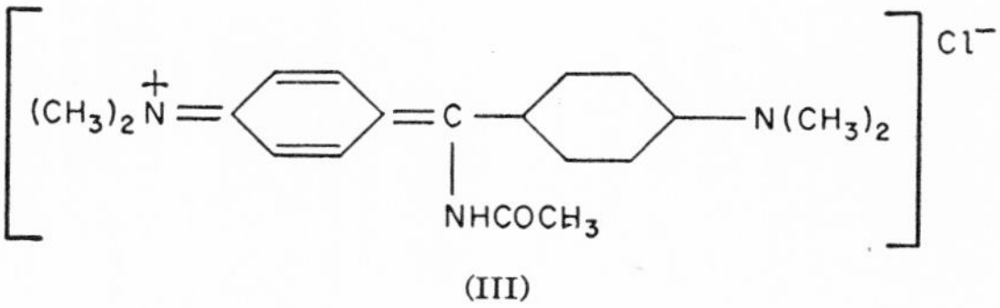

(III)

The yellow color of Auramine indicates that its conjugate chain is shorter; this is explained on the basis of the salt formation being primarily at the

$\diagdown$
C=NH grouping, so that the major part of the resonance energy must
$\diagup$

be confined to the shorter chain of 7 atoms.

Two common synthetic methods for the preparation of ketone imine colors are:

(1) *The Auramine Process*[2]. This procedure, discovered by Sandmeyer but commonly credited to Feer, is used for the commercial manufacture of Auramine. It involves the action of sulfur, sodium chloride, ammonium chloride, and ammonia on p,p'-methylenebis[N,N-dimethylaniline] (IV), thio-Michler's ketone [4,4'-bis(dimethylamino)thiobenzophenone] (V) being formed as an intermediate product[3].

(III)

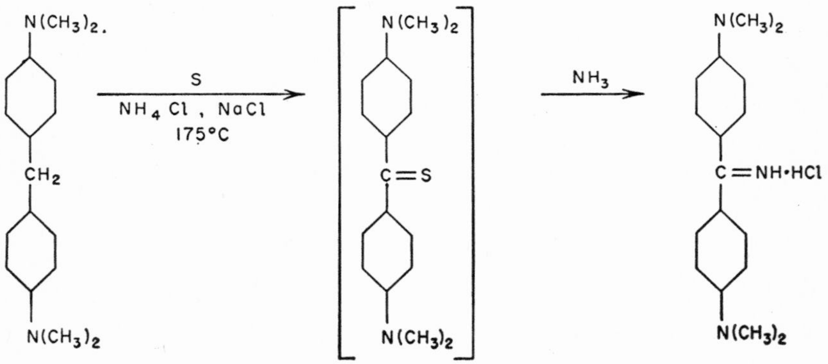

(IV)   (V)

(2) *The Ketone Chloride Process.* The ketone chloride process is used to prepare alkyl- or aryl-substituted ketone imines. It proceeds as follows[5]:

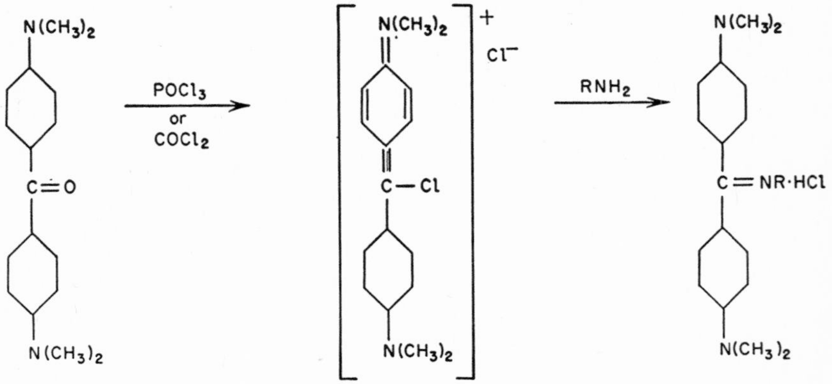

Many ketone imine dyes have been prepared and evaluated (e.g., Auramine G, CI 656), but none has achieved the importance of Auramine. It is a bright yellow of poor light fastness and water solution stability (it hydrolyzes quite rapidly at temperatures above 60°C), but its cheapness and high tinctorial strength have resulted in its wide use, primarily for the dyeing of paper.

Literature Cited

1. Caro and Kern, U.S. Patent 301,802 (1884).
2. Fierz-David and Blangey, "Fundamental Processes of Dye Chemistry," p. 298, New York, Interscience Publishers, Inc., 1949.
3. German Patent 37,730 (1886).
4. Hodgson, *J. Soc. Dyers Colourists*, **62**, 176 (1946).
5. I. G. Farbenindustrie, PB 70336, frame 7462.
6. U.S. Tariff Commission Report No. 173, "Synthetic Organic Chemicals. U. S. Production and Sales, 1950," p. 22.

Metallized Azomethine Dyes

The metallized azomethines, one of the newer dye types, are metal complexes of aromatic azomethines which have hydroxy groups ortho to the —CH=N— bridge.

The azomethine colors are prepared generally by condensation of an aromatic o-hydroxyaldehyde and an aromatic o-aminophenol to give a Schiff's base, followed by metallizing. An example is the synthesis of Zapon Fast Yellow G[4] (I):

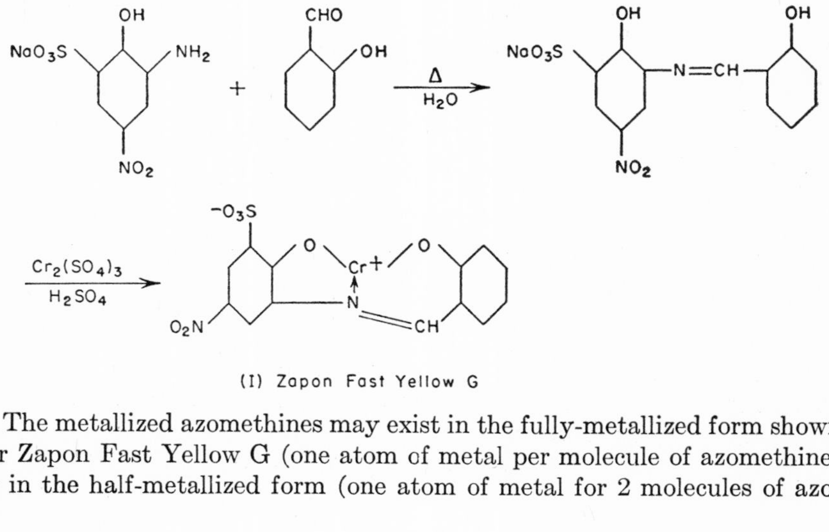

(I) Zapon Fast Yellow G

The metallized azomethines may exist in the fully-metallized form shown for Zapon Fast Yellow G (one atom of metal per molecule of azomethine) or in the half-metallized form (one atom of metal for 2 molecules of azomethine). In the half-metallized group, of which Perlon Fast Yellow RS[3] (II) is a member, the residual negative charges are neutralized by salt formation, the dye chromophore being the anion:

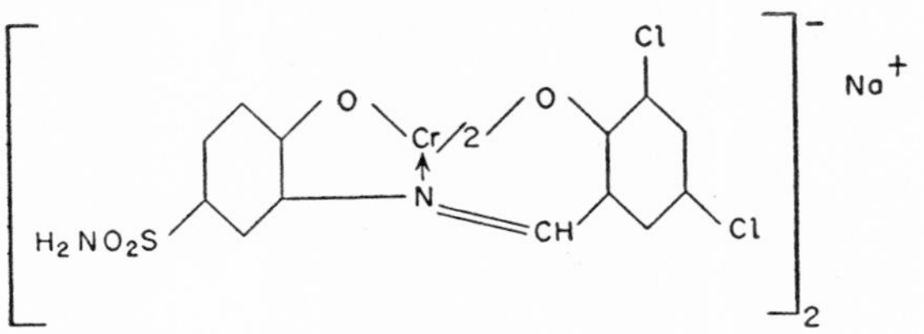

(II) Perlon Fast Yellow RS

In general the structure of the metallized compound can be predicted from the coordination number of the metal used. Trivalent chromium with its coordination number of six can exist in both the half- and fully-metallized forms, the presence of a sulfonic acid group favoring the latter[5]. Dyes based on divalent cobalt sometimes exist in the fully metallized form, the cobalt showing a coordination number of four[2], but trivalent cobalt usually gives half-metallized compounds, its coordination number being six[5].

The dyes of this group are substantive to silk, wool and nylon, their shade range being from yellow to orange. The dyeings of both the chromium types shown earlier and those based on cobalt[1] are characterized by excellent lightfastness.

Literature Cited

1. British Patent 629,473 (1949).
2. Callis, Nielsen and Bailar, *J. Am. Chem. Soc.*, **74**, 3461 (1952).
3. I. G. Farbenindustrie, BIOS 20, p. 30; Appendix No. 38, pp. 1, 6 (PB 31004).
4. ——, PB 70135, frames 1343–1346.
5. Pfitzner, *Angew. Chem.*, **62**, 244 (1950).

Methine, Cyanine and Polymethine Dyes

The methine, cyanine and polymethine dyes fall into one group since they each contain one or more methine (—CH=) linkages as part of their chromophoric system.

The methine and polymethine colors, though a fairly old class, have been exploited only recently as dyes for cellulose acetate. The cyanines could be classed as methine or polymethine dyes, but they are grouped separately since they are used as photographic sensitizers rather than textile dyes. The two groups are discussed separately.

Methines and Polymethines. The first dyes of the polymethine type were prepared by Koenig[14] in 1904 by rupture of the pyridine ring with cyanogen bromide in the presence of aromatic amines:

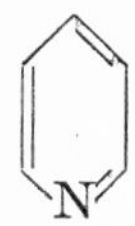

$$\text{(pyridine)} + 2\text{ArNH}_2 \xrightarrow{\text{BrCN}} \left[\text{ArNH}-(\text{CH}=\text{CH})_2-\text{CH}=\overset{\text{H}}{\text{N}}-\text{Ar}\right]^+ \text{Br}^-$$

These products were substantive to animal and vegetable fibers, giving bright shades of red, but they were of no commercial importance due to their extreme lack of fastness to alkali. In 1925, Koenig[15] patented a very similar dye which had the bright red shade of his earlier compounds but was fast to alkali and acid. This dye was marketed as Astraphloxine FF (I):

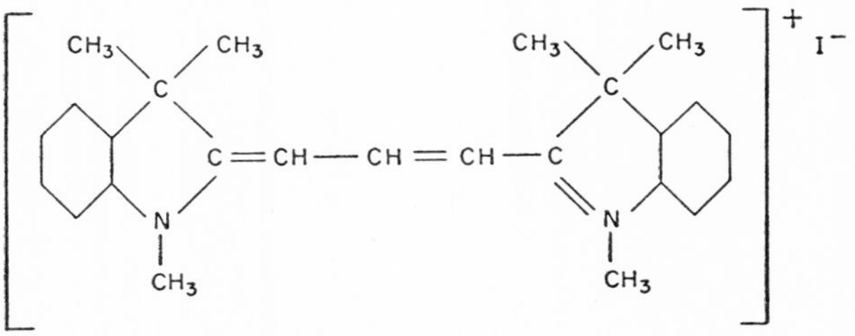

(I) Astraphloxine FF

In the decade just preceding World War II, the I. G. Farbenindustrie patented a color range of polymethine dyes of the Astraphloxine type, which were sold under the trade name Astrazone. These are bright, fairly fast, water-soluble printing colors for cellulose acetate, but as yet they have attained relatively little importance for this use in the American market.

The methine colors have not been of particular importance, though some of them have been patented as yellow disperse dyes for cellulose acetate[17, 18].

Synthetic routes to these dyes are:

(1) *Methines.* A typical methine dye synthesis is the condensation of ethyl cyanoacetate and *p*-[butyl(2-chloroethyl)amino]benzaldehyde to give a yellow dye (II)[7a, 17], known as Celliton Fast Yellow 7G, Pr. 420.

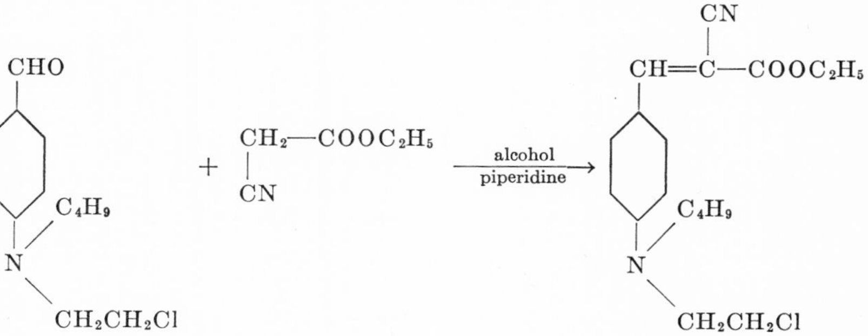

(2) *Polymethines.* Two processes were used for the synthesis of the Astrazones.

(a) *Fischer's Base Synthesis.* This involves the condensation of Fischer's base (1,3,3-trimethyl-2-methyleneindoline) (III)[8] and an aromatic aldehyde in the presence of acetic acid. The preparation of Astrazone Pink FG (IV)[9] is typical.

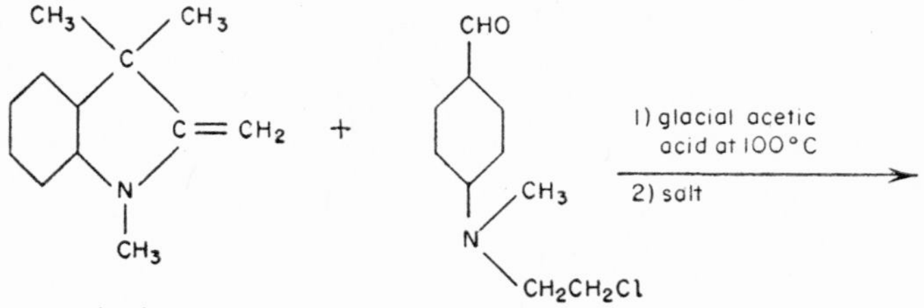

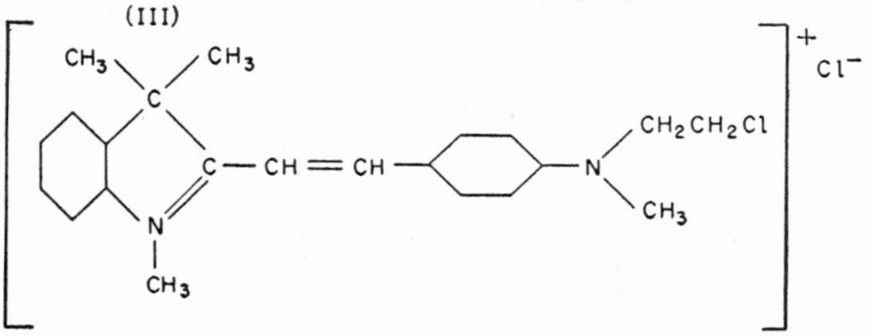

(IV) Astrazone Pink FG

(b) *Fischer's Aldehyde Synthesis.* This comprises condensation of Fischer's aldehyde (1,3,3-trimethyl-$\Delta^{2,\alpha}$-indolineacetaldehyde) (V)[22] and an aromatic amine in the presence of mineral acid. This process is used for Astrazone Yellow 3G (VI)[10]:

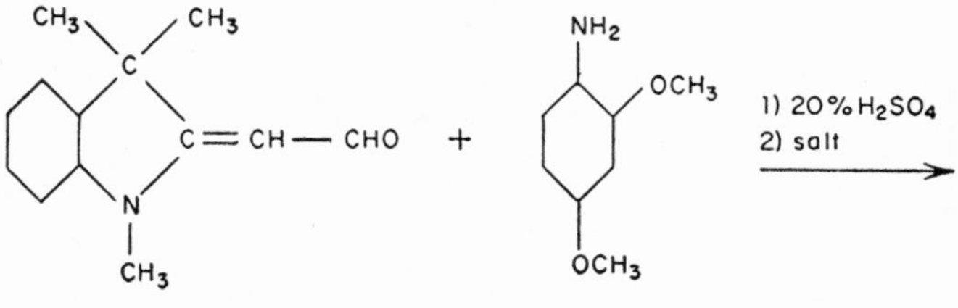

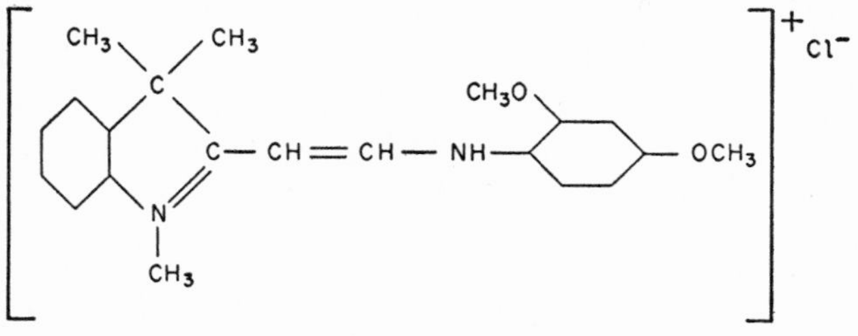

(VI) Astrazone Yellow 3G

Cyanines. Prior to the development of the cyanine dyes, the sensitivity of the silver halide emulsions used in photography was limited almost completely to the ultraviolet, violet and blue region of the spectrum. This resulted in photographic prints in which the shadings differed sharply from those seen by the eye.

Vogel, in 1873[19], discovered that the range of spectral sensitivity of the emulsions could be extended by tinting them with dyes. In 1875, he reported that the blue dye Cyanine, CI 806 (VII), was effective in increasing the orange sensitivity of the emulsion[20]. These discoveries led to an entirely new group of photographic sensitizers which were given the generic name cyanine.

By suitable selection of sensitizing dyes, the photographic film can be made equally sensitive to the whole visible spectrum (panchromatic), to any desired part of it or even sensitive to the near infrared.

Cyanine itself was prepared originally by Williams in 1856 by the reaction of ammonia on the amyl iodide quaternary salt of impure quinoline (which contained some 4-methylquinoline)[21]. Its structure was shown later[16] to be

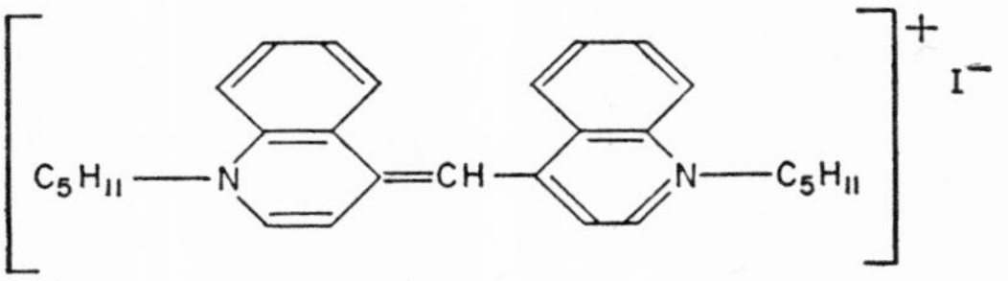

(VII) Cyanine

It was too light-fugitive to be useful as a fabric dye, but it led to the series of related compounds which bear its name.

The cyanines are resonance hybrids[3] based on systems (VIII-a) and (VIII-b) in which both nitrogen atoms are members of heterocyclic ring

(VIII-a)　　　　　　　　　(VIII-b)

systems. The heterocyclic nuclei are quite varied and include quinoline, pyridine, thiazole, benzothiazole, benzoxazole and benzoselenazole as well as many others.

The cyanines are classified according to the value of n in formula VIII. Where $n = 0$, there is only one methine group between the heterocyclic nuclei and the dye is classified as a monomethine or simple cyanine. If there are three methine groups ($n = 1$), the dye is called a trimethine or carbocyanine. In those cases where $n = 2$ or higher, the appropriate prefix is added to carbocyanine—e.g., a tricarbocyanine is a dye where $n = 3$

and in which there are 7 methine groups in the chain between the hetero-cyclic nuclei.

An extremely large group of cyanine dyes has been synthesized and patented. Each photographic concern produces its own sensitizers in small batches and uses its own combinations of dyes to achieve the desired range of emulsion sensitivity. These dyes are not useful for textile application due to their poor lightfastness.

In view of the complexity of the field of photographic sensitizers and the limited range of application of the dyes themselves, the synthetic routes which follow have been restricted to one example each for the simple cyanines, carbocyanines, di- and tricarbocyanines. For further and more complete information as to syntheses and dye properties references 3, 5, 7, and 11 are suggested.

Simple Cyanine. The condensation of quinaldine ethiodide (IX) and 2-iodoquinoline ethiodide (X) in the presence of triethylamine yields the simple cyanine, 1,1'-diethyl-2,2'-cyanine iodide (XI)[2, 4].

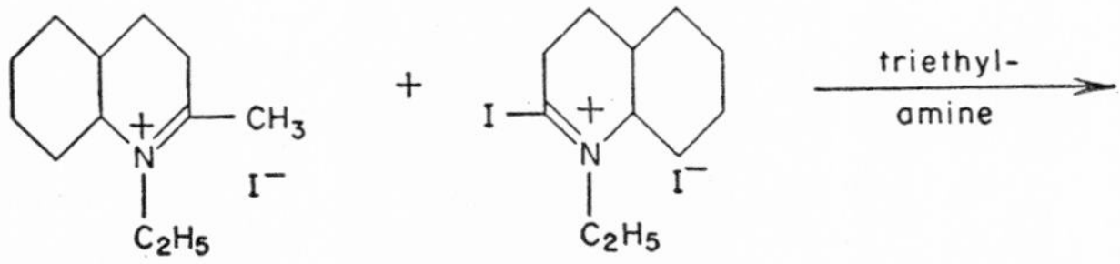

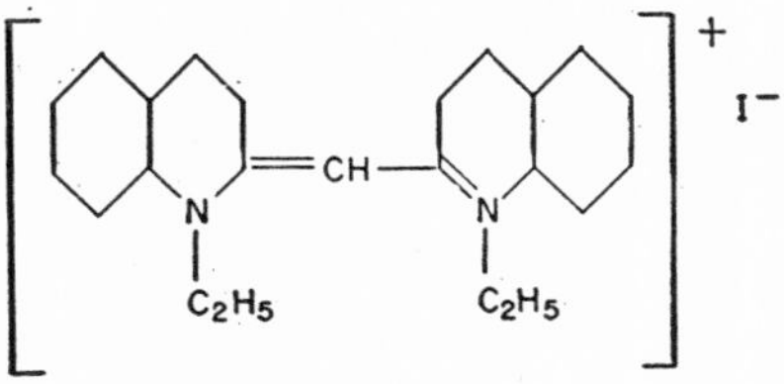

Carbocyanine. The synthesis of Pinacyanol, CI 808 (XII), by the con-densation of quinaldine ethiodide and triethyl orthoformate[13] is typical:

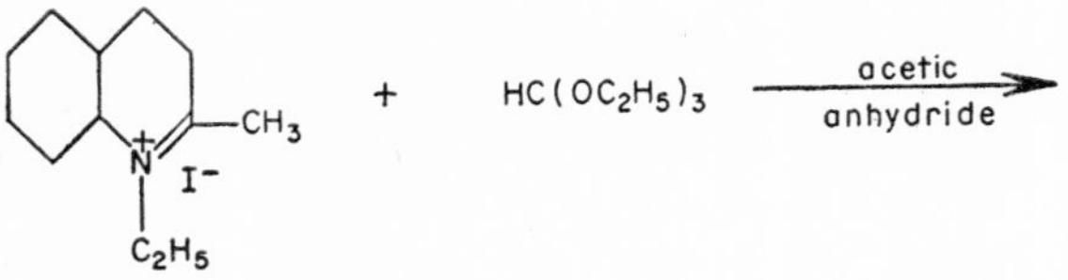

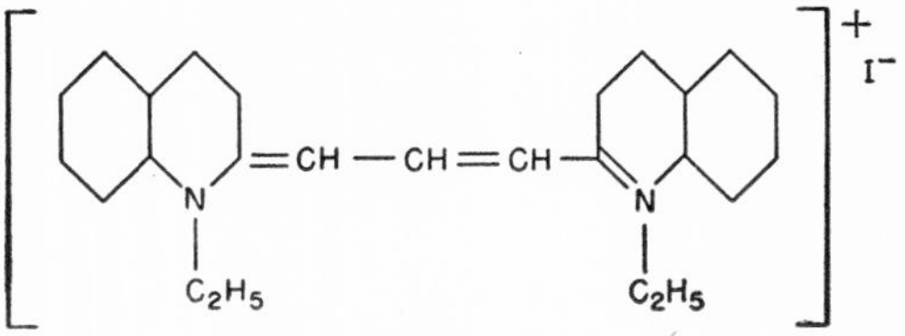

(XII)   Pinacyanol

Dicarbocyanine. An example of this class is the condensation of 2-methyl-benzoxazole ethiodide (XIII) and *N*-(2-chloro-3-phenyliminopropenyl)-aniline (XIV) to give 10-chloro-3,3'-diethyloxadicarbocyanine iodide (XV)[1]:

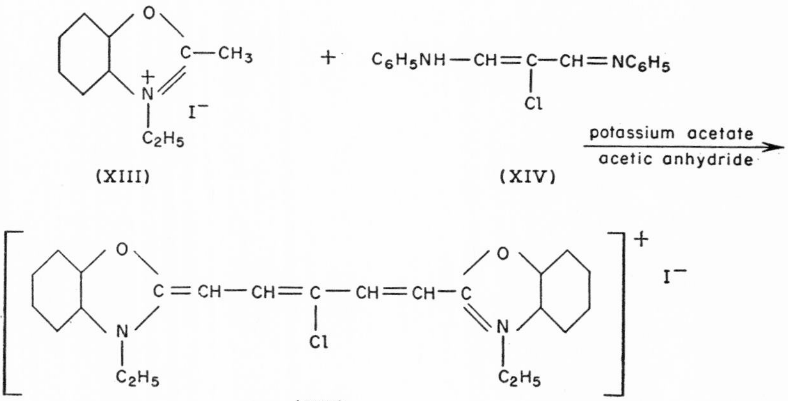

(XIII)   (XIV)

(XV)

Tricarbocyanine. One tricarbocyanine synthesis uses a polymethine dye as an intermediate. Condensation of *N*-(5-phenylimino-1,3-pentadienyl)ani-line hydrochloride (XVII) and 2-methylbenzothiazole ethiodide (XVI) gives 3,3'-diethylthiatricarbocyanine iodide (XVIII)[6]:

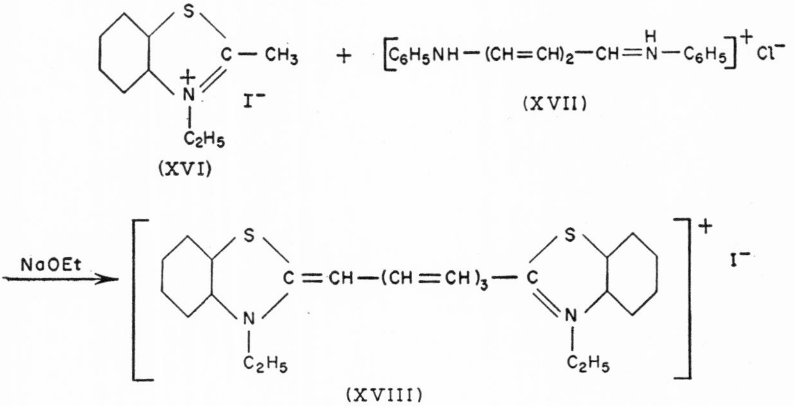

(XVI)

(XVIII)

Due to their complex nature, the cyanines are difficult to name in an unambiguous fashion. Their nomenclature is discussed in reference 12 and the system used therein is the one used for the compounds cited in this text.

Literature Cited

1. Beattie, Heilbron and Irving, *J. Chem. Soc.*, **1932**, 260.
2. British Patent 408,571 (1934).
3. Brooker, "The Sensitizing and Desensitizing Dyes," in Mees, "The Theory of the Photographic Process," p. 987, New York, Macmillan Co., 1942.
4. Brooker and Keyes, *J. Am. Chem. Soc.*, **57**, 2488 (1935).
5. Doja, *Chem. Revs.*, **11**, 273 (1932).
6. Fisher and Hamer, *J. Chem. Soc.*, **1933**, 189.
7. Hamer, *Quart. Revs. (London)*, **4**, 327 (1950).
7a. I. G. Farbenindustrie, PB 74025, frame 1869.
8. ——, PB 82058, frames 6153, 6154.
9. ——, PB 31004, Appendix 37, p. 12.
10. ——, *ibid.*, p. 11.
11. Kendall, *Chemistry & Industry*, **1950**, 121.
12. Kirk and Othmer, "Encyclopedia of Chemical Technology," Vol. 4, pp. 744 745, New York, Interscience Publishers, Inc., 1949.
13. Koenig, *Ber.*, **55**, 3293 (1922).
14. ——, *J. prakt. Chem.*, **69**, 105 (1904).
15. ——, U.S. Patent 1,524,791 (1925).
16. Mills and Wishart, *J. Chem. Soc.*, **117**, 579 (1920).
17. Mueller and Berres, U.S. Patent 2,179,895 (1939).
18. ——, U.S. Patent 2,206,108 (1940).
19. Vogel, *Ber.*, **6**, 1302 (1873).
20. ——, *ibid.*, **8**, 1635 (1875).
21. Williams, *Chem. News*, **1**, 15 (1860).
22. Wolff and Sieglitz, U.S. Patent 2,126,852 (1938).

Nitro Dyes

A nitro dye, picric acid, is considered to be the oldest artificial organic dye, since Woulfe produced it as early as 1771 by the action of nitric acid on indigo. It was used to give greenish-yellow tints on animal fibers long before Perkin synthesized Mauve.

The early nitro dyes were acidic compounds, mainly o-nitrophenols and nitronaphthols, the nitro group being the chromophore and the hydroxy group an auxochrome. The newer colors usually have one or more amino groups as auxochromes and may or may not be acidic.

Hantzsch's work[3] on the ethers of o-nitrophenols indicated that their strong color was probably due to a shift from a benzenoid (I) to a quinonoid (II) structure.

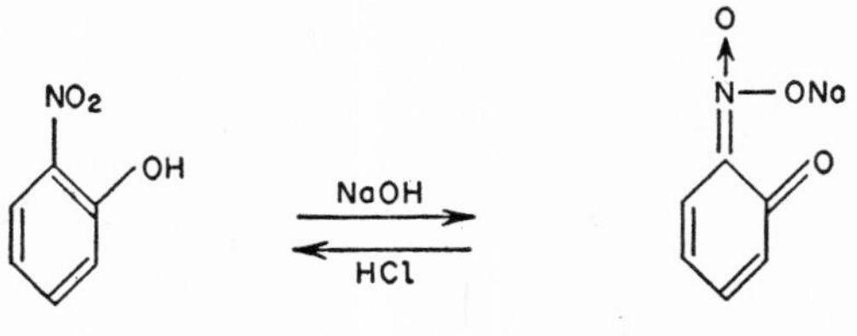

(I)   (II)

Hantzsch was able to show the existence of two methyl ethers of *o*-nitrophenol, one of which was colorless and had the structure (III) while the other (IV) was red.

(III)   (IV)

The nitro dyes fall into four general groups—the nitrophenols, the nitrodiphenylamines, heterocyclic nitro compounds and those based on *p*-quinone. These groups are discussed separately.

The Nitrophenols. Only two nitrophenols, Martius Yellow, CI 9 (V), and Naphthol Yellow S, CI 10 (VI), are of commercial importance today. They are produced by di- or trisulfonation of 1-naphthol, followed by replacement of sulfonic acid groups with nitro groups by means of dilute nitric acid[2].

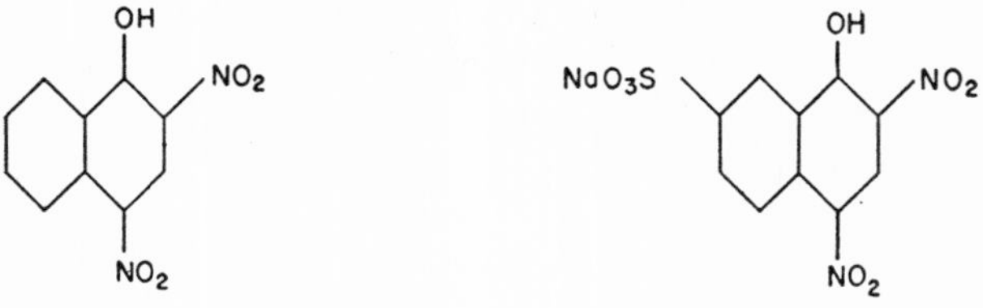

(V) Martius Yellow   (VI) Naphthol Yellow S

These dyes are used to a limited extent for leather and paper but are fugitive to light and to most other color-destroying agents.

The Nitrodiphenylamines. Today the nitrodiphenylamine colors are by far the most important members of the nitro class. The chemistry involved in their preparation is very simple—an aromatic amine and an aromatic compound containing an active halogen are condensed in water in the presence of an acid binding agent such as sodium or calcium carbonate, sodium acetate or magnesium oxide. The synthesis of Amido Naphthol

Brown 3G, Pr. 209 (VII)[7], illustrates the process:

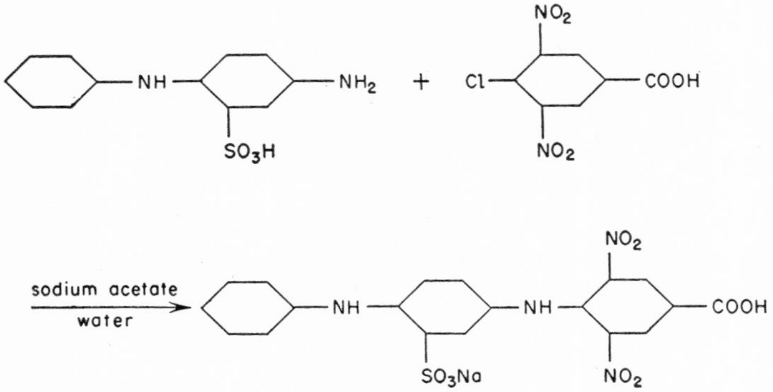

(VII) Amido Naphthol Brown 3G

The shade range of the nitrodiphenylamines includes yellows, oranges and browns. The sulfonated dyes, such as Amido Naphthol Brown 3G and related compounds, give attractive yellow and brown shades on wool and leather; the dyeings show good lightfastness but only fair washing fastness.

A fairly large outlet for nitrodiphenylamine dyes is their use in dispersed form for the dyeing of cellulose acetate and nylon. A yellow (VIII)[9] and an orange (IX)[1] of this type are disclosed in the recent patent literature as being light- and wash-fast colors.

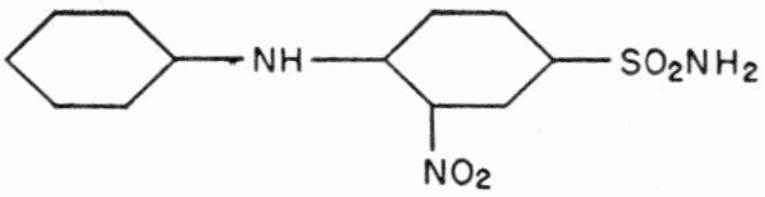

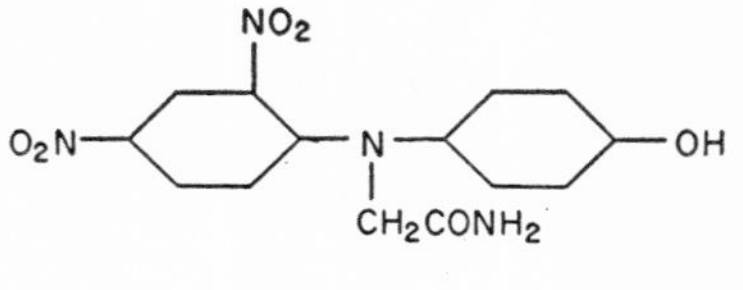

(VIII)   (IX)

The Heterocyclic Nitro Dyes. The heterocyclic nitro dyes shown below are of interest chemically because of their syntheses; only one was considered of sufficient commercial merit (by the I. G. Farbenindustrie) to be given a name.

Supramine Brown GR (X) was produced by the cyclization of a diphenylamine derivative with 2,4,6-trinitroanisole[6].

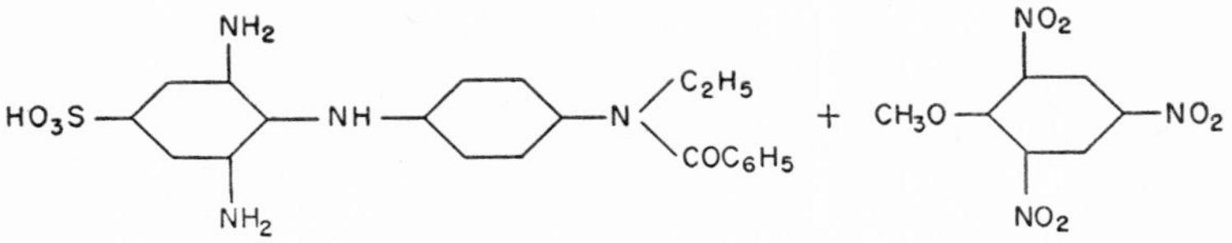

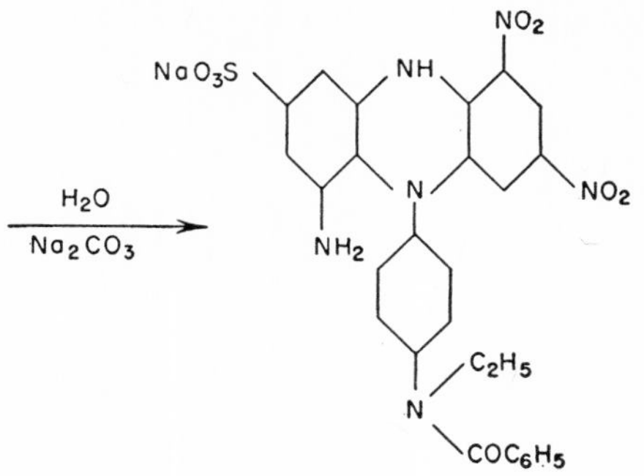

(X) Supramine Brown GR

A second dye was synthesized as follows[5]:

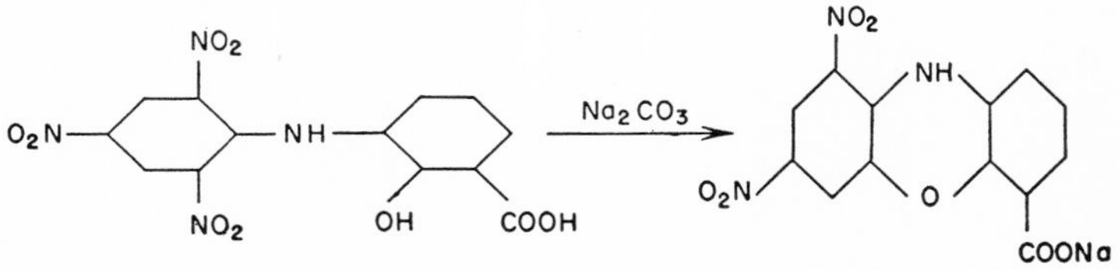

The colors illustrated above give brown shades on wool and leather.

Dyes Based on p-Quinone. The nitro dyes based on p-quinone are prepared by oxidative condensation of an aromatic amine and p-quinone or the direct condensation of the amine and chloranil. The oxidative synthesis is used for Acid Leather Brown EGB (XI)[8]:

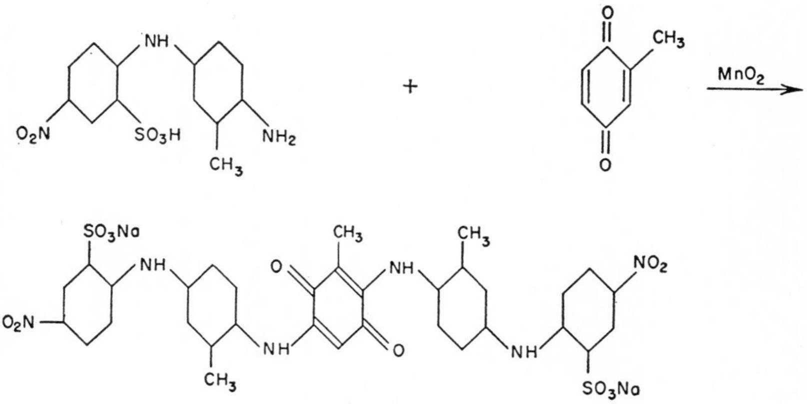

(XI) Acid Leather Brown EGB

The p-quinone nitro dyes are fast-to-light browns for leather, reputed to have the very valuable property of deep penetration during the dyeing process[4].

Literature Cited

1. Dickey and McNally, U.S. Patent 2,269,147 (1942).
2. German Patent 10,785 (1879).
3. Hantzsch and Gorke, *Ber.*, **39,** 1073 (1906).
4. Hess, Hager and Pense, U.S. Patent 2,107,941 (1938).
5. —— and Pardon, U.S. Patent 2,225,476 (1940).
6. I. G. Farbenindustrie, PB 70276, frames 3783–3785.
7. ——, PB 73497, frame 3736.
8. ——, *ibid.*, frame 3743.
9. McNally and Dickey, U.S. Patent 2,422,029 (1947).

Nitroso Dyes

Aromatic compounds containing nitroso and hydroxy groups ortho to each other can form colored chelate compounds with various metals, including iron, chromium, cobalt and nickel. This chelate formation (III) is based on the possible tautomeric shift of the *o*-nitrosophenols (I) to *o*-quinone monoximes (II):

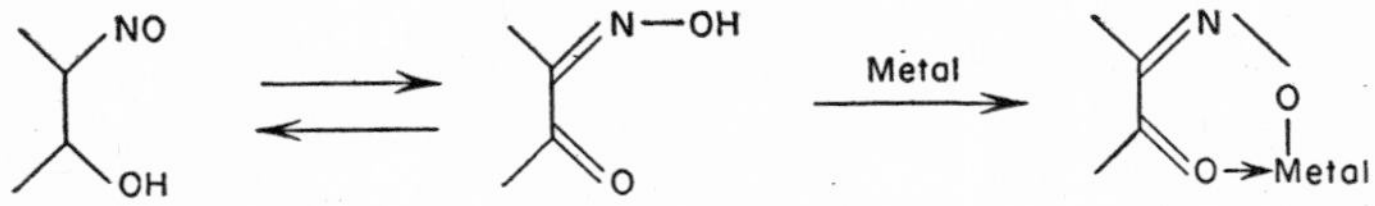

(I)   (II)   (III)

Naphthol Green B, CI 5 (IV), is the only dye of commercial importance which belongs to this class. It is synthesized by the nitrosation of Schaeffer's acid (2-naphthol-6-sulfonic acid), followed by conversion to the iron complex[1]:

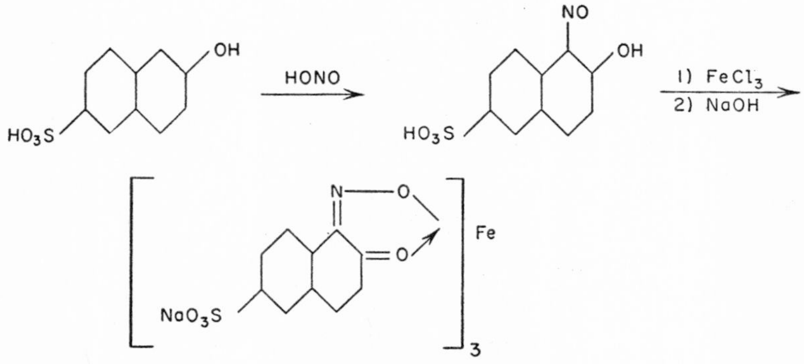

(IV) Naphthol Green B

The nitroso dyes range in shade from the dull green of Naphthol Green B to the brown nickel complex of 2,4-dinitrosoresorcinol. Green B is a cheap green of good lightfastness, used chiefly for the dyeing of paper.

The colored chelate-forming nature of the nitrosophenols has made them useful precipitants in analytical chemistry[2].

Literature Cited

1. Bloch and Schnerb, U.S. Patent 2,383,762 (1945).
2. Cronheim, *J. Org. Chem.*, **12**, 1 (1947).

Oxazine Dyes

The first oxazine dye was prepared by Meldola[4] in 1879, when he heated an equimolar mixture of 2-naphthol and *N*,*N*-dimethyl-*p*-nitrosoaniline hydrochloride in acetic acid. The blue dye thus formed was thought at first to be an indophenol, but it was shown later to be an oxazine derivative, Meldola's Blue (or New Blue R), CI 909 (I):

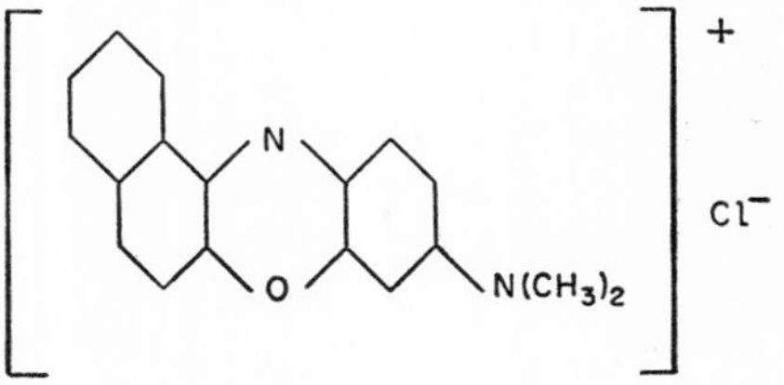

(I) Meldola's Blue

Although Meldola's Blue was sensitive to alkali, it was used widely for the dyeing of mordanted cotton. It is used very little for textile dyeing at the present time, but it is used to a limited degree for the dyeing of leather.

The oxazine dye chromophore is the phenoxazonium group (III). Phenoxazine (II) itself can be oxidized to phenoxazonium bromide, a red salt[2].

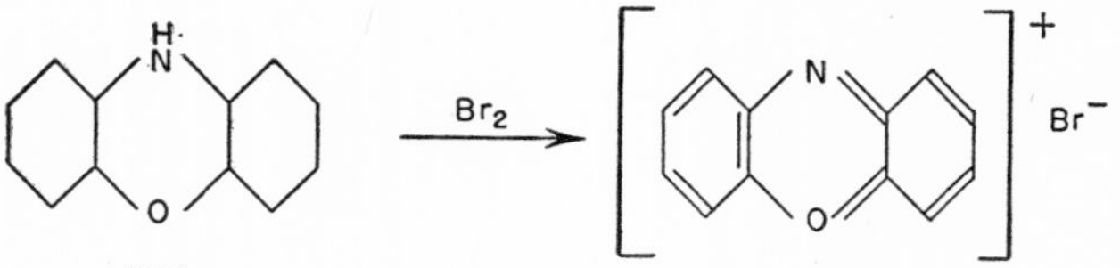

(II)   (III)

The color of the salt indicates that it exists in the *o*-quinonoid form. The dyes of the oxazine group have amino or hydroxy groups para to the ring nitrogen as auxochromes, permitting resonance stabilization related to contributing forms of both the *o*- and *p*-quinonoid type[3]. The dyes range in shade from greenish to reddish-blue.

Meldola's original synthesis is the common process for the preparation of the oxazine dyes. The preparatory routes for Gallocyanine, CI 883 (IV)[7], the oldest dye of the chrome mordant type, and Nile Blue A, CI 913 (V)[5], illustrate two modifications.

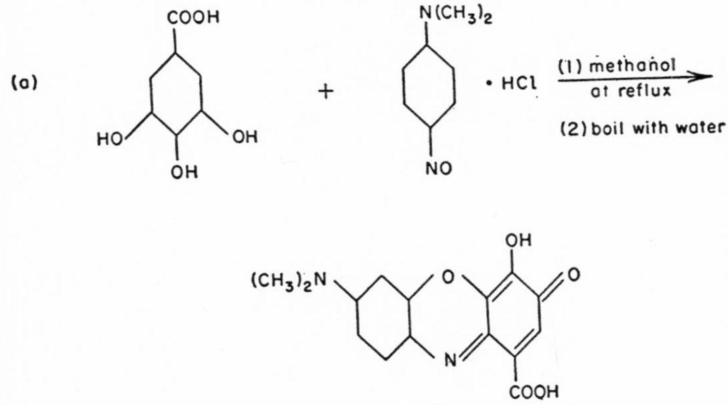

(IV) Gallocyanine

Three moles of N,N-dimethyl-p-nitrosoaniline hydrochloride are used for every two moles of gallic acid. The leuco form of the dye forms first and is oxidized to the dye by the excess nitroso compound, N,N-dimethyl-p-phenylenediamine being formed.

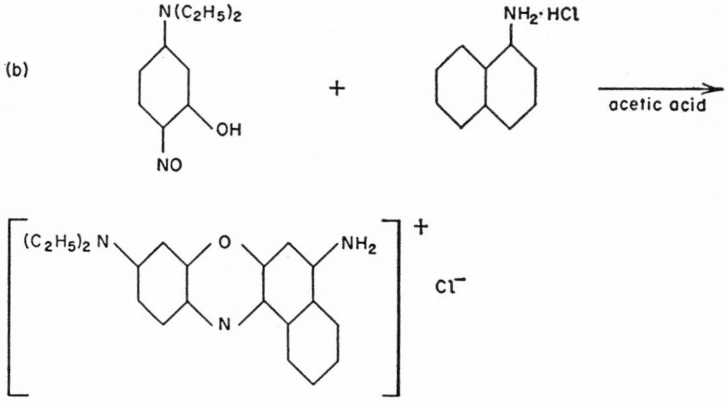

(V) Nile Blue A

The oxazines are not a particularly important dye class at the present time, Gallocyanine, New Blue R and Nile Blue A being the only three for which any sale or production was reported in the United States during 1950[8]. Gallocyanine and its derivative, Delphine Blue B, CI 878, are used for the chrome-printing of cotton and the dyeing of wool in the presence of chromium salts, giving blues of good washfastness and moderate lightfastness. Nile Blue A is used as the Smith and Mair fat stain[1], due to its ability to hydrolyze in the presence of a dilute mineral acid to the corresponding red oxazone (VI)[6].

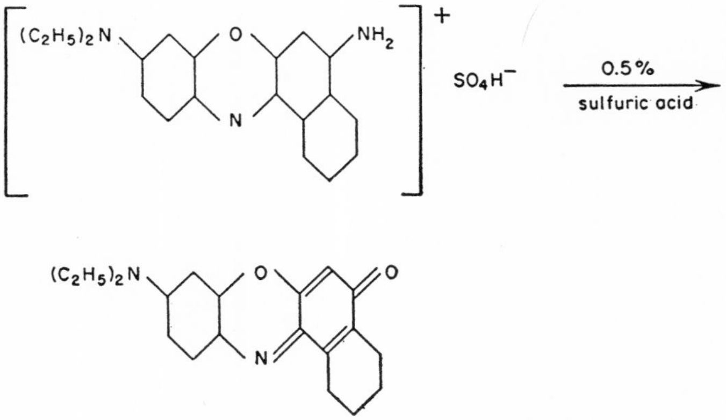

(VI)

Literature Cited

1. Conn, "Biological Stains," 4th ed., p. 92, Geneva, N. Y., Biotech Publications, 1940.
2. Kehrmann, *Ann.*, **322,** 1 (1902).
3. ——, *Helv. Chim. Acta*, **4,** 527 (1921).
4. Meldola, *Ber.*, **12,** 2065 (1879).
5. Moehlau and Uhlmann, *Ann.*, **289,** 115 (1896).
6. Thorpe, *J. Chem. Soc.*, **91,** 324 (1907).
7. Thorpe and Linstead, "Synthetic Dyestuffs," p. 388, London, Charles Griffin & Co., Ltd., 1933.
8. U.S. Tariff Commission Report No. 173, "Synthetic Organic Chemicals, U. S. Production and Sales, 1950," p. 77.

Quinoline Dyes

In 1883 Jacobsen and Reimer reported that fusion of quinaldine and phthalic anhydride yielded the alcohol-soluble pigment, quinophthalone, CI 800 (I)[7]. Sulfonation of quinophthalone gave the yellow dye, Quinoline Yellow, CI 801 (II).

With minor modifications[4], Jacobsen's process still is used in the manufacture of quinoline dyes:

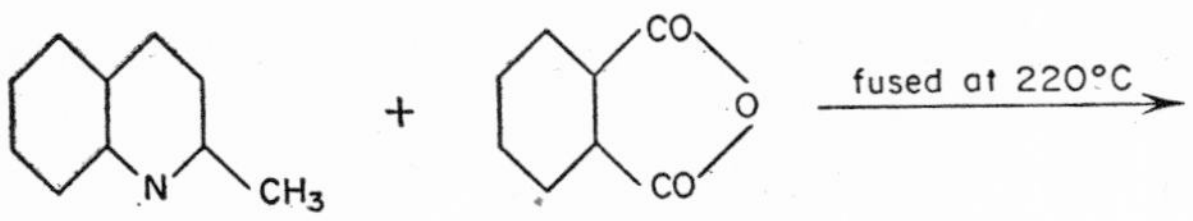

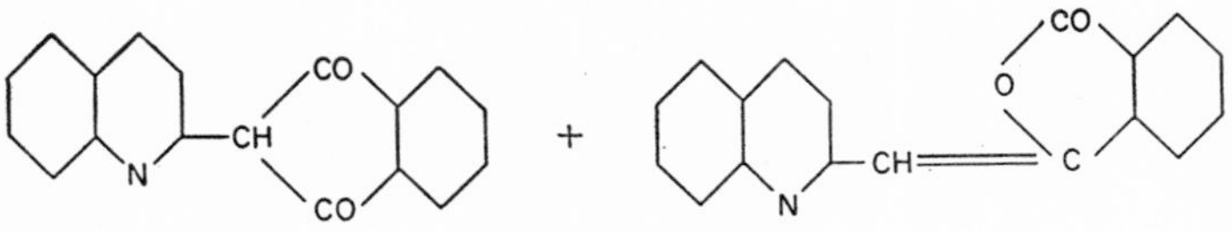

(I) Quinophthalone   (III)

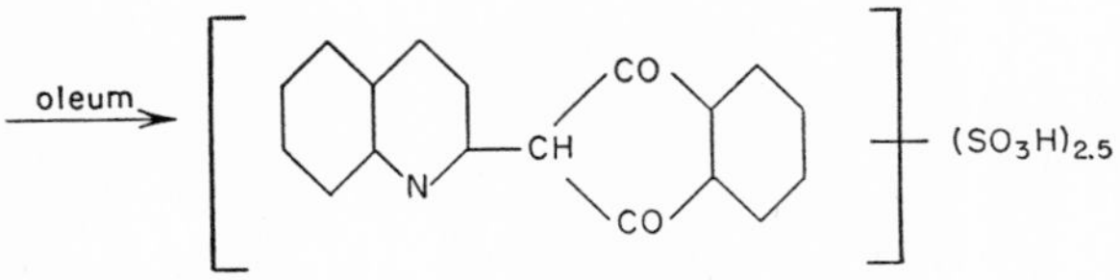

(II) Quinoline Yellow

The research of Eibner[1] showed that the symmetrical structure (I) is that of the dye. During its preparation the phthalide form (III) is produced first and persists to some extent in the final product. Eibner found also that digestion with sodium ethoxide converted the phthalide to the quinophthalone[2, 3].

The quinoline dyes are yellows, ranging from the reddish yellow of Quinoline Yellow KT (IV)[5] to the greenish-yellow of Quinoline Yellow itself. They are not particularly light-fast as a class, but a recent discovery has shown that a hydroxy group in the 3 position in the quinoline ring enhances the lightfastness. Such a product is the German dye Supra Light Yellow GGL (V)[6, 8].

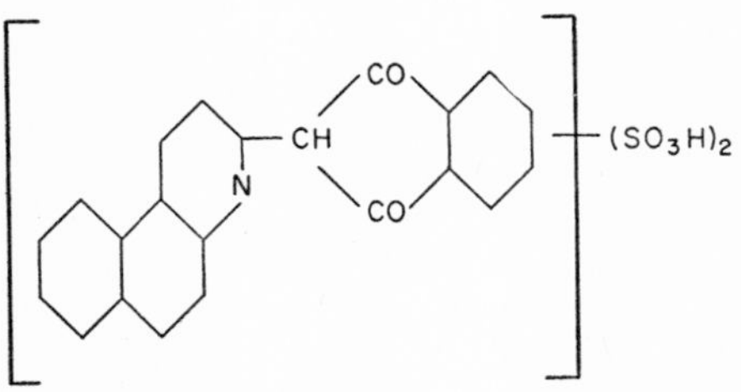

(IV) Quinoline Yellow KT 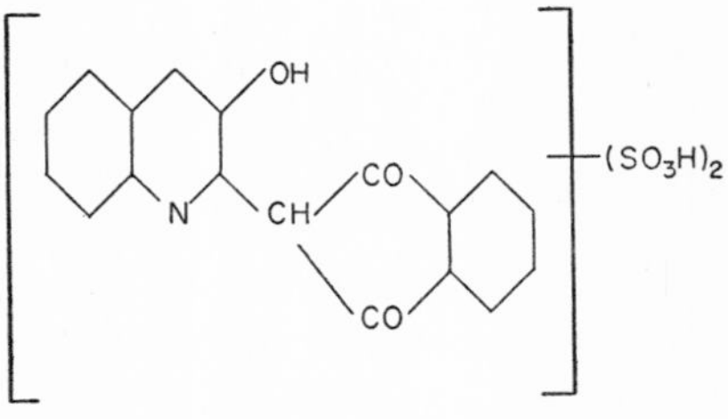   (V) Supra Light Yellow GGL

Quinoline colors find their main use on paper, where they give yellow shades of much better lightfastness than those obtainable with Auramine (see section on Ketone Imines, p. 245). Supra Light Yellow GGL is a wool dye.

Literature Cited

1. Eibner, *Chem. Ztg.*, **28,** 1206 (1904); *Chem. Zentr.*, **76**(I), 263 (1905).
2. Eibner and Merkel, *Ber.*, **37,** 3006 (1904).
3. German Patent 158,761 (1905).
4. I. G. Farbenindustrie, FIAT 1313, Vol. II, p. 384 (PB 85172).
5. ——, *ibid.*, p. 386.
6. ——, PB 70256, frames 9577–9582.
7. Jacobsen and Reimer, *Ber.*, **16,** 1082 (1883).
8. Kraenzlein, Schlichenmaier and Schoerning, U.S. Patent 2,006,022 (1935).

p-Quinone Imine Dyes

The *p*-quinone imine dyes are a very old class of colors based on *p*-quinone, from which they are derived by replacement of one or both oxygen atoms by $=NH$ groups.

The parent structures of this group are indamine (I), indoaniline (II) and indophenol (III).

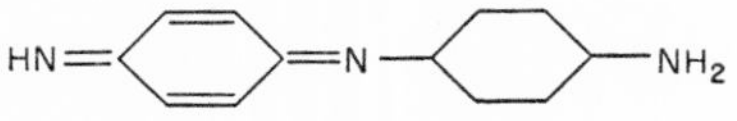

(I) 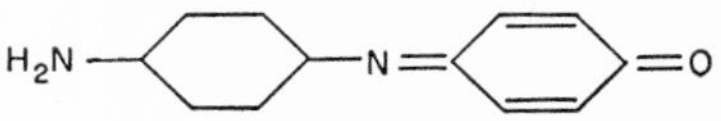   (II)

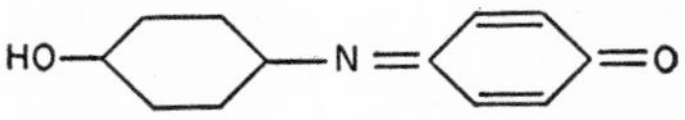

(III)

In actual usage, the term indophenol has been broadened to embrace the indoanilines as well.

As dyes for fiber application, the indamines and indophenols are blues and greens of chiefly historical interest, since they decompose when treated with acids into the corresponding quinone and amine or phenol. They are, however, of great importance as intermediates—the indamines yield safranines on oxidation with aniline hydrochloride (see Azines, p. 238) and the indophenols are used in sulfur dye manufacture (see Chapter 6 on Sulfur Dyes). A new application of the indophenols is in color photography, which is discussed later in this section.

Two synthetic routes to these products are:

(1) *Oxidation*. The oxidation of a *p*-phenylenediamine and a phenol or naphthol yields an indophenol. For example[5]:

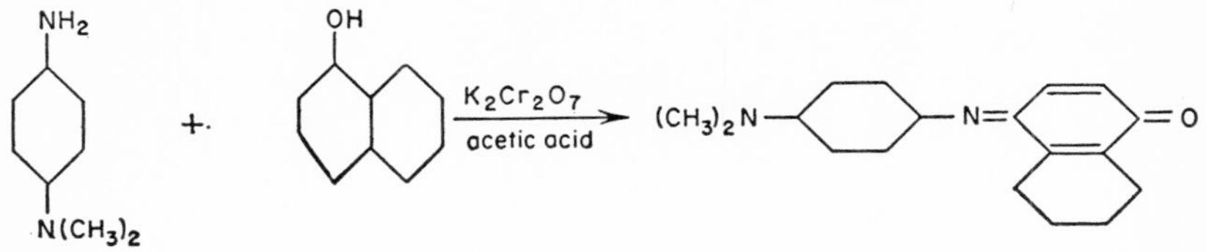

Indophenol Blue,
CI 821

(2) *Condensation.* The condensation of equimolecular amounts of N,N-dimethyl-p-nitrosoaniline hydrochloride and toluene-2,4-diamine gives Toluylene Blue, CI 820 (IV)[7]:

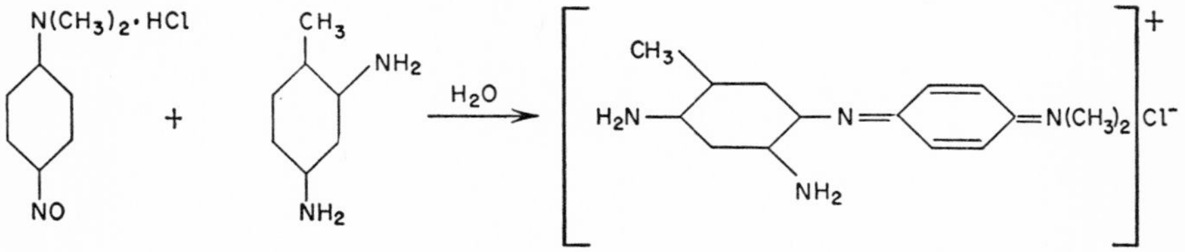

(IV) Toluylene Blue

The oxidative formation of indophenols has been used most successfully in color photography. The principle involved in the Agfacolor reversal process[4] is the inclusion in the silver bromide film emulsion of components, rendered nondiffusing in their gelatin layers by the attachment of long aliphatic chains, which are capable of coupling with N,N-diethyl-p-phenylenediamine or an analog to give a dye of one of three colors, blue-green, magenta or yellow. The actual coupling occurs during the developing operation, silver bromide acting as the oxidizing agent. The silver image then is removed by a potassium ferricyanide bleaching process, leaving a transparent, positive multi-colored picture of the object.

Three dyes formed in the Agfacolor reversal process by coupling with N,N-diethyl-p-phenylenediamine during the developing operation are the following[3]:

(1) *Blue-green Component:*

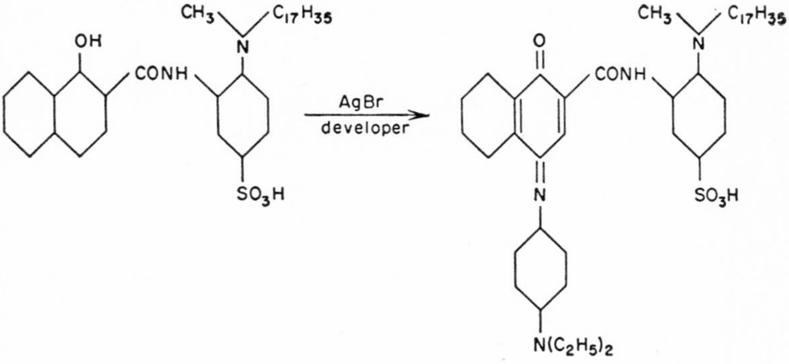

(2) *Magenta Component:*

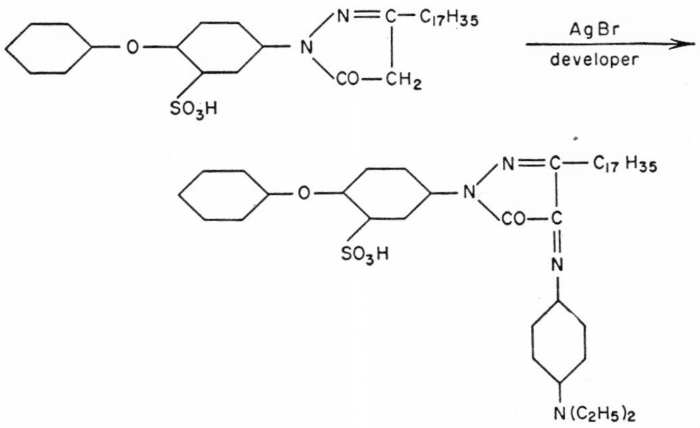

(3) *Yellow Component:*

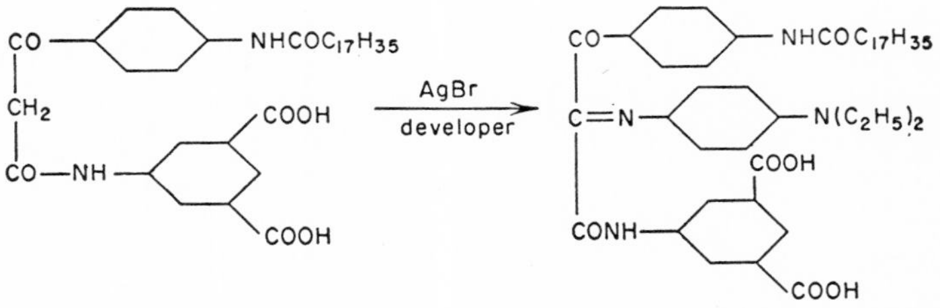

In general, the blue-green coupler is a phenol or naphthol, the magenta coupler, a substituted pyrazolone and the yellow coupler, a ketomethylene compound, such as an acetoacetanilide or a cyanoacetic ester. While the dyes produced from the blue-green couplers with N,N-diethyl-p-phenylene-diamine are indophenols, those from the magenta and yellow couplers are azomethine dyes. The azomethines are made by the oxidation of the active methylene groups of the pyrazolones and ketomethylene compounds with the unsubstituted amino group of the developing agent. It has been necessary to use the azomethines because the phenolic couplers give only blue and blue-green shades.

Other color photographic systems are based on similar dyes. Discussion of these systems is beyond the scope of this book, but further and more complete information may be obtained from references 1, 2 and 6.

Literature Cited

1. Cornwell-Clyne, "Colour Cinematography," 3rd ed., London, Chapman & Hall, Ltd., 1951.
2. Friedman, "History of Color Photography," Boston, American Photographic Publishing Company, 1944.
3. I. G. Farbenindustrie, FIAT 943, pp. 3, 14, 15, 62, 67, 76, 87 (PB 78248).

4. ——, FIAT 976, pp. 13–29 (PB 79559).
5. Thorpe and Linstead, "The Synthetic Dyestuffs," p. 386, London, Charles Griffin & Co., Ltd., 1933.
6. Wahl, *Angew. Chem.*, **64**, 259 (1952).
7. Witt, *J. Chem. Soc.*, **35**, 356 (1879).

Thiazine Dyes

The first thiazine dye was prepared by Lauth in 1876, when he obtained a violet dye by the ferric chloride oxidation of *p*-phenylenediamine in the presence of hydrogen sulfide. Later, Bernthsen[1] showed that Lauth's Violet, CI 920 (I), had the structure

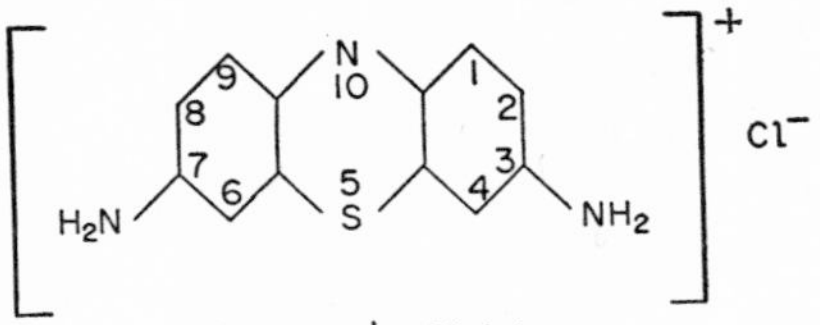

(I)   Lauth's Violet

and that it could be derived from phenothiazine by nitration, reduction and oxidation.

Caro applied Lauth's reaction to *N*,*N*-dimethyl-*p*-phenylenediamine and prepared the important dye, Methylene Blue, CI 922 (II)[4]:

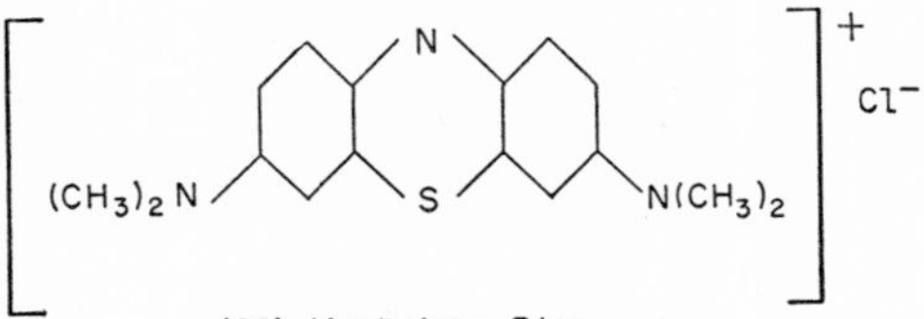

(II) Methylene Blue

In 1950[11] the total production of this dye in the United States was 349,000 pounds.

The thiazine chromophore is the phenazathionium nucleus, with amino groups in positions 3 and 7 as auxochromes. The dyes of this group have a color range from green to blue and have been used as colorants for paper, tannin-mordanted cotton and silk. In addition, Methylene Blue is a very important biological stain[2].

Two syntheses for thiazine dyes are presented—the first is the commercial or "thiosulfate" route and the second is a novel preparation of considerable academic interest.

(1) *Thiosulfate Process*[3]. This procedure comprises oxidation of an *N*-

alkyl-*p*-phenylenediamine and an *N*-alkylaniline in the presence of sodium thiosulfate and zinc chloride. The synthetic route may be represented as follows:

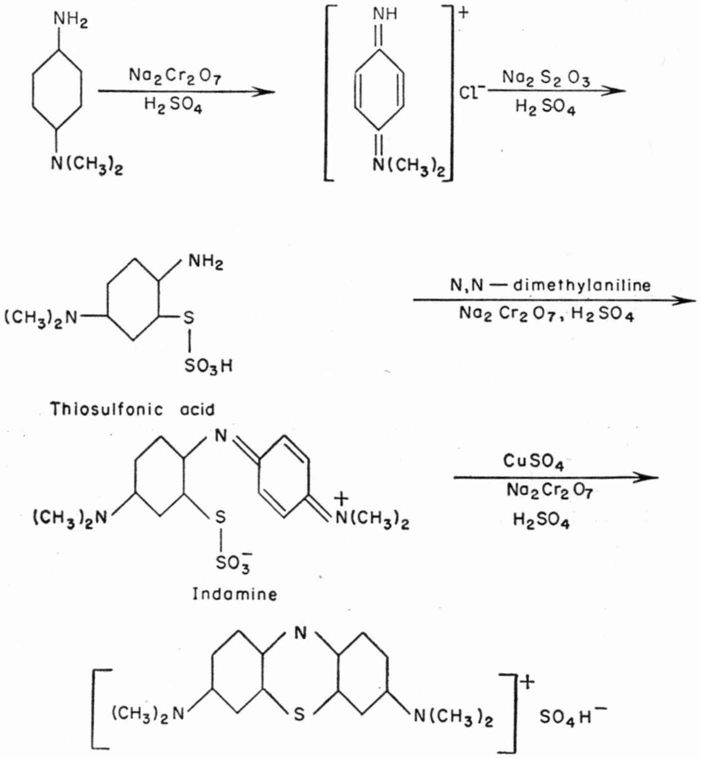

Thiosulfonic acid

Indamine

Methylene Blue (sulfate)

Methylene Blue is converted to its chloride for medicinal use or isolated as the zinc chloride double salt of the chloride for dye use.

The procedure for unsymmetrical thiazines is similar through the thiosulfonic acid stage; the second constituent is added prior to oxidation to the indamine. An example[6] is Thionine Blue GO (III).

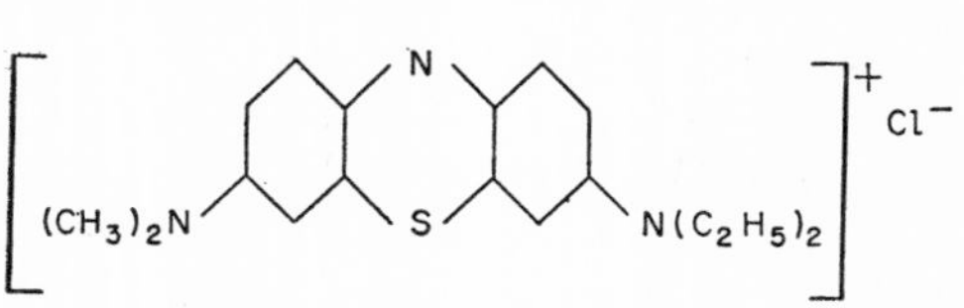

(III) Thionine Blue GO

(2) *Kehrmann's Synthesis*[8, 9]. This scientifically interesting method in-

volves the acetic acid bromination of phenothiazine (IV) to phenazathionium perbromide (V), followed by treatment of the latter with alcoholic dimethylamine to give Methylene Blue in almost quantitative yield (the dimethylamine adds across the quinonoid nucleus and the addition product is oxidized to the dye by bromine):

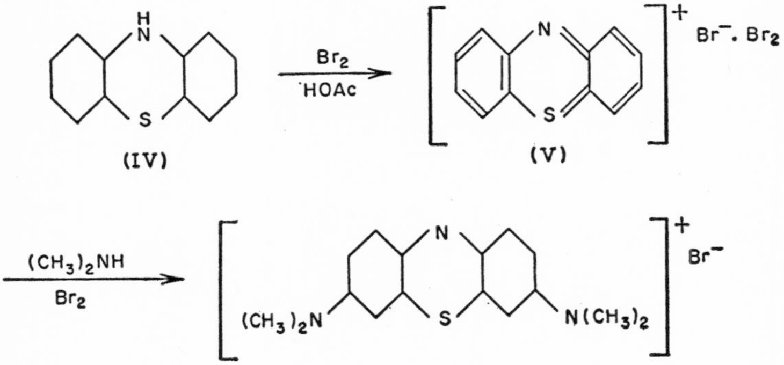

The current availability of phenothiazine and a wide variety of alkylamines should make Kehrmann's synthesis a useful laboratory procedure for symmetrically substituted thiazines.

Two other commercially important dyes of this group are Methylene Green B, CI 924 (VI), prepared by the nitration of Methylene Blue[7], and New Methylene Blue N, CI 927. The structure of the latter dye is variously represented as VII or VIII[5, 10].

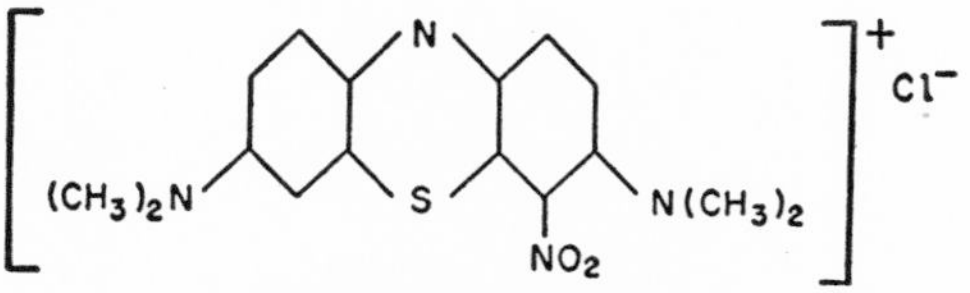

(VI) Methylene Green B

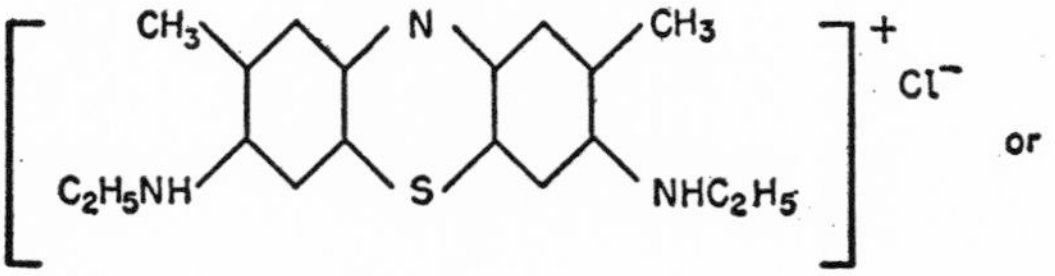

(VII)

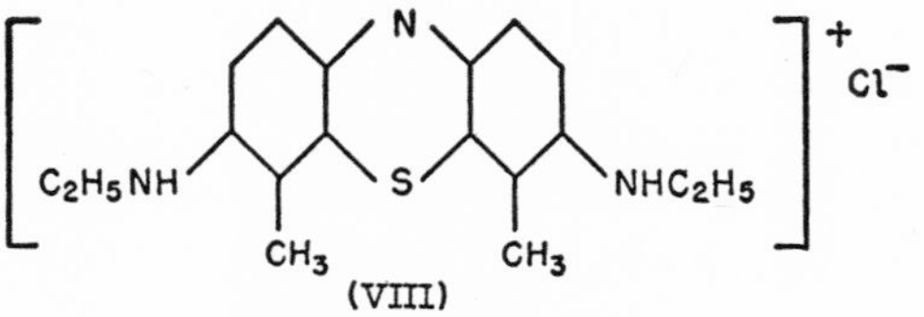

(VIII)
New Methylene Blue N

Literature Cited

1. Bernthsen, *Ber.*, **17,** 611 (1884).
2. Conn, "Biological Stains," 4th ed., p. 80, Geneva, N. Y., Biotech Publications, 1940.
3. Fierz-David and Blangey, "Fundamental Processes of Dye Chemistry," p. 311, New York, Interscience Publishers, Inc., 1949.
4. German Patent 1,886 (1877).
5. I. G. Farbenindustrie, FIAT 1313, Vol. II, p. 373 (PB 85172).
6. ——, *ibid.*, p. 375.
7. ——, PB 74067, frame 220.
8. Kehrmann, *Ber.*, **49,** 53 (1916).
9. —— and Diserens, *ibid.*, **48,** 318 (1915).
10. Rowe, "Colour Index," 1st ed., p. 228, 1924.
11. U.S. Tariff Commission Report No. 173, "Synthetic Organic Chemicals, U. S. Production and Sales, 1950," p. 17.

Thiazole Dyes

The thiazole dyes are a closely related group, inasmuch as they all contain the thiazole ring (I)

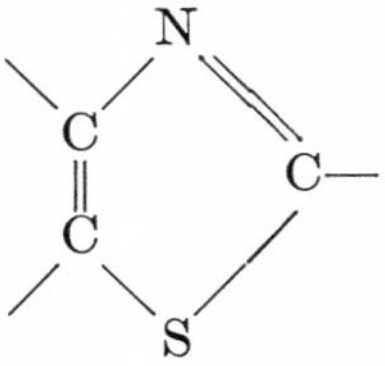

(I)

and are all produced from dehydrothio-*p*-toluidine [2-(*p*-aminophenyl)-6-methylbenzothiazole] (II).

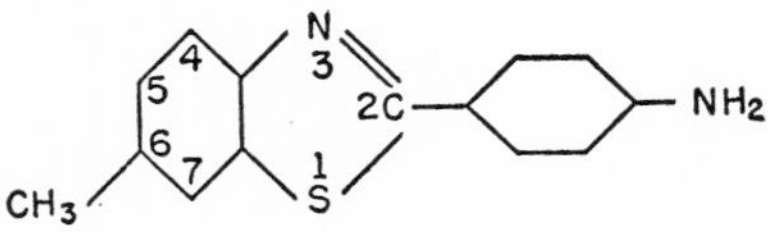

(II)

This class of colors is based on the discovery by Green (1887) that the fusion of *p*-toluidine and sulfur at 200 to 280°C gives a mixture of bases[2]. Green and later investigators found that the fusion first produces dehydrothio-*p*-toluidine (II). Further fusion causes the monothiazole derivative to condense again, the final product being a mixture of it and di- (III) and trithiazoles.

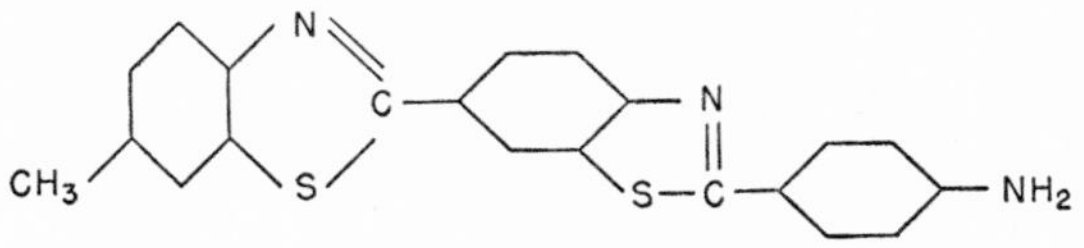

(III)

Green also discovered that the mixture of di- and trithiazoles could be sulfonated to a product which he named Primuline, CI 812, and which could be used for the preparation of cotton-substantive azo dyes[3].

In commercial practice, the fusion mass is sulfonated[1] and the dehydrothio-*p*-toluidinemonosulfonic acid [2-(*p*-aminophenyl)-6-methyl-7-benzothiazolesulfonic acid] (IV)[6] is separated from the primuline. Unsulfonated dehydrothio-*p*-toluidine may be isolated from the fusion by vacuum distillation[1]. The three products are the parent compounds for several dye classes—direct (azo), developed, basic and sulfur. The first three of these are discussed below and the fourth is discussed in the chapter on sulfur colors.

Azo Dyes. Several azo dyes are based on dehydrothio-*p*-toluidine. Preparative methods involve a unique oxidative route as well as the usual diazotization and coupling techniques.

(1) *Oxidative Synthesis.* Chloramine Yellow, CI 814 (V), is prepared by the hypochlorite oxidation[1] of dehydrothio-*p*-toluidinemonosulfonic acid and is the only important azo dye made by the oxidative route. Only recently it has been shown by the excellent work of Schubert[6] to be a mixture, 60 per cent of which is the azo dye (Va), 25 per cent an azine dye (Vb) and the other 15 per cent unidentified products.

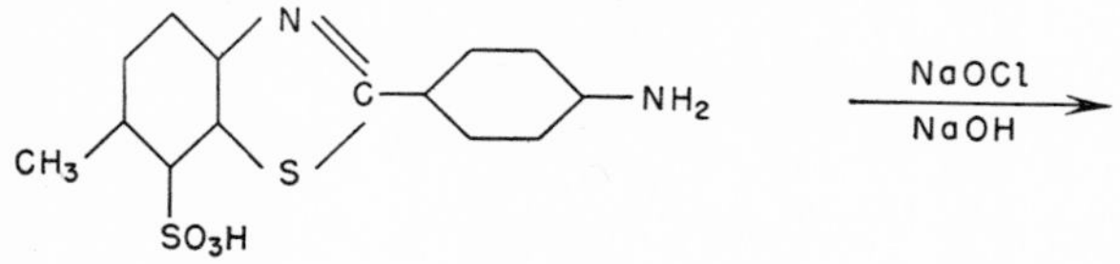

(IV)

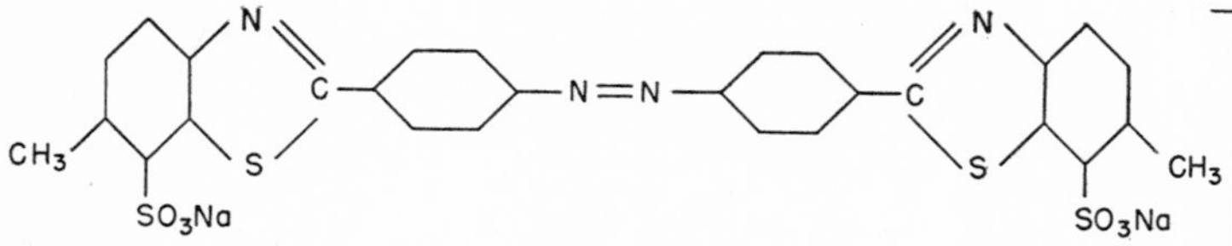

(Va)

+

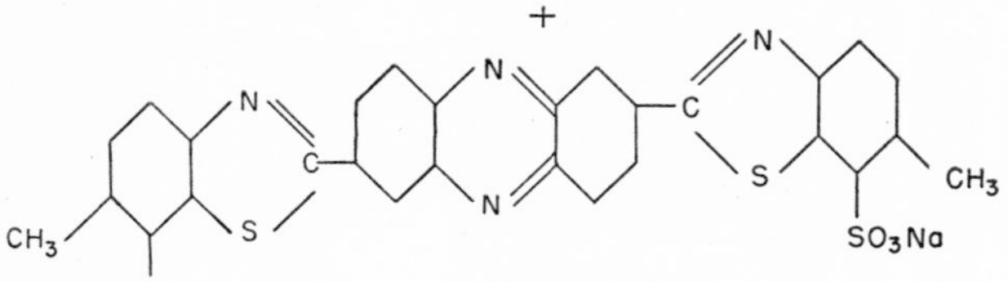

(Vb)

Chloramine
Yellow
(V)

Chloramine Yellow is one of the best direct yellows known due to its good fastness to light and bleach. It is a very important dye; 486,000 pounds of it was produced in the United States in 1950[7].

(2) *Coupling.* Erika 2GN, CI 126 (VI), is prepared by diazotization of dehydrothio-*p*-toluidine, followed by coupling with 1-naphthol-3,8-disulfonic acid[5].

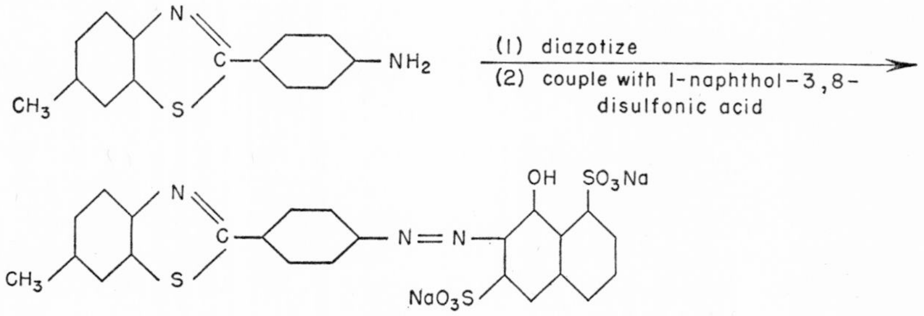

(VI) Erika 2GN

Erika 2GN, Rosophenine 10B, CI 225, and other azo coupled colors of this group are direct dyeing pinks of moderate fastness to light, but they are not comparable in light resistance to Chloramine Yellow.

Developed Dyes. Green's early work with primuline showed that it was substantive to cotton and that it could be diazotized on the fiber. If the fiber containing the diazotized primuline was coupled with phenols or amines, dyeings from yellow to maroon and brown were obtained[3]. The developed or "ingrain" colors thus obtained have only moderate lightfastness but excellent washfastness.

Basic Dyes. Green[2] also showed that methylation of dehydrothio-*p*-toluidine with methanol and hydrogen chloride[4] gave a bright greenish-yellow basic dye. This product is known now as Thioflavine T, CI 815 (VII).

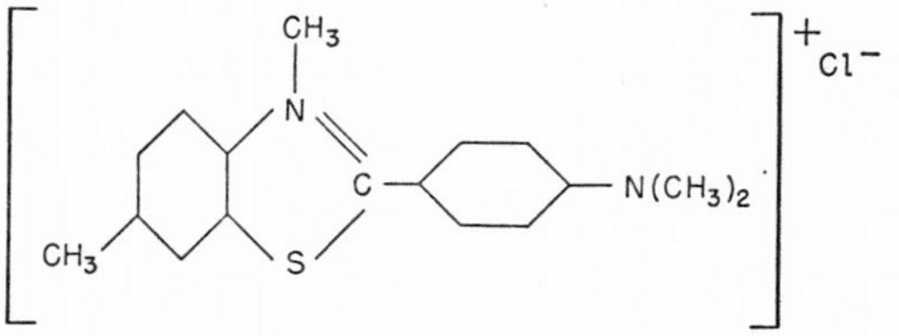

(VII) Thioflavine T

Thioflavine T gives a light-fugitive canary yellow shade on paper and it is used also to an appreciable extent in the manufacture of yellow-green phosphotungstate lakes for use in printing inks.

Literature Cited

1. Fierz-David and Blangey, "Fundamental Processes of Dye Chemistry," pp. 332–337, New York, Interscience Publishers, Inc., 1949.

2. Green, *J. Chem. Soc.*, **55**, 227 (1889).

3. ——, *J. Soc. Dyers Colourists*, **4**, 39 (1888).

4. I. G. Farbenindustrie, PB 25626, frames 1184–1186.

5. Paul, *Z. angew. Chem.*, **9**, 683 (1896).

6. Schubert, *Ann.*, **558**, 10 (1947).

7. U.S. Tariff Commission Report No. 173, "Synthetic Organic Chemicals, U. S. Production and Sales, 1950," p. 17.

Triarylmethane Dyes

The largest and most important group of miscellaneous colors are the triarylmethane dyes. These products, most of which are derivatives of triphenyl- or diphenylnaphthylmethane, have been of continued commercial importance since Verguin's discovery of Fuchsine, CI 677 (I), in 1858. Their 1950 production in the United States constituted 3.9 per cent[32] of the total dye output.

Verguin synthesized Fuchsine by the stannic chloride oxidation of crude aniline. Later investigators showed that Verguin's dye was actually a triamino derivative of triphenylmethane[6, 10] and that its synthesis was possible due to the presence of *o*- and *p*-toluidines in crude aniline.

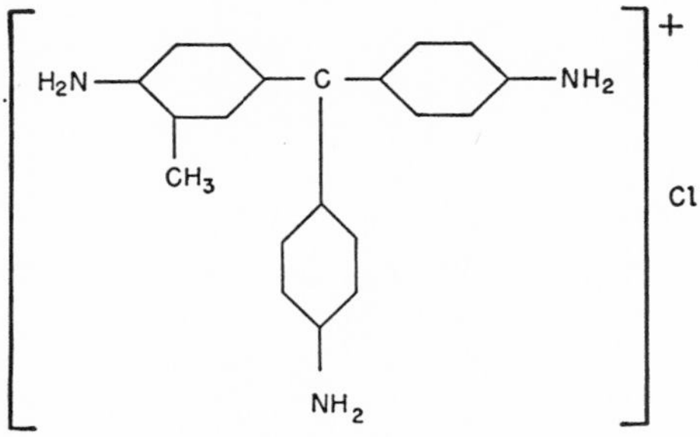

(I) Fuchsine

The triarylmethanes may be regarded as having the fuchsone imine (II) structure as their chromophore. Fuchsone imine itself is a colored substance capable of forming orange-red salts. Introduction of one amino group into

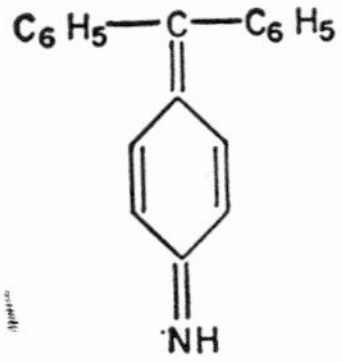

(II) Fuchsone imine

one of the phenyl nuclei in the position para to the methane carbon atom gives the first true dye of the series, Doebner's Violet; and the entrance of a second amino group in the remaining phenyl nucleus gives the bluish-red Pararosaniline, CI 676. The dyes of this group may have either amino or hydroxy groups in the positions para to the methane carbon as auxochromes. The dye shades include red, blue, green and violet.

The dyes are very similar in their general chemical reactions. Using Pararosaniline as a representative member, the following diagram illustrates the reactions of the class:

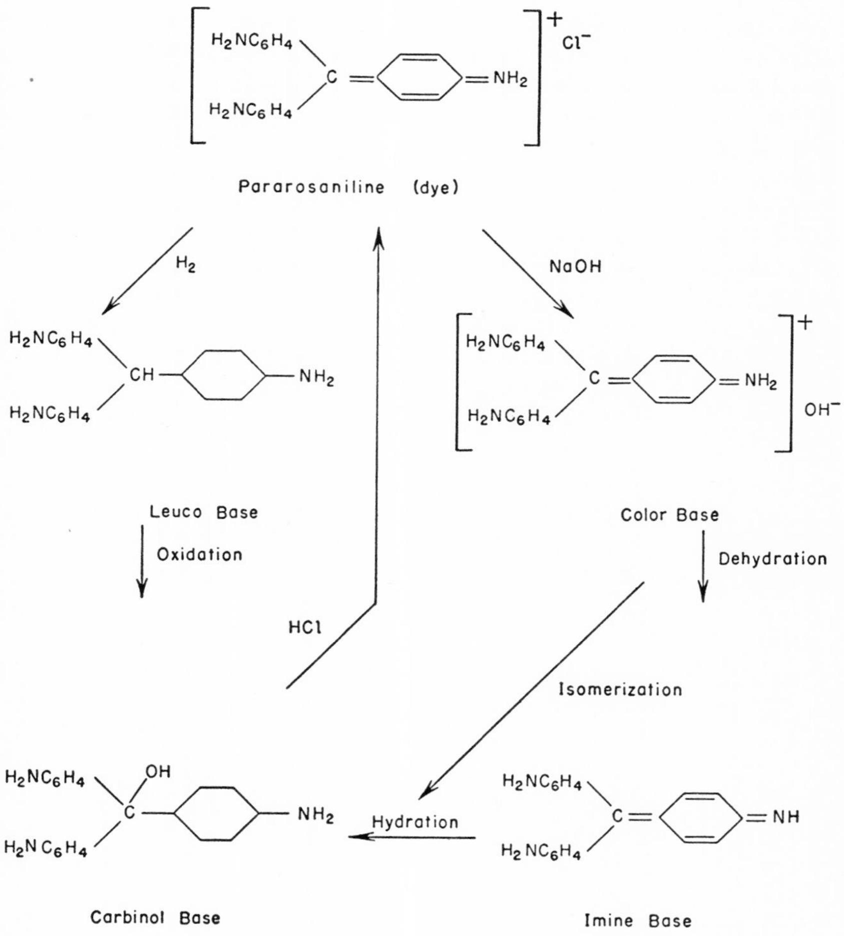

In general the true ammonium or color bases are capable only of a transitory existence in solution; they isomerize rapidly to the colorless, stable carbinol bases. In some cases the imine bases are sufficiently stable to permit their isolation and characterization.

The triarylmethane dyes include basic colors (those in which the chromophore is a cation), acid colors (those in which the chromophore is an anion and which usually show "zwitter-ion" properties) and chromable colors (usually acidic in nature, but carrying metallizable groups). They give dyeings of extreme brightness and purity, but their fastness properties, particularly to light, are quite poor. They find wide usage despite their light fugitiveness, due to their brilliance of shade, their extremely high tinctorial values and their relative cheapness.

The *basic* colors of this group are used primarily for the dyeing of paper, for the production of printing and hectograph duplicating inks and as biological stains. In ink manufacture and paper tinting they frequently are employed as their faster-to-light, insoluble phosphotungstomolybdate lakes.

The *acid dyes* are used chiefly for the dyeing of wool and silk, but they find considerable use as tints for writing inks, as bluing compositions and as lake colors. The *chrome colors* are used for the dyeing of wool and silk.

The triarylmethanes fall naturally into the following subclasses:

      (a) Diamino derivatives of triphenylmethane
      (b) Triamino derivatives of triphenylmethane
      (c) Aminohydroxy derivatives of triphenylmethane
      (d) Hydroxy derivatives of triphenylmethane
      (e) Derivatives of diphenylnaphthylmethane
      (f) Miscellaneous

These subclasses are treated separately in the discussion which follows.

Diamino Derivatives of Triphenylmethane. The simplest member of this series, Doebner's Violet (III), is of academic interest only. Methylation of the amino groups in Doebner's Violet gives the commercially important dye, Malachite Green, CI 657 (IV), which was first prepared by Fischer in 1877[7].

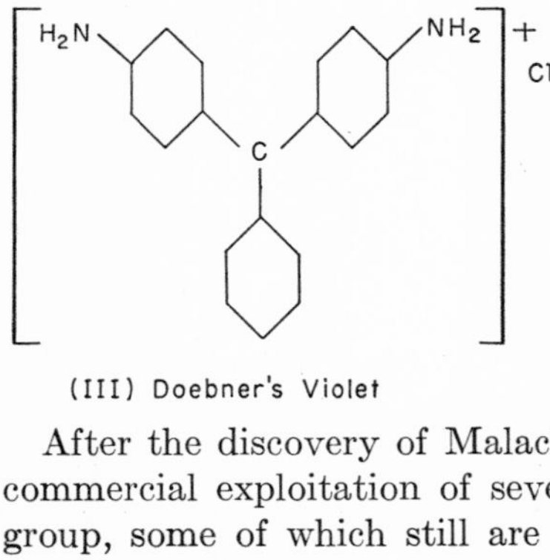

(III) Doebner's Violet 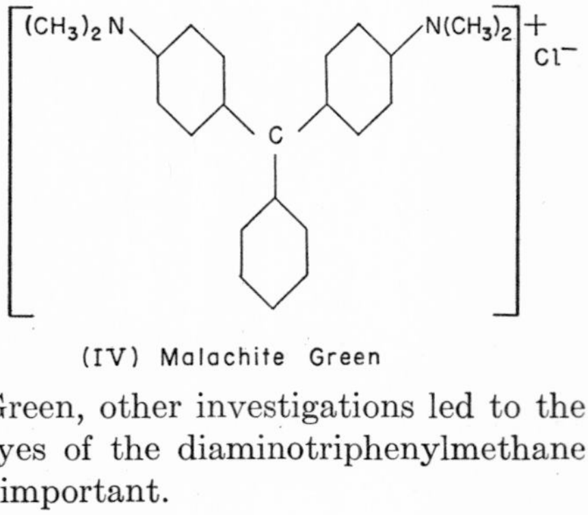   (IV) Malachite Green

After the discovery of Malachite Green, other investigations led to the commercial exploitation of several dyes of the diaminotriphenylmethane group, some of which still are very important.

One general synthetic method is used for these dyes—the condensation of two moles of an aromatic amine with an aromatic aldehyde to the leuco dye, followed by chemical oxidation to the dye. The following two examples illustrate the method:

(1) *Malachite Green*[4]:

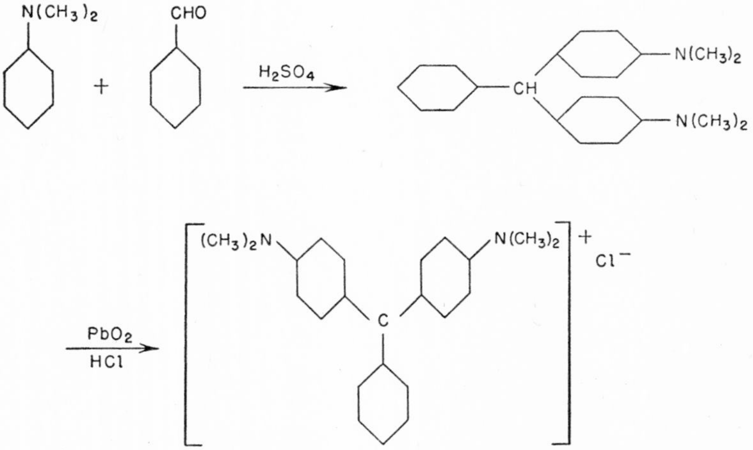

In common practice the dye is converted to the carbinol and reacidified with oxalic acid to form the easily crystallizable oxalate.

(2) *Erioglaucine, CI 671 (V)*[11]:

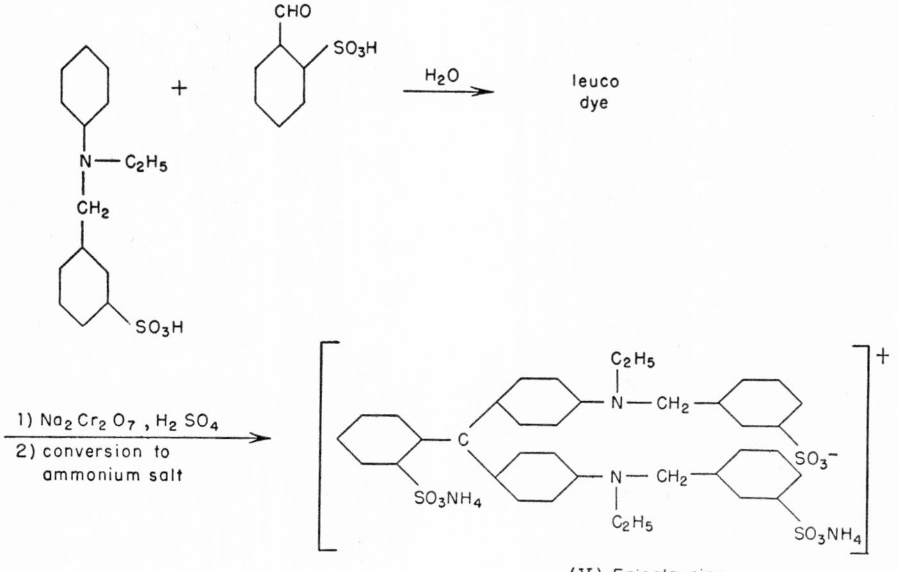

(V) Erioglaucine

Erioglaucine and other sulfonated dyes to be illustrated later are presented as inner salts ("zwitter-ions"). It is also possible to represent them as an inner anhydride between the sulfonic acid group and the carbinol hydroxy group of the triphenylmethane, e.g., formula (VI)[5].

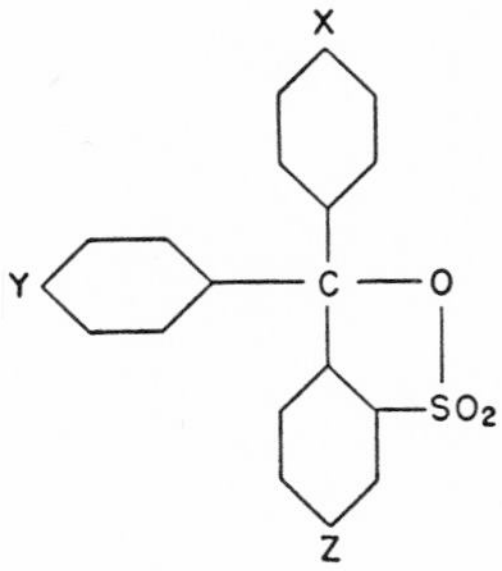

(VI)

In the older literature the structure of the monosulfonic acid of N-ethyl-N-phenylbenzylamine is given generally with the sulfonic acid group in the benzyl nucleus para to the methylene group; recent work has proved the predominant isomer to be the meta one shown above[1].

The shade range of this subclass is from blue to green.

The technically important *basic dyes* of this group include Malachite Green, Setoglaucine, CI 658 (VII)[18], and Brilliant Green, CI 662 (VIII)[16].

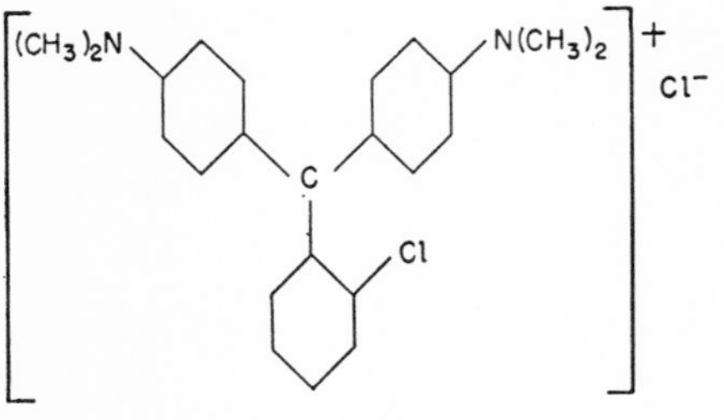

(VII) Setoglaucine 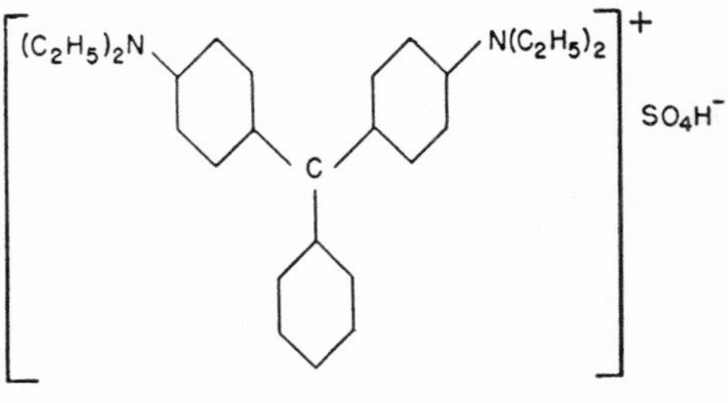   (VIII) Brilliant Green

Of the *acid dyes* the most important is Erioglaucine, which is used in large quantities for the preparation of peacock blue lakes, of value in printing inks. Other less important dyes include Guinea Green B, CI 666 (IX)[9], and Brilliant Milling Green B, CI 667 (X)[23]. (Reference 23 discloses a closely analogous process.)

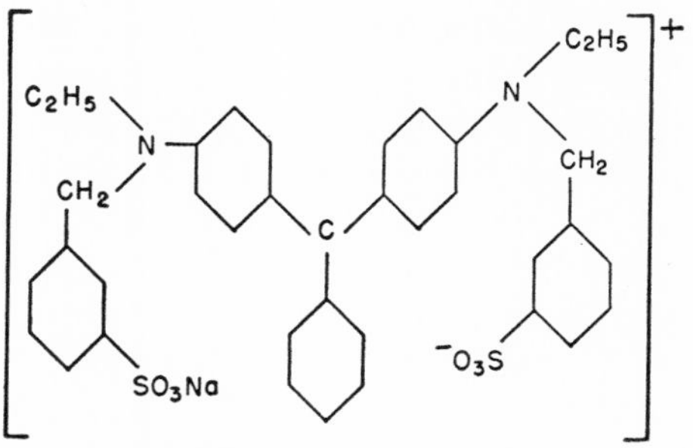

(IX) Guinea Green B

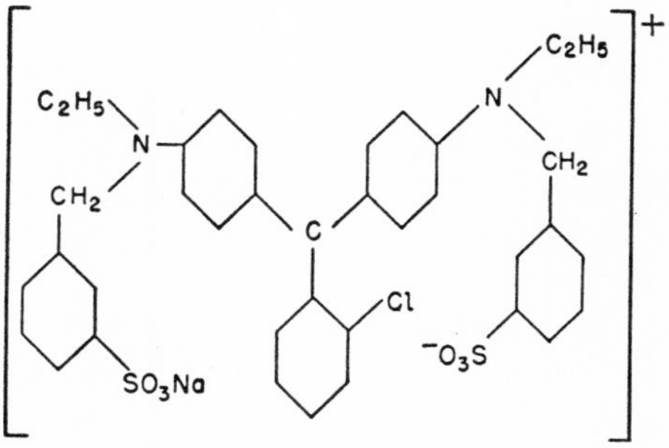

(X) Brilliant Milling Green B

Triamino Derivatives of Triphenylmethane. Verguin's synthesis of Fuchsine (see p. 272) led to a comprehensive study of triaminotriphenyl-methane dyes. Other important discoveries followed closely that of Verguin:

(1) Lauth's synthesis of Methyl Violet B (1861).

(2) Girard and de Laire's discovery of the phenylation of Fuchsine to Spirit Blue (1861).

(3) Nicholson's sulfonation of phenylated-Fuchsine to a water-soluble blue dye (1862).

(4) Caro and Kern's synthesis of Crystal Violet (1883).

The brilliant shades and the versatility of the products of this subclass have resulted in their continued commercial importance. Two dyes, Crystal Violet, CI 681, and Methyl Violet B, CI 680, are produced on a very large scale (the 1950 United States productions of these dyes were, respectively, 1 million and 1.6 million lb[31]).

The *basic colors* of this group are technically more important than the *acid colors*. In addition to Crystal Violet and Methyl Violet B, Para Magenta (Pararosaniline), CI 676, Fuchsine, CI 677, Ethyl Violet, CI 682, and Spirit Blue, CI 689, are used in appreciable quantities.

The *acid colors* are gradually being displaced by acid dyes from the azo and anthraquinone groups, since the latter exhibit better fastness properties, especially to light. The fairly cheap sulfonated arylated triaminotriphenylmethanes (Alkali Blue, CI 704, Methyl Blue, CI 705, and Soluble Blue, CI 707) do find considerable use, however, in writing inks, laundry and commercial blue tinting compositions, etc. Some violets and blues are still important wool dyes—Acid Violet 6B, CI 697, Formyl Violet S4B, CI 698, Brilliant Indocyanine 6B, Pr. 222, and Brilliant Wool Blue FFR, Pr. 40, being examples.

The common syntheses used in their production include:

(1) *Fuchsine Melt*[17]. In Fuchsine manufacture, a mixture of aniline, *o*-, *m*- and *p*-toluidines, *o*-, *m*- and *p*-nitrotoluenes, zinc chloride and ferrous chloride is heated to 175°C over several hours. The dye is isolated by careful extraction of the melt. The reactions which occur involve first the oxidation of some of the methyl groups to aldehyde equivalents, followed by condensation to triphenylmethane derivatives. Ortho condensation occurs to some extent, yielding Chrysaniline (see section on Acridine dyes), and this product is removed during the extractive purification.

(2) *Synthetic route to Pararosaniline, CI 676 (XI)*[25]:

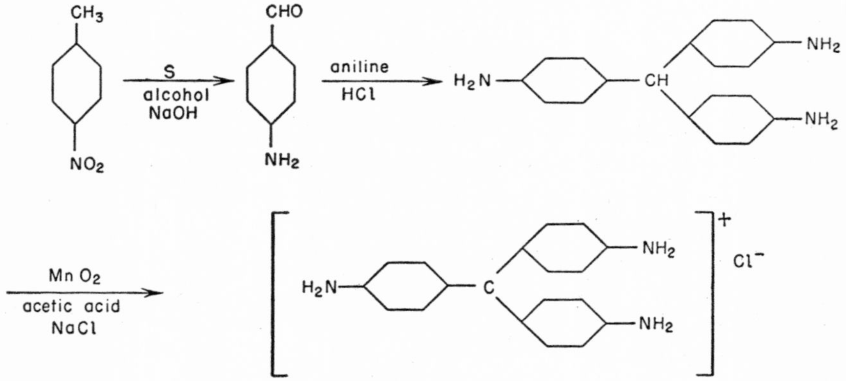

(XI) Pararosaniline (Para Magenta)

(3) *Methyl Violet B, CI 680 (XII), Synthesis*[12]:

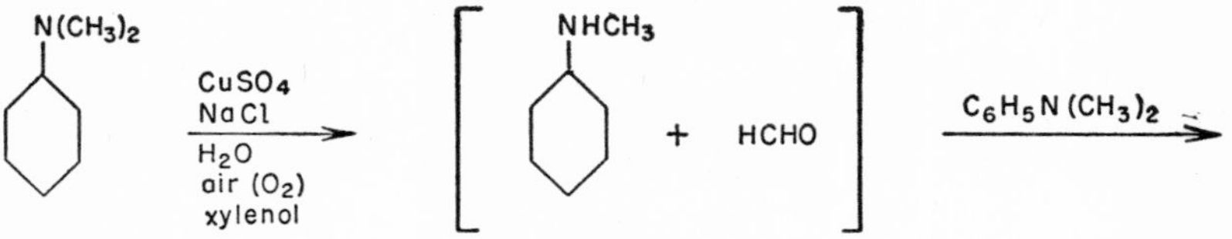

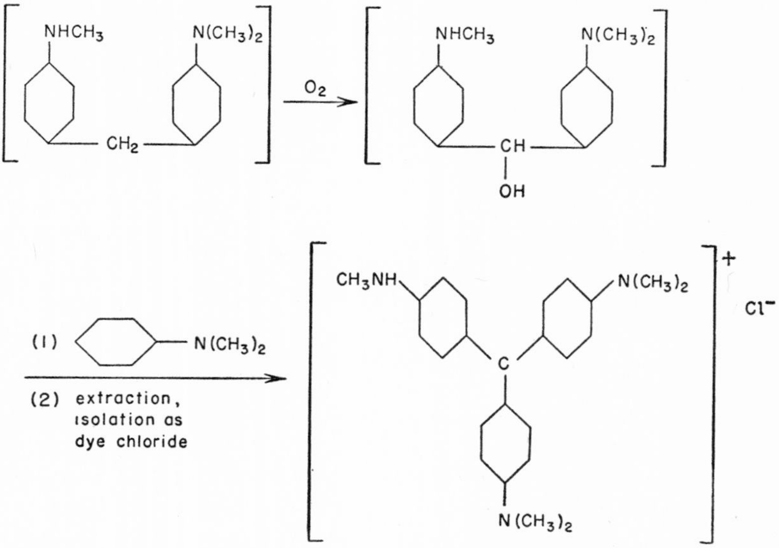

(XII) Methyl Violet B

The dye also contains some hexamethyl- and some tetramethyltriaminotri-phenylmethane.

(4) *The "Phosgene" Synthesis.* This synthesis involves the condensation of one mole of phosgene and 2 moles of an N,N-dialkylarylamine to form a benzophenone. The latter reacts further with phosgene to give an intermediate addition product or "dichloride," which condenses with a third mole of the amine to give the dye. This procedure, applied to Crystal Violet, CI 681 (XIII), is shown below[13]:

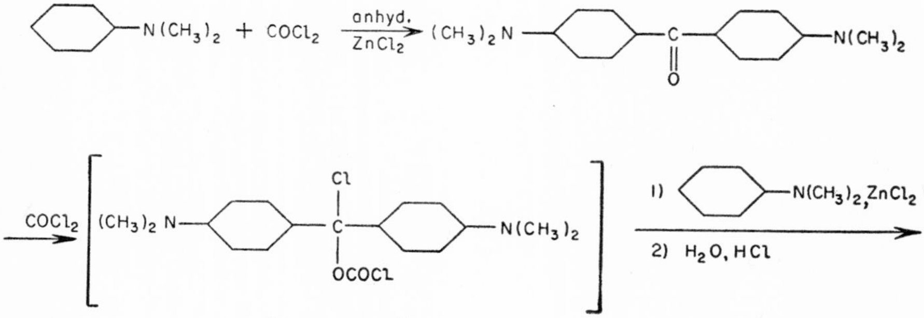

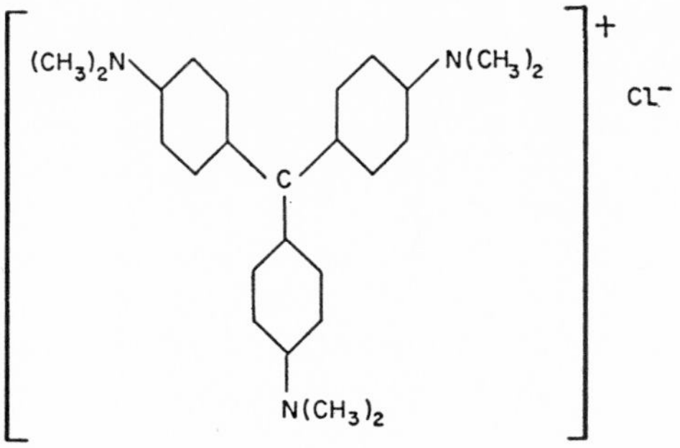

(XIII) Crystal Violet

The reaction is carried from dimethylaniline to color without isolation of the intermediate products.

(5) *The "Ketone Chloride" Process.* The "ketone chloride" method is a modification of the phosgene process, in which the intermediate benzophenone is isolated. The preparation of Ethyl Violet, CI 682 (XIV)[8], from "Ethyl Ketone" [4,4'-bis(diethylamino)benzophenone][28] is given below:

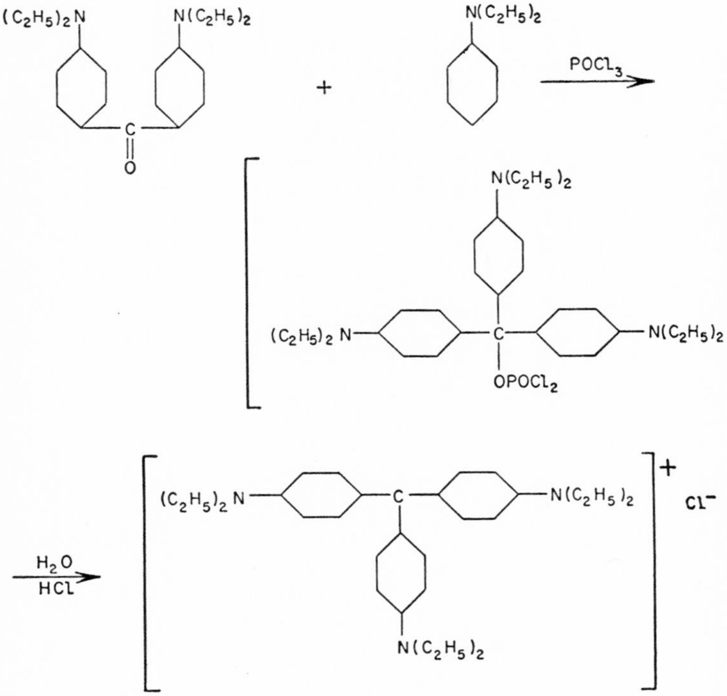

(XIV) Ethyl Violet

(6) *The "Spirit Blue" Synthesis.* The so-called "spirit blues" are chiefly phenylated Fuchsine and Pararosaniline. They have little water solubility but possess satisfactory solubility in alcohol—hence the name. Synthesis of these colors involves the fusion of a mixture of the triaminotriphenyl-methane and an excess of aniline or some other arylamine in the presence of benzoic acid. The degree of phenylation is controlled empirically by a carefully defined heating schedule during the fusion; samples are taken frequently and compared with a standard dye until the desired shade is obtained. An example is [29]:

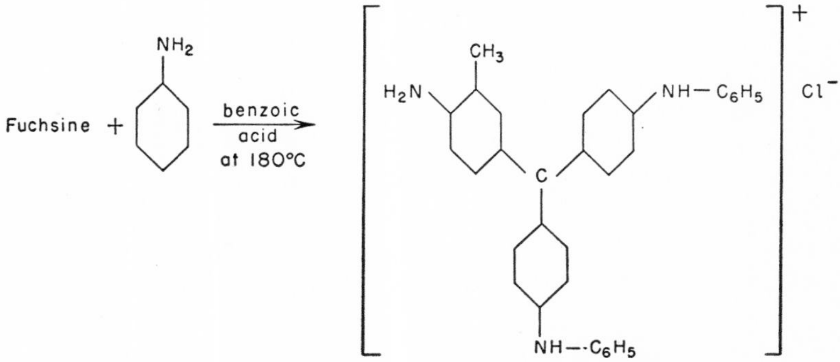

Spirit Blue, CI 689

(+ mono – and tri phenylated products)

The six syntheses given above are used mainly for the basic dyes of this group. The acid dyes are prepared by similar routes, such as:

(7) *The "Hydrol" Synthesis.* This procedure involves the oxidation of a diphenylmethane to the corresponding diphenylcarbinol (or "hydrol"), condensation of the latter with an aromatic amine to the leuco product and oxidation of the latter to the dye. An example is the synthesis of Acid Violet 6B, CI 697 (XV)[21], which is illustrated on pages 281 and 282.

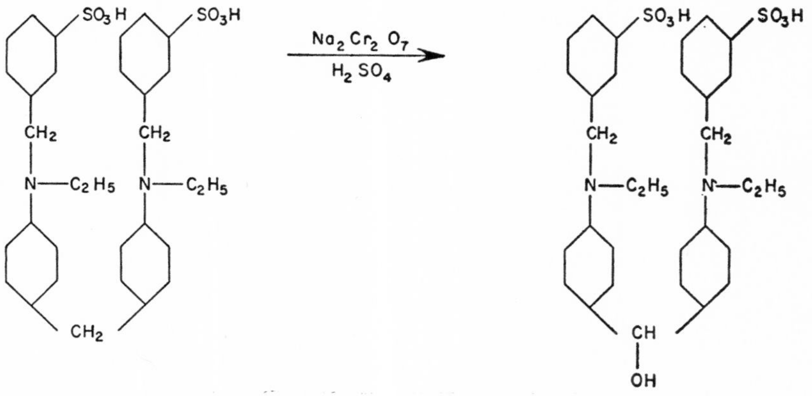

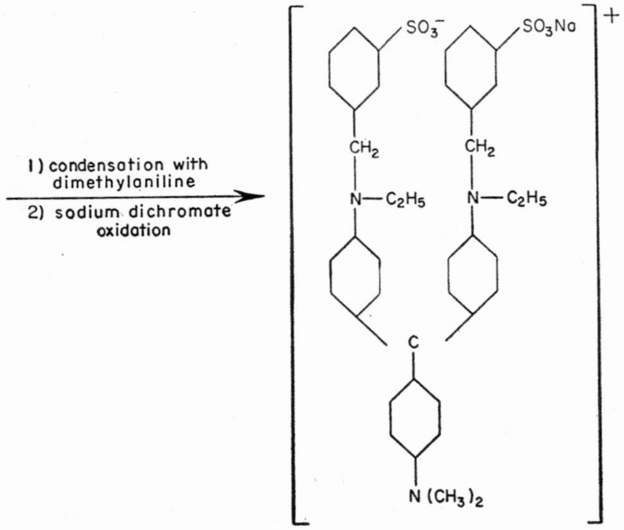
1) condensation with dimethylaniline
2) sodium dichromate oxidation
SO3−
SO3Na
CH2
CH2
N—C2H5
N—C2H5
C
N(CH3)2
+

(XV) Acid Violet 6B

(8) *Direct Sulfonation.* The conversion of the "spirit blues" to the "soluble blues" is accomplished by direct sulfonation, the degree of sulfonation being controlled by the degree of solubility required and the product being a mixture of mono-, di- and trisulfonates. For example[30]:

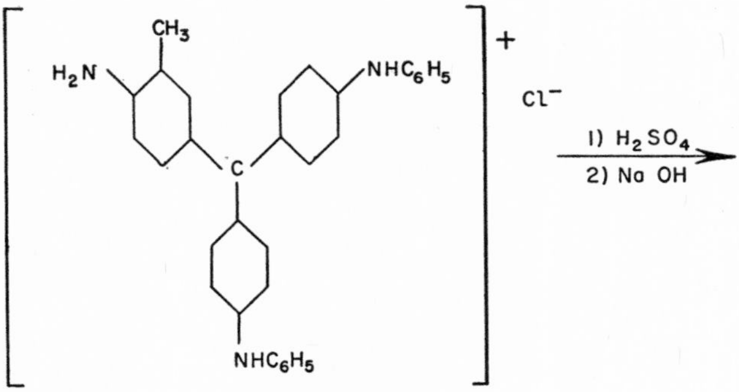
CH3
H2N
NHC6H5
C
NHC6H5
+
Cl−
1) H2SO4
2) Na OH

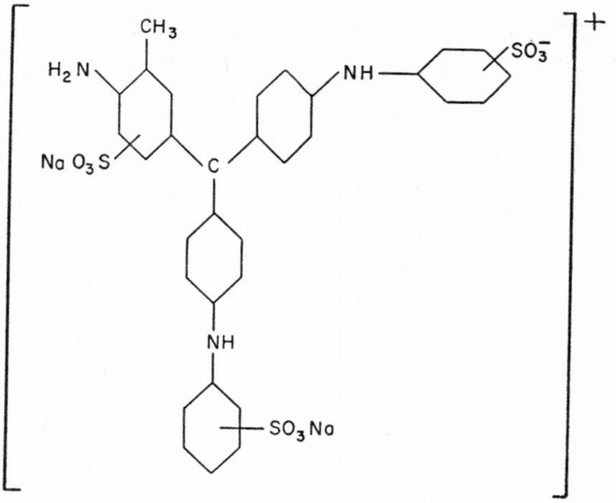

Soluble Blue, CI 707

(9) *Brilliant Indocyanine 6B, Pr. 222, Synthesis*[20]. Brilliant Indocyanine. 6B (XVI) and similar dyes are prepared by a process which introduces the third auxochromic amino group after the condensation to the triphenylmethane. This is accomplished by condensing two moles of aromatic amine with one mole of *p*-chlorobenzaldehyde, oxidizing the triphenylmethane thus formed to the diaminotriphenylmethane dye and, finally, replacing the chlorine atom in the benzaldehyde portion of the molecule with an amine.

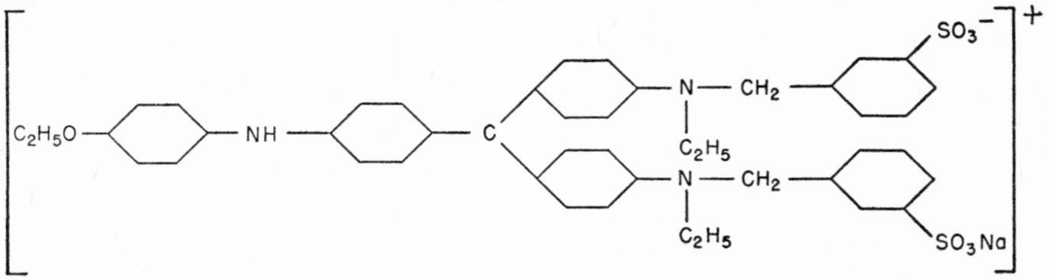

(XVI) Brilliant Indocyanine 6B

Aminohydroxy Derivatives of Triphenylmethane. This small group includes some of the most recently developed of the triphenylmethane dyes, the I. G. Farbenindustrie's Chromoxane violets. These bright and fairly fast-to-light chromable wool colors were just beginning to be exploited at the onset of World War II.

The syntheses of these dyes follow common triphenylmethane routes— condensation of a hydroxybenzaldehyde and an aromatic amine, sulfonation (if necessary) and oxidation to the dye. Patent Blue V, CI 712 (XVII)[27], and Chromoxane Brilliant Violet 5R (XVIII)[24] are typical products:

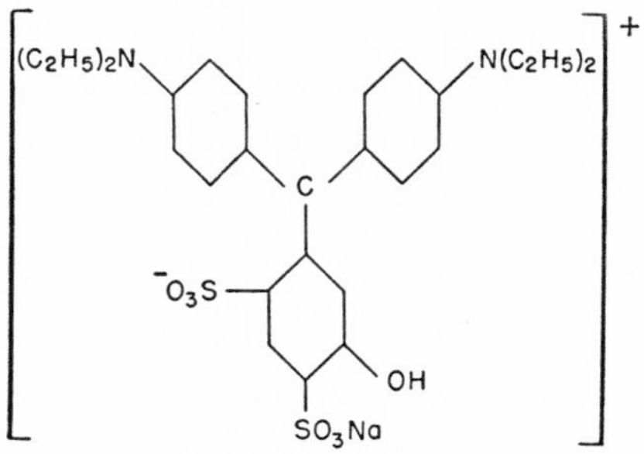

(XVII) Patent Blue V

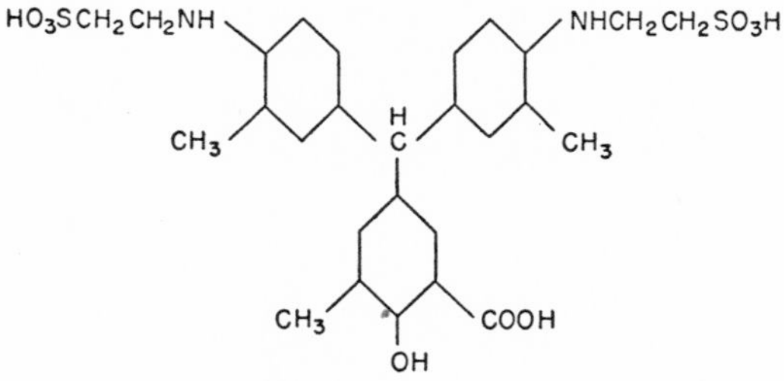

(XVIII) Chromoxane Brilliant Violet 5R

The Chromoxane violets were marketed in the leuco form, the chroming treatment during the dyeing operation forming a chromium complex with the ortho-hydroxy-carboxy grouping and simultaneously oxidizing the products to their dye form. These dyes, though not as fast to light as Chromoxane Brilliant Red BL (see section on Xanthenes, p. 298), were considered with it as the beginning of a new line of faster-to-light triphenylmethane dyes.

Patent Blue V and Patent Blue A, CI 714, are bright blues for wool and silk.

Hydroxy Derivatives of Triphenylmethane. The dyes of this subclass have hydroxy groups para to the center triphenylmethane carbon as auxochromes and are similar in shade to the corresponding amino compounds. They are much less versatile, however, and are considerably less important.

The simplest member of this class is Aurine, CI 724 (XIX), which is no longer of commercial importance. Its synthesis involves the condensation of phenol and oxalic acid[26].

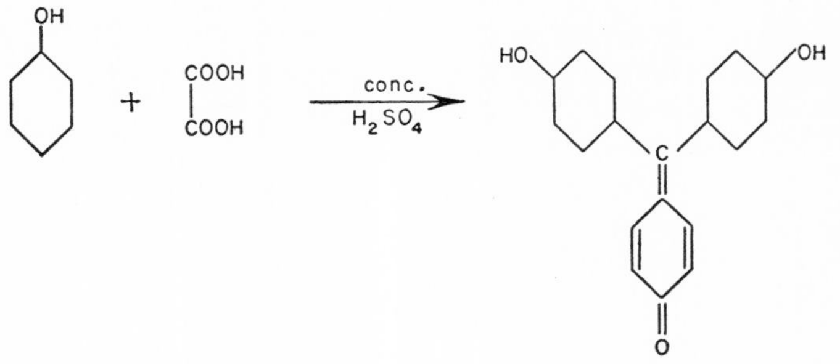

(XIX) Aurine

Of considerable importance, however, are the chrome-mordant blues, Eriochrome Azurol B, CI 720 (XX), and Eriochrome Cyanine R, CI 722 (XXI), which were discovered by Conzetti in 1906[2, 3]. These moderately fast-to-light wool blues have been used quite widely. Their 1950 sales in the United States were 149,000 and 42,000 pounds, respectively[31].

The Eriochromes are prepared by condensation of the appropriate benzaldehyde with 2,3-cresotic acid to the leuco, followed by sodium nitrite oxidation to the dye[24].

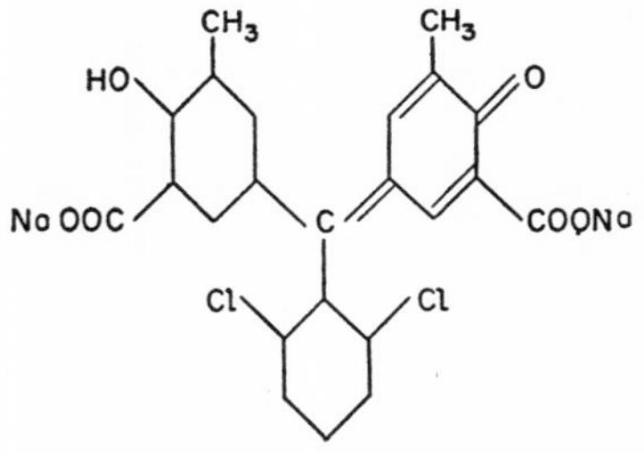

(XX) Eriochrome Azurol B

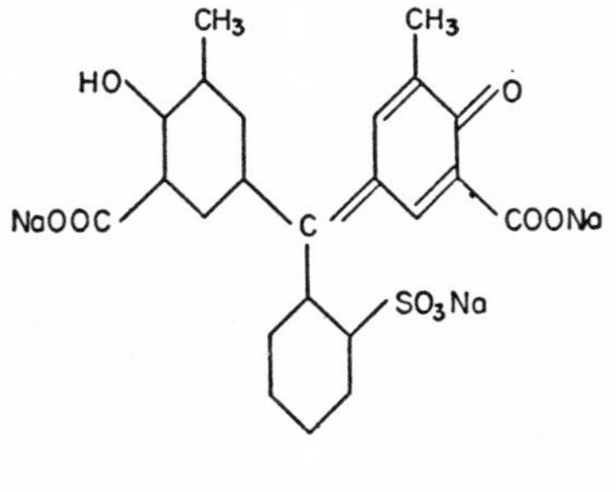

(XXI) Eriochrome Cyanine R

Derivatives of Diphenylnaphthylmethane. The diphenylnaphthyl-methanes serve to round out the shade range of the triarylmethane dyes, since they include good basic blues and acid greens.

Three important colors of this group are Victoria Blue B, CI 729 (XXII)[14], Victoria Pure Blue BO (XXIII)[15] and Wool Green S, CI 737 (XXIV)[22]. The processes used for their manufacture are the same as those used for triaminotriphenylmethanes—the basic dyes are produced by the "ketone chloride" method and the acid dye by the "hydrol" synthesis.

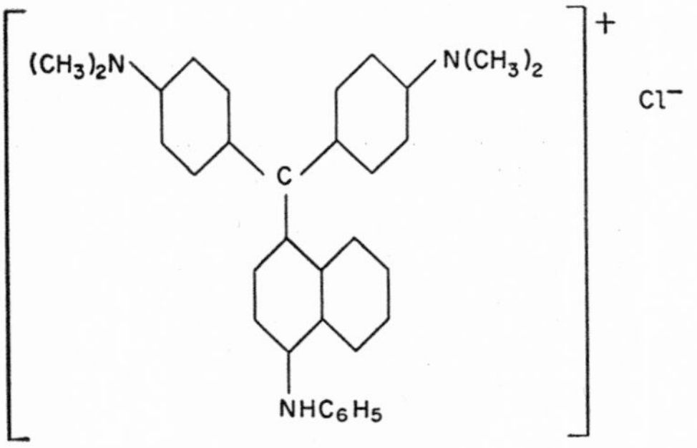

(XXII) Victoria Blue B

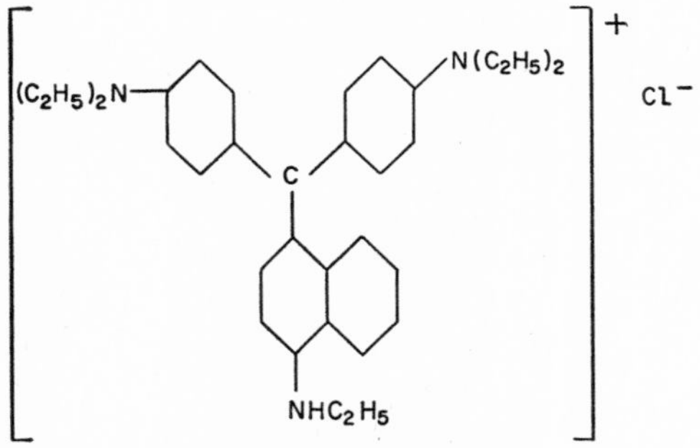

(XXIII) Victoria Pure Blue BO

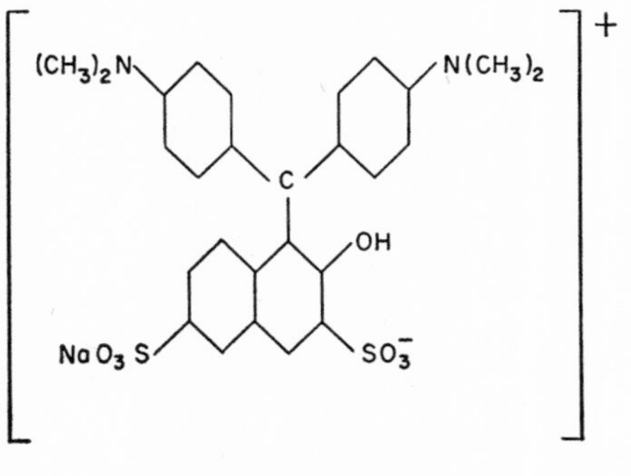

(XXIV) Wool Green S

The Victoria blues are used chiefly in the manufacture of blue lakes, particularly of the phosphomolybdotungstate type. Wool Green S has been quite important as a wool dye, despite its poor lightfastness.

Miscellaneous Triarylmethanes. The relatively new colors, Wool Fast Blues FBL and FGL, are novel members of the triarylmethane group, inasmuch as they are derivatives of diphenylindolylmethane. They are bright wool blues of moderate lightfastness[19] (a fastness rating considerably superior to that of other wool dyes of this group).

Wool Fast Blues FBL (XXV) and FGL (XXVI) are produced by the reaction of 4,4'-dichlorobenzophenone and an indole, followed by replacement of the halogen atoms with aromatic amino groups and sulfonation to the dye[33].

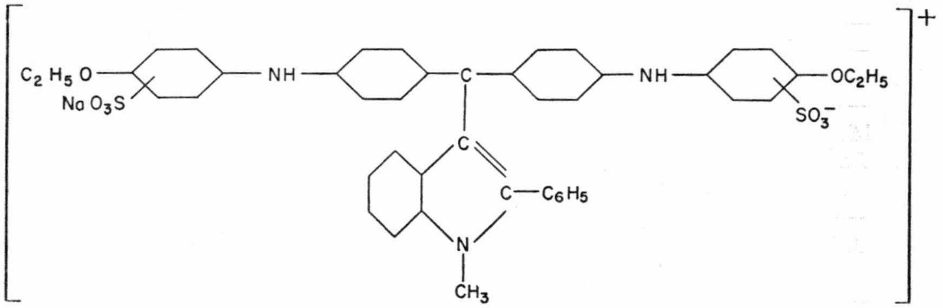

(XXV) Wool Fast Blue FBL

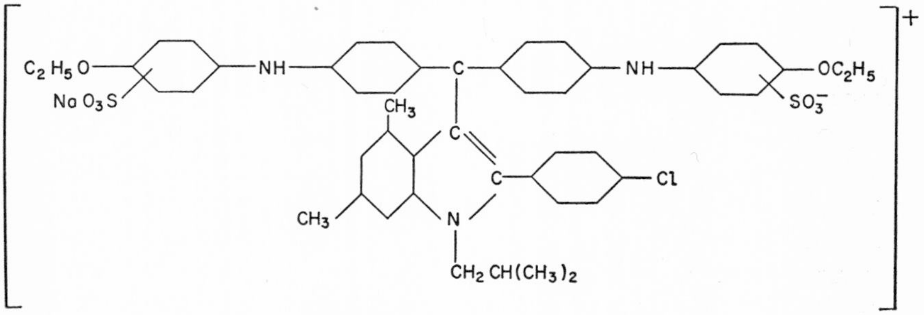

(XXVI) Wool Fast Blue FGL

Literature Cited

1. Blangey, Fierz-David and Stamm, *Helv. Chim. Acta*, **25**, 1162 (1942).
2. Conzetti, U.S. Patent 877,052 (1908).
3. ——, U.S. Patent 877,054 (1908).
4. Fierz-David and Blangey." "Fundamental Processes of Dye Chemistry," p. 299, New York, Interscience Publishers, Inc., 1949.
5. ——and——, *ibid.*, p. 302.
6. Fischer, E., and Fischer, O., *Ber.*, **13**, 2204 (1880).
7. Fischer, O., *ibid.*, **10**, 1624 (1877).
8. German Patent 27,789 (1884).

9. German Patent 50,782 (1890).
10. Hofmann, *Ann.*, **132,** 296 (1864).
11. I. G. Farbenindustrie, BIOS 1433, p. 20 (PB 81029).
12. ——, FIAT 1313, Vol. II, p. 314 (PB 85172).
13. ——, *ibid.*, p. 317.
14. ——, *ibid.*, p. 321.
15. ——, *ibid.*, p. 323.
16. ——, *ibid.*, p. 328.
17. ——, *ibid.*, p. 330.
18. ——, *ibid.*, p. 333.
19. ——, *ibid.*, p. 336.
20. ——, *ibid.*, p. 337.
21. ——, *ibid.*, p. 345.
22. ——, *ibid.*, p. 350.
23. ——, *ibid.*, p. 351.
24. ——, *ibid.*, p. 365.
25. ——, PB 25626, frames 1219–1228; 1236–1242.
26. ——, PB 70135, frame 1629.
27. ——, PB 74067, frame 145.
28. Michler and Gradmann, *Ber.*, **9,** 1912 (1876).
29. Thorpe and Linstead, "The Synthetic Dyestuffs," p. 373, London, Charles Griffin & Co., Ltd., 1933.
30. ——and——, *ibid.*, p. 376.
31. U.S. Tariff Commission Report No. 173, "Synthetic Organic Chemicals, U. S. Production and Sales, 1950," p. 17.
32. ——, *ibid.*, p. 22.
33. Wolff, U.S. Patent 2,032,033 (1936).

Triphenodioxazine Dyes

In 1912, the colored product obtained by heating 2,5-dichloro-3,6-bis(2-naphthylamino)-*p*-quinone in nitrobenzene[3] was patented, and a second patent issued one year later disclosed anlogous products from 2,5-dianilino-3,6-dichloro-*p*-quinone[4]. Fierz-David[2] later demonstrated that the products obtained were the polynuclear triphenodioxazines, that from 2,5-dianilino-3,6-dichloro-*p*-quinone being the simplest and having the structure (I):

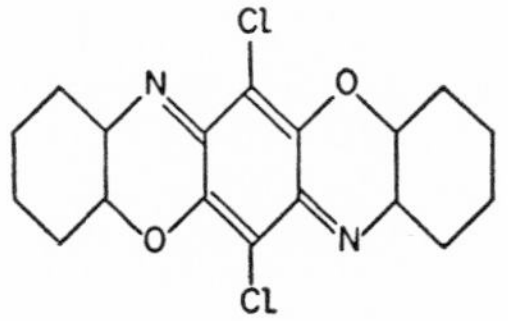

(I)

This relatively new chromophore was not exploited until two decades later when the I. G. Farbenindustrie launched its new series of fast-to-light blue dyes for cotton, the Sirius Light Blues, a group of sulfonated triphenodioxazines.

The triphenodioxazines have a shade range from reddish-orange to green, but to date only the blues have achieved commercial importance. The Sirius blues were sold in large volume for the printing and dyeing of cellulosic materials in the instances where excellent lightfastness was required.

These colors were synthesized in two steps. The first step, the preparation of the intermediate diarylaminoquinone (IV), was the condensation of chloranil (II) and the required arylamine (III) in water or alcohol and in the presence of an acid binder such as magnesium oxide or sodium acetate[8, 9]:

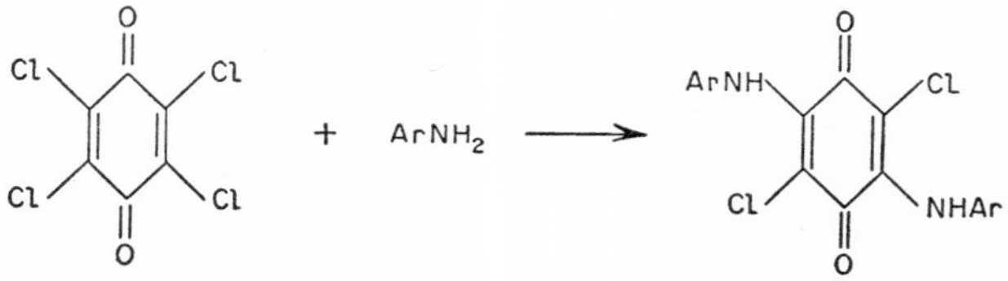

(II)   (III)   (IV)

Two general methods were used for ring closure of the diarylaminoquinone to the triphenodioxazine:

(1) *Oxidative Ring Closure.* The oxidative ring closures generally were carried out at reflux in a high-boiling solvent, such as nitrobenzene or o-dichlorobenzene, and in the presence of a catalyst such as phosphorus pentachloride, ferric chloride, p-toluenesulfonyl chloride, etc. The exact combinations were quite specific and were selected based on the yield obtained. The ring closure to the triphenodioxazine for Sirius Light Blue F3GL (V) illustrates the procedure[7]:

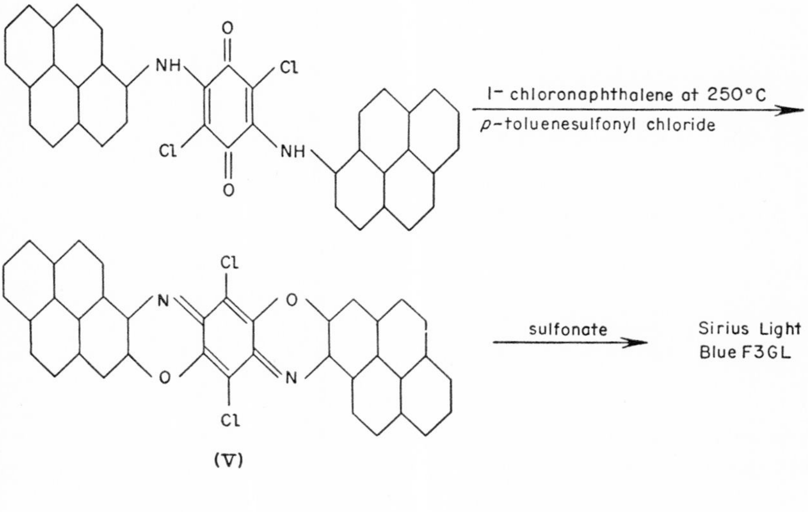

(V)

The oxidative ring closure and sulfonation may be combined—the mono-hydrate sulfonation of the product from 3-amino-9-ethylcarbazole and chloranil gives Sirius Light Blue FFGL[6].

(2) *Nonoxidative Ring Closure*. Nonoxidative ring closure can be effected if the diarylaminoquinone intermediate has methoxy groups ortho to the amino groups. Methyl alcohol splits off during the reaction and volatilizes away or reacts with the aromatic acid chloride used as catalyst. The tri-phenodioxazine formed is purer than a corresponding product made by the oxidative ring closure route. For example[1]:

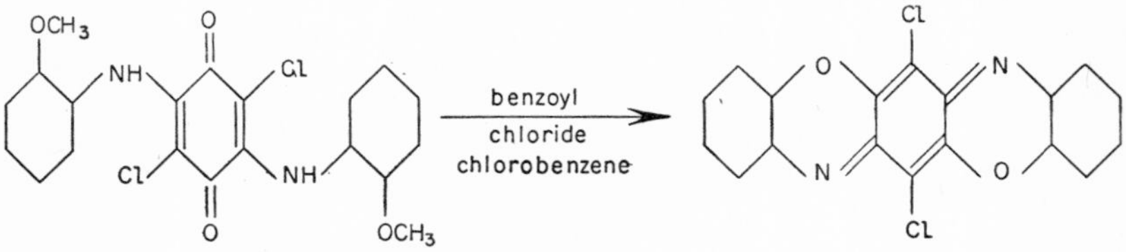

Unsymmetrical triphenodioxazines are prepared by similar ring closure methods, but a different procedure is used for the required diarylamino-quinone. The method is illustrated below as applied to the synthesis of an unsymmetrical dioxazine (VI):

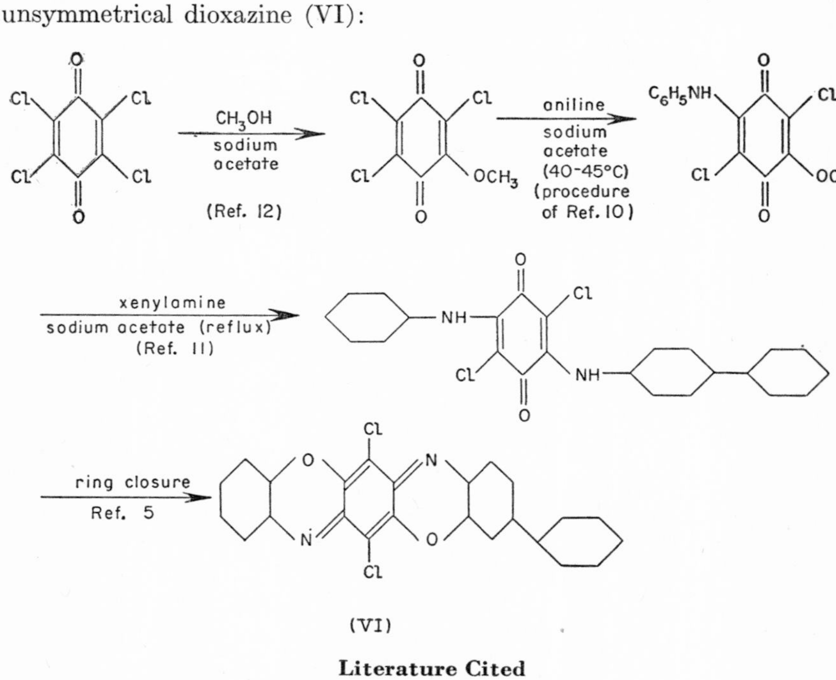

(VI)

Literature Cited

1. Brunner and Thiess, U.S. Patent 2,092,387 (1937).
2. Fierz-David, Brassell and Probst, *Helv. Chim. Acta*, **22**, 1348 (1939).

3. German Patent 253,091 (1912).
4. German Patent 255,642 (1913).
5. Greune and Langbein, U.S. Patent 2,278,260 (1942).
6. I. G. Farbenindustrie, BIOS 960, p. 79 (PB 65657).
7. ——, *ibid.*, p. 85.
8. ——, BIOS 1482, p. 23 (PB 86136).
9. ——, *ibid.*, p. 26.
10. Langbein, U.S. Patent 2,229,099 (1941).
11. ——, U.S. Patent 2,267,741 (1941).
12. ——, U.S. Patent 2,288,198 (1942).

Xanthene Dyes

The dyes of the xanthene class are noted for their brilliant shades of red, pink and greenish-yellow, and for the strong fluorescence which they exhibit.

Fluorescein, CI 766 (I), was the first dye of this group to be discovered. Its synthesis by Baeyer in 1871[3] was followed by a concentrated study of hydroxyphenylxanthenes (phthaleins) which led to many technically important dyes.

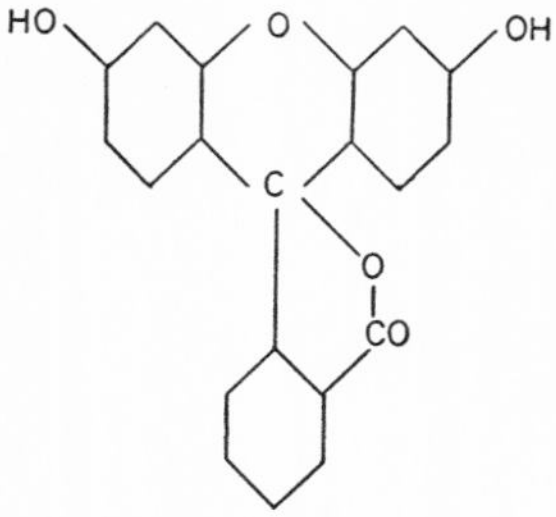

(I) Fluorescein

In 1887, Ceresole[5] synthesized an aminophenylxanthene which he called a rhodamine. This dye is known as Rhodamine B, CI 749 (II), and has had wide commercial usage due to its brilliant bluish-red shade.

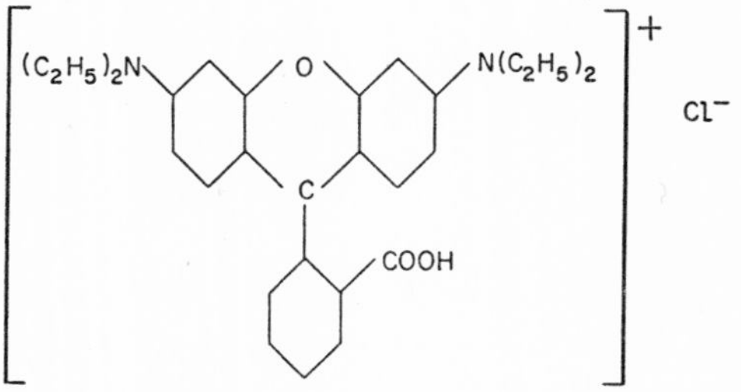

(II) Rhodamine B

The dyes of this group are based on xanthene (III), the chromophore being the xanthylium nucleus and the usual auxochromes being amino or hydroxy groups meta to the oxygen atom.

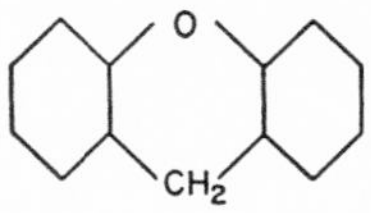

(III) Xanthene

The xanthenes range in shade from yellow through violet, the most important products being reds and pinks. They are used for the dyeing of cellulosic fibers, wool and silk and for the production of various brilliant insoluble lakes, such as those of the phosphomolybdotungstic acid type.

The dyes of this group fall into several subclasses:

  (a) Pyronines   (d) Rhodamines
  (b) Sacchareins and succineins   (e) Rhodoles
  (c) Rosamines   (f) Phthaleins

These are discussed separately.

Pyronines. The pyronines are a small group of red and violet dyes. The oldest and best-known, Pyronine G, CI 739 (IV), is prepared by the condensation of m-dimethylaminophenol and formaldehyde, followed by sulfuric acid ring closure to the leuco form and oxidation to the dye[4].

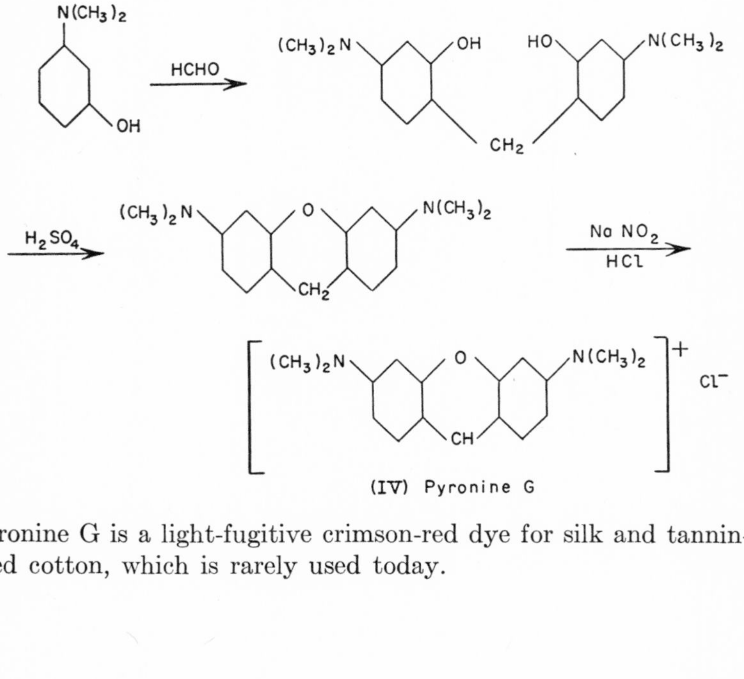

(IV) Pyronine G

Pyronine G is a light-fugitive crimson-red dye for silk and tannin-mordanted cotton, which is rarely used today.

Recently indolylpyronines have been disclosed in the patent literature. The synthesis of one such color (V) follows[27]:

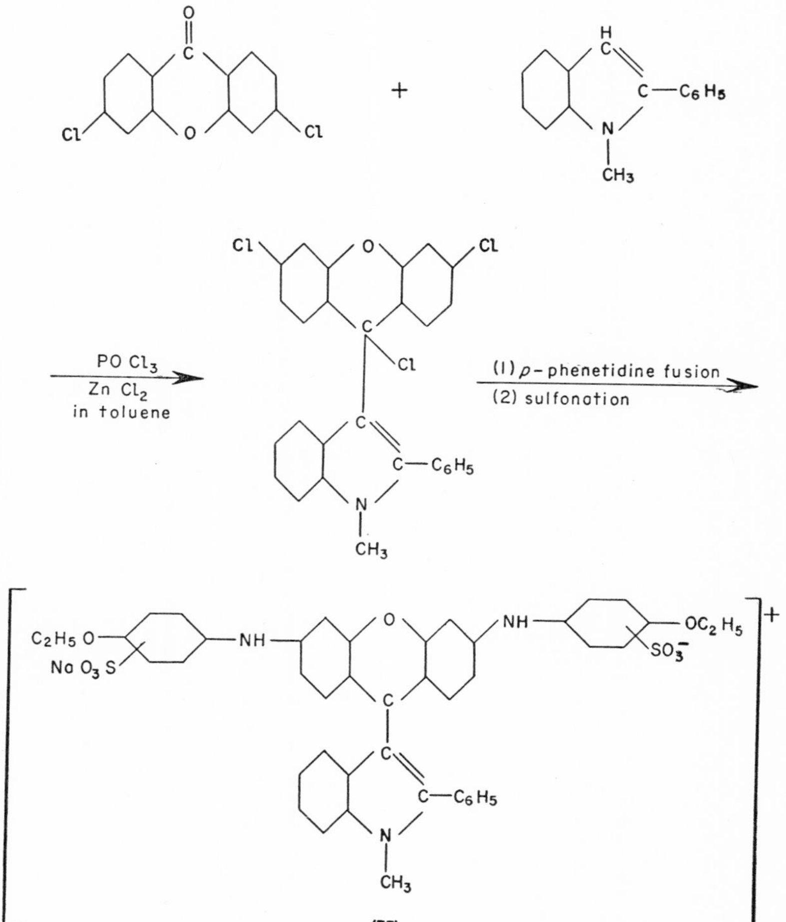

Sacchareins and Succineins. Sacchareins and succineins are dye types which no longer have commercial importance but which are of interest from a chemical standpoint.

Saccharein, CI 744 (VI), itself is a bluish-red dye for tannin-mordanted cotton, prepared by the fusion of saccharin and *m*-diethylaminophenol at 165°C, followed by acidification of the condensation product[9]:

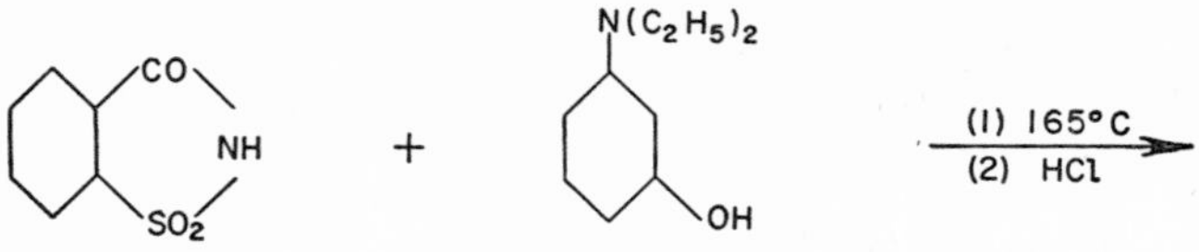

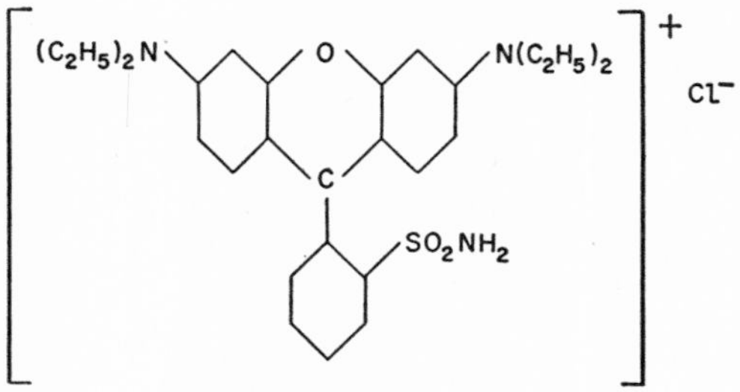

(VI) Saccharein

The sacchareins are closely related to the rhodamines, the carboxy group of the latter being replaced by a sulfonamide group.

The only succinein exploited was the pink dye, Rhodamine S, CI 743 (VII), prepared by a process similar to that shown above but using m-dimethylaminophenol and succinic anhydride[6]:

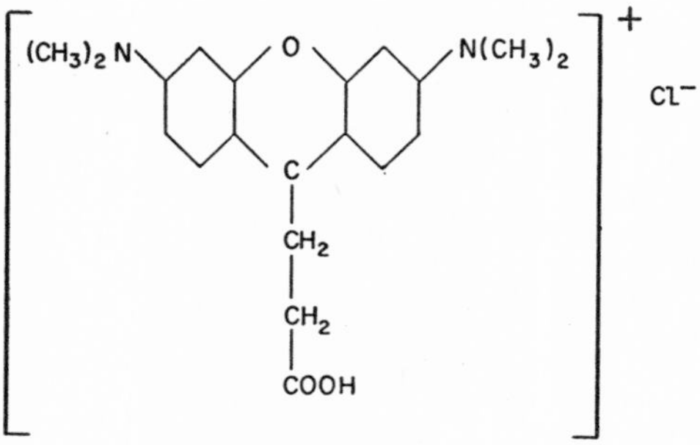

(VII) Rhodamine S

Rosamines. The rosamines are phenylated pyronines, synthesized by the condensation of benzaldehyde or a derivative thereof with a m-amino-phenol, ring closure to the leuco product and oxidation to the dye. The synthesis of Sulpho Rhodamine B, CI 748 (VIII)[16], is typical:

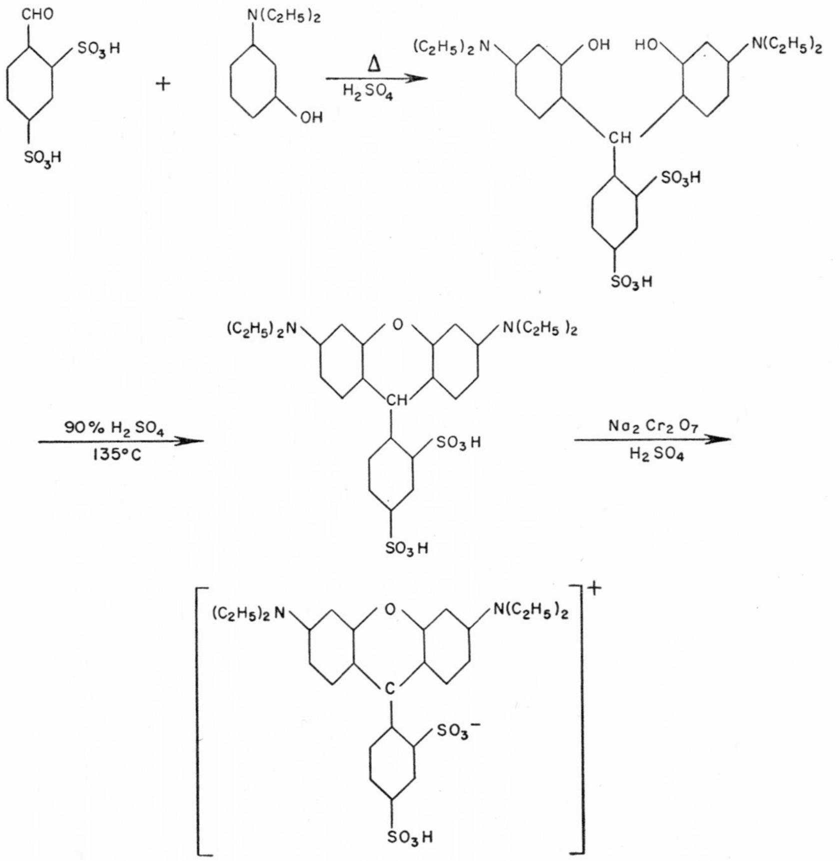

(VIII) Sulpho Rhodamine B

A basic rosamine, Rhodamine 5G, CI 746 (IX)[26], is used abroad as a bluish-pink shading component for pink phosphomolybdotungstate lakes. Sulpho Rhodamine B and its close relative, Sulfo Rhodamine G (X)[17], are bright bluish-pink wool and silk dyes of poor fastness to light.

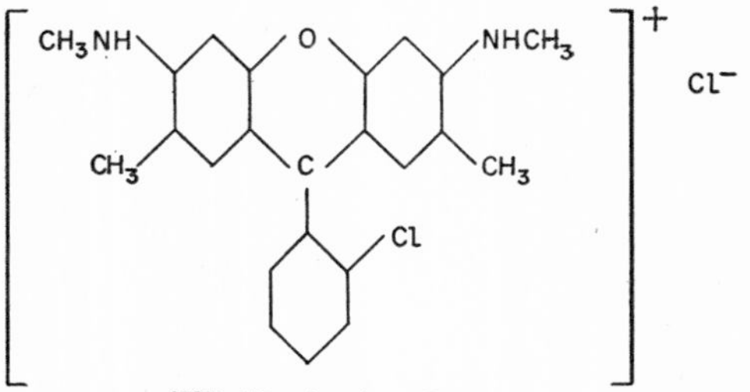

(IX) Rhodamine 5G

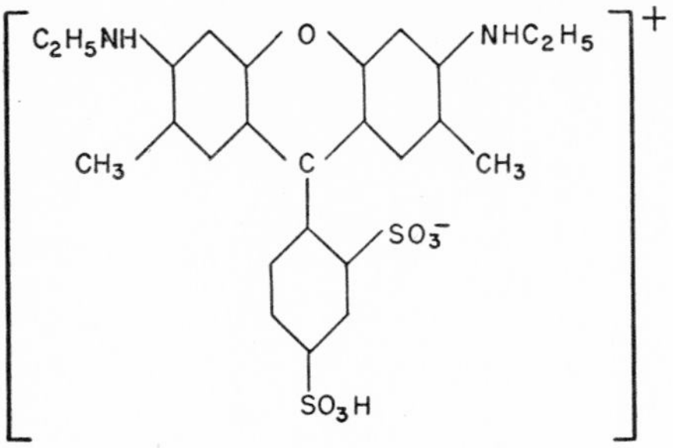

(X) Sulpho Rhodamine G

With the possible exception of the Sulpho Rhodamines, the rosamines are an unimportant group technically, since their properties are not unlike those of the cheaper and more versatile rhodamines.

Rhodamines. The rhodamines are a very important group comprising basic, acid and chromable dyes. Several general synthetic routes are used for their manufacture.

(1) *Rhodamine B Fusion.* The fusion of 2 moles of *m*-diethylaminophenol and 1 mole of phthalic anhydride, followed by acidification of the fusion mass, gives Rhodamine B (II)[14]. This is a general method for symmetrical rhodamines.

(2) *Action of Amines on Fluorescein Dichloride.* Fluorescein dichloride (3′,6′-dichlorofluoran) is fused with an aliphatic or aromatic amine in the presence of zinc chloride to give the basic dye. Arylated rhodamines, prepared this way, frequently are sulfonated to acid dyes. The synthesis of Violamine R, CI 758 (XI)[13], illustrates both procedures.

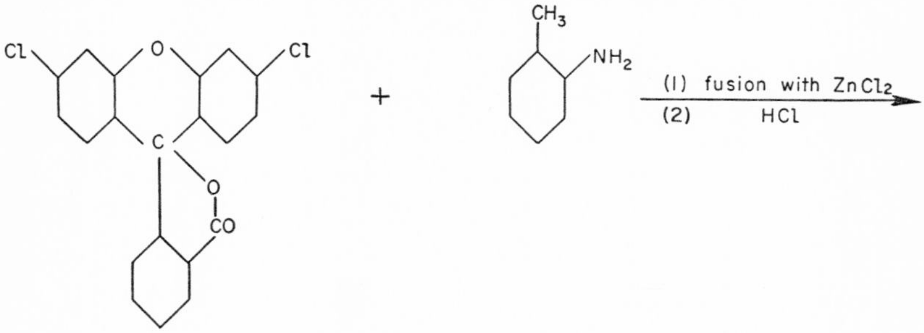

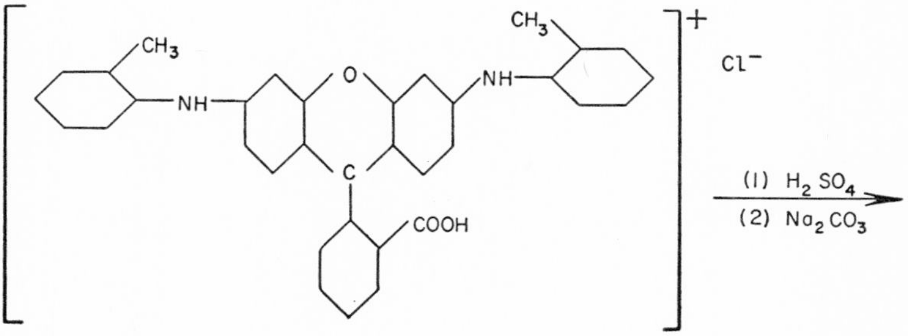

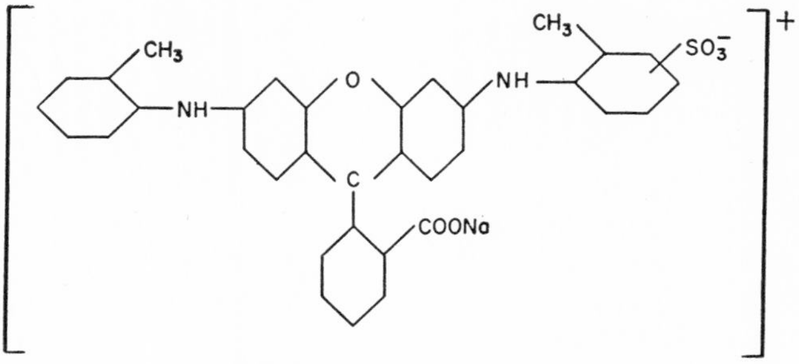

(XI) Violamine R

(3) *Unsymmetrical Rhodamine Synthesis.* The preparation of unsymmetrical rhodamines usually involves condensation of a *m*-aminophenol and phthalic anhydride to the corresponding *o*-benzoylbenzoic acid and condensation of the latter with a second *m*-aminophenol to give the dye. One route to Rhodamine 3GO, CI 753 (XII)[12], is typical of this synthesis.

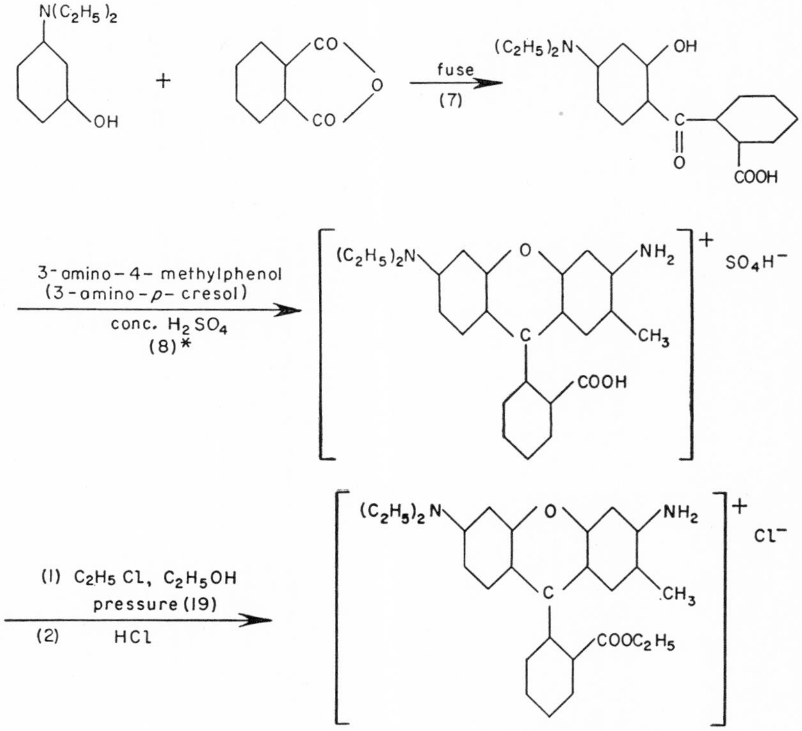

(XII) Rhodamine 3GO

Ethylation of the rhodamine carboxy group [see Rhodamine 3GO (XII)]

* The method disclosed in this reference yields an isomer.

is a general method which is used to improve the solubility of these dyes in alcohol-type solvents.

The rhodamines range in shade from yellowish-red to blue. The *basic rhodamines*, of which the two most commonly used are Rhodamine B and Rhodamine 6G (XIII)[15], are used chiefly for the dyeing of paper in red shades and for the preparation of red and pink lakes for use as pigments. They are used to some extent for the dyeing of silk and wool where brilliant shades of fluorescent effects are desired and where light fastness requirements are of secondary importance.

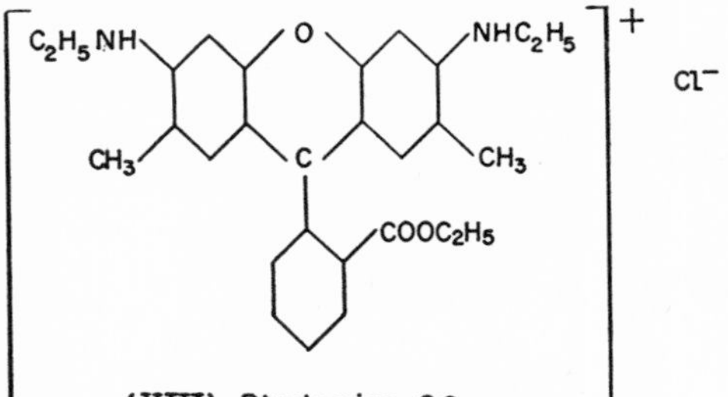

(XIII) Rhodamine 6G

The *acid rhodamines* are primarily violets and blues, obtained by the sulfonation of arylated rhodamines [e.g., Violamine R (XI)]. They are silk and wool dyes of fair fastness properties.

A subgroup of acid rhodamines containing the chromable o-hydroxycarboxy grouping constitute the most important new dyes of the xanthene class. Chemists of the I. G. Farbenindustrie discovered that these new wool dyes showed a lightfastness of 5–6 (on a scale of 8) after metallizing, as contrasted to a fastness rating of 2 for the unchromed color. Commercial exploitation of several of these colors either had begun or was contemplated by I. G. Farbenindustrie in the period immediately preceding World War II.

The chromable xanthenes were synthesized by the usual methods, using 5-hydroxytrimellitic acid[25] in place of phthalic anhydride. The most important was the rhodamine, Chromoxane Brilliant Red BL (XIV)[18].

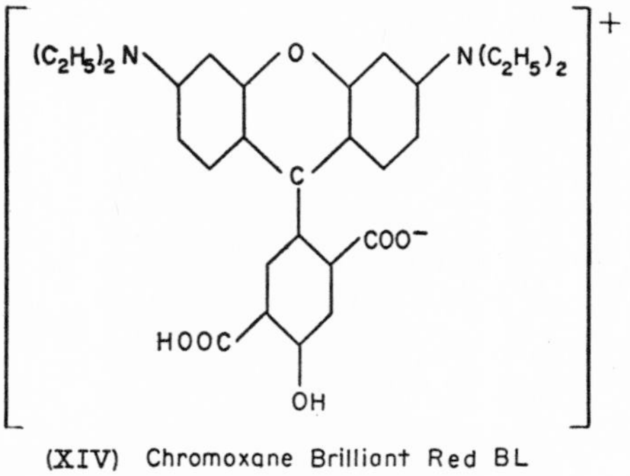

(XIV) Chromoxane Brilliant Red BL

Rhodoles. The rhodoles are red aminohydroxy-xanthenes and are of little importance as a class. They are prepared by the method used for unsymmetrical rhodamines. Two dyes which have been of some slight interest are the basic Rhodamine 12GM, CI 761 (XV)[10, 11], and the chrome dye, Chromogen Red B (XVI)[24].

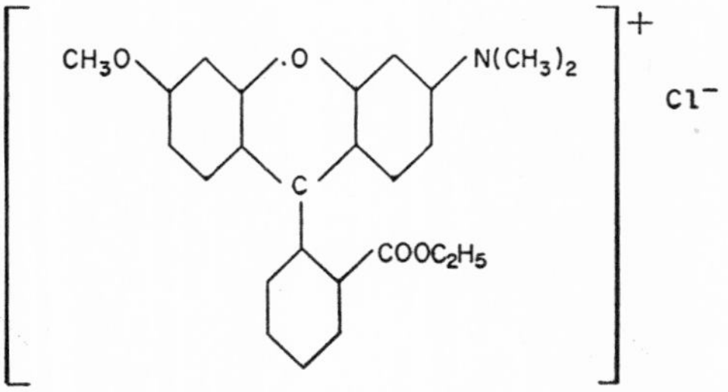

(XV) Rhodamine 12GM

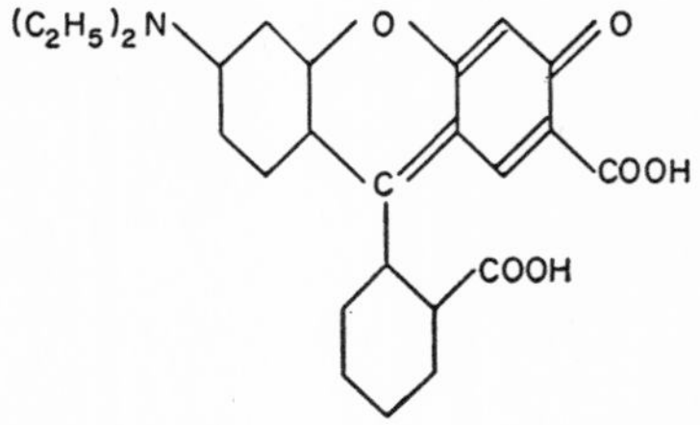

(XVI) Chromogen Red B

Phthaleins. The phthaleins or hydroxyxanthenes are widely used. They are derivatives of Fluorescein, CI 766 (I), or its sodium salt, Uranine (XVII), and are noted for their strong fluorescence.

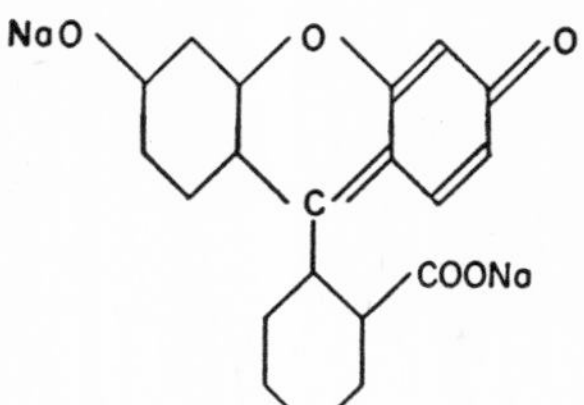

(XVII) Uranine

Fluorescein and its derivatives are prepared by the fusion of resorcinol and phthalic anhydride[23] or a chlorinated phthalic anhydride. Other dyes of this series are made by the halogenation or nitration of Fluorescein or its chlorinated derivatives. In addition, the carboxy group may be esterified to improve the solubility of the product in alcohol-type solvents.

Today the most important color in this group is Eosine G, CI 768 (XVIII)[21]. It, Erythrosine Bluish, CI 773 (XIX)[22], and Rose Bengale, CI 777 (XX)[20], are typical phthalein dyes.

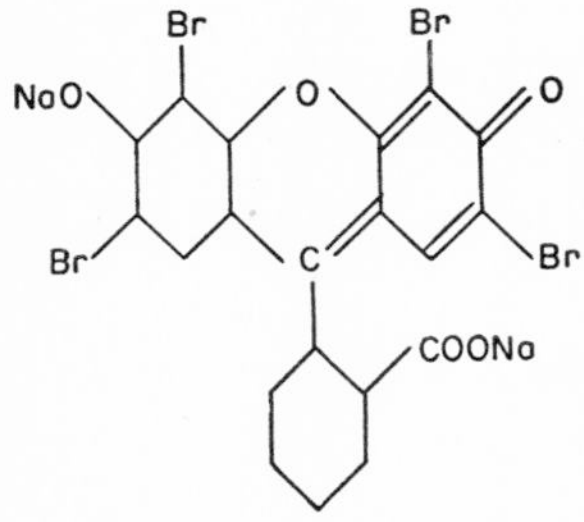

(XVIII)   Eosine G

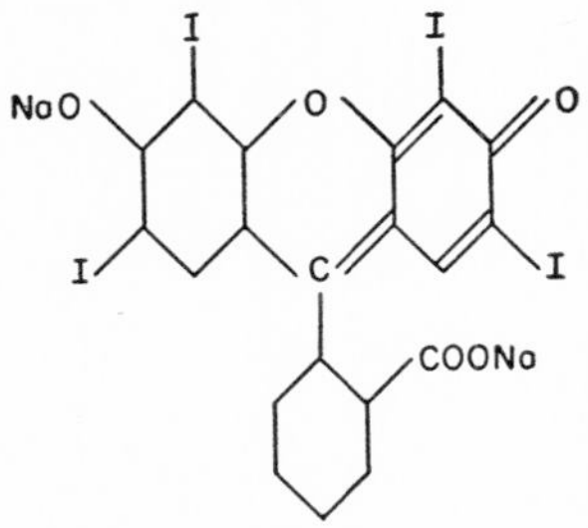

(XIX) Erythrosine Bluish

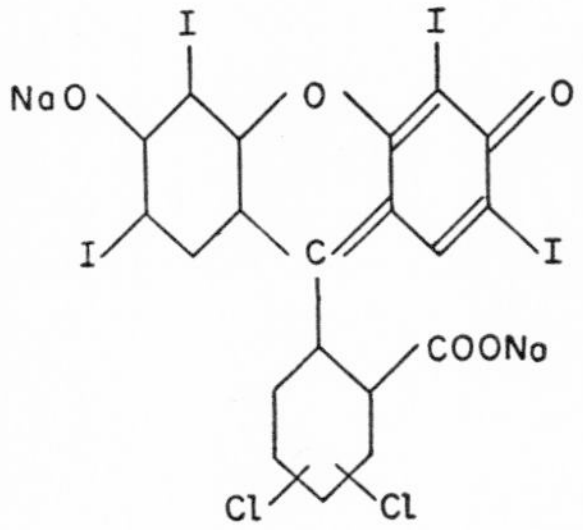

(XX) Rose Bengale

The phthaleins are acid dyes ranging in shade from the yellow of Fluorescein to the bluish-red of Rose Bengale. Fluorescein, itself, is not used to an appreciable extent as a textile dye due to its poor lightfastness. It is used as a water tracer dye, since its green fluorescence is visible at dilutions as high as 1:40,000,000 in water. The halogenated phthaleins, though not very fast to light, are used as bright yellowish-to-bluish-red dyes for wool and paper and for conversion to pigment-type lakes.

Two chromable phthaleins merit mention. Gallein, CI 781 (XXI)[1], is made from pyrogallol by the usual phthalein synthesis; at high temperature sulfuric acid dehydrates it to Coerulein, CI 783 (XXII)[2]. These dye chrome-mordanted wool and silk bluish-violet and green shades, respectively, of fair lightfastness.

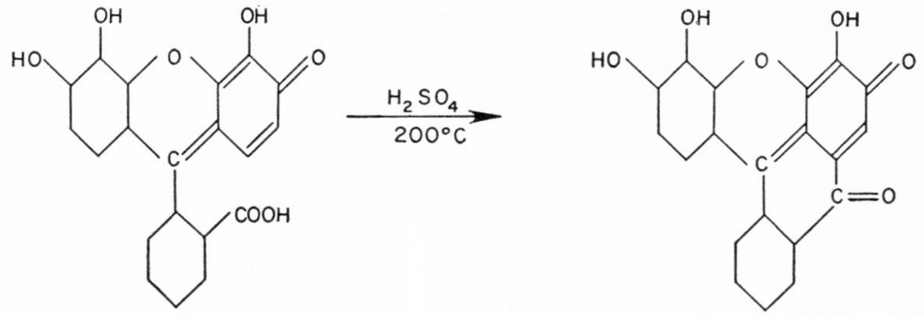

(XXI) Gollein   (XXII) Coerulein

Literature Cited

1. Baeyer, *Ber.*, **4,** 457, 663 (1871).
2. ——, *ibid.*, **4,** 556, 663, (1871).
3. ——, *ibid.*, **4,** 558, 662, (1871).
4. Bender, U.S. Patent 445,648 (1891).
5. Ceresole, U.S. Patent 377,350 (1888).
6. German Patent 51,983 (1890).
7. German Patent 85,931 (1896).
8. German Patent 96,108 (1898).
9. German Patent 100,779 (1898).
10. German Patent 119,061 (1901).
11. German Patent 122,289 (1901).
12. I. G. Farbenindustrie, BIOS 959, p. 12 (PB 63858).
13. ——, *ibid.*, pp. 21, 24.
14. ——, *ibid.*, p. 32.
15. ——, *ibid.*, pp. 37–41.
16. ——, *ibid.*, p. 66.
17. ——, *ibid.*, p. 71.
18. ——, FIAT 1313, Vol. II, pp. 354, 363 (PB 85172).
19. ——, PB 70135, frames 913–923.
20. ——, *ibid.*, frames 1062–1071.
21. ——, *ibid.*, frames 1092–1098.
22. ——, *ibid.*, frames 1099–1110.
23. ——, *ibid.*, frames 1125–1135.
24. ——, *ibid.*, frames 1277–1281.
25. ——, PB 70254, frames 7090–7111.
26. Nastvogel, U.S. Patent 738,227 (1903).
27. Wolff and Frank, U.S. Patent 2,197,846 (1940).

6. SULFUR DYES

N. M. Bigelow and Otto Stallmann

HISTORY AND INTRODUCTION

The sulfur dyes are a class of highly colored water-insoluble products reducible by dilute aqueous sodium sulfide to water-soluble derivatives which are substantive to cellulosic fibers. On exposure to air or other oxidizing agents, they revert to their highly colored, water-insoluble oxidized form. They are prepared by the reaction of sulfur or sodium polysulfide with a wide variety of organic compounds, mainly hydroxy, amino, or nitro derivatives of aromatic hydrocarbons. With a few exceptions, they are amorphous colloidal materials of high molecular weight and variable composition. Their exact structures have never been positively determined, although the nature of their active chromophores is well established. They are used mainly in the dyeing of cheap cotton goods, and have been used to a very minor extent in the dyeing of wool, silk, leather and paper. As a group, they are among the cheapest of the synthetic dyes. Their fastness to light is good; their fastness to washing varies between different types, but in general is excellent. Their main disadvantages are that they are relatively dull and that their fastness to hypochlorite and similar bleaching agents is poor. A complete shade range is lacking, since sulfur dyes of a true red shade are not available.

Traditionally, the history of the sulfur dyes begins with the chance observation that cotton cloth was stained on contact with sawdust which had been used to absorb sodium sulfide leaking from a reaction vessel. This observation was pursued further by Croissant and Bretonniere and the first patent on sulfur colors was issued to these inventors in 1873[25]. This patent covered the manufacture of sulfur colors from a wide variety of organic materials, mainly cellulosic in character, by heating them with sulfur or sodium polysulfide to temperatures ranging between 100 and 350°C. The product was hardly a true dye in the modern sense of the word; nevertheless, it was accepted to a minor extent by the trade, and was sold under the name Cachou de Laval for some years thereafter.

Twenty years later, Vidal discovered that treatment of a large number of aromatic intermediates with sulfur or with sodium polysulfide yielded black or brown dyes which could be reduced with sodium sulfide and applied to the fabric in this form[32, 138, 139]. These products, while still unsatisfactory by modern standards, were far superior to the Cachou de Laval. Although the trade acceptance of these dyes was slow, the potential value of this new class of colors was quickly recognized by the German dye industry, and a large number of patents soon issued, covering the thionation of an exceedingly wide variety of aromatic intermediates.

The next great stride in the development of sulfur colors was the preparation of Immedial Black in 1897, by the thionation of 4'-hydroxy-2,4-dinitrodiphenylamine (*p*-(2,4-dinitroanilino)phenol)[107]. This dye was again a vast improvement over the sulfur dyes known at the time, and was eagerly accepted by the dyers. The commercial use of sulfur colors rapidly became widespread. During this period, much was learned about thionation, and especially about purification of the crude thionation products. The use of inert liquid solvents to control the thionation made possible the discovery of Immedial Pure Blue, CI 957, the thionation product of 4-dimethylamino-4'-hydroxydiphenylamine (*p*-(*p*-dimethylaminoanilino)-phenol), and the use of solvent thionation was rapidly extended to a number of other intermediates. The tan and brown sulfur colors derived from toluene-2,4-diamine and the red-brown shades derived from aminohydroxyphenazines were also discovered in this period. The pioneering phase of the development of sulfur colors ended around 1905. While a few new examples have been discovered since this time, the greater part of the research activity in this field has been directed toward the improvement of established types.

STRUCTURE OF THE SULFUR DYES

The sulfur colors are amorphous, and have no readily determined physical constants, nor can they be converted to well characterized closely related derivatives. It is very difficult to purify a sulfur dye without altering the very physical and chemical properties which determine its commercial value. It is therefore not surprising that empirical knowledge regarding the sulfur dyes has always progressed far ahead of fundamental understanding of their nature, and that their manufacture has been based on art rather than on science. However, thanks to indirect reasoning based on a careful study of synthetically prepared analogs of the sulfur dyes, the basic structures and the fundamental chemistry of these dyes are quite well understood today.

The sulfur content of these dyes is bound in the molecule in three different manners. It may exist as part of the fundamental chromophore; in the form of disulfide or disulfoxide linkages; or in the form of loosely bound polysulfide ("thiozonide") sulfur.

The basic chromophores in the sulfur dyes are the thiazole (I), the thiazone (3H-isophenothiazin-3-one) (II) and the thianthrene (III) groups:

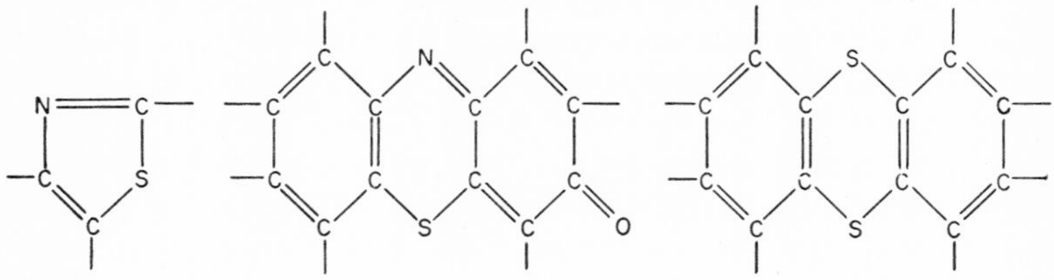

(I)   (II)   (III)

The presence of the thiazole group in certain sulfur dyes is indicated by the fact that degradation of these dyes gives known thiazole derivatives. The presence of the thiazone ring in one sulfur color was first proved by Gnehm and Kaufler[48], who isolated and identified tetrabromodimethylaminothiazone as the chief bromination product of Immedial Pure Blue, CI 957. Its presence in some classes of sulfur dyes is also indicated by a method used in the manufacture of certain sulfur colors[6, 40, 41, 42]. By this method, the thiosulfate derivatives of substituted *p*-diamines are condensed with the thiosulfates from chlorinated hydroquinones to yield chloroaminothiazinethiosulfates:

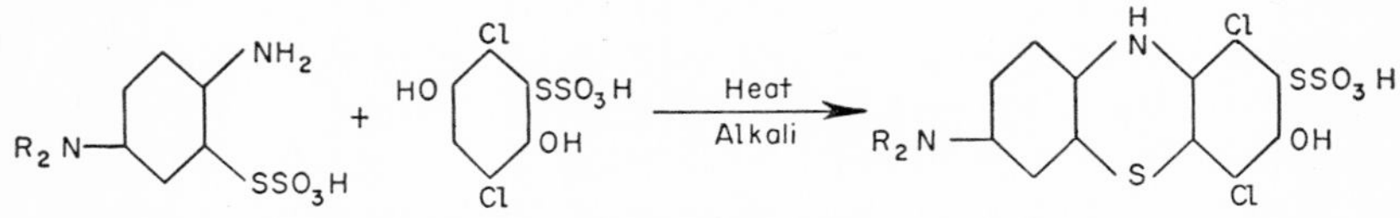

On hydrolysis and oxidation, these thiosulfate derivatives yield aminochloromercapto substituted thiazones, sometimes of crystalline character. The dyes so produced are very similar in analysis, shade and working properties to the commercial sulfur colors prepared by the thionation of analogously substituted indophenols. In another method for the preparation of "synthetic" sulfur colors, originally developed by Herz[66], an *o*-aminothiophenol is caused to react with a halogen-substituted quinone:

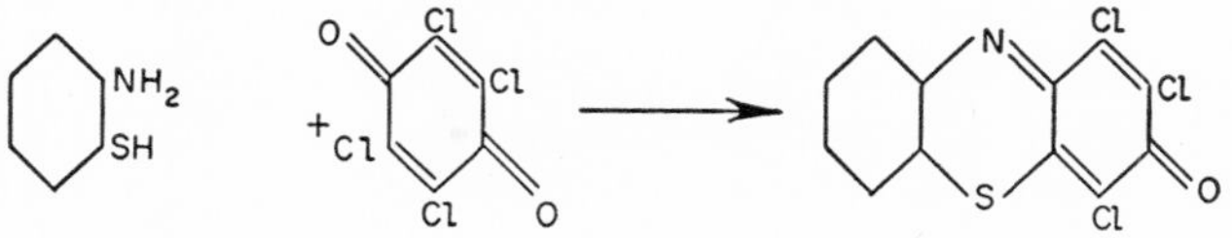

The substituted thiazones so produced show many of the properties of sulfur colors. Their chlorine atoms may be replaced by mercapto groups on treatment with boiling alcoholic sodium polysulfide, yielding synthetic sulfur dyes which in some cases are hard to distinguish from those manufactured by orthodox thionation methods from similarly substituted indophenols[5],[22, 146, 149]. Both of the above methods have been of great help in the determination of the approximate constitution of sulfur colors.

The presence of the thianthrene ring in some sulfur dyes was suggested by Fierz-David and Valpiana[134] and has been demonstrated by Zerweck and his collaborators[149].

Only a portion of the sulfur present in a typical sulfur color is bound in thiazole, thiazone, or thianthrene ring systems. Some of the remaining sulfur is attached to the aromatic rings in the form of disulfide or disulfoxide bridges. When these dyes are reduced, these linkages are transformed to mercapto groups. The sulfur bound in this manner has no significant influence on the shade of the color; however, its capacity for reduction to mercapto groups and reoxidation to disulfide linkages plays an important role in the solution of sulfur colors in a sodium sulfide vat. The capacity of these mercapto groups to form intermolecular and intramolecular disulfide linkages is the determining factor in the high molecular weight and heterogeneity of the sulfur colors.

Besides the sulfur which is integrally bound in the molecule, the commercial sulfur dyes contain large amounts of "loosely bound" sulfur; in the black sulfur dyes the amount of sulfur bound in this fashion may amount to 25 per cent of the total sulfur content of the dye[147]. This sulfur is without doubt bound in polysulfide ("thiozonide") form[21]. Loosely bound sulfur is not removed by extractions with caustic or solvents[148], but is lost on repeated vatting and reoxidation or on prolonged oxidation with air. In certain dyes it is slowly oxidized to sulfuric acid on storage, and may cause fabric dyed therewith to lose some of its original tensile strength on storage.

METHODS OF MANUFACTURE

There are three general methods for the commercial production of sulfur colors: the sulfur bake, the polysulfide bake and the solvent fusion. Each is peculiarly adapted to certain intermediates and to the manufacture of specific types of dyes.

The Sulfur Bake

The sulfur bake technique is used in the manufacture of yellow, orange and brown sulfur dyes. It is commonly applied to aromatic amines or diamines or their acylated derivatives, either singly or in mixtures. The sulfur bake is the cheapest method of producing sulfur colors. Because of the methods used, local overheating is hard to avoid; as a result, the thionated product varies in quality and strength from charge to charge and requires careful blending for standardization.

Sulfur bakes are usually carried out in stationary iron kettles or in rotary bakers, which are heated with flue gas or direct flame. In commercial practice, the sulfur is usually melted in the kettle by itself. The intermediate is then added, and the charge is heated slowly to its final temperature, usually between 200 and 250°C. Hydrogen sulfide is evolved; the reaction mass becomes increasingly viscous and finally solidifies. The reaction mixture is heated until spot tests indicate that the product has reached the desired tinctorial strength and shade. Increasing temperature or time of reaction produces darker, stronger and duller shades.

When the thionation is complete, the mass is cooled somewhat and treated with aqueous sodium hydroxide. The purpose of this treatment is to remove residual free sulfur, according to the equation:

$$6NaOH + 4S \rightarrow 2Na_2S + Na_2S_2O_3 + 3H_2O$$

When this reaction is completed, the mass is evaporated to dryness. In the cases of the cheaper sulfur colors, this dried material constitutes the semifinished dye; standardization consists merely in grinding the powder and diluting with an inert material to standard tinctorial strength. Some of these dyes contain sufficient quantities of residual sodium sulfide to make them directly water soluble. Other dry baked sulfur colors contain too large quantities of unreacted starting material or of partially charred by-products to permit this simple standardization. In these cases, the solution obtained by the addition of sodium hydroxide to the primary thionation mass is passed through a clarification press, and the sulfur color is isolated from the filtered liquor by evaporation on a drum dryer, or by acidification. In the latter case the dye is precipitated in its leuco form, which is almost insoluble in water; this product is filtered, washed and dried.

The Polysulfide Bake

Another commonly used method in the manufacture of sulfur colors is the polysulfide bake. This method differs from the sulfur bake only in that sodium polysulfide is used in place of free sulfur. It is widely used in the manufacture of brown, olive and dull green sulfur dyes from aromatic amines, diamines, nitroamines and phenols. Many common organic intermediates can be subjected to either the sulfur bake or the polysulfide bake; the latter method usually produces darker, stronger and more soluble dyes. As in the sulfur bake, close temperature control is difficult and as a result the sulfur dyes manufactured by the polysulfide bake method tend to be variable in shade and chemical constitution.

The sodium polysulfide used in this reaction may be prepared by heating an aqueous solution of sodium sulfide and sulfur:

$$Na_2S + nS \rightarrow Na_2S_{(n+1)}$$

or by boiling aqueous sodium hydroxide with sulfur:

$$6\text{NaOH} + (2n + 2)\ \text{S} \rightarrow 2\text{Na}_2\text{S}_n + \text{Na}_2\text{S}_2\text{O}_3 + 3\text{H}_2\text{O}$$

When the sulfur is completely dissolved, the intermediate is added, and the reaction mixture is heated slowly to a final temperature ranging from 180 to 250°C, where it is held until the desired reaction is completed. At this point, aqueous sodium hydroxide is added in a quantity sufficient to convert the residual sodium polysulfide to sodium sulfide. Following this, the entire reaction mass may be evaporated to dryness, or the aqueous solution may be clarified and the dye isolated either by drum drying or by acidification.

Solvent Thionation

In solvent thionation, the intermediate is treated with sodium polysulfide in an inert liquid medium. The thionation mass remains fluid and stirrable throughout the reaction; the problems of homogeneity and local overheating are thus avoided. The solvent-fusion method is not as widely applicable as the dry bake procedures. The intermediate used must be capable of accepting sulfur readily at relatively low temperatures; its practical application is limited to the manufacture of sulfur colors from nitrophenols, indophenols, indamines, phenazines and quinone imines.

Water is the most commonly used solvent in this reaction; organic solvents are used when a dye of the highest purity and brightness is required, or when the polysulfide ratio required is higher than can be maintained in water[29, 64, 98]. The upper limit of stability of aqueous sodium polysulfide in boiling water is roughly represented by the formula $\text{Na}_2\text{S}_{4.5}$, while polysulfides represented by the formula Na_2S_8 can easily be prepared in organic solvents. Most of the commonly used solvents are alcohols, such as ethyl alcohol, butyl alcohol, and amyl alcohol. Cyclohexanol and mono ethers of aliphatic glycols also are frequently used[96, 108, 118].

In solvent thionation, the required amount of sulfur is completely dissolved in an aqueous or alcoholic solution of sodium sulfide or sodium hydroxide. The intermediate is added, and the thionation is allowed to proceed under vigorous reflux. The thionation is considered complete when no unchanged starting material can be detected in the thionation mass or when a dye of the proper shade and strength has been attained.

At the end of the thionation, the reaction mass consists chiefly of the so-called leuco form of the dye, partly dissolved and partly suspended in the reaction medium. Sodium hydroxide is added to the reaction mixture to convert the residual polysulfide to sodium disulfide. If an organic solvent has been used, it is distilled off and recovered. The crude thionation product is sometimes precipitated from the resultant aqueous suspension by the addition of salt, and is freed of polysulfide and other by-products by filtration and thorough washing of the filter cake with brine. More often, the aqueous mass is diluted with water, made alkaline by the addition of more sodium hydroxide and oxidized by the passage of air through the suspension. Sodium disulfide in the mixture is oxidized to thiosulfate:

$$2Na_2S_2 + 3O_2 \rightarrow 2Na_2S_2O_3$$

When all of the polysulfide has been consumed, the dye is precipitated in its oxidized form, which is almost insoluble in water. This suspension is filtered, washed and dried.

After-treatments

Sulfur dyes which are made by solvent thionations are often subjected to oxidative after-treatments[30, 125]. These treatments cause a number of beneficial effects. The shade of the dye is usually brightened and altered, sometimes to a surprising degree; the content of loosely bound sulfur in the dye is decreased; and the exhaust rate and degree of exhaustion of the dye are modified. After-oxidized dyes, when applied to fibers, attain their final oxidized shade much more rapidly than those which have not been so treated[5].

After-oxidation is usually performed by simply prolonging the aeration of the precipitated crude dye. Less commonly, the press cake of the leuco form of the dye (obtained by salting out of the diluted thionation mass) may be suspended in water and treated with hydrogen peroxide, sodium perborate or sodium hypochlorite.

PROPERTIES OF THE SULFUR COLORS

Physical Properties

With very few exceptions, the commercial sulfur dyes are amorphous. A crystalline addition compound of the thionation product of 4-dimethylamino-4'-hydroxydiphenylamine has been reported[38, 46], and a few analogs of sulfur colors, prepared by the Herz synthesis, exist in crystalline form. However, the great majority of the sulfur colors show no crystalline character, either by microscopic observation or by examination by the x-ray diffraction technique[22, 105]. Sulfur dyes exist in a highly polymerized state; all attempts to determine their molecular weight have been unsuccessful[105]. Sulfur colors are soluble in sulfuric acid and to a certain extent in ethylene chlorhydrin. They are, of course, soluble in dilute sodium sulfide solution by virtue of reduction; however, the constitution and tinctorial properties of sulfur colors are altered considerably by treatment with either sulfuric acid or sodium sulfide, so that neither of these "solvents" can be used as means of purification in attempts to determine the constitution. Even exhaustive extraction with water is not a satisfactory means of purification, since the sulfur colors become virtually unfilterable when freed of inorganic electrolytes. The most satisfactory method of purifying sulfur colors that has yet been developed consists in successive extractions with dilute aqueous acid and alkali, followed by exhaustive extraction of the dry powder with alcohol and ether[5, 22]. The difficulty in purifying sulfur colors and in establishing accurate and reproducible physical constants has been a great obstacle in all efforts to study their composition.

Solutions of sulfur colors in sulfuric acid, as well as their aqueous reduced solutions, are colored; unfortunately, the absorption bands of most of the commercial dyes of similar shade all lie within the same region, and are lacking in sharp, easily defined maxima[5, 24].

Most sulfur colors are colloidal in character[1, 3]. They are easily coagulated by electrolytes, and therefore do not normally show this behavior; however, when the electrolytes are removed by exhaustive extraction or dialysis the dyes swell, retain water and give unfilterable suspensions. The ultimate particles are negatively charged[2]; they exhibit the Tyndall effect characteristic of all colloids.

Chemical Properties

Reduction. The most important chemical property of the sulfur colors is their common capacity for reduction by sodium sulfide. The alkali metal salts of the leuco derivatives are soluble in water; the free leuco acid, as well as almost all of its heavy metal salts, are practically insoluble. There are wide differences between the solubilities of different types of sulfur colors. Naturally, only those sulfur dyes which have reasonably good solubility in dilute sodium sulfide solutions are selected for commercial exploitation.

The mechanism by which reduction takes place is not entirely clear. In the case of brown and yellow sulfur dyes derived from toluene-2,4-diamine or 2-(*p*-aminophenyl)-6-methylbenzothiazole ("dehydrothio-*p*-toluidine") in which the thiazole ring is the basic chromophore, reduction must consist in the conversion of disulfide and sulfoxide linkages to mercapto groups[49]. In sulfur colors containing the thiazone ring, reduction consists in the reduction of the latter ring to the thiazine structure as well as in the reduction of disulfide or sulfoxide linkages. The evidence on this point is convincing, although indirect. Chemists of the I. G. Farbenindustrie have prepared, by modifications of the Herz synthesis, a number of synthetic sulfur dyes which contain no disulfide or mercapto groups[103], but which are nevertheless reduced by sodium sulfide to yield colored vats which dye cotton in the manner of the orthodox sulfur colors of similar structure. There is also the case of Direct Sulfur Blue, CI 956, the thionation product of 4'-hydroxy-2,4-dinitrodiphenylamine. This dye yields a blue vat on normal reduction with sodium sulfide solution; this is taken as evidence that its thiazone structure has not been altered[55]. Further reduction of this dye with hydrosulfite yields the yellow vat which is characteristic of most sulfur colors; however, the reduction of the dye to this extent has a harmful effect on its tinctorial properties. Reduced solutions of Hydron Blue, CI 961, and the thionation product of the leuco indophenol derived from diphenylamine (CI 969) may be cautiously re-oxidized to deeply colored water-soluble compounds[5]; in products of this type it is assumed that the thiazone ring has re-oxidized, while the mercapto groups remain reduced.

In the commercial application of the sulfur colors to textiles, the preliminary reduction is intentionally left incomplete. It is easy to carry the reduction of a sulfur color too far, especially when hydrosulfite or other strong reducing agents are used. An over-reduced dye does not exhaust well on the fabric, and yields a weak coloration which is very slow in oxidizing to its final shade. The role played by "loosely bound" or thiozonide sulfur is another mysterious but important factor in the reduction of sulfur dyes. Diminution of loosely bound sulfur in a dye beyond a certain limit decreases not only its solubility but also its exhausting properties.

Sulfur colors may be reduced by agents other than sodium sulfide. Strong reducing agents such as hydrosulfite may be used, although care must be taken to avoid over-reduction with these agents. Mixtures of glucose and sodium hydroxide are also effective reducing agents for certain colors and are sometimes used in special applications where the presence of sodium sulfide must be avoided. In general, however, sodium sulfide is the most widely used reducing agent for this class of colors because of its cheapness and simplicity of operation.

Oxidation. The leuco derivatives of sulfur colors in aqueous solution are very readily re-oxidized by atmospheric oxygen, hydrogen peroxide, sodium perborate, or weakly acid dichromate solutions. The rate and extent of oxidation must be controlled to avoid damage to the dye. Sulfur dyes are quite susceptible to over-oxidation, both in the wet and dry states. In the early days of the development of sulfur colors, commercial preparations sometimes underwent spontaneous combustion on storage, as the result of reaction with atmospheric oxygen[15, 77]. Thanks to more precise methods of manufacture, cases of spontaneous combustion are now very rare.

The "tendering," or loss of tensile strength, of cotton fibers dyed with certain sulfur dyes, is also the result of over-oxidation. Older methods for the isolation of sulfur colors left a considerable quantity of loosely bound ("thiozonide") sulfur in their molecules[12, 18, 19]. When cotton goods dyed with these colors were stored, the loosely bound sulfur slowly was oxidized to sulfuric acid, which in turn attacked the fabric. At one time "tendering" was a very serious problem, and much attention was devoted to its correction[3, 16, 17, 20, 110, 120]. It is seldom encountered today.

Strong oxidizing agents such as hypochlorite[19], nitric acid[105], or acid dichromate[132] usually destroy the sulfur colors completely; only very rarely has it been possible to isolate and identify any degradation products from such reaction mixtures.

Alkylation. Sulfur colors containing the thiazone ring either do not react with alkylating or acylating agents, or else give tarry, poorly characterized products[105]. Attempts to convert sulfur dyes to direct dyes by reaction with alkyl sulfates have not as of the present yielded products of commercial interest. The leuco derivatives of the sulfur dyes of either the thiazole or thiazone types contain free mercapto groups which will react with acetic anhydride, acetyl chloride, chloroacetic acid[105, 109], or diazomethane[8]. In general, these alkylation products are amorphous, usually tarry, and are unstable, undergoing spontaneous decomposition even in an inert atmosphere.

Other Reactions of the Sulfur Colors. Most sulfur colors may be sulfonated by cautious treatment of a sulfuric acid solution of the dye with chlorosulfonic acid or fuming sulfuric acid[5]. The introduction of the sulfonic acid group increases the solubility of the dye and lowers its exhaust, usually very markedly. When the presence of a sulfonic acid group is desired in a sulfur color, the better procedure is to sulfonate the intermediate rather than the thionation product.

In general, nitration leads to complete decomposition of the dye molecule[105], although the successful nitration of Hydron Blue has been reported[106].

Many reduced sulfur colors will react with sodium bisulfite, forming water-soluble thiosulfate derivatives[27, 38, 113]. In some cases the products are completely water-soluble; the bisulfite addition product derived from 4-dimethylamino-4'-hydroxydiphenylamine is crystalline[38]. These dyes are not substantive to cotton, but become so when heated with sodium sulfide.

Fusion of sulfur dyes containing the thiazone nucleus with sodium hydroxide usually causes complete decomposition of the molecule; no identifiable products are formed[105]. However, caustic fusion has been used successfully in a very interesting study of sulfur colors containing the thiazole nucleus. In this case, the primary decomposition products, mostly amino- and carboxy-thiophenols, were stabilized at once by reaction with chloroacetic acid[149].

When certain sulfur dye intermediates are thionated in the presence of a metal oxide or salt, metal complexes are formed[22, 146]. A number of metals such as copper, cobalt, nickel, iron and molybdenum are capable of this complex formation; only the copper derivatives are of technical importance. The effect of the copper is usually to produce a brighter and yellower dye. Copper is frequently used in the manufacture of green sulfur dyes from Phenyl Peri acid (8-anilino-1-naphthalenesulfonic acid) (CI 1006) and bordeaux shades from aminohydroxyphenazines (CI 1012). The metal is held very firmly, and cannot be extracted with dilute acids or even with sodium cyanide. The amount of metal required depends on the intermediate used; the copper complex of the green sulfur dye from Phenyl Peri acid contains approximately one atom of copper for every two thiazone rings.

APPLICATIONS

Sulfur colors are used chiefly in the dyeing of natural and regenerated cellulose. They are substantive to wool, silk, and leather, but are not often used commercially to dye these fibers because of the destructive effect of the sodium sulfide bath from which they must be applied. The sulfur dyes are not substantive to the commercial hydrophobic fibers. They have been used successfully in the coloration of paper; their use in this application is small. Leather has been dyed with sulfur colors in Europe, but the practice has not found favor in the United States.

Sulfur colors are used in dyeing applications where good fastness to washing and light are required, where relative dullness is not objectionable, and where the dyed goods will not be exposed to bleaching agents. Their main applications are in work clothes and inexpensive dress goods; in dyeing cotton cloth which is to be used as a lining for trunks and baggage, or as a backing fabric for rubberized or leatherized goods; and in the dyeing of tarpaulins and cotton webbing. Much of the cotton raw stock used as padding for upholstered furniture is dyed with sulfur colors. The sulfur dyes derived from indophenols are bright enough to compete with dyes of other classes, and are used, within the limits of their fastness, thoughout the dyeing industry.

REVIEW OF THE MOST IMPORTANT COMMERCIAL SULFUR-DYE TYPES

The classification of the sulfur dyes is a difficult matter. Arrangement of the various types in terms of their structures is impossible, since the constitution of many important species has never been established. From a chemical viewpoint, sulfur dyes are most logically classified in terms of the intermediates from which they are prepared. The following section is arranged in terms of intermediates of increasing complexity, following the Beilstein system of classification.

Sulfur Dyes From Aliphatic Intermediates

Few, if any, of the modern sulfur dyes are prepared from aliphatic intermediates. This group is of historic interest in that it includes the intermediate from which the first sulfur dye, *Cachou de Laval*, CI 933, was prepared. This dye was manufactured by heating cellulosic materials (sawdust, bran, leaves, etc.) with sulfur or sodium polysulfide at temperatures as high as 350°C[25, 140]. The product was crushed and used without purification.

A dull brown sulfur dye of good fastness properties (*Sulphaniline Brown 4B*, CI 935) was prepared by baking the concentrated waste liquors from the sulfite-cellulose industry with sodium polysulfide[127, 131]. Modifications of this dye are still found in commerce.

Dyes from Aromatic Intermediates

Dyes Derived from Hydrocarbons and Their Nitro Derivatives. Several sulfur dyes of minor importance are manufactured from aromatic hydrocarbons or their nitro derivatives. In Germany, brown and cutch dyes having good fastness properties were manufactured from decacyclene and its nitrated derivatives[52, 53, 54, 102]. Very dark brown sulfur dyes (*Kryogene Brown S*, CI 940) are manufactured by baking 1,8-dinitronaphthalene with sodium polysulfide; copper sulfate is sometimes added to deepen the shade[52, 53, 70, 79]. Black dyes (CI 996) were formerly produced from this same intermediate by modified thionation conditions[10, 11]. *Hydron Olive GX* is manufactured by the thionation of anthracene with sulfur[79].

The structures of these dyes have never been elucidated.

Dyes Derived From Phenol and Its Substitution Products. Phenol itself is not a suitable intermediate for the manufacture of sulfur dyes, although it is sometimes used in conjunction with other intermediates. Phenol forms addition and substitution products with sulfur; under certain conditions it reacts with aqueous sodium polysulfide to form a colorless product which is substantive to cotton and serves as a synthetic mordant for basic dyes[133].

Cresol is a rather important intermediate for the manufacture of sulfur dyes. This material, baked with sodium polysulfide in the presence of copper sulfate, yields *Immedial Black Brown GN*[79]. The thionation of a mixture of cresol and phenol with sodium polysulfide at high temperatures yields a Sulfur Brown which is of commercial importance in Europe[34], and is also manufactured in the United States. The shade of this product resembles that of Cachou de Laval, but its fastness and application properties are much superior.

The constitution of the sulfur dyes derived from phenol and cresol has never been determined. This is unfortunate, since a comparison of the structures of these nitrogen-free dyes with the far more common nitrogen-containing sulfur dyes would be of considerable theoretical interest.

The mono-nitro derivatives of phenol are also of some importance in the manufacture of sulfur dyes; the most important dye of this category is

Pyrogene Green, CI 1002. This dye is manufactured by heating *p*-nitrophenol with sodium polysulfide, either under reflux or by the dry bake procedure[26, 36, 70]. Copper salts are sometimes added to give a yellower shade[33]. The dye colors cotton in deep olive green shades, rather dull but possessing good solubility and fastness properties. Another dye of some importance is *Immedial Brown BR Extra*, which is prepared by heating a mixture of 1,5-dinitronaphthalene and crude cresol with aqueous sodium polysulfide, and subsequently fusing the primary product[80].

Black Sulfur Dyes from Dinitrophenol. The black sulfur dyes derived from dinitrophenol are among the earliest commercially important types of sulfur colors and still are being used in very large quantities. The usual starting material is commercial chlorodinitrobenzene, which consists chiefly of the 1,2,4 and 1,2,6 isomers. This intermediate is easily hydrolyzed by boiling water containing the theoretical amount of sodium hydroxide, and the aqueous hydrolysate is run slowly into aqueous sodium polysulfide. The reaction is vigorous and exothermic; hydrogen sulfide and ammonia are evolved copiously[146]. At the end of the thionation the reaction mass is diluted and aerated until the dye is precipitated in its oxidized, water-insoluble form[23, 123, 135]. The sodium thiosulfate formed by the oxidation of the polysulfide is a profitable by-product.

The thionation of dinitrophenol may also be performed under pressure in an autoclave[124].

By control of thionation conditions and by the use of additives, the shade and working properties of the dinitrophenol blacks may be varied over a surprisingly wide range. Deliberate underthionation, which may be achieved either by shortening the thionation period or by reducing the amount of polysulfide, produces black dyes with a reddish undertone[111, 115]; prolonged thionation produces bluer shades. The addition of *p*-nitrophenol or *p*-aminophenol produces a somewhat greeener shade, while the addition of trinitrophenol gives a very much redder shade. Thionation of a mixture of dinitrophenol and 4'-hydroxy-2,4-dinitrodiphenylamine produces an exceptionally full and "bloomy" shade of black. All present American sulfur black standards that were made either from dinitrophenol alone or from mixtures of this product and any of the above mentioned secondary intermediates are now listed under CI 978, which originally was limited to dyes equivalent to *Sulfur Black T Extra*, made from straight dinitrophenol[129].

The chemistry of this thionation process is obscure; according to Khmelnitzkaya[111, 112] the reaction proceeds in two stages. The primary reaction consists in the reduction of the nitro groups of dinitrophenol by sodium disulfide which is provided by the sodium polysulfide; the nascent sulfur thus set free combines with the reduction products of the phenol to form thiazine rings. The second stage of the reaction is oxidative in character; sodium nitrite may be added as an oxidizing agent.

In spite of much effort, the structure of the dinitrophenol blacks remains obscure. Three possible structures for dinitrophenol black have been suggested: (IV) and (V) by Kubota[115] and (VI) by Khmelnitzkaya and Werchowskaya[113].

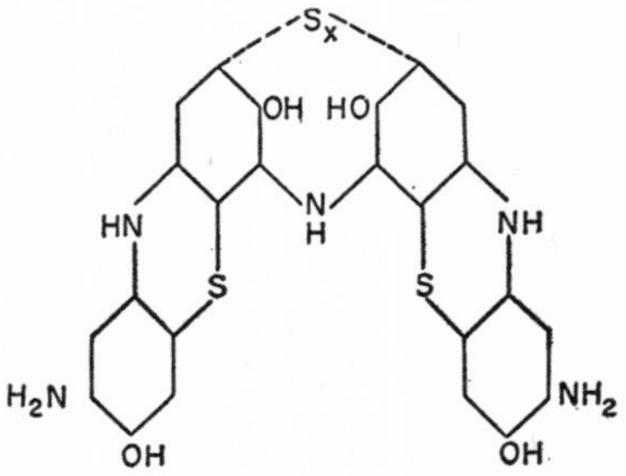

(IV)

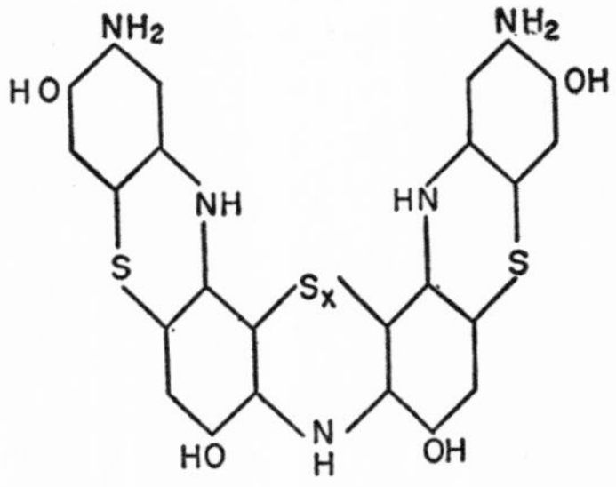

(V)

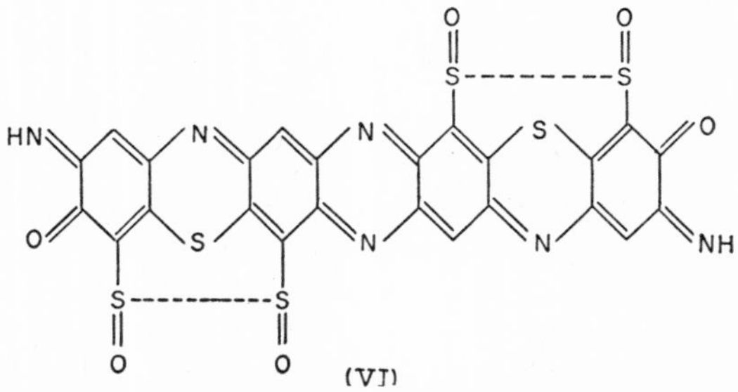

(VI)

These hypotheses are based on empirical analyses; objections can be raised against all three.

Sulfur Blacks Derived from Trinitrophenol. Trinitrophenol can be thionated with aqueous polysulfide[35]. The product dyes cotton in purplish or reddish black shades. The exhaust of this dye is rather poor, and it does not build up to attractive full shades; in other respects it bears a close resemblance to the dinitrophenol blacks.

Dyes Derived from Aromatic Amines and Diamines. The simple aromatic amines react with sulfur to form compounds analogous to p,p'-thiodianiline (VII) or phenothiazine (VIII).

(VII)   (VIII)

Such compounds are not dyes, and further treatment with sulfur or sodium polysulfide does not convert them to dyes. However, the introduction of nitro groups into aromatic amines makes them capable of conversion to sulfur colors. The most important representative of this class is *Immedial Yellow G Extra*, which is prepared by baking 2,4-dinitroacetanilide and phthalic anhydride with sodium polysulfide at 180°C[89, 93]. A mixture of p-nitroaniline and o-toluidine, baked with sulfur at 250°C, yields *Immedial Yellow 3GT*[93].

The aromatic diamines are much more important as intermediates for the manufacture of sulfur dyes. Thionation of p-phenylenediamine and o-toluidine with sodium polysulfide yields *Immedial Olive FF Extra*[87]. p-Aminoacetanilide, thionated with sodium polysulfide, yields *Sulfur Brown R*, CI 936[121]. The same intermediate, thionated in admixture with o-aminoacetanilide, produces *Thiophore Bronze 5G*, CI 946[44]. The structures of these colors have not been determined.

The presence of a methyl group in an ortho position to one of the amino groups in an aromatic diamine greatly increases its usefulness as an intermediate for the manufacture of sulfur colors. The presence of this group makes possible the formation of the thiazole ring, a very effective chromophore. Toluene-2,4-diamine, the most commonly used member of this group, when baked with sulfur under varied conditions of time and temperature, produces a number of commercially important sulfur dyes, ranging in shade from yellow and orange to tan and brown. Increase in temperature or time produces deeper and duller shades.

The fundamental chemical structure of the sulfur dyes derived from toluene-2,4-diamine has been elucidated by the brilliant work of Zerweck and his collaborators[149]. *Immedial Orange C*, CI 949, an important member of this class of dye, was fused with sodium hydroxide; the complex mixture of amines and thioamines was stabilized by reaction with chloroacetic acid and isolated as crystalline and identifiable degradation products. Basing his conclusions on the nature and relative amounts of these degradation products, Zerweck has proposed two alternative structures (IX) and (X) for *Immedial Orange C*:

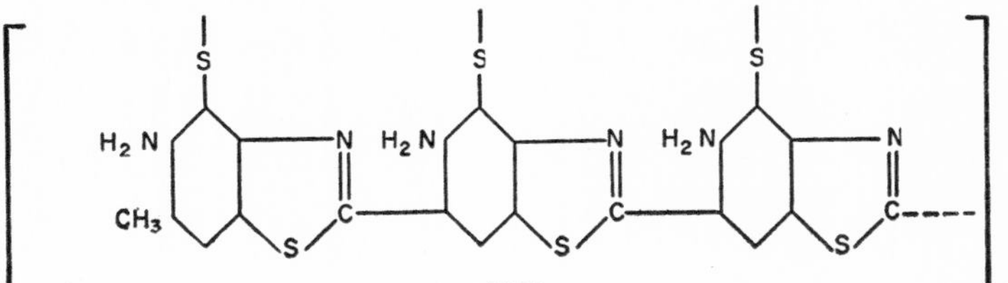

(IX)

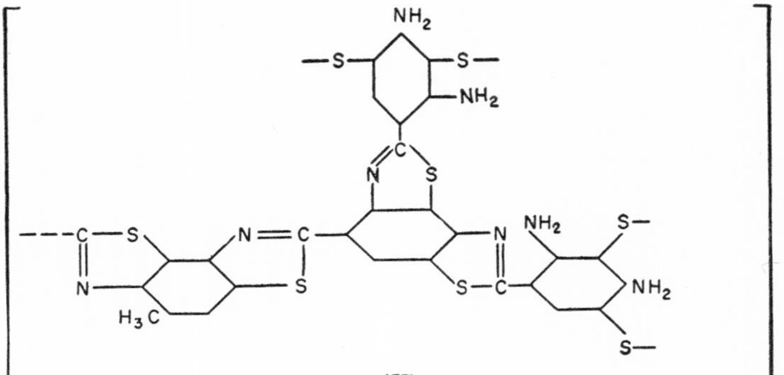

(X)

Attempts to prove the correctness of these structures by synthesis have not yet been successful; however, they are probably fundamentally correct.

Toluene-2,4-diamine is commonly co-thionated with other aromatic amines or diamines[104, 122, 145]. Thionation of such mixtures frequently yields more valuable dyes than can be produced by the thionation of either of the components alone. The use of benzidine in this manner is an interesting example. Benzidine itself reacts with sulfur to produce 3,7-dibenzothiophenediamine, which is not a dye and is not soluble in sodium sulfide solution[116]. However, a number of very valuable sulfur dyes are produced by baking mixtures of benzidine and other aromatic amines or diamines with sulfur. Benzidine is not a catalyst or carrier of sulfur; it enters the reaction and becomes an integral part of the dye produced. *Immedial Yellow D*, CI 948, is manufactured by heating a mixture of toluene-2,4-diamine and benzidine with sulfur at 190 to 220°C[144]. The reaction mass is digested with sodium hydroxide, and the dye is isolated by acidification[30, 72, 102, 103, 120]. The dye colors cotton in neutral yellow shades; it is widely used to disguise or "standardize" the shade of unbleached cotton in lining fabrics.

Many different diamines are used, both singly and in admixture, as intermediates for the manufacture of sulfur dyes. The more important members of this type of sulfur dyes are listed in Table 1.

Sulfur Colors Derived from *p*-Aminophenol. *p*-Aminophenol and several of its simply substituted derivatives are among the intermediates

TABLE 1. SULFUR DYES DERIVED FROM MIXED AROMATIC AMINES AND
DIAMINES

Name	Ingredients	Ref.
Immedial Green Yellow G	MTD* and p-nitroaniline	60, 74, 82
Immedial Yellow Olive 3GR	MTD and p-nitroaniline	60, 73, 92
Immedial Yellow 4RT Extra	MTD, m-nitroaniline and benzidine	90
Immedial Orange Brown 3RL	MTD and 4-nitro-2-aminotoluene (5-nitro-o-toluidine)	14, 76
Immedial Yellow Brown O Base	MTD and p-aminophenol	94
Immedial Yellow 6RT Extra	MTD and m-phenylenediamine	91
Immedial Orange FR Base	MTD and N,N'-p-phenylenediphthalimide	93
Immedial Yellow Brown G 26 Base	MTD and toluene-2,6-diamine	94
Eclipse Yellow, CI 951	Diformyl MTD (N,N'-2,4-tolylenebisformamide) and benzidine	126
Immedial Orange FRR	Benzidine and 2-nitro-p-acetotoluidide	93
Immedial Yellow RT	Benzidine and 2-thio-1-(2,5-xylyl)urea	73

* MTD stands for toluene-2,4-diamine.

disclosed by Vidal in his pioneering patents on the manufacture of sulfur dyes[136, 138, 139].

St. Denis Black, CI 973, which attained some commercial importance during the early development of the sulfur colors, was prepared by heating a mixture of p-aminophenol and p-phenylenediamine with sodium polysulfide. A mild thionation of this mixture yielded a blue sulfur dye; under more drastic conditions a black dye was formed. Both dyes have been replaced by others having better working properties. They still are of theoretical interest in that consideration of their properties by their discoverer led him to propose the thiazine ring as the fundamental chromophore for such dyes[137].

Sulfur Dyes Derived from p-Hydroxydiarylamines and Quinone Imines. The p-hydroxydiarylamines constitute a useful class of intermediates for the manufacture of sulfur dyes. These compounds may be oxidized readily to deeply colored quinone imines:

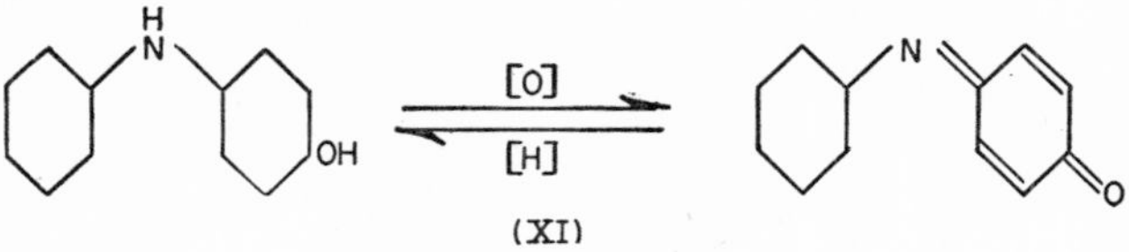

(XI)

These colored quinone imines are rather unstable; however, they react readily with sodium polysulfide, yielding sulfur colors of good tinctorial strength, excellent fastness and pleasing shades. The thionation of p-hydroxydiphenylamine (p-anilinophenol) itself yields an attractive reddish brown dye which is considerably stronger and brighter than the brown dyes prepared from aromatic diamines by the bake process[56, 57, 58]. The thionation is carried out with sodium polysulfide in an organic medium; the product is isolated by aeration of the diluted thionation mass.

The structural formula (XII) below has been proposed by Zerweck and his collaborators[103]; loosely bound sulfur and disulfide groups are not indicated:

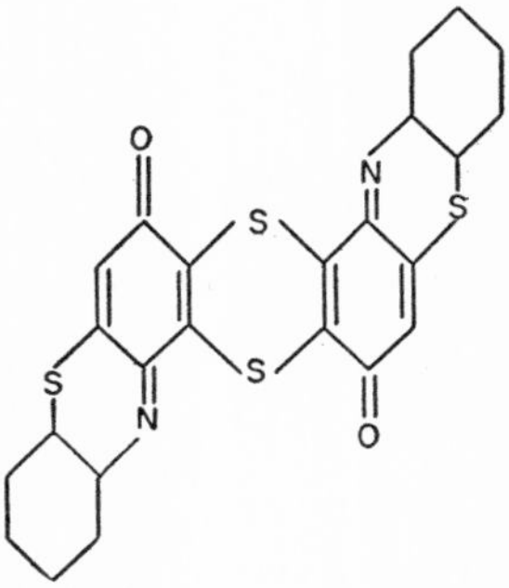

(XII)

This hypothesis is supported by the empirical analysis and chemical properties of the dye, and by its close similarity to synthetic dyes of known structure prepared by the Herz synthesis. The properties of three of these synthetic dyes of the structures shown below give very convincing indirect evidence for the existence of the thianthrene ring:

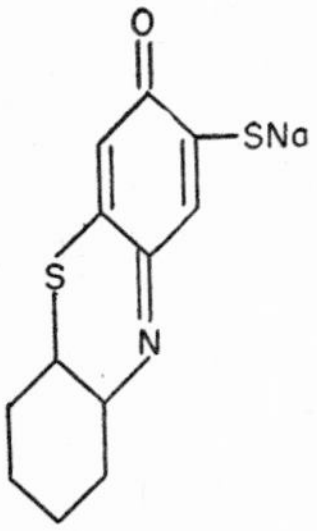

(XIII) 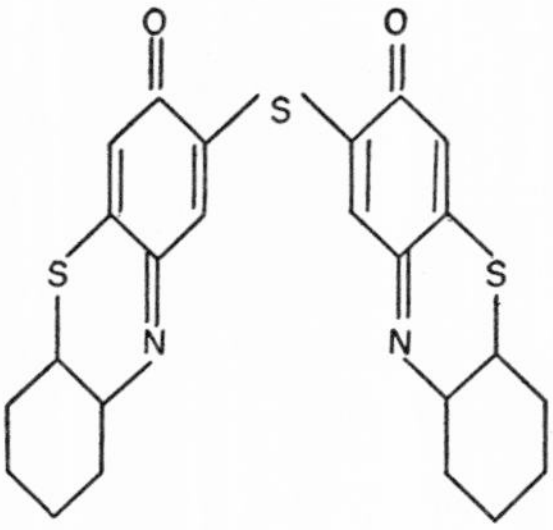   (XIV) 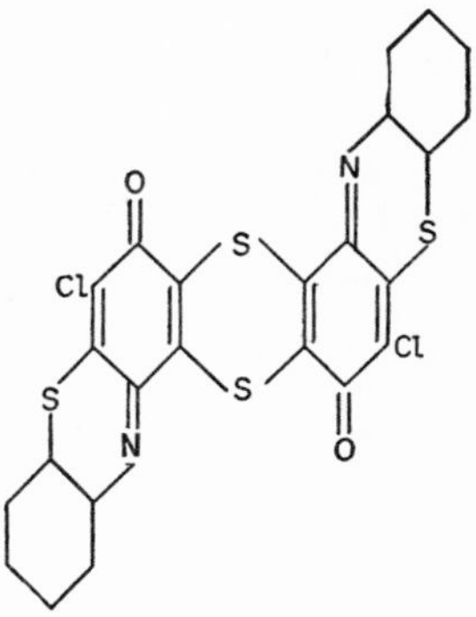   (XV)

The first (XIII) was deeply colored, but was very soluble in sodium sulfide and had very little affinity for cotton. The dye having the structure

(XIV) showed a decreased solubility and a markedly increased affinity for cotton; while the dye corresponding to (XV) resembled the thionation product of p-hydroxydiphenylamine very closely in its shade, solubility and affinity to cotton.

Indocarbon CL, Pr. 126. This dye, one of the most important of the quinone imine-type sulfur dyes, is prepared by the thionation of N-(p-hydroxyphenyl)-2-naphthylamine (p-(2-naphthylamino)phenol) with high-ratio sodium polysulfide in an organic solvent[59, 78].

Indocarbon CL dyes cotton in attractive deep black shades. The fastness properties of the dye are good; it has the greatest resistance of all of the black sulfur dyes to hypochlorite, and will survive moderate concentrations of this reagent without serious loss of strength[110]. Unlike the dinitrophenol blacks, it has no tendency to tender cotton goods which have been dyed with it.

Valpiana[134] has proposed the structure (XVI) for Indocarbon CL:

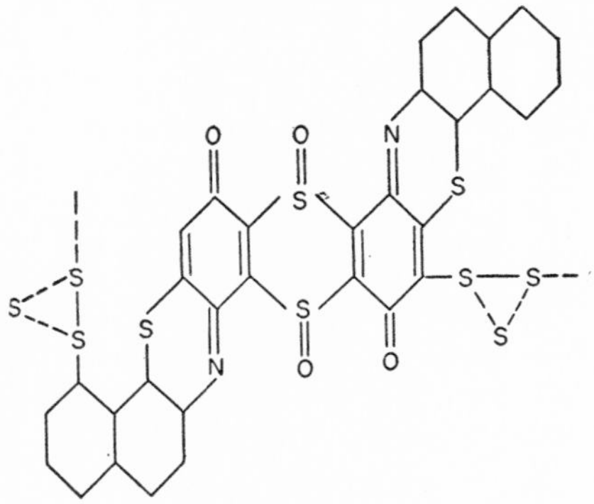

(XVI)

The sulfoxide groups and the thiozonide sulfur are included to bring the formula into agreement with the empirical formula of the commercial dye; the side-chain sulfur is attached asymmetrically to explain the fact that alkylation of the leuco form of the dye yields two distinct types of alkylation products.

A basic chromophore of the same type has been proposed independently by Zerweck[103].

Another valuable intermediate of the quinone-imine type is 4'-hydroxy-2,4-dinitrodiphenylamine (p-(2,4-dinitroanilino)phenol). When thionated with aqueous or alcoholic sodium polysulfide, this compound yields either blue[7] or black[107] sulfur colors, depending on the intensity of thionation; when it is treated with sodium hydroxide and then baked with sodium polysulfide, valuable brown dyes are produced[67].

Direct Sulfur Blues, CI 956. The direct sulfur blues are prepared by the thionation of 4'-hydroxy-2,4-dinitrodiphenylamine with a solution of fairly low-ratio sodium polysulfide in water or alcohol[7, 103]. This dye is unusually responsive to the conditions employed in its preparation and isolation; a very wide range of shades can be produced from this one intermediate by choice of solvent, polysulfide ratio, and particularly by varied degrees of after-oxidation[69].

The direct sulfur blues are so named because their vats in sodium sulfide are blue in color, quite unlike the yellow vats which are characteristic of most sulfur colors. This does not mean that the dye is not reduced by sulfide, but rather that the reduction involves only the disulfide linkages in the molecule, the thiazone ring being left in its oxidized form.

The structure of the direct sulfur blue type has not been determined.

When 4'-hydroxy-2,4-dinitrodiphenylamine is baked with sodium polysulfide, *Immedial Black V Extra*, CI 988, is produced[95, 107]. Treatment of the same intermediate with sodium hydroxide, followed by a polysulfide bake yields *Immedial Dark Brown A*, CI 939[67, 69, 81]. The constitution of these colors has not been determined.

Sulfur Dyes Derived from Indophenols and Leucoindophenols. The indophenols and their leuco derivatives constitute a very important class of intermediates for the manufacture of sulfur dyes. The greater part of the sulfur blues and greens, which are the brightest and cleanest of the sulfur colors, are manufactured from intermediates of this type. The indophenols themselves are deeply colored, and can be dyed on cotton from a sulfide or hydrosulfite bath; the indophenol prepared by the reaction of N,N-dimethyl-p-nitrosoaniline with 1-naphthol (CI 821) was, in fact, once used commercially for brightening goods which had previously been dyed with Indigo[31]. However, the indophenols are not stable to acids, and are no longer used as dyes; they are valuable today solely as intermediates for the manufacture of sulfur dyes.

Several methods are used for the manufacture of these compounds. The most general method is based on the reaction of aromatic amines having a free para position with p-nitrosophenol[28, 31, 47]:

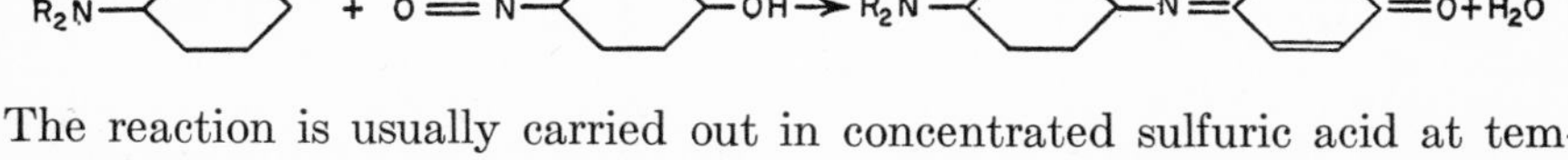

The reaction is usually carried out in concentrated sulfuric acid at temperatures below 5°C. The condensation is fairly rapid. The indophenol may be isolated by drowning the sulfuric acid solutions, filtering off the precipitated product and washing it free of acid. More often the primary product is reduced at once to its leuco derivative by drowning the sulfuric acid solution of the indophenol in water containing somewhat more than the theoretically necessary amount of sodium sulfide. The leuco indophenol is then filtered and washed free of acid.

A less commonly used method for the preparation of indophenols involves the simultaneous oxidation with dichromate of p-aminophenol and an aromatic amine having an unsubstituted para position, usually in sulfuric acid[31]:

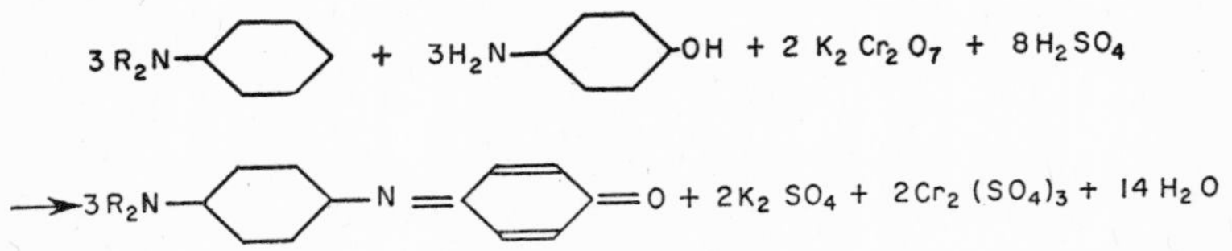

Water-soluble amines, such as the sulfonated or carboxylated amines, are usually converted to indophenols by oxidation together with p-aminophenol by means of sodium hypochlorite[31]:

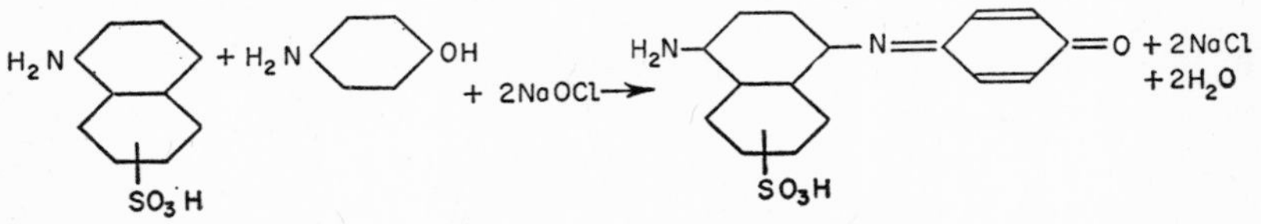

The reaction is carried out as rapidly as possible in alkaline aqueous solution at 0°C; the indophenol is reduced with sodium sulfide and salted out or precipitated by acidification. A less commonly used modification of the above method depends on the simultaneous oxidation of an aromatic p-diamine and phenol with sodium hypochlorite[125]:

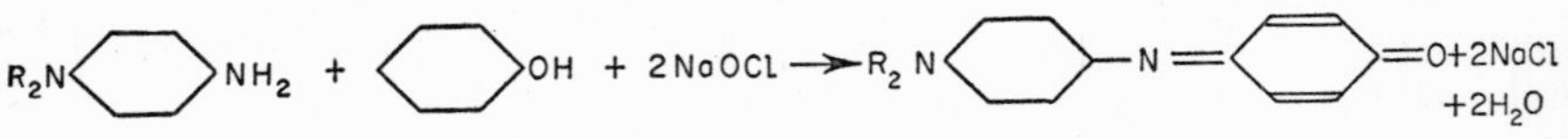

Indophenols may also be prepared by the reaction of aromatic amines having free para positions with quinone chlorimide (N-chloro-p-quinone imine) in sulfuric or acetic acid[28, 101]:

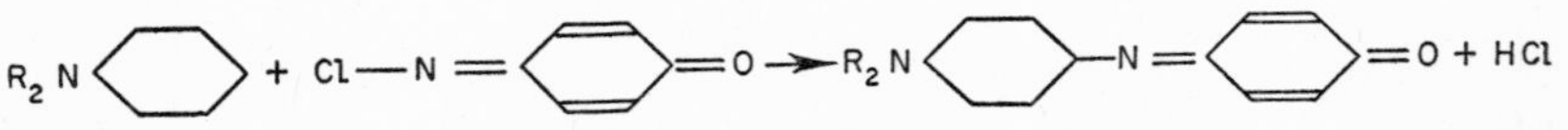

This method is seldom used commercially, although it is a very convenient method for the laboratory preparation of indophenols.

Indophenols and leucoindophenols react very readily with sodium polysulfide to form sulfur dyes. The reaction consists in the addition and substitution of sulfur, with simultaneous ring closure to form thiazone derivatives. Usually, an indophenol and its leuco derivative both yield an identical sulfur color, although slight differences in physical properties sometimes favor the use of one type over the other. Solvent thionations are used almost exclusively, since the dry baking method usually yields a duller product.

The simplest of the leucoindophenols is 4,4'-dihydroxydiphenylamine (p,p'-iminodiphenol). This was originally prepared by the reaction of p-nitrosophenol with phenol[28], but is now manufactured by the oxidation of phenol and p-aminophenol with hypochlorite[98]. A number of blue dyes of minor importance are made by the aqueous thionation of this intermediate with sodium polysulfide, followed by aeration[75, 86]. These dyes are attractive in shade but do not exhaust well.

The indophenol derived from o-toluidine and p-nitrosophenol is a very important intermediate, yielding on thionation the extensively used Sulfur Navy Blues.

Sulfur Navy Blues, CI 959. These colors are manufactured by the thionation of N-o-tolyl-p-quinone imine, or its leuco derivative, with sodium polysulfide[43, 47, 61, 63, 128]. A wide range of shades can be produced by choice of solvent and degree of afteroxidation. Aqueous thionation produces the greenest shade; redder and brigher shades are produced by the use of organic solvents. Redness and brightness are also enhanced by afteroxidation. The Navy blues are the cheapest of the blue sulfur dyes, and are widely used in dyeing cotton in deep blue tones.

Jones and Reed have proposed the structural formula

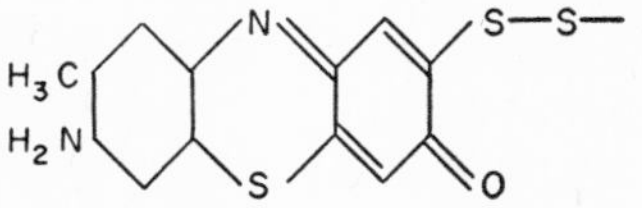

(XVII)

for Sulfur Navy Blue[105]. It is more probable, however, that the dye has a thianthrene structure of the type proposed by Zerweck.

Sulfur Brilliant Blues, CI 961. The Sulfur Brilliant Blues are produced by the thionation of 4-anilino-4'-hydroxydiphenylamine (p-(p-anilino-anilino)phenol) or its corresponding indophenol[62, 80, 114]. Either water or organic solvents may be used.

Bernasconi[5] has proposed the formula (XVIII) for the unoxidized dye, as it is isolated from the thionation mass:

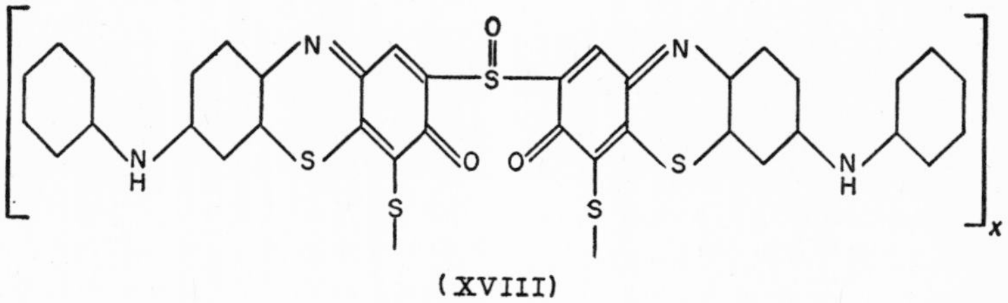

(XVIII)

The sulfur content of this dye is not altered by mild afteroxidation, although its oxygen content is increased. Bernasconi believes that afteroxidation consists in the oxidation of disulfide bonds to disulfoxide bonds. He proposes the typical formula (XIX) for the afteroxidized product:

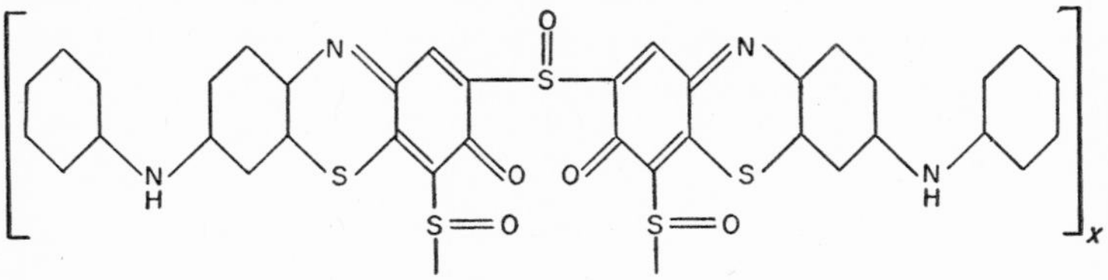

(XIX)

Bernasconi's hypotheses are based on analyses of carefully purified samples of commercial dyes, and on analogy with a synthetic dye of the following structure (XX), which he prepared by the Herz synthesis:

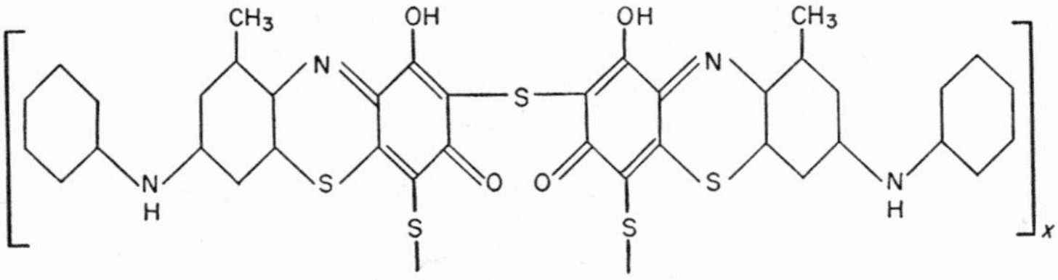

(XX)

During World War II the German dye industry was devoting much research effort to the sulfur dyes derived from diphenylamine[99]. Several new dyes derived from 4-(p-hydroxyanilino)-4'-sulfodiphenylamine (N-(p-(p-hydroxyanilino)phenyl)sulfanilic acid)[75, 85] and a dye derived from 2-carboxy-4'-(p-hydroxyanilino)-diphenylamine (N-(p-(p-hydroxyanilino)-phenyl)anthranilic acid) were already in commercial use; sulfur dyes prepared from acetylated aminohydroxydiphenylamines were under investigation.

Immedial Pure Blue, CI 957. This dye is manufactured by the thionation of 4-dimethylamino-4'-hydroxydiphenylamine (p-(p-dimethylamino-anilino)phenol). The latter intermediate is prepared by the reaction of N,N-dimethyl-p-nitrosoaniline with phenol followed by reduction to the leucoindophenol. The thionation may be carried out in water or alcohol[46, 47, 125, 141, 142]. The product is isolated by aerating the aqueous thionation mass and salting out the dye.

Immedial Pure Blue is attractive in shade; its working properties are normal, with the exception of a rather poor exhaust.

Immedial Pure Blue was one of the first of the indophenol dyes to be prepared. The presence of a thiazone ring in this dye was demonstrated early in this century by Gnehm and his collaborators, who treated the dye with hydrobromic acid and potassium bromate under pressure, and isolated a crystalline product from the reaction mixture. This was identified[48, 49] as 2,4,6,8-tetrabromo-7-dimethylaminothiazone (2,4,6,8-tetrabromo-7-dimethylamino-3H-isophenothiazin-3-one):

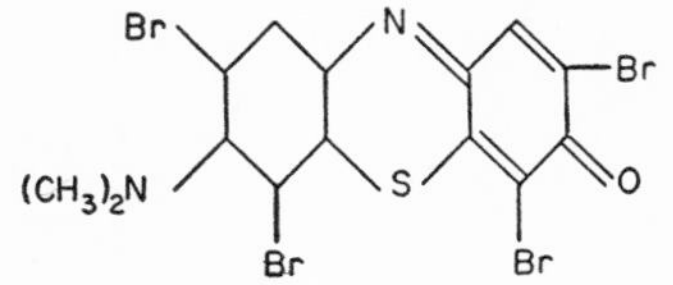

The dye was capable of forming a crystalline addition product with sodium bisulfite[38], which simplified its purification. A considerable amount of work has been performed with the object of determining its structure. The three most plausible structures are given below:

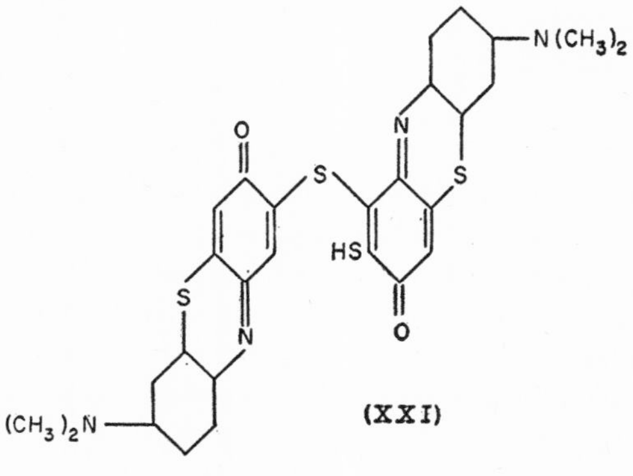

(XXI)

Bernthsen[6]

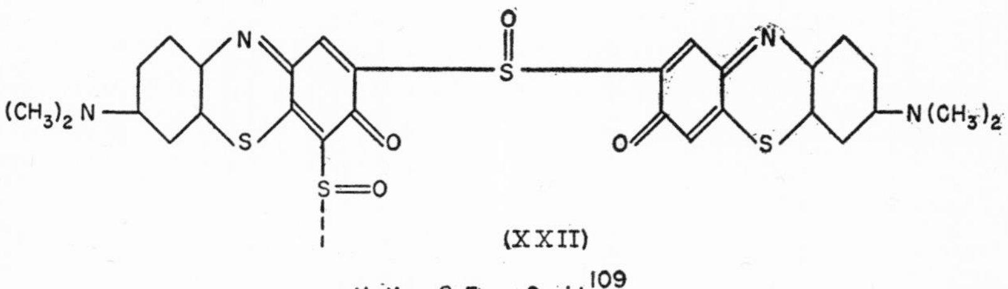

(XXII)

Keller & Fierz-David[109]

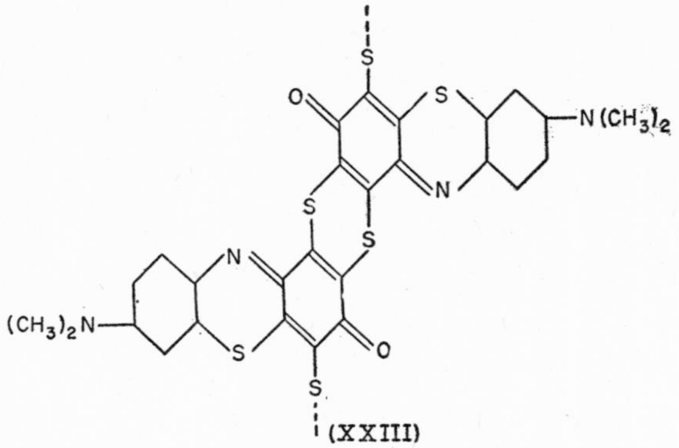

(XXIII)

Zerweck[149]

All of these proposed structures are based on the empirical formulas of commercial dyes and on analogy with synthetic dyes of related constitution. Bernthsen used the reaction of chlorosubstituted hydroquinone thiosulfate with a thiosulfate of p-amino-N,N-dimethylaniline[40, 41] in the preparation of his synthetic analog; he stated that further condensation was possible by this synthetic method, but that it did not alter the properties of the dye. Zerweck employed a modification of the Herz synthesis in the preparation of his analog, and on the basis of its properties assigned the thianthrene structure to the commercial dye. The structure of Keller and Fierz-David is of interest in that it attempts to assign a position in the molecule to the oxygen atoms that are introduced in the working up of the dye.

Fast Sulfur Greens, Pr. 65. These dyes are prepared by the thionation of the leucoindophenols derived from 5(or 8)-amino-2-naphthalenesulfonic acid (1,6 or 1,7 Cleve's acid), or from mixtures of the two. The thionation may be carried out in aqueous or alcoholic polysulfide[4, 9, 37, 45, 117]. The color may be salted out of the thionation mass after the elimination of excess polysulfide, or may be isolated by aeration.

Brilliant Sulfur Greens, CI 1006. The Brilliant Sulfur Greens are manufactured from the leucoindophenol derived from 8-anilino-1-naphthalenesulfonic acid (Phenyl Peri acid)[4, 9, 39]. The commercial dyes are usually copper complexes, prepared by thionation in the presence of a copper salt, which intensifies the yellowness of the dye. These dyes, either with or without copper, are usually yellower and brighter than those drived from Cleve's acid.

Fierz-David[22] has proposed the following structural formula (XXIV) for the thionation product of 8-anilino-5-(p-hydroxyanilino)-1-naphthalenesulfonic acid:

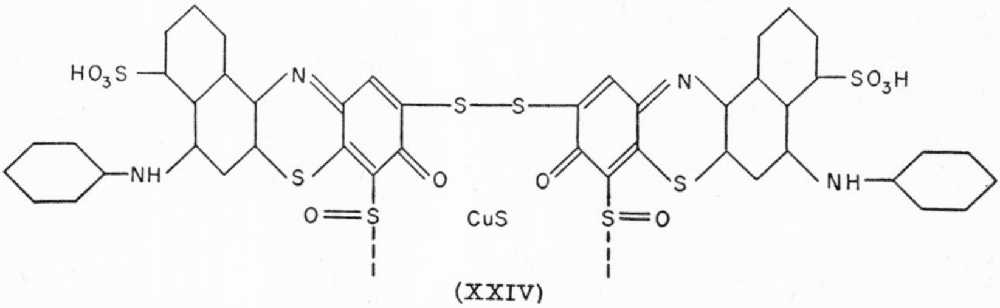

(XXIV)

His hypothesis is based on the empirical formula of the commercial dye, and is supported by the synthesis of a dye of similar properties through the Herz synthesis.

Sulfur Colors Derived from Heterocyclic Intermediates

Hydron Blue R, CI 969. Hydron Blue R is still an important color and is manufactured by the thionation of *N*-3-carbazolyl-*p*-quinone imine or its corresponding leuco derivative with sodium polysulfide. The indophenol is prepared by the reaction between *p*-nitrosophenol and carbazole in concentrated sulfuric acid at low temperature; the sulfuric acid solution is drowned in ice and water. To prepare the corresponding leucoindophenol, the sulfuric acid solution of the indophenol is run into water containing somewhat more than the amount of sodium sulfide necessary for its reduction[97]. Thionation of the indophenol or leucoindophenol is carried out with a fairly high-ratio polysulfide under reflux in an organic solvent[50, 51, 64, 68].

Sodium hydrosulfite is required to reduce Hydron Blue R completely. It is compatible with other vat dyes, and is sometimes used in combination with them. It dyes cotton in attractive reddish-blue shades which have good fastness to light and washing, and are somewhat resistant to hypochlorite.

A number of structural formulas have been proposed for Hydron Blue R, the most plausible of which is that of Fierz-David and Valpiani[134]:

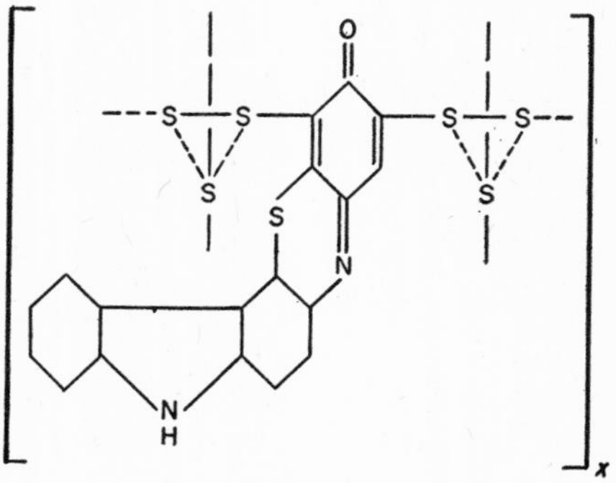

(XXV)

The vertical barred lines indicate the boundaries of the repeating molecular unit; the dotted lines represent the thiozonide linkage of sulfur. Zerweck's investigations[149] suggest strongly that a considerable portion of the sulfur content of this dye may be bound in thianthrene rings.

Hydron Blue G, CI 971. Hydron Blue G is the thionation product of the leucoindophenol derived from 9-ethylcarbazole[65]. This dye is distinctly greener in shade than Hydron Blue R; in its preparation, and in its other tinctorial properties, it resembles the latter dye very closely.

Bordeaux Shade Sulfur Dyes. A number of valuable sulfur dyes are prepared by the thionation of 2-amino-7-hydroxy-phenazine (8-amino-2-phenazinol) or its 3-methyl derivative. These are usually prepared by the two-stage oxidation of equimolecular amounts of *m*-phenylenediamine or toluene-2,4-diamine and *p*-aminophenol. The first stage consists in the chemical oxidation of the two components to an indamine:

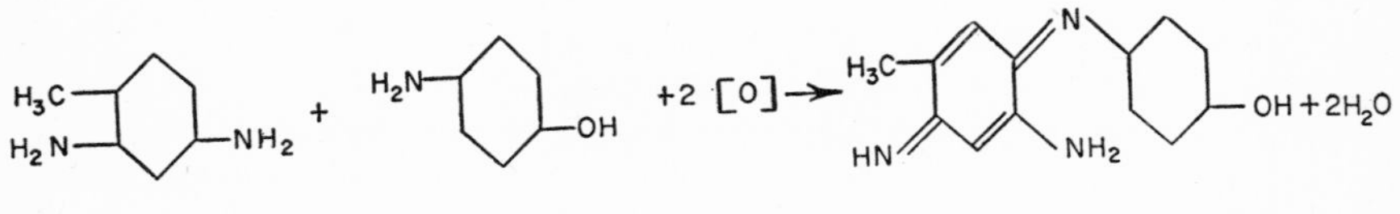

The further oxidation of this indamine with air results in the formation of the phenazine:

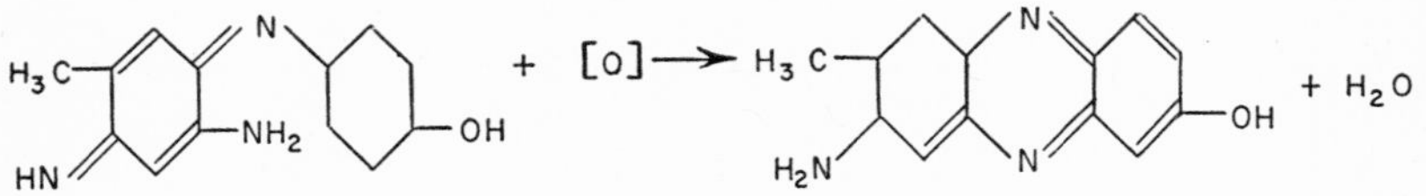

Immedial Bordeaux, CI 1012. The most important intermediate of the phenazine type is 3-methyl-2-amino-7-hydroxy-phenazine (8-amino-7-methyl-2-phenazinol), prepared from toluene-2,4-diamine and *p*-aminophenol[143]. This intermediate is converted to a sulfur dye by refluxing with aqueous polysulfide[69, 84]; the product is isolated by drying the entire thionation mass, or by acidification. Two types of this dye are manufactured: one contains copper, the other is copper free. The addition of copper renders the dye considerably yellower and somewhat duller, and decreases its exhaust.

The structure of the Sulfur Bordeaux dyes has not been determined.

Sulfur Bordeaux shades of lesser importance are also prepared by the thionation of 2-amino-7-hydroxy-phenazine (8-amino-2-phenazinol) both with and without copper[83].

Sulfur Yellows from Dehydrothio-*p*-toluidine, CI 955. When *p*-toluidine is heated with sulfur, the primary reaction product is 2-(*p*-

aminophenyl)-6-methylbenzothiazole ("dehydrothio-*p*-toluidine"):

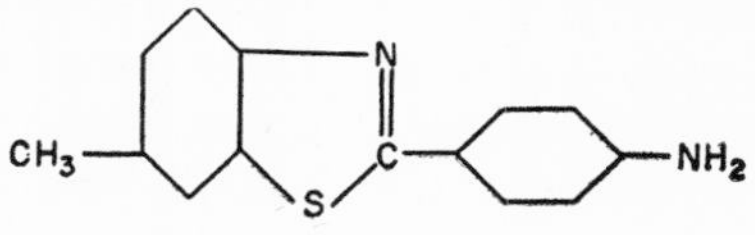

(XXVI)

This product is not a sulfur dye, nor can it be converted to one by further heating with sulfur. When, however, a mixture of dehydrothio-*p*-toluidine and benzidine is heated with sulfur, a very valuable sulfur dye, *Immedial Yellow GG*, is formed[130]. The thionation is carried out at 220 to 225°C; the product is isolated by digestion of the thionation mass with sodium hydroxide, clarification and aeration of the diluted filtrate[72, 89].

Immedial Yellow GG dyes cotton in fairly bright yellow shades. The fastness and the working properties of the dye are good.

Zerweck and his collaborators have established the constitution of Immedial Yellow GG by fusing the dye with sodium hydroxide and identifying the cleavage products, after stabilization by conversion into mercaptoacetic acid derivatives[149]. According to this evidence, the commercial dye is a mixture of the four types shown below:

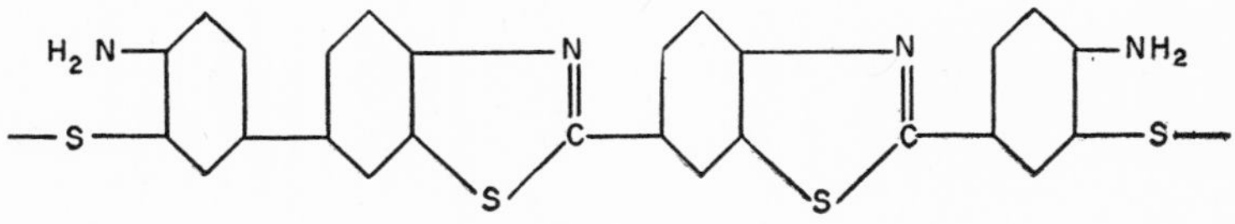

(XXVII)

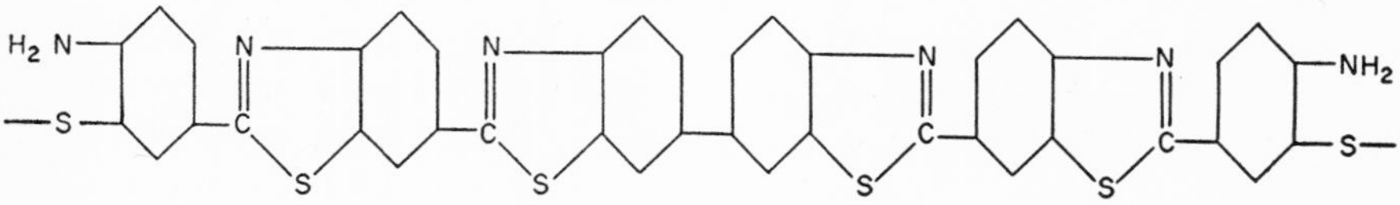

(XXVIII)

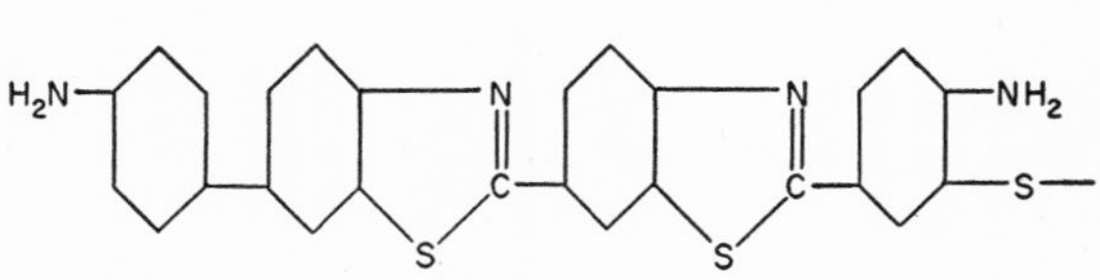

(XXIX)

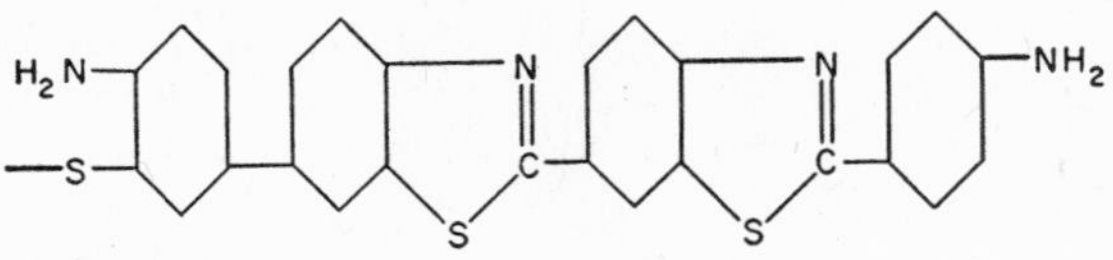

(XXX)

Compounds (XXVII) and (XXVIII) predominate in the mixture. All of these compounds were prepared synthetically in order to prove their structures; a mixture of the four in the proper proportions practically duplicates the properties of the commercial dye.

Sulfur Colors Derived From Substituted Thiazones. The preparation of substituted thiazones by the condensation of thiosulfate derivatives of aromatic diamines with hydroquinone thiosulfates, or by the reaction of *o*-aminothiols with chloroquinones has already been described. When these thiazone derivatives are heated with sodium polysulfide solution, sulfur is introduced into the molecule; at the same time the remaining chlorine atoms are replaced by sulfur, either in the form of mercapto groups, sulfoxy links or thianthrene rings. In this manner one can prepare synthetic dyes of known basic constitution which resemble very closely the commercial dyes prepared from indophenols or quinone imines of comparable structure. *Immedial Red Brown CL3R* is manufactured in this fashion, by the thionation of 1,2,4-trichloro-7-methylthiazone (1,2,4-trichloro-7-methyl-3H-isophenothiazin-3-one)[88] of the following structure:

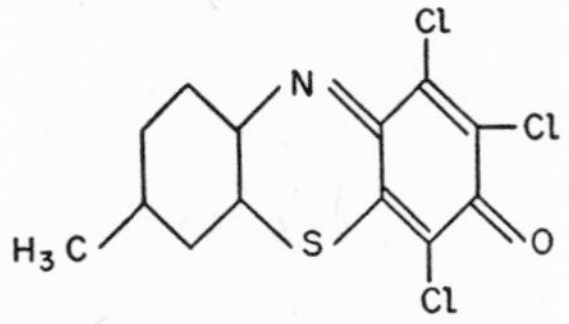

The method is not very important commercially; however, it has been of outstanding value as a means of determining the approximate constitution of a wide variety of sulfur colors, and has also been very useful in indicating the effect of substitution in sulfur dyes. Since thiazone (3H-isophenothiazin-3-one) (XXXI) differs from the quinone imines or indophenols (XXXII) only by a sulfur bridge

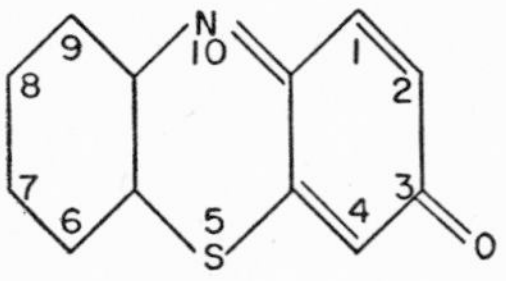

(XXXI)

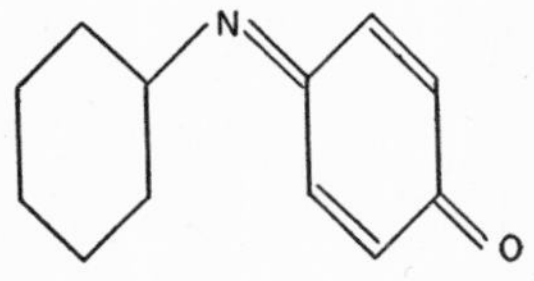

(XXXII)

any conclusions regarding the effect of substitution on the former molecule have application to the latter. Zerweck[103, 149] has summarized very well the results of his own studies, as well as those of others, on the effect of substitution on the sulfur dyes derived from the thiazones. For the conversion of a substituted thiazone to a true sulfur color, it is necessary that each of the 1, 2 and 4 positions be substituted with sulfur atoms, or with chlorine which is replaced by sulfur during thionation. Sulfur in the 4 position may be in the form of a mercapto or sulfoxy group; that in the 1 and 2 positions probably forms part of a thianthrene ring or its disulfoxide analog. Zerweck suggests strongly that all sulfur colors containing the thiazone ring also contain thianthrene rings or related disulfoxide rings. The idea is reasonable, but cannot be considered as proved for all cases. Substitution of the 1, 2 and 4 positions with anything save sulfur affects the properties of the compound as a sulfur dye adversely; for instance, blocking of the 4 position produces a dye which requires hydrosulfite for its reduction, and thiazones in which the 1 and 2 positions are blocked (as for instance 1,2-dimethylthiazone or 1,2-benzothiazone) do not yield true sulfur colors on thionation. Substitution in the benzenoid portion of the molecule (6, 7, 8, or 9 positions) determines the shade, solubility, fastness, and tinctorial properties of the dye but has no influence on the ease of thionation. Thiazone itself yields a red-brown sulfur dye on thionation. Substitution of the hydrogen in the 7 position with methyl, methoxy, methylmercapto or acylamino groups yields brown dyes of only slightly altered shade and properties. Substitution in the 7 position by amino, alkylamino or hydroxy groups produces dyes ranging between blue and blue-violet in shade. The substitution of an amino group in the 8 position yields an olive green dye; and the thionation of thiazones substituted in the 7 and 9 positions by amino groups yields a black dye. The presence of the benzo nucleus fused to the 6, 7 side produces the earlier discussed Indocarbon CL. A black dye also is obtained when the benzo nucleus is fused to the 8, 9 side. Apparently the normal thionation of a thiazone introduces no sulfur in the benzenoid portion of the ring. Thiazones substituted in the benzenoid ring by synthetically introduced sulfur are not true sulfur dyes; and a thiazone in which the 1, 2 and 4 positions have been blocked by nonreplaceable substituents cannot be thionated at all.

Literature Cited

1. Belen'kii, *Anilinokrasochnaya Prom.*, **5**, 11 (1935); *C.A.*, **29**, 3519 (1935).
2. ——, *Kolloid-Z.*, **67**, 79 (1934); *C.A.*, **28**, 3906 (1934).
3. ——, *Melliand Textilber.*, **14**, 555 (1933).
4. Bergdolt, Neelmeier and Nocken, U.S. Patent 1,733,443 (1929).
5. Bernasconi, *Helv. Chim. Acta*, **15**, 287 (1932).
6. Bernthsen, *Chem. Ztg.*, **32**, 956 (1908).
7. Bertschmann, U.S. Patent 665,726 (1901).

8. Binz and Rath, *Ber.*, **58**, 309 (1925).
9. Boeniger, U.S. Patent 776,885 (1904).
10. Bohn, U.S. Patent 545,336 (1895).
11. ——, U.S. Patent 545,337 (1895).
12. Brass, *Z. angew. Chem.*, **39**, 697 (1926).
13. ——, *Monatschr. Textil-Ind.*, **41**, 316 (1926); *C.A.*, **26**, 4475 (1932).
14. British Patent 23,312 (1895).
15. Creevey, *Chemical Age (London)*, **46**, 257 (1942); *C.A.*, **36**, 5350 (1942).
16. Crist, *Am. Dyestuff Reptr.*, **21**, 367 (1932).
17. ——, *ibid.*, **25**, 11 (1936).
18. ——, *ibid.*, **31**, 133 (1942).
19. Davidson, *ibid.*, **19**, 709 (1930).
20. Eppendahl, *Faerber-Ztg.*, **22**, 44 (1911); *C.A.*, **6**, 297 (1912).
21. Erdmann, *Ann.*, **362**, 134 (1908).
22. Fierz-David, *J. Soc. Dyers Colourists*, **51**, 50 (1935).
23. Flachslaender, U.S. Patent 935,009 (1909).
24. Formánek and Knop, "Untersuchung und Nachweis organischer Farbstoffe," p. 9, Berlin, Julius Springer, 1927.
25. French Patent 98,915 (1873).
26. French Patent 255,473 (1896).
27. French Patent 308,669 (1901).
28. French Patent 332,884 (1903).
29. French Patent 656,907 (1910), Equiv. U.S. 1,759,261.
30. Friedlaender, *Z. angew. Chem.*, **19**, 615 (1906).
31. German Patent 15,915 (1881), Equiv. B. 1,393.
32. German Patent 84,632 (1895).
33. German Patent 101,577 (1899).
34. German Patent 102,897 (1899), Equiv. U.S. 603,755.
35. German Patent 116,791 (1900), Equiv. B. 7,332.
36. German Patent 123,569 (1901).
37. German Patent 132,212 (1898).
38. German Patent 135,952 (1902), Equiv. B. 20,741.
39. German Patent 162,156 (1905).
40. German Patent 167,012 (1905).
41. German Patent 178,940 (1906).
42. German Patent 179,225 (1906).
43. German Patent 199,963 (1908).
44. German Patent 220,064 (1910).
45. Gley, U.S. Patent 741,030 (1903).
46. Gnehm, *Z. angew. Chem.*, **1901**, 226.
47. ——, Bots and Weber, *J. prakt. Chem.*, **69**, 161, 223 (1904).
48. —— and Kaufler, *Ber.*, **37**, 2617, 3032 (1904).
49. —— and ——, *ibid.*, **37**, 3032 (1904).
50. Haas, U.S. Patent 919,572 (1909).
51. ——, U.S. Patent 931,598 (1909).
52. Hagge and Haagen, U.S. Patent 2,076,143 (1937).
53. —— and ——, U.S. Patent 2,076,144 (1937).
54. —— and ——, U.S. Patent 2,151,513 (1939).
55. Haskell, *Am. Dyestuff Reptr.*, **18**, 42 (1929).
56. Heimann, U.S. Patent 1,096,715 (1914).

57. ——, U.S. Patent 1,098,260 (1914).
58. —— and Virck, U.S. Patent 1,099,039 (1914).
59. ——, U.S. Patent 1,105,515 (1914).
60. Herre and Jaeckel, U.S. Patent 895,637 (1908).
61. Herz, U.S. Patent 709,151 (1902).
62. ——, U.S. Patent 723,154 (1903).
63. ——, U.S. Patent 742,189 (1903).
64. ——, U.S. Patent 956,348 (1910).
65. ——, U.S. Patent 966,092 (1910).
66. ——, U.S. Patent 1,588,384 (1926).
67. Hoffmann and Kalischer, U.S. Patent 660,058 (1900).
68. I. G. Farbenindustrie, BIOS 983, pp. 43, 71 (PB 79226).
69. ——, *ibid.*, p. 44.
70. ——, *ibid.*, p. 45.
71. ——, *ibid.*, pp. 45, 83–86
72. ——, *ibid.*, p. 46.
73. ——, *ibid.*, p. 47.
74. ——, *ibid.*, p. 49.
75. ——, *ibid.*, p. 50.
76. ——, *ibid.*, p. 51.
77. ——, *ibid.*, p. 64.
78. ——, *ibid.*, p. 117.
79. ——, BIOS 1155, p. 5 (PB 79309).
80. ——, *ibid.*, p. 12.
81. ——, *ibid.*, p. 16.
82. ——, *ibid.*, p. 20.
83. ——, *ibid.*, p. 23.
84. ——, *ibid.*, pp. 23–32.
85. ——, *ibid.*, p. 24.
86. ——, *ibid.*, p. 25.
87. ——, *ibid.*, p. 26.
88. ——, *ibid.*, p. 31.
89. ——, *ibid.*, pp. 33–34.
90. ——, *ibid.*, p. 37.
91. ——, *ibid.*, p. 38.
92. ——, *ibid.*, p. 39.
93. ——, *ibid.*, p. 41.
94. ——, *ibid.*, p. 42.
95. ——, Economic Study—Tabulations (PB 548–561).
96. ——, FIAT 1313, Vol. II, p. 304 (PB 85172).
97. ——, *ibid.*, p. 310.
98. ——, *ibid.*, Vol. III, p. 228.
99. ——, *ibid.*, pp. 228–234.
100. ——, *ibid.*, p. 238.
101. ——, *ibid.*, p. 247.
102. ——, PB 74236, frames 201–221.
103. ——, *ibid.*, frames 760–772.
104. Jaeckel, U.S. Patent 896,916 (1908).
105. Jones and Reid, *J. Am. Chem. Soc.*, **54**, 4393 (1932).
106. Justin-Mueller, *Bull. Soc. Ind. Mulhouse*, **94,** 185 (1928); *C.A.*, **22**, 3781 (1928).

107. Kalischer, U.S. Patent 610,541 (1898).
108. —— and Ritter, U.S. Patent 1,759,261 (1930).
109. Keller and Fierz-David, Helv. Chim. Acta, 16, 585 (1933).
110. Kertess, Melliand Textilber., 8, 56 (1927).
111. Khmelnitzkaya, Anilinokrasochnaya Prom., 1, 22 (1931); C.A., 28, 5244 (1934).
112. —— and Werchowskaja, ibid., 2, 31 (1932); C.A., 26, 4590 (1932).
113. —— and ——, ibid., 5, 67 (1935); C.A., 29, 4943 (1935).
114. Kraus, U.S. Patent 727,387 (1903).
115. Kubota, J. Chem. Soc. Japan, 55, 565 (1934); C.A., 28, 5448 (1934).
116. Lange, "Die Schwefelfarbstoffe," 2nd ed., p. 167, Leipzig, O. Spamer, 1925.
117. Levinstein and Naef, U.S. Patent 802,049 (1905).
118. Lubs and Strouse, U.S. Patent 1,944,250 (1934).
119. Mueller and Stober, U.S. Patent 1,165,531 (1915).
120. Nanson, Textile Colorist, 48, 239, 383 (1926).
121. Poirrier, U.S. Patent 561,276 (1896).
122. ——, U.S. Patent 561,277 (1896).
123. Priebs and Kaltwasser, U.S. Patent 655,659 (1900).
124. Reinhart and Hoerlin, U.S. Patent 1,026,881 (1912).
125. Ris, U.S. Patent 696,751 (1902).
126. —— and Mylius, U.S. Patent 722,630 (1903).
127. Robeson, U.S. Patent 1,316,742 (1919).
128. Rongger, U.S. Patent 747,643 (1903).
129. Rowe, "Colour Index," Soc. Dyers Colourists (1924 edition).
130. Schmidt, U.S. Patent 892,455 (1908).
131. Seidel, U.S. Patent 687,581 (1901).
132. Selivanov, Chemie et Ind. 25, 1497 (1931); C.A., 25, 5565 (1931).
133. Thauss and Guenther, U.S. Patent 1,450,463 (1923), Re 17,940 (1931).
134. Valpiana, thesis, Eidg. Tech. Hochschule, Zurich (1946).
135. Vidal, U.S. Patent 618,152 (1899).
136. ——, Mon. scient., (4) 11, 655 (1897).
137. ——, ibid., (4) 17, 427 (1903); Chem. Zentr., 1903, II, 266.
138. Vidal and Poirrier, U.S. Patent 532,484 (1895).
139. —— and ——, U.S. Patent 532,503 (1895).
140. ——, U.S. Patent 549,036 (1895).
141. Weinberg and Herz, U.S. Patent 693,632 (1902).
142. —— and ——, U.S. Patent 693,633 (1902).
143. ——, U.S. Patent 701,435 (1902).
144. —— and Lange, U.S. Patent 712,747 (1902).
145. —— and ——, U.S. Patent 714,542 (1902).
146. ——, Ber., 63A, 117 (1930).
147. Zaenker, Faerber-Ztg., 27, 273 (1916); Chem. Zentr., 1916, II, 1200.
148. ——, Z. angew. Chem., 32, 49 (1919).
149. Zerweck, Ritter and Schubert, Z. angew. Chem., A60, 141 (1948).

7. ANTHRAQUINONE DYES AND INTERMEDIATES

INTRODUCTORY COMMENTS

Melvin A. Perkins

9,10-Anthraquinone and all its derivatives, as well as iso- and hetero-cyclic compounds related to it or built up from it, can be considered as colored compounds. In order to possess sufficient color for use as a dye, however, the anthraquinone molecule must be substituted in specific ways or else increased resonance must be accumulated by building up more highly condensed systems. Thus a line is drawn between intermediates of the anthraquinone series and dyes derivable therefrom. This dividing line becomes less sharp however when we consider that some intermediates are capable of yielding satisfactory dyeings on certain fibers such as cellulose acetate, nylon, "Dacron" polyester fiber and "Orlon" acrylic fiber. For this reason, anthraquinone intermediates and dyes are treated in this same chapter, although in separate sections.

The economic importance of anthraquinone colors and their rate of growth can be seen from the fact that total sales value of these products in the United States increased from $12 million in 1935 to $43 million in 1948 and to over $60 million in 1951! Of the 1948 value, 81 per cent was due to vat dyes, 13 per cent to acid dyes and 6 per cent to disperse types. The very small sales of metallizable types are included with acid dyes in this case.

Both acid and disperse type anthraquinone colors, as they appear on the market at the present time, supplement dyes of other classes, particularly azo and (to a much lesser extent) triphenylmethane, azine and dioxazine colors. The generalization can be made that acid types and disperse type anthraquinones in largest volume use are those which give blue, violet, green, olive, brown and gray shades while the supplementary azo colors, for example, are mostly in the yellow, orange, red and black range. Thus this holds true for the colors presently used for dyeing cellulose acetate, nylon and wool. When it comes to cotton dyes, however, the situation is quite different.

Historically, the metallizable colors as typified by alizarin red or purpurin were very important for a long time but they have been largely replaced by dyes which may be more expensive but which give more reliable results and which can be applied with less expenditure of time and effort. This is true of the vat colors. They have the further advantage of providing an essentially complete shade range.

As a class, anthraquinone colors are generally considered to have excellent fastness properties, superior to those of other chemical classes. However, such generalizations are misleading in the dye field and can be made honestly only with certain reservations. Outstanding individual dyes are to be found in many different chemical classes. Perhaps a larger number of products with outstanding fastness properties are to be found in the anthraquinone field than in any other single class, and this is particularly true of anthraquinone vat colors. These show very good fastness to washing on all fibers when properly applied. On cellulosic and wool fibers (as well as on some of the new man-made fibers such as "Orlon" acrylic fiber) they also show good to excellent lightfastness.

Coloring materials of the anthraquinone class are often used for purposes other than the dyeing of textile fibers. Examples of this are to be found in the coloration of paper, rubber, paints, printing inks, plastics for various uses, petroleum products, etc. Since the present work deals with the chemistry of dyes rather than with their uses, these latter are referred to only as indicating relative importance of the products discussed.

Classification

For purposes of this monograph, anthraquinone compounds of technical importance will be discussed under the following broad headings:
(1) Intermediates.
(2) Acid Dyes (for wool, nylon, "Orlon" acrylic fiber, etc.).
(3) Disperse Dyes (for cellulose acetate, nylon, "Dacron" polyester fiber, etc.).
(4) Metallizable Dyes (for mordanted cotton and wool).
(5) Vat Dyes (for cellulosic and miscellaneous fibers).
This last type is subdivided into carbocyclic and heterocyclic quinones and solubilized vat dyes.

For the purpose of completeness, all types of quinonoid vat colors are considered regardless of whether they are strictly "anthraquinone" or not (e.g., benzoquinones, naphthoquinones as well as quinones containing 4, 5, 6 or more condensed rings). Intermediates just one step removed from the dyes are discussed along with the latter, while those further removed are considered in the section on Intermediates which follows.

ANTHRAQUINONE INTERMEDIATES

Frederick B. Stilmar and Melvin A. Perkins

The synthesis and properties of 9,10-anthraquinone, its commonly known substitution products and benzanthrones derived from anthraquinone are discussed under the following headings:

Chemical Reactivity of Anthraquinone
Synthesis of the Anthraquinone Ring System
Preparation and Reactions of Haloanthraquinones
Preparation and Reactions of Nitroanthraquinones
Preparation and Reactions of Anthraquinonesulfonic Acids
Preparation and Reactions of Alkylanthraquinones, Anthraquinonecarboxylic Acids and Aldehydes
Preparation and Reactions of Aminoanthraquinones
Preparation and Reactions of Hydroxyanthraquinones
Preparation and Reactions of Anthraquinone Ethers
Preparation and Reactions of Anthraquinonethiols and Thioethers
Preparation and Reactions of Leucoquinizarin and Leuco-1,4-diaminoanthraquinones
Benzanthrone Intermediates

Chemical Reactivity of 9,10-Anthraquinone

Anthraquinone is relatively unreactive, being stable even at rather high temperatures toward sulfuric acid, nitric acid and the usual halogenating agents. In addition to being resistant to attack by the above electrophilic reagents, anthraquinone also resists attack by nucleophilic reagents such as sodium hydroxide. Yet, under drastic conditions, both types of reagents yield substituted anthraquinones as illustrated below[48, 192]:

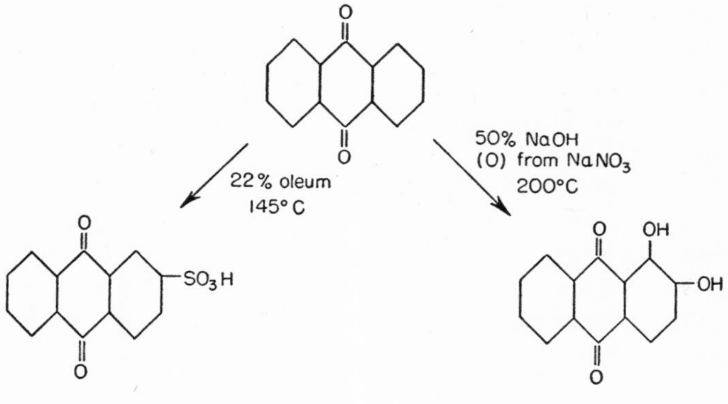

The chemical inertness of anthraquinone is somewhat similar to that of nitrobenzene, both compounds having electron-deficient systems[193].

The polarization of the C=O dipole and the relaying of the positive charge both to alpha and beta positions may be represented as follows:

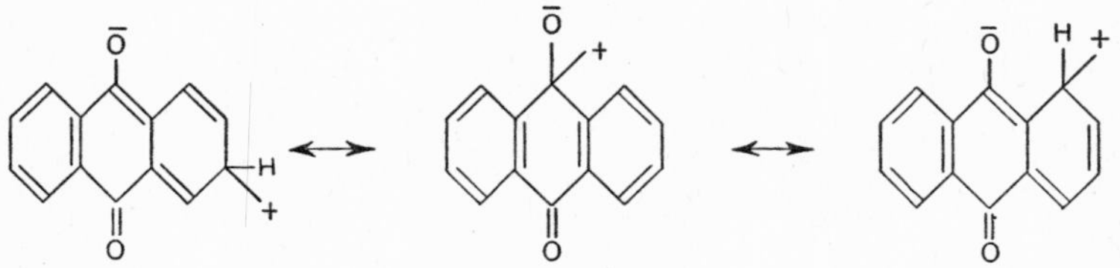

The properties of the carbonyl groups in anthraquinone are subdued, as would be expected from the structure. A ketone reagent such as hydroxylamine yields an oxime only under "forcing" conditions (180°C).

Anthraquinone is not reduced by sulfur dioxide (cf. benzoquinone) and yields anthrahydroquinone only with powerful reducing agents such as sodium hydrosulfite and formamidinesulfinic acid. This results from the larger resonance energy of anthraquinone as compared to that of benzoquinone. The reduction potentials are a measurement of this effect:

Benzoquinone	$E_0^{alc.}$	0.715 volts
Naphthoquinone	$E_0^{alc.}$	0.484 volts
Anthraquinone	$E_0^{alc.}$	0.154 volts.

Synthesis of the Anthraquinone Ring

o-**Benzoylbenzoic Acid Route.** Phthalic anhydride is the cornerstone of the anthraquinone dye industry, reaction with benzene and aluminum chloride yielding *o*-benzoylbenzoic acid in high yield and purity[220]. Ringclosure of this intermediate, or of its substituted derivatives, with concentrated sulfuric acid or oleum gives the corresponding anthraquinone. The following reactions are illustrative[15, 74, 136, 242].

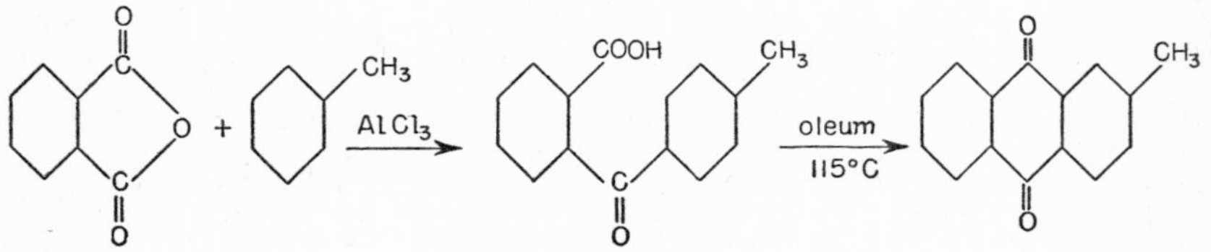

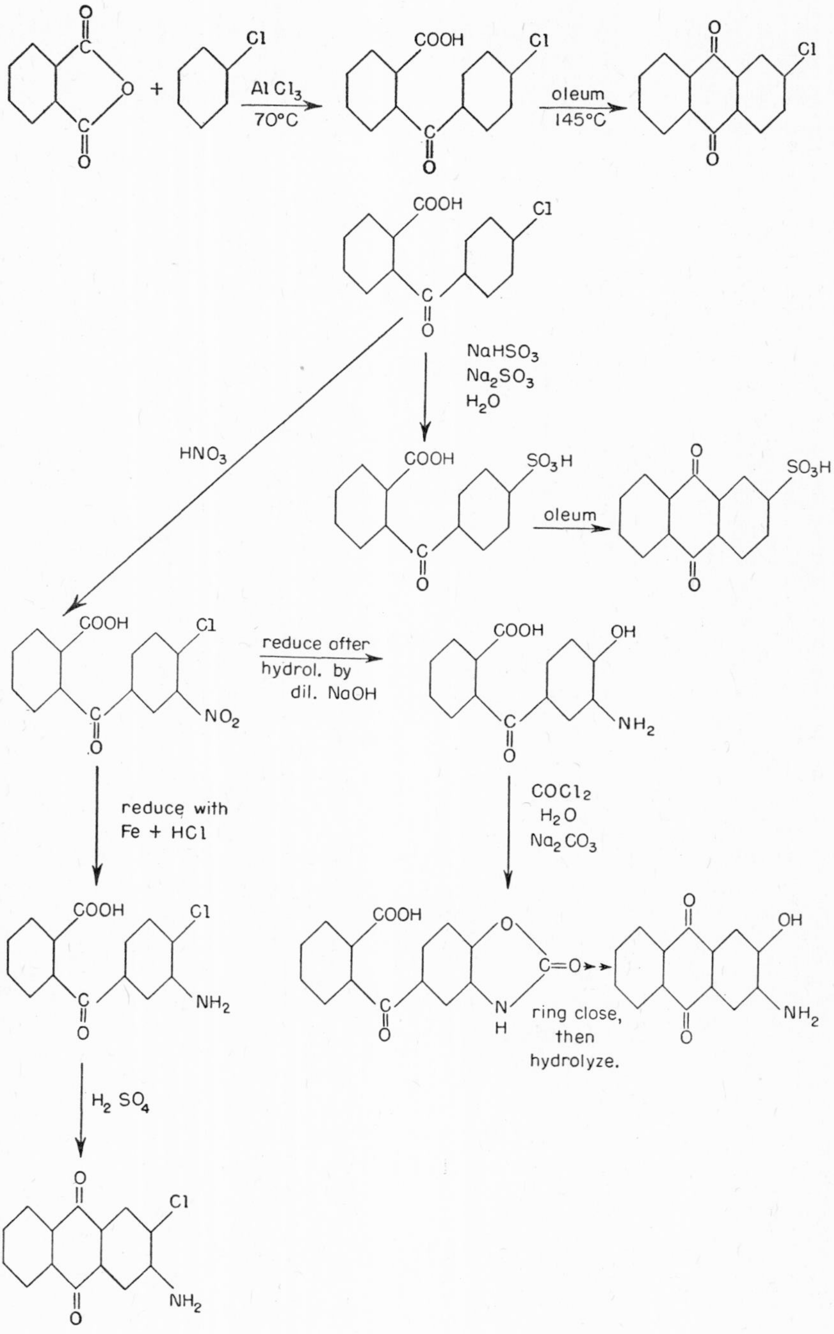
Cl
AlCl3
70°C
COOH
oleum
145°C
NaHSO3
Na2SO3
H2O
HNO3
SO3H
reduce after
hydrol. by
dil. NaOH
OH
NO2
NH2
reduce with
Fe + HCl
COCl2
H2O
Na2CO3
ring close,
then
hydrolyze.
H2 SO4

The anthraquinone ring-closure probably proceeds through an intermediate 3-phenylphthalidyl sulfate.

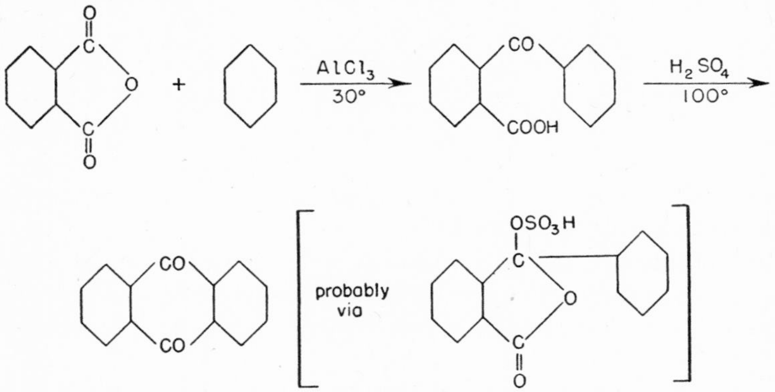

When *o*-benzoylbenzoic acid is ring-closed to anthraquinone, the product is rarely isolated as such but is usually carried on to benzanthrone (see page **377**) or to 1-anthraquinonesulfonic acid (see page 352) in situ.

Weaker "acid" condensing agents may often assist condensation, for example in the following[22, 258]:

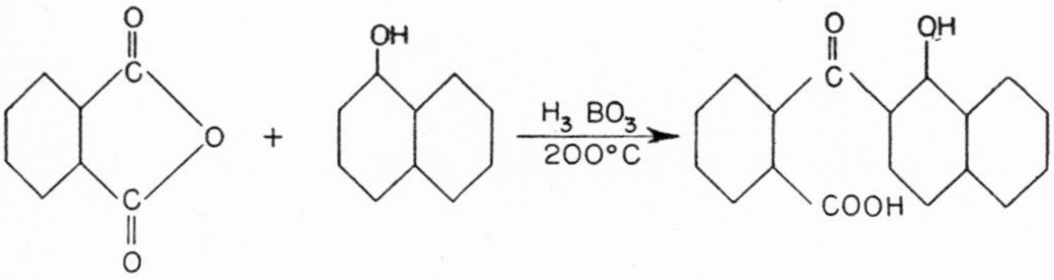

The preparation of quinizarin from phthalic anhydride and *p*-chlorophenol is undoubtedly a special case of the *o*-benzoylbenzoic acid synthesis. This reaction is unique in that sulfuric acid acts as a condensing agent to form the *o*-benzoylbenzoic acid derivative, as a ring-closing agent, and also as a hydrolytic agent for the intermediate 1-chloro-4-hydroxyanthraquinone[216].

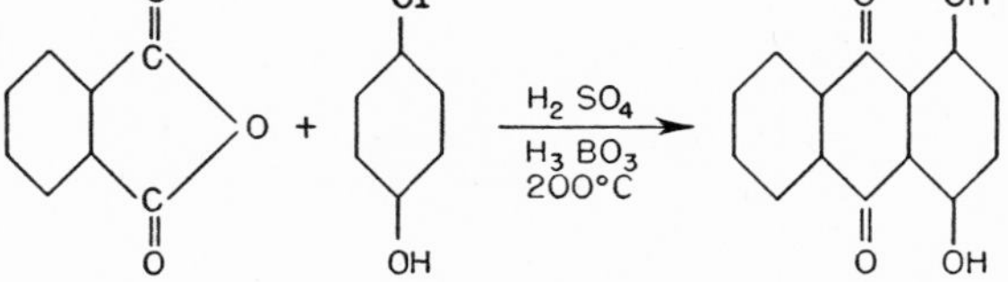

Aluminum chloride can be substituted for sulfuric acid in this reaction[58], but chlorine is thereby retained.

Quinizarin also results from hydroquinone when aluminum chloride is employed as condensing agent:

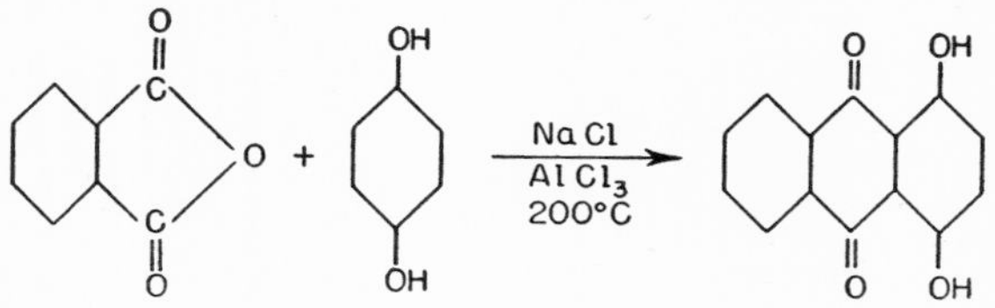

If the fusion is carried out at 125°C, the corresponding o-benzoylbenzoic acid derivative may be isolated[263].

Diaryl phthalides are often formed as by-products in the o-benzoylbenzoic acid synthesis. The use of tetrachloroethane as a solvent helps to prevent this difficulty, which is particularly evident in phenol condensations[243, 249].

An amino o-benzoylbenzoic acid can sometimes be obtained from certain acetanilides, for instance[190]:

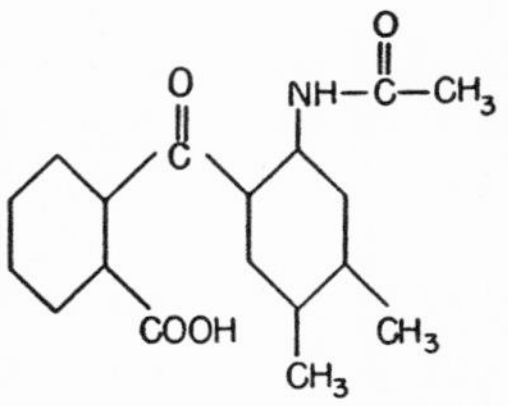

Finally, phthalimides can be rearranged as illustrated below[19]:

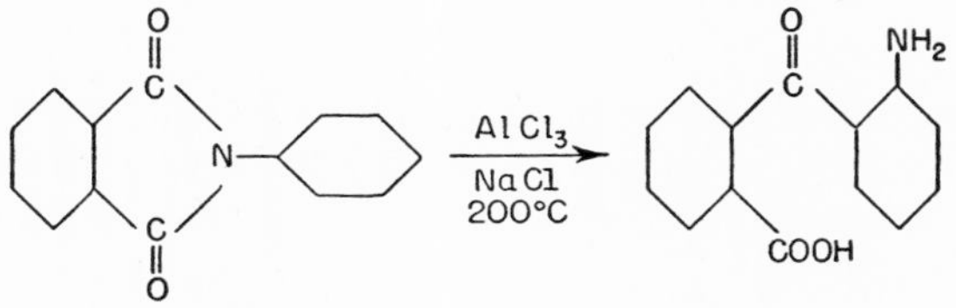

Occasionally, heat in the presence of sulfuric acid is sufficient to cause both condensation and ring-closure without the aid of boric acid[6].

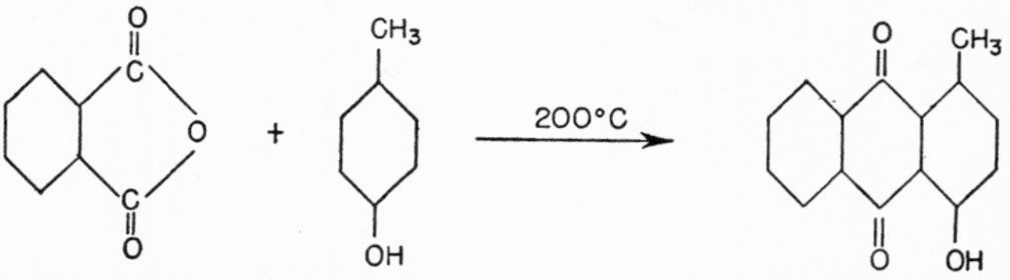

Widespread use has been made of the Grignard reagent in preparing complicated o-benzoylbenzoic acids[257]:

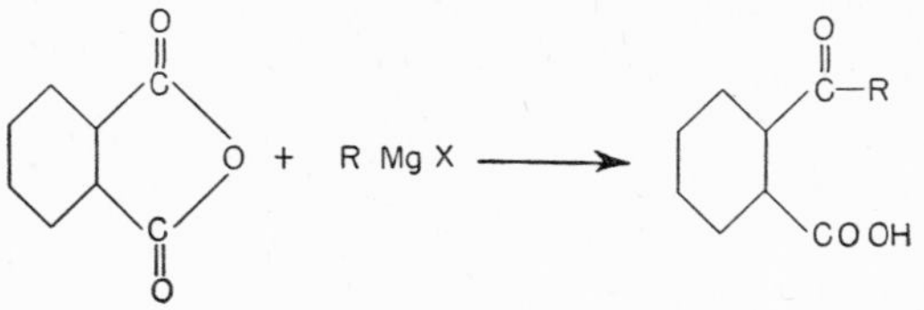

Occasionally an *o*-benzoylbenzoic acid resists ring-closure in which case the *o*-benzylbenzoic acid may be used[5, 234]. The latter is best obtained by reducing the former by means of zinc and ammonia according to the reaction:

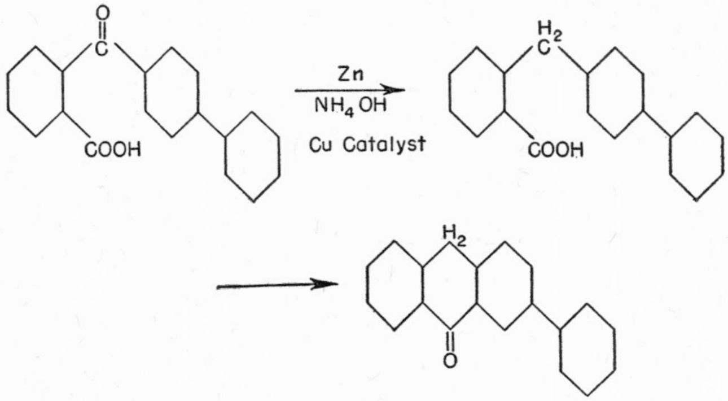

The anthrone may then be oxidized to the anthraquinone.

As a variation, the benzylbenzoic acid may be ring-closed to the anthryl acetate[30] and subsequently oxidized to the anthraquinone:

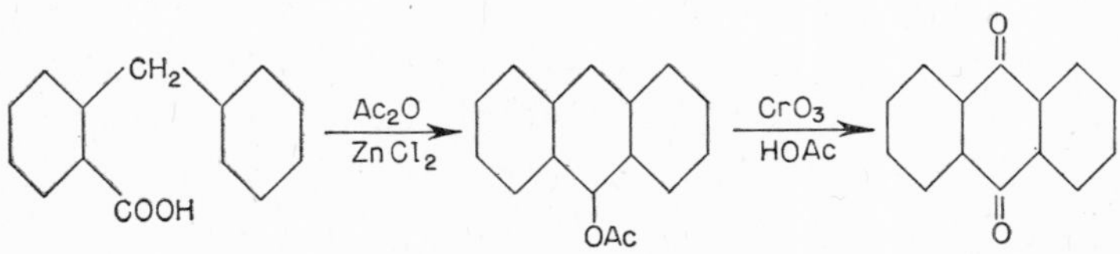

Occasionally, substituents can migrate during the *o*-benzoylbenzoic acid condensation due to the action of the condensing agent, anhydrous aluminum chloride:

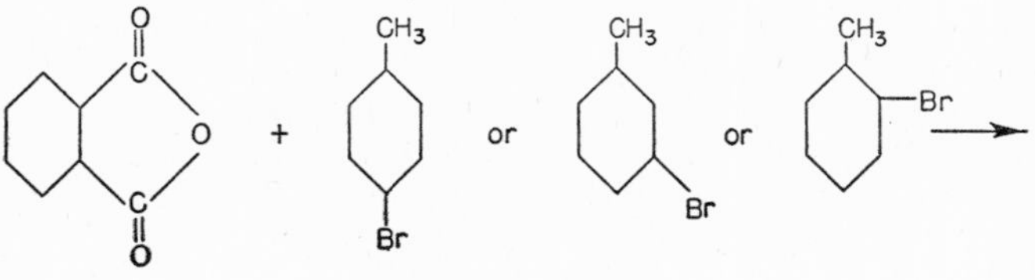

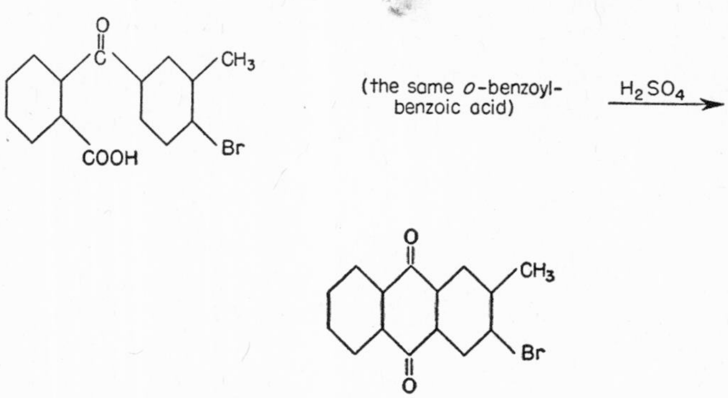

(the same *o*-benzoyl-benzoic acid) $\xrightarrow{H_2SO_4}$

Although the bromine wanders, chlorine in the chlorotoluenes behaves normally[80].

Although sulfuric acid is the most common ring-closing agent, mention should be made of P_2O_5 in nitrobenzene[252], anhydrous HF[17] and benzoyl chloride with a trace of sulfuric acid[252].

An interesting rearrangement of a 2,6-disubstituted benzophenone, without ring-closure, has been reported[78].

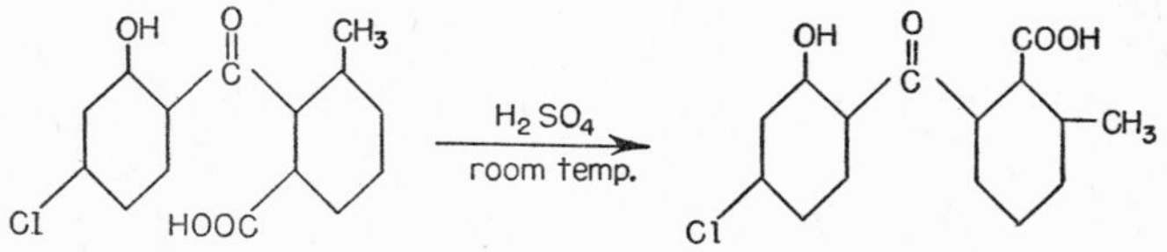

A rearrangement with subsequent ring-closure has been reported in special cases, under drastic conditions[31, 32].

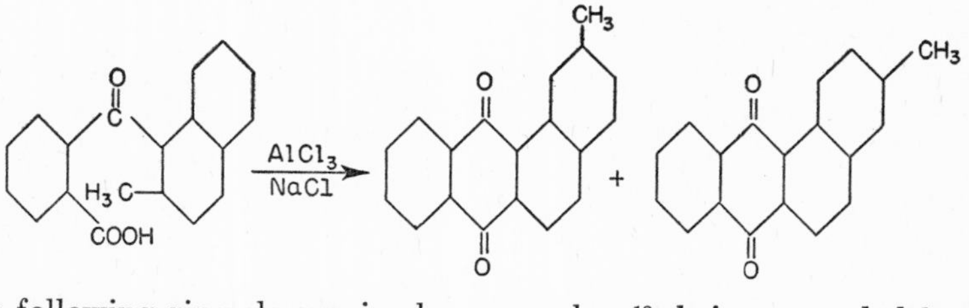

The following ring-closure is also anomalous[18], being preceded by rearrangement:

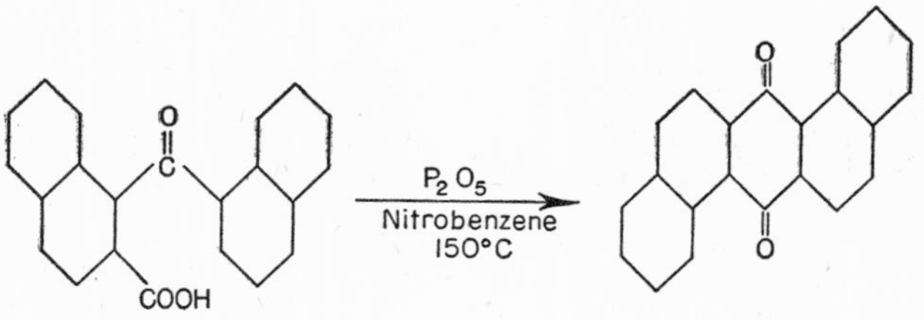

Anthracene Route to Anthraquinone. Anthracene from coal tar is contaminated with phenanthrene and carbazole; the latter impurity yields harmful contaminants when oxidized. An efficient 85 per cent sulfuric acid countercurrent extraction is claimed to remove the carbazole leaving anthracene of high purity.

The I.G. Farbenindustrie process for anthraquinone involved the oxidation of anthracene with dichromate in 25 per cent sulfuric acid and subliming the crude reaction product[127].

A survey of anthracene derivatives as obtained by the Elbs reaction can be found in "Organic Reactions"[29]. The simplest case is shown below and the reaction has been utilized to prepare many alkylanthracenes as well as anthraquinonecarboxylic acids[26]:

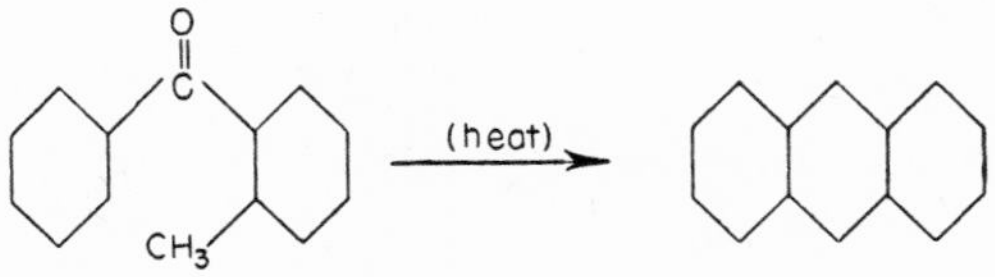

Diene Route to Anthraquinone. Anthraquinone results smoothly when *p*-benzoquinone is condensed with two moles of butadiene and the octahydroanthraquinone adduct is oxidized[24, 201]:

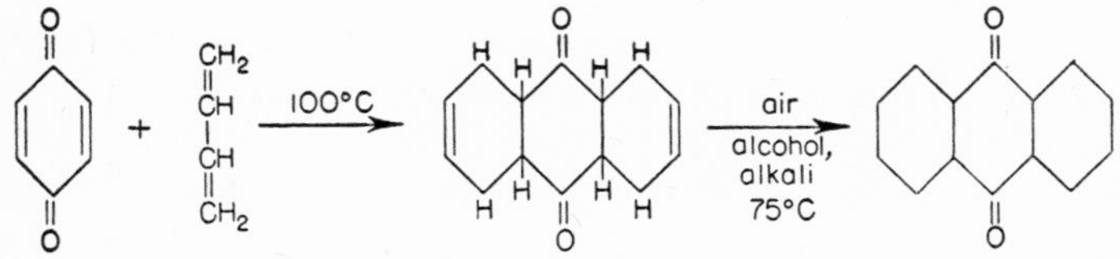

The diene method is subject to wide variation as the intermediate tetrahydronaphthoquinone may be condensed with a different diene[24], e.g.:

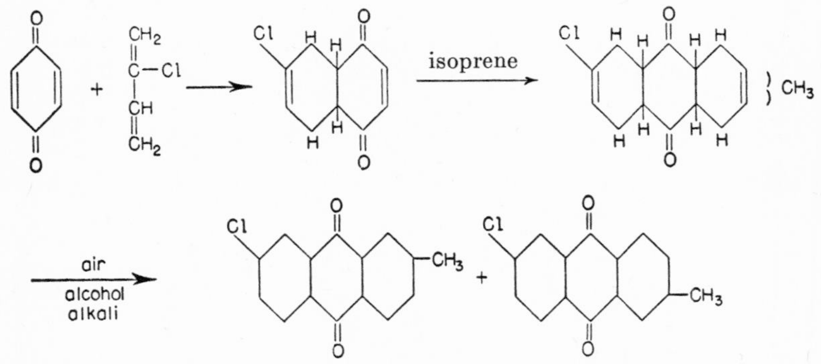

A limiting factor in this synthesis is the polymerizing tendency of the diene.

2-Chloro-1,3-butadiene is not sufficiently stable thermally to be used in the second step with good results.

An isobenzofuran may replace the diene[9], in which case the aromatic system is produced directly:

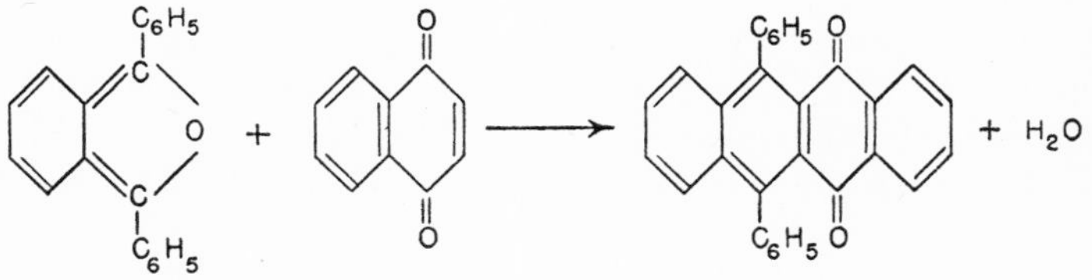

A summary of the diene reaction and the preparation of complicated isocyclic anthraquinones is given in "Chemical Reviews"[209].

Haloanthraquinones

Preparation of Chloroanthraquinones. The direct chlorination of anthraquinone in oleum cannot be controlled to yield a monochloro product, but 1,4,5,8-tetrachloroanthraquinone can be prepared by this route[7, 51]. Careful chlorination of 2-methylanthraquinone yields the 1-chloro derivative[137].

2-Chloroanthraquinone is best prepared from o-(p-chlorobenzoyl)benzoic acid as described previously[3].

Replacement of Sulfo Groups, Nitro Groups. A technically important method is the replacement of either an alpha or a beta sulfo group by nascent chlorine (from $KClO_3$ and HCl at the boil).

The following table lists a number of such replacements, all of which were effected at 100°C by treating the aqueous sulfonic acid with hydrochloric acid and gradually adding sodium or potassium chlorate solution.

Anthraquinone Starting Material	Anthraquinone Reaction Product	Ref.
1-SO₃H	1-Cl	135
1,5-Di-SO₃H	1,5-Di-Cl	135
1,8-Di-SO₃H	1,8-Di-Cl	135
2,6-Di-SO₃H	2,6-Di-Cl	99, 135
1-SO₃H-5-NO₂	1-Cl-5-NO₂	99, 135

Of limited importance is the replacement of the nitro group by gaseous chlorine at high temperature[53, 55].

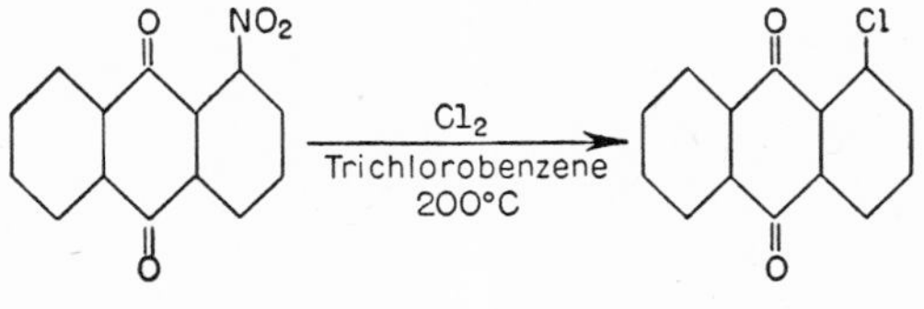

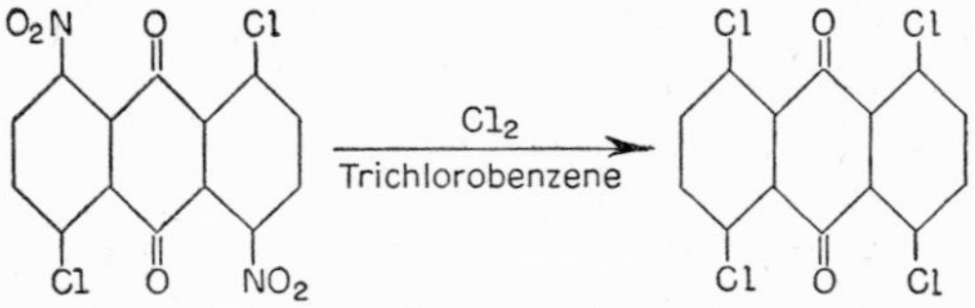

Direct Halogenation. Many substituted anthraquinones such as alkyl, hydroxy and amino derivatives are readily chlorinated by using relatively mild reagents such as sulfuryl chloride. Definite chloro derivatives are obtained in good yields. Some illustrations of these reactions, and of the direct chlorination of anthraquinone, are given in the following table.

Anthraquinone Starting Material	Reaction Conditions	Anthraquinone Reaction Product	Ref.
Anthraquinone	Cl_2 oleum	1,4,5,8-Tetra-Cl	7, 51
2-CH_3	Cl_2 H_2SO_4	1-Cl-2-CH_3	137
2-NH_2	SO_2Cl_2 nitrobenzene, 30°C	1-Cl-2-NH_2	134
1-C_6H_5CONH	SO_2Cl_2 nitrobenzene, 60°C	1-C_6H_5CONH-4-Cl	133
1,4-Di-NH_2	SO_2Cl_2 nitrobenzene, 45°C	1,4-Di-NH_2 2,3-Di-Cl	120
1,5-Di-NH_2	SO_2Cl_2 o-dichlorobenzene, 75°C	1,5-Di-NH_2 2,4,6,8-Tetra-Cl	164
3,7-Di-NH_2 2,6-Di-SO_3H	Cl_2, H_2O 30°C	3,7-Di-NH_2 4,8-Di-Cl 2,6-Di-SO_3H	217

Bromoanthraquinones. Bromoanthraquinones are frequently used for synthetic work. They often result in good yields from the action of free bromine or nascent bromine on the properly substituted anthraquinone. A molecular mixture of sulfuryl chloride and bromine often yields the pure bromo derivative with evolution of HCl[212]. Other oxidizing agents such as sodium hypochlorite or sodium chlorate can be used in aqueous brominations, permitting full utilization of the bromine[160].

Although the sulfo group in 1-anthraquinonesulfonic acid is replaced by bromine only at 250°C[21], 3-amino-2-anthraquinonesulfonic acid readily yields 2-amino-1,3-dibromoanthraquinone when treated with bromine in aqueous solution at 80° or below[247]. Likewise, 1-amino-2,4-dibromoanthraquinone is obtained in the aqueous bromination of 1-amino-2-anthraquinonesulfonic acid along with the intermediate 1-amino-4-bromo-2-anthraquinonesulfonic acid (see following table).

Preparation of Bromoanthraquinones by Bromination.

Anthraquinone Starting Material	Reaction Conditions	Anthraquinone Reaction Product	Ref.
$1\text{-}NH_2$	Br_2 , nitrobenzene	$1\text{-}NH_2$ 2,4-Di-Br	245
$1\text{-}NH_2\text{-}2\text{-}SO_3H$	Br_2 , H_2O, NaOCl	$1\text{-}NH_2\text{-}4\text{-}Br\text{-}2\text{-}SO_3H$ and $1\text{-}NH_2\text{-}2,4\text{-}Di\text{-}Br$	160
$2\text{-}NH_2$	Br_2 , dil. H_2SO_4	$2\text{-}NH_2\text{-}1,3\text{-}Di\text{-}Br$	247
$1\text{-}CH_3NH$	$Br_2 + Cl_2$, H_2O, HCl	$1\text{-}Br\text{-}4\text{-}CH_3NH$	165
$1\text{-}OH$	Br_2 , HOAc, NaOAc	$1\text{-}Br\text{-}4\text{-}OH$	37
$1,4\text{-}Di\text{-}OH$	Br_2 , nitrobenzene	$2\text{-}Br\text{-}1,4\text{-}Di\text{-}OH$	116

Reactivity of Haloanthraquinones. 1-Chloroanthraquinone is more reactive than 2-chloroanthraquinone as is illustrated in the following table where it is shown that the formation of the beta isomers requires more drastic conditions. (N. R. means "no reaction" and it is understood that "anthraquinone" is the essential nucleus involved throughout, except in the first column.)

Chemical Reagent	Substituent Introduced (anthraquinone deriv.)	Reaction Conditions for 1-Chloro	Ref.	Reaction Conditions for 2-Chloro	Ref.
KOH, CH_3OH	CH_3O-	80°C	52	130°C	52
$p\text{-}CH_3C_6H_4NH_2$, Cu cat.	C_7H_7NH-	120°C amyl alc.	256	N.R.	—
H_2NNH_2	H_2NNH-	115°C pyridine	207	170°C pyridine	207
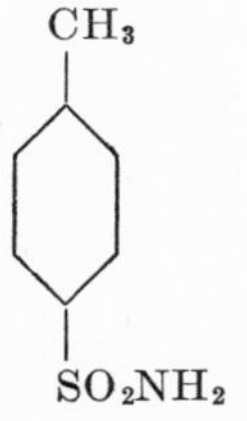 CH₃ structure with SO₂NH₂	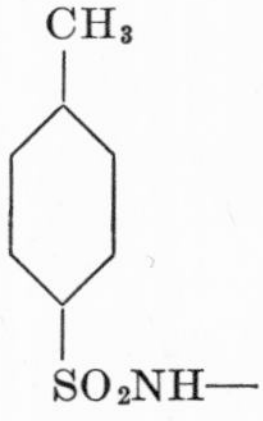 CH₃ structure with SO₂NH—	Na_2CO_3 , Cu cat. nitrobenzene 180°C	246	N.R.	246

Chemical Reagent	Substituent Introduced (anthraquinone deriv.)	Reaction Conditions for 1-Chloro	Ref.	Reaction Conditions for 2-Chloro	Ref.
CuCN	NC—	200°C PhCH$_2$CN	35	N.R. at 240°C	35
1-NH$_2$AQ	1-AQ-NH—	180°C Na$_2$CO$_3$, Cu cat. nitrobenzene	248	210°C Na$_2$CO$_3$, Cu cat. nitrobenzene	—
Na$_2$S$_x$	HS—	80°C	41	130°C	41, 50
conc. NH$_4$OH	H$_2$N—	ca. 160°C	—	210°C	77, 130

The greater reactivity of the alpha chlorine is also shown in 1,6-dichloro-anthraquinone which yields 1-amino-6-chloroanthraquinone by the *p*-toluenesulfonamide route at 180°C[259].

Furthermore, 1,3-dichloroanthraquinone yields 1-amino-3-chloroanthra-quinone with NH$_4$OH at 170°C[173], and it is important to avoid exceeding this temperature. 1,3-Dibromoanthraquinone is also aminated preferentially in the 1 position[245].

The reactivity of the halogen in anthraquinone increases in the order Cl < Br < I[191].

A negative group in ortho position activates the chlorine in anthraquinone as would be expected. 1-Chloro-2-anthraquinonecarboxylic acid reacts with many amines in aqueous solution at 50 to 100°C in the presence of a copper catalyts[261].

The beta chlorine of 3-chloro-2-anthraquinonecarboxylic acid reacts with ammonia at 140°C in the presence of a copper catalyst[121].

Surprisingly, 2-amino-1-chloroanthraquinone reacts more readily with sodium polysulfide than does 1-chloroanthraquinone. The reason for this anomalous behavior may possibly be a tautomeric form that confers quinonoid activity on the outer ring and hence activates the chlorine.

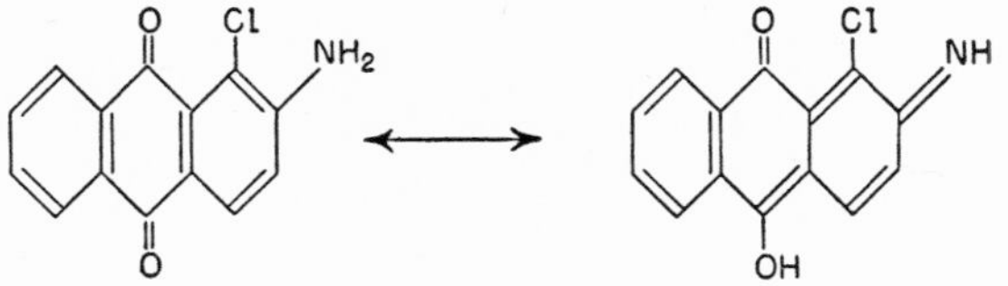

The numerous reactions of haloanthraquinones with amines will be listed in the section on Aminoanthraquinones.

Two moles of 1-chloro-2-methylanthraquinone combine when heated with copper to yield 2,2'-dimethyl-1,1'-bianthraquinone (intermediate for pyranthrone[227]) as shown.

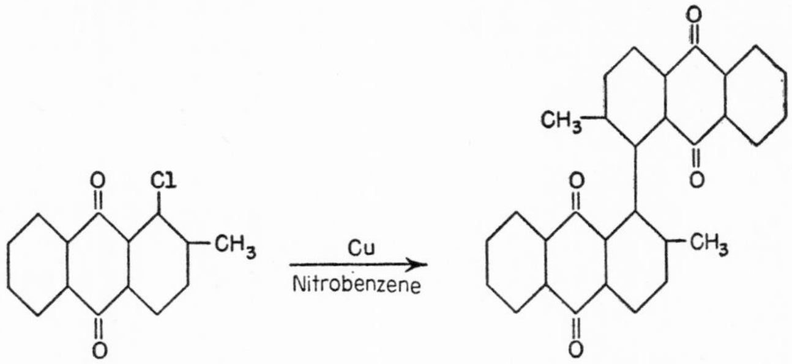

2-Chloroanthraquinone is too unreactive to undergo coupling to the biaryl derivative, although the coupling of the more reactive 2-iodoanthraquinone has been reported[27, 234]. The selective coupling of 1,3-dichloroanthraquinone to 3,3'-dichloro-1,1'-bianthraquinone has been reported[25].

Hydrolysis of Haloanthraquinones. Certain haloanthraquinones can be hydrolyzed in strong sulfuric acid to the hydroxy derivative. A para amino or a para hydroxy group strongly aids this replacement.

Acid Hydrolysis of Anthraquinone Halogen Compounds.

Starting Material	Reaction Conditions	Reaction Product	Ref.
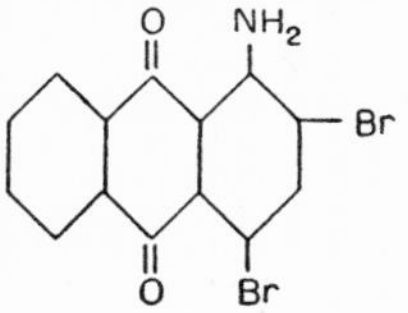	5% oleum H_3BO_3 120°C	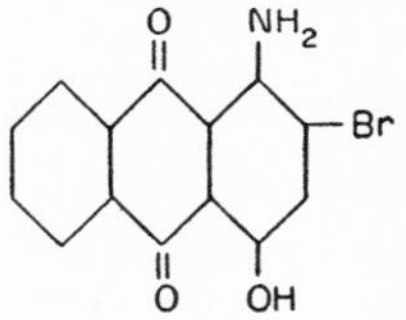	93
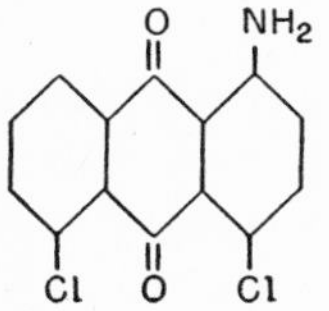	conc. H_2SO_4, H_3BO_3 145°C	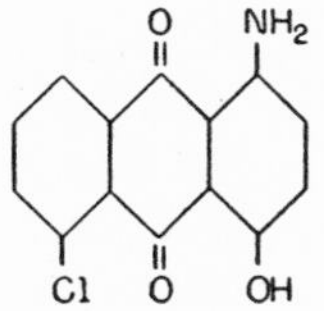	23
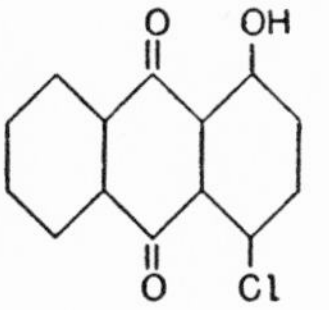	conc. H_2SO_4, H_3BO_3 160°C	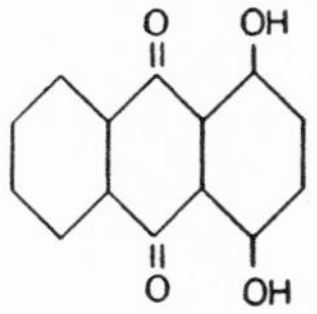	244
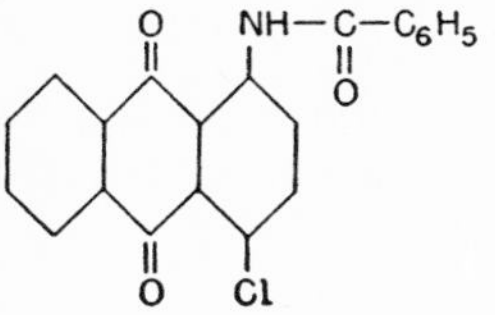	weak oleum 140°C H_3BO_3	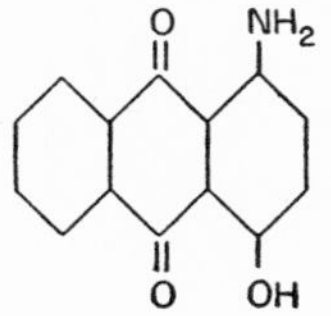	154

Starting Material	Reaction Conditions	Reaction Product	Ref.

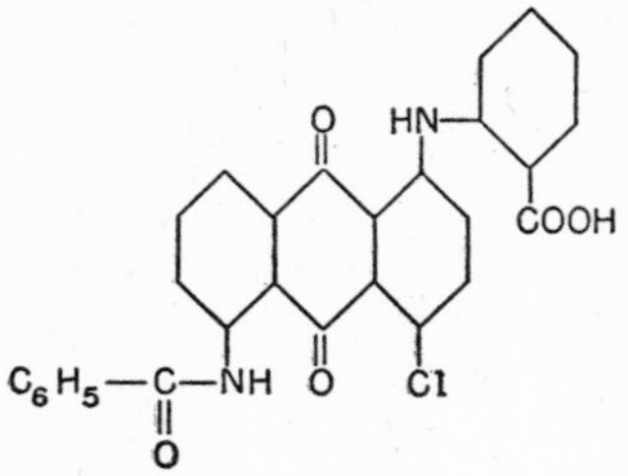

conc. H_2SO_4
30°C

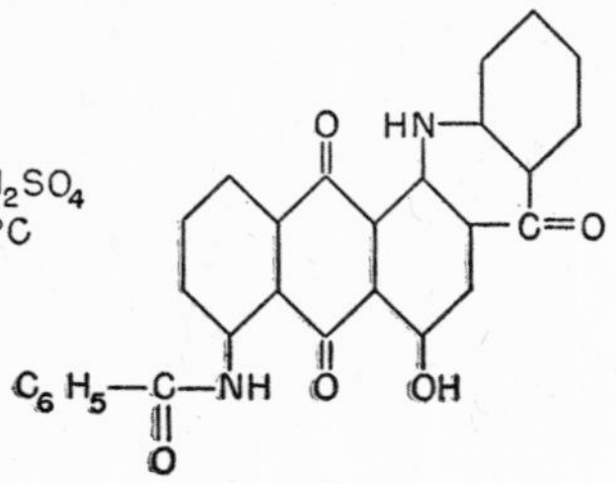

184

Nitroanthraquinones

Preparation. Anthraquinone is mainly nitrated in the 1 position when treated with nitric acid in sulfuric acid or by fuming nitric acid alone[8], but the resulting product is too impure for use to prepare the technically important 1-aminoanthraquinone. Nitration in 85 per cent sulfuric acid is claimed to give a pure product, as the resulting 1-nitroanthraquinone precipitates out of the reaction medium and is not further attacked[260]. Dinitration yields the mixed 1,5 and 1,8 isomers in addition to less well-defined products. The 1,5 isomer is separated by solvent or sulfuric acid crystallization.

The important 2-methyl-1-nitroanthraquinone and 5-nitro-1-anthraquinonesulfonic acid are prepared by direct nitration of 2-methylanthraquinone and of 1-anthraquinonesulfonic acid, respectively.

The nitration conditions are sufficiently drastic so that any hydroxy or amino groups present in the starting material must be protected (e.g., by H_3BO_3, CH_2O, or organic acyl groups).

Anthraquinone Nitrations.

Anthraquinone Starting Material	Reaction Conditions	Position of Entering Nitro Group	Ref.
Anthraquinone	85% H_2SO_4 , HNO_3	1	260
Anthraquinone	100% H_2SO_4 , HNO_3 80–100°C	1,5 and 1,8	163
2-CH₃	HNO_3 , H_2SO_4 14°C	1	88
1-SO₃H	HNO_3 , 96% H_2SO_4 95°C	5 (and 8)	119
1,8-Di-Cl	HNO_3 , 96% H_2SO_4 20°C	4	99
1-NH₂-2-COOH	CH_2O (to form a complex) HNO_3 , H_2SO_4 −5°C	4	147

Anthraquinone Starting Material	Reaction Conditions	Position of Entering Nitro Group	Ref.

1,5-Di-(—N—C—COOH) with H O		4,8	157
(SO₂ fused ring structure) (from 1,4-di-NH₂Aq and oleum)	HNO₃ , H₂SO₄	5	103
1-OH	H₃BO₃ , HNO₃ , H₂SO₄ 25°C	4	94
1-OCH₃	HNO₃ , H₂SO₄ 30°C	4	94
1,2-Di-OH	62% HNO₃ , o-Dichloro-benzene 40°C	3	102
1,5-Di-OC₆H₅	HNO₃ , 100% H₂SO₄	4,8 (additional nitration in C₆H₅O groups)	118
1,5-Di-OH 2,6-Di-SO₃H	HNO₃ , H₂SO₄ 50°C	4,8	158

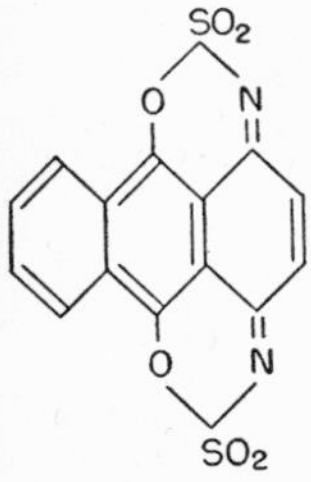

Reactivity of Nitroanthraquinones. Alpha-nitroanthraquinones undergo nucleophilic displacements in a manner analogous to that undergone by o-dinitrobenzene[81]. For example, 1-methoxyanthraquinone results from the reaction with methanol and caustic at 65°C which shows that 1-nitroanthraquinone is more active than 1-chloroanthraquinone in this type of displacement[42]. Other illustrations are given in the following table:

Reactions of Nitroanthraquinones with Nucleophilic Reagents.

Anthraquinone Starting Material	Reaction Conditions	Anthraquinone Reaction Product	Ref.
1-NO₂	KOH, CH₃OH 65°C	1-OCH₃	42
1-NO₂	Na₂SO₃ , H₂O 100°C	1-SO₃H	224
1-NO₂	C₆H₅NH₂ 180°C	1-NHC₆H₅	225

Anthraquinone Starting Material	Reaction Conditions	Anthraquinone Reaction Product	Ref.
1-NO₂-2-COOH	KOH, MgO, H₂O H₂NC₆H₄COOH(p) 100°C	1-NHC₆H₄COOH(p)- 2-COOH	92
1,5-Di-OH-4,8-Di-NO₂	C₆H₅NH₂ , H₂O 120°C	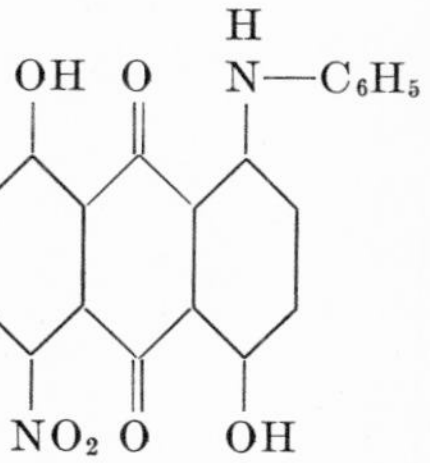	239

The reduction of nitroanthraquinones to the amines may be effected by treatment with hot sodium sulfide solution, sodium hydrosulfide, and also by vatting the nitro compound with alkaline hydrosulfite.

The nitro group may be replaced with chlorine under drastic conditions:

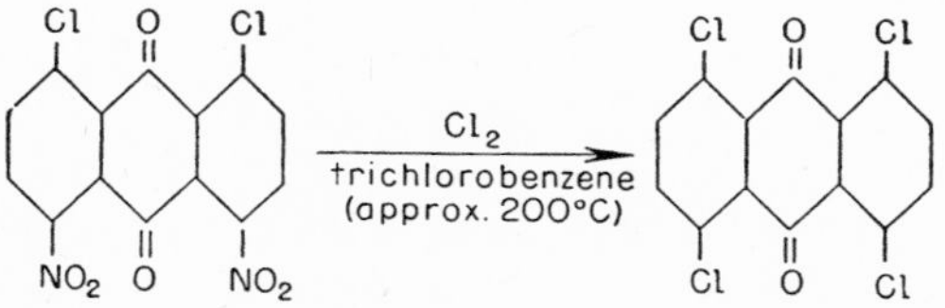

However, the nitro group is relatively unaffected in the following commercial process although some slight nitro replacement is claimed[119].

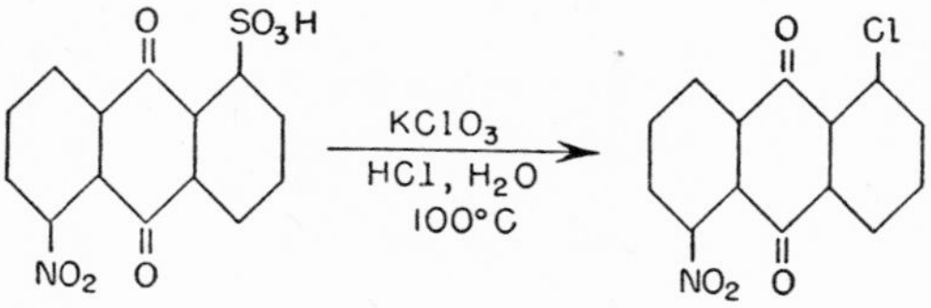

Anthraquinonesulfonic Acids

Preparation. Anthraquinone yields the 2 sulfonic acid with 22 per cent oleum at 145°C. Stronger oleum yields the 2,6 and 2,7 disulfonic acids. The 2,6 isomer may be crystallized out by gradually diluting the sulfonation mass, or it may be salted out in aqueous solution from the more soluble 2,7 isomer. The presence of one sulfonic acid group prevents any further sulfonation in the same ring.

A mercury catalyst in the oleum directs the sulfonic acid into the 1 position. Stronger oleum (40 per cent) with a mercury catalyst yields the mixed 1,5 and 1,8 disulfonic acids. The (symmetrical) 1,5 isomer is salted out from the more soluble 1,8 isomer after dilution.

Although mercury does influence certain other sulfonations, the effect is not nearly so pronounced as in the anthraquinone series[96, 142, 143, 144].

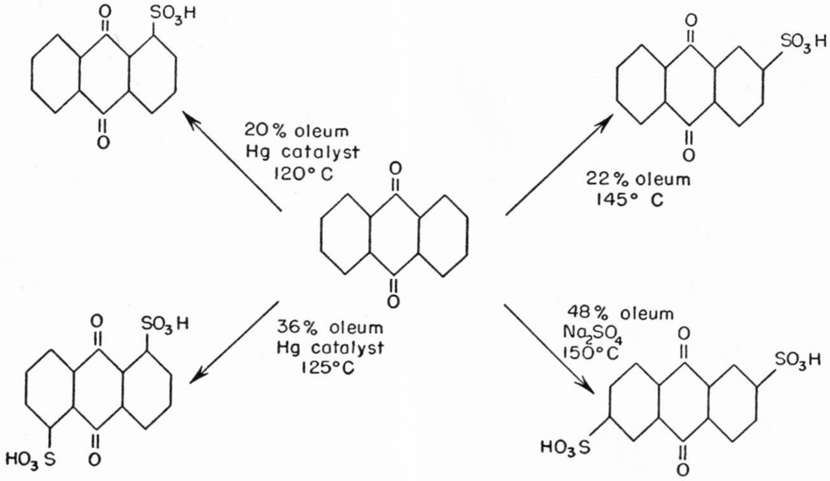

1-Aminoanthraquinone is more readily sulfonated, yielding 1-amino-2-anthraquinonesulfonic acid with only a small excess of chlorosulfonic acid in nitrobenzene[160] or in *o*-dichlorobenzene[196]. The same product also results from baking the sulfate of 1-aminoanthraquinone at 200°C[86].

Some other technically important sulfonations are listed below:

Anthraquinone Starting Material	Sulfonation Conditions	Position of Entering Sulfo Group	Ref.
1,5-Di-NH₂	20% oleum 145°C	2	105
2-NH₂	20% oleum 100°C	3	247
1,5-Di-OH	20% oleum 120°C Na₂SO₄	2,6	158
1,2-Di-OH	20% oleum 105°C Na₂SO₄	3	166
1,4-Di-OH	oleum, HgSO₄ 180°C H₃BO₃	6	114

The "sulfiting" of 1,4-dihydroxyanthraquinone (quinizarin) to yield the 2 sulfonic acid[115] is perhaps analogous to the "sulfiting" of hydroquinone. The following replacement of —Cl by —SO₃H is of interest, although not of great importance as a preparative method[110, 254]:

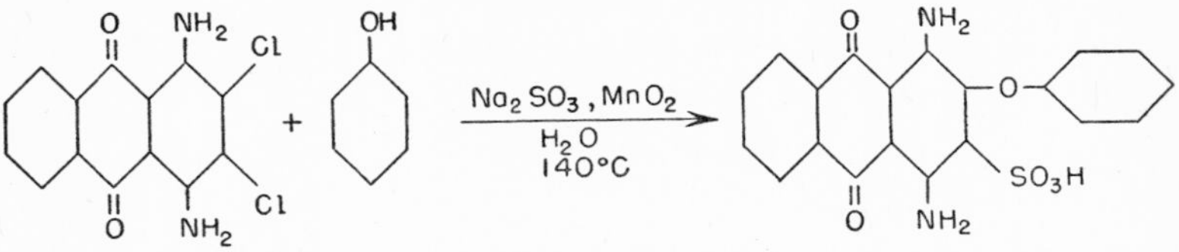

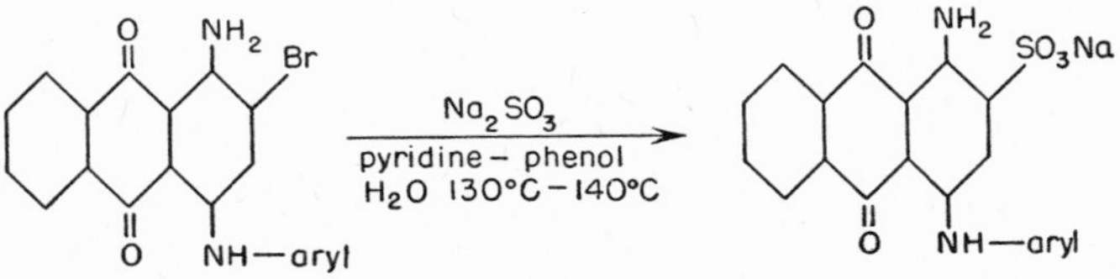

Reactivity of Anthraquinonesulfonic Acids. The alpha sulfonic acid group of anthraquinone is particularly easily displaced by nucleophilic reagents. (This is analogous to the reactivity of *o*-nitrobenzenesulfonic acid.) 1-Anthraquinonesulfonic acid yields 1-methoxyanthraquinone at 60°C with caustic and methanol, while the less reactive 1-chloroanthraquinone requires a temperature of 70°C.

Treatment of either 1- or 2-anthraquinonesulfonic acid with alkalies or alkaline earths leads to hydrolysis and the salts can be acidified to give the corresponding hydroxy compounds[43, 47].

Particularly noteworthy is the reactivity of 1,4-di(amino or hydroxy)-2-anthraquinonesulfonic acids (see table). Quinizarin type compounds can have "quinonoid" structures in the outer ring and hence should be especially reactive:

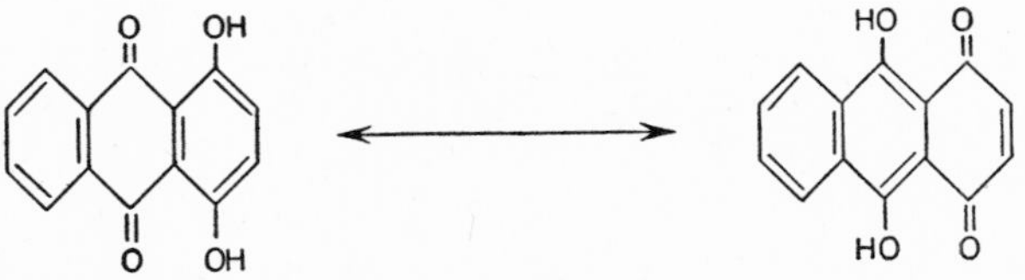

Reactions of Anthraquinonesulfonic Acids with Nucleophilic Reagents.

Anthraquinone Starting Material	Reaction Conditions	Anthraquinone Product	Ref.
1-SO₃H	CH₃OH, KOH, 60°C	1-OCH₃	224
1-SO₃H	H₂O, CH₃NH₂, 128°C (*m*-nitrobenzenesulfonic acid)	1-NHCH₃	101
1-SO₃H	30% NH₄OH, (*m*-nitrobenzenesulfonic acid) 175°C	1-NH₂	128

Anthraquinone Starting Material	Reaction Conditions	Anthraquinone Product	Ref.
1,5-Di-SO_3H	25% NH_4OH (*m*-nitrobenzenesulfonic acid) 175°C	1,5-Di-NH_2	138
2,6-Di-SO_3H	25% NH_4OH, oxid. agent, 200°C	2,6-Di-NH_2	98
1-NH_2-2-SO_3H	25% NH_4OH, $C_6H_5NO_2$ and H_3AsO_4, 197°C	1,2-Di-NH_2	150
1-NH_2-4-CH_3NH-2-SO_3H	K_2CO_3, NaCN, H_2O 127°	1-NH_2-4-$NHCH_3$-2-CN	111
1,4-Di-OH-2-SO_3H	KCN, Na_2CO_3, H_2O air, room temp.	1,4-Di-OH 2-SO_3H-3-CN	202
1,4-Di-OH-2-SO_3H	KCN, Na_2CO_3, H_2O, 90°C, then oxid. the leuco	1,4-Di-OH 2,3-Di-CN	202

The replacement of both alpha and beta sulfo groups by nascent chlorine (from $KClO_3$ and HCl at the boil) is a very important preparative method which is discussed under chloroanthraquinones.

Desulfonation. The desulfonation of anthraquinonesulfonic acids is of some importance (see section on leucoquinizarin and leuco-1,4-diaminoanthraquinone). In general, it can be effected by heating in aqueous sulfuric acid (e.g., 60 to 85 per cent) or by alkaline reductions with sodium sulfide, hydrosulfite or glucose solutions[56, 57]:

Anthraquinone Starting Material | Desulfonation Conditions | Reaction Product | Ref.

NH2 O OH SO3H
HO3S
OH O NH2
96% H2 SO4
H3 BO3
130°C
NH2 O OH SO3 H
OH O NH2

159

NH2 O OH SO3H
HO3 S
OH O NH2
H2O, NaOH
Na2 S2 O4
104°C
OH O OH (leuco)
OH O OH

154

O SO3H
O (the β isomer is stable)
60–85% H2 SO4
boil
O
O

192

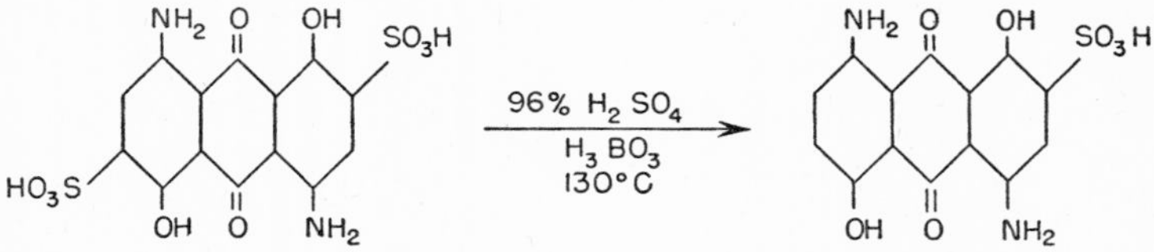

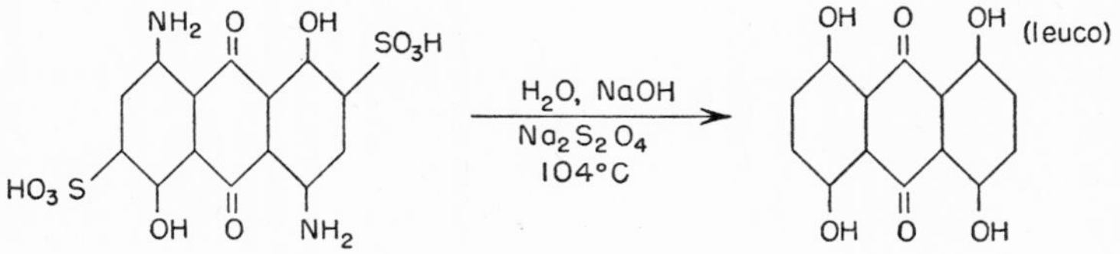

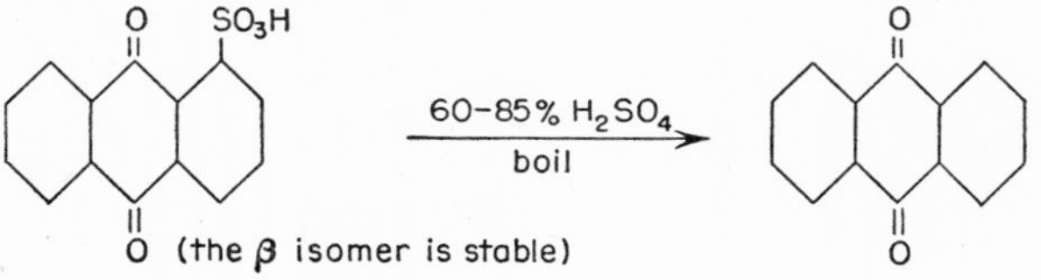

Anthraquinone Starting Material	Desulfonation Conditions	Reaction Product	Ref.
	H_2SO_4, 130°C		54
	H_2SO_4, 170°C		218
	NH_4OH, hydrosulfite, H_2O, 70°C		214

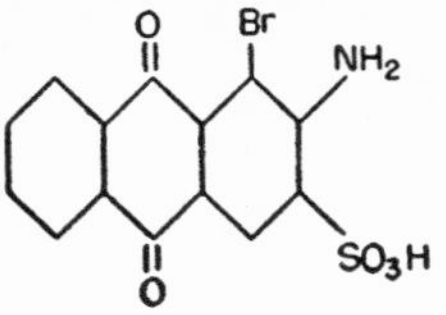

Alkylanthraquinones, Anthraquinonecarboxylic Acids and Aldehydes

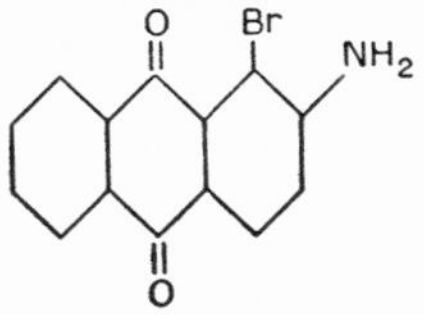

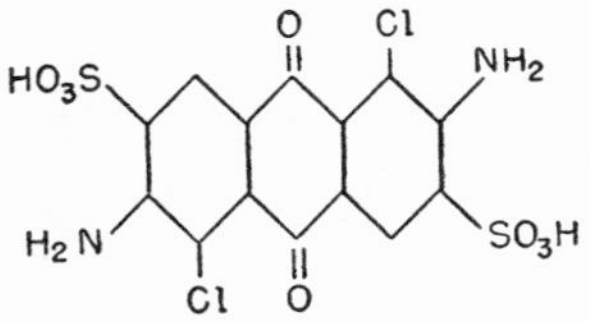

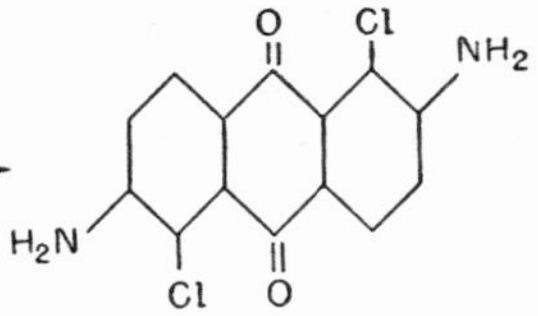

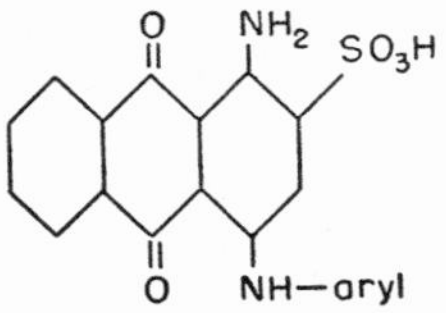

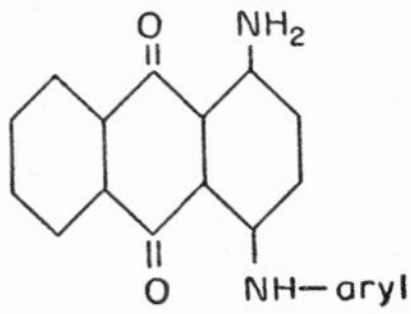

Preparation of Alkylanthraquinones. The technically important 2-methylanthraquinone is prepared from toluene and phthalic anhydride via the *o*-(*p*-toluyl)benzoic acid[136].

2-Ethylanthraquinone (from ethylbenzene) was used during the war by the Germans to prepare hydrogen peroxide [124]. The catalytically prepared leuco derivative was oxidized with air to hydrogen peroxide and the original quinone, which was re-reduced and thus used over and over, the net reaction being $H_2 + O_2 \rightarrow H_2O_2$. The ethyl derivative was used instead of the cheaper 2-methylanthraquinone because of greater solubility in the solvent mixture employed.

Preparation of Anthraquinonecarboxylic Acids. Anthraquinone acids may be prepared from the nitriles which result from heating haloanthraquinones in nitrobenzene with a cuprous cyanide-pyridine addition compound[182, 233].

The nitriles also can be made via the diazonium salt and cuprous cyanide[232]. The following two oxidation reactions are of importance[146, 241].

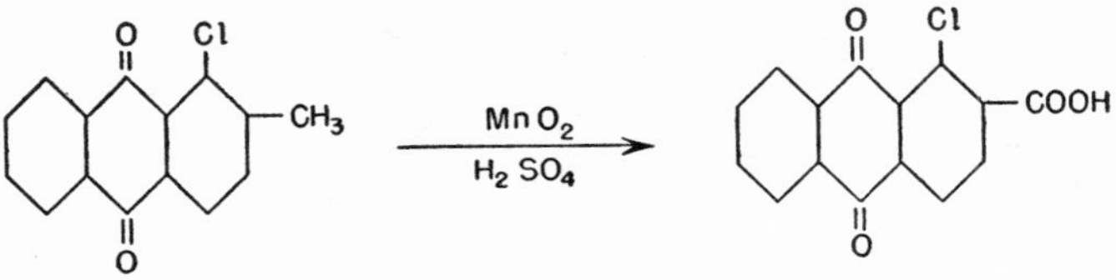

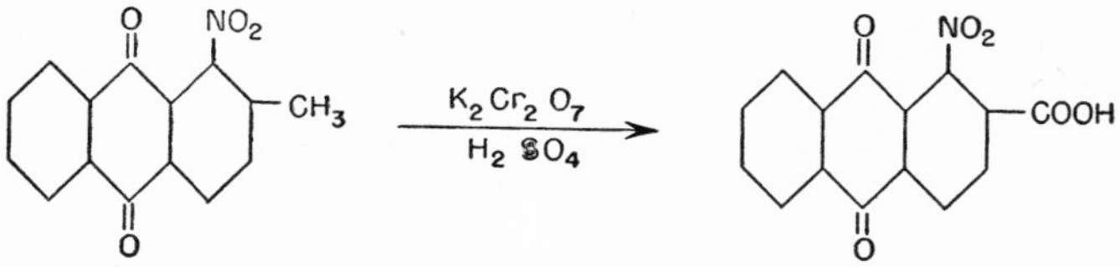

Of interest also is the oxidation of 1,3-dimethylanthraquinone and of 1,4-dihydroxy-2-methylanthraquinone[230, 250]:

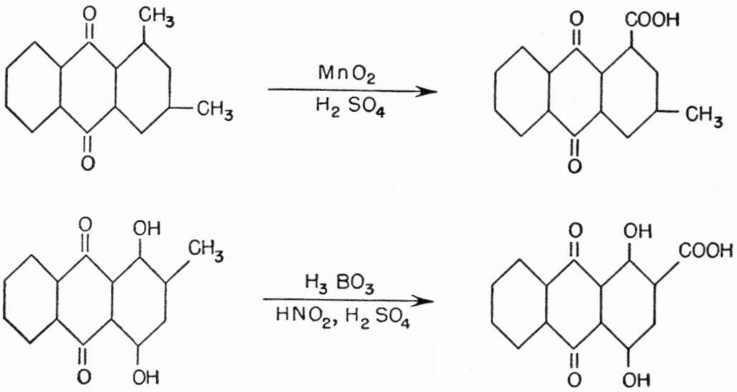

The oxidation of polycyclic compounds (with more than three condensed rings) often leads to decomposition or ring rupture with formation of the more stable anthraquinonecarboxylic acids, as for example[31, 210]:

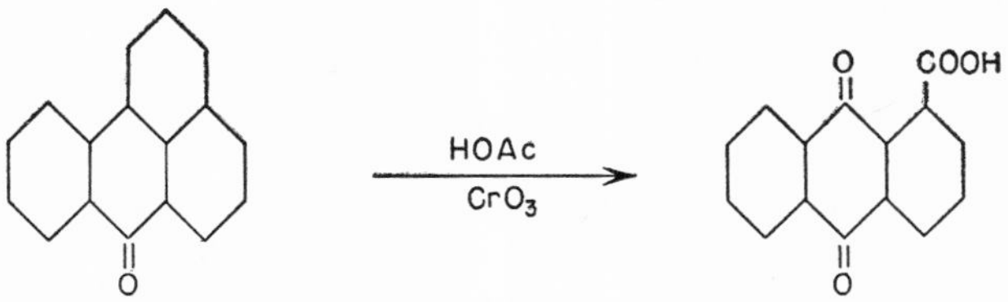

Substituents such as nitro, halogen and alkyl groups may be present. However, selenium dioxide is a useful reagent as ring rupture is minimized and a benzanthronecarboxylic acid can be isolated[179]:

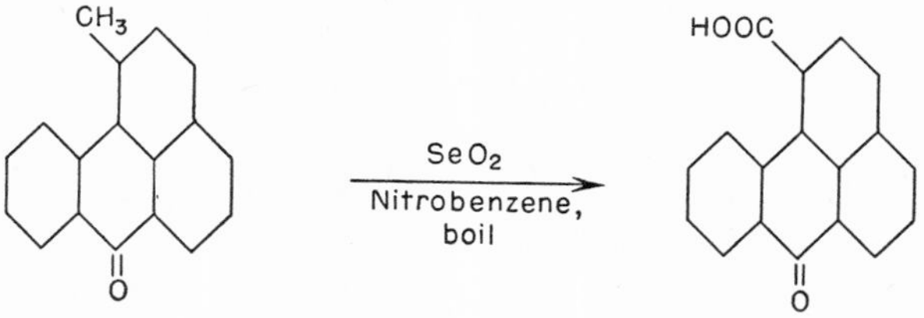

Potassium hydroxide-nitrobenzene has been reported to oxidize the methyl groups in many isocyclic and heterocyclic compounds[66].

The preparation of an isoxazole from 2-methyl-1-nitroanthraquinone may be considered to represent an internal oxidation-reduction reaction[64, 65]:

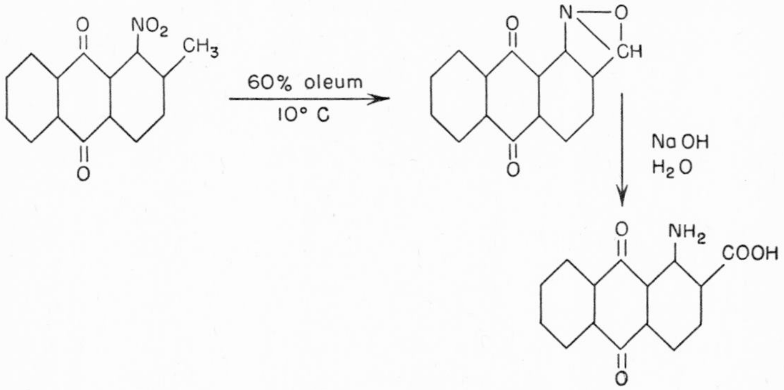

The same product was reported to have been obtained by treatment with aluminum chloride and SO_2 at 125°C[183].

The methyl group may often be oxidized more effectively at the o-(p-toluyl)benzoic acid stage (prior to ring-closure)[97, 126]:

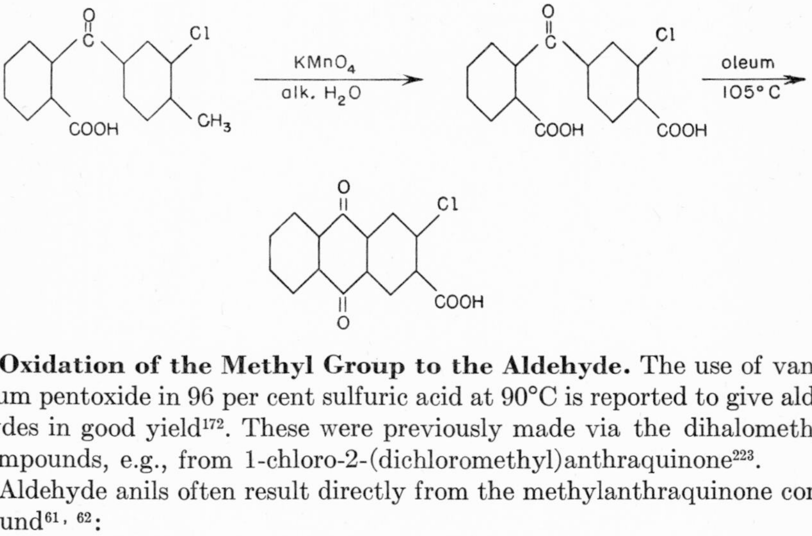

Oxidation of the Methyl Group to the Aldehyde. The use of vanadium pentoxide in 96 per cent sulfuric acid at 90°C is reported to give aldehydes in good yield[172]. These were previously made via the dihalomethyl compounds, e.g., from 1-chloro-2-(dichloromethyl)anthraquinone[223].

Aldehyde anils often result directly from the methylanthraquinone compound[61, 62]:

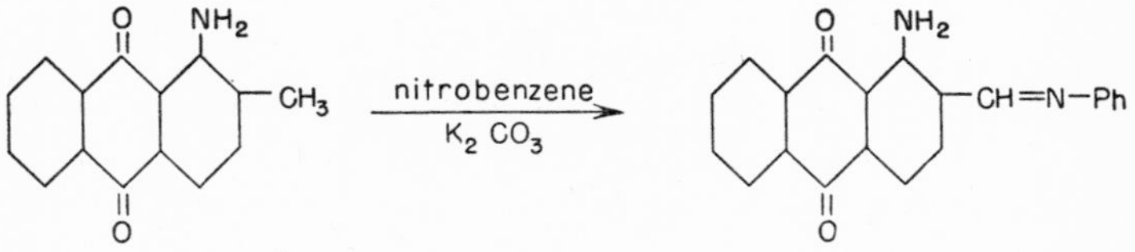

The dianil from 2,6-dimethylanthraquinone is also disclosed in the literature, as well as the anil from 2-methylanthraquinone[63].

Trifluoromethylanthraquinones. Side chain chlorination of 2-methylanthraquinone gives the trichloromethyl compound, which may be fluorinated[125]:

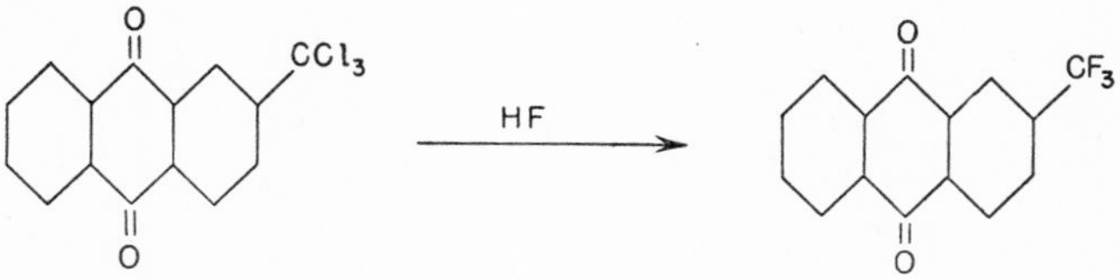

Aminoanthraquinones

Preparation. Aminoanthraquinones result from reduction of the nitro compounds, but even more important are the replacement reactions applied to halogen, nitro- or sulfo-substituted anthraquinones. As a special case, many 1,4-dihydroxyanthraquinones can be aminated to 1,4-diaminoanthraquinones via the leuco derivatives. Finally, amines can be obtained by the direct amino replacement of the hydroxy in certain hydroxyanthraquinones without intermediate leuco formation.

Preparation of Aminoanthraquinones by Reduction.

Anthraquinone Starting Material	Reaction Conditions	Anthraquinone Reaction Product	Ref.
$1-NO_2-2-CH_3$	Na_2S, H_2O boil	$1-NH_2-2-CH_3$	226
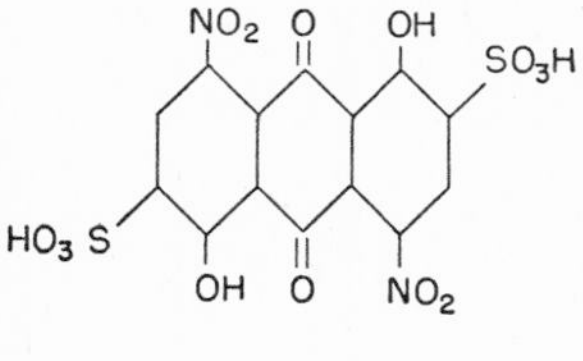	Na_2S, H_2O 90°C	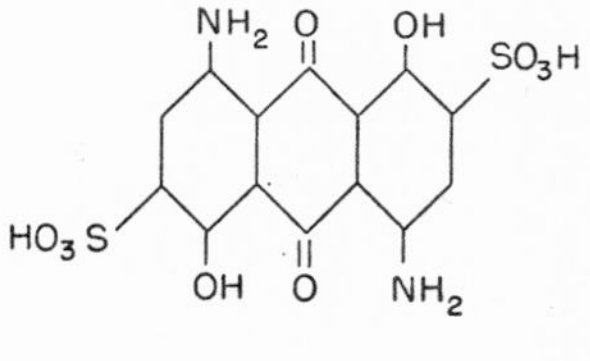	158
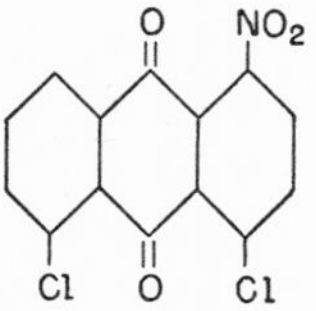	30% oleum $S + H_3BO_3$ 99°C	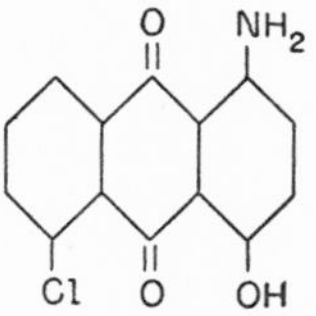	223

Preparation of Aminoanthraquinones by Replacing Halogen.

Anthraquinone Starting Material	Reaction Conditions	Anthraquinone Reaction Product	Ref.
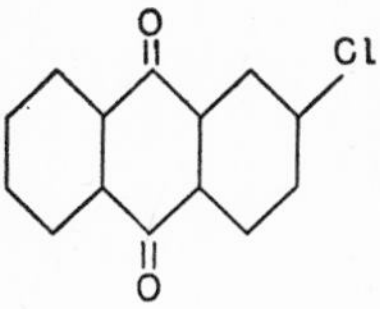	20% NH_4OH, H_3AsO_4 217°C	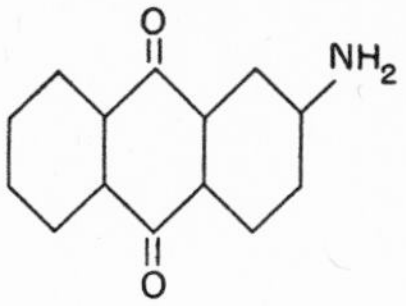	130

Anthraquinone Starting Material	Reaction Conditions	Anthraquinone Reaction Product	Ref.

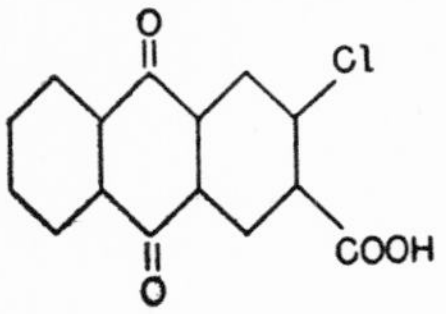

20% NH_4OH,
Cu
140°C

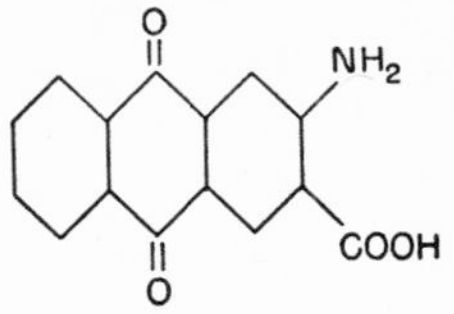

121

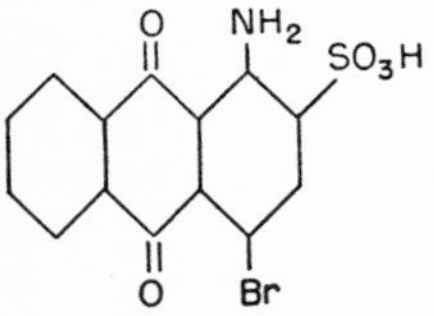

CH_3NH_2, H_2O
Na_2CO_3, $CuSO_4$
80°C

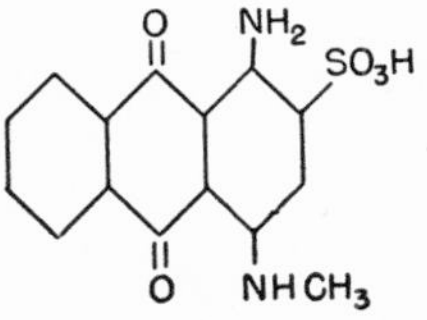

95

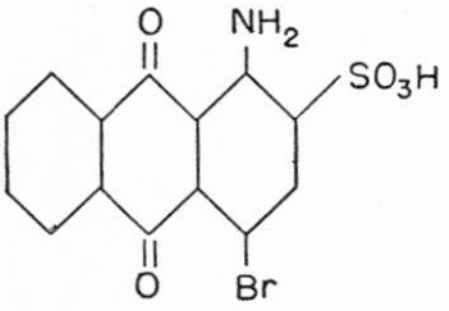

arylamine, H_2O,
$NaHCO_3$, Cu_2Cl_2
70–100°C

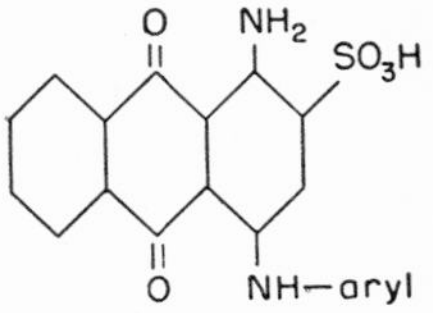

151

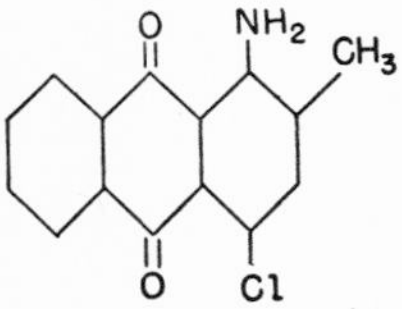

p–toluidine,
NaOAc, $CuSO_4$
150°C

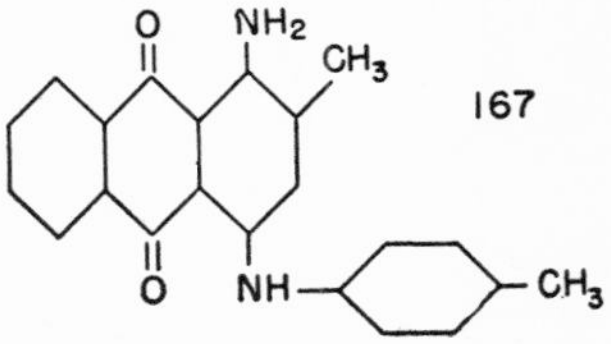

167

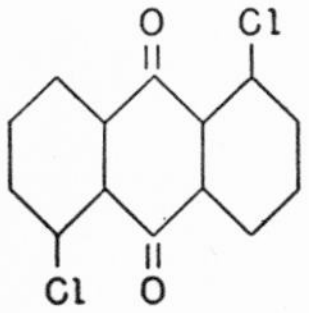

potassium
anthranilate,
MgO, CuO,
isobutanol
150°C

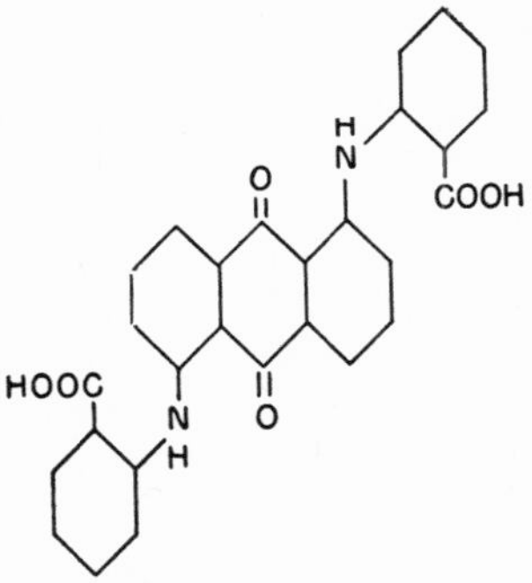

153

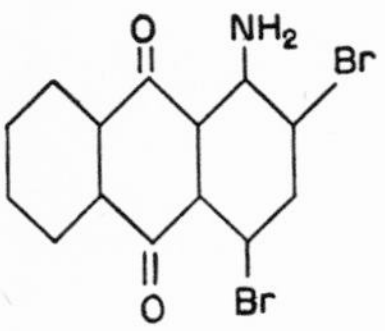

p–toluidine,
Na OAc
190°C

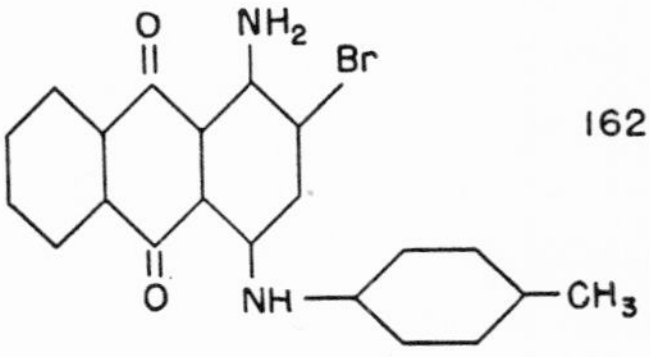

162

Preparation of Aminoanthraquinones by Replacing the Nitro Group.

Anthraquinone Starting Material	Reaction Conditions	Reaction Product	Ref.

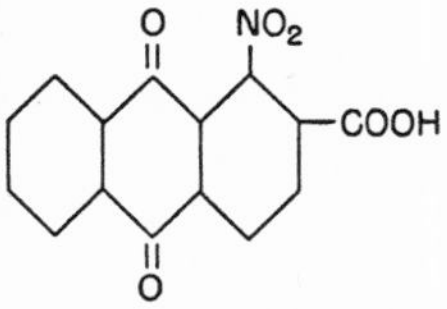

15% NH_4OH
130°C

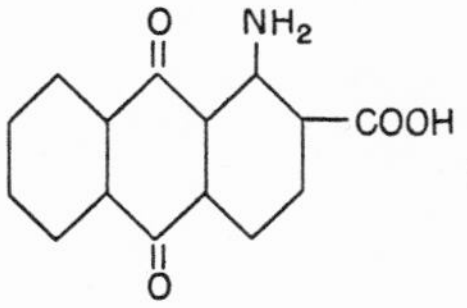

146

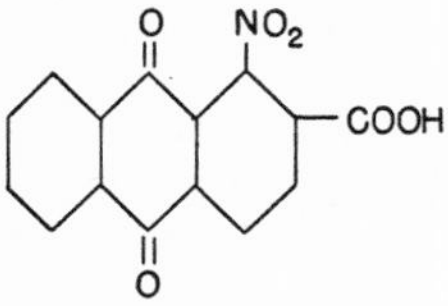

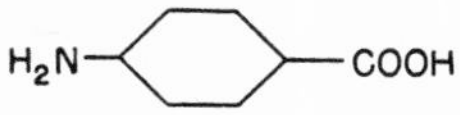

H_2N—⟨ ⟩—COOH

MgO, H_2O
100°C

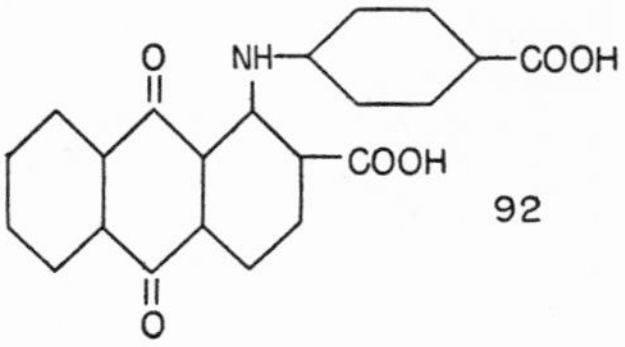

92

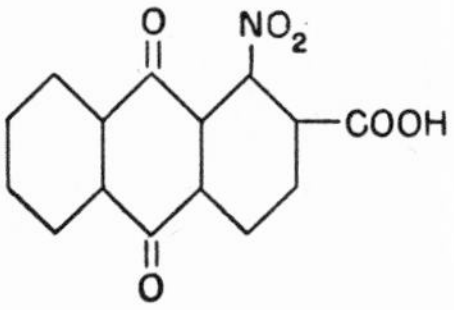

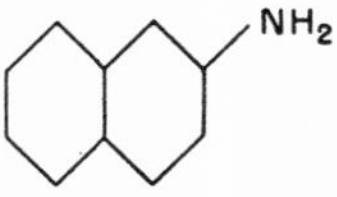

$AsCl_3$
o-dichlorobenzene
155°C

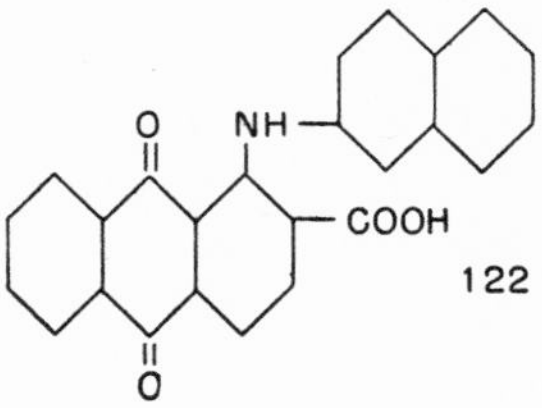

122

Preparation of Aminoanthraquinones by Replacing the Sulfo Group.

Anthraquinone Starting Material	Reaction Conditions	Anthraquinone Reaction Product	Ref.
1-SO$_3$H	30% NH$_4$OH, *m*-nitrobenzenesulfonic acid 175°C	1-NH$_2$	128
1,5-Di-SO$_3$H	25% NH$_4$OH, *m*-nitrobenzenesulfonic acid 175°C	1,5-Di-NH$_2$	138
2,6-Di-SO$_3$H	20% NH$_4$OH, oxid. agent, 200°C	2,6-Di-NH$_2$	98
1-NH$_2$-2-SO$_3$H	25% NH$_4$OH, C$_6$H$_5$NO$_2$, H$_3$AsO$_4$, CuSO$_4$, 197°C	1,2-Di-NH$_2$	150
1-SO$_3$H	CH$_3$NH$_2$, H$_2$O, CuSO$_4$ (*m*-nitrobenzene-sulfonic acid) 128°C	1-NHCH$_3$	100

It will be noted that these aminations require autogenous pressure, often as high as 700 psi.

Preparation of Anthraquinone Amines from Leucoquinizarin and Related Types:

Anthraquinone Starting Material	Reaction Conditions	Anthraquinone Reaction Product	Ref.
Leuco-1,4-Di-OH (leucoquinizarin)	5–6% NH₄OH 75–85°C	1-NH₂-4-OH (after oxidation)	174
Leuco-1,4-Di-OH (leucoquinizarin)	18% NH₄OH 90°C	1,4-Di-NH₂ (after oxidation)	141
1,4-Di-OH	CH₃NH₂, H₂O 120°C Zn (to give leuco)	1,4-Di-NHCH₃	156
1,4-Di-OH	p-toluidine, H₃BO₃, HCl Zn (to give leuco) 95°C	1,4-Di-p-toluidino	161
1,4-Di-OH	p-toluidine, H₃BO₃, HCl, C₂H₅OH Zn (to give leuco) 78–80°C	1-OH-4-p-toluidino	108, 262

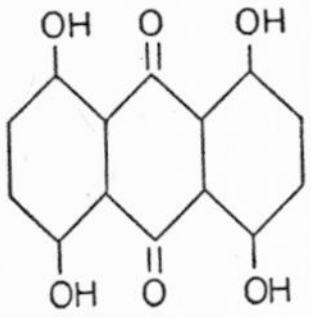

(after oxidation)

$H_2NCH_2CH_2OH$, H_2O, MeOH $Na_2S_2O_4$ 78°C   112

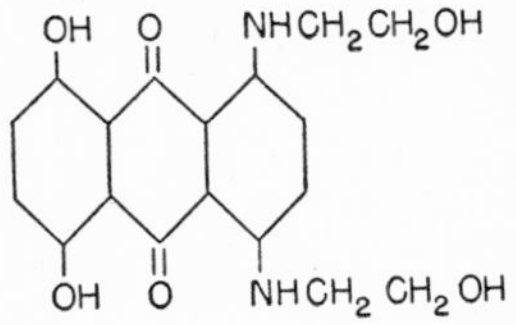

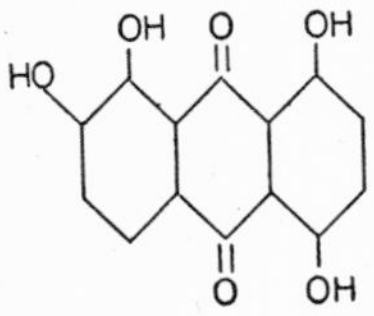

p-toluidine, H_3BO_3, H_2O, HCl Zn (to give leuco) 92°C   169

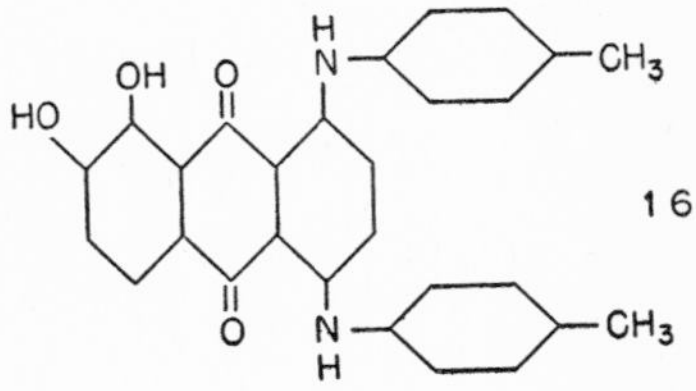

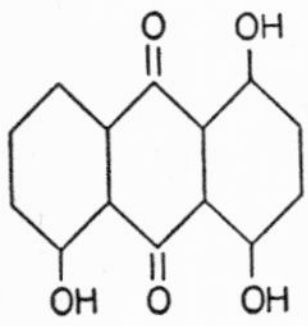

p-toluidine, H_3BO_3, H_2O, HCl Zn (to give leuco) 95°C   107

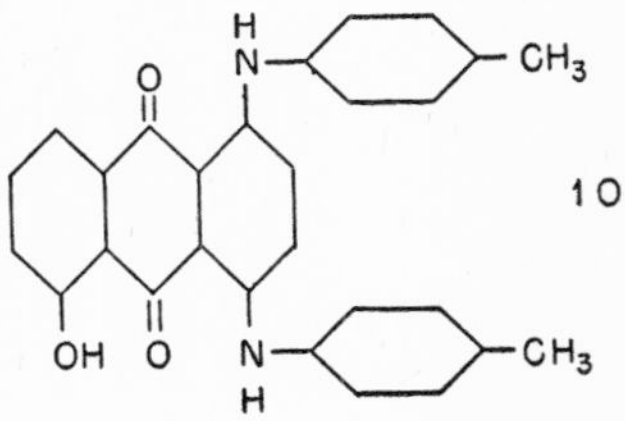

Anthraquinone Starting Material	Reaction Conditions	Anthraquinone Reaction Product	Ref.
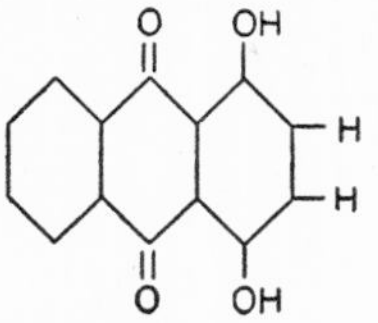 (quinizarin structure, O OH / H H / O OH)	arylamine, H_3BO_3, alcohol 80°C	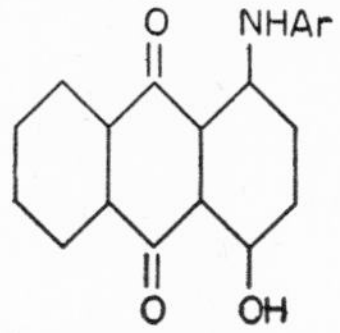 (structure, O NHAr / O OH)	189, 262

Halo-substituted quinizarin can be reacted with amines, anthranilic acid, o-mercaptobenzoic acid, etc., whereupon either —OH or halogen is displaced depending on the conditions used[36].

In the case of alkoxyanthraquinones, alkoxy can be replaced by aliphatic or aromatic amines when used in excess[49].

Reactions of Aminoanthraquinones. *Acylation.* The benzoylation of aminoanthraquinones is of great importance since many vat dyes contain one or more benzamido groups in an alpha position. The monobenzoylation of 1,4- and 1,5-diaminoanthraquinone is of particular value. Other acylations are of some importance likewise. Those leading directly to vat dyes are discussed in the sections on Anthraquinone Dyes rather than under Intermediates.

Anthraquinone Starting Material	Reaction Conditions	Anthraquinone Reaction Product	Ref.
1–NH₂	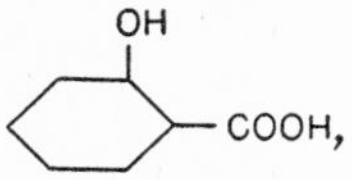 (OH-substituted benzene—COOH), SOCl₂, nitrobenzene 120°C	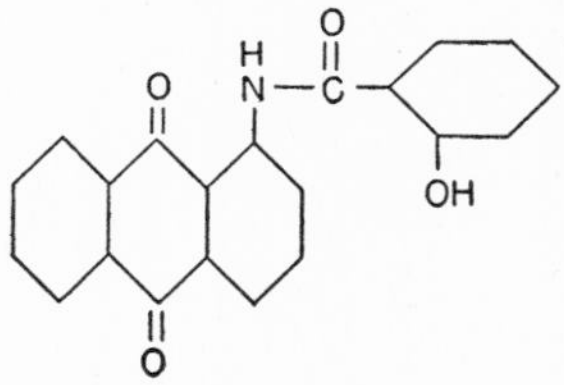 (structure with N—C=O / OH)	117
1–NH₂–5–Cl	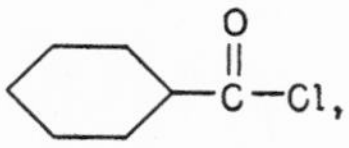 (C₆H₅—C(=O)—Cl), o-dichlorobenzene 125°C	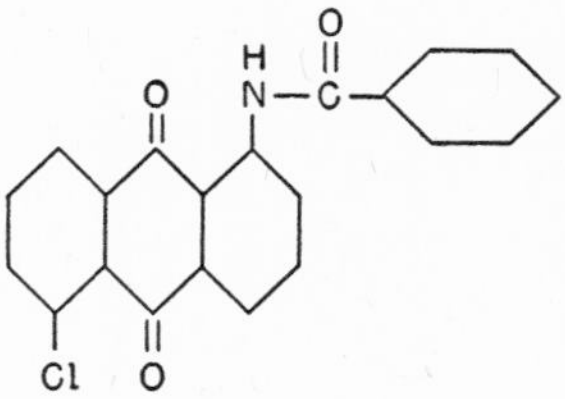 (structure with N—C=O, Cl)	133
1–NH₂–4–OH	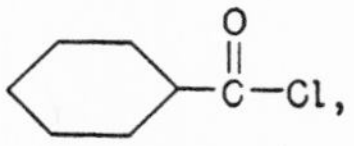 (C₆H₅—C(=O)—Cl), o-dichlorobenzene 120°C	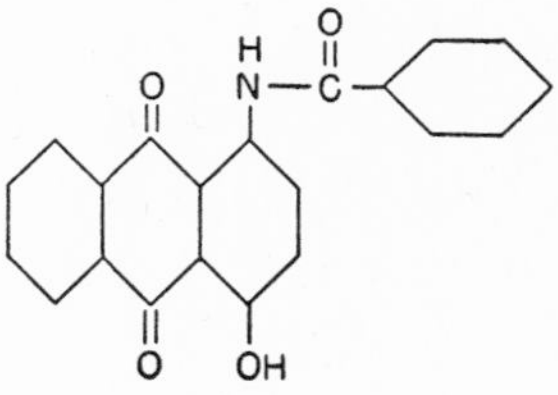 (structure with N—C=O, O OH)	113

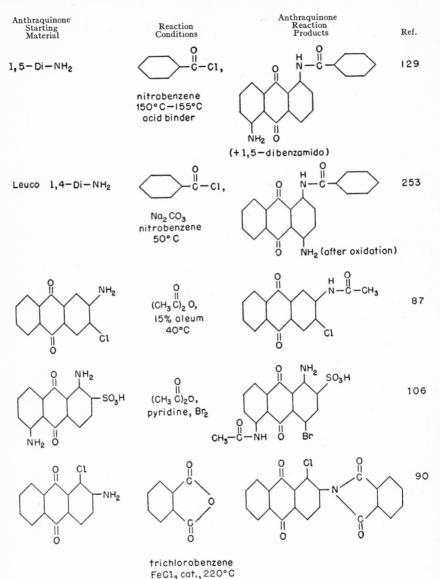

Anthraquinone Starting Material	Reaction Conditions	Anthraquinone Reaction Products	Ref.

Direct Nucleophilic Substitution of Aminoanthraquinones. The "quinonoid" reactivity of anthraquinone amines was postulated early by European chemists, particularly in the formation of indanthrone from the caustic fusion of 2-aminoanthraquinone[83, 231].

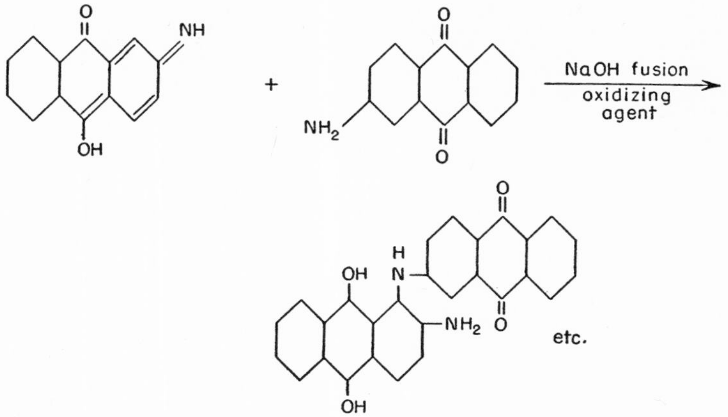

In this connection, the most recent publications of Bradley and co-workers throw more light on this mechanism[12]. The above enolization is apparently not required, since the following intermediate will ring-close under alkaline conditions.

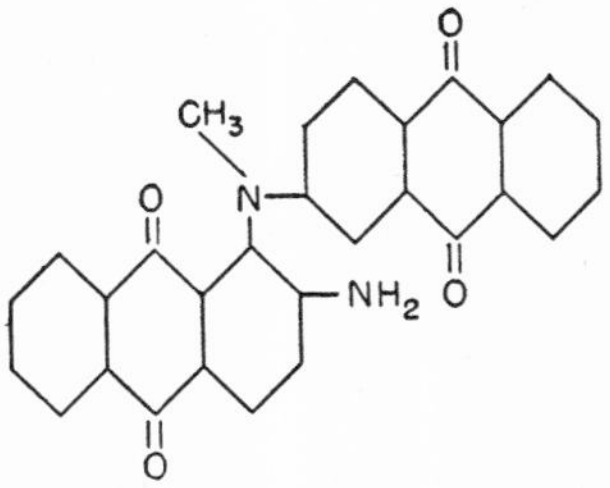

Starting Material (Ph=phenyl)	Nucleo-philic Reagent	Solvent and Temperature	Oxidizing Agent	Anthraquinone Reaction Product	Ref.
1-NH$_2$	NH$_4$OH	H$_2$O, 200°C	NaNO$_3$	1,2-Di-NH$_2$	69
2-NH$_2$	NH$_4$OH	H$_2$O, 210°C	H$_3$AsO$_4$	1,2-Di-NH$_2$	69
1-NH$_2$-2-CH$_3$	NaNHPh	PhNH$_2$, 50°C	air	1-NH$_2$-2-CH$_3$-4-NHPh	199
1-NHPh	NaNHPh	PhNH$_2$, 60°C	air	1,4-Di-NHPh	199
2-NHPh	NaNHPh	PhNH$_2$, 45°C	air	a dianilino-aq. M.P. 152°	199
1-NH$_2$	Na$_2$S	H$_2$O, 140°C	S(?)	1-NH$_2$-2-SH	60, 221

Starting Material	Nucleophilic Reagent	Solvent and Temperature	Oxidizing Agent	Anthraquinone Reaction Product	Ref.
1-NH$_2$-4-OH-2-SO$_3$H	KCN	H$_2$O, 90°C–95°C	persulfate	1,4-Di-OH-2,3-Di-CN	202
1-OH-4-NHBu-2-SO$_3$H	NaCN	H$_2$O, 90°C		1-OH-4-BuNH-2,3-Di-CN	238
1-NH$_2$-4-NHCO-COOH	Na$_2$SO$_3$	H$_2$O, 115°C (autoclave)	MnO$_2$	1,4-Di-NH$_2$-2-SO$_3$H	59

Diazotization. Diazotization of aminoanthraquinones proceeds normally in most cases except that special techniques have to be used because of the low solubility of the starting materials.

The anthraquinone diazonium compounds are used in a wide variety of reactions. The alpha isomers give better yields. The diazotization is usually performed in 90 to 96 per cent sulfuric acid at 0 to 25°C by gradually adding sodium nitrite.

Although 1,4-diaminoanthraquinone behaves abnormally, 1,5-diaminoanthraquinone can be tetrazotized and the usual replacements can be effected[188].

Reaction of stabilized diazonium salts with aromatic hydrocarbons in the presence of Friedel-Crafts catalysts has been reported to give arylanthraquinones[265]:

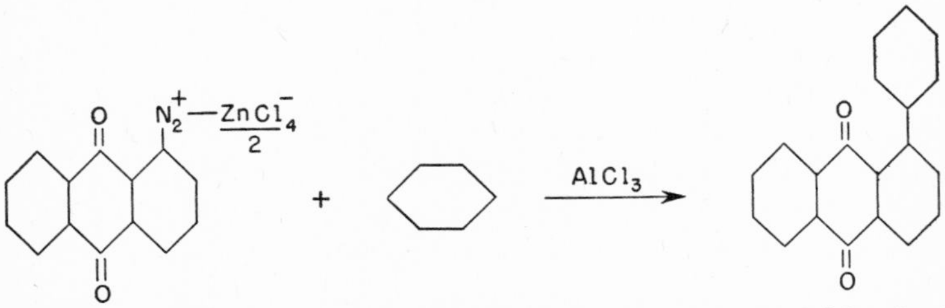

The following diazonium replacements have been disclosed in the literature.

	Conditions	Ref.
N$_2$X by H	Heat in alcohol	187
by OH	Heat in 80–96% H$_2$SO$_4$	219
by Cl	HCl, Cu$_2$Cl$_2$	237
by Br	HBr, CuBr	44
by I	KI, H$_2$O	191
by CN	KCu(CN)$_2$, H$_2$O	232
by SCN	KSCN, H$_2$O	40
by NO$_2$	NaNO$_2$	72
by N$_3$	NaN$_3$	71

Coupling of Diazonium Salts to Form Biaryl Compounds. Certain negatively substituted diazonium compounds may often be converted to biaryls by treatment with cuprous salts, e.g., the preparation of diphenic acid from diazotized anthranilic acid. Similarly, 1-amino-2-methylanthraquinone may be converted to the biaryl compound, 2,2'-dimethyl-1,1'-bianthraquinone, which is a pyranthrone intermediate[226].

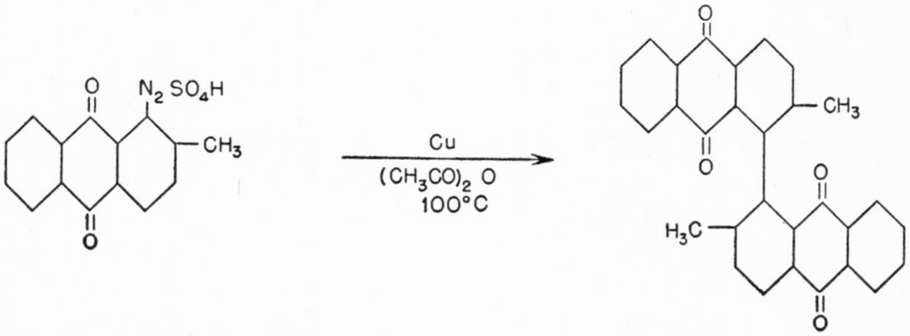

Hydroxyanthraquinones

Preparation. Many anthraquinones may be directly hydroxylated by treatment with oleum, although this procedure usually gives impure products.

Quinizarin (1,4-dihydroxyanthraquinone) results from the direct condensation of phthalic anhydride and *p*-chlorophenol in which sulfuric acid acts as condensing agent, ring-closing agent, and hydrolytic agent for the intermediate chlorohydroxyanthraquinone[139] (see Hydrolysis of Haloanthraquinones).

Most chloro, nitro and sulfo anthraquinones can be converted to hydroxyanthraquinones by alkaline hydrolysis.

Decomposition of anthraquinonediazonium salts in hot sulfuric acid offers a convenient route to many hydroxyanthraquinones[219].

Preparation of Hydroxyanthraquinones by Oleum Oxidation.

Starting Material	Reaction Conditions	Reaction Product	Ref.
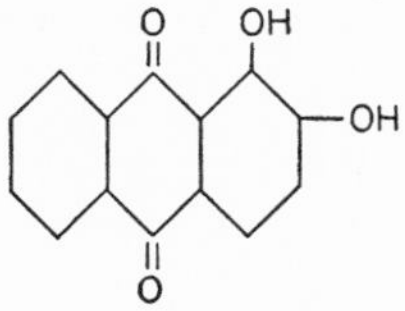	MnO_2, H_2SO_4 20°C	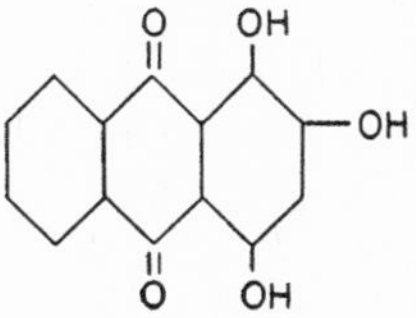	131
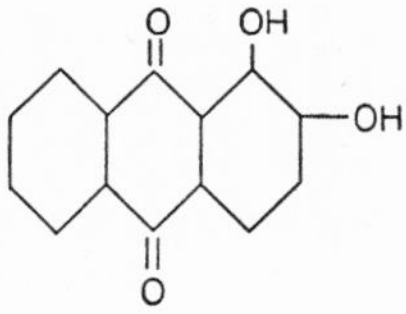	80% oleum, 28°C	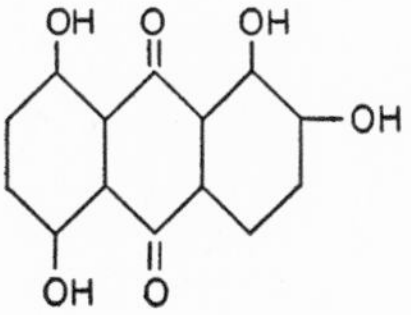	168

Starting Material	Reaction Conditions	Reaction Product	Ref.
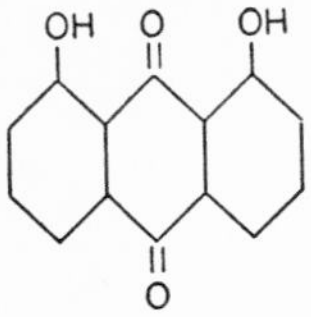	80% oleum, H_3BO_3 27°C	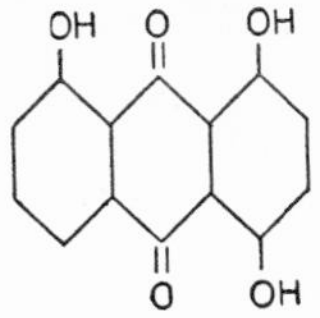	104
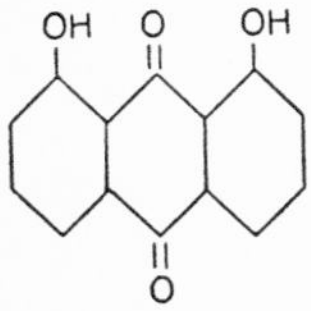	80% oleum, 37°C	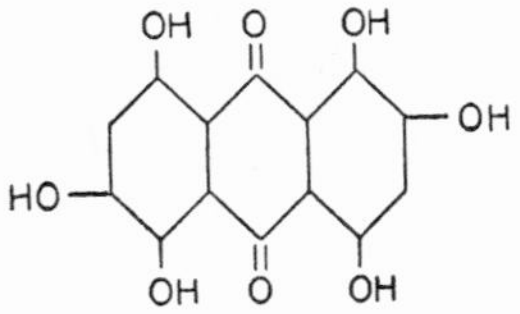	

Preparation of Hydroxyanthraquinones by Replacing —SO₃H.

1-SO₃H	Ca(OH)₂	180°C	1-OH	140
1,5-Di-SO₃H	Ca(OH)₂ MgCl₂	230°C	1,5-Di-OH	140
1,8-Di-SO₃H	Ca(OH)₂ MgCl₂	215°C	1,8-Di-OH	140
2-SO₃H	20% NaOH	160°C	2-OH	240
2-SO₃H	50% NaOH NaNO₃	200°C	1,2-Di-OH	76

Direct Nucleophilic Substitution of Hydroxyanthraquinones.
Hydroxy(and amino)anthraquinones often show "quinonoid" activity, reacting with nucleophilic reagents more readily than does anthraquinone. Particularly active is quinizarin which can yield a "benzoquinone type" mesomeric anion[202].

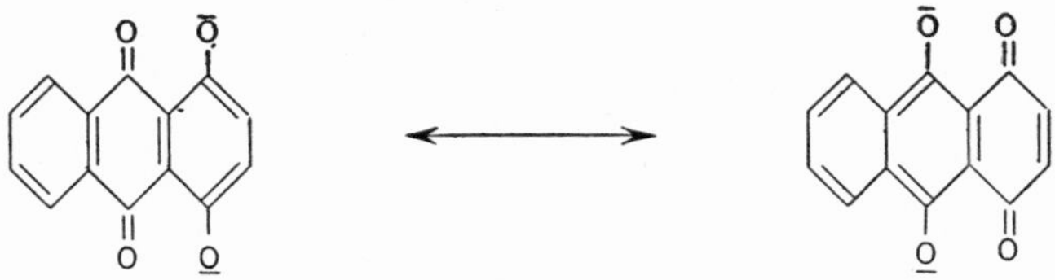

Similar to benzoquinone, quinizarin is attacked even by the weakly nucleophilic reagent sodium cyanide to yield 2,3-quinizarindicarbonitrile.

The activity of 1-hydroxyanthraquinone to nucleophilic reagents has been thought to be due to its possible existence in the tautomeric forms as follows[82]:

Since most nucleophilic reactions take place on the alkaline side, the hydroxyanthraquinones would exist as mesomeric ions. Scholl[228] gives a correlation of color and constitution of mesomeric anions. However, certain arylamines and mercaptans can substitute for hydrogen under acid conditions also.

Nucleophilic substitution requires the elimination of hydrogen. The ability of the anthraquinone molecule to form the leuco derivative is one means of accommodating the "excess" hydrogen. Oxidizing agents are often employed. The point of attack is a position vinylogous to a carbonyl group. The yields are often poor in this type of reaction.

Anthraquinone Starting Material	Nucleophilic Reagent	Temp.	Oxidizing Agent	Reaction Product	Ref.
1-OH	KOH	(caustic fusion)		1,2-Di-OH (minor product)	197
1,5-Di-OH	KOH	180°C	$NaNO_3$	1,2,5-Tri-OH	75
1,3-Di-OH	KOH	135°C	air	1,2,4-Tri-OH	198
2-OH	NH_4OH	180°C	m-nitrobenzene-sulfonic acid	1-NH₂-2-OH	—
1,4-Di-OH	H_2NOH	90°C	probably via leuco derivative	1,4-Di-OH-2-NH₂	203
1,4-Di-OH	Na_2S	150°C	probably via leuco derivative	1,4-Di-OH-2-SH	60
1,4-Di-OH	$PhNH_2$	160°C	nitrobenzene	1,4-Di-OH-2-NHPh	20, 171, 180
1,4-Di-OH	NaCN, H_2O	90°C	isolated as leuco derivative	1,4-Di-OH-2,3-Di-CN	202
1,4-Di-OH	Na_2SO_3	90°C	air or MnO_2	1,4-Di-OH-2-SO₃H	115

Anthraquinone Ethers

Preparation. The technically important anthraquinone ethers are prepared by displacement of —Cl or —SO₃H groups in substituted anthraquinones. Only unsymmetrical ethers, i.e., alkoxy or aryloxy anthraquinones where the aryl group is of the benzene series, have any great importance. Dianthraquinonyl ethers are known but are not important.

The following table lists some ether preparations:

Anthraquinone Starting Material	Conditions	Product	Ref.
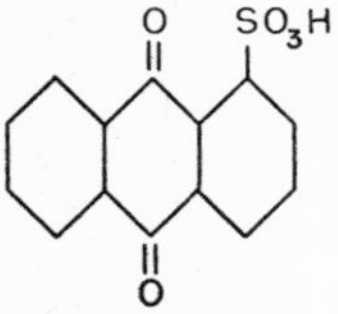 (structure: anthraquinone with SO_3H)	CH_3OH, KOH 65°C	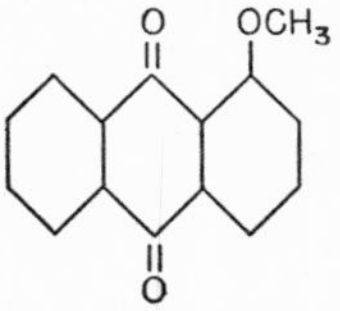 (structure: anthraquinone with OCH_3)	45,224
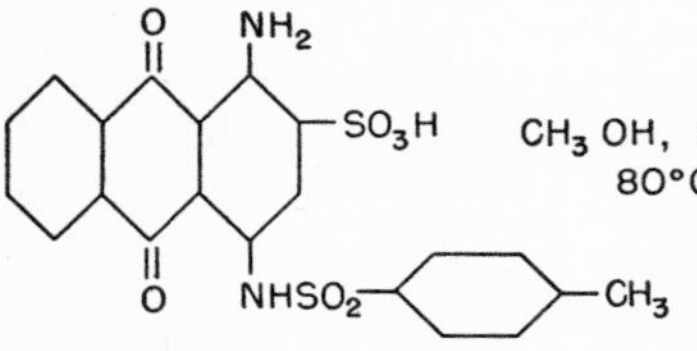 (structure: anthraquinone with NH_2, SO_3H, $NHSO_2$-C$_6$H$_4$-CH_3)	CH_3OH, KOH 80°C	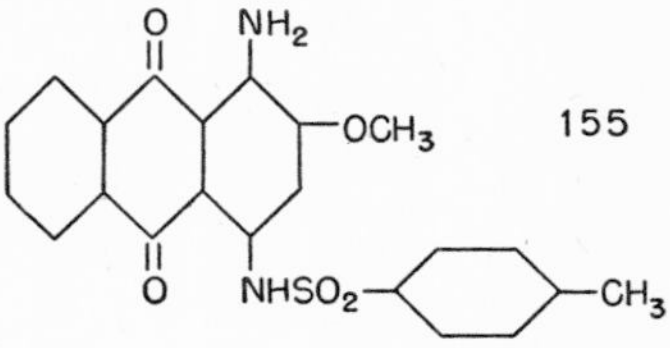 (structure: anthraquinone with NH_2, OCH_3, $NHSO_2$-C$_6$H$_4$-CH_3)	155
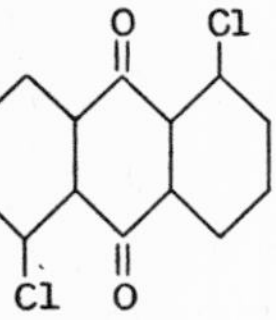 (structure: anthraquinone with Cl, Cl)	C_6H_5OH, NaOH 160°C	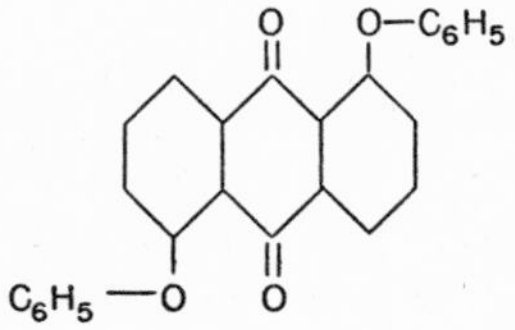 (structure: anthraquinone with O-C_6H_5, C_6H_5-O)	118
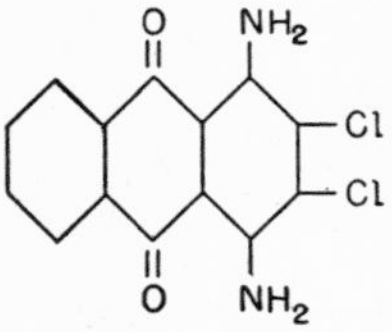 (structure: anthraquinone with NH_2, Cl, Cl, NH_2)	C_6H_5OH, Na_2SO_3 140°C	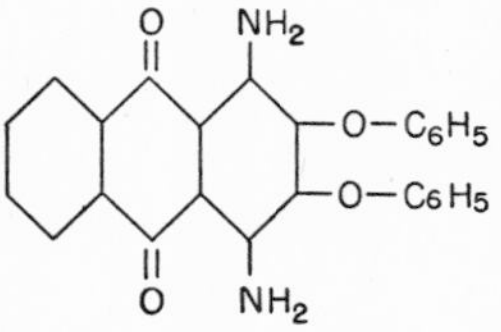 (structure: anthraquinone with NH_2, O-C_6H_5, O-C_6H_5, NH_2)	109
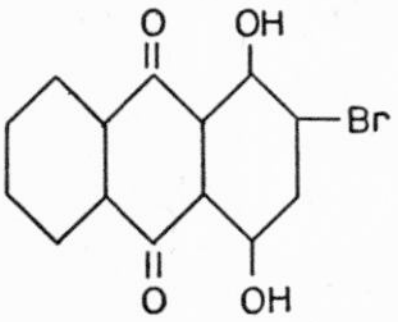 (structure: anthraquinone with OH, Br, OH)	C_6H_5OH, K_2CO_3 155°C	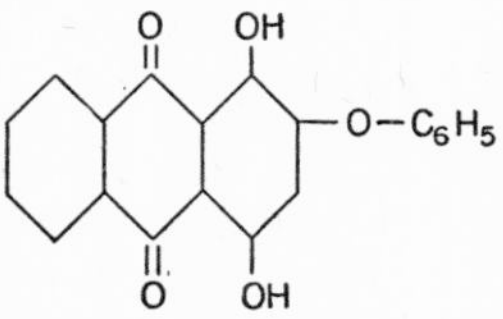 (structure: anthraquinone with OH, O-C_6H_5, OH)	116

Reactions of Anthraquinone Ethers. Anthraquinone ethers may be ammonolyzed, although not as readily as benzoquinone ethers. They also may be alcoholized and, when substituted by nitro groups, even hydrolyzed by dilute caustic.

Ammonolysis of Anthraquinone Ethers.

Anthraquinone Starting Material	Conditions	Product	Ref.
	CH_3NH_2, pyridine 150°C		46
			175

Alcoholysis of Anthraquinone Ethers.

	KOH, CH_3OH 80°C		70,176
	KOH, CH_3OH 80°C		208
	KOH, C_4H_9OH 100°C		208

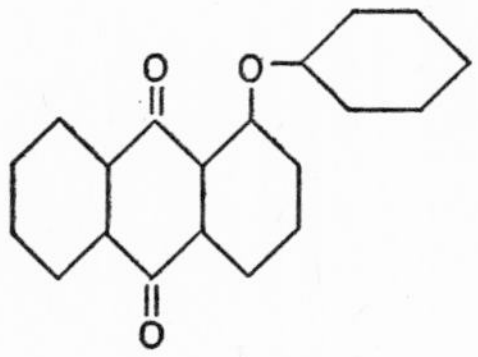

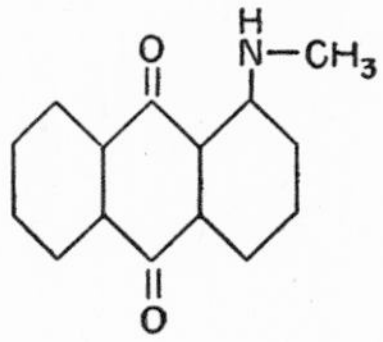

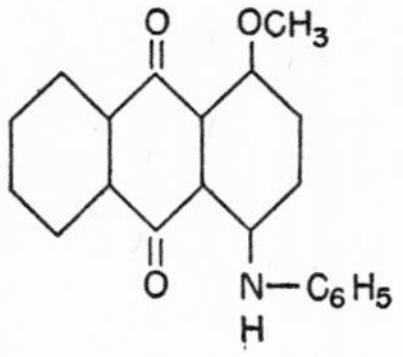

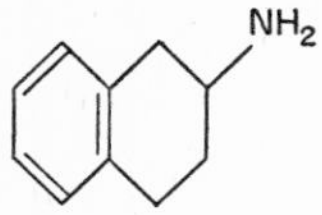

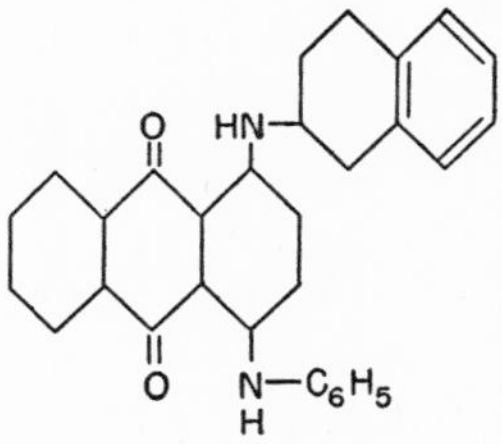

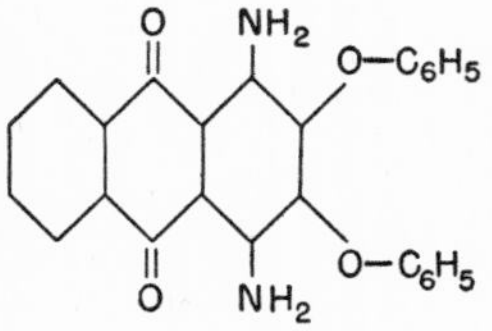

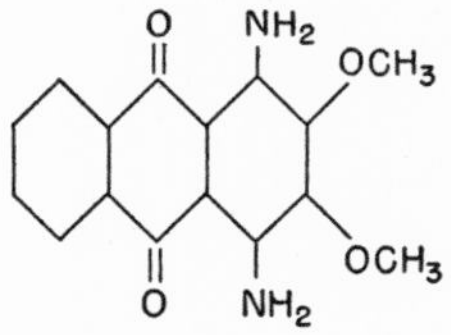

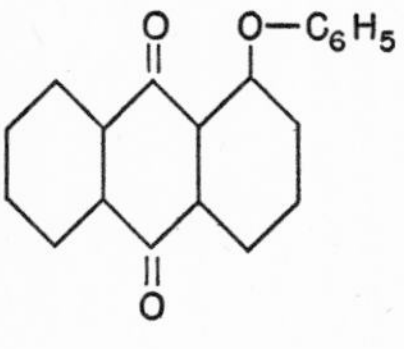

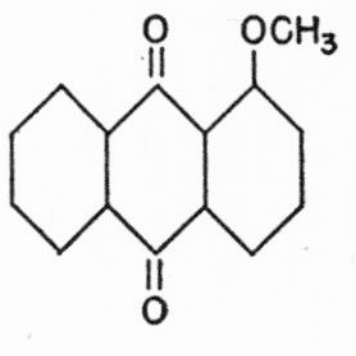

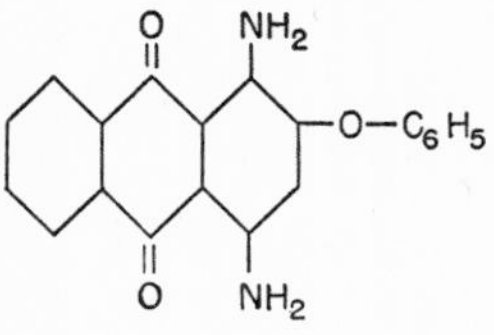

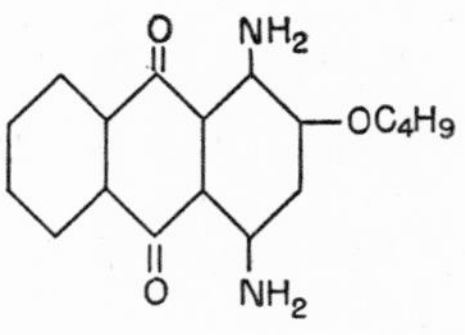

Hydrolysis of Anthraquinone Ethers.

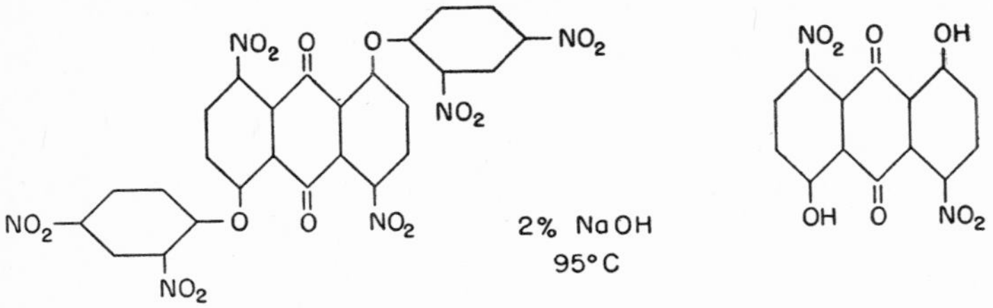

2% NaOH
95°C

Anthraquinonethiols and Thioethers

The technically important anthraquinonethiols are usually prepared from the corresponding halogen compounds. The diazonium replacement by thiocyanate is mentioned in the literature[39].

Some of these preparations are illustrated below:

Anthraquinone Starting Material	Conditions	Product	Ref.
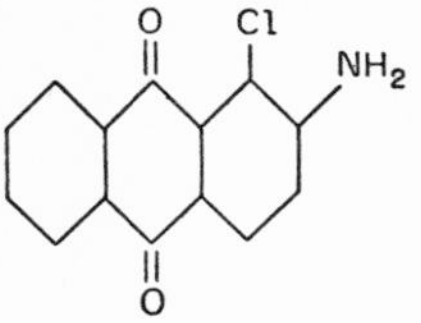	Na$_2$S + S, alcohol, H$_2$O 80–105° C	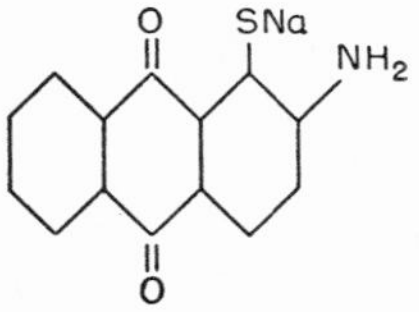	145
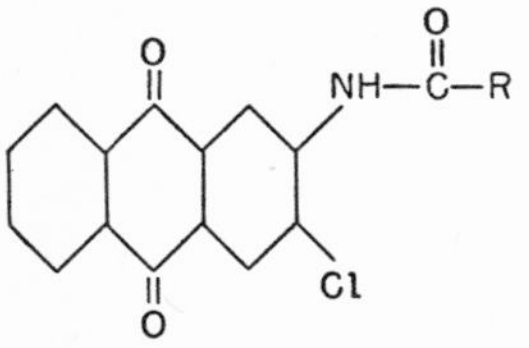	pyridine, Na$_2$S$_2$, H$_2$O 100° C	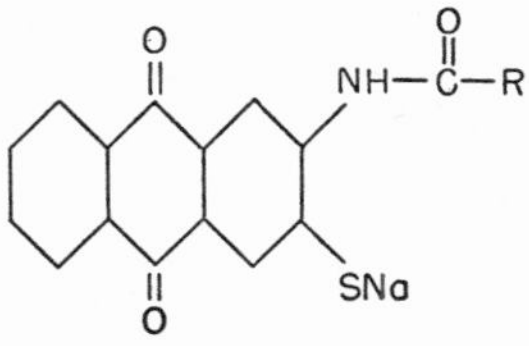	89
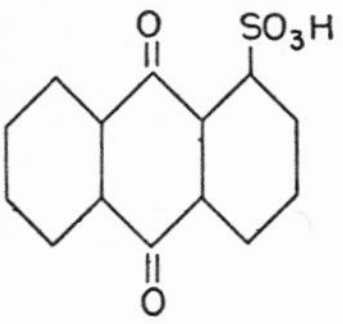	NaOH, RSH 100°C	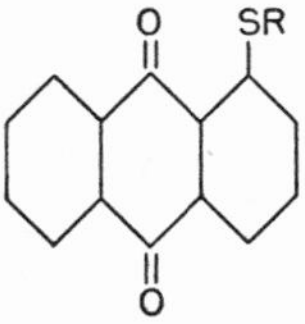	215

Leucoquinizarin and Leuco-1,4-diaminoanthraquinone

Exchange of —OH by —NH₂ in Leucoquinizarin. Quinizarin, 1-amino-4-hydroxyanthraquinone and 1,4-diaminoanthraquinone are unique in that they and their related types can form stable leuco derivatives. Most anthrahydroquinones are only stable in alkaline solution and the free leuco compounds disproportionate to yield oxanthrones:

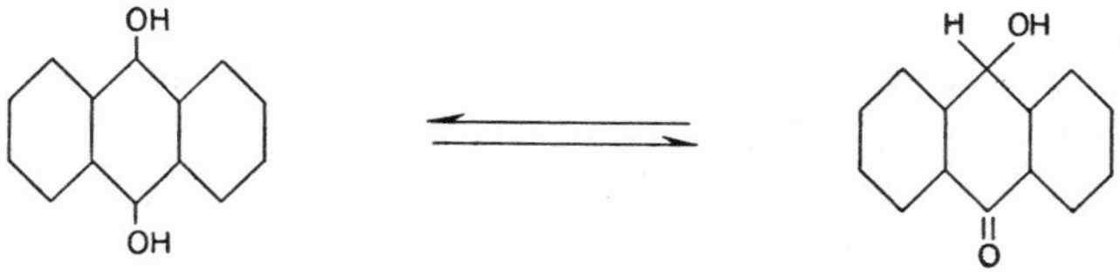

In most cases the latter are more stable than are the anthrahydroquinones. Leucoquinizarin may be variously represented as follows:

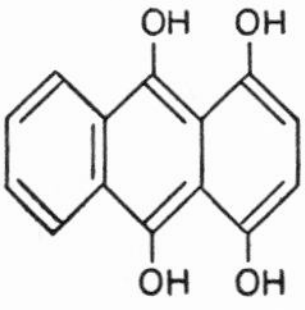

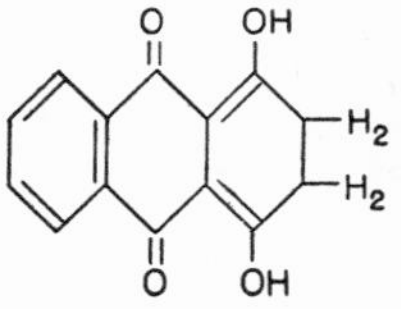

The stability of leucoquinizarin as well as its slight solubility in caustic does not agree with formula (I). Infrared measurements seem to support a resonance hybrid of (II) and (III)[33].

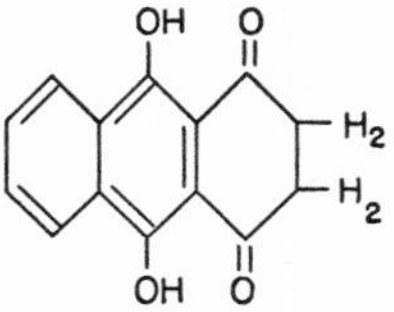

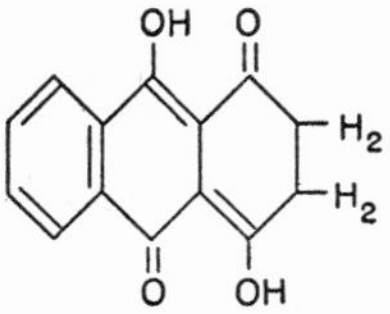

The easy reaction with ammonia at 30°C to yield leuco-1-amino-4-hydroxyanthraquinone and at 100°C to yield leuco-1,4-diaminoanthraquinone is most unusual.

The condensations of leucoquinizarin with aromatic amines are catalyzed by either weak acids (H_3BO_3) or small amounts of strong acids. These reactions are perhaps analogous to the reactions of beta-diketones and beta-ketoesters with ammonia and aromatic amines.

The I.G. Farbenindustrie scientists favored the Zahn formula (III, above) and prepared a further reduction product which still was capable of being aminated in a manner similar to that of leucoquinizarin[177], as shown by the following scheme:

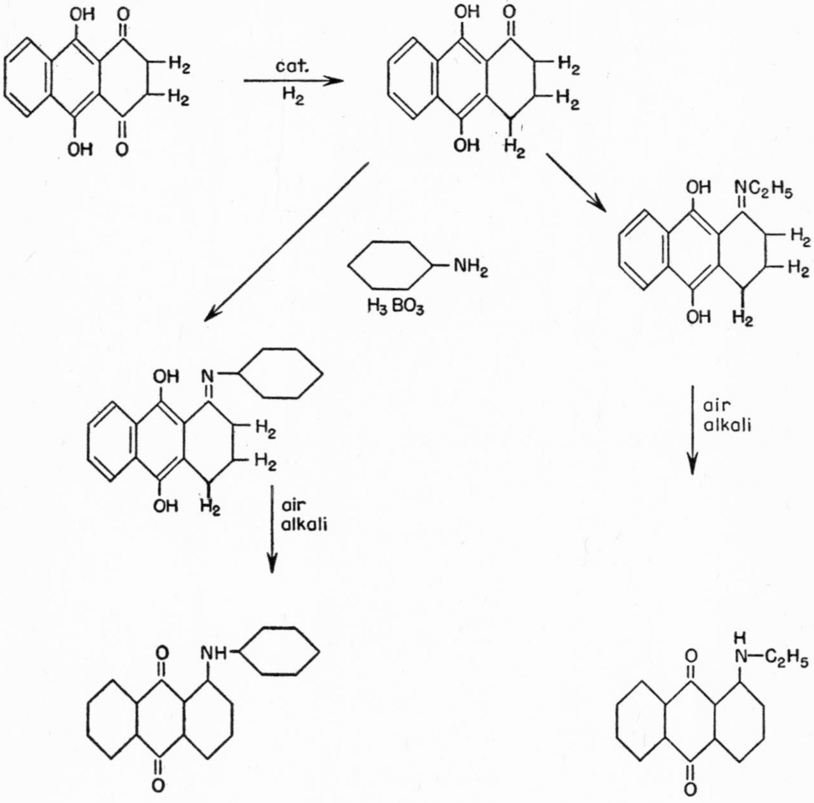

Some very important technical products are listed below, formed by the replacement of one or both of the hydroxy groups of quinizarin via the leuco (see Preparation of Aminoanthraquinones)[108, 141, 161, 174, 189, 262].

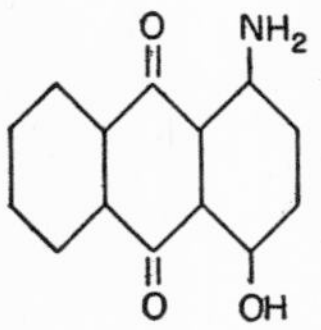

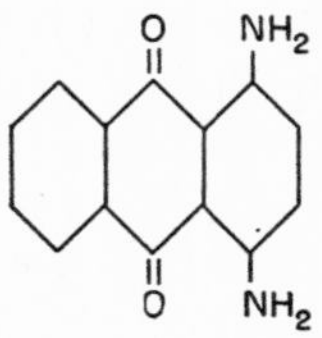

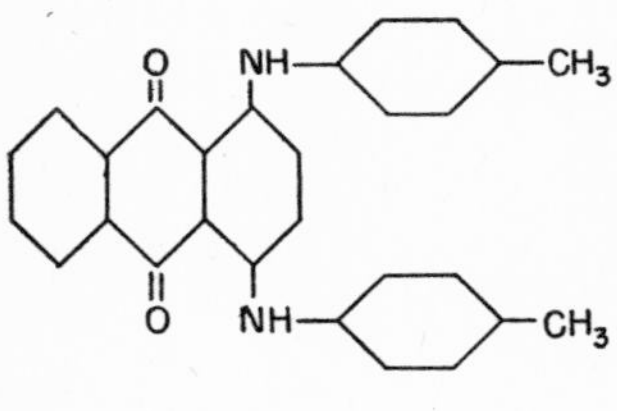

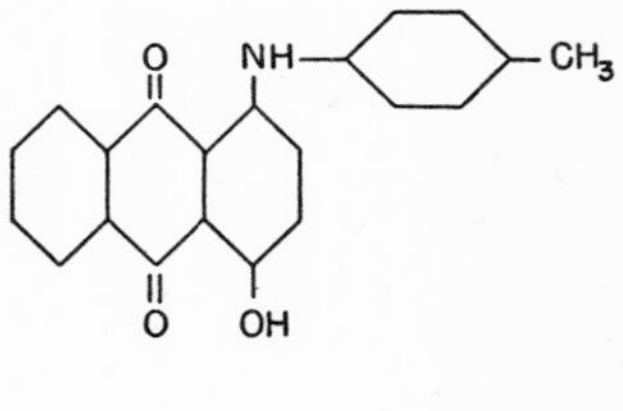

The difference in the mode of reaction of 5,8-dichloroquinizarin and its leuco derivative is illustrated by the following reactions[263].

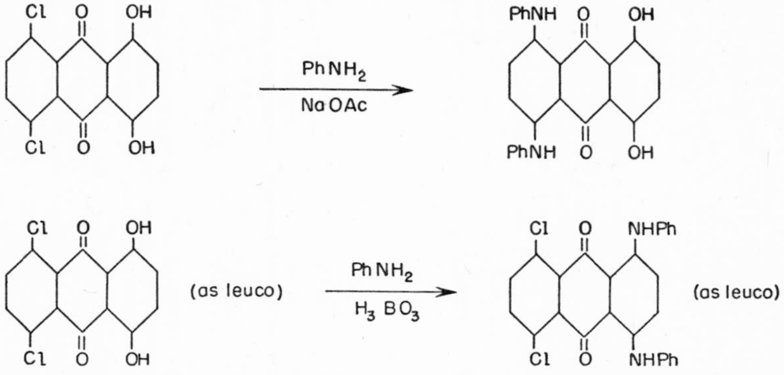

The leucoquinizarin type amination may take place in certain analogous heterocyclics[73]:

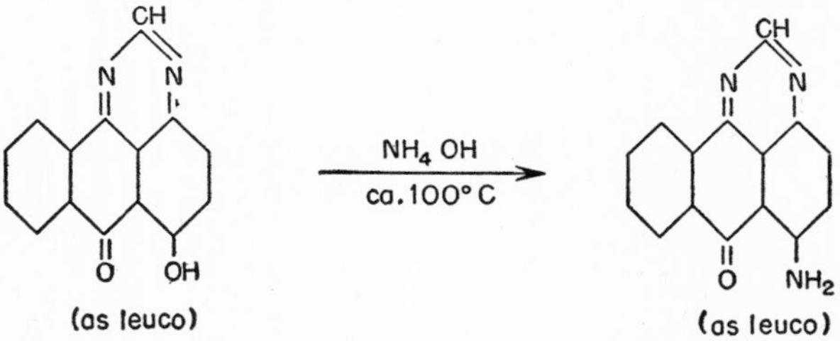

The amination of leucoquinizarin is a reversible reaction and leuco-1,4-diaminoanthraquinone may be reverted to leucoquinizarin by aqueous caustic. This deamination may be accomplished even in heterocyclics that have the 1,4-diamine structure[181]:

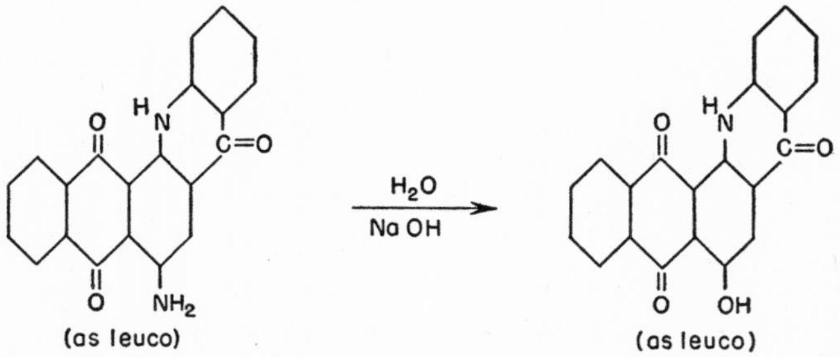

The corresponding aminothiaxanthenone also reacts similarly[181].

Leuco-1,4-diaminoanthraquinone is readily oxidized to the 1,4-diaminoanthraquinone by nitrobenzene at 150°C with a trace of piperidine[141]. Leuco-hydroxyanthraquinones are easily oxidized by sodium *m*-nitrobenzenesulfonate in aqueous alkali.

Alkylation of Leucoquinizarin. When quinizarin is treated with caustic and hydrosulfite in the presence of an aldehyde, a 2,3-dialkylation product results[205]:

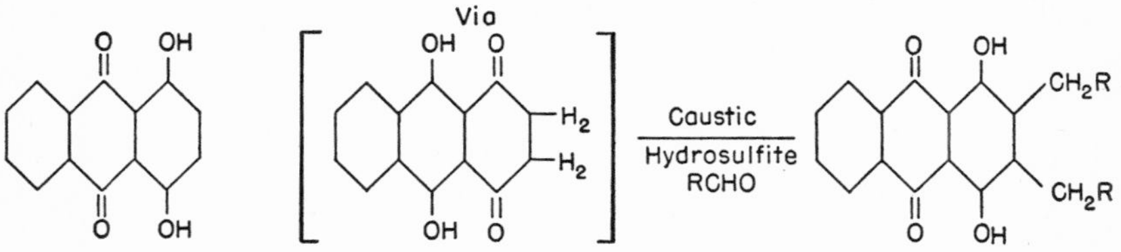

It is believed that the leuco intermediates are best represented by formula III to explain the above reaction.

The following alkylation products may be made directly from the amino or hydroxyanthraquinones. The reaction reminds one of the behavior of quinizarin and of 1,4-diaminoanthraquinone[205].

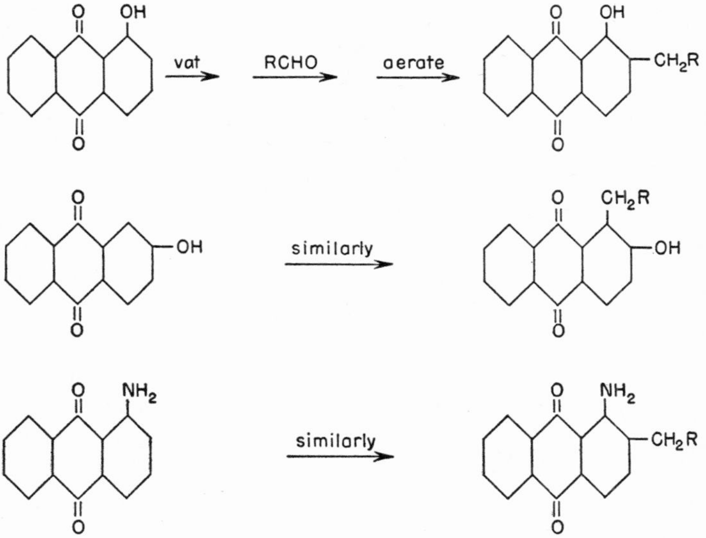

Decarboxylation, Dehalogenation and Desulfonation of 2-Substituted 1,4-Dihydroxy and 1,4-Diaminoanthraquinones. It is not surprising that 2-substituents may sometimes be removed by vatting, considering the activity of the 2 position toward hydrogen "addition"[185, 204].

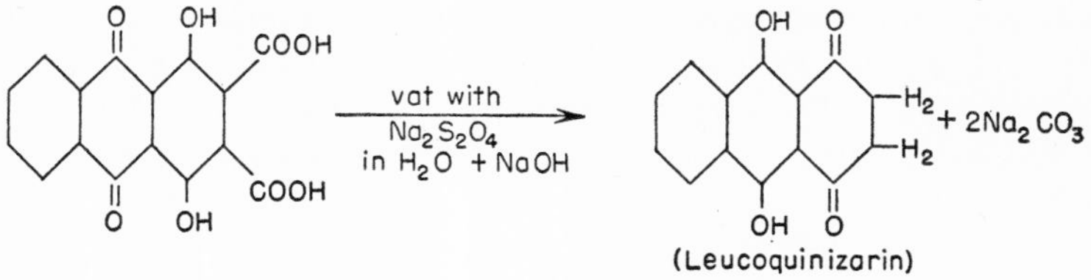

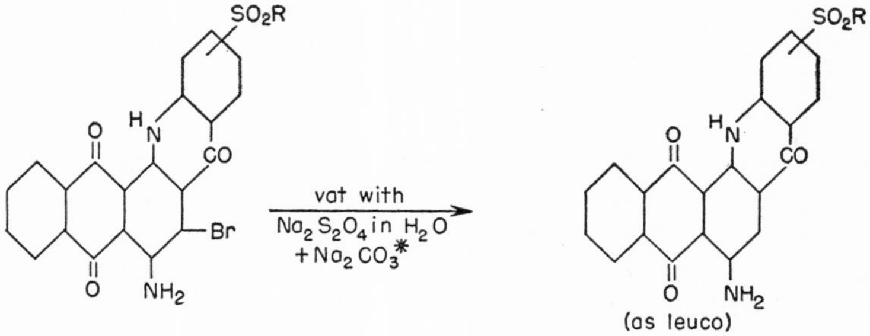

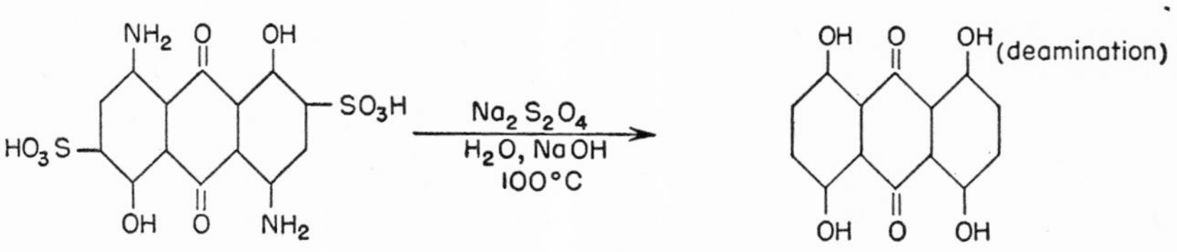

(Leucoquinizarin)

(as leuco)

(deamination)

Benzanthrone Intermediates

Preparation of Benzanthrone (7H-Benz[de]anthracen-7-one). *Glycerine Synthesis* (Aldehyde-Anthrone Condensations). Anthraquinone gives benzanthrone when treated in 82 per cent sulfuric acid with metal (Fe, Cu) powder and glycerine. The glycerine is converted to acrolein and the anthraquinone to anthrone (9,10-dihydro-9-oxoanthracene), the reac-

---

* *Note:* As 1,4-diamine products can deaminate with caustic and hydrosulfite, soda ash should be used in place of caustic in the vatting operation if nitrogen retention is desired.

tion taking place as follows[2, 132]:

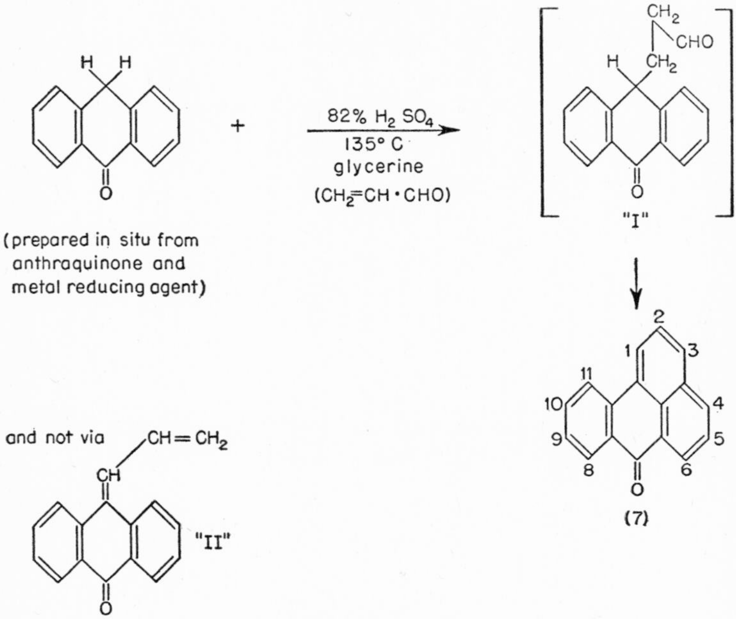
H H
82% H_2SO_4
135° C
glycerine
(CH_2=CH·CHO)
CH_2
CHO
H CH_2
O
"I"
(prepared in situ from
anthraquinone and
metal reducing agent)
and not via
CH=CH_2
CH
"II"
1 2 3 4 5 6 8 9 10 11
(7)

The use of a substituted acrolein has shown that the reaction proceeds via "I," e.g.[34, 178, 179],

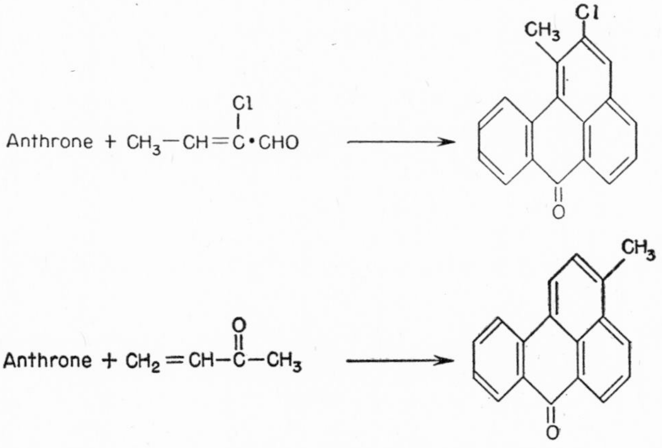
Anthrone + CH_3—CH=C(Cl)·CHO
CH_3
Cl
Anthrone + CH_2=CH—C(=O)—CH_3
CH_3

According to the normal practice for anthraquinone, the double bonds in benzanthrone will be omitted in the following formulas unless necessary to illustrate a point. Furthermore, intermediates of type I may be isolated when anthrone is condensed with an alpha-beta unsaturated ketone and a basic catalyst such as piperidine[38, 251]. Most of such compounds do not cyclize to give benzanthrones however.

The similarity of the Skraup and the benzanthrone reactions has been noted[2].

However, cinnamaldehyde reacts with anthrone presumably according to the scheme[170]:

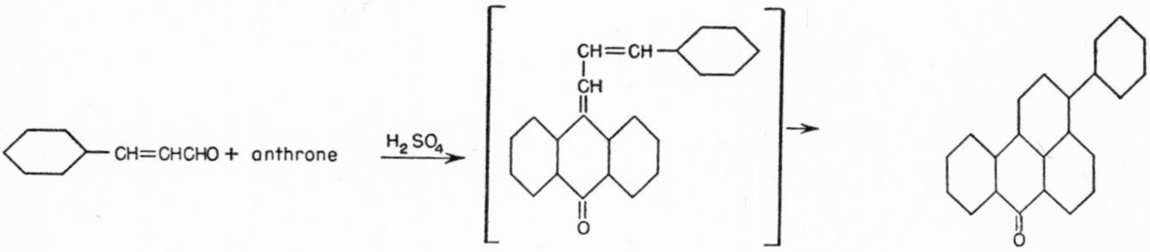

Scholl Method. Benzanthrone may also result by the Scholl peri ring-closure method from 1-benzoylnaphthalene as follows[235, 236]:

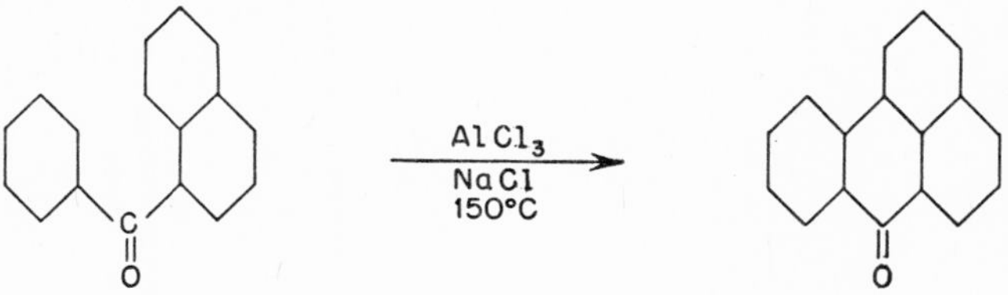

A recent innovation uses sodium *m*-nitrobenzenesulfonate as the oxidizing agent[206].

The vigorous conditions of the Scholl ring-closure often give isomerization, as shown below, so that a fluorenone sometimes is the chief product[28].

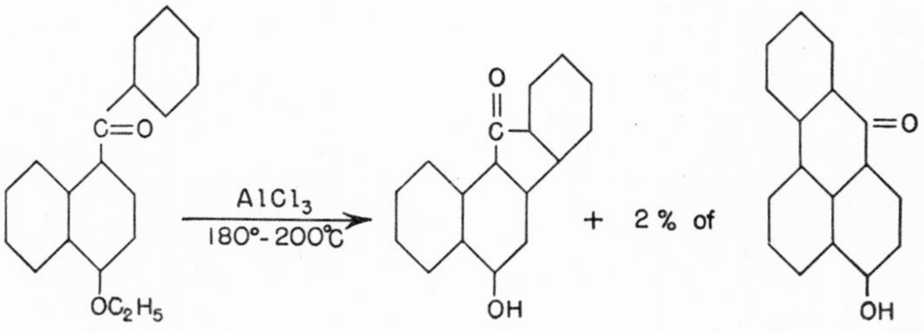

Diene Route. Methyleneanthrone, which may be considered a condensed diene, gives substituted benzanthrones in good yield and quality when condensed with alpha-beta unsaturated ketones[1, 16, 186]:

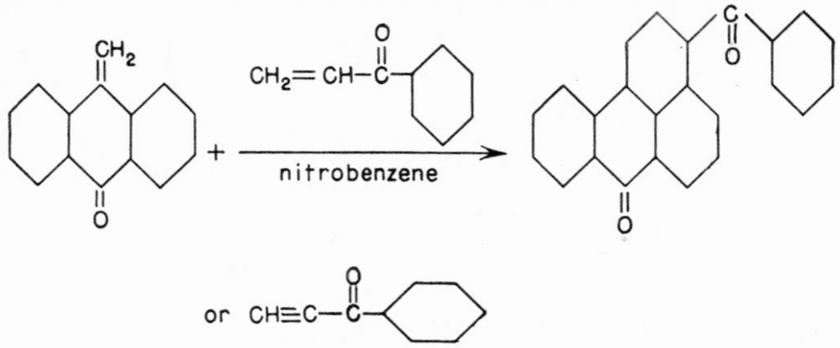

Mixed Biaryl Route. The Gomberg reaction can give appropriately substituted biaryls which may be ring-closed to benzanthrones[79].

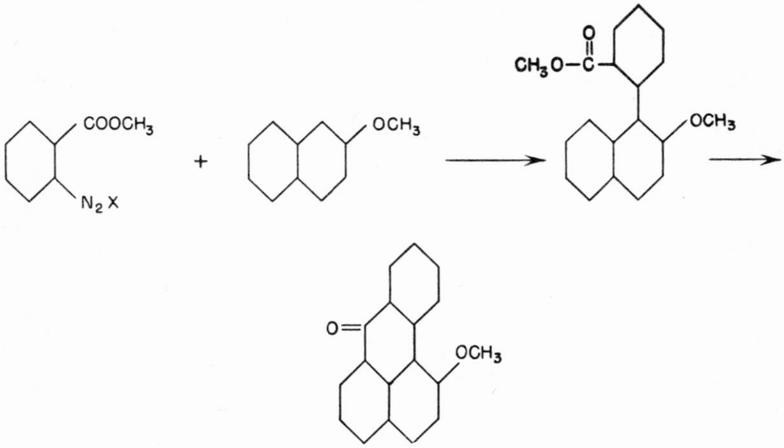

Similarly, a mixed Ullmann reaction may be used (in which a halobenzene derivative is condensed with a halonaphthalene one), the product then being ring-closed[222].

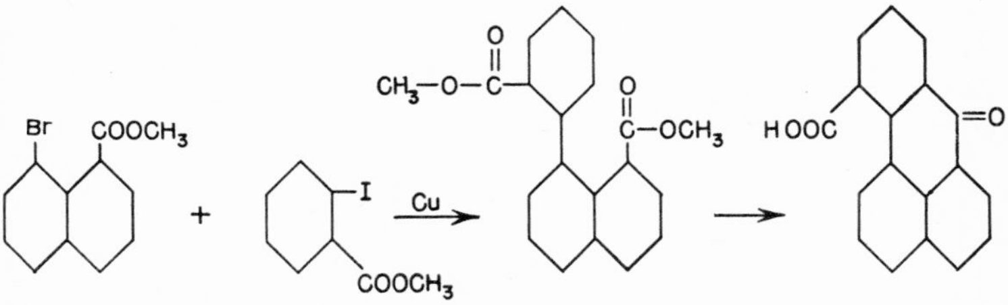

Chemistry of Benzanthrone. *Electrophilic and Nucleophilic Attack on Benzanthrone.* Benzanthrone is substituted more readily by both nucleophilic and electrophilic reagents than is anthraquinone. The susceptibility of benzanthrone to nucleophilic attack can be rationalized by the following resonance structures:

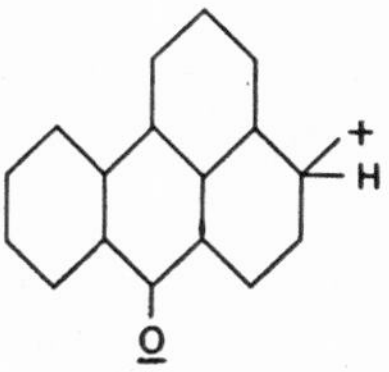

Nucleophilic attack yields the following derivatives, as would be expected, although there is no theory to explain which of the vinylogous points will be substituted[10, 13, 200, 211].

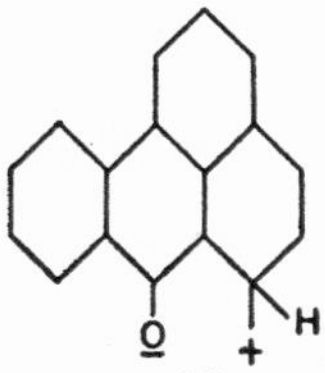

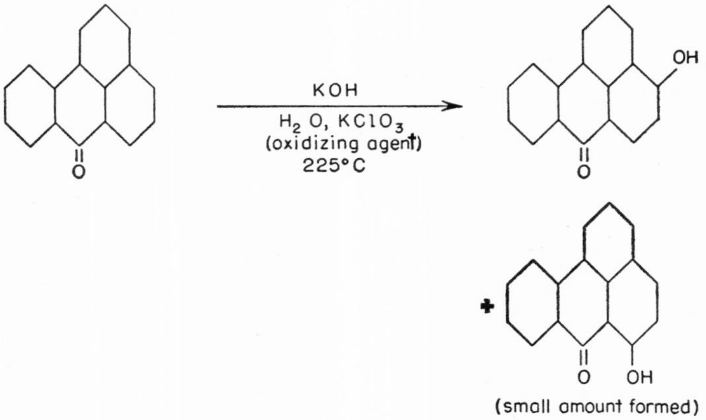

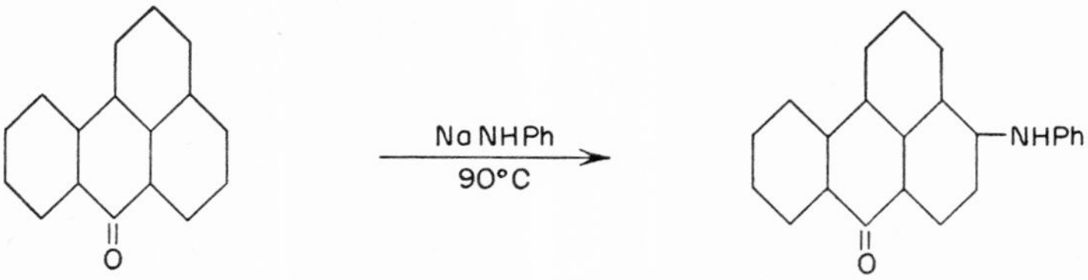

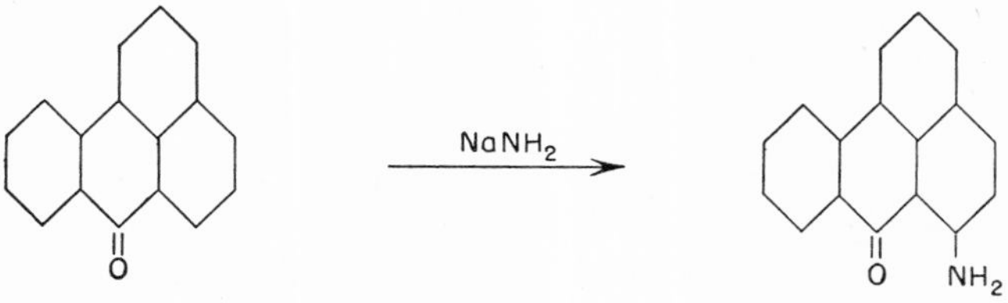

(small amount formed)

Electrophilic reagents also act upon benzanthrone. Bromine gives an addition compound from which the benzanthrone may be recovered by heating with thiosulfate[14]. Under mild heating the addition compound is converted into 3-bromobenzanthrone. Excess bromine yields 3,9-dibromobenzanthrone:

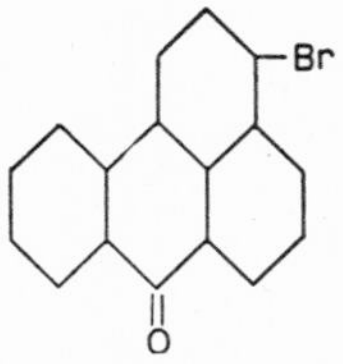

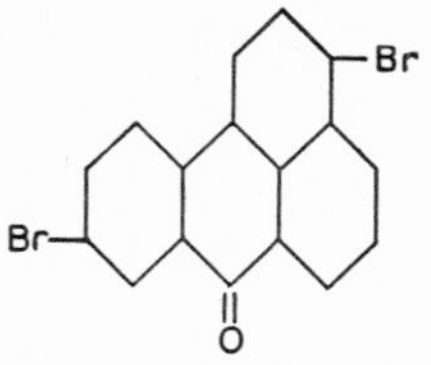

Nitric acid in nitrobenzene gives the 3-nitro product[194], but sulfuric acid substitutes the 9 position[213].

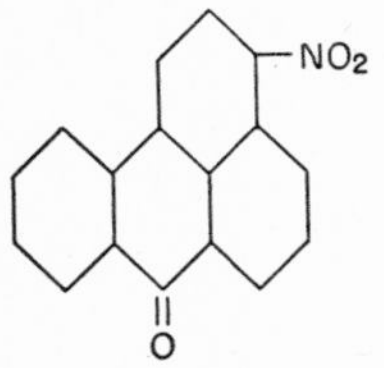

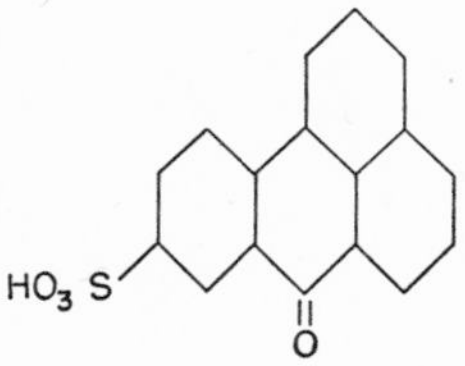

The 4,4'-Bibenzanthrone Fusion. One of the most important reactions of benzanthrone is its condensation to 4,4'-bibenzanthrone ([4,4'-bi-7H-benz[de]anthracene]-7,7'-dione) under alkaline conditions[148].

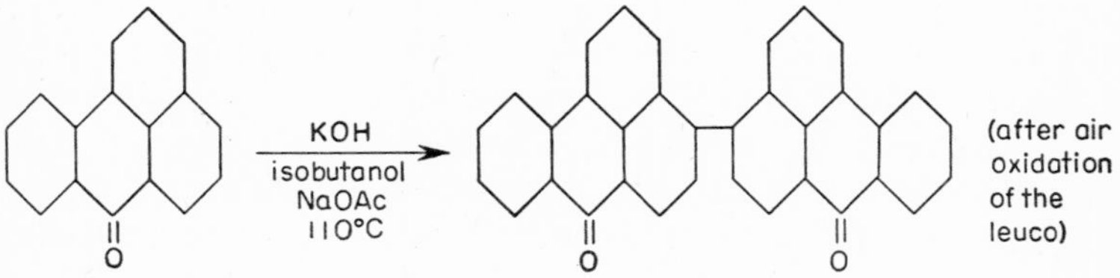

The explanation by Luettringhaus[200] of the mechanism of this reaction as proceeding through a divalent radical intermediate seems unlikely. The most significant factor is that coupling takes place at the most positive point in the benzanthrone molecule. This is the point of nucleophilic attack under *oxidizing* conditions. Yet the fusion occurs under nonoxidizing, or even mildly reducing conditions.

Bradley's theories[11] indicate that the strongly alkaline conditions give rise to minute amounts of a benzanthrone carbanion. This may then attack a molecule of benzanthrone that has the normal induced positive charge at the 2 position, as indicated by the scheme:

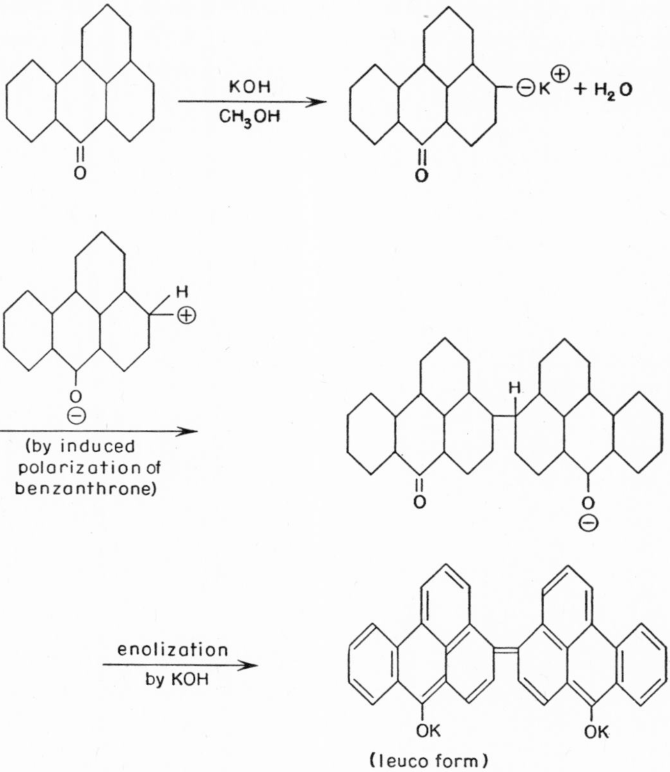

(by induced
polarization of
benzanthrone)

enolization
by KOH

(leuco form)

Although the coupling fusion takes place under reducing conditions (which should inhibit nucleophilic substitution of OH) it is not surprising that a small amount of nucleophilic substitution takes place. 4-Hydroxybenzanthrone has been isolated from the KOH—CH₃OH coupling fusion and 4-anilinobenzanthrone is a by-product in the sodium anilide coupling fusion.

The known reaction of benzanthrone with carbanions lends support to Bradley's explanation[67, 68]:

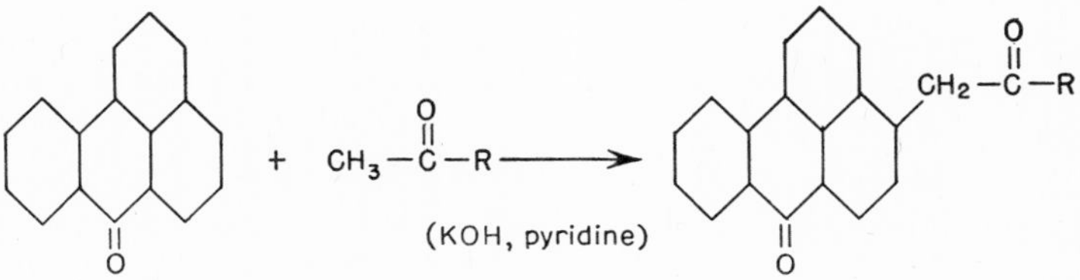

The 3,3'-Bibenzanthrone Coupling. The oxidative coupling of electron-rich aromatic systems to biaryls is a rather common reaction in aromatic chemistry, e.g., the oxidation of 2-naphthol to 1,1'-bi-2-naphthol and of diphenylamine to N,N'-diphenylbenzidine. The point of union is the location of negative aromatic carbon, namely a point where electrophilic substitution takes place.

Similarly, benzanthrones may be oxidatively coupled at the point of electrophilic substitution[84, 149, 195].

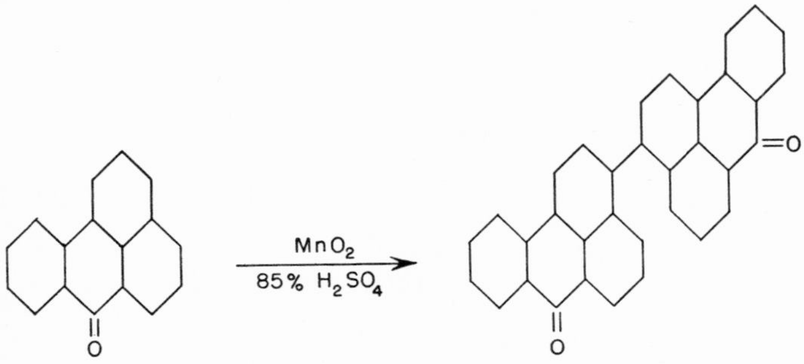

MnO$_2$
85% H$_2$SO$_4$

3, 3'-Bibenzanthrone
([3, 3'- Bi -7H-benz [de] anthracen]-
7, 7'-dione)

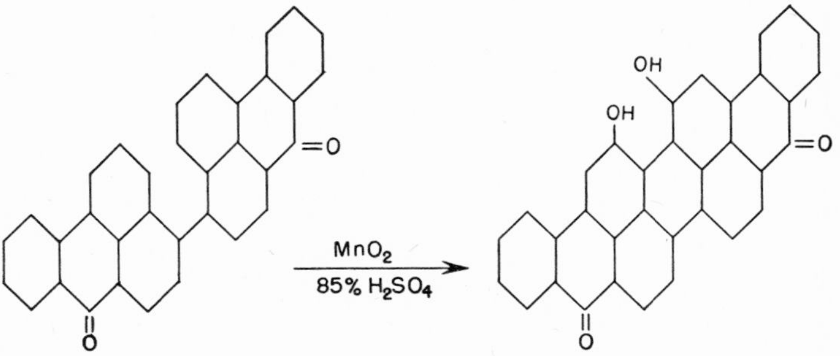

MnO$_2$
85% H$_2$SO$_4$

The subsequent hydroxylation may be avoided by using H$_3$AsO$_4$ in H$_2$SO$_4$[85].

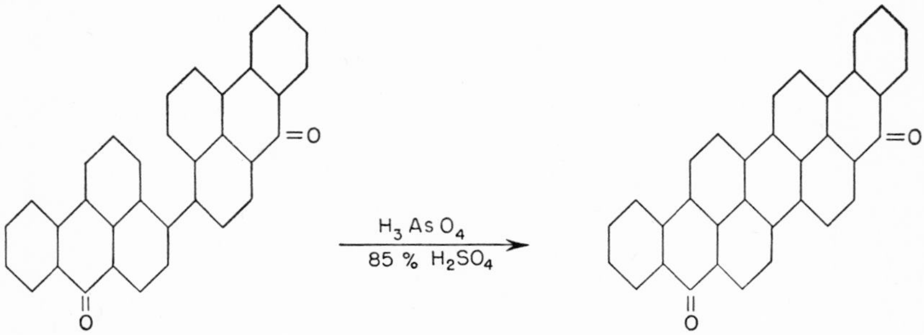

H$_3$AsO$_4$
85 % H$_2$SO$_4$

It will be recognized that the last two reactions give rise to vat dyes of the dibenzanthrone type. These and other vat dyes (exclusive of indigo and thioindigo and their derivatives) are discussed in subsequent sections, following those on acid, metallizable and disperse types of anthraquinone dyes.

Literature Cited

1. Allen, Bell (A.C.), Bell (Alan), and Van Allan, *J. Am. Chem. Soc.*, **62**, 656 (1940).
2. —— and Overbaugh, *ibid.*, **57**, 1322 (1935).
3. Bailey, U. S. Patent 1,515,325 (1924).
4. Barnett and Hewitt, *J. Chem. Soc.*, **1932**, 506.
5. —— and Wiltshire, *ibid.*, **1928**, 1822.
6. Baeyer and Drewsen, *Ann.*, **212**, 345 (1882).
7. Beard, U. S. Patent 2,378,745 (1945).
8. Beisler and Jones, *J. Am. Chem. Soc.*, **44**, 2296 (1922).
9. Bergmann, *J. Chem. Soc.*, **1938**, 1147.
10. Bradley, *ibid.*, **1948**, 1175.
11. —— and Jadhav, *ibid.*, **1948**, 1622.
12. —— and Leete, *ibid.*, **1951**, 2129, 2147.
13. Bradshaw and Perkin, *ibid.*, **121**, 911 (1922).
14. Brass and Clar, *Ber.*, **69**, 690 (1936).
15. British Patent 334,166 (*C.A.*, **25**, 1100) (1930).
16. British Patent 604,491 (1948).
17. Calcott, Tinker and Linch, U. S. Patent 2,174,118 (1939).
18. Cook, *J. Chem. Soc.*, **1932**, 1472.
19. Corbellini and Cecchi, *Gazz. chim. ital*, **63**, 489 (1933).
20. Crowell, U. S. Patent 1,892,871 (1933).
21. Day, *J. Chem. Soc.*, **1939**, 816.
22. Deichler and Weizmann, *Ber.*, **36**, 547 (1903).
23. Deinet and Stilmar, U. S. Patent 2,487,110 (1949).
24. Diels and Alder, *Ber.*, **62**, 2337 (1929).
25. Eckert and Tomaschek, *Monatsh.*, **39**, 839 (1918).
26. Elbs, *J. prakt. Chem.*, **41**, 1 and 121 (1890).
27. Fanta, *Chem. Revs.*, **38**, 139 (1946).
28. Fierz-David and Jaccard, *Helv. Chim. Acta*, **11**, 1042 (1928).
29. Fieser, "Organic Reactions," Vol. I, p. 129.
30. —— and Hershberg, *J. Am. Chem. Soc.*, **59**, 1028 (1937).
31. —— and Martin, *ibid.*, **58**, 1443 (1936).
32. —— and Peters, *ibid.*, **54**, 3742 (1932).
33. Flett, *J. Chem. Soc.*, **1948**, 1441.
34. French Patent 631,995 (1927).
35. French Patent 828,202 (*C.A.*, **33**, 176) (1938).
36. Frey, *Ber.*, **45**, 1359 (1912).
37. Fries and Schurmann, *ibid.*, **52**, 2182 (1919).
38. Gagnon and Gravel, *Can. J. Research*, **8**, 600 (1933).
39. Gattermann, *Ann.*, **393**, 113 (1912).
40. ——, *ibid.*, **393**, 158, 166, 170, 174 (1912).
41. ——, *ibid.*, **393**, 150 (1912).
42. German Patent 75,054 (1894).
43. German Patent 106,505 (1899).
44. German Patent 131,538 (1902).
45. German Patent 156,762 (1904).

46. German Patent 165,728 (1905).
47. German Patent 172,642 (1906).
48. German Patent 186,526 (1907).
49. German Patent 205,881 (1909).
50. German Patent 206,536 (1909).
51. German Patent 228,901 (1910).
52. German Patent 229,316 (1910).
53. German Patent 252,578 (1912).
54. German Patent 253,683 (1912).
55. German Patent 254,450 (1912).
56. German Patent 263,395 (1913).
57. German Patent 266,563 (1913).
58. German Patent 282,493 (1915).
59. German Patent 289,112 (1915).
60. German Patent 290,084 (1916).
61. German Patent 343,064 (1921).
62. German Patent 346,188 (1921).
63. German Patent 359,138 (1922).
64. German Patent 360,422 (1922).
65. German Patent 364,181 (1922).
66. German Patent 479,917 (1929).
67. German Patent 499,320 (1930).
68. German Patent 501,082 (1930).
69. German Patent 523,523 (1931).
70. German Patent 538,014 (1931).
71. German Patent 580,647 (1933).
72. German Patent 581,439 (1933).
73. German Patent 651,431 (1937).
74. Gleason and Dougherty, *J. Am. Chem. Soc.*, **51**, 310 (1929).
75. Graebe, *Ann.*, **349**, 215 (1906).
76. —— and Liebermann, *ibid.*, **160**, 121, 130, 141 (1871).
77. Groggins and Newton, *Ind. Eng. Chem.*, **21**, 369 (1929).
78. Hayashi, *J. Chem. Soc.*, **1930**, 1520, 1524.
79. Heilbron, Hey and Wilkinson, *ibid.*, **1938**, 699.
80. Heller, *Ber.*, **45**, 792 (1912).
81. Houben, "Das Anthracen und die Anthrachinone," p. 284.
82. ——, *ibid.*, pp. 319, 321.
83. ——, *ibid.*, p. 714.
84. Howell, U.S. Patent 2,001,063 (1935).
85. ——, U.S. Patent 2,388,743 (1945).
86. Huber, *Helv. Chim. Acta*, **15**, 1372 (1932).
87. I.G. Farbenindustrie, BIOS 987, p. 12 (PB 75860).
88. ——, *ibid.*, p. 13.
89. ——, *ibid.*, p. 17.
90. ——, *ibid.*, p. 36.
91. ——, *ibid.*, pp. 60–63.
92. ——, *ibid.*, pp. 63–64.
93. ——, BIOS 1484, p. 5 (PB 86139).
94. ——, *ibid.*, p. 7.
95. ——, *ibid.*, p. 8.
96. ——, *ibid.*, p. 11.

97. ——, *ibid.*, p. 12.
98. ——, *ibid.*, p. 14.
99. ——, *ibid.*, p. 15.
100. ——, *ibid.*, p. 18.
101. ——, *ibid.*, pp. 18, 62.
102. ——, *ibid.*, p. 19.
103. ——, *ibid.*, p. 20.
104. ——, *ibid.*, p. 22.
105. ——, *ibid.*, p. 28.
106. ——, *ibid.*, p. 29.
107. ——, *ibid.*, p. 33.
108. ——, *ibid.*, p. 48.
109. ——, *ibid.*, p. 49.
110. ——, *ibid.*, p. 50.
111. ——, *ibid.*, p. 55.
112. ——, *ibid.*, p. 59.
113. ——, *ibid.*, p. 63.
114. ——, *ibid.*, p. 64.
115. ——, *ibid.*, p. 65.
116. ——, *ibid.*, p. 67.
117. ——, *ibid.*, p. 68.
118. ——, BIOS 1493, p. 8 (PB 81611).
119. ——, *ibid.*, p. 15.
120. ——, *ibid.*, p. 18.
121. ——, *ibid.*, p. 19.
122. ——, *ibid.*, p. 41.
123. ——, *ibid.*, p. 44.
124. ——, FIAT 917 (PB 44961).
125. ——, FIAT 1313, Vol. I, pp. 318, 378 (PB 85172).
126. ——, *ibid.*, p. 348.
127. ——, FIAT 1313, Vol. II, p. 19 (PB 85172).
128. ——, *ibid.*, p. 22.
129. ——, *ibid.*, pp. 25, 26.
130. ——, *ibid.*, p. 28.
131. ——, *ibid.*, pp. 28, 60.
132. ——, *ibid.*, p. 31.
133. ——, *ibid.*, p. 34.
134. ——, *ibid.*, p. 35.
135. ——, *ibid.*, pp. 36, 37.
136. ——, *ibid.*, p. 40.
137. ——, *ibid.*, p. 41.
138. ——, *ibid.*, p. 43.
139. ——, *ibid.*, p. 47.
140. ——, *ibid.*, pp. 50–56.
141. ——, *ibid.*, p. 51.
142. ——, *ibid.*, p. 52.
143. ——, *ibid.*, p. 54.
144. ——, *ibid.*, p. 56.
145. ——, *ibid.*, p. 64.
146. ——, *ibid.*, p. 69.
147. ——, *ibid.*, p. 70.

148. ——, *ibid.*, p. 83.
149. ——, *ibid.*, p. 85.
150. ——, *ibid.*, p. 98.
151. ——, *ibid.*, pp. 143, 227–230.
152. ——, *ibid.*, pp. 154–157.
153. ——, *ibid.*, p. 172.
154. ——, *ibid.*, p. 201.
155. ——, *ibid.*, p. 203.
156. ——, *ibid.*, p. 206.
157. ——, *ibid.*, p. 207.
158. ——, *ibid.*, p. 212.
159. ——, *ibid.*, p. 213.
160. ——, *ibid.*, p. 214.
161. ——, *ibid.*, p. 215.
162. ——, *ibid.*, p. 216.
163. ——, *ibid.*, p. 220.
164. ——, *ibid.*, p. 221.
165. ——, *ibid.*, p. 222.
166. ——, *ibid.*, p. 223.
167. ——, *ibid.*, p. 224.
168. ——, *ibid.*, p. 225.
169. ——, *ibid.*, p. 226.
170. ——, FIAT 1313, Vol. III, p. 28 (PB 85172).
171. ——, *ibid.*, p. 74.
172. ——, *ibid.*, p. 85.
173. ——, PB 70057, frames 8366, 8368.
174. ——, PB 70332, frame 437.
175. ——, PB 70338, frame 9949.
176. ——, *ibid.*, frame 10292.
177. ——, *ibid.*, frame 10303.
178. ——, *ibid.*, frame 10487.
179. ——, *ibid.*, frame 10627.
180. ——, PB 70340, frame 12516.
181. ——, PB 70342, frame 14653.
182. ——, *ibid.*, frame 14806.
183. ——, *ibid.*, frame 14880.
184. ——, PB 74898, frame 9536.
185. Irving, Heslop and Livingston, U.S. Patent 2,481,744 (1949).
186. —— and Johnson, *J. Chem. Soc.*, **1948**, 2037.
187. Junghaus, *Ann.*, **399**, 326 (1913).
188. Kacer and Scholl, *Ber.*, **37**, 4185 (1904).
189. Klein, U.S. Patent 2,419,405 (1947).
190. Kraenzlein, *Ber.*, **70**, 1952 (1937).
191. Laube, *ibid.*, **40**, 3562 (1907).
192. Lauer, *J. prakt. Chem.*, **130**, 185 (1931).
193. ——, *ibid.*, **135**, 164 (1932).
194. —— and Atarashi, *Ber.*, **68**, 1373 (1935).
195. Lee and Howell, U.S. Patent 2,413,507 (1946).
196. —— and Klein, U.S. Patent 2,169,196 (1939).
197. Liebermann, *Ann.*, **183**, 145, 205, 217 (1876).
198. —— and Kostanecki, *ibid.*, **240**, 267 (1887).

199. Luettringhaus and Eifflaender, U.S. Patent 1,394,851 (1921).
200. —— and Neresheimer, *Ann.*, **473**, 259 (1929).
201. ——, Neresheimer, Eichholz, Boehner and Schneider, U.S. Patent 1,890,040 (1932).
202. Marschalk, *Bull. soc. chim. France* [5], **2**, 1810 (1935).
203. ——, *ibid.*, **4**, 629 (1937).
204. ——, *ibid.*, **2**, 1821 (1935).
205. ——, Koenig and Ouroussoff, *ibid.*, [5], **3**, 1545 (1936).
206. Moergeli, Krauer and Bommer, U.S. Patent 2,238,180 (1941).
207. Moehlau, *Ber.*, **45**, 2244 (1912).
208. Nawiasky, Stein and Krause, U.S. Patent 1,943,876 (1934).
209. Norton, *Chem. Revs.*, **31**, 319 (1942).
210. Perkin, *J. Chem. Soc.*, **117**, 706 (1920).
211. —— and Spencer, *ibid.*, **121**, 474 (1922).
212. Perkins and Deinet, U.S. Patent 2,180,835 (1939).
213. Pritchard and Simonsen, *J. Chem. Soc.*, **1938**, 2047.
214. Randall and Renfrew, U.S. Patent 2,560,887 (1951).
215. Reid, MacKall and Miller, *J. Am. Chem. Soc.*, **43**, 2104 (1921).
216. Reynolds and Bigelow, *ibid.*, **48**, 420 (1926).
217. Rintelman, U.S. Patent 1,899,986 (1933).
218. ——, U.S. Patent 1,899,987 (1933).
219. Roemer, *Ber.*, **15**, 1793 (1882).
220. Rubidge and Qua, *J. Am. Chem. Soc.*, **36**, 732 (1914).
221. Ruggli and Heitz, *Helv. Chim. Acta*, **14**, 257 (1931).
222. Rule, Pursell and Barnett, *J. Chem. Soc.*, **1935**, 571.
223. Schaarschmidt and Herzenberg, *Ber.*, **53**, 1807 (1920).
224. Schmidt, *ibid.*, **37**, 66 (1904).
225. ——, *Bull. Soc. Ind. Mulhouse*, **84**, 409 (1914).
226. Scholl, *Ber.*, **40**, 1696 (1907).
227. ——, *ibid.*, **43**, 346 (1910).
228. —— and Dahll, *ibid.*, **74B**, 1129 (1941).
229. —— and Dischendorfer, *ibid.*, **51**, 441 (1918).
230. ——, Donat and Boettger, *Ann.*, **512**, 124 (1934).
231. —— and Eberle, *Monatsh.*, **32**, 1036 (1911).
232. ——, Hass and Meyer, *Ber.*, **62**, 107 (1929).
233. ——, Meyer and Keller, *Ann.*, **513**, 295 (1934).
234. —— and Neovius, *Ber.*, **44**, 1075 (1911).
235. —— and Seer, *Ann.*, **394**, 111 (1912).
236. —— and ——, *Monatsh.*, **33**, 1 (1912).
237. —— and Ziegs, *Ber.*, **67**, 1746 (1934).
238. Seymour, Salvin and Hieserman, U.S. Patent 2,445,007 (1948).
239. —— and Salvin, U.S. Patent 2,480,269 (1949).
240. Simon, *Ber.*, **14**, 464 (1881).
241. Thomas, U. S. Patent 1,504,164 (1924).
242. —— and Drescher, U.S. Patent 1,779,221 (1930).
243. Ullmann and Conzetti, *Ber.*, **53**, 830 (1920).
244. —— and ——, *ibid.*, **53**, 833 (1920).
245. —— and Eiser, *ibid.*, **49**, 2154 (1916).
246. —— and Fodor, *Ann.*, **380**, 317 (1911).
247. —— and Medenwald, *Ber.*, **46**, 1798 (1913).
248. —— and Minajeff, *ibid.*, **45**, 687 (1912).

249. —— and Schmidt, *ibid.*, **52**, 2098 (1919).
250. —— and ——, *ibid.*, **52**, 2111 (1919).
251. Vachon, Gagnon and Kane, *Can. J. Research*, **11**, 644 (1934).
252. Waldmann and Polak, *J. prakt. Chem.*, **150**, 113 (1938).
253. Waldron and Franklin, U.S. Patent 2,378,812 (1945).
254. Weinand and Kalckbrenner, U.S. Patent 2,027,658 (1936).
255. Weinmayr, U.S. Patent 2,242,842 (1941).
256. Weiss and Knapp, *Monatsh.*, **47**, 485 (1926).
257. Weizmann, Bergmann (E), and Bergmann (F), *J. Chem. Soc.*, **1935**, 1367.
258. ——, Haskelberg and Berlin, *ibid.*, **1939**, 398.
259. Whelen, U.S. Patent 2,181,034 (1939).
260. ——, U.S. Patent 2,302,729 (1942).
261. Wuertz, U.S. Patent 1,950,348 (1934).
262. —— and Klein, U.S. Patent 2,353,108 (1944).
263. Zahn and Ochwat, *Ann.*, **462**, 76, 95 (1928).
264. —— and ——, *ibid.*, **462**, 72 (1928).
265. Zerweck and Schutz, U.S. Patent 2,280,504 (1942).

ANTHRAQUINONE ACID DYES

Edwin C. Buxbaum

These colors will be treated under the following headings:

Sulfonation of anthraquinone acid color bases.

Anthraquinone acid dyes derived from dihydroxyanthraquinones.

Heterocyclic acid dyes.

Anthrimides and naphthocarbazoles.

Dyes derived from bromamine acid.

The anthraquinone acid colors appeared early in the history of anthraquinone dyes in the period from about 1893 to about 1907. The first anthraquinone vat dye was discovered by Bohn in 1901. A great many of the anthraquinone acid colors which were discovered in that period are still of great commercial importance. Chief among these colors are the following

Dye	Discoverer	Date of Discovery	CI
Alizarine Sky Blue B	Unger	1899	1088
Cyananthrol	Isler	1900	1076
Alizarine Astrol	Schmidt	1901	1075
Alizarine Irisol R	Schmidt	1894	1074
Alizarine Blue Black B	Schmidt	1894	1085
Alizarine Cyanine Green	Schmidt	1894	1078
Alizarine Saphirol B	Schmidt	1897	1054
Alizarine Saphirol SE	Schmidt	1897	1053
Anthraquinone Violet	Isler	1898	1080
Alizarine Rubinol R	Thomaschewski	1907	1091

Their impact on the wool-dyeing world was tremendous since here for the first time was a class of dyes that could be easily applied like the triphenylmethane, azine or azo dyes of that period but far exceeded them in lightfastness. Their great advantage over the older mordant dyes for wool lay in their simplicity of application. Unlike the mordant colors, they required no previous preparation of the fiber and were applied in a single bath in a weak acid solution at a temperature close to the boiling point.

Their fastness properties, by present standards, are good since they are fairly resistant to light, washing treatments and perspiration. They give bright clear shades of a wide range of colors. They are especially rich in blue, violet and green shades. While the older colors of this group were chiefly in the violet-indigo-blue part of the spectrum, that condition is not true today. Modern acid colors in the yellow, orange and red shade are quite common and often have the brilliancy of the azo colors in that shade range plus fastness properties of a degree not known even in the older anthraquinone types. Brown, gray and black shades of good fastness properties can also be obtained. The United States production and sales figures for this class of colors taken from the reports of the U. S. Tariff Commission on Synthetic Organic Chemicals are given below.

Year	Production (Lb)	Unit Value
1951	7,051,000	$1.99
1950	6,312,000	2.16
1949	4,359,000	1.61
1948	7,840,000	1.76
1947	6,687,000	1.45

They are, in general, of a lower molecular weight than the anthraquinone vat dyes. Most of them are sulfonic acids of amino- or aminohydroxyanthraquinone compounds which may carry one or more of a great variety of substituents. Many of them are prepared by sulfonating arylamino groups present in the anthraquinone derivative. Such compounds, called "bases," usually contain an anilino or *p*-toluidino group which is easily sulfonated. Hundreds of other arylamino groups can be used.

Acid color bases are generally prepared from haloanthraquinones by means of a reaction worked out by Ullmann. He is generally credited with working out the details of the arylation reaction which is quite widely used in anthraquinone chemistry[56].

This reaction is extremely valuable in the preparation of the anthraquinone acid color bases and has wide commercial application. It consists of the condensation of a halogen-containing anthraquinone compound with an organic amine in the presence of a copper catalyst and an acid binding agent. A simple example is shown below:

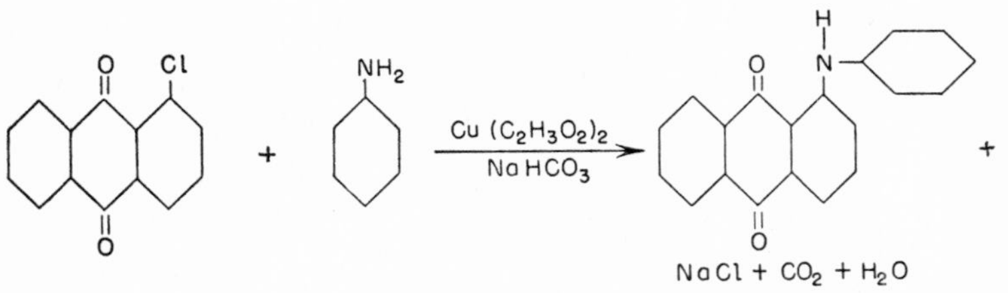

$$NaCl + CO_2 + H_2O$$

The reaction is usually carried out either in the presence of an unreactive solvent or in an excess of the amine itself acting as solvent. Almost any inert organic solvent may be used; the commonest ones in commercial practice are alcohol, mono- or dichlorobenzene, nitrobenzene, pyridine or solvent naphtha.

The copper catalyst varies greatly but the commonest one is basic copper acetate. Other copper salts such as the sulfate or chloride may be employed. Sometimes metallic copper can be used advantageously. Some condensations proceed better with one copper catalyst than another and exact conditions must be ascertained for new compounds. Sodium carbonate, sodium bicarbonate or the acetates of sodium, ammonia, and potassium are usually employed as the acid acceptors.

The condensation may be either the "dry" type in which conditions are anhydrous and the temperature of reaction is usually from about 130 to 180°C or the "wet" condensation type in which substantial amounts of water are present and in which the condensation is conducted at 100 to 110°C.

Chloroanthraquinone compounds, as would be expected, require higher temperatures and take a longer time to react than do the corresponding bromoanthraquinone compounds. Usually, the initiation of the reaction can be detected by a gradual darkening of the reaction mass, and in most cases the reaction is 95 per cent complete during the first few hours of the condensation. The resulting bases are isolated by diluting the reaction mass with a suitable diluent such as ethanol, then filtering and washing. In general, the anthraquinone acid color bases are very well defined, crystalline, dark bronzy compounds with sharp melting points. If impure, they can be readily purified from either sulfuric acid or organic solvents in which they are very soluble. Because of their solvent solubility and bright shades many of these anthraquinone acid color bases are used as dyes for gasoline.

The Preparation of Typical Anthraquinone Acid Color Bases:

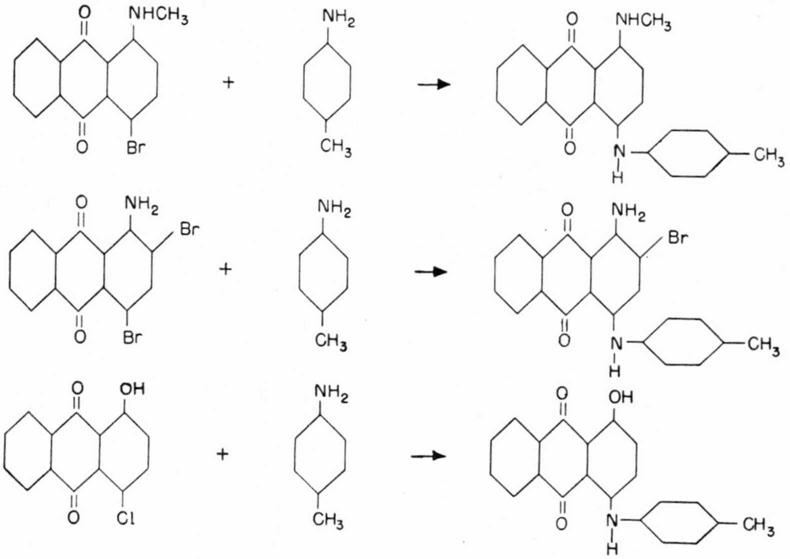

Sulfonation of Anthraquinone Acid Color Bases

To dye wool, the anthraquinone acid color bases must be put into a soluble form. In some cases the presence of COOH groups is sufficient to give this solubility[64] but this is the exception and the commonest way is to introduce one or more sulfonic acid groups. There are several ways in which this can be done. The position of the sulfonic acid group in the anthraquinone nucleus is also important as the solubility characteristics and dyeing properties vary substantially according to the placement of these groups. Solubility can be obtained by the following methods.

Replacement of a Halogen by a Sulfonic Acid Group. An example of such a replacement is the following:

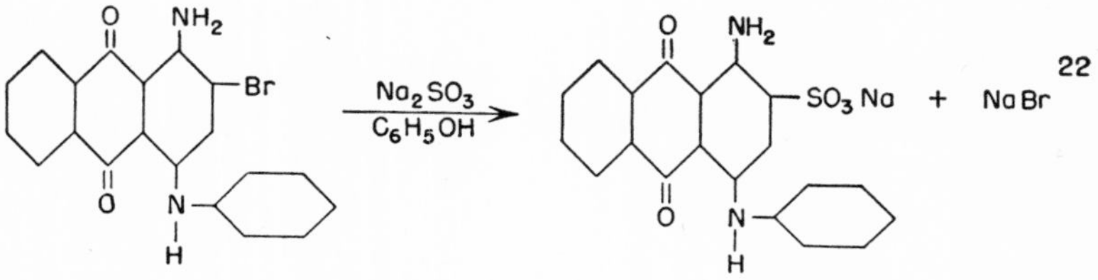

The insoluble base containing a halogen atom is treated with sodium or potassium sulfite or bisulfite in a suitable solvent which may be water, phenol or alcohol. Very often this must be done under pressure.

Sulfonation with Sulfuric Acid or Oleum. The commonest method and the one in widest commercial use is the sulfonation which employs sulfuric acid or "oleum," which is sulfuric acid containing dissolved sulfur trioxide. The optimum conditions for the sulfonation of anthraquinone color bases vary from compound to compound. A great amount of art attends the sulfonation procedure and the isolation of the product.

Sulfuric acid of about 80 per cent strength can be used on some compounds while most require 100 per cent sulfuric acid (commonly called monohydrate) plus the addition of various amounts of oleum. Most compounds can be sulfonated at ordinary temperatures of 20 to 30°C but higher temperatures are often employed. Usually five to ten parts of acid per part of compound are used[8].

Some compounds, especially those anthraquinone compounds which contain benzylamino and phenoxy groups, are very easily sulfonated at 20 to 30°C with acids as low as 80 to 90 per cent.

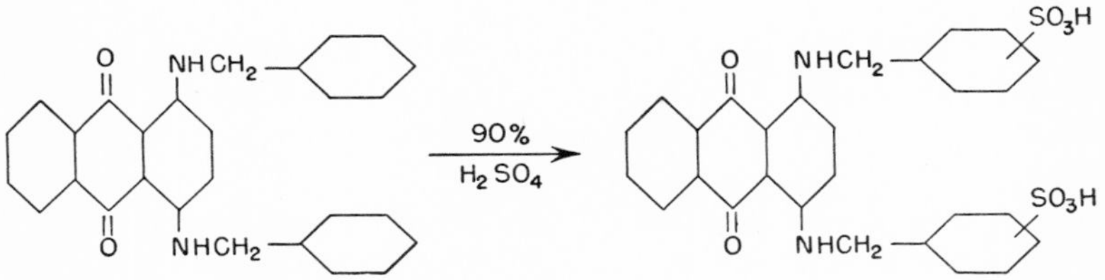

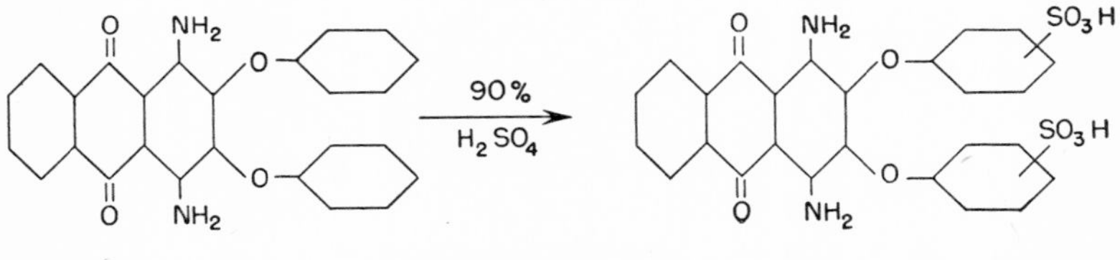

The sulfonation procedure which is used most is that in which the anthraquinone compound contains an arylamino group such as anilino or toluidino. In these cases, the usual procedure is to dissolve the base in 100 per cent sulfuric acid and follow this with varying amounts of oleum depending in amount on the nature of the compound to be sulfonated[15, 17].

Compounds of this type are illustrated by the following:

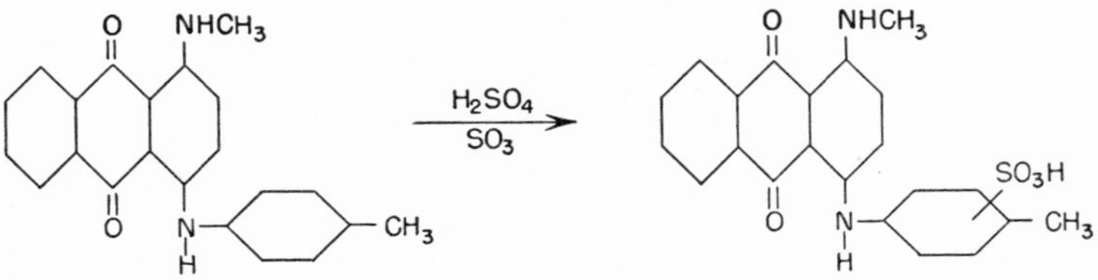

! If the arylamino group happens to contain two or more substituents such as methyl, chloro or nitro, sulfonation may be very difficult. Such products will require high temperatures or strong oleum. In some cases, sulfonation may be impossible because decomposition and oxidation take place before sulfonation. In other cases, it is desirable to modify the action of the sulfuric acid with inorganic compounds such as sodium sulfate or boric acid, which are often used when sulfonating anthraquinone compounds containing the hydroxy group. In some cases, chlorosulfonic acid is used in place of sulfuric acid.

In order to obtain the dye in a usable form it must be isolated and freed from the acid when sulfonation is complete. Numerous tests have been devised to ascertain when sulfonation is complete. Generally speaking, sulfonation is complete when a drop of the sulfonation mixture is completely soluble in water and when no base can be extracted with an organic solvent. There are many exceptions to this rule as some free sulfonic acids are entirely insoluble in water and some are soluble in organic solvents. Isolation is achieved by pouring into water or brine which precipitates the color, which can then be filtered off and washed free of acid with water or brine. Brine washing is usually sufficient to convert the relatively insoluble free acid into the more soluble sodium salt which is usually required. In some cases the sodium salt is not sufficiently soluble to be useful and other more soluble salts may have to be made. Such may be the potassium, lithium or ammonium salts or organic salts such as that obtained from 2-amino-ethanol[40].

Sulfonation may proceed to various degrees. Continued sulfonation may lead to over-sulfonation with a loss of some desirable dyeing characteristics. The neutral-dyeing property of a dye, for instance, may be affected adversely by such over-sulfonation.

In many cases sulfonation takes place in the anthraquinone nucleus itself rather than in any external group. To do this stronger acids and higher temperatures are usually required. The following are examples:

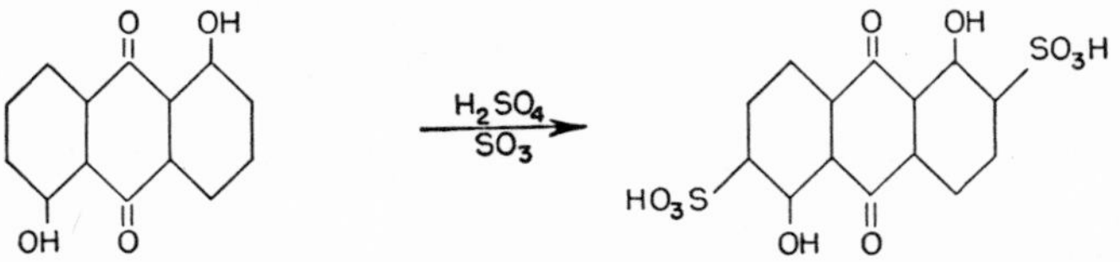

Sulfonation of arylaminoanthraquinone compounds is usually considered as introducing the sulfonic acid group ortho to the amino group of the aryl-amino nucleus if the para position is occupied as in the example below.

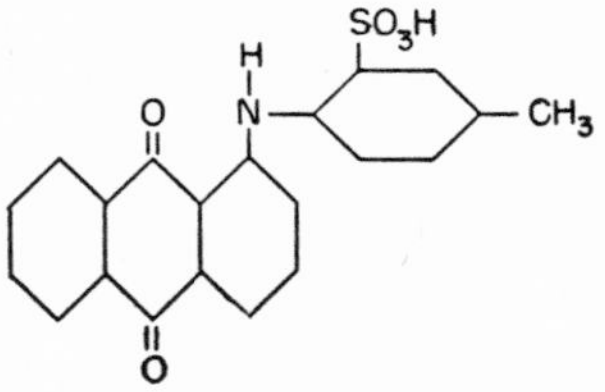

However, in the case of unsubstituted arylaminoanthraquinone compounds, such as the following, sulfonation occurs in the para position.

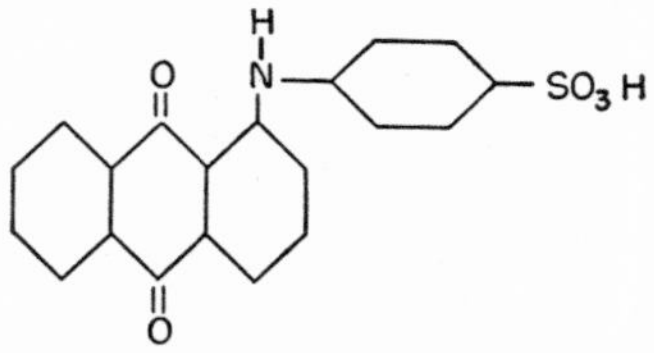

In the case of p-toluidinoanthraquinone compounds, Allen, Frame and Wilson have proved that substitution takes place in the ortho position[1]. This is probably true for most compounds in which approximately one sulfonic group enters the arylamino nucleus. However, sulfonation with sulfuric acid or oleum is not an entirely clean or simple reaction. It can be expected that, at the end of a sulfonation which is properly done, there will be a large percentage of a monosubstituted product, a small percentage of di- and polysubstituted products and a definite and usually small amount of an entirely unsulfonated base which may, or may not, be separated from the soluble portions.

For this reason sulfonation in arylamines is often indicated without reference to position as follows:

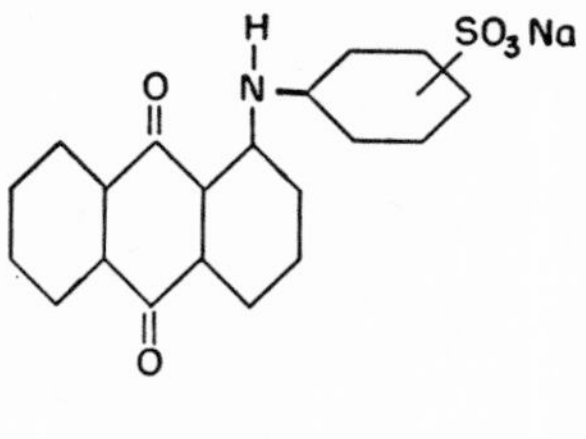

Similar dyes containing the sulfonic acid group in other positions can be obtained by condensing with the proper sulfonated arylamine as follows:

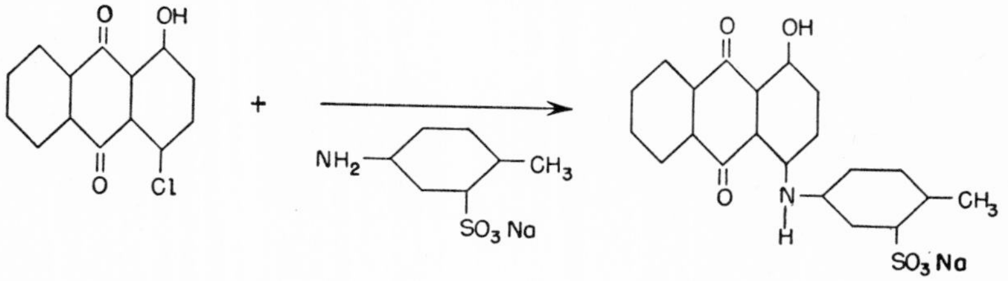

However, these reactions do not go too well nor do they give pure products. The dyes prepared in this manner are much more expensive than the products prepared by direct sulfonation over which they have little advantage.

Anthraquinone Acid Dyes Derived From Dihydroxyanthraquinones

The dihydroxyanthraquinones such as 1,5-dihydroxyanthraquinone (anthrarufin), 1,8-dihydroxyanthraquinone (chrysazin) and especially 1,4-dihydroxyanthraquinone (quinizarin) are the starting materials for a large number of anthraquinone acid dyes among which are some of the most important. The dyes derived from these compounds often carry one or more sulfonic acid groups attached directly to the anthraquinone nucleus and may or may not have arylamino groups present which can also carry sulfonic acid groups.

One of the most important of this class is the dye known as Alizarine Saphirol B, CI 1054, which is derived from 1,5-dihydroxyanthraquinone according to the following scheme.

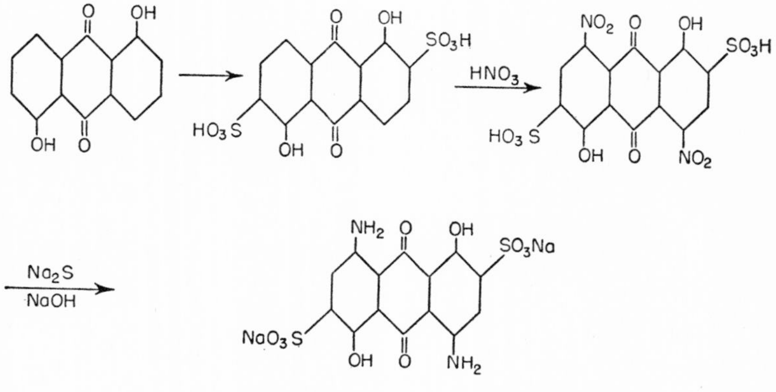

Alizarine Saphirol B, CI 1054

A similar compound is obtained if one starts with 1,8-dihydroxyanthraquinone instead of 1,5-dihydroxyanthraquinone[14].

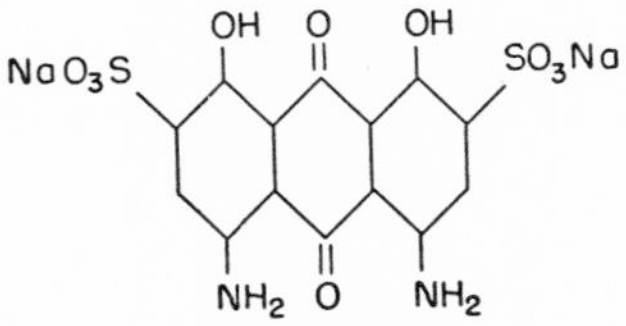

Both of these products are bright blues of good fastness properties. Both of them can be partially desulfonated, resulting in products which have unusually good resistance to salt water and to water spotting.

The dyes derived from 1,4-dihydroxyanthraquinone (quinizarin) are extremely numerous and of great value and commercial interest. Chemically, quinizarin is unique among the dihydroxyanthraquinones. It is very reactive and behaves quite differently from the isomeric 1,5- and 1,8-dihydroxyanthraquinones.

While it is a simple matter, for instance, to condense only *one* of the two hydroxy groups in quinizarin with an amine leaving the other group free, this is practically impossible in the case of anthrarufin or chrysazin. The reactivity of quinizarin is also much greater than that of its isomers. Consequently, there are an enormous number of compounds, chiefly aminated derivatives, which have been prepared from the interaction of quinizarin with amines of all kinds. Presented in its simplest form, the reaction proceeds as follows:

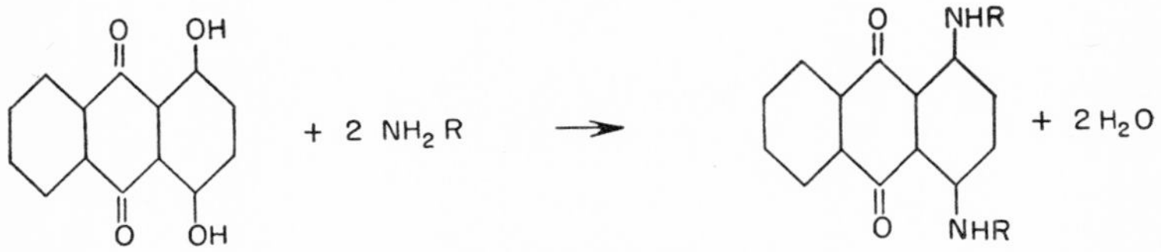

R = hydrogen, alkyl, aryl or other
organic residue

Actually, the reaction is not so simple. It is usually necessary to conduct this condensation in the presence of boric acid, which forms esters of the hydroxy groups, and in the presence of various amounts of a reduced form of quinizarin called the leuco form or, probably more correctly, 2,3-dihydroquinizarin.

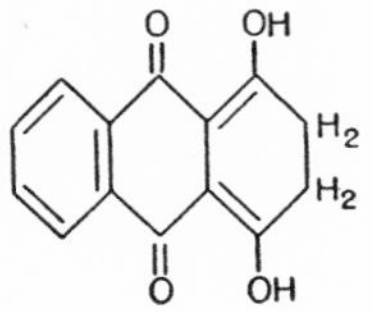

Such a reduced quinizarin can be obtained by a variety of methods[23]. A common ratio for condensation with amines is two-thirds quinizarin and one-third dihydroquinizarin. Such a mixture is extremely reactive and in the presence of any one of a large number of organic solvents will react with ammonia, alkylamines and arylamines. Since quinizarin is a relatively low cost intermediate, the dyes prepared from it are likely to have a favorable economic aspect.

The dyes derived from quinizarin are usually blues or greens if both the 1 and 4 positions are substituted, and usually violets if only one of these two positions is filled by an amine. In order to convert such aminoanthraquinone compounds into dyes for wool, solubilizing groups such as sulfonic acid groups are necessary. Hydroxy groups which can be esterified serve the same purpose. These may be present in a side chain or substituent group such as an arylamine. Substituents of various kinds such as cyano, methyl or other alkyl groups, alkoxy, halogen and many others will cause the shade to vary considerably from the corresponding unsubstituted derivatives.

The 1,4-disubstituted aminoanthraquinone compounds can be obtained not only from the 1,4-dihydroxyanthraquinones (quinizarin) but also from 1,4-dichloroanthraquinone with amines according to the following reaction,

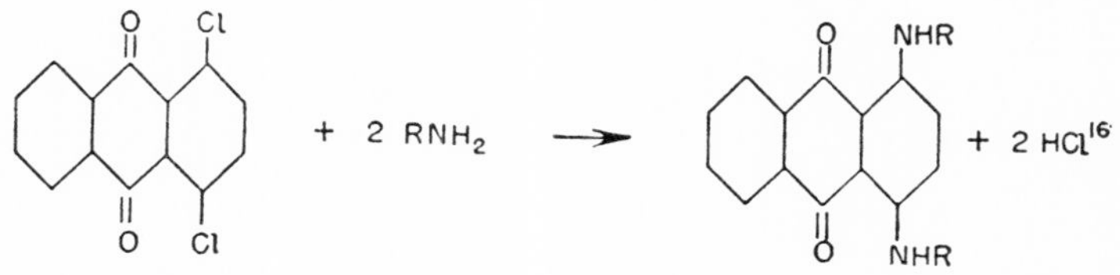

$$\text{(1,4-dichloroanthraquinone)} + 2\ RNH_2 \longrightarrow \text{(1,4-di-NHR-anthraquinone)} + 2\ HCl \quad [16]$$

or from 1,4-diaminoanthraquinones by reacting with aryl halides such as chlorobenzene, dichlorobenzene or similar compounds.

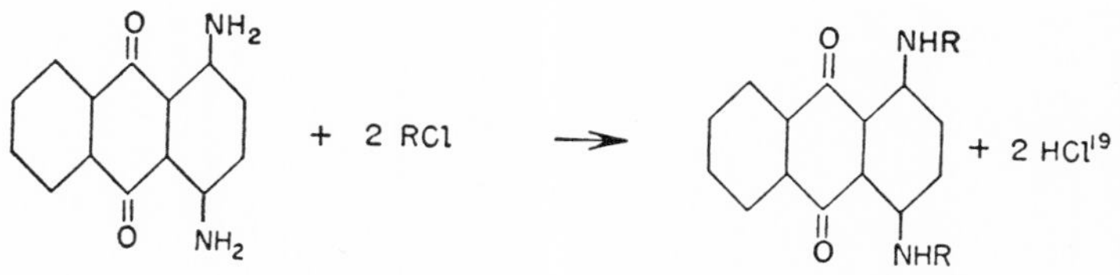

$$\text{(1,4-diaminoanthraquinone)} + 2\ RCl \longrightarrow \text{(1,4-di-NHR-anthraquinone)} + 2\ HCl \quad [19]$$

While both of these methods of preparation are possible they are not generally used because of poor yields, high cost or other considerations. The method generally employed is the route which uses a mixture of quinizarin and 2,3-dihydroquinizarin as previously shown.

The anthraquinone acid dyes of the substituted 1,4-diaminoanthraquinone class in which both amino groups are substituted by aryl groups, principally of the benzene or naphthalene series, are an important group.

Among them is Alizarine Cyanine Green G (I), a color discovered by Robert E. Schmidt in the period 1894–1897 when Alizarine Blue Black and Alizarine Saphirol were also found. From the examples given in the following table, it can be seen that the presence of hydrogenated arylamino groups such as in (VI), (VII) and (VIII) tends to confer considerable brightness, but the structure must contain a nonhydrogenated nucleus which will allow room for the necessary sulfonations. In example (V), in which both ortho positions to the amino group are filled, the shade is changed from what would be a green, if these positions were not filled, to a blue. The presence of long alkyl chains or several short alkyl chains on the arylamino groups, as in (III), lends extraordinary fastness to washing and wet treatments. Other substituents in the anthraquinone nucleus, such as the hydroxy groups in (IV), change the shade markedly—in this case, from the blue-green of the unsubstituted compound to a yellow-green.

Dyes in Which the 1,4 Positions are Filled by Arylamino Groups.

Structure	Characteristics
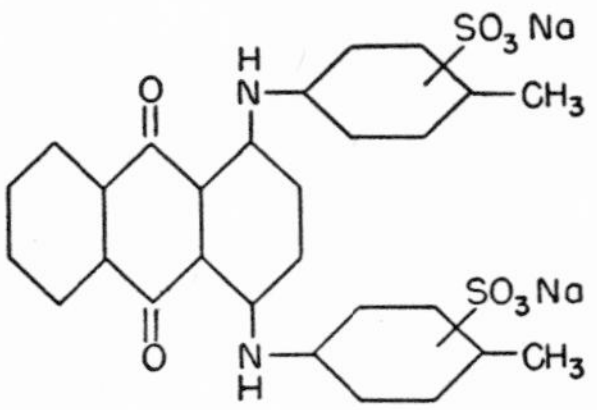 I Alizarine Cyanine Green G, CI 1078	Bluish-green. Good fastness properties[11, 12, 13].
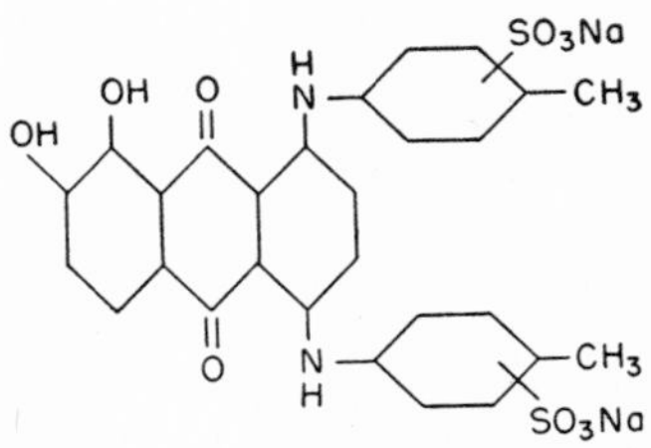 II Alizarine Viridine FF	Similar in properties to Alizarine Cyanine Green G but of yellower shade[27]

Structure   Characteristics

III

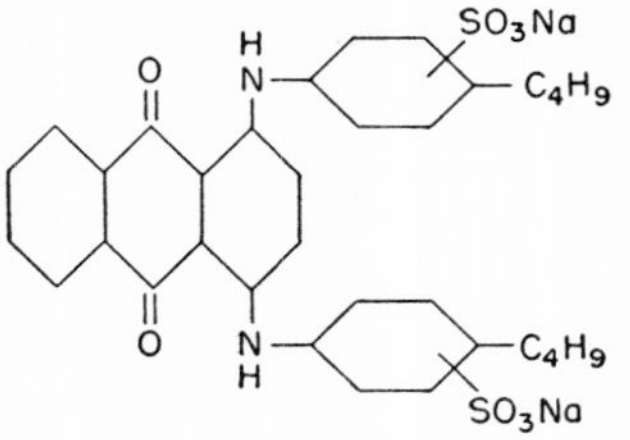

Bluish-green. Ex-
tremely fast to
washing and wet
treatments[26]

IV

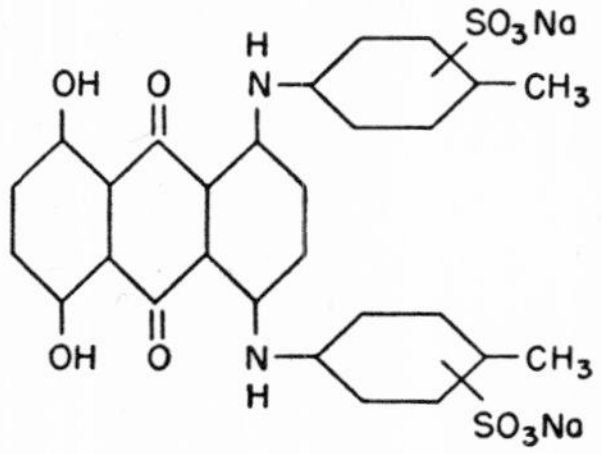

A yellow-green,
much yellower
than Alizarine Cy-
anine Green G[60]

Alizarine Cyanine Green 5G

V

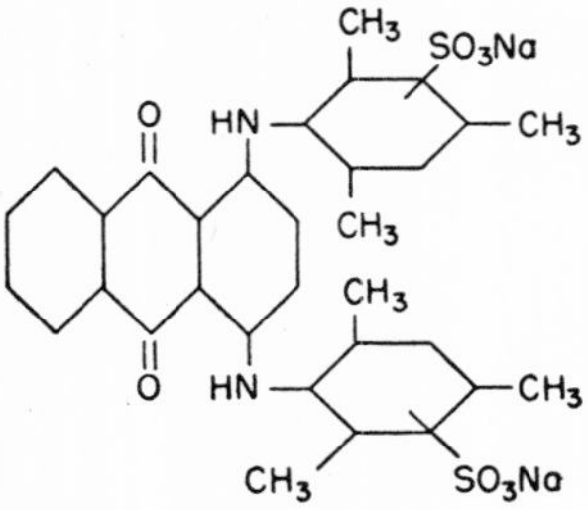

Bright blue. Fast
to wet treat-
ment[49]

VI

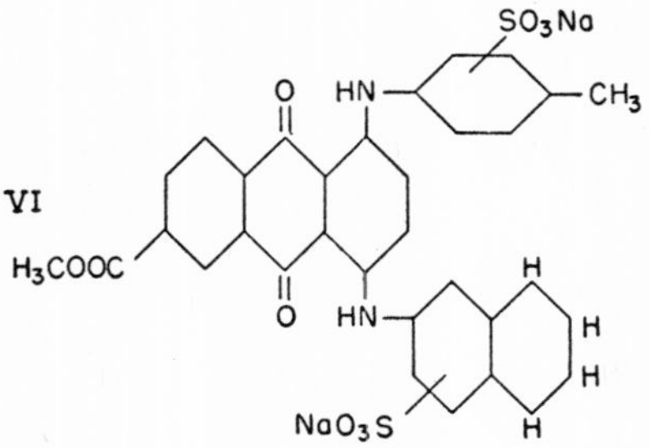

Green, with good
leveling proper-
ties[45]

Structure   Characteristics

VII

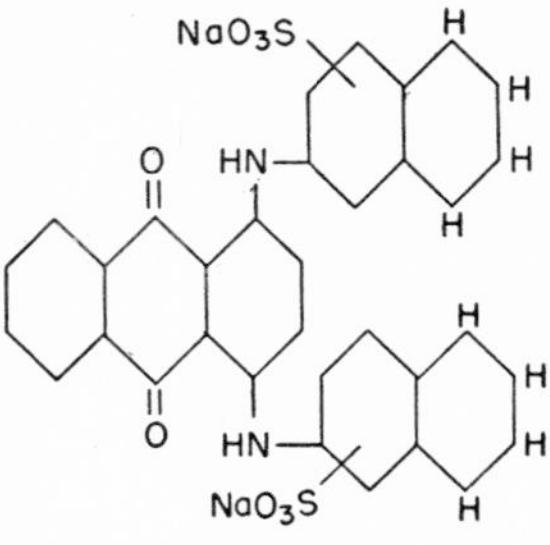

Alizarine Supra Blue SE

Bright blue of good
fastness proper-
ties[63]

VIII

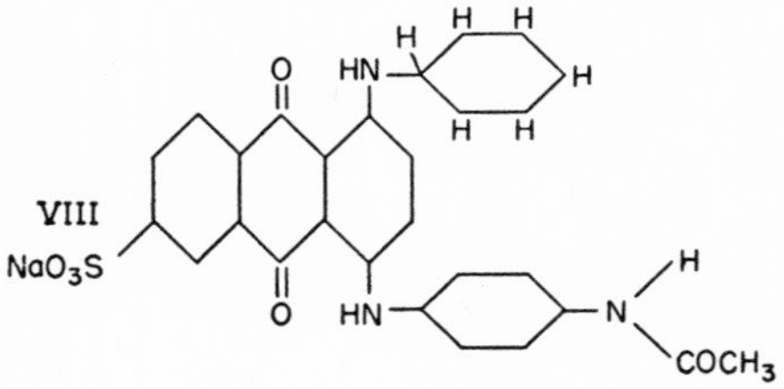

Alizarine Brilliant Green B

Ref. 28

IX

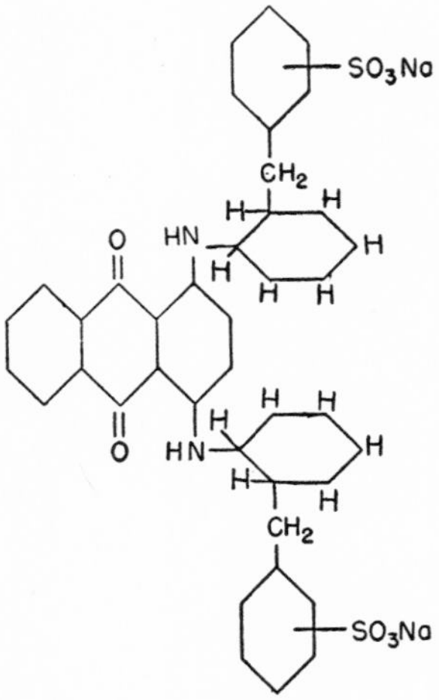

Clear blue of great-
est brilliance[5]

X

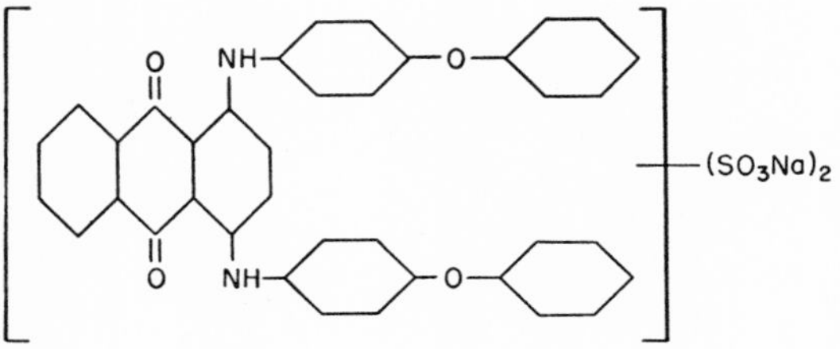

Blue-green. Fast to
wash treatments[42]

While a great many valuable acid colors of the anthraquinone series are derived from 1,4-diaminoanthraquinone in which both amino groups are substituted by aryl groups, there is another useful class in which the 1,4-diamino groups are unsubstituted but which carry substituents in one or both of the 2, 3 positions. Among these compounds there exist particularly wide variations in shade and application properties. From the table following it can be seen, for instance, that compounds I and IV, which are the mono- and disulfonic acids respectively of 1,4-diaminoanthraquinone, vary greatly in color. The monosulfonic acid is a red-violet, the disulfonic acid a greenish-blue. Both have very poor lightfastness. The introduction of two phenoxy groups in the 2, 3 positions gives a bright red-violet shade of excellent fastness to light when sulfonated (II). If in place of one of these phenoxy groups one substitutes one sulfonic acid group, there is obtained a bright blue-violet or purple of good fastness properties (III). The 2, 3 positions can also be substituted by halogen and mercapto or substituted mercapto groups to produce blue shades of good fastness properties. Many similar anomalies are found in great variety in this interesting 1,4-substituted series of anthraquinone compounds.

1,4-Diaminoanthraquinone Compounds in Which the 2 or 3 or 2,3 Positions are Substituted.

Structure   Characteristics

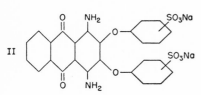

I   Red violet dye, poor fastness properties[20]

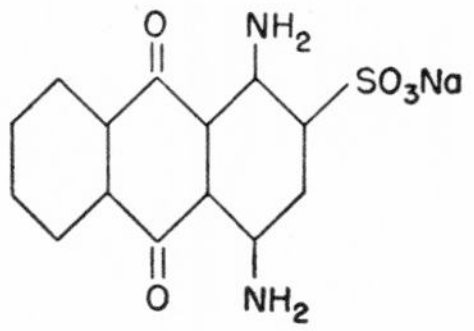

II   Bright red-violet. Excellent lightfastness[35]

Alizarine Geranol

III   Bright violet shade. Good fastness properties[54, 55]

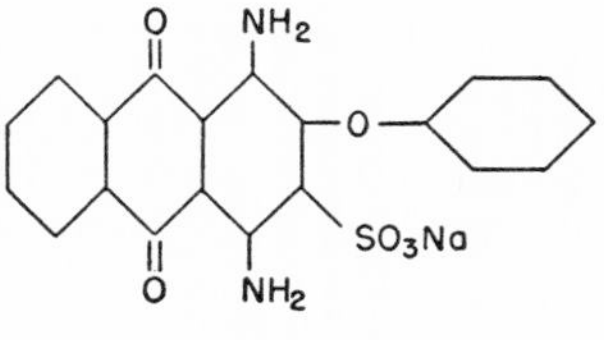

Anthralan Violet 4BF

Structure   Characteristics

IV   Bright blue. Poor lightfastness[2]

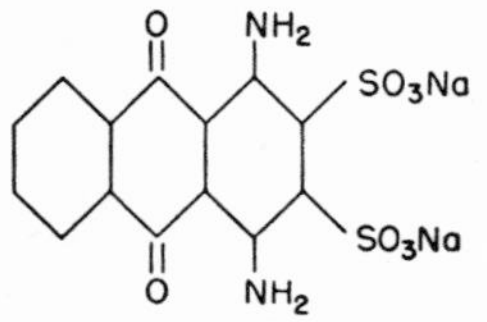

1,4-Diaminoanthraquinones in Which Only One of the Two Amino Groups is Substituted by an Aryl Group. This constitutes a large class and includes many of the oldest anthraquinone acid colors of which some are still of commercial importance. A large number of them are blues and violets on wool but other shades such as grays and greens can be obtained by such after-treatments as nitration and chroming.

Substitution in the 2 position with an alkyl group such as methyl or an alkoxy group shifts the shade from a blue to a violet as in examples (I), (V), (VI), (X), below. If the substituent in the 2 position is halogen or sulfonic acid, the shade of the unsubstituted compound is not greatly changed. The lightfastness of such compounds, in general, is superior to those in which the 2 position is filled by an alkyl or alkoxy group.

Solubility can also be obtained in these dyes by making the sulfuric acid ester of a hydroxy group as in examples (VIII) and (X). If there are sufficient external carboxylic acid groups as in example (XII), sufficient water solubility is obtained so that the added presence of sulfonic acid groups is unnecessary or even undesirable. Example (XI) shows a compound in which exceptional fastness to wet treatments has been obtained by the introduction of a long chain alkyl group.

Structure   Characteristics

I   Reddish-blue. Lightfastness only
                                             fair[34]. CI 1076

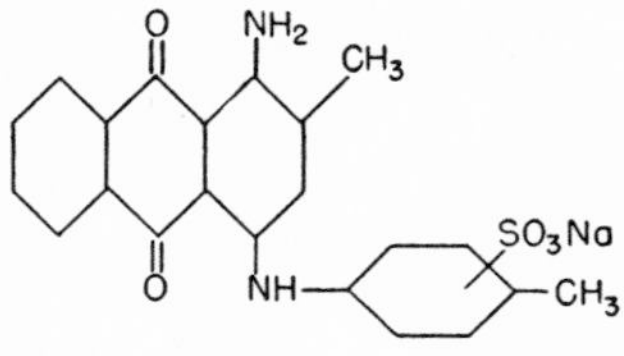

Cyananthrol R

II   Bright blue. Good fastness proper-
                                             ties[57, 58]

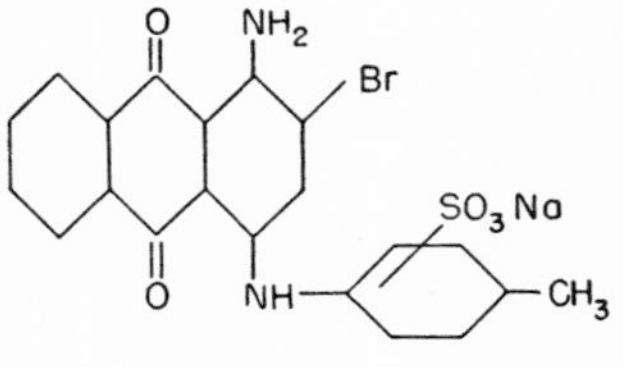

Alizarine Sky Blue B, CI 1088

Structure   Characteristics

III

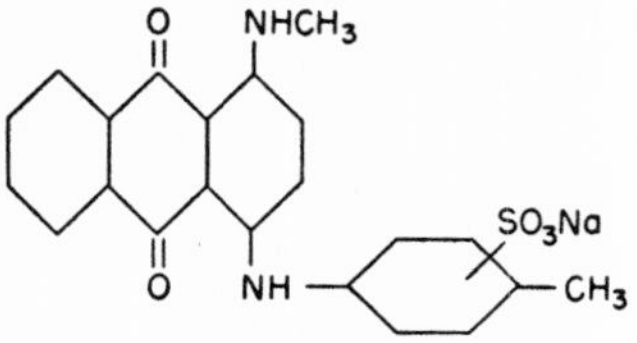

Alizarine Astrol B, CI 1075

Very bright greenish-blue. Fair lightfastness[18]

IV

Alizarine Direct Blue A, Pr. 12

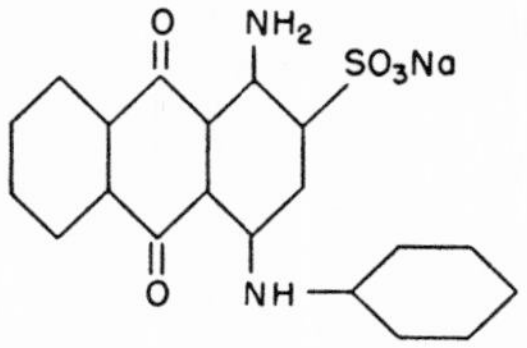

Bright blue. Good properties.
See section on derivatives of bromamine acid

V

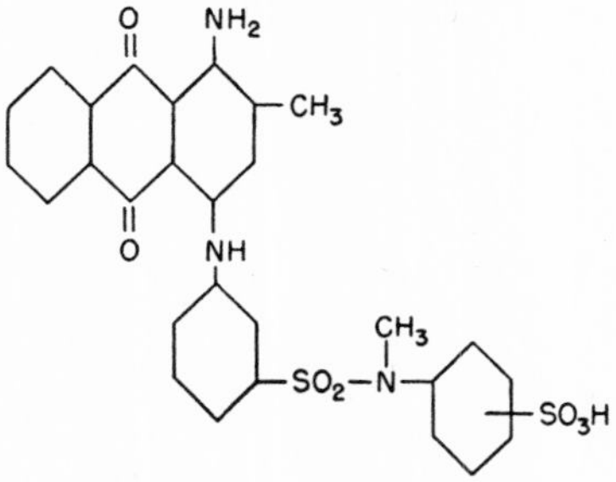

Dyes neutral very well. Violet shade[62]

VI

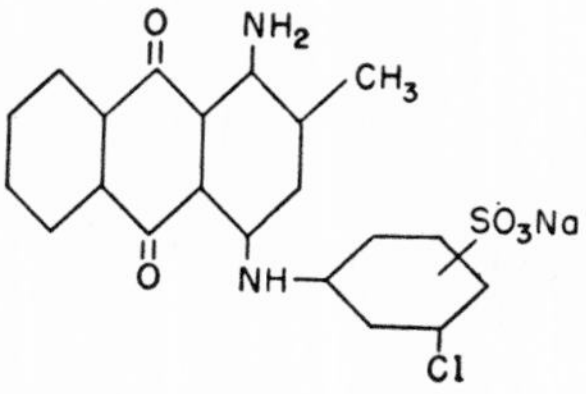

Bright violet. Little change in shade
on chroming[59]

VII

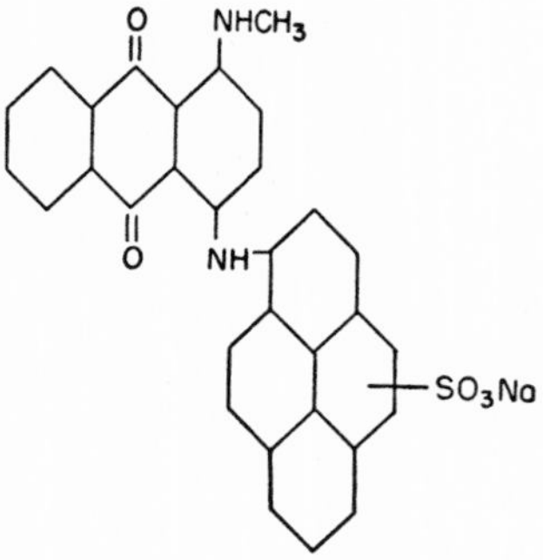

Fast olive-green shade[36]

Structure   Characteristics

VIII

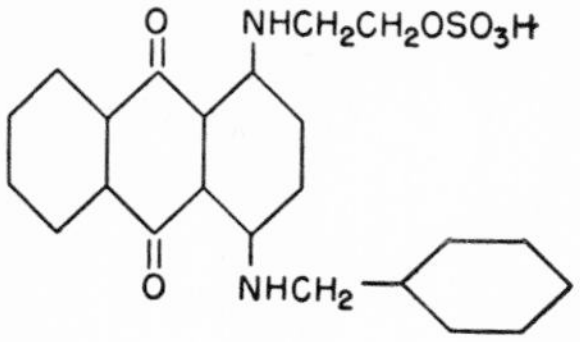

O $NHCH_2CH_2OSO_3H$

O $NHCH_2$—

Blue shade[4]

IX

O $NHCH_3$

O NH— SO_3H

OH $COOH$

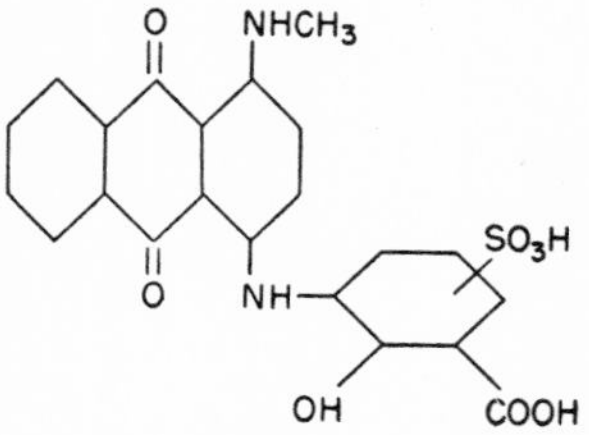

Blue shade turning to green-blue on chroming[37]

X

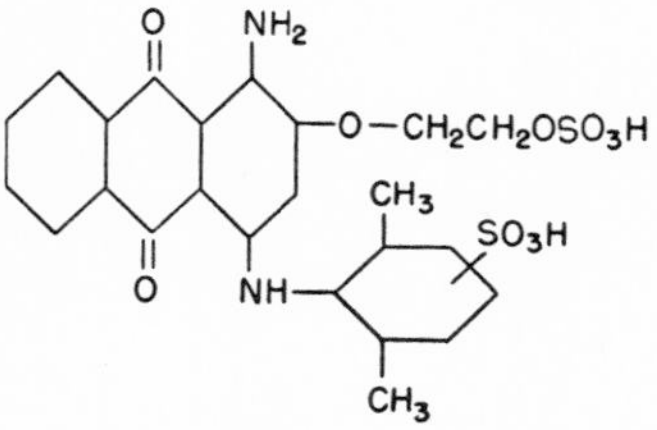

O NH_2

O—$CH_2CH_2OSO_3H$

CH_3 SO_3H

O NH—

CH_3

Bright violet, fast-to-light[50]

XI

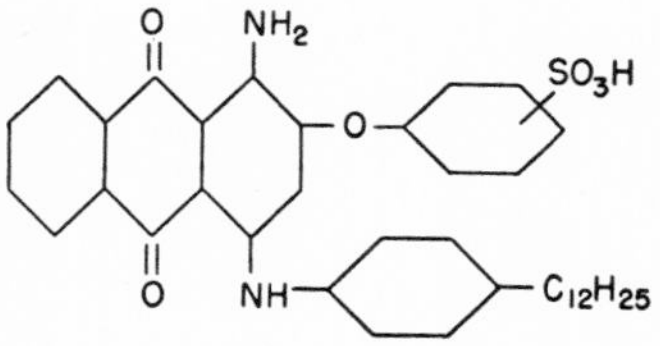

O NH_2

SO_3H

O—

O NH— $C_{12}H_{25}$

Reddish-blue, very fast to milling[41]

XII

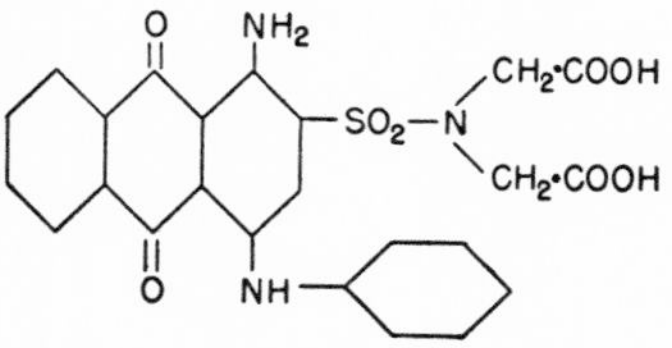

O NH_2

SO_2—N $CH_2 \cdot COOH$

$CH_2 \cdot COOH$

O NH—

Good leveling blue. Soluble in water. No sulfonic acid groups[64]

Aminohydroxyanthraquinone Compounds. A well known old dye of this class is Alizarine Irisol R, CI 1073, example (2), which is a bright violet shade. In common with all compounds of this class which carry an unsubstituted hydroxy group in the anthraquinone, it changes shade upon chroming, in this case becoming green. Its use is as a violet shade; the chromed shade is not of interest nor of value.

The exact reverse is true of another old and still important color—Alizarine Blue Black B, CI 1085, example (4). This is prepared from quinizarin, purpurin, or 2-chloroquinizarin by condensation with aniline to give what was formerly believed to be a mixture of 1 and 2

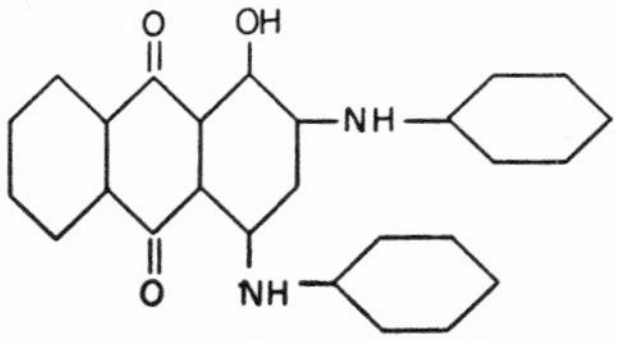

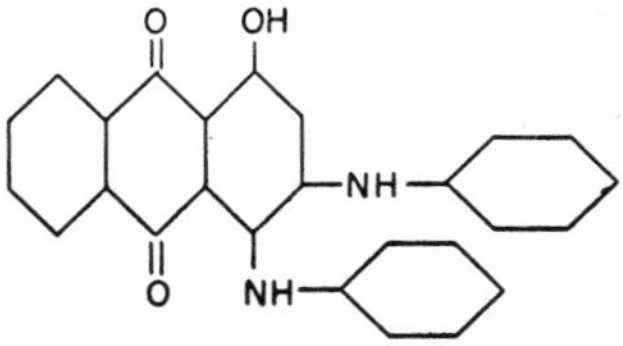

which was then sulfonated. It is now known that most brands of this color are mixtures of 3 and 4, each of which is sulfonated.

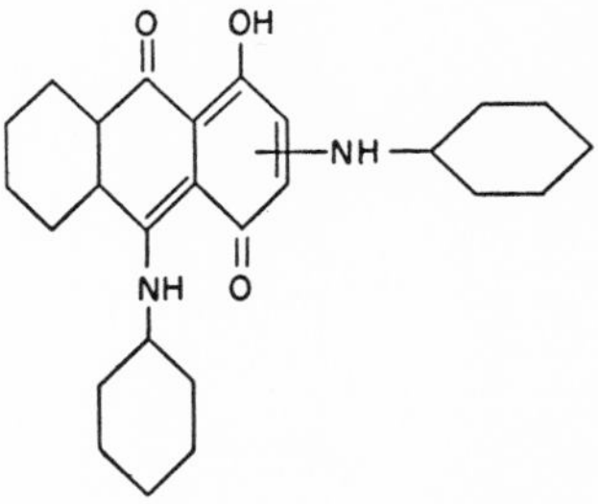

The sulfonated color is a dull violet of no interest, but unlike Alizarine Irisol R, it is the chromed shade (a deep black) which is of interest. This color also has a favorable economic picture although the lightfastness is not as good as that of many other colors in modern usage. Nevertheless, because of its comparatively low cost and its good working properties it is still of considerable commercial importance.

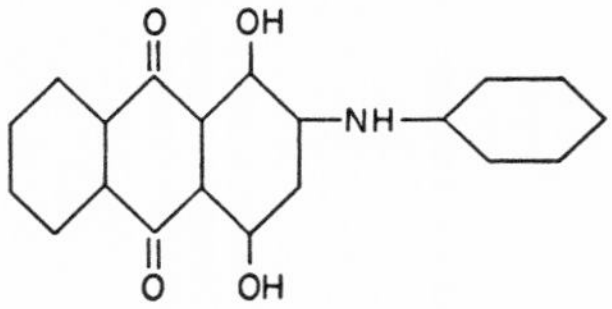

Compounds such as example (III), which carry both a hydroxy and a carboxy group in ortho position to each other, give shades which after chroming have very good fastness properties.

Structure	Characteristics
I	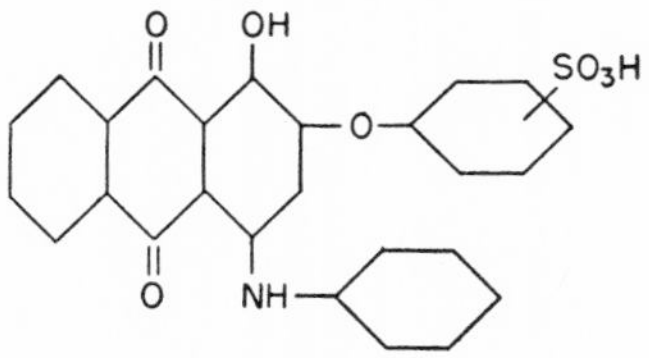 Red-violet. Black on chroming[6]
II	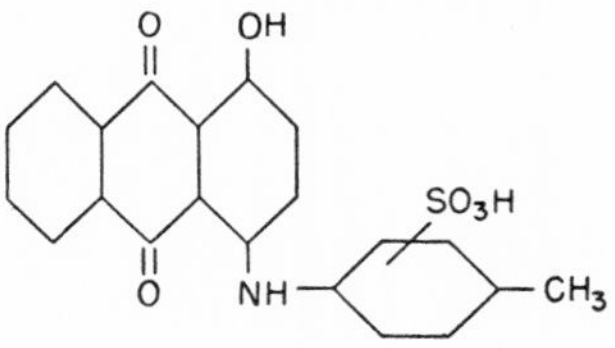 Violet. Green on chroming[10]

Structure   Characteristics

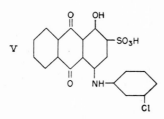

III

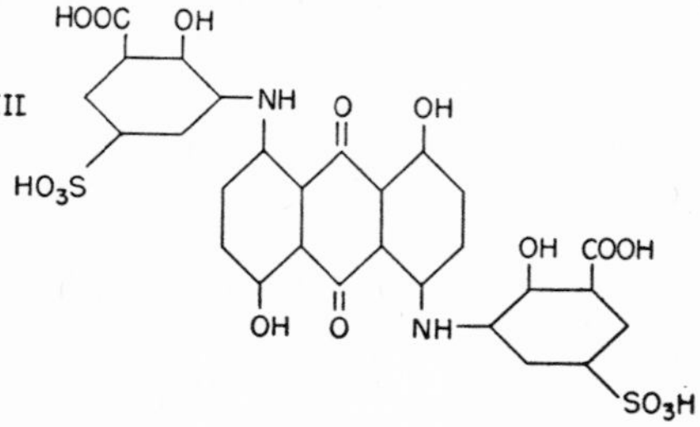

Blue. Green after chroming.
Good fastness properties[38]

Dull violet which changes to
black on chroming[10, 33]

IV

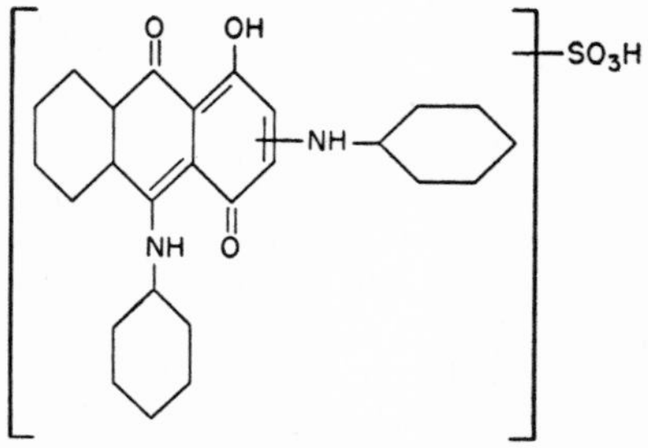

Alizarine Blue Black B, CI 1085

Blue-violet shades. Good fastness properties[59]

V

Heterocyclic Acid Dyes

The heterocyclic anthraquinone compounds contain some of the newest, brightest and most useful acid dyes in the yellow, orange and red range and are of relatively recent origin. In brightness, they compete with the azo dyes in this color range while retaining, and even improving upon, the good lightfastness characteristic of anthraquinone acid colors. In most cases the lightfastness of these dyes is definitely superior to that of the older dyes in the blue, green and violet classes which were discovered over fifty years ago. Their other application properties have made them valuable additions to the older acid colors.

Chemically, most of these are anthraquinone derivatives which carry a heterocyclic ring with one or more atoms of nitrogen, sulfur or oxygen. Some of the general classes of these compounds are illustrated below. The names accompanying the formulas refer to the major ring system and are not complete names for the compounds.

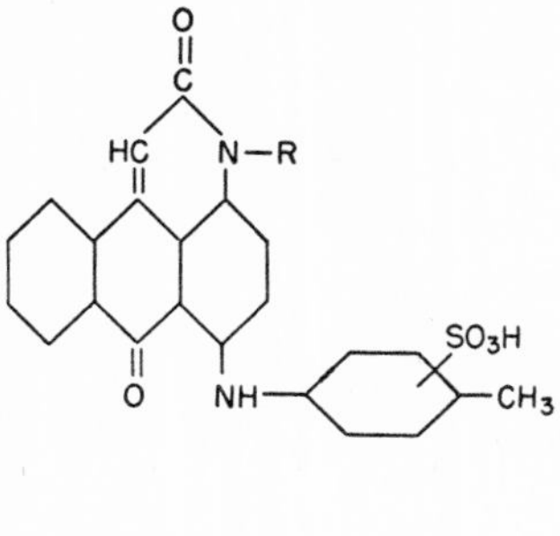

Anthrapyridone

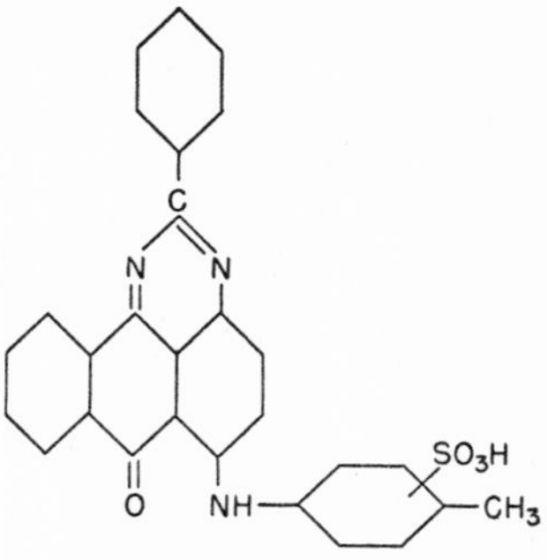

Anthrapyrimidine

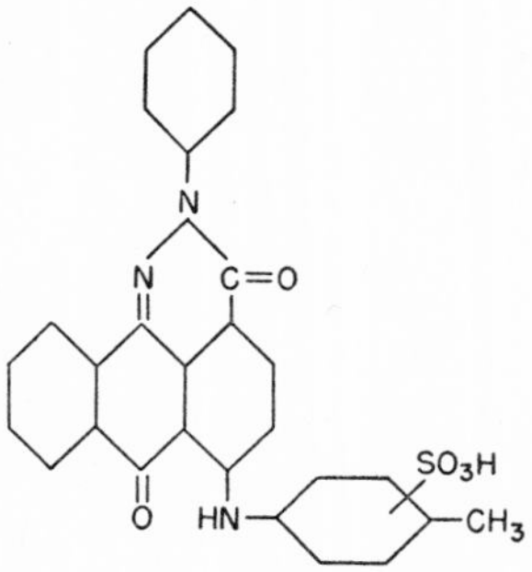

Anthrapyridazone

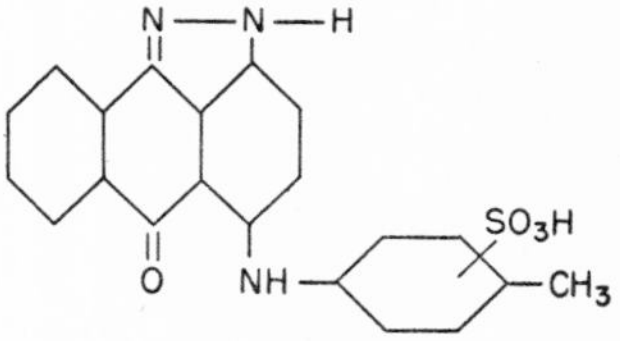

Anthrapyrazole

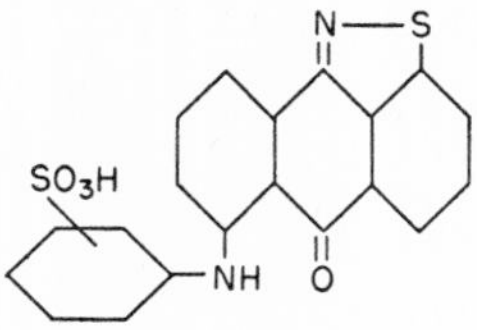

Anthraisothiazole

The anthrapyridones are mostly reds of which Alizarine Rubinol R, CI 1091, discovered by Thomaschewski in 1907 is the oldest. While this has fairly good fastness properties and is still used to some extent, it has been superseded by the newer and better anthrapyrimidine reds which are very bright and vary from a yellow-scarlet to a bluish-red. Yellow shades can also be obtained from anthrapyrazoles, anthrapyridones, anthrapyrimidines and anthrapyridazones. These are often very brilliant and of excellent fastness properties but few have reached the market because of high cost.

Anthrimides and Naphthocarbazoles

Until recently, gray and black direct-dyeing acid wool colors of the anthraquinone series were almost unknown. Alizarine Blue Black B, CI 1085, which is a gray or black only upon chroming, does not have the high degree of lightfastness required today. More important, it was desirable that such a color should dye "direct" without the necessity of chroming and yet substantially retain its shade if chromed along with other chrome colors. These requirements were well met by the anthraquinone anthrimide sulfonic acids.

The anthraquinone anthrimides, or dianthraquinonylamines, can be looked upon as derivatives of the usual amino(arylamino)anthraquinone dyes of formula (A) in that R may be an organic radical of the benzene series typified by (B), which is a bright blue dye on wool. If in place of the benzene ring we substitute a naphthalene nucleus, as in (C), a blue dye is still obtained but it is considerably duller than (B). If, however, we substitute an anthraquinone nucleus for the benzene or naphthalene ring, we obtain what amounts to an extremely dull blue or, as in the case of (D), what would be called a blue-gray. Nearly all of the grays and blacks in the anthraquinone acid color series are of this type of degraded blue dye.

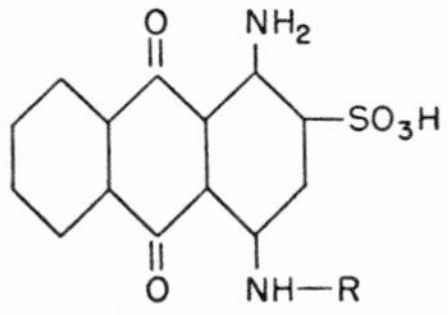

(A)

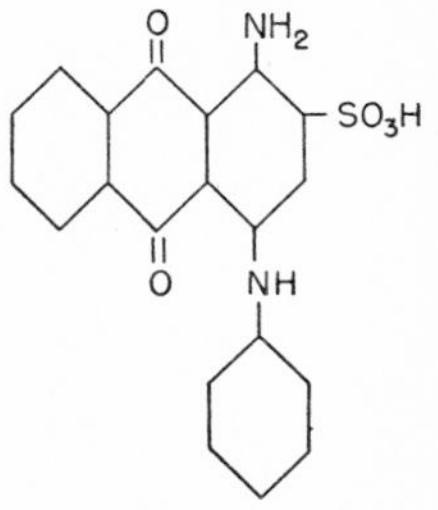

(B)

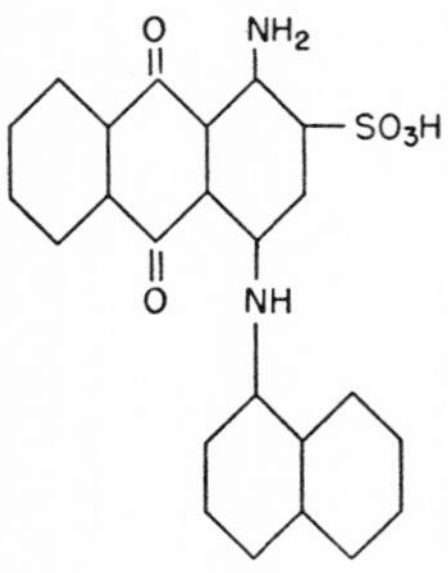

(C)

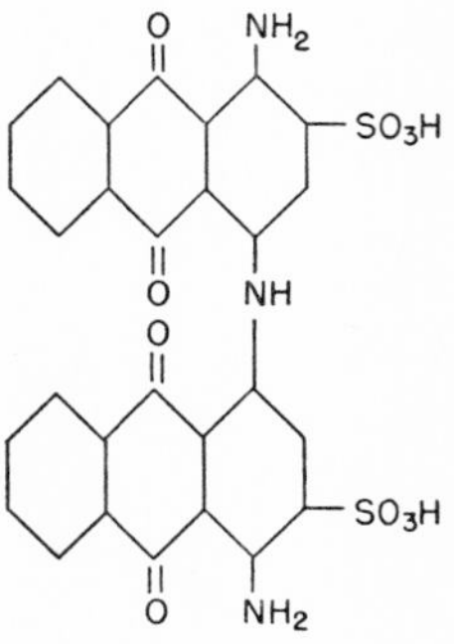

(D)

One of the most useful of this type is Alizarine Fast Gray BBLW, Pr. 206 (D), which is a very fast-to-light blue-gray[51]. It is widely used in mixture with other fast wool colors to give browns and taupes. The shade obtained can be varied within wide limits depending upon the conditions of sulfonation. Alizarine Light Gray RLL (I) is a fast-to-light "red-gray" of similar good properties and is one of the few good wool colors containing a benzanthrone nucleus. Formulas II and III are two of a great number of dianthrimides similar to Alizarine Fast Gray BBLW which can be prepared and which give various shades of gray and black.

Wool browns of excellent lightfastness can be obtained from the naphthocarbazole type of which Alizarine Light Brown BL[24] (IV) is the best known. Colors of this type have excellent fastness and application properties and are widely used today. Various shades of yellow to brown can be obtained by proper substitution of the basic nucleus. The sulfonation and carbazolation require considerable care to effect proper ring-closure to result in the correct shade.

Structure		Characteristics

I

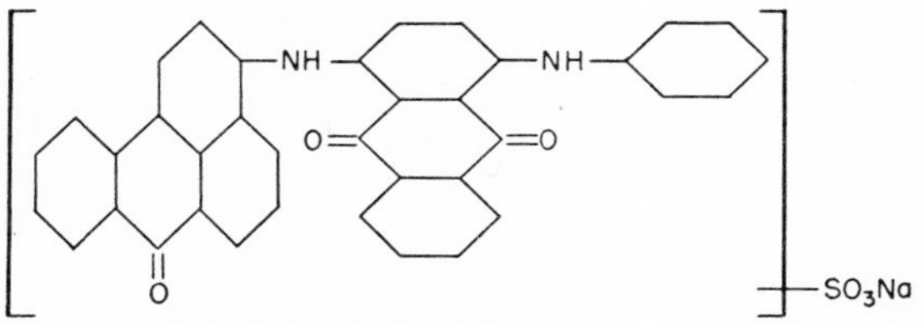

Alizarine Light Gray RLL

Very fast-to-light
reddish-gray[25]

II

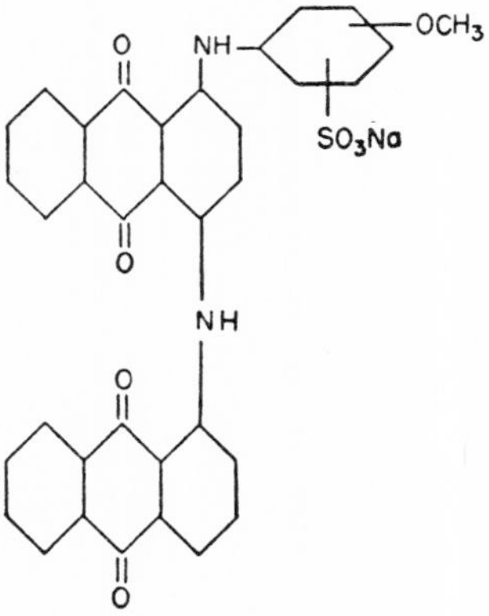

Greenish-grays[43]

III

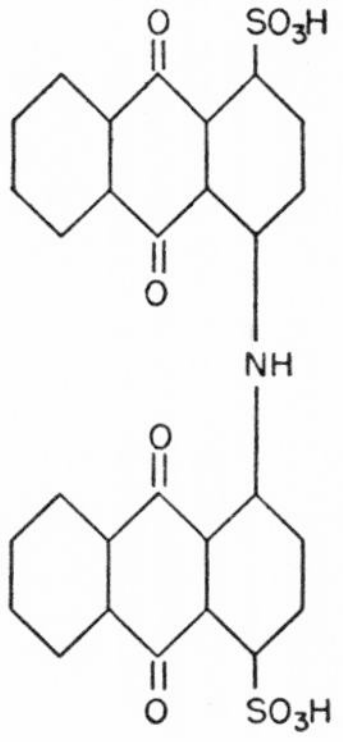

Yellow brown shades.
Quite fast-to-light.
Not good wet fastness[44]

Structure   Characteristics

IV

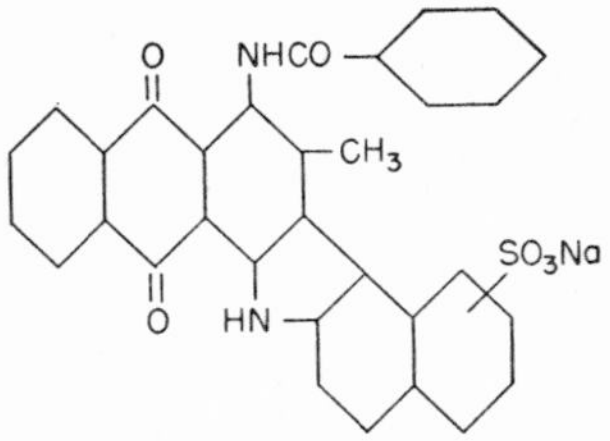

Brown shades of excel-
lent fastness to light
and wet treatment[24]

Alizarine Light Brown BL

Dyes Derived from Bromamine Acid

This intermediate is the parent compound of a great many dyes for wool.
Known commonly as bromamine acid, its constitution is 1-amino-4-bromo-
2-anthraquinonesulfonic acid,

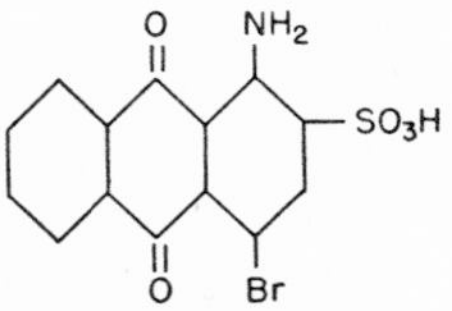

"Bromamine Acid"

This compound is important because of its favorable economic position
and its easily replaceable bromine atom in the 4 position. Literally thousands of new compounds have been prepared by reacting bromamine acid
with an immense variety of primary arylamines according to the following
reaction:

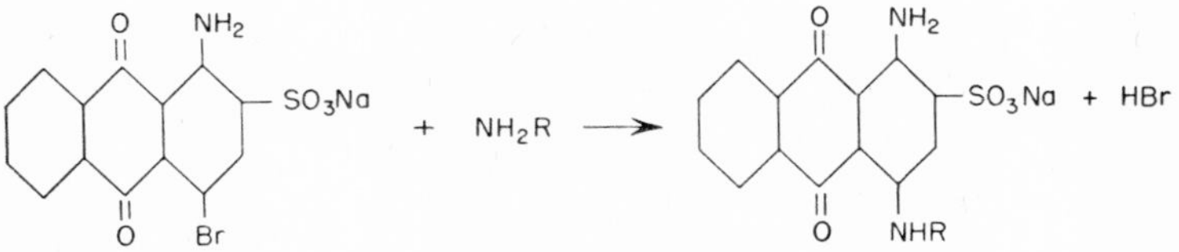

Many hundreds of patents have been granted on the condensation products of bromamine acid and arylamines. The earliest patents were concerned with arylamines like aniline, p-toluidine, p-aminoacetanilide and
similar relatively simple compounds of the benzene series. Substitutions in
the aryl ring were of a great variety and consisted of alkoxy, alkyl, mercapto, cyano, nitro, amino and many other groups.

More complex arylamines were soon employed, including those of the
naphthalene, biphenyl, diphenyl ether, and diphenylmethane series as well
as hydrogenated arylamines. Arylamines containing chromable groups such
as hydroxy and carboxy groups were found to give valuable dyes of this

class. More complex amines such as aminopyrenes and aminofurans were also used. In fact, there is hardly a primary amine available today which has not been reacted with bromamine acid in an effort to obtain new dyes.

An obvious advantage of such dyes is the fact that, after condensation and appropriate isolation which may involve one or more purifications, they are immediately available as dyes for wool because of the presence of the sulfonic acid group in the 2 position. In order to dye wool, the dye must be soluble in water. While other solubilizing groups such as COOH, OH, and SH have been used as a means of obtaining solution of dyes, the commonest, the most satisfactory, and usually the cheapest method is to introduce one or more sulfonic acid groups, by methods described earlier. In the case of the bromamine acid condensations with arylamines the compounds are isolated directly as the sulfonic acids. Difficulties involving over- or under-sulfonation which often attend the sulfonation of acid color "bases" are avoided.

The solubility of dyes of the bromamine acid class varies in quite a marked manner from the colors which are prepared from the color bases by direct sulfonation with sulfuric acid. Bromamine acid colors have solubilities which are usually substantially less than those of dyes prepared by direct sulfonation although there are exceptions. Usually one or two per cent of acid or salts such as sodium chloride will precipitate such colors from their water solution. There are many anomalies among the solubilities of these colors. Some of the free acids are almost insoluble in water and may even be soluble to some extent in solvents. Some sodium salts may be so insoluble in water that no coloration is observed. In other cases, the solubility of the compound may be so low that it is desirable to have another sulfonic group present, either in the arylamine nucleus or perhaps in the other side of the anthraquinone nucleus.

The shade of ninety per cent of the colors derived from bromamine acid with arylamines is blue. This encompasses a wide range of blue from a very greenish-blue to a red-blue approaching a violet. In general, the dyes formed from simple arylamines such as aniline and other substituted derivatives are brighter than those formed from more complex amines. However, there are many exceptions to this rule. Very large, heavy molecules usually give very dull shades. Condensation with amines of three or more condensed rings is usually very difficult to effect. Hydrogenated arylamines confer unusual brightness—a very desirable characteristic—to bromamine acid dyes. Arylamines containing hydroxy, carboxy or other chromable groups are usually on the dull side of blue although the chromed color usually has other desirable properties such as fastness to light or washing.

While blue dyes are usually obtained, other colors are possible. Substitutions in the meta position or 2, 6 substitution in the arylamino group tend toward redness. Violets can be obtained by the use of the proper amine.

Shades ranging from green to black can be obtained by after-treatment of bromamine acid colors with nitric acid and various other reagents. Further variation in this type of dye can be obtained by substituting the primary amino group in the 1 position. In general, substitutions of such amines result in quite greenish-blue shades. Still other variations in shade can be effected by substituting positions 5, 6, 7 or 8 in the anthraquinone nucleus. Substituents such as Cl, NO_2, SO_3H or SH tend to make blues greener while OH and OCH_3 tend to redden the shade.

Preparation of Bromamine Acid. Bromamine acid can be prepared from *o*-(3-amino-4-sulfobenzoyl)benzoic acid by treating this compound with phosgene and then ring-closing with fuming sulfuric acid[21]. The 1-amino-2-anthraquinonesulfonic acid which is formed can then be brominated to 1-amino-4-bromo-2-anthraquinonesulfonic acid or bromamine acid by the usual bromination method. However, the preparations which start with 1-aminoanthraquinone have more practical importance. As long ago as 1913, bromamine acid was prepared by heating 1-aminoanthraquinone with five parts of sulfuric acid containing 12 per cent sulfur trioxide at 120°C, followed by bromination. The bromination of 1-amino-2-anthraquinonesulfonic acid in this way gives a low yield of a product whose quality is inferior to that obtained by newer and more efficient methods.

In general, all of the methods for the preparation of bromamine acid which use sulfuric acid or acid sulfate depend on the initial formation of a sulfuric acid salt of the amine. On further heating, the attached sulfuric acid is split off from the amino group and sulfonates the anthraquinone nucleus in the 2 position. The product is then isolated and brominated to bromamine acid[3, 7, 9, 39, 46, 47, 48, 52, 53, 61].

"Bromamine Acid"

Bromamine Acid Derivatives in Commercial Use. A considerable number of dyes derived from bromamine acid are of commercial importance. Of the thousands of dyes of this class which have been prepared or tested, the following are some that have been chosen for commercial use because of unusually good dyeing or fastness properties combined with a favorable economic picture.

Formula | Trade Name

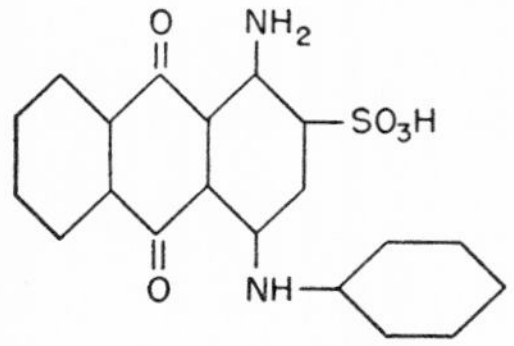

Alizarine Saphirol A[29], Pr. 12

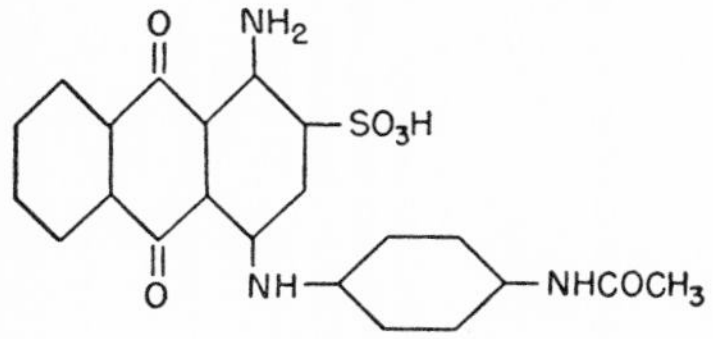

Alizarine Direct Blue A2G[30], Pr. 10

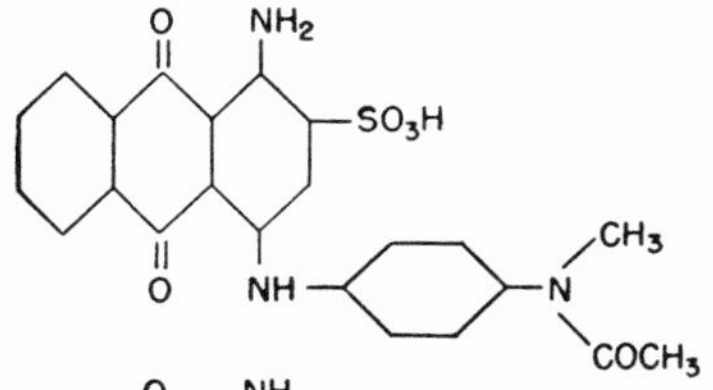

Alizarine Direct Blue ARA[31], Pr. 11

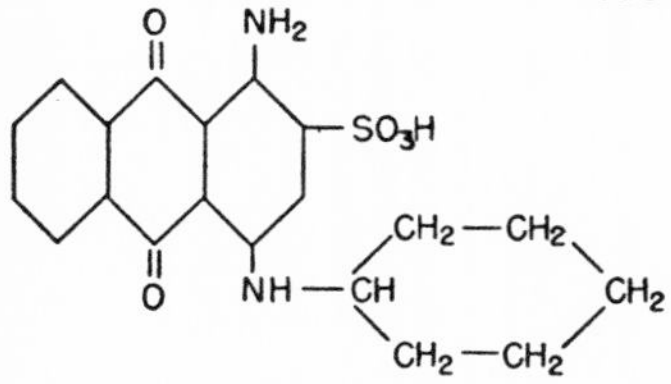

Alizarine Brilliant Pure Blue R[30] (Supra Sky R), Pr. 207

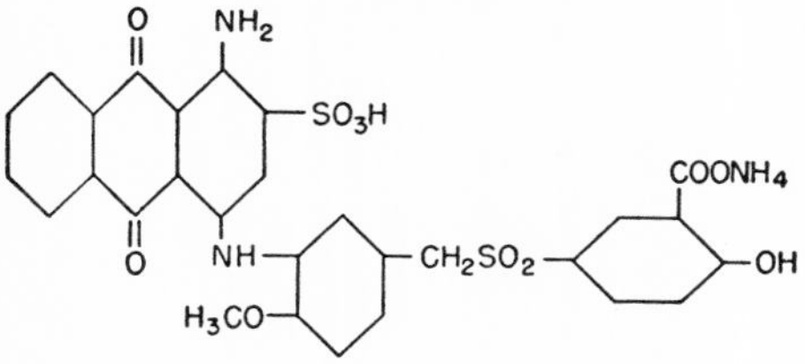

Alizarine Chrome Blue FFG[30]

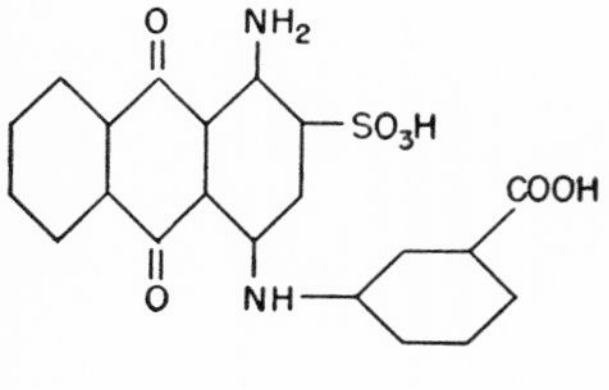

Alizarine Pure Blue FFB[32]

Literature Cited

1. Allen, Frame and Wilson, *J. Org. Chem.*, **6**, 732–49 (1941).
2. Baumann, U. S. Patent 1,975,386 (1934).
3. British Patent 311,977 (1929).
4. British Patent 473,762 (1937).
5. Buckley and Piggott, U.S. Patent 2,426,547 (1947).
6. Buxbaum, U.S. Patent 2,151,634 (1939).
7. Davidson, Tatum and Watts, U.S. Patent 1,873,300 (1932).
8. Fierz-David, "Kuenstliche Organische Farbstoffe," p. 516, Berlin, Julius Springer, 1926.
9. Freudenberg, U.S. Patent 2,503,254 (1950).
10. German Patent 86,150 (1896).
11. German Patent 91,149 (1897).
12. German Patent 91,152 (1897).
13. German Patent 92,591 (1897).
14. German Patent 100,136 (1898).
15. German Patent 121,685 (1901).
16. German Patent 125,698 (1901).
17. German Patent 151,513 (1904).
18. German Patent 164,791 (1905).
19. German Patent 172,464 (1906).
20. German Patent 263,395 (1913).
21. German Patent 281,010 (1914).
22. German Patent 288,878 (1915).
23. Grandmougin, *J. prakt. Chem.* [*2*], **76**, 139 (1907).
24. Gutzweiller, U.S. Patent 2,093,355 (1937).
25. ——, U.S. Patent 2,227,543 (1941).
26. Haddock, Lodge, and Lumsden, U.S. Patent 2,091,812 (1937).
27. Hess, U.S. Patent 734,325 (1903).
28. I. G. Farbenindustrie, BIOS 1484, p. 28 (PB 86139).
29. ——, FIAT 764, Vol. I, p. 17 (PB 60946).
30. ——, *ibid.*, p. 14.
31. ——, *ibid.*, p. 15.
32. ——, *ibid.*, p. 16.
33. ——, PB 70340, frames 12516–18.
34. Isler, U.S. Patent 715,662 (1902).
35. Jacobi, U.S. Patent 1,038,589 (1912).
36. Kern, U.S. Patent 2,225,013 (1940).
37. Kraenzlein, Schlichenmaier and Meissner, U.S. Patent 2,081,359 (1937).
38. ——, —— and ——, U.S. Patent 2,159,506 (1939).
39. Lee and Klein, U.S. Patent 2,135,346 (1938).
40. —— and Young, U.S. Patent 2,314,356 (1943).
41. Lodge, U.S. Patent 2,113,054 (1938).
42. Mettler, U.S. Patent 2,158,473 (1939).
43. Mieg and Raab, U.S. Patent 2,230,574 (1941).
44. —— and Raeder, U.S. Patent 1,735,123 (1929).
45. Nawiasky, Zell and Kuehne, U.S. Patent 2,046,835 (1936).
46. Ogilvie, U.S. Patent 2,360,010 (1944).
47. —— and Hoare, U.S. Patent 2,251,688 (1941).
48. Peter, U.S. Patent 1,871,466 (1932).
49. ——, U.S. Patent 2,101,094 (1937).

50. ——, U.S. Patent 2,117,569 (1938).
51. Raeder and Mieg, U.S. Patent 1,508,409 (1924).
52. Seymour, Salvin and Edwards, U.S. Patent 2,440,760 (1948).
53. ——, —— and Miville, U.S. Patent 2,413,790 (1947).
54. Stein, U.S. Patent 1,957,858 (1934).
55. —— and Baumann, U.S. Patent 2,001,221 (1935).
56. Ullmann and Bincer, *Ber.*, **49, 747** (1916).
57. Unger, U.S. Patent 654,294 (1900).
58. ——, U.S. Patent 654,295 (1900).
59. Von Allmen, U.S. Patent 1,898,861 (1933).
60. Weinand, U.S. Patent 1,713,576 (1929).
61. ——, U.S. Patent 1,841,997 (1932).
62. —— and Bamberger, U.S. Patent 2,195,067 (1940).
63. Zahn, Koch and Weinand, U.S. Patent 2,042,757 (1936).
64. Zerweck, Heinrich and Troesken, U.S. Patent 2,150,793 (1939).

DISPERSE DYES

Clarence F. Belcher

Anthraquinone Dyes for Cellulose Acetate, Nylon and Other Hydrophobic Fibers

Cellulose acetate fiber began to assume commercial importance shortly after the end of World War I and with this development came the need for suitable dyes. Early efforts were directed toward devising new methods of applying known dyes and, until the Ionamine[49] dyes were announced in 1922, there were no special dyes for cellulose acetate.

The British pioneered in the development of dyes for cellulose acetate. British Dyestuffs Corporation and British Celanese Corporation were originators of the disperse water-insoluble dyes for cellulose acetate. Sulforicinoleic acid as the dispersing agent gave rise to the SRA dyes[43]. As other dispersing agents found use, Dispersol, Duranol, Celatene, Celanthrene, Celliton and other brands of disperse dyes came onto the market[88, 95].

Although the proportion of anthraquinone acetate dyes is not recorded, Tariff Commission reports show that the United States production of dyes for acetate rayon increased from 1.2 million pounds in 1934 to 8.4 million pounds in 1951. This was 4.5 per cent of the domestic dye production totaling 187 million pounds.

These dyes are generally simple aminoanthraquinones or derivatives in which one or more of the hydrogens of the amino groups are replaced by alkyl, aryl, aralkyl, hydroaryl, hydroxyalkyl or other groups. A serious disadvantage in many of these dyes is the fading and shade change caused by gas fumes. Introduction of substituents such as halogen, hydroxy, alkoxy, nitro, cyano and other groups is reported to improve the fastness properties.

However, halogen, nitro and arylamino groups also tend to decrease affinity although certain combinations of arylamino and nitro groups with free amino and hydroxy groups in the anthraquinone nucleus do give dyes of good tinctorial strength with increased resistance to gas fading.

Strong salt-forming groups and groups promoting water solubility generally decrease the affinity of the dye. The first indication that either soluble or insoluble anthraquinone compounds would dye cellulose acetate was the disclosure by Clavel[6] in 1922 of the use of suspensions of several hydroxyanthraquinones, with the notation that if dyes were sulfonated they should not contain more than one sulfonic acid group. The following year British Dyestuffs Corporation claimed dyes containing carboxylic acid but no sulfonic acid groups obtained by condensing aminoanthraquinones with 5-(chlorosulfonyl)salicylic acid or haloanthraquinones with anthranilic acid[7]. In 1924, they claimed the use of aminoanthraquinones in a state of fine suspension or in a colloidal state and in the presence of an emulsifying agent or colloid[8]. Since then there have been extensive disclosures of anthraquinone derivatives made for the purpose of broadening the shade range, improving application properties and increasing the resistance to fading by light and gas fumes.

It is now generally agreed that the dyeing of acetate, nylon and some of the newer synthetic fibers such as "Dynel," "Orlon" acrylic fiber and "Dacron" polyester fiber with water-insoluble disperse dyes results through adsorption and diffusion of the dye into the fiber to form a solid solution. It is also probable that other forces, such as hydrogen bonding, assist in adsorption and retention of the dye on and in the fiber.

Many of the anthraquinone dyes for acetate are discussed in the section on Anthraquinone Intermediates. Only a small number of the possible derivatives have been described. These have been arranged in tables according to shade range as follows: (1) yellow to orange; (2) red; (3) violet; (4) blue to green. Miscellaneous polycyclic derivatives are listed in Table 5 and chemically identified commercial dyes with their trade names are shown in Table 6.

The shade of anthraquinone dyes for acetate depends upon the kind of auxochromes, their number and orientation. Auxochromes in the alpha positions (1, 4, 5, 8) are more effective in shade changes than those in the beta positions (2, 3, 6, 7). In general the effect of auxochromes is additive in developing deeper shades, with 1,4 disubstitutions giving greater depth of shade than 1,5 or 1,8 disubstitutions. The auxochromes in order of greatest to least effect are $NH_2 > SH > OH > Br > Cl > NO_2$[52]. Hundreds of anthraquinone compounds containing various auxochrome combinations and modifications have been examined as dyes for acetate. Derivatives listed in the following tables have been selected to show a general relationship between constitution and color. Simple hydroxy-, alkoxy-, and alkylmercaptoanthraquinones and monoaminoanthraquinones, as such or acylated or alkylated, are yellow to orange dyes for acetate (see Table 1).

TABLE 1

Anthraquinone Derivative	Color on Acetate	Ref.
1,2-Dihydroxy	Yellow	6
1,4-Dihydroxy	Orange	13
1,5-Dihydroxy	Yellow	13
1,5-Dimethoxy	Yellow	20
1,4,5-Trimethoxy	Greenish-yellow	20
1-Chloro-4-hydroxy	Yellow	13
1-Ethylmercapto	Yellow	21
1-Amino	Yellow	8
1-Acetamido	Greenish-yellow	15
2-Amino	Yellow	9
2-Methylamino	Yellow-orange	18
1-Amino-4-chloro	Yellow	9
1-Amino-4-guanidino	Yellow	24
1-Amino-2-methoxy	Orange	1
1-Amino-2-methyl	Orange	8
1-Amino-2,4-dibromo	Orange	9

Various shades of red on acetate are obtained largely by the use of modified monoaminoanthraquinones containing other auxochromes and from 1,5- and 1,8-diaminoanthraquinone as such or modified by alkylation or arylation. Acylation or aroylation of 1,4-diaminoanthraquinone also gives derivatives which dye acetate in red shades. Some of these derivatives are shown in Table 2.

TABLE 2

Anthraquinone Derivative	Color on Acetate	Ref.
1-Methylamino	Red	8, 53
1-(2-Hydroxyethylamino)	Red	93
1-Anilino	Rose	77
1-(4-Morpholinyl)	Red	22
1-(N-[2-Hydroxyethyl]anilino)	Rose-red	32
1-Amino-2-isopropylmercapto	Red	21
2-Isobutylmercapto-1-methylamino	Pink	21
1-Amino-4-hydroxy	Crimson	8, 53
1-Guanidino-4-hydroxy	Red	24
1,4-Diamino-2-methoxy	Pink	1, 53, 89
1,4-Bis(propionylamino)	Bright red	15
1-Amino-4-hydroxy-2-methoxy	Yellowish-rose	28, 53
1-Acetamido-4-amino	Red	44
1,5-Diamino	Red	8
1,8-Diamino	Red	8
1,5-Bis(N-[2-hydroxyethyl]anilino)	Bluish-red	93
1,8-Bis(methylamino)	Red	18
1,4,5-Triguanidino	Red	24
2-Amino-1-anilino-3-chloro	Red	17

Although some 1,5- and 1,8-diaminoanthraquinone derivatives dye acetate bluish-red, most of the violet dyes are 1,4-diaminoanthraquinones modified by alkylation or arylation of one or both amino groups. Also, the anthraquinone nucleus may contain other auxochromes and the alkyl or

TABLE 3

Anthraquinone Derivative	Color on Acetate	Ref.
1,4-Diamino	Red-violet	8, 53, 85
1-Amino-4-methylamino	Blue-violet	19, 53
1-Amino-4-(p-[2-hydroxyethyl]anilino)	Blue-violet	32
1-Amino-2-methoxy-4-methylamino	Violet	84
1-Amino-4-anilino-2-methoxy	Reddish-violet	84
1-Amino-4-anilino-2-(2-hydroxyethoxy)	Violet	48
1,4-Diamino-2,3-dimethoxy	Blue-violet	26
1,4-Diamino-5-nitro	Violet	47, 53
1,4,5-Triamino	Violet	10
4-Amino-2-carbamyl-1-hydroxy	Violet	90
1-Hydroxy-4-methylamino	Violet	85
1,5-Diamino-2-methyl	Red-violet	83
1,8-Diamino-2-methyl	Red-violet	83
1,5-Dianilino	Violet	77

TABLE 4

Anthraquinone Derivative	Color on Acetate	Ref.
1-Amino-4-anilino	Blue	78
1-Anilino-4-methylamino	Greenish-blue	18, 100
1,4-Bis(methylamino)	Blue	37, 50, 53, 85
1-Butylamino-4-methylamino	Blue	34
1-(p-Aminoanilino)-4-methylamino	Bluish-green	2, 98
1-(2-Hydroxyethylamino)-4-methylamino	Blue	33, 34, 36, 37, 53
1-Arylamino-4-hydroxyalkylamino	Greenish-blue	29
1,4-Bis(hydroxyalkylamino)	Blue	4, 29, 51, 85
1,4-Bis(m-hydroxyanilino)	Blue-green	25
1,4-Bis(cyclohexylamino)	Blue	31
1-Hydroxy-4-(m-toluidino)	Blue	27
1,4-Diamino-2-cyano	Blue	82
1,4-Diamino-2-carbamyl	Blue	90
1-Amino-2-carbamyl-4-methylamino	Blue	53, 90
4-Anilino-1-(2-hydroxyethylamino)-2-methylcarbamyl	Greenish-blue	38
1-Amino-4-arylamino-5-hydroxy	Blue	45
5-Hydroxy-1,4-bis(p-hydroxyanilino)	Green	25
4-(p-Aminoanilino)-1-methylamino-5-nitro	Greenish-blue	100
1,5-Diamino-2-(2-hydroxyethylmercapto)	Blue	81
1,4,5,8-Tetraamino	Blue	11, 41, 42, 53, 54, 99
1,5-Diamino-4,8-dihydroxy	Reddish-blue	8
Alkylated 1,5-diamino-4,8-dihydroxy	Sky blue	8, 96
Alkylated 1,8-diamino-4,5-dihydroxy	Blue	30
1,4-Dihydroxy-5,8-bis(2-hydroxyethylamino)	Blue-green	4, 51, 53, 86

aryl radicals may contain modifying substituents. 1,4-Diaminoanthraqui-none is a red-violet dye for acetate which has been used commercially for many years. A representative number of these derivatives are shown in Table 3.

The search for blue and green dyes having good lightfastness and resist-ance to change by gas fumes has led to the investigation of a very large number of anthraquinone derivatives. These are substituted 1,4-diamino-anthraquinones or 1,5- and 1,8-diaminoanthraquinones containing other amino or hydroxy groups in para positions. Like the derivatives dyeing in violet shades many of the blue and green dyes contain alkylated or arylated amino groups. They may also contain various additional auxochromes in the nucleus or in substituent groups all of which have more or less effect on shade and properties.

The dyes listed in Table 4 are only a small portion of those described in the literature but many of them have been produced commercially.

Besides the simple anthraquinones many derivatives having attached carbocyclic or heterocyclic rings, such as benzanthraquinones, benzan-thrones, anthrapyridones, anthrapyrimidines, anthrapyrimidones and pyr-imidinoanthraquinones containing suitable auxochromes are reported to dye acetate in brilliant shades. The shades are dependent on the kind and orientation of the auxochromes as illustrated in Table 5. The nomenclature of the references is used here.

TABLE 5

Compound	Color on Acetate	Ref.

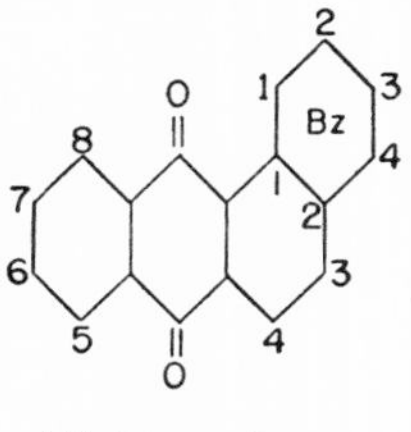

1,2-benzanthra-quinone

5,8-Diamino-1,2-benzan-thraquinone — Reddish-blue — 23

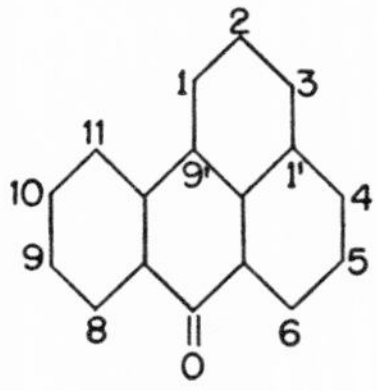

(7)

Benzanthrone

3-Methoxybenzanthrone — Greenish-yellow — 35, 96

TABLE 5—*Continued*

Compound	Color on Acetate	Ref.

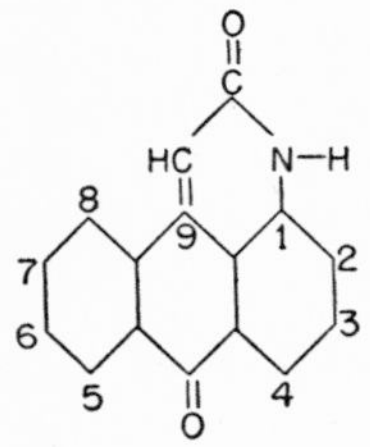

1,9-Anthrapyridone

Substituted 1,9-anthra-pyridones	Yellow, orange, red, blue	16

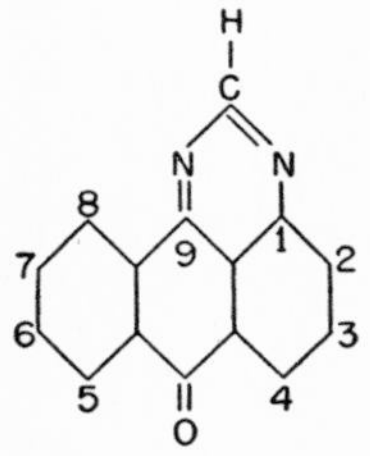

1,9-anthrapyrimidine

4-Amino-2-methoxy-1,9-anthrapyrimidine	Greenish-yellow	79
5(or 8)-Amino-1,9-anthra-pyrimidine	Red	79
Polyamino-1,9-anthrapyr-imidines	Yellow, red, violet	97
5-Methylamino-1,9-anthra-pyrimidine	Red-violet	79
3-(3-Amino-2-hydroxypro-pyl)-1,9-anthrapyrimidine	Yellow	39

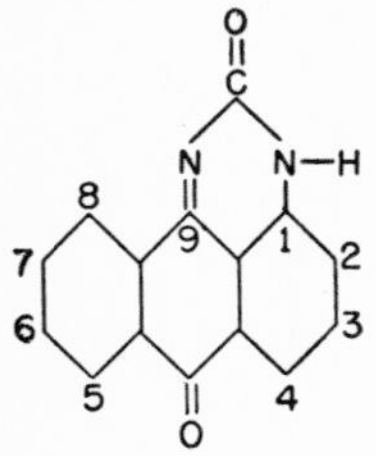

1,9-Anthrapyrimidone

1,9-Anthrapyrimidines and 1,9-anthrapyrimidones	Yellows, oranges	80

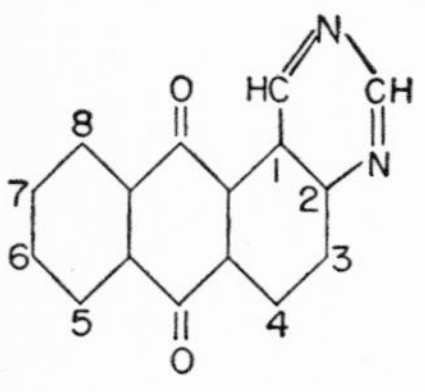

1,2-Pyrimidino-anthraquinone

1,2-Pyrimidinoanthra-quinones	Orange, red, blue	5

Although most of the anthraquinone dyes for acetate are the insoluble disperse types, a considerable amount of research has been devoted to the investigation of derivatives which are slightly to very soluble in water. Solubility has been attained by the introduction of sulfonic or carboxylic

TABLE 6

Trade Name	Chemical Compound	Ref.
Duranol Brilliant Yellow 6G	3-Methoxybenzanthrone	41, 42, 96
Celliton Orange	1-Amino-2-methylanthraquinone	76
Celliton Orange R ⎱ Duranol Red B ⎰	1-Methylaminoanthraquinone	53, 99
Celliton Fast Pink RF, Pr. 370	1-Amino 4-hydroxy-2-methoxy-anthraquinone	53
Celliton Fast Pink B, Pr. 234	1-Amino-4-hydroxyanthraquinone	53, 59
Celliton Fast Pink FF3B ⎱ Duranol Red X3B, Pr. 235 ⎰	1,4-Diamino-2-methoxyanthra-quinone	53, 54, 99
Celliton Fast Red Violet R ⎫ Artisil Direct Violet RRP, ⎬ Pr. 237 ⎭	1,4-Diaminoanthraquinone	53, 65, 67
Celliton Fast Violet B, Pr. 240	1,4-Diamino-5-nitroanthraquinone	53, 68
Celliton Fast Violet 6B	Partly methylated 1,4-diaminoan-thraquinone	53, 54, 63
Celliton Fast Blue B ⎱ Duranol Brilliant Blue B ⎰	1,4-Bis(methylamino)anthra-quinone	41, 42, 53, 54, 99
Celliton Fast Blue BF	1,4-Bis(2-hydroxyethylamino)an-thraquinone	59, 61
Celliton Fast Blue FFR, Pr. 228	1-(2-Hydroxyethylamino)-4-methyl-aminoanthraquinone	53, 64, 71
Celliton Fast Blue FW	4-(2-[2-Hydroxyethoxy]ethyl-amino)-1-methylaminoanthra-quinone	53, 72, 74
Celliton Fast Blue FFB	1-Amino-4-methylamino-2-anthra-quinonecarboxamide	53, 56, 70, 73
Celliton Fast Blue FFG	1-Amino-4-cyclohexylamino-2-an-thraquinonecarboxamide	53, 69
Celliton Blue Extra ⎱ Duranol Blue CB ⎰	1,4,5,8-Tetraaminoanthraquinone	41, 42, 53, 99
Duranol Blue G	1,5-Dihydroxy-4,8-bis(methyl-amino)anthraquinone	41, 42, 99
Celliton Blue 3G	Methylated Celliton Blue Extra	53
Celliton Fast Blue Green B ⎱ SRA Green Blue II, Pr. 229 ⎰	1,4-Dihydroxy-5,8-bis(2-hydroxy-ethylamino)anthraquinone	53, 54, 58, 62, 66
Celliton Fast Green 5B	1-(p-[2-Hydroxyethylamino]anilino)-4-methylaminoanthraquinone	55, 75

acid groups into the nucleus or into substituent groups. Among these are derivatives of aminoanthraquinonesulfonic or -carboxylic acids[45a, 87], anthranilic acid derivatives[7, 77], and glycine[12,46], alanine[40], thioglycolic acid[14], and phosphoric acid derivatives[3]. The Ionamines are N-substituted aminomethanesulfonic acids represented as "Dye-NHCH$_2$SO$_3$H"[92]. The violet, blue and green Solacets are believed to be sulfuric acid esters of (2-hydroxyethylamino)anthraquinones[57, 91]. In general, the water-soluble compounds dye weaker than the disperse types[60]; however, the solubility of the Solacet and Ionamine types does not appear to depress the affinity for the fiber[41, 42, 49].

Both the disperse types and Solacets have been used for dyeing nylon[41, 42] as well as cellulose esters, and they will undoubtedly find greater use as new synthetic fibers are developed.

The anthraquinone acetate colors have not been described in the Colour Index[94] but a number have been identified and disclosed in published literature. The brand names and chemical compositions of these are shown in Table 6.

Literature Cited

1. Albrecht and Mueller, U.S. Patent 1,964,971 (1934).
2. Bally, Grossmann and Felix, U.S. Patent 1,856,802 (1932).
3. Baumann, U.S. Patent 2,104,286 (1938).
4. ——, Friedrich and Zeh, U.S. Patent 1,843,313 (1932).
5. Braun and Koeberle, U.S. Patent 2,154,889 (1939).
6. British Patent 182,830 (1922).
7. British Patent 207,711 (1923).
8. British Patent 211,720 (1924).
9. British Patent 214,112 (1924).
10. British Patent 230,130 (1925).
11. British Patents 231,206 (1925); 460,027 (1937).
12. British Patent 232,599 (1925).
13. British Patent 238,936 (1925).
14. British Patent 252,646 (1926).
15. British Patent 263,260 (1926).
16. British Patent 263,946 (1927).
17. British Patent 278,417 (1927).
18. British Patent 282,853 (1927).
19. British Patents 291,814 (1928); 396,662 (1933).
20. British Patent 307,813 (1929).
21. British Patent 308,242 (1929).
22. British Patent 317,555 (1929).
23. British Patent 334,565 (1930).
24. British Patent 348,661 (1931).
25. British Patent 362,846 (1931).
26. British Patent 362,921 (1931).
27. British Patent 402,391 (1933).
28. British Patent 402,505 (1933).

29. British Patent 423,256 (1935).
30. British Patent 430,658 (1935).
31. British Patent 434,906 (1935).
32. British Patent 439,885 (1935).
33. British Patent 441,043 (1936).
34. British Patents 447,088 (1936); 447,090 (1936).
35. British Patent 447,134 (1936).
36. British Patents 461,427 (1937); 461,428 (1937).
37. British Patent 461,428 (1937).
38. British Patent 603,880 (1948).
39. Dreyfus, U.S. Patent 1,883,350 (1932).
40. Duisberg, Hentrich and Zeh, U.S. Patent 1,749,242 (1930).
41. Egerton, *Am. Dyestuff Reptr.*, **38,** 608 (1949).
42. ——, *J. Soc. Dyers Colourists*, **64,** 336 (1948).
43. Ellis, *ibid.*, **40,** 285 (1924).
44. ——, U.S. Patent 1,989,133 (1935).
45. —— and Brown, U.S. Patent 2,053,273 (1936).
45a. ——, Mosby and Olpin, U.S. Patent 1,935,623 (1933).
46. German Patent 232,127 (1911).
47. German Patent 268,984 (1914).
48. German Patent 541,637 (1932).
49. Green and Saunders, *J. Soc. Dyers Colourists*, **39,** 10 (1923).
50. Grossmann, U.S. Patent 1,898,953 (1933).
51. Hauser and Bommer, U.S. Patent 1,911,316 (1933).
52. Houben, "Das Anthracen und Die Anthrachinone," p. 15, Leipzig, Georg Thieme, 1929.
53. I. G. Farbenindustrie, BIOS 1484, pp. 52–62 (PB 86139).
54. ——, FIAT 1313, Vol. II, pp. 200–207 (PB 85172).
55. ——, PB 70254, frames 7167–78.
56. ——, PB 70338, frame 9575.
57. ——, *ibid.*, frame 10123.
58. ——, PB 70340, frames 12435, 12441.
59. ——, PB 70341, frame 13370–75.
60. ——, *ibid.*, frame 13795.
61. ——, PB 70342, frame 14287.
62. ——, *ibid.*, frames 14287, 14474–82.
63. ——, *ibid.*, frame 15154.
64. ——, PB 70343, frame 15275.
65. ——, PB 73490, frame 8660.
66. ——, PB 73726, frame 275.
67. ——, *ibid.*, frame 289.
68. ——, *ibid.*, frame 293.
69. ——, *ibid.*, frame 308.
70. ——, *ibid.*, frame 312.
71. ——, *ibid.*, frames 316–24.
72. ——, *ibid.*, frame 332.
73. ——, *ibid.*, frames 686–88.
74. ——, PB 82170, frame 2765.
75. ——, *ibid.*, frame 2816.
76. ——, *ibid.*, frame 2905.
77. Kartaschoff, *Helv. Chim. Acta*, **9,** 169 (1926).

78. —— and Farine, *ibid.*, **11,** 820 (1928).
79. Koeberle and Mueller, U.S. Patent 1,947,855 (1934).
80. —— and Steigerwald, U.S. Patent 2,138,381 (1938).
81. Kraenzlein and Corell, U.S. Patent 1,710,992 (1929).
82. Kugel, U.S. Patent 1,938,029 (1933).
83. Locher and Fierz, *Helv. Chim. Acta*, **10,** 655 (1927).
84. Lodge and Tatum, U.S. Patent 1,881,752 (1932).
85. Lord and Reeves, U.S. Patent 2,128,307 (1938).
86. —— and ——, U.S. Patent 2,183,652 (1939).
87. Mueller, U.S. Patent 1,587,669 (1926).
88. Mullin, "Acetate Silk and Its Dyes," Chapter XXII, p. 298, New York, D. Van Nostrand Company, 1927.
89. Nawiasky, U.S. Patent 1,736,088 (1929).
90. —— and Krause, U.S. Patent 1,871,821 (1932).
91. Olpin, U.S. Patent 1,688,553 (1928).
92. Perkin, Fyfe and Mendoza, U.S. Patent 1,636,485 (1927).
93. Reddelien and Mueller, U.S. Patent 1,717,809 (1929).
94. Rowe, "Colour Index," Bradford, Yorkshire, England, The Society of Dyers and Colourists, 1924.
95. ——, "The Development of the Chemistry of Commercial Synthetic Dyes," p. 96, The Institute of Great Britain and Ireland, 1938.
96. ——, *ibid.*, p. 97.
97. Schlichting, U.S. Patent 2,123,749 (1938).
98. Shepherdson and Tatum, U.S. Patent 1,898,693 (1933).
99. Thomson, *J. Soc. Dyers Colourists*, **52,** 246 (1936).
100. —— and Tatum, U.S. Patent 1,898,750 (1933).

METALLIZABLE DYES

Edwin C. Buxbaum

Anthraquinone Alizarin Mordant Colors

The alizarin type anthraquinone mordant colors are mainly of historical interest in the United States today, having been superseded by dyes which are easier to apply. They are still used to an appreciable extent in Europe and some other parts of the world. They comprise a wide shade range but require a mordant in order to develop their shade and characteristic fastness properties. In many cases the mordant is first applied to the cotton or wool fabric and the dyeing is then made, which is a two-step operation. In other dyeing methods involving mordant dyes containing solubilizing sulfonic acid groups, the shade of the unmetallized dye is of no interest and the dye must be insolubilized by the addition of some metallic salt, usually chromium.

Although chromium was the most widely used metal to prepare these dyes, many other metallic salts were used to a lesser extent and provided a means of getting a variety of shades from a single dye. The commonest metallic salts used were those of chromium, copper, cobalt, aluminum, iron and nickel. An alizarinsulfonic acid which might be red when metallized with aluminum would be violet with iron and brown with chromium.

Alizarin, 1,2-dihydroxyanthraquinone, is the oldest and best known of the series and was familiar to the ancient Egyptians. Its synthesis was one of the landmarks of dye chemistry[5]. Alizarin is the basis of the well known Turkey Red which was applied by a very involved, tedious procedure.

Chemically, these compounds are hydroxyanthraquinones which may carry, in addition to at least two hydroxy groups which are usually ortho to each other, one or more groups such as nitro, amino, or sulfo. As many as eight positions of the anthraquinone nucleus may be substituted.

A group of sulfonated hydroxyanthraquinone compounds such as sulfonated alizarin and sulfonated quinizarin give dyes which not only can be dyed on wool but which have some use in the pigment field (see Chapter 11). Amino and nitro derivatives give various red, orange and brown shades with a chromium mordant. Polyhydroxyanthraquinone molecules containing four, five, six or more hydroxy groups give various shades of blue upon mordanted cotton and wool and once had wide use both for dyeing and printing. A variant of the polyhydroxyanthraquinone type of dye is the Anthracene Blue group which is a highly substituted anthraquinone nucleus whose exact constitution is not known. By starting with a compound such as 1,5-dinitroanthraquinone and treating it with fuming sulfuric acid (Bohn-Schmidt reaction) a hexahydroxyanthraquinonedisulfonic acid is obtained. In addition some nitrogen-containing compounds are also obtained, probably aminohydroxyanthraquinonesulfonic acids. The mixture gives deep blue shades of relatively good lightfastness when the dyeings are chromed by any of the usual methods[11].

The Bohn-Schmidt reaction, which was discovered in 1886, was an important tool for the manufacture of these dyes since it provided the means of direct hydroxylation of the anthraquinone nucleus. By the use of sulfuric acid containing sulfur trioxide, the introduction of hydroxy and sulfonic acid groups is easily accomplished. The procedure works very well on many compounds including amino- and nitroanthraquinones.

Another variety of chrome mordant alizarin dye is derived from 3(or 4)-nitro(or amino)alizarin by treatment with glycerol and sulfuric acid (Skraup synthesis). An anthraquinonequinoline structure is formed which can be applied to mordanted wool in the usual manner. Blue, green and black shades are known in this series. By treatment of these water-insoluble compounds with sodium bisulfite, water-soluble addition compounds are formed which have some application advantages.

Structure   Characteristics

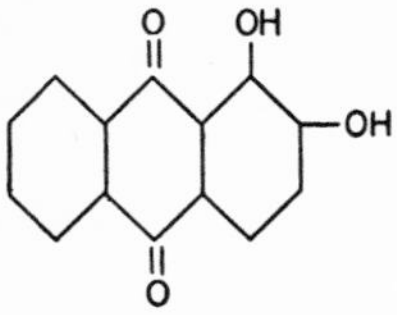

Alizarin

Dyes red[4]. CI 1027

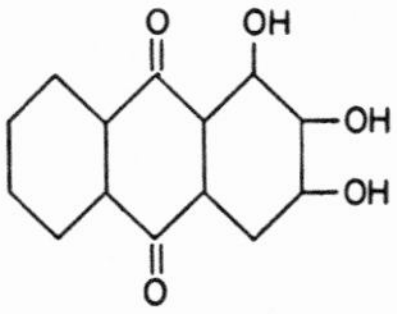

Anthracene Brown

Dyes brown[16]. CI 1035

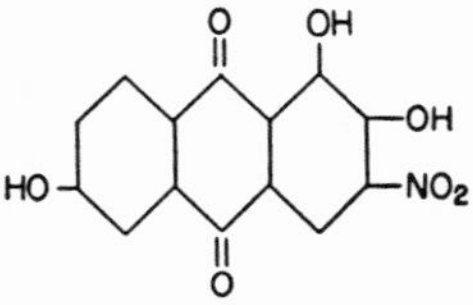

Alizarin Orange G

Dyes orange shades[10]. CI 1042

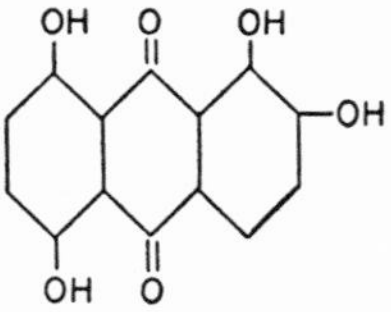

Alizarin Bordeaux BA

Dyes wool violet blue[18]. Dyes cotton in bordeaux shades. CI 1045

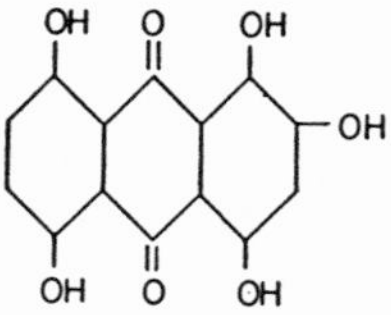

Alizarin Cyanine AC

Dyes blue. CI 1050

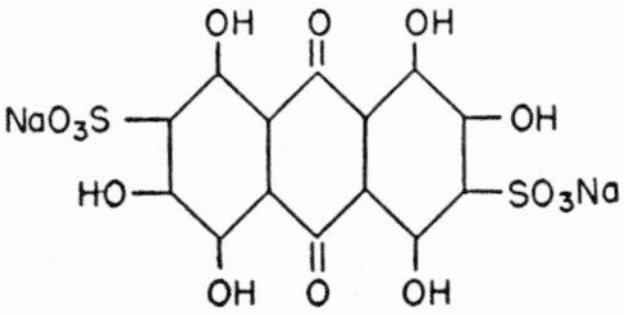

Anthracene Blue SWX

Dyes blue. CI 1063

Structure   Characteristics

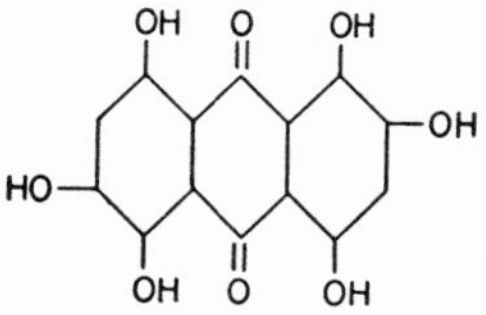

Anthracene Blue WR

Dyes blue. CI 1062

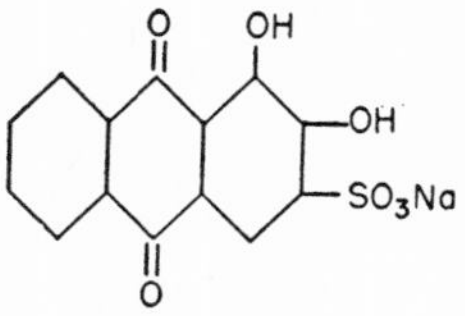

Alizarin Red S

Scarlet. CI 1034

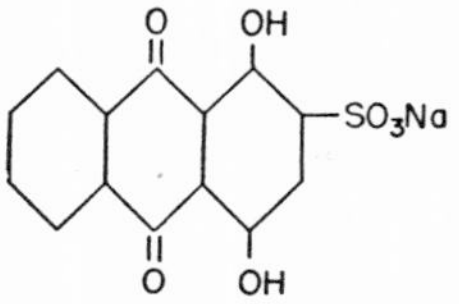

Helio Fast Rubine 4BL

Used as a pigment[13]. Pr. 406

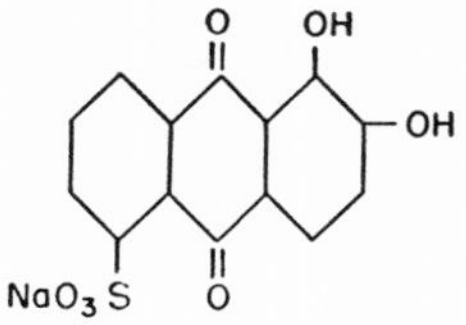

Dyes bordeaux shades[14]

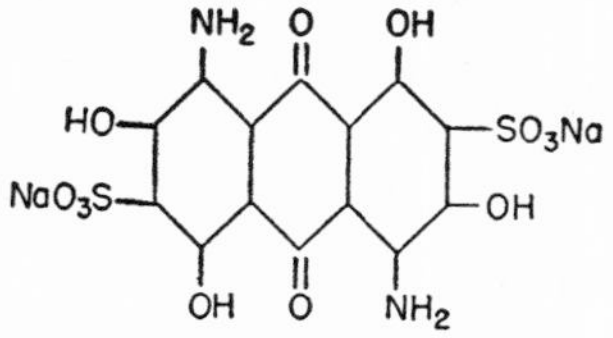

Acid Alizarin Blue GR

Dyes in blue shades. CI 1048

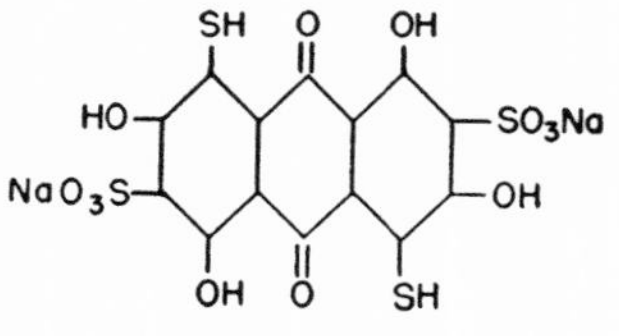

Dyes in green shades[9]. Acid Alizarin Green B, CI 1049

Structure   Characteristics

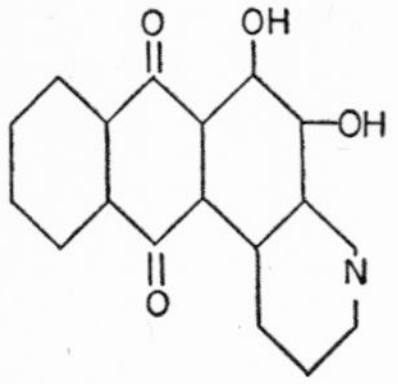

Alizarin Blue

Dyes blue[3, 12]. CI 1066

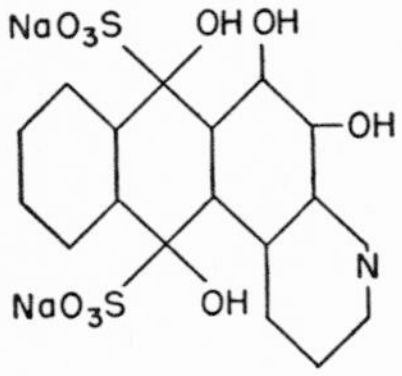

Water-soluble form of Alizarin Blue[2]

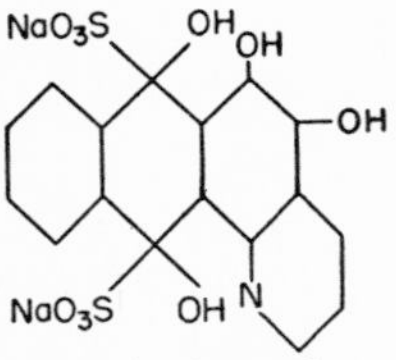

Alizarin Green S

Dyes dull blue-green[8]. CI 1068

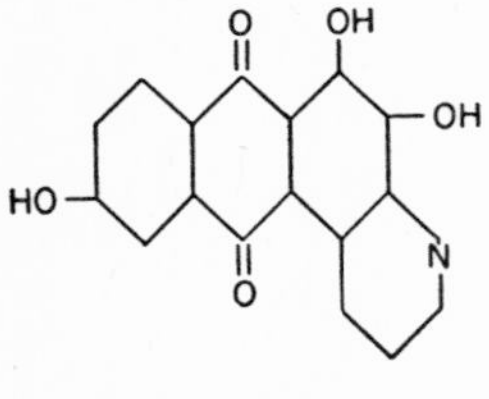

Alizarin Black P

Dyes black[7]. CI 1069

Literature Cited

1. Bohn, U. S. Patent 502,603 (1893).
2. Brunck, U. S. Patent 258,530 (1882).
3. Caro, U.S. Patent 186,032 (1877).
4. ——, Graebe, and Lieberman, U.S. Patent 153,536 (1874).
5. Fieser, *J. Chem. Educ.*, **7,** 2609 (1930).
6. German Patent 3565 (1878).
7. German Patent 54,624 (1890).
8. German Patent 67,470 (1893).
9. German Patent 73,684 (1894).
10. German Patent 74,562 (1894).
11. German Patent 79,768 (1895).
12. Graebe, *Ber.*, **11,** 522 (1878).

13. I. G. Farbenindustrie, FIAT 764, Vol. I, p. 91 (PB 60946).
14. Iljinsky, U.S. Patent 826,509 (1906).
15. Lifschuetz, U.S. Patent 500,917 (1893).
16. Seuberlich, *Ber.*, **10**, 38 (1877).
17. Schmidt, U.S. Patent 446,892 (1891).
18. ——, U.S. Patent 446,893 (1891).

VAT DYES

Melvin A. Perkins

The oldest known vat dye is indigo. Many of its derivatives, as well as thioindigo and its derivatives, are important vat dyes whose chemistry is discussed in Chapter 8 of this monograph. In this chapter, discussion is limited to carbocyclic and heterocyclic quinones. These may be derivatives of simple quinones like benzoquinone, naphthoquinone and anthraquinone, or they may be complex structures containing as many as nineteen condensed rings and ten keto groups.

Vat dyes are made up of any organic coloring matter (with the exception of basic and sulfur colors) which is capable of undergoing a reversible reduction-oxidation cycle without serious color loss or change of shade. No general formula can be written for a vat dye. It is almost always a colored

organic compound containing two or more keto groups $\left(\begin{array}{c} C \\ \| \\ O \end{array}\right)$ which are

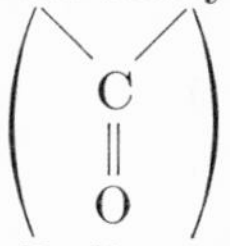

capable of being reduced by sodium hydrosulfite and alkali to give a leuco

compound $\left(\begin{array}{c} C \\ | \\ ONa \end{array}\right)$ which has affinity for cellulosic fiber. In many cases

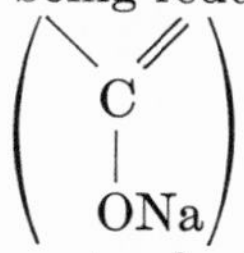

this affinity extends also to other fibers such as wool, nylon, "Orlon" acrylic fiber, and even to cellulose acetate.

Vat dyes were the largest application class produced in the United States in 1951, amounting to 36 per cent of the total. The most notable increase is output since World War II was in nonindigoid vat dyes.

Carbocyclic Vat Dyes

BENZOQUINONES AND NAPHTHOQUINONES

Melvin A. Perkins

The simplest vat colors possible are those related to p-quinone since the latter lends itself to the reduction-oxidation cycle which is characteristic of a vat dye:

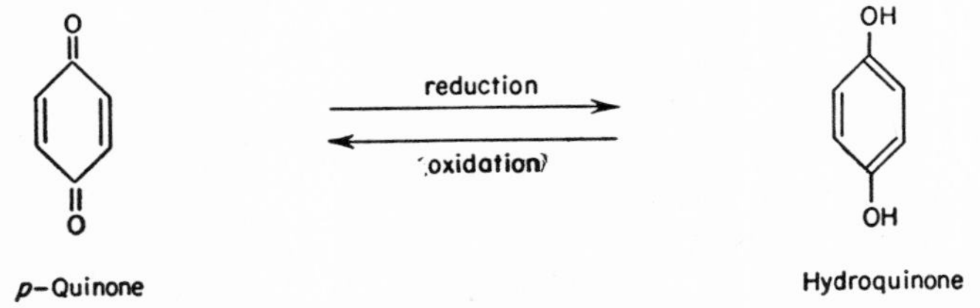

p-Quinone   Hydroquinone

p-Quinone is a very reactive substance and readily undergoes addition reactions which result in 2,5-disubstituted-p-quinones plus hydroquinone. Aniline, for example, reacts with p-quinone in hot alcoholic solution to give 2,5-dianilino-p-quinone and hydroquinone.

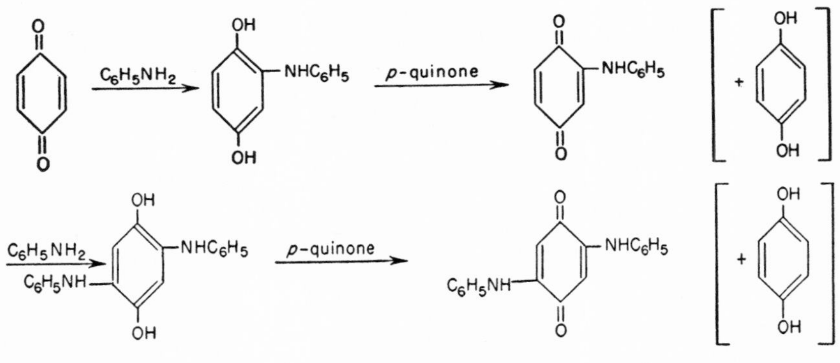

2,5-Dianilino-p-quinones themselves have vat dye properties. In fact they have been used to a considerable extent in Europe for vat dyeing of wool[6]. Examples of such products are Vat Yellow G and Vat Brown G. On cotton they are too weak and dull to be of practical interest as vat dyes. In spite of this, however, the leuco sulfuric acid ester of 2,5-bis(p-chloroanilino)-p-quinone[8] has been sold in considerable volume under the name of Indigosol or Anthrasol Yellow HCG[9, 10]. It prints and dyes cotton and wool in dull yellow shades of surprisingly good fastness.

No derivatives of the isomeric *o*-quinone have been found to be of interest as dyes. Similar relationships are found in the naphthoquinone field. While 1,2- and 2,6-naphthoquinones are known, only the 1,4-naphthoquinones are of interest as dyes. This product itself may be regarded as intermediate between *p*-quinone and anthraquinone in that one side of the quinone ring is protected by a benzo ring while anthraquinone has both sides so protected.

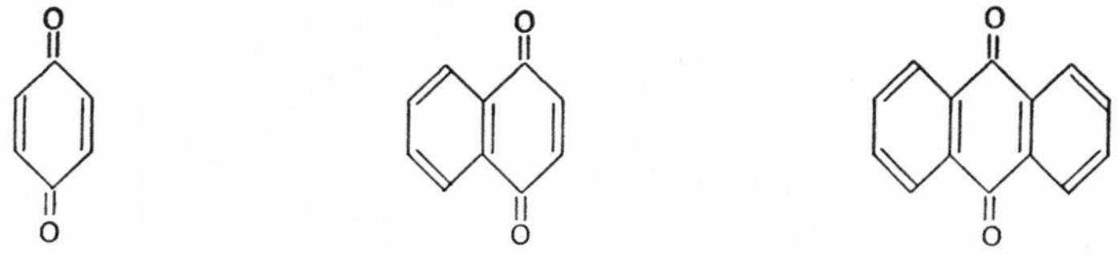

In actual practice this "protection" is of little significance unless the other side of the quinone nucleus is also covered. An example of this is found in Indanthrene Yellow 6GD which is obtainable by condensation of 1,8-naphthosultam-5,6-phenazine (5H-[1,2]benzisothiazolo[4,3-ab]phenazine, 4,4-dioxide) with 2,3-dichloro-1,4-naphthoquinone and which has the configuration shown[7].

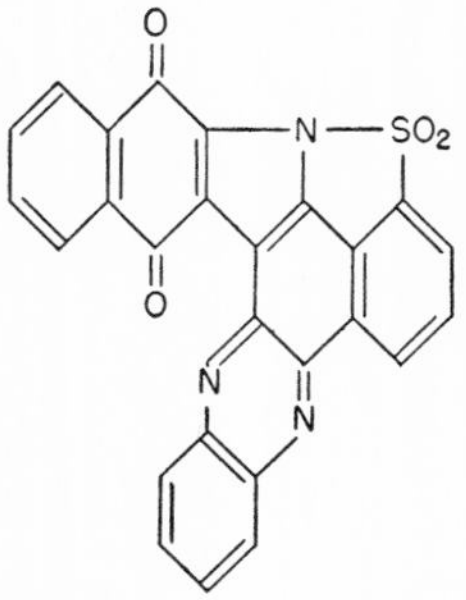

This and related colors of this type have been used to dye wool as well as to give very greenish-yellow shades on cotton, particularly for chartreuse shades when printed in blends with vat greens[5, 11]. The product is said to be a "nontenderer," an important factor in the field of yellow and orange vat dyes, in that fiber dyed therewith shows no loss of tensile strength after prolonged light exposure, compared to a similar sample of undyed fiber[12, 13].

No other naphthoquinones are known to be of importance as vat dyes. A few selected products of this class are known which are dyes for gasoline, cellulose acetate and "Dacron" polyester fiber, but they are not strictly naphthoquinones (except "naphthazarin")[4], being quinone imines of the type illustrated by the following formula[1, 2, 3]:

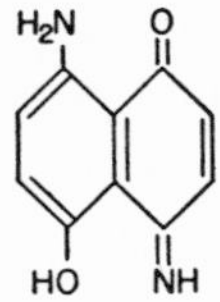

Literature Cited

1. Bally, U.S. Patent 619,115 (1899).
2. Bohn, U.S. Patent 667,486 (1901).
3. ——, U.S. Patent 669,894 (1901).
4. Dimroth and Ruck, *Ann.*, **446**, 123 (1925).
5. Herzberg and Hoppe, U.S. Patent 1,431,656 (1922).
6. I.G. Farbenindustrie, BIOS (Misc.) 20, p. 23 (PB 31004).
7. ——, BIOS 987, p. 126 (PB 75860).
8. ——, BIOS 1493, p. 6 (PB 81611).
9. ——, *ibid.*, p. 72.
10. ——, FIAT 1313, Vol. II, p. 195 (PB 85172).
11. Kraenzlein, Greune and Vollmann, U.S. Patent 1,767,377 (1930).
12. Kunz, *Angew. Chem.*, **52**, 269 (1939).
13. ——, *Bull. soc. ind. Mulhouse*, **100**, 3 (1933).

ACYLAMINOANTHRAQUINONES

Myron S. Whelen

The acylaminoanthraquinones are the products obtained by the acylation of an aminoanthraquinone with an acid halide or its equivalent. They may be represented by the formula RCONHAq where Aq is an anthraquinone radical and R is the radical from the acid chloride utilized.

Historically they represent a very important group of vat dyes originally known as Algol colors. Algol is the trade name of the Bayer Company, while Indanthrene was the trade name used for vat colors of the Badische Anilin-und Soda-Fabrik. At a later date under the I.G. Farbenindustrie, the Algol name was used to refer to a degree of fastness—good, but admittedly below that of Indanthrene. At the time of their discovery the commercial vat dyes of the anthraquinone type were limited to indanthrone, flavanthrone and pyranthrone, all condensed systems. It may be said that the advent of the Algol colors marked the second milestone in the anthraquinone vat color field, the first being Bohn's discovery of indanthrone in 1901.

The first acylaminoanthraquinone dye of interest was prepared in 1908 utilizing an aliphatic acid chloride[12], but to establish this class of dye it remained for J. Deinet, then with the Bayer Company at Elberfeld, to discover that the acylation of aminoanthraquinones with an aromatic acid chloride[5], especially benzoyl chloride, gave rise to a valuable series of dyes. A number of these were quickly produced by the Bayer Company and they greatly extended the range of shade and thus more firmly established the use of vat dyes. Many of these same dyes are currently being produced—a tribute to their all-around good properties. The development of the acyl-aminoanthraquinones simultaneously created great interest in aminoanthra-quinones and their derivatives and from them new types of anthraquinone vat dyes were obtained, the anthrimide carbazoles containing acylamino groups being an outstanding example.

Methods of Preparation. The commonly used procedure for the conversion of an aminoanthraquinone to an acylaminoanthraquinone is to allow it to react with the acid chloride at an elevated temperature in an inert organic solvent such as *o*-dichlorobenzene, nitrobenzene or naphthalene[4]. Nitrobenzene is most commonly used and the temperature employed is of the order of 150 to 190°C. In some cases it is possible to acylate by means of the anhydride[18]. Acylation of an aminoanthraquinone is always accompanied by a great increase in dyeing strength, strong vat dyes being obtained from an aromatic acid chloride such as benzoyl chloride. Acylation may also be accomplished by heating a haloanthraquinone with an acid amide[13]. This reaction is carried out in an inert solvent in the presence of a copper catalyst and an acid-binding agent. This method is not commercially important. Acylaminoanthraquinones are usually obtained as highly crystalline compounds in high yield and quality.

General Properties. Acylation of aminoanthraquinones with aliphatic acid chlorides does not produce valuable dyes. The products obtained by acylation of 1-aminoanthraquinone with aromatic acid chlorides, especially benzoyl chloride or its derivatives, or with other complex aromatic acid chlorides obtained from anthraquinone[22] or other condensed systems, are the vat dyes of this type now being sold. Products obtained by acylation with acid chlorides derived from naphthalene are of little value[20]. Acylation of 2-aminoanthraquinone in general gives rise to weak dyes of no commercial importance.

The acylaminoanthraquinones dye cotton from a sodium hydrosulfite-sodium hydroxide vat in shades ranging from greenish-yellow through orange and red to violet. They dye best by the so-called "cold" method—reduction at 120°F and dyeing at 80°F with low sodium hydroxide concentration. They are in general good dyeing and printing colors, and a few are used as pigment colors. They possess good brightness and have good fastness to chlorine and washing. Their lightfastness as a class is satisfactory.

Lightfastness increases as the depth of shade increases; the greenish-yellows tend to be poor, while the red shades show good lightfastness.

Types of Acylaminoanthraquinones. Acylaminoanthraquinones can be prepared from mono- or polyaminoanthraquinones with mono- or dicarboxylic acid chlorides[9, 11]. The aminoanthraquinone or the acid chloride can also contain suitable substituent groups. The following illustrations represent the various types and the examples are the more important dyes in this class.

Monoaminoanthraquinones and Aromatic Monocarboxylic Acid Chlorides:

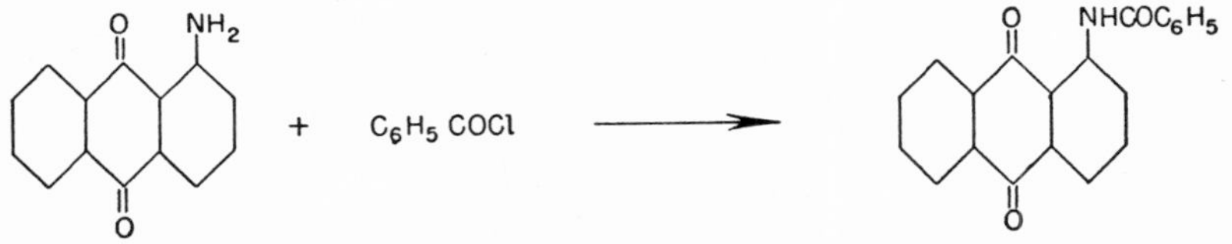

1- Aminoanthraquinone   Benzoyl chloride   1- Benzamido-
                                                      anthraquinone

This greenish-yellow dye was at one time sold as Algol Yellow WG. It lacks adequate tinctorial strength and is no longer commercially important.

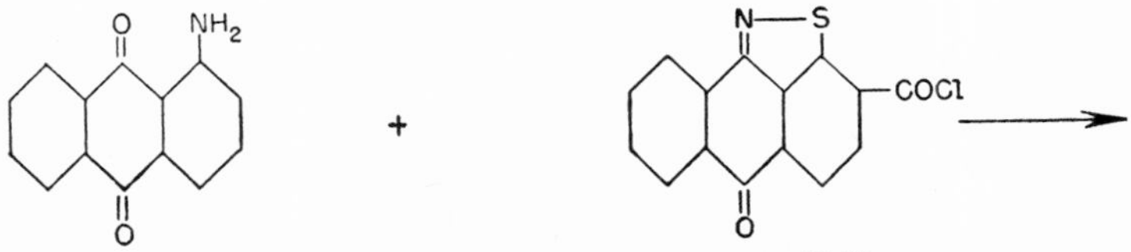

1-Aminoanthraquinone   6-Oxo-6H-anthr [9,1] isothiazole-
                            3-carbonyl chloride

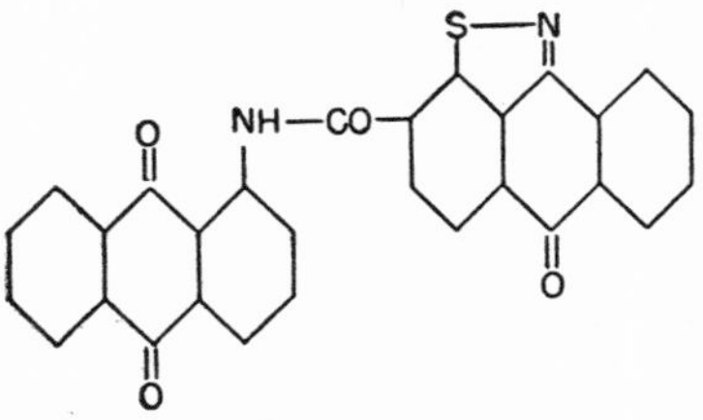

This is a yellow dye[16] possessing very good tinctorial and fastness properties.

Monoaminoanthraquinones and Dicarboxylic Acid Chlorides:

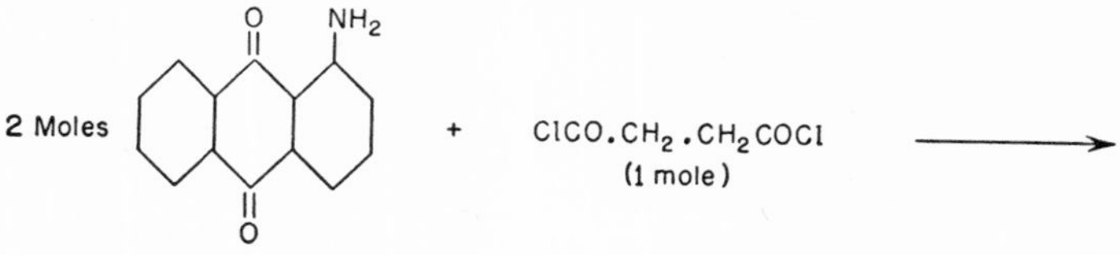
2 Moles
+
ClCO.CH2.CH2COCl
(1 mole)

1-Aminoanthraquinone   Succinyl chloride

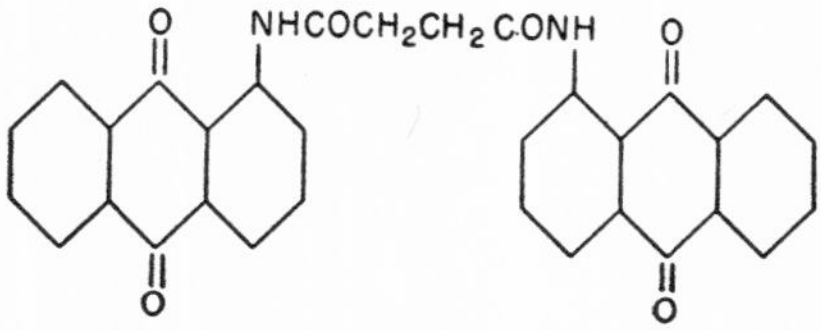
NHCOCH2CH2CONH

Algol Yellow 3G[12]

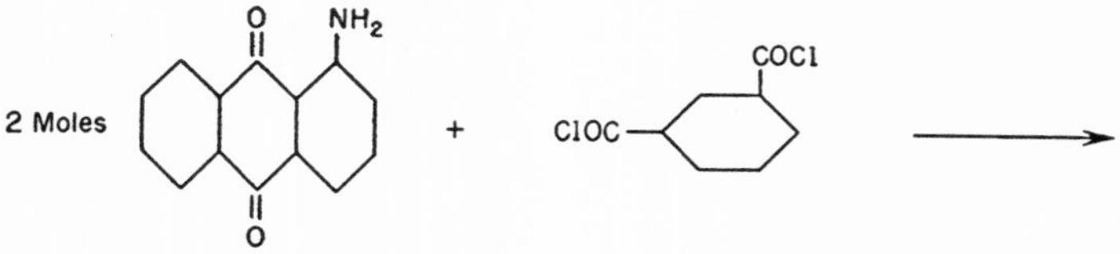
2 Moles
+
ClOC
COCl

1-Aminoanthraquinone   Isophthaloyl chloride

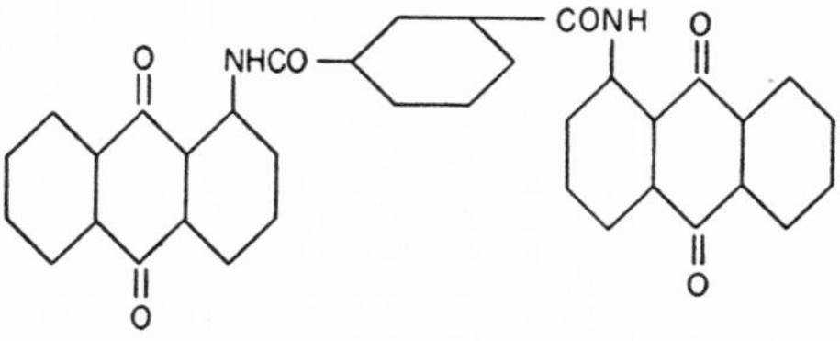
NHCO
CONH

Indanthrene Yellow 5 GK[11]

This is a greenish-yellow dye with poor tinctorial properties, and is not commercially important, although it is used to some extent for blending with vat greens to obtain yellower greens.

Diaminoanthraquinones and Aromatic Monocarboxylic Acids:

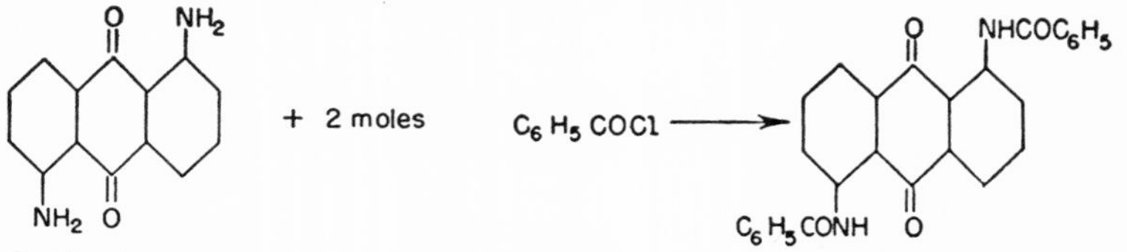
+ 2 moles
C6 H5 COCl
NHCOC6H5
C6 H5 CONH

1,5-Diaminoanthraquinone   Benzoyl chloride   1,5-Dibenzamidoanthraquinone (Indanthrene Yellow GK) CI 1132

It is in this class that the most important colors are found.

1,5-Dibenzamidoanthraquinone is probably the best known. It is a yellow dye possessing good tinctorial properties and good all-around fastness. 1,4-Dibenzamidoanthraquinone, similarly prepared from 1,4-diaminoanthraquinone, dyes red[10] (Indanthrene Red 5GK) showing the bathochromic effect derived from an amino group in the 4 position as contrasted with one in the 5 position (changing the shade from yellow to red). Incidentally, this red, although very weak tinctorially, has excellent lightfastness. 1,8-Dibenzamidoanthraquinone[6] is a yellow dye close in shade to 1,5-dibenzamidoanthraquinone but with inferior lightfastness, a property often encountered in 1,8 derivatives of anthraquinone. The utilization of a mixture of 1,5- and 1,8-dibenzamidoanthraquinone is stated to produce superior application properties[19], due to a synergistic effect.

The acylation of β-aminoanthraquinones gives products of no value as dyes. 2,3-Dibenzamidoanthraquinone will not dye, 2,6-dibenzamidoanthraquinone vats but is practically colorless, and even the "mixed" 1,2-dibenzamidoanthraquinone is weak tinctorially. Tribenzamidoanthraquinones[8] are known but are of little technical interest.

Introduction of a simple substituent group into the 4 position of a 1-acylaminoanthraquinone is commonly employed to secure dyes with greater depth of shade. Likewise the introduction of a suitable substituent in the ring of the aromatic acid chloride may be used to produce the same effect. An example of the latter is the acylation of aminoanthraquinones with 1-amino-2-anthraquinonecarbonyl chloride to give reddish type dyes of commercial interest[17].

Acylaminoanthraquinones Containing Hydroxy and Alkoxy Groups. Hydroxy and alkoxy groups are well known auxochrome groups. The most commonly used procedure for obtaining acylaminohydroxyanthraquinones is to acylate the corresponding aminohydroxyanthraquinone. Substitution in the 4 position of a 1-aminoanthraquinone produces a bathochromic effect in that it deepens the shade, 1-benzamido-4-hydroxyanthraquinone[17] (Algol Red R) being a pink dye while 1-benzamidoanthraquinone is a greenish-yellow. Dyes of this class are inferior in washing properties as compared to the corresponding unsubstituted products. They do, however, possess very good lightfastness and are used as pigment colors.

1,5-Dibenzamido-4-hydroxyanthraquinone prepared either by the benzoylation of 1,5-diamino-4-hydroxyanthraquinone[4], or by treatment of 1,5-dibenzamidoanthraquinone in oleum with manganese dioxide[14] is a red dye which finds very limited use in cotton dyeing (Algol Red FF).

Introduction of hydroxy groups into positions other than the 4 position of the anthraquinone nucleus produces little effect on shade except in those cases where there is a "doubling up effect" of the hydroxy group. The dyes obtained from 1,5-diamino-4,8-dihydroxyanthraquinone (diaminoanthrarufin) by acylation with either benzoyl or anisoyl chloride[3] (Indanthrene Brilliant Violet RK, CI 1135) are examples of the "doubling up effect." These products with two hydroxy groups, each in para position to an amino group, exhibit the greatest depth of shade (violet) of any of the simple acylaminoanthraquinones. The use of anisoyl chloride in the above example to introduce a methoxy group into the aromatic nucleus produces somewhat of a hypsochromic effect. The introduction of an hydroxy group into the aromatic nucleus is also known, an example being the acylation of 1-aminoanthraquinone with salicyloyl chloride to produce a yellow dye valuable as a pigment color[21] (Helio Fast Yellow 6GL).

The introduction of a methoxy group in the anthraquinone nucleus of acylaminoanthraquinones gives a hypsochromic effect, shifting the shade toward the yellow when compared to the corresponding hydroxy compound. It is usually accomplished by acylation of the desired aminomethoxyanthraquinone[7] rather than by methylation of the hydroxy group, or by displacement of a halogen atom by means of methyl alcohol and potassium hydroxide. The methoxy derivatives have better washfastness but poorer lightfastness than the corresponding hydroxy derivatives. They are not commercially important.

Substitution by chlorine or methyl groups has little effect. The introduction of a sulfonic acid group creates water-soluble products unsatisfactory as cotton dyes and lacking interest as wool dyes.

In summation, substitution in the anthraquinone ring of α-acylaminoanthraquinones by groups other than the amino group in positions other than 4 has little effect. Substituents other than halogen in the 4 position have a marked bathochromic effect.

Acylaminoanthraquinones Containing a Free Amino Group. Anthraquinone vat dyes containing a free amino group are in general of no value as vat dyes, and this is well shown in the acylaminoanthraquinones. Such products lack affinity for the fiber and in any event lack chlorinefastness. Aminobenzamidoanthraquinones are readily obtained by mono-benzoylation of the corresponding diaminoanthraquinones[2]. The 1-amino-4-, 5- and 8-benzamidoanthraquinones are well known. They have practically no affinity for cotton but are very important intermediates for vat dye synthesis. There are, however, well known exceptions in which the introduction of an amino group confers valuable properties, exemplified by an intense reddening of shade as well as fastness toward chlorine. There are numerous acylaminoanthraquinone dyes known wherein an amino group has been acylated with 1-amino-2-anthraquinonecarbonyl chloride, the resulting product containing a so-called "free amino" group. Such products are usually red in shade. Acylation of 1,5-diaminoanthraquinone with two moles of 1-amino-2-anthraquinonecarbonyl chloride[17] produces the red vat dye shown as follows:

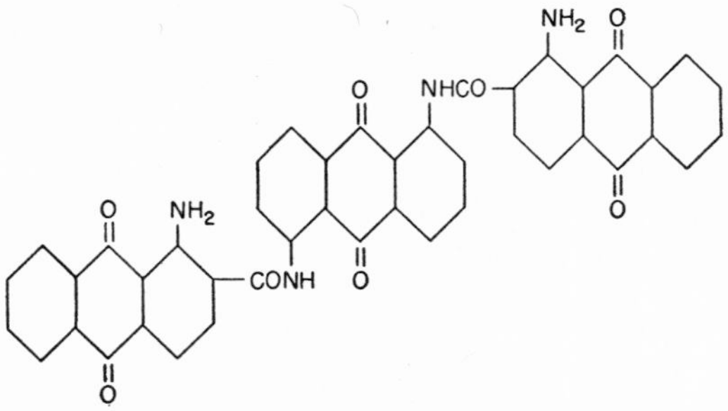

This product has good tinctorial strength and good light- and chlorine-fastness. Though it contains two so-called "free amino" groups which ordinarily would produce poor chlorinefastness, these amino groups are actually not free, and the resistance to chlorine arises from the fact that the amine is protected by hydrogen bonding to the oxygen of the carbonyl group, represented as follows:

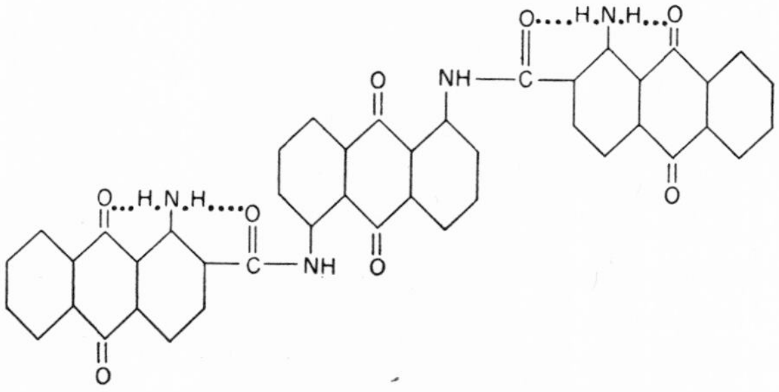

The use of other anthraquinonecarbonyl chlorides as acylating agents to introduce a substituted anthraquinone nucleus is known. The acid chloride is usually in the 2 position as this leads to dyes having better tinctorial strength. A nitro group, which may be reduced after condensation, is commonly employed, which in turn may be converted to an acylamino group. The use of 5-nitro-2-anthraquinonecarbonyl chloride or 5-benzamido-2-anthraquinonecarbonyl chloride[1] is an example where an acylamino group is introduced to produce dyes of the type R-CONHR′, where R is an acyl-aminoanthraquinone and R′ is an anthraquinone nucleus which may or may not be substituted by acylamino or other groups.

Numerous acylaminoanthraquinones of bridged type are known, which may be represented as follows where R is an anthraquinone radical and R' may be CH$_2$, CH=CH, CO, S, SO$_2$, NH or N=N. Many variations of such bridged types are known. The introduction of such bridging groups, with the exception of the azo and the ethylene groups, usually does not add anything to the value of the dye. The increase in molecular weight without a compensating contribution of an auxochrome group makes them tinctorially weaker than the corresponding unbridged component.

The introduction of an azo group as a bridge between two acylamino-anthraquinone groups is however of distinct advantage. The yellow dye obtained by the condensation of two moles of 1-amino-5-benzamidoanthra-quinone with one mole of 4',4'''-azobis-4-biphenylcarbonyl chloride[15] (Indanthrene Yellow GGF):

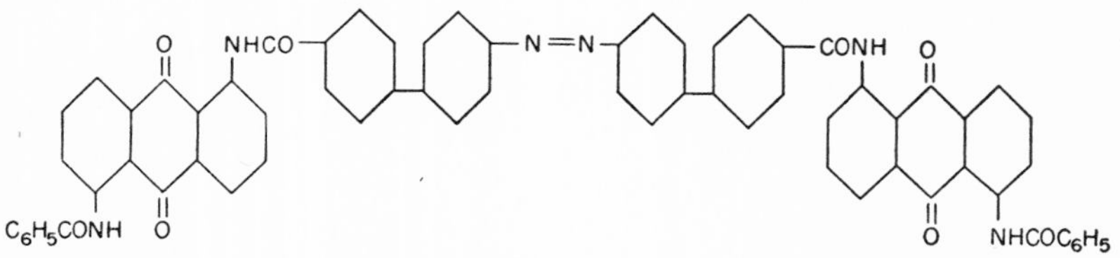

is an outstanding example of the introduction of an azo group into an acyl-aminoanthraquinone system which produces an intense yellow effect and simultaneously imparts enhanced affinity as well as improved lightfastness. It is interesting to note that this dye is not destroyed by vatting with alkaline hydrosulfite, the azo group when so linked being stable to vatting.

In addition to the various types of acylaminoanthraquinones already described there are many products known wherein molecules of the various types are linked together. Many of complex nature are known wherein an acylaminoanthraquinone is joined through a CONH, NHCO, NH or other linkage to systems containing an anthraquinone nucleus to which a heterocyclic system is attached. Such dyes are outside the scope of this section and fall under the type of the particular heterocyclic system involved.

Literature Cited

1. Beard, U.S. Patent 2,001,701 (1935).
2. Buchloh, Meig and Stoetzer, U.S. Patent 1,867,058 (1932).
3. Deinet, U.S. Patent 935,590 (1909).
4. ——, U.S. Patent 935,781 (1909).
5. ——, U.S. Patent 938,618 (1909).
6. ——, U.S. Patent 938,619 (1909).
7. ——, U.S. Patent 957,039 (1910).
8. ——, U.S. Patent 957,040 (1910).
9. ——, U.S. Patent 957,041 (1910).
10. ——, U.S. Patent 957,042 (1910).
11. Fischer, U.S. Patent 938,565 (1909).

12. German Patent 210,019 (1909).
13. German Patent 216,772 (1909).
14. German Patent 238,488 (1911).
15. Honold and Schubert, U.S. Patent 2,228,455 (1941).
16. Lulek, *Ind. Eng. Chem.*, **23**, 96 (1931).
17. Nawiasky and Saurwein, U.S. Patent 1,539,689 (1925).
18. Perkin and Bunbury, U.S. Patent 1,660,090 (1928).
19. Stott and Beard, U.S. Patent 2,022,748 (1935).
20. Thomaschewski, U.S. Patent 935,827 (1909).
21. ——, U.S. Patent 957,125 (1910).
22. Wolman, U.S. Patent 935,878 (1909).

BENZANTHRAQUINONES AND PYRENEDIONES

Melvin A. Perkins

Of the various carbocyclic quinones containing either four or five condensed rings, there is none which constitutes an important dye. 1,2-Benz-
anthraquinone (benz[a]anthracene-7,12-dione)

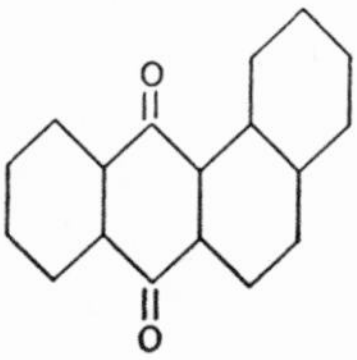

has been synthesized from naphthalene and phthalic anhydride [along with
smaller quantities of the isomeric 2,3-benzanthraquinone (naphthacenequinone)] by sulfuric acid ring-closure of the naphthoylbenzoic acid in a
manner analogous to that used for anthraquinone itself[2]. This is a yellow
substance which, although vattable, has little or no affinity for cellulosic
or other fiber. Reactivity of this material has been studied rather extensively
but no dye worthy of comment has arisen from this work.

Two isomeric pyrenediones are known which are dyes[1, 5]. They are represented by the following formulas:

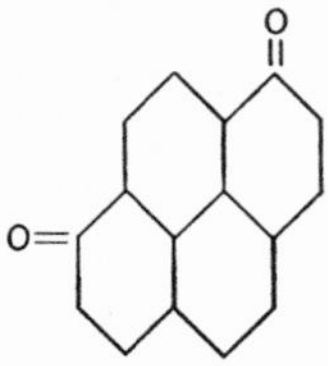

1,8-Pyrenedione   and   1,6-Pyrenedione

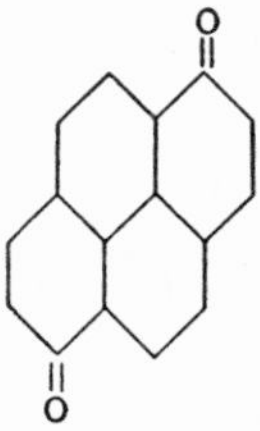

The 1,8 compound is orange-red while the 1,6 is yellow. They can be separated by selective reduction with alkaline hydrosulfite solutions, the former being more readily soluble. Without further condensed rings [as in the technically important 2,3-7,8-dibenzopyrene-1,6-dione (dibenzo[a,h]-pyrene-7,14-dione)] these products have no practical usefulness because of poor affinity and insufficient fastness to washing[5]. There is, however, one product of this class which is worthy of note because of its unusually attractive bright green shade. Because of low affinity it is marketed and used as a leuco sulfuric acid ester rather than as a vat dye[3, 4]. The parent dye is 5,10-dianilino-3,8-dichloro-1,6-pyrenedione and is prepared from pyrene by the following steps.

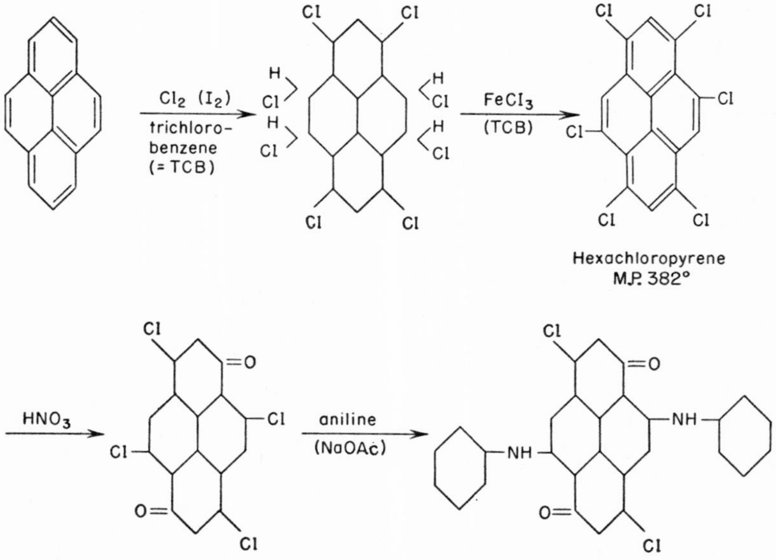

Hexachloropyrene
M.P. 382°

Tetrachloropyrenedione

Base Color for Anthrasol Green I3G

There is literature indicating that other derivatives of pyrenedione have dye properties but neither these nor monobenzopyrenediones appear to have sufficient technical merit to warrant marketing.

Dibenzopyrenediones are of sufficient importance to justify a separate section (see p. 446).

Literature Cited

1. German Patent 613,914 (1935).
2. Heller and Schulke, *Ber.*, **41**, 3627 (1908).
3. I. G. Farbenindustrie, BIOS 1493, pp. 64–68 (PB 81611).
4. ——, FIAT 1313, Vol. II, p. 191 (PB 85172).
5. Vollmann, Becker, Corell and Streeck, *Ann.*, **531**, 1–159 (1937).

ANTHANTHRONES

Myron S. Whelen

Anthanthrone (dibenzo[cd,jk]pyrene-6,12-dione), a six-ringed pyrene derivative, may be visualized as two internally condensed anthrone systems.

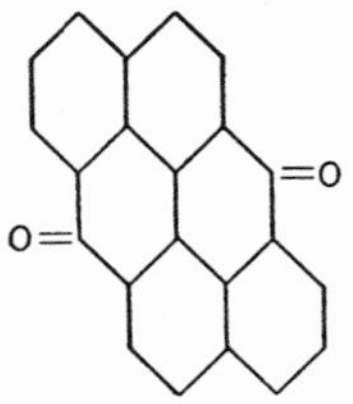

It was discovered by Kalb[4] in 1914, who prepared it from both 1,1'-binaphthalene-8,8'-dicarboxylic acid and 1,1'-binaphthalene-2,2'-dicarboxylic acid by ring-closure methods.

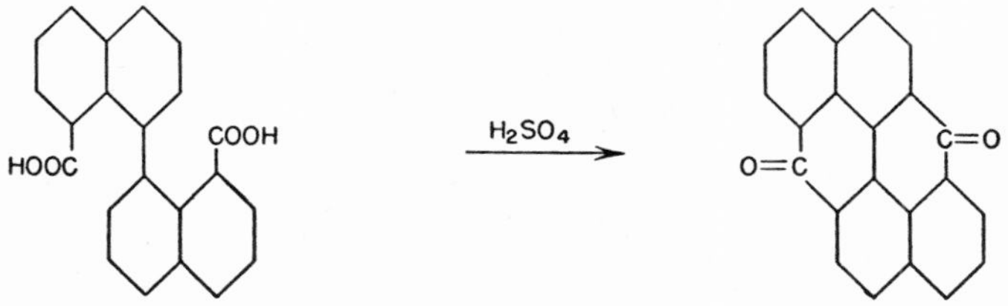

1,1'-Binaphthalene-8,8'-
dicarboxylic acid

Anthanthrone

The use of 1,1'-binaphthalene-8,8'-dicarboxylic acid is the more practical. The synthesis of this intermediate and its conversion to anthanthrone and its halogenated derivatives is outlined as follows[3]:

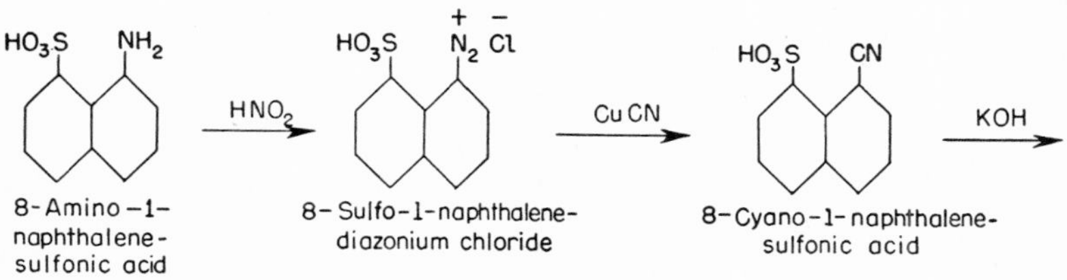

8-Amino-1-
naphthalene-
sulfonic acid

8-Sulfo-1-naphthalene-
diazonium chloride

8-Cyano-1-naphthalene-
sulfonic acid

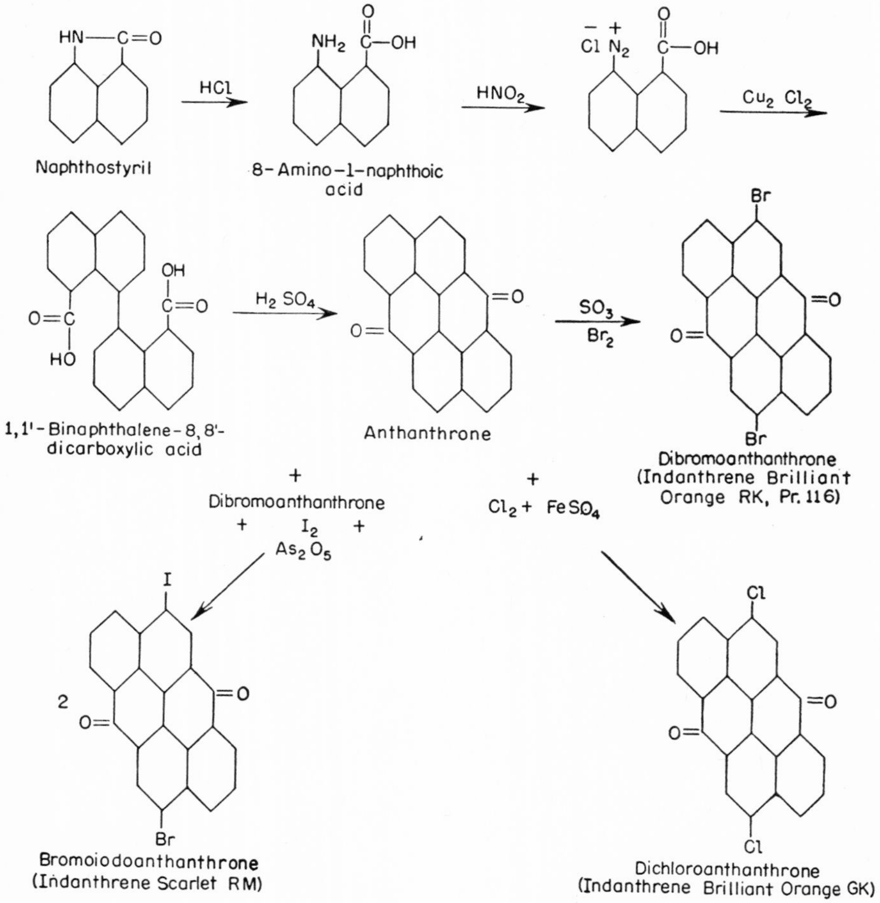

Naphthostyril → 8-Amino-1-naphthoic acid → (diazonium) → 1,1'-Binaphthalene-8,8'-dicarboxylic acid → Anthanthrone → Dibromoanthanthrone (Indanthrene Brilliant Orange RK, Pr. 116)

Bromoiodoanthanthrone (Indanthrene Scarlet RM)

Dichloroanthanthrone (Indanthrene Brilliant Orange GK)

Anthanthrone is a yellowish-orange colored compound which dyes cotton in orange shades from a sodium hydrosulfite ($Na_2S_2O_4$) sodium hydroxide vat. It is not used commercially due to the fact that it shows poor tinctorial properties and is lacking in lightfastness. Its dihalogenated derivatives, however, overcome these shortcomings. This phenomenon of increasing tinctorial strength and lightfastness by halogenation is common to many isocyclic keto hydrocarbons. Halogenation beyond two bromine or chlorine atoms may cause loss in tinctorial value, and tetrabromoanthanthrone, for example, is quite weak tinctorially. The dihalo derivatives are accordingly the best products and the dibromo derivative, Indanthrene Brilliant Orange RK[1], is the most important commercially. Redness of shade increases by halogenation through chlorine, bromine to iodine, the chlorine derivatives being classed as yellow-oranges and the iodo derivatives being scarlets. Numerous mixed types are known. A mixture of Indanthrene Scarlet RM and Indanthrene Brilliant Orange RK is sold as Indanthrene Scarlet GK[5].

The anthanthrone colors are characterized by their brilliance of shade, good level-dyeing and good fastness properties, especially bleach- and light-fastness. They are primarily used as dyeing colors but they are also satisfactory printing colors. Due to their relatively high cost they are not consumed in large volume but tend to be used in specialty work.

Dibromoanthanthrone may be used as an intermediate for condensation purposes. On condensation with two moles of 1-amino-4-benzamidoanthraquinone a mixture of di- and trianthrimides is formed. This is Indanthrene Gray BG[2], a gray dye having good fastness properties but inferior in light-fastness as compared to the parent compound. It is said to be excellent for dyeing tightly woven materials because of slow, even dyeing and complete penetration.

Literature Cited

1. Herz and Zerweck, U.S. Patent 1,803,757 (1931).
2. I. G. Farbenindustrie, BIOS 1493, p. 23 (PB 81611).
3. ——, FIAT 1313, Vol. II, p. 89 (PB 85172).
4. Kalb, *Ber.*, **47**, 1724 (1914).
5. Kunz, Koeberle and Berthold, U.S. Patent 1,926,155 (1933).

DIBENZOPYRENEDIONES

Frederick B. Stilmar

Dibenzo[a,h]pyrene-7,14-dione was first synthesized by Kraenzlein, Corell and Sedlmayr in 1922[7].

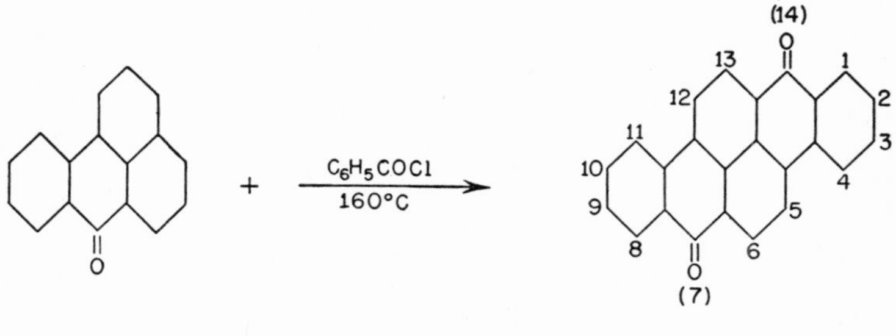

Benzanthrone was condensed with benzoyl chloride in aluminum chloride to form the golden yellow dibenzo[a,h]pyrene-7,14-dione. Scholl[18] had previously failed in an attempt to cyclize 1,5-dibenzoylnaphthalene to dibenzopyrenedione although he was successful in preparing the isomeric red dibenzo[a,i]pyrene-5,8-dione from 1,4-dibenzoylnaphthalene

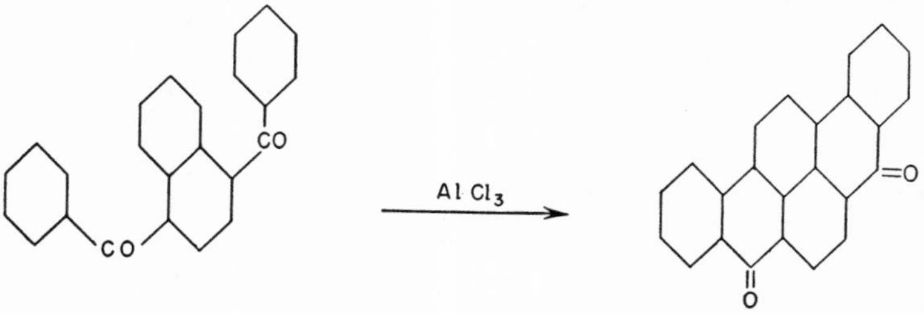

The 5,8-quinone has not assumed any commercial importance because the vat dyes based on it possess low affinity and poor working properties.

For dibenzo[a,h]pyrene-7,14-dione the best methods of synthesis are the original route (benzoylation of benzanthrone), ring-closure of 1,5-dibenzoylnaphthalene[10, 11], benzoylation/ring-closure of 1-benzoylnaphthalene[9] or direct condensation of naphthalene with benzoyl chloride/aluminum chloride[19] as in the scheme:

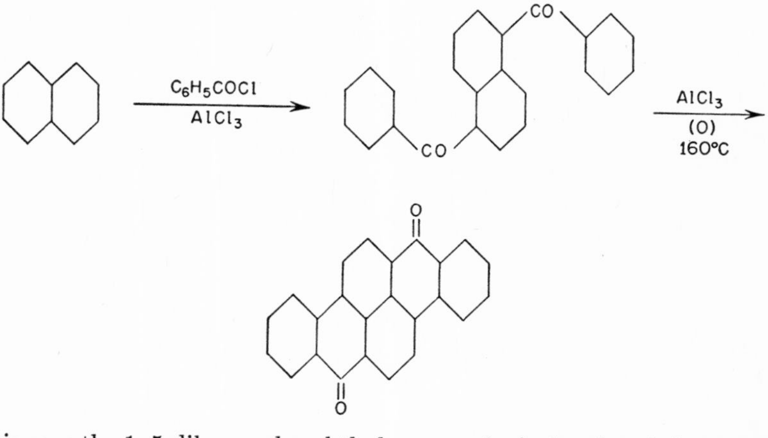

In this case the 1,5-dibenzoylnaphthalene may be isolated and then cyclized or the reaction may be carried all the way through successfully. In the second step an oxidizing agent is essential. After purification by vatting to remove vat-insoluble by-products, the over-all yield by either of the above procedures is about 55 per cent according to I. G. Farbenindustrie data[3].

Dibenzo[a,h]pyrene-7,14-dione is readily halogenated by standard methods[13, 16] but the most successful are unquestionably a bromination of the crude product in an aluminum chloride melt at 160 to 170°C[4], and the bromination in chlorosulfonic acid at relatively low temperatures in the presence of a large amount of iodine catalyst to produce a more homogeneous product[8, 17] presumably represented by the formula:

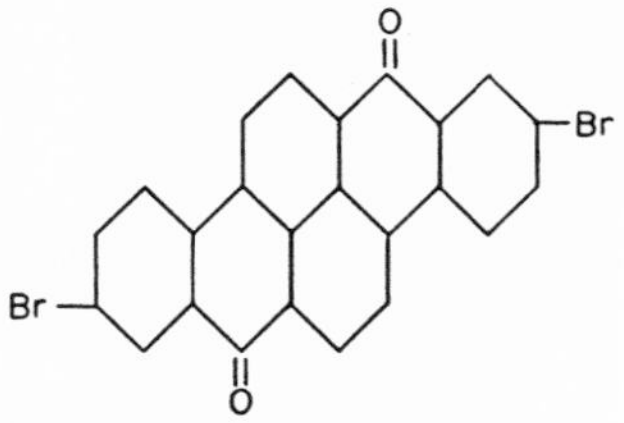

The 2 and 9 positions would appear to be the most logical points for attack since they are meta to a carbonyl group and at the terminalpara position in a biphenyl nucleus.

Other methods which may be employed to prepare specific substitution products of dibenzo[a,h]pyrene-7,14-dione include the condensation of 1,5-naphthalenedicarbonyl chloride or of 3-benzanthronecarbonyl chloride with substituted benzene derivatives, and a novel and useful diene synthesis involving 10-methyleneanthrone and substituted propiolophenones followed by the usual AlCl$_3$ ring-closure, as illustrated by the scheme:

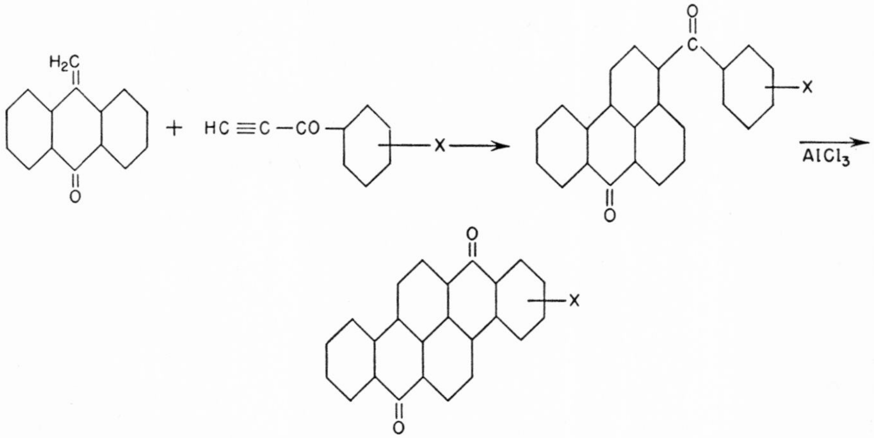

where X may represent halo, methoxy, another benzo ring, etc.[5]

Hydroxy and dihydroxy derivatives are accessible by Fries rearrangement through 2,6-dibenzoxynaphthalene or 2-benzoxybenzanthrone[6, 12].

Substitution products are also available by nitration[10, 14]. The corresponding amines have been acylated[15], but none of this work has afforded colors equivalent to the simple molecules, Indanthrene Golden Yellow GK, Pr. 291, or the 2,9-dibromo product, Indanthrene Golden Yellow RK, Pr. 292.

The range of hues obtainable with this nucleus is illustrated in the following table, wherein the groups are probably in the 2 (or 2,9) position as indicated above (AQ = anthraquinone nucleus).

NO_2	yellow
H	golden yellow
Cl, Br	golden yellow-orange
I	reddish-yellow
$(OCH_3)_2$	brownish-red
OH	red-brown
NH_2	violet
$NHCOC_6H_5$	orange-red
(NH-AQ-1)	orange-brown
Benzo	orange-brown
$(NH-AQ-1)^4$	blue-black

Commercially, only the parent molecule, Golden Yellow GK, and the dibromo derivative, Golden Yellow RK, have assumed importance. Golden Yellow GK affords clear, bright golden yellow prints with only fair lightfastness but the dye has excellent working (printing) properties. Golden Yellow RK, which is slightly redder in hue, is both a dyeing and a printing color, and shows definitely better fastness to washing, sodium carbonate boil and light then the unsubstituted "GK." A dichlorobromo derivative (Yellow GOW) and a dibromo derivative (Yellow GD) isomeric with "RK," but greener and duller in shade, have been marketed[1] but are of less importance than the "GK" and "RK" brands. United States production of Golden Yellow GK totaled 587,000 pounds in 1951. An appreciable amount of the Golden Yellow RK has been used in the manufacture of mixtures such as Indanthrene Printing Brown TM[2].

Literature Cited

1. I. G. Farbenindustrie, "Economic Study of I. G. Farbenindustrie A. G." (PB 548–561).
2. ——, PB 39562; Suppl. to BIOS (Misc.) 20 (PB 31004).
3. ——, FIAT 1313, Vol. II, pp. 123–128 (PB 85172).
4. ——, *ibid.*, p. 128.
5. Irving and Johnson, *J. Chem. Soc.*, **1948**, 2037.
6. Kraenzlein and Corell, U.S. Patent 1,714,677 (1929).
7. ——, Corell and Sedlmayr, U.S. Patent 1,564,584 (1925).
8. ——, —— and Vollmann, U.S. Patent 1,856,710 (1932).
9. —— and Vollmann, U.S. Patent 1,792,169 (1931).
10. ——, Vollmann and Corell, U.S. Patent 1,876,966 (1932).
11. ——, —— and ——, U.S. Patent 1,901,307 (1931).
12. ——, Zahn, Ochwat and Corell, U.S. Patent 1,693,447 (1928).

13. Kunz and Koeberle, U.S. Patent 1,952,677 (1934).
14. ——, Koeberle and Berthold, U.S. Patent 1,804,880 (1931).
15. ——, —— and ——, U.S. Patent 1,863,662 (1932).
16. ——, Kraenzlein, Koeberle, Corell, Berthold and Vollmann, U.S. Patent 1,887,812 (1932).
17. ——, ——, ——, —— and Vollmann, U.S. Patent 1,988,205 (1935).
18. Scholl and Newmann, *Ber.*, **55,** 118 (1922).
19. Wulff, Sedlmayr and Eckert, U.S. Patent 1,747,535 (1930).

PYRANTHRONES

Melvin A. Perkins

Pyranthrone (8,16-pyranthrenedione) is the product of the following formula,

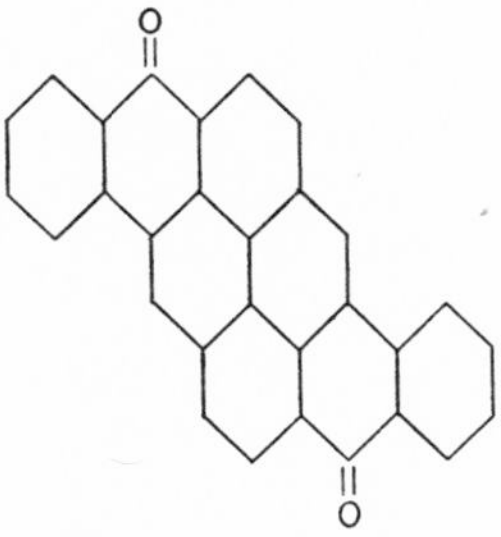

which was originally prepared by the Badische Anilin- u. Soda-Fabrik in 1905[2]. The method of preparation is the coupling of two 2-methylanthraquinone nuclei through the 1 positions followed by ring-closure with the elimination of water according to the scheme:

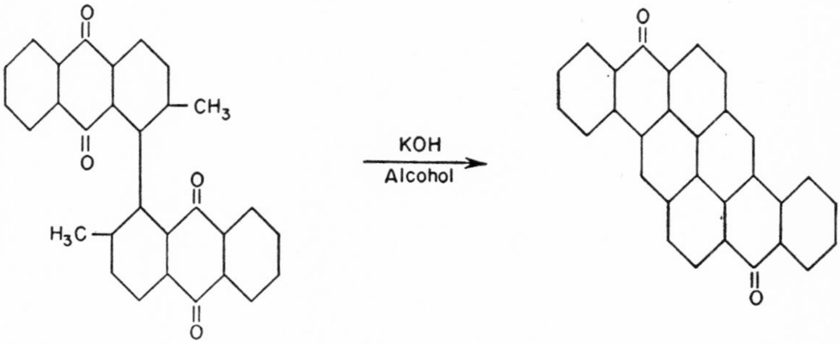

This condensation is brought about by the action of alcoholic caustic, preferably potassium hydroxide, at temperatures above 110°C[11]. The 2,2'-dimethyl-1,1'-bianthraquinone used as starting material for the synthesis of this dye may be prepared by either of two methods of technical importance:

(a) Condensation of two molecules of 1-chloro-2-methylanthraquinone with elimination of chlorine[3, 7]. This is normally carried out in a high-boiling solvent with addition of copper powder and an acid binder. Alternatively, 1-bromo-2-methylanthraquinone may also be employed[1].

(b) Diazotization of 1-amino-2-methylanthraquinone in concentrated sulfuric acid followed by reduction with cuprous chloride to obtain the biaryl coupling[4].

The preparation and properties of pyranthrone were studied rather intensively by Roland Scholl[11]. His work was concerned also with the behavior of dyeings of this material when soaped. This is an intriguing subject because of the very large change in shade which occurs upon boiling the dyeings with a soap solution. Scholl[12] attributed this phenomenon to a hydrate formation but more recent studies indicate that a change in the physical state of the dye on or in the fiber is primarily responsible[14].

Scholl and Seer also discovered a new route to pyranthrone which involved building it up from pyrene[13]. The latter was benzoylated and the 1,6-dibenzoyl derivative (freed of mono- and tribenzoyl compounds) was baked with anhydrous aluminum chloride.

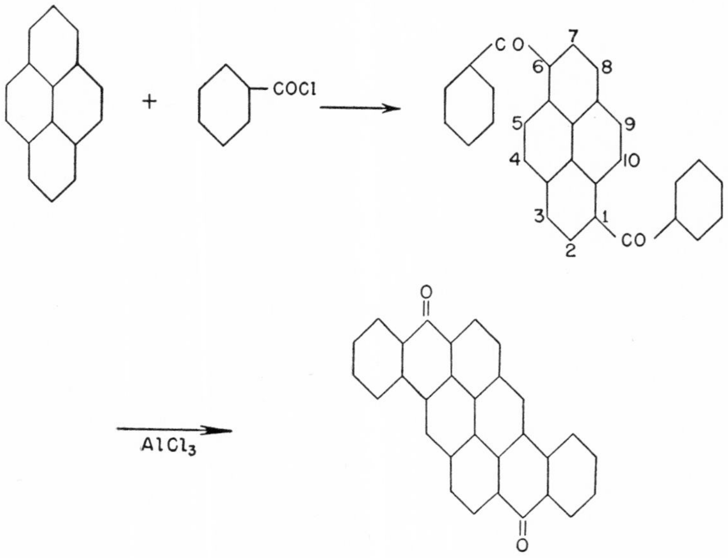

Pyranthrone and its simple derivatives are characterized by extreme tinctorial power. This behavior is, in fact, characteristic of most polyiso-cyclic quinones. By comparison with the pyranthrones, most other vat oranges are considerably weaker tinctorially. Pyranthrone dyes textile fibers in strong golden orange shades from a violet vat and has very good application properties. As stated above, its soaping change is undesirable and for this reason it has been customary to halogenate pyranthrone to obtain better soaping fastness. The dichloro derivative was on the market for a number of years[6], but more recently this has given way to the corresponding dibromo compound[15], e.g., Indanthrene Golden Orange RRT[7]. The exact position of the halogen in the molecule is not known. By continued bromination, a tetrabromo compound is obtainable, but this product has little if any tinctorial power because of insolubility of the vat[10]. The reddest shade brominated pyranthrone which is useful for the dyeing of textiles is obtained by bromination to a bromine content somewhat below that required for a tetrabromo compound[15].

Halogenated pyranthrones can be condensed with amino compounds, such as 1-aminoanthraquinone and aminodibenzanthrone (aminoviolanthrone), to give valuable vat colors of dark brown, olive and gray-black shades[5, 8, 9]. For example, Indanthrene Direct Black RB is obtained by condensation of tetrabromopyranthrone with two molecular proportions of aminodibenzanthrone and two molecular proportions of 1-aminoanthraquinone[7]. All of these products have good dyeing properties, showing high tinctorial value, good solubility, good rate of dyeing and reasonably good fastness properties, combined with very deep shades.

Pyranthrone derivatives, other than the halogenated ones cited above and their condensation products, have little practical importance. The parent material can be mono and dinitrated in suitable media such as nitrobenzene or sulfuric acid but neither the nitro compounds nor the amines derived from them by reduction have any commercial value.

Commercial pyranthrone derivatives comprise[7]:

Indanthrene Golden Orange G—pyranthrone itself, CI 1096
Indanthrene Orange RRT—dibromopyranthrone, CI 1098
Indanthrene Orange 4R—tri- to tetrabromopyranthrone, Pr. 381
Indanthrene Direct Black RB—bis(1-anthraquinonylamino)bis(dibenzan-thronylamino)pyranthrone, Pr. 289

Literature Cited

1. Deinet and Gottlieb, U.S. Patent 2,396,989 (1946).
2. German Patent 174,494 (1906).
3. German Patent 175,067 (1907).
4. German Patent 215,006 (1909).
5. Gubelmann, U.S. Patent 1,596,528 (1926).
6. Houben, "Das Anthracen und die Anthrachinone," p. 767, Leipzig, Georg Thieme, 1929.

7. I. G. Farbenindustrie, BIOS 987, pp. 60–63 (PB 75860).
8. Kunz and Koeberle, U.S. Patent 1,855,295 (1932).
9. —— and ——, U.S. Patent 1,859,742 (1932).
10. ——, —— and Berthold, U.S. Patent 1,904,145 (1933).
11. Scholl, *Ber.*, **43**, 346 (1910).
12. ——, *ibid.*, **44**, 1448 (1911).
13. —— and Seer, *Ann.*, **394**, 121 (1912).
14. Valko, *J. Am. Chem. Soc.*, **63**, 1433 (1941).
15. Waldron, U.S. Patent 1,735,941 (1929).

DIBENZANTHRONES (VIOLANTHRONES)

Melvin A. Perkins

The term dibenzanthrone is used here to include both dibenzanthrone it-self (violanthrone in Chemical Abstracts usage) and isodibenzanthrone

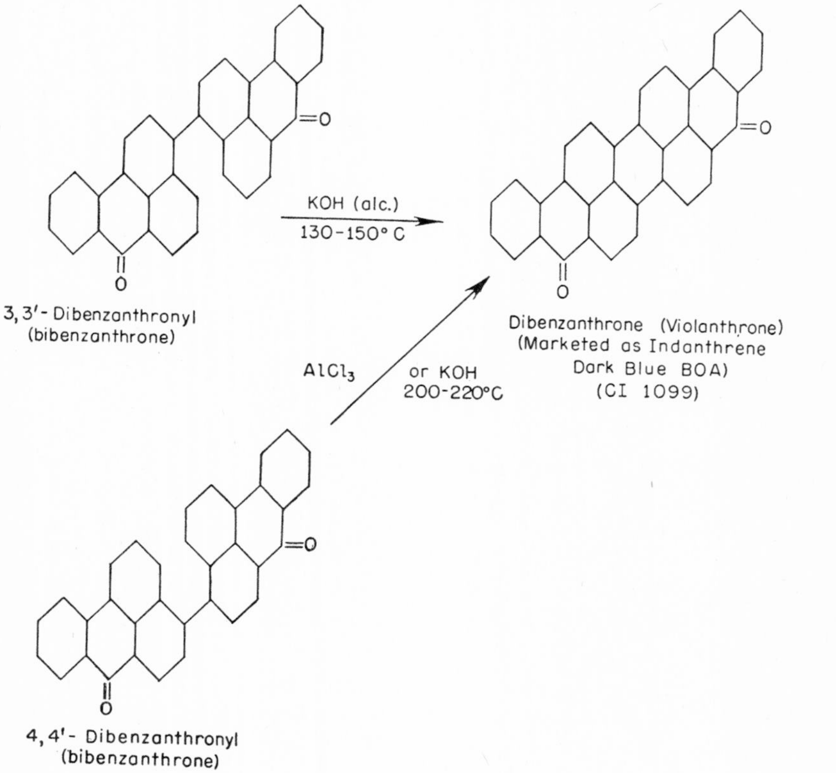

3,3′- Dibenzanthronyl
(bibenzanthrone)

KOH (alc.)
130–150° C

Dibenzanthrone (Violanthrone)
(Marketed as Indanthrene
Dark Blue BOA)
(CI 1099)

AlCl₃   or KOH
200–220°C

4,4′- Dibenzanthronyl
(bibenzanthrone)

(isoviolanthrone) as well as derivatives. Both products are polyisocyclic quinones containing a perylene nucleus and are made up of nine condensed benzene rings and two keto groups. They are among the oldest of the known anthraquinone vat dyes, having been discovered by Oskar Bally in 1904. The method first used for their preparation is still important commercially and consists in the fusion through a common benzene ring of two molecules of benzanthrone (7H-benz[de]anthracen-7-one)[1]. Bally remarked that this was the first blue dye for the direct coloration of vegetable fibers (i.e., without mordanting) which (dye) did not contain nitrogen. In the case of dibenzanthrone the benzanthrone nuclei are joined either as 4,4'-dibenzanthronyl or 3,3'-dibenzanthronyl and these products are further ring-closed as indicated on the preceding page [18, 20]. From the formulas for dibenzanthrones it will be apparent that these materials may also be regarded as derivatives of perylene and it was shown in later work by Zincke and others[29] that isodibenzanthrone may be obtained in fact by suitable ring-closure of 3,9-dibenzoylperylene obtainable by benzoylation of perylene with benzoyl chloride in the presence of aluminum chloride. In this operation the 3,10 isomer is also obtained and this material upon ring-closure should be expected to give dibenzanthrone, but Zincke was apparently unsuccessful in attempts to carry this out. The classical way of obtaining isodibenzanthrone has been the simpler route of alcoholic caustic fusion of 3-chloro- or bromobenzanthrone[27] according to the scheme

It is probable that this fusion operation proceeds by way of 3,4'-dibenzanthronyl which has been synthesized[19] and shown to ring-close upon alcoholic caustic fusion to yield isodibenzanthrone. A number of 3-substituted benzanthrones have been found to yield isodibenzanthrone on caustic fusion. Among these may be mentioned the sulfinic acid[23], alkoxy derivatives[3], sulfides including di-3-benzanthronyl sulfide[8], and selenides[25, 26] including di-3-benz-anthronyl selenide[24].

Ever since their discovery the dibenzanthrones have been important dyes and starting materials for others. Most important of the derivatives are simple chlorinated and nitrated (or nitrated and reduced) ones, as well as alkyl ethers of dihydroxydibenzanthrone. Both dibenzanthrone and iso-dibenzanthrone are intensely colored compounds. The former dissolves in sulfuric acid with a reddish-violet color and dyes cotton deep blue-violet shades from a highly fluorescent red-violet vat. Isodibenzanthrone, on the other hand, dissolves in sulfuric acid with a green color and dyes dull red-dish-violet shades from a blue vat which has relatively little fluorescence. As originally obtained, isodibenzanthrone was sufficiently impure so that its vatting and dyeing properties were reasonably satisfactory and the product was marketed as Indanthrene Violet R Extra[9, 27], but it was subsequently found that pure isodibenzanthrone is almost entirely unvattable and therefore is not a dye in the strict sense of the word. In order to obtain a satisfactory dye from it, the common procedure is to chlorinate the parent compound[4] essentially to a dichloro derivative which has good vattability and gives very strong and bright reddish-violet shades on cellulosic fibers. The dichloro derivative also enjoys some popularity as a pigment color because of very good lightfastness. Also readily vattable but much more bluish in shade are the bromination products of isodibenzanthrone containing one to two atoms of bromine[7]. Commercial representatives of the iso-dibenzanthrones are:

(1) Indanthrene Brilliant Violet 2R, 4R, 4RN (chlorinated), CI 1104
(2) Indanthrene Brilliant Violet 3B (brominated), Pr. 288

Dyeings of the violet mentioned above and of dibenzanthrone have the serious defect of becoming very much redder when spotted by water. This lack of fastness to water spotting can be corrected by an extremely vigorous chlorination wherein three to four chlorine atoms are introduced at a relatively elevated temperature[21, 22]. Simultaneous with this improvement in water-spotting fastness, a decided shift in shade results from the chlorination so that the final product is no longer a violet but a navy blue.

Dibenzanthrone Blacks

Because of their very high tinctorial power and excellent printing properties, combined with low cost, dibenzanthrones have been used as bases for a rather large number of vat grays and blacks. Most of these depend upon nitrated derivatives. Dibenzanthrones can be nitrated readily and both mono and dinitro compounds have been isolated. Nitration is normally carried out in an organic solvent such as nitrobenzene or acetic acid, and the nitro compounds can be reduced in a variety of ways such as with sodium sulfide, metal powders in sulfuric acid, and by vatting[2, 5]. Usually these nitro compounds (actually amino compounds as dyed) dye cellulosic fibers in green shades but these are converted to black upon treatment with sodium hypochlorite, sodium nitrite or sodium dichromate solutions. The blacks thus obtained have excellent fastness properties. So-called direct blacks (i.e., those which do not require a subsequent oxidative treatment after dyeing) are said to be obtainable by certain specific procedures such as caustic fusion of nitrodibenzanthrones[28], alkali fusion of a nitrogen-containing 3,3'-dibenzanthronyl[10], continued condensation of nitrodibenzanthrone in nitrobenzene in the presence of sodium carbonate[17] or action of hydroxylamine on dibenzanthrone in sulfuric acid in the presence of ferrous sulfate[16].

Ethers of Dihydroxydibenzanthrones

Another very important class of dibenzanthrone derivatives is constituted by the alkyl or alkylene ethers of dihydroxydibenzanthrone or isodibenzanthrone. In the synthesis of these, a dibenzanthrone is oxidized by manganese dioxide in sulfuric acid to give a tetraoxo compound which is converted by mild reducing agents to a dihydroxydibenzanthrone. In the case of dibenzanthrone itself, it has been established that the hydroxy groups are in the "2" positions of the benzanthrone nuclei. These dihydroxydibenzanthrones are extremely insoluble materials which dye cotton from deeply colored vats but the dyeings change shade in dilute acids or dilute alkalies, and thus are not practical for general use. The hydroxy compounds can, however, be alkylated under suitable conditions to obtain dyes which give dyeings entirely fast to dilute acids and alkalies and these are extremely valuable because of brilliance of shade, high tinctorial power, good application properties including printing, and excellent all-around fastness. The shades obtained vary with the alkylating agent and the particular dihydroxydibenzanthrone used to give products dyeing from reddish-blue to green[6].

Dibenzanthrone type vat dyes of known constitution are listed alphabetically below, along with some statement as to constitution. The Indanthrene name is used throughout with the usual understanding that there are many competitive types under different trade names where the base name may or may not be the same.

Name	Constitution	Ref.
Black BA, BB, BBN, BGA, CI 1102	nitrated dibenzanthrone	13
Blue Green 3B	tetrabromodihydroxydibenzanthrone ethylene ether	11
Brilliant Green B, FFB (Jade Green), CI 1101	dimethoxydibenzanthrone	12
Brilliant Green 3B	diethoxydibenzanthrone	12
Brilliant Green 2G	brominated dimethoxydibenzanthrone	12
Dark Blue BOA, CI 1099	dibenzanthrone	27
Gray 3B	dibenzanthrone + hydroxylamine	16
Gray 3G	4,4'-dibenzanthronyl nitrated, reduced and fused with alcoholic potash	12

Navy Blue BF	bromodibenzanthrone	12
Navy Blue RB, CI 1100	tetrachlorodibenzanthrone	11
Navy Blue G	dihydroxydibenzanthrone ethylene ether	14
Violet R (Extra), CI 1103	isodibenzanthrone (impure)	27
(Brilliant) Violet 3B, Pr. 288	brominated isodibenzanthrone	15
(Brilliant) Violet RR, 4R, CI 1104	dichloroisodibenzanthrone	4

Literature Cited

1. Bally, *Ber.*, **38,** 195 (1905).
2. ——, U.S. Patent 796,393 (1905).
3. British Patent 257,618 (1927).
4. Caswell and Marshall, U.S. Patent 1,525,117 (1925).
5. Daniels, U.S. Patent 1,464,598 (1923).
6. Davies and Thomson, U.S. Patent 1,531,261 (1925).
7. German Patent 217,570 (1909).
8. German Patent 448,262 (1924).
9. Houben, "Das Anthracen und die Anthrachinone," p. 785, Leipzig, Georg Thieme, 1929.
10. Howell, U.S. Patent 1,957,459 (1934).
11. I.G. Farbenindustrie, BIOS (Misc.) 20, pp. 41, 43 (PB 31004).
12. ——, BIOS 987, pp. 69–75 (PB 75860).
13. ——, FIAT 764, Vol. II, p. 120 (PB 60946).
14. ——, FIAT 1313, Vol. II, pp. 134–5 (PB 85172).
15. ——, *ibid.*, p. 170.
16. Kunz, U.S. Patent 1,464,079 (1923).
17. ——, Koeberle and Bruck, U.S. Patent 1,837,274 (1931).
18. Luettringhaus, *Ann.*, **473,** 259–289 (1929).
19. ——, Neresheimer and Wolff, U.S. Patent 1,633,866 (1927).
20. ——, —— and Emmer, U.S. Patent 1,899,579 (1933).
21. Mayer and Siebenbuerger, U.S. Patent 1,728,068 (1929).
22. —— and ——, U.S. Patent 1,771,802 (1930).
23. Neresheimer and Emmer, U.S. Patent 1,644,851 (1927).
24. Perkins, U.S. Patent 1,924,456 (1933).
25. ——, U.S. Patent 1,965,855 (1934).
26. ——, U.S. Patent 1,999,999 (1935).
27. Scholl, *Ann.*, **394,** 128 (1912) (footnote).
28. Wilke and Josef, U.S. Patent 1,538,419 (1925).
29. Zincke, Linner and Wolfbauer, *Ber.*, **58,** 323 (1925).

MISCELLANEOUS POLYISOCYCLIC QUINONES

Frederick B. Stilmar

Acedianthrone (aceanthra[2,1-a]aceanthrylene-5,13-dione) is an important new keto hydrocarbon which has unusually good lightfastness. The preparation is as follows[2, 5]:

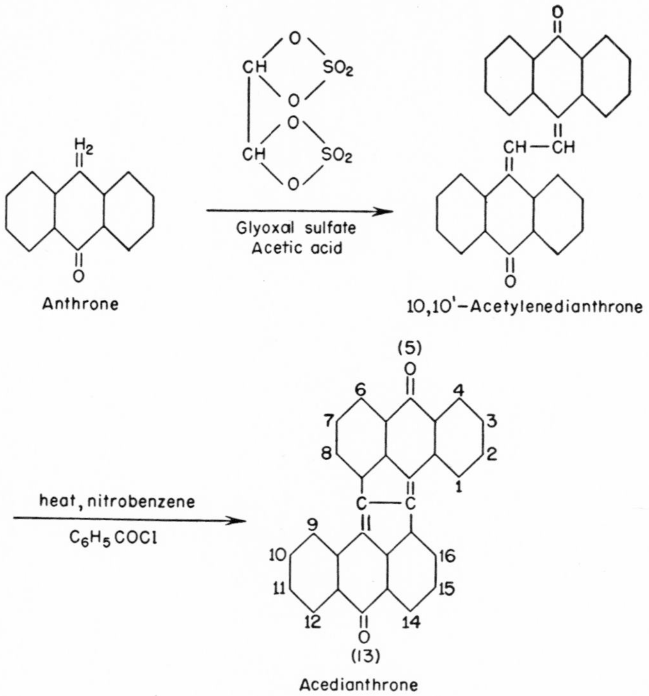

Anthrone

Glyoxal sulfate
Acetic acid

10,10'-Acetylenedianthrone

heat, nitrobenzene

C_6H_5COCl

Acedianthrone

The structure has been proved by oxidation to both 1-anthraquinonecarboxylic acid and 1,1'-oxalyldianthraquinone[1].

Indanthrene Red Brown RR is 8,16 or 3,11-dichloroacedianthrone. Indanthrene Brown NG is the carbazole obtained by ring-closure of the anthrimide from 6,14 or 4,12-dichloroacedianthrone and two moles of 1-amino-5-benzamidoanthraquinone[2]. All products of this class appear to have good printing properties. All have good lightfastness and all are brown vat dyes.

The phthaloyl derivatives of highly condensed hydrocarbons are often colored, but are reported to be too weak to be of interest[3, 4, 6].

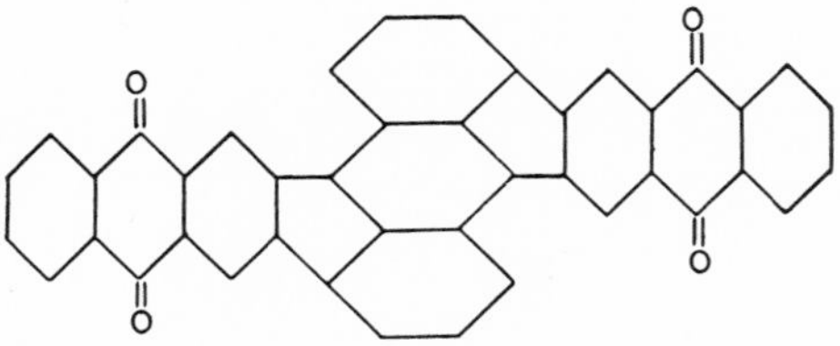

red-violet

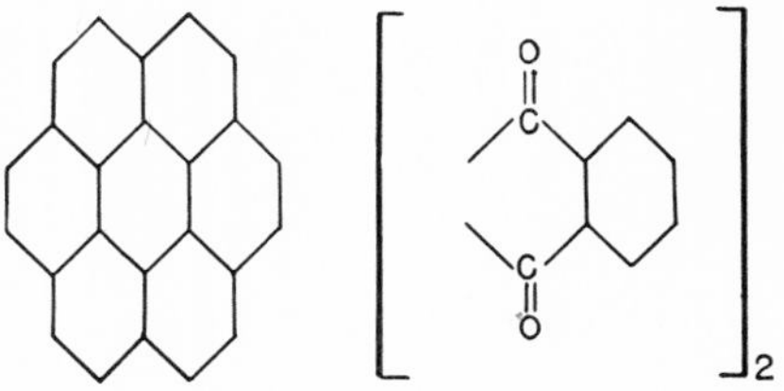

orange

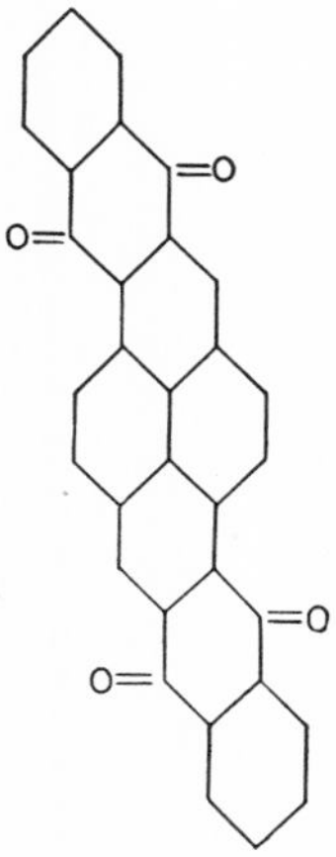

yellow

Literature Cited

1. Clar, *Ber.*, **72B,** 2134 (1939).
2. I. G. Farbenindustrie, FIAT 1313, Vol. II, pp. 105, 149 (PB 85172).
3. ——, PB 70338, frame 9812.
4. ——, PB 70342, frame 14263.
5. Scheyer, U.S. Patent 1,990,841 (1935).
6. Vollmann, Becker, Corell and Streeck, *Ann.*, **531,** 1 (1937).

Five-membered Heterocyclic Vat Dyes

ANTHRAQUINONECARBAZOLES

(Including Anthrimides)

Myron S. Whelen

The term anthrimide, or dianthrimide (iminodianthraquinone), is used to mean R—NH—R' where R and R' are anthraquinone nuclei, and R may or may not be the same as R'. Anthrimides are also known throughout the literature as anthraquinonylamines. Trianthrimides of the structure R—NH—R—NH—R and polyanthrimides of the structure R(NHR)$_x$ are likewise known wherein R is again an anthraquinone nucleus which may or may not contain substituent groups. In all cases the prefix (di, tri, tetra, etc.) signifies the total number of anthraquinone nuclei involved in the molecule. Isomers are of course possible, occasioned by the position of attachment of one anthraquinone nucleus to another through nitrogen as well as by the position of substituents. This subject is complex and is considered more closely with simple illustrative examples later.

Anthrimides are no longer important as vat dyes, but they are necessary intermediates in the preparation of the anthraquinonecarbazoles, a class of dyes characterized by excellent fastness properties and a wide range of shade.

The earliest preparation of an anthrimide was reported by Isler in 1905[7], and the first anthrimide of value as a dye was probably made by him[8] in 1907. Historically it is of interest to note that the development of aminobenzamidoanthraquinones made it possible to prepare anthrimides and subsequently anthraquinonecarbazoles containing benzamido groups[13]. The anthrimides possessed poor affinity for cotton and in order to obtain these dyes in a finely divided physical form suitable for application, the anthrimides were treated with concentrated sulfuric acid. In so doing valuable vat dyes were obtained. The chemistry involved was for many years obscure, but in fact the anthrimides had been converted to anthraquinonecarbazoles and a new and excellent class of vat dyes evolved. As the art progressed it was possible to produce them in shades of yellow, orange, brown, olive and khaki—shades which up to that time were largely unattainable in the vat dye field. Their excellent fastness properties gave a great stimulus to developments in the entire field of vat dyes.

In this discussion it is not proposed to give an exhaustive summary of the very large number of dyes which have been prepared. Instead it is intended to indicate the directions in which advance has been made by reference to dyes of representative character and of commercial importance. In this way it is hoped to convey a broad picture of the course of progress.

Anthrimides

Methods of Preparation. Anthrimides are produced by the condensation of a haloanthraquinone with an aminoanthraquinone. The reaction is carried out by heating them together in a high-boiling, inert, organic solvent, usually nitrobenzene or naphthalene, in the presence of an acid-binding agent such as sodium carbonate or sodium acetate and a copper salt as a catalyst, usually copper acetate. This reaction is generally referred to as the "anthrimide condensation." A modification of this method wherein the ingredients are baked together at elevated temperatures without the use of a solvent is known[29].

Types. Three isomeric forms of a simple, unsubstituted dianthrimide are possible. They may be illustrated as follows:

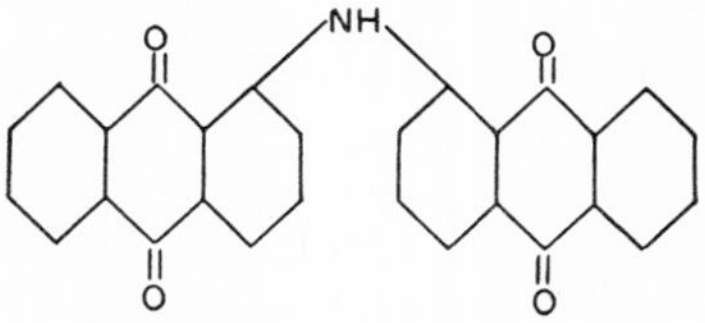

1,1'– Dianthrimide
(1,1'–iminodianthraquinone)

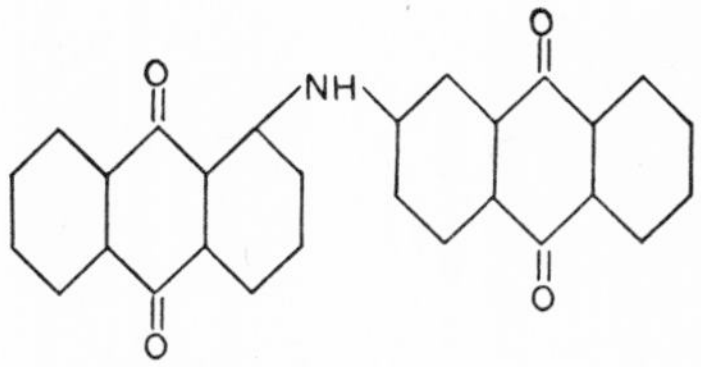

1, 2'- Dianthrimide
(1,2'-iminodianthraquinone)

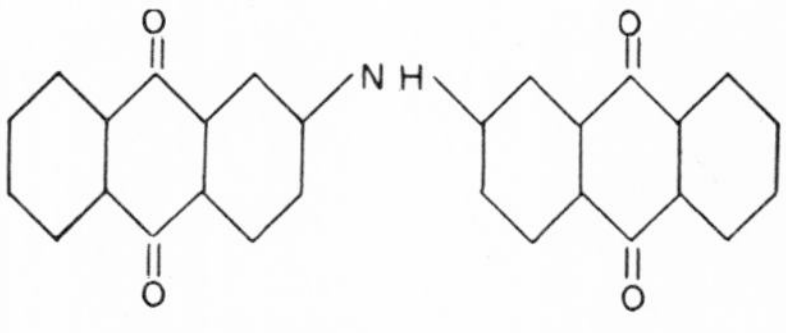

2, 2'- Dianthrimide
(2, 2'-iminodianthraquinone)

Of the three types the 1,1'-type is most important, while the 2,2'-type is of little or no importance.

The ease of anthrimide formation depends upon the position of the amino group and of the halogen atom in the anthraquinone nuclei employed. When both are in the 1 positions the reaction takes place readily and high yields of 1,1'-dianthrimides are obtained. If one group is in the 2 position, 1,2'-dianthrimide formation is much harder and it is desirable to condense a 2-haloanthraquinone with 1-aminoanthraquinone. When both the amino group and the halogen atom are in 2 positions the condensation proceeds with difficulty and low yields are obtained. 2,2'-Dianthrimides can also be prepared from the condensation of 2-anthraquinonediazonium salts with ammonia followed by heating the resulting product in a high-boiling solvent preferably in the presence of a condensing agent[15].

Condensation of dihaloanthraquinones with monoaminoanthraquinones gives rise to a series of trianthrimides[17]. In this fashion polyanthrimides may likewise be prepared. In this case it is often desirable to employ an aminodianthrimide as an intermediate. For example, 4,4'-diamino-1,1'-dianthrimide on condensation with two moles of 1-chloroanthraquinone produces a tetraanthrimide[14].

Di-, tri- and polyanthrimide types in which heterocyclic rings are present may likewise be prepared by employing halo or aminoanthraquinone nuclei to which a heterocyclic group is attached, for example, a pyridone ring[9].

Substituted Anthrimides. A great number of anthrimide derivatives have been prepared either by introduction of groups into the anthrimide or by direct condensation of substituted halo or aminoanthraquinones. The presence of an auxochrome group invariably imparts marked modification. Nitration of anthrimides followed by reduction is commonly employed to produce amino derivatives. Nitration of a 1,1'-dianthrimide takes place in the positions para to the imino group. The most important intermediate prepared in this manner is 4,4'-dinitro-1,1'-dianthrimide[24]. The same nitro body is obtained by the condensation of 1-chloro-4-nitroanthraquinone with 1-amino-4-nitroanthraquinone, thus proving its constitution[20]. Reduction with sodium sulfide gives the diamine—a valuable intermediate. The nitro groups in anthrimides may be replaced by alkoxy groups by heating with alcoholic potassium hydroxide. Halogen-substituted anthrimides may be prepared, and these may be further condensed with aminoanthraquinones to produce polyanthrimides.

Acylaminoanthrimides, especially where the acylamino group is benzamido, are the most important substituted anthrimides. While they are not good dyes due to their weak tinctorial properties, they are valuable as intermediates for carbazole dyes as will subsequently be shown. They can be prepared either by benzoylation of aminoanthrimides, for example,

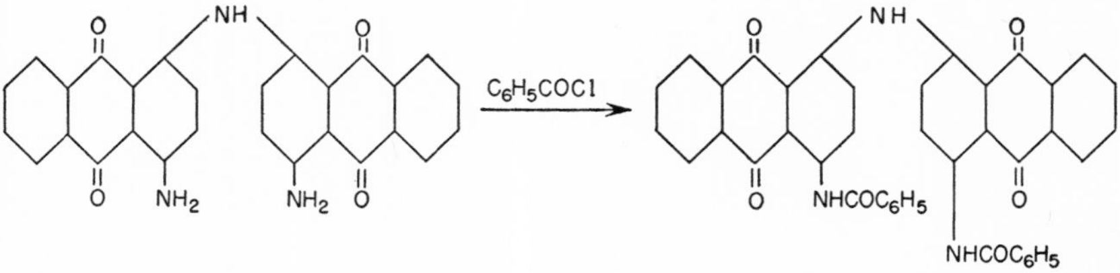

4,4'-Diamino-1,1'-dianthrimide   4,4'-Dibenzamido-1,1'-dianthrimide

or by condensation of 1-amino-4-benzamidoanthraquinone with 1-benz-amido-4-chloroanthraquinone to produce the same compound.

As dyes, anthrimides have only moderate affinity for cotton at best and have only fair fastness properties. They dye mostly in red to bordeaux shades. They are now mostly of historic interest as they have been replaced by other types with better tinctorial and fastness properties. The following dyes were at one time commercial products, although they are now largely obsolete.

Algol Red B[3], an anthrapyridone derivative, was the first red vat dye of the anthraquinone series prepared. It was made by the condensation of 4-bromo-N-methyl-1(N),9-anthrapyridone   (6-bromo-3-methyl-7H-dibenz-[f,i,j]isoquinoline-2,7(3H)-dione) with 2-aminoanthraquinone.

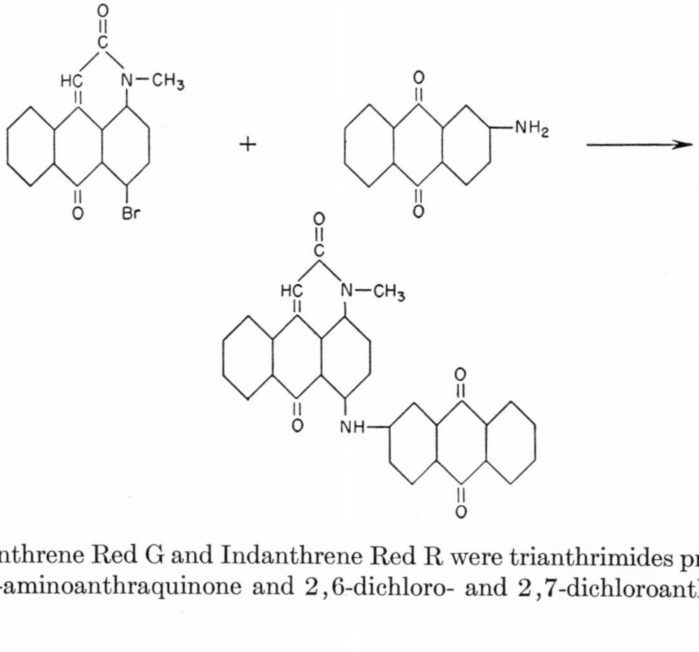

Indanthrene Red G and Indanthrene Red R were trianthrimides prepared from 1-aminoanthraquinone and 2,6-dichloro- and 2,7-dichloroanthraquinone, respectively[10]. Indanthrene Bordeaux R[11] was a chlorine-containing trianthrimide prepared from one mole of 2,7-dichloroanthraquinone and two moles of 1-amino-6-chloroanthraquinone. Algol Bordeaux 3B[12] was a trianthrimide prepared from one mole of 2,6-dichloroanthraquinone and two moles of 1-amino-4-methoxyanthraquinone.

Indanthrene Corinth B[18] is 4-benzamido-1,2'-dianthrimide prepared by condensation of 1-amino-4-benzamidoanthraquinone with 2-chloroanthraquinone.

Carbazoles

The conversion of an anthrimide to an anthraquinonecarbazole, whereby a carbazole ring is formed between two anthraquinone nuclei, is brought about by one of two methods.

(1) Treatment with concentrated sulfuric acid.
(2) Fusion with aluminum chloride.
    (a) Dry fusion with aluminum chloride or sodium chloride/aluminum chloride melts.
    (b) In presence of aluminum chloride complexes with nitrogen-containing compounds, acid chlorides or nitriles.

Ring-closure with Sulfuric Acid. This method of ring-closure is applicable to all dianthrimides containing at least two benzamido groups, one in each of the anthraquinone nuclei in the 4 or 5 positions.

A typical example is Indanthrene Olive R[25].

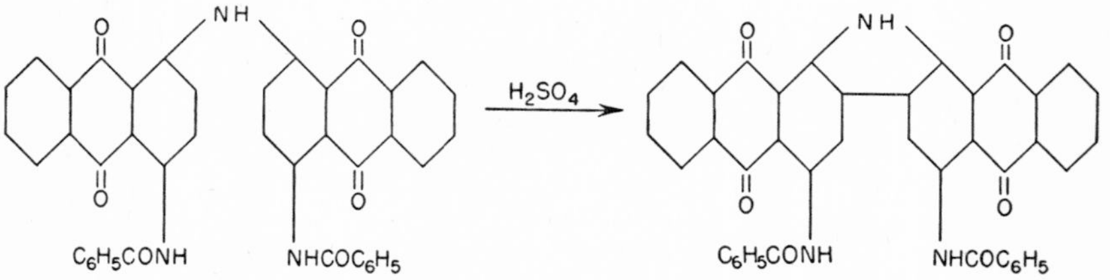

The method employed is simply to dissolve the anthrimide in concentrated sulfuric acid, at a temperature below 15°C (to prevent hydrolysis of the benzamido groups). After stirring a number of hours below 25°C the color of the sulfuric acid solution changes from green to brown and the ring-closure is then complete. The addition of small amounts of ferrous chloride or copper catalyzes the reaction. The dye is recovered by slowly pouring the sulfuric acid solution into ice and water.

An anthrimide derived from two anthraquinoneacridone nuclei (see p. 487).

will ring-close in the above described manner, in which case the acridone structure acts like a benzamido group[5, 30].

Ring-closure with Aluminum Chloride. (a) This method is particularly applicable to the ring-closure of unsubstituted anthrimides. The procedure consists in fusion of the anthrimide in an anhydrous aluminum chloride/sodium chloride melt at an elevated temperature often in the presence of an oxidizing agent. 1,1'-Dianthrimide[22] and 1,1'-4,1''-5,1'''-8,1''''-pentaanthrimide[14] are converted to carbazoles in this fashion.

(b) A modification of this procedure is commonly used to carbazolate anthrimides which will not ring-close in sulfuric acid, but which contain benzamido groups. This consists in forming a complex of aluminum chloride with nitrogen-containing solvents such as nitrobenzene[16] or with tertiary nitrogenous bases such as pyridine[26], or by the addition of acid halides[27] or organic nitriles[4]. 4-Benzamido-1,1'-dianthrimide[26], 8,8'-dibenzamido-1,1'-dianthrimide[26], 5',5''-dibenzamido-1,1'-5,1''-trianthrimide[23] and 1,1'-4,1''-trianthrimide[26] are examples of anthrimides which may be converted to carbazoles using these methods. The methods utilizing nitrobenzene or tertiary nitrogenous bases are the ones commonly used. Anthrimides of the anthraquinoneacridone type (and related heterocyles) are commonly carbazolated by this method.

After carbazolation of an anthrimide the dye is obtained in a reduced form and it is necessary to subject it to an oxidation procedure, which is usually acid oxidation by means of sodium dichromate and sulfuric acid. This is customarily done on the dye in a finely divided form suitable for application purposes. This treatment oxidizes the reduced form of the dye and at the same time destroys impurities present and produces maximum strength and brightness of shade in the residual dye.

Anthraquinonecarbazoles as a class are one of the most important types of vat dyes known in that they exhibit excellent properties, being outstanding in their light- and bleachfastness. They are obtainable in yellow, orange, olive, brown and khaki shades. They dye best by the cold method, producing level dyeings with very good tinctorial strength. They are not good printing colors, and a few of them are dyeing tenderers—that is, the tensile strength of the dyed goods is lowered in comparison to that of undyed goods. The following summation shows some of the better known commercial products typical of the anthraquinonecarbazole class. All are carbazoles prepared by ring-closure of the corresponding anthrimides, and none contains other heterocyclic groupings. There are in addition a number of anthraquinonecarbazoles which contain acridone groupings and these products are dealt with in the acridone series (see p. 500). The component parts are shown, though the anthrimides are not necessarily prepared directly from them.

Color-name	Shade	Component Intermediates
Indanthrene Yellow FFRK[22], Pr. 450	yellow	1-Aminoanthraquinone (1 mole) 1-Chloroanthraquinone (1 mole)
Indanthrene Yellow 3R[21], Pr. 452	reddish-yellow	1,5-Diaminoanthraquinone (1 mole) 1-Chloroanthraquinone (2 moles)
Indanthrene Golden Orange 3G[6], Pr. 290	golden orange	1-Amino-5-benzamidoanthraquinone (1 mole) 1-Benzamido-5-chloroanthraquinone (1 mole)
Indanthrene Brown BR[26], Pr. 118	brown	1,4-Diaminoanthraquinone (1 mole) 1-Chloroanthraquinone (2 moles)
Indanthrene Red Brown GR[19]	red-brown	1,5-Diaminoanthraquinone (1 mole) 1-Benzamido-4-chloroanthraquinone (2 moles)
Indanthrene Red Brown 5RF[2], Pr. 448	red-brown	1-Amino-4-benzamidoanthraquinone (1 mole) 1-Benzamido-5-chloro-4-methoxyanthraquinone (1 mole)
Indanthrene Brown R[28], CI 1151	yellow-brown	1-Amino-4-benzamidoanthraquinone (1 mole) 1-Benzamido-5-chloroanthraquinone (1 mole)
Indanthrene Olive R[25], CI 1150	olive	1-Amino-4-benzamidoanthraquinone (1 mole) 1-Benzamido-4-chloroanthraquinone (1 mole)
Indanthrene Olive 3G[1],	olive-green	N-(4-Amino-1-anthraquinonyl)-2-anthraquinonecarboxamide (1 mole) N-(4-Chloro-1-anthraquinonyl)-2-anthraquinonecarboxamide (1 mole)

Color-name	Shade	Component Intermediates
Indanthrene Khaki 2G[14], Pr. 122	khaki	1-Aminoanthraquinone (4 moles) 1,4,5,8-Tetrachloroanthraquinone (1 mole)

Of these colors, Indanthrene Brown R, Indanthrene Olive R and Indanthrene Khaki 2G are the most important. These colors are those utilized for the dyeing of military uniforms and equipment (cotton) in a range of olive drab shades. In peacetime they are produced in good volume, but in wartime their production becomes enormous; the production of the Indanthrene Khaki 2G type (Pr. 122), for example, in 1944 in the United States was 12.7 million pounds with a unit value of $1.22 per pound.

The over-all picture of the anthraquinonecarbazoles is attractive. Their cost of production is reasonable and manufacture is well established. With their use in the trade so extensive there is little likelihood that they will be superseded for dyeing or padding where the duller shades of fast oranges and browns contributed by them are desired.

Literature Cited

1. Baumann, U.S. Patent 1,819,014 (1931).
2. ——, U.S. Patent 1,885,172 (1932).
3. British Patent 13,686 (1907).
4. Burneleit, Mieg, and Wieners, U.S. Patent 2,187,815 (1940).
5. Dettwyler, U.S. Patent 2,373,817 (1945).
6. Gassner, U.S. Patent 1,667,848 (1928).
7. German Patent 162,824 (1905).
8. German Patent 184,905 (1907).
9. German Patent 194,253 (1907).
10. German Patent 197,554 (1908).
11. German Patent 206,717 (1909).
12. German Patent 216,668 (1909).
13. German Patent 220,581 (1910).
14. German Patent 282,788 (1913).
15. German Patent 308,666 (1918).
16. German Patent 566,708 (1932).
17. Houben, "Das Anthracen und die Anthrachinone," p. 469, Leipzig, Georg Thieme, 1929.
18. I. G. Farbenindustrie, BIOS 1493, p. 14 (PB 81611).
19. ——, *ibid.*, p. 42.
20. Isler, U.S. Patent 814,137 (1906.)
21. Kalischer, U.S. Patent 999,798 (1911).
22. Kraenzlein and Ebert, U.S. Patent 1,709,985 (1929).
23. Lulek, U.S. Patent 2,212,028 (1940).
24. Mieg, U.S. Patent 960,182 (1910).
25. ——, U.S. Patent 996,109 (1911).
26. ——, U.S. Patent 1,690,236 (1928).
27. —— and Wieners, U.S. Patent 2,073,022 (1937).
28. Thomaschewski, U.S. Patent 971,225 (1910).
29. Tinker and Stallmann, U.S. Patent 2,420,022 (1947).
30. Weiland and Dettwyler, U.S. Patent 2,036,663 (1936).

ANTHRAPYRAZOLONE DYES

Frederick B. Stilmar

Anthra[1,9]pyrazol-6(2H)-one results by acid ring-closure of 1-anthra-quinonylhydrazine or its N-sulfonic acid[13].

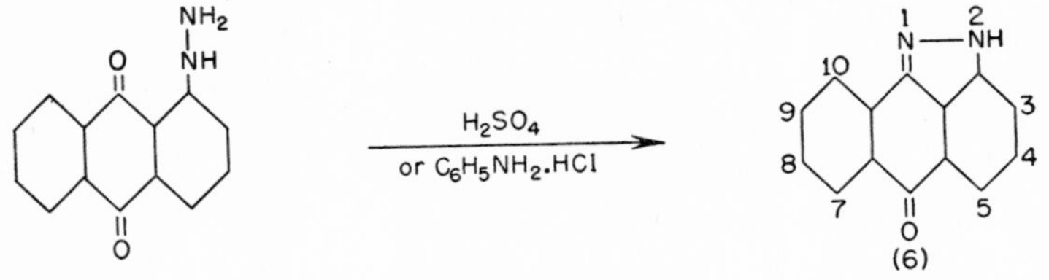

Bianthrapyrazoledione Dyes

The potassium hydroxide/alcohol fusion of anthra[1,9]pyrazol-6(2H)-one to [3,3'-bianthra[1,9]pyrazole]-6,6'(2H,2'H)-dione is reminiscent of the formation of 4,4'-dibenzanthronyl[1, 2]. 3,3'-Bianthrapyrazoledione dyes cotton yellow, but it spots blue with excess alkali. Alkylation of the dipotassium salt in nitrobenzene with alkyl halides, sulfates, or benzenesulfonic acid alkyl esters yields alkali-fast red dyes[16]. The 1,1'-diethyl derivative is Indanthrene Rubine R[7], Pr. 124.

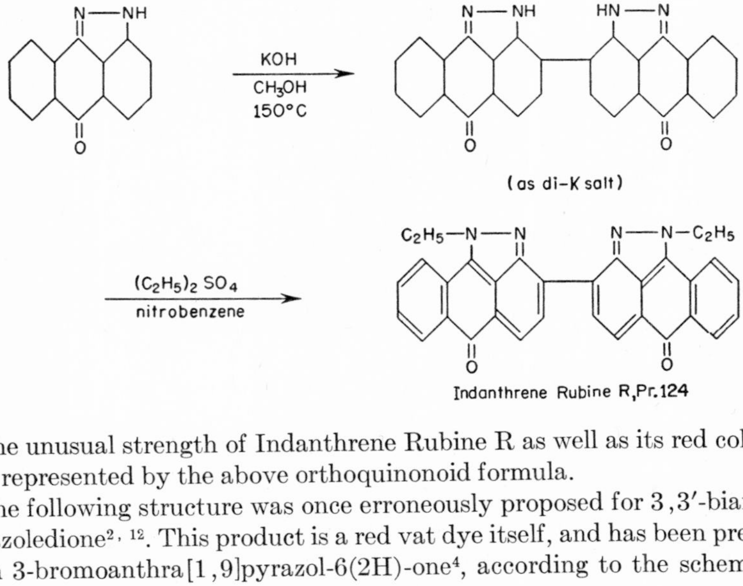

Indanthrene Rubine R,Pr.124

The unusual strength of Indanthrene Rubine R as well as its red color are best represented by the above orthoquinonoid formula.

The following structure was once erroneously proposed for 3,3'-bianthrapyrazoledione[2, 12]. This product is a red vat dye itself, and has been prepared from 3-bromoanthra[1,9]pyrazol-6(2H)-one[4], according to the scheme:

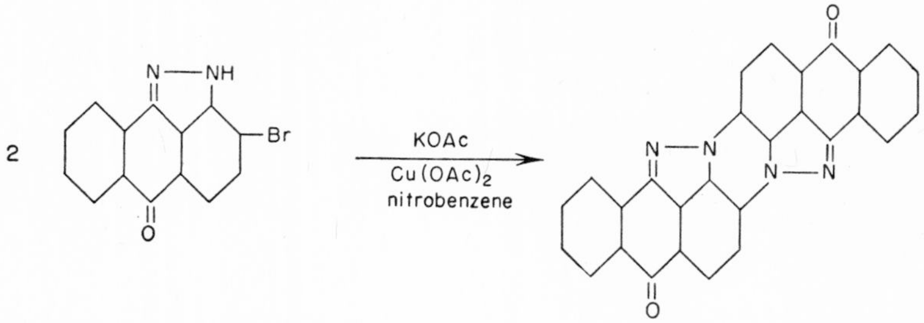

The following mixed pyrazoledihydroazine molecule is a violet vat dye[14]. It may be considered as a half-way step between the above dye and indanthrone.

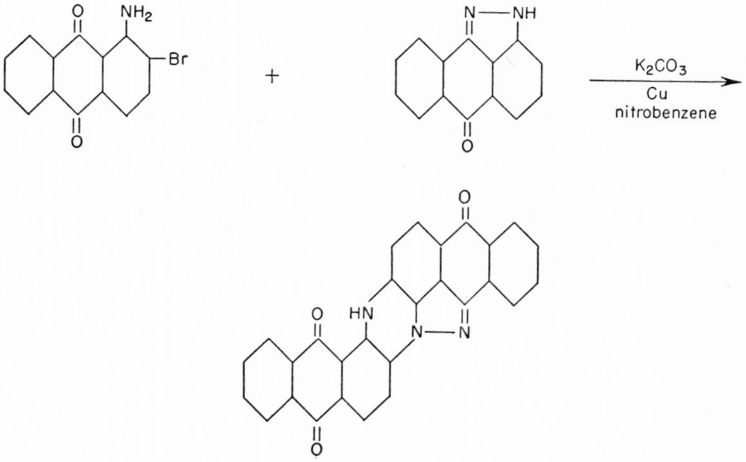

Alkylation of 3,3'-bianthrapyrazoledione with formaldehyde in sulfuric acid yields an alkali-fast yellow dye, which undoubtedly is of the paraquinonoid type (2,2'-dimethyl derivative), as shown[17]:

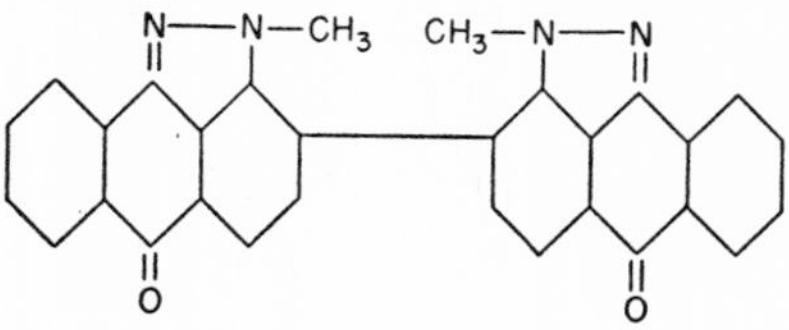

Paradoxically, acid alkylation of anthra[1,9]pyrazol-6(2H)-one yields an orthoquinonoid alkylation product which may be caustic fused to a red dye. Alkaline alkylation yields the paraquinonoid isomer which will not yield a red dye on potassium hydroxide/alcohol fusion. This relationship is illustrated as follows[10, 15]:

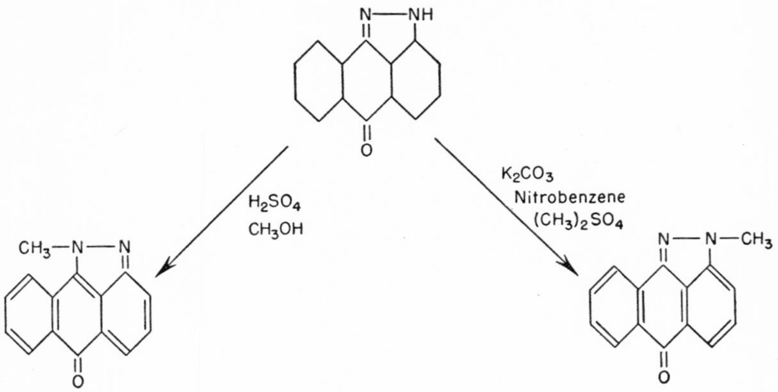

Benzanthrone-Anthrapyrazolone

Anthra[1,9]pyrazol-6(2H)-one reacts with active aromatic halogen compounds to yield the 2-aryl derivatives. The condensation product with 3-bromobenzanthrone may be easily ring-closed by a potassium hydroxide/alcohol fusion. This is obviously analogous to the alkaline ring-closure of 3,3′-dibenzanthronyl to violanthrone[1].

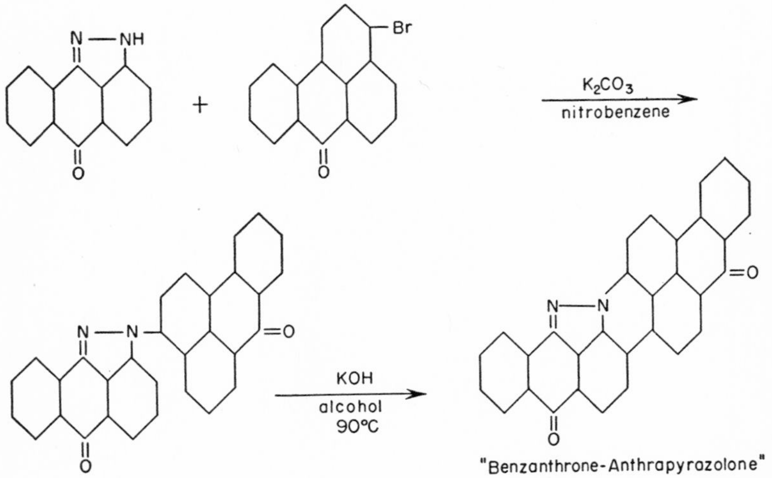

"Benzanthrone-Anthrapyrazolone"

Benzanthrone-anthrapyrazolone is a navy blue vat dye, which is also analogous to violanthrone in that its dyeings "water spot." The I.G. Farbenindustrie marketed the product as Indanthrene Navy Blue R but it is now of little commercial importance[5].

Of much greater importance is Indanthrene Gray M, an anthraquinonylamino derivative of benzanthrone-anthrapyrazolone. This results from the interaction of 3,9-dibromobenzanthrone with one mole of anthrapyrazolone followed by condensation with one mole of 1-aminoanthraquinone and subsequent potassium hydroxide/alcohol ring-closure[6].

1,2-Anthraquinonepyrazoles

The following two pyrazole intermediates are readily available but have no practical dye use[3, 11].

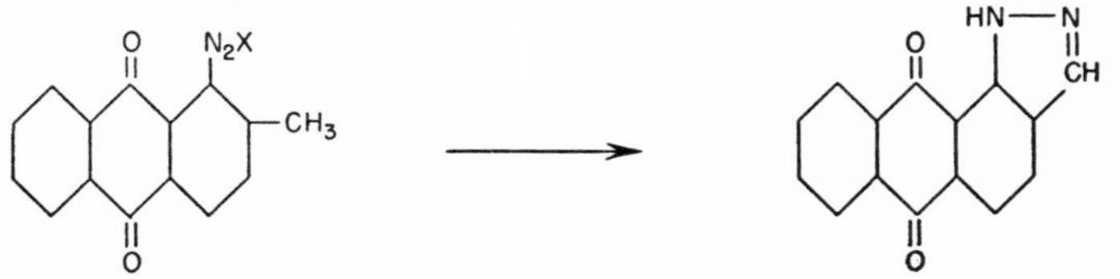

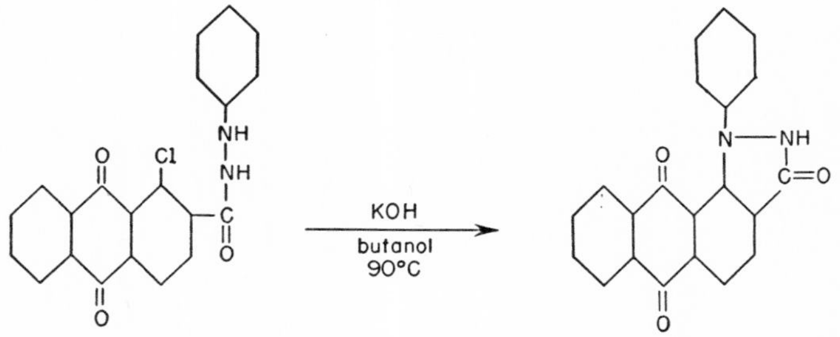

The following carboxylic acids have been used to prepare acylamino vat types by conversion to acid chlorides and condensation with aminoanthraquinones. Preparation of the acids is illustrated as follows[8, 9]:

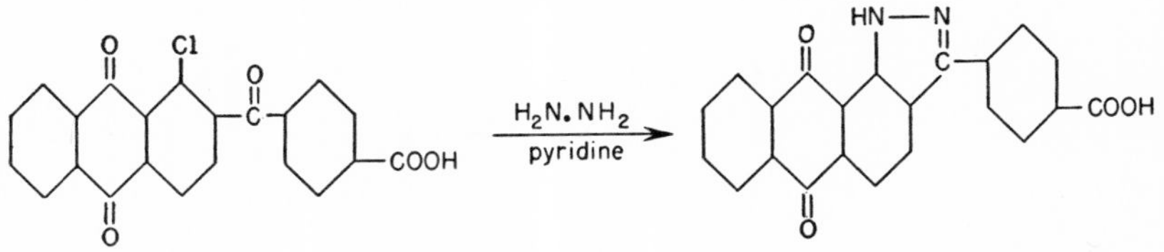

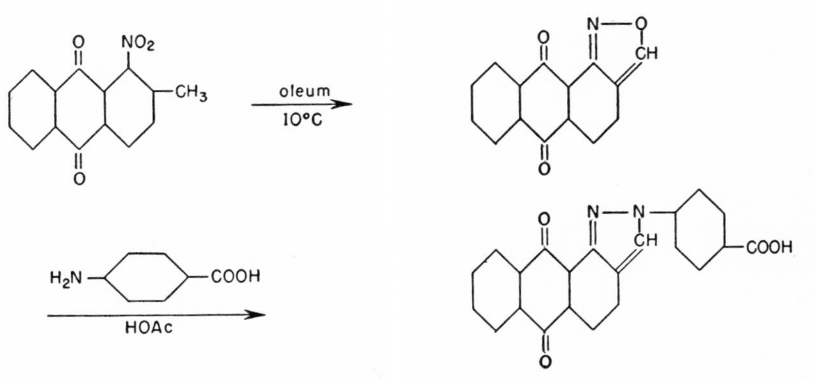

Literature Cited

1. Bradley and Jadhav, *J. Chem. Soc.*, **1948**, 1622.
2. German Patent 255,641 (1912).
3. German Patent 269,842 (1914).
4. German Patent 454,425 (1926).
5. I. G. Farbenindustrie, BIOS 1493, p. 26 (PB 81611).
6. ——, FIAT 1313, Vol. II, p. 111 (PB 85172).
7. ——, *ibid.*, p. 162.
8. ——, FIAT 1313, Vol. III, p. 12 (PB 85172).
9. ——, PB 70338, frame 9677.
10. ——, PB 70339, frame 11319.
11. ——, PB 74898, frame 9649.
12. Mayer and Heil, *Ber.*, **55**, 2155 (1922).
13. Moehlau, *ibid.*, **45**, 2233 (1912).
14. Nawiasky and Krauch, U.S. Patent 1,838,232 (1931).
15. —— and Krause, U.S. Patent 1,766,719 (1930).
16. Singer and Holl, U.S. Patent 1,329,435 (1920).
17. Wilke, U.S. Patent 1,790,780 (1931).

ANTHRAQUINONEOXAZOLES, THIAZOLES AND IMIDAZOLES

Frederick B. Stilmar

Anthraquinoneoxazoles

Anthraquinoneoxazoles result conveniently from acid ring-closure of *o*-hydroxy-*N*-acylamines[10]. They also result from dehydrohalogenation of *o*-halo-*N*-acylamines[24, 29] in a solvent in the presence of sodium carbonate and a copper salt. The preparation of Indanthrene Red FBB, Pr. 296, by both routes is illustrative [20].

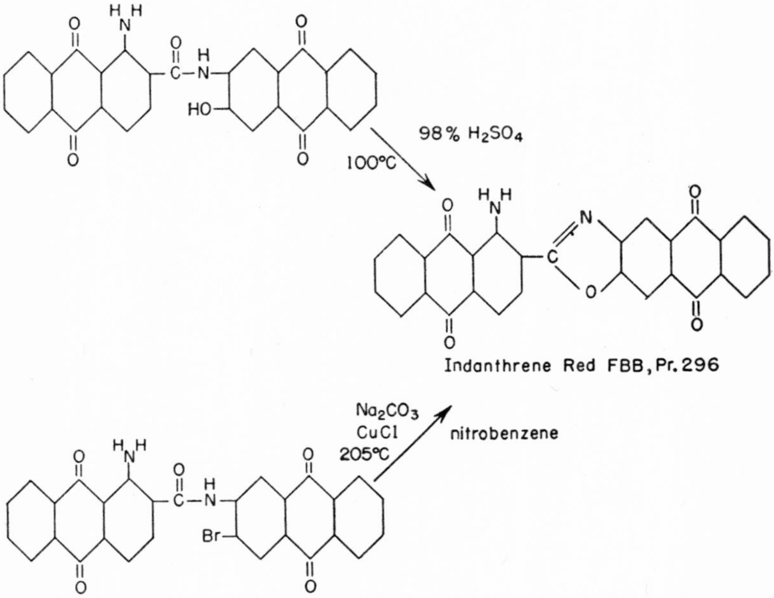

98% H_2SO_4
100°C

Indanthrene Red FBB, Pr. 296

Na_2CO_3
CuCl   nitrobenzene
205°C

The remarkable resistance of the amino group in Indanthrene Red FBB to bleach may be explained by hydrogen bonding. One of the amino hydrogens is bonded to the peri carbonyl oxygen while the other amino hydrogen is bonded to either the nitrogen or oxygen of the oxazole ring. This principle of amino protection is also effective in thiazole combinations.

Anthraquinonethiazoles (including Anthraisothiazolones)

Thiazoles. Algol Yellow GC, Pr. 9, because of brightness of shade and low cost, is an important greenish-yellow vat dye of this class in spite of its poor lightfastness. The following preparations are illustrative of thiazole syntheses in general[1, 17, 18, 25, 30, 32]:

1.

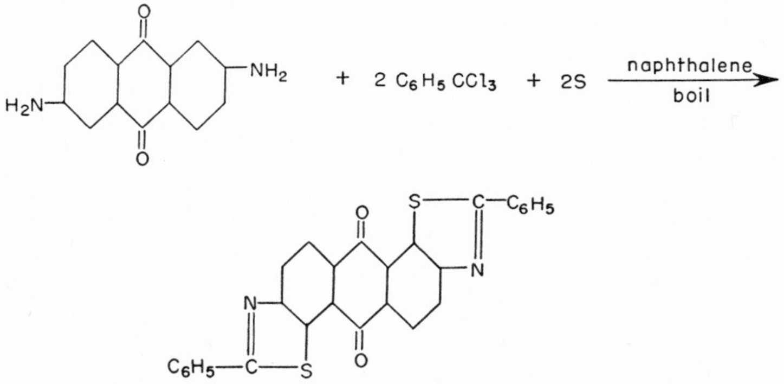

Algol Yellow GC, Pr. 9

2.

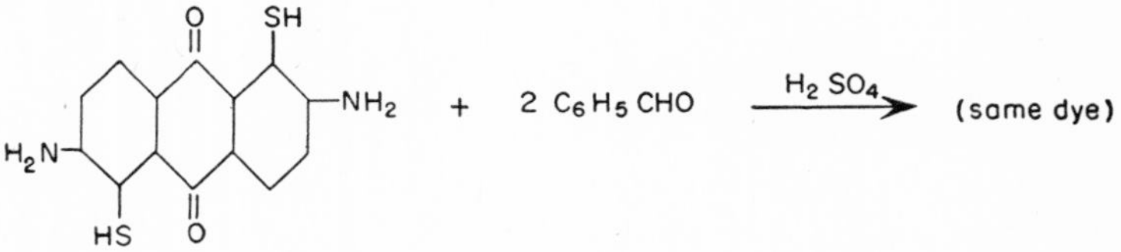

3.

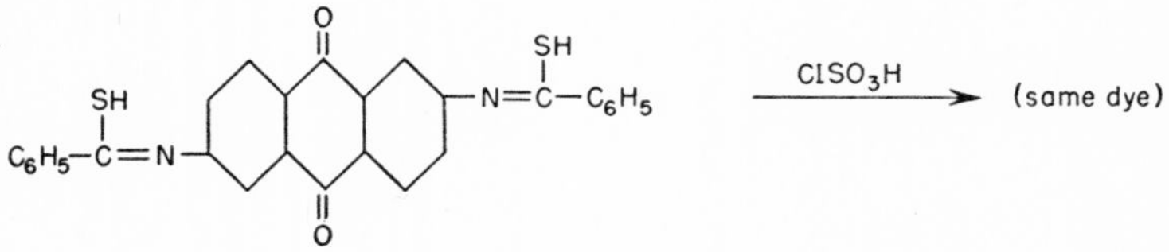

4.

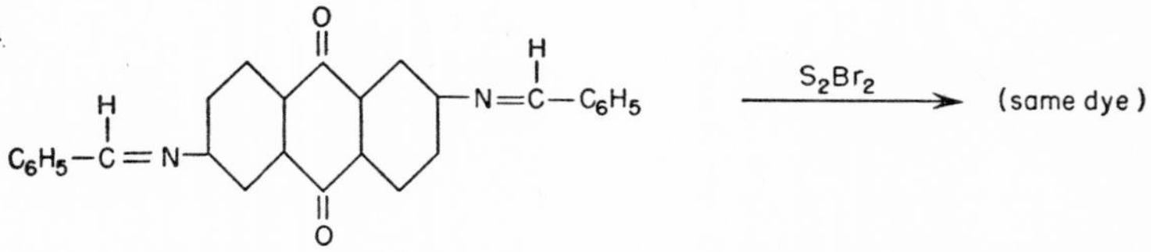

Indanthrene Rubine B is the thiazole analog of Indanthrene Red FBB[8],

Pr. 296. Although of good fastness, it is not widely used because of its dull shade.

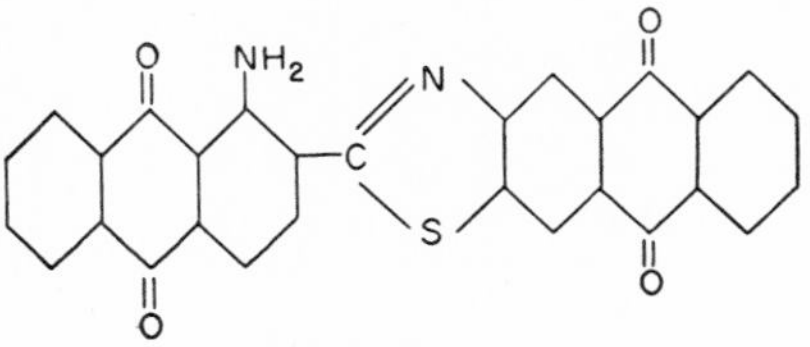

Indanthrene Rubine B

The I.G. Farbenindustrie developed two bleach-fast blue specialties of the following formulas[9]. Because of relative weakness, dullness and high cost they have found very limited use.

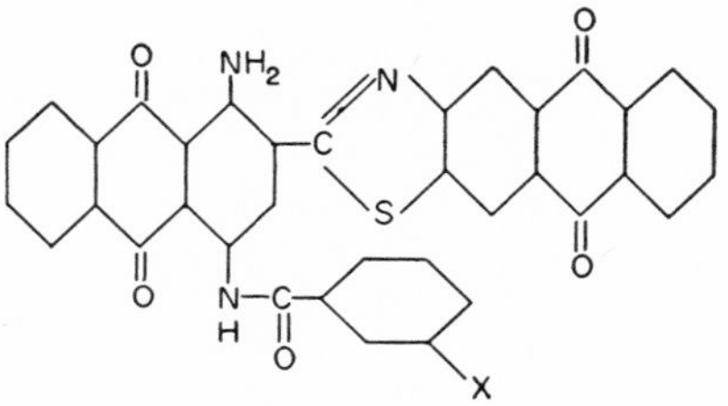

Indanthrene Blue CLG (X = H)
Indanthrene Blue CLB (X = CF₃)

Acylation of 2-amino-3-chloroanthraquinone with 1-amino-4-nitro-2-anthraquinonecarbonyl chloride followed by sulfide reduction of the nitro group and simultaneous mercaptanization of the chloro group, then sulfuric acid ring-closure to the thiazole, gives the amine base. Acylation with the appropriate benzoyl halide then yields the above blue dyes[9, 27].

Anthraisothiazolones.

The isothiazole ring is outstandingly stable to both acid and alkaline agents. 1-Chloro-2-anthraquinonecarboxylic acid yields 6-oxo-6H-anthra-[9,1]isothiazole-3-carboxylic acid on heating with sodium polysulfide and ammonia as indicated below[23].

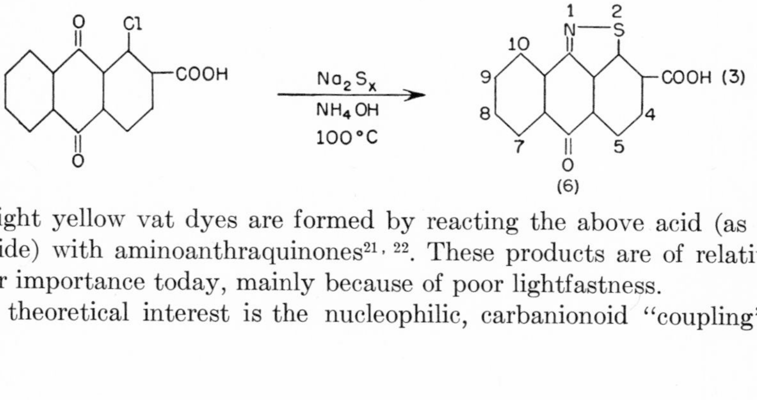

Bright yellow vat dyes are formed by reacting the above acid (as acid chloride) with aminoanthraquinones[21, 22]. These products are of relatively minor importance today, mainly because of poor lightfastness.

Of theoretical interest is the nucleophilic, carbanionoid "coupling" of anthraisothiazole, analogous to those of benzanthrone and of anthra[1,9]-pyrazol-6(2H)-one[2, 6].

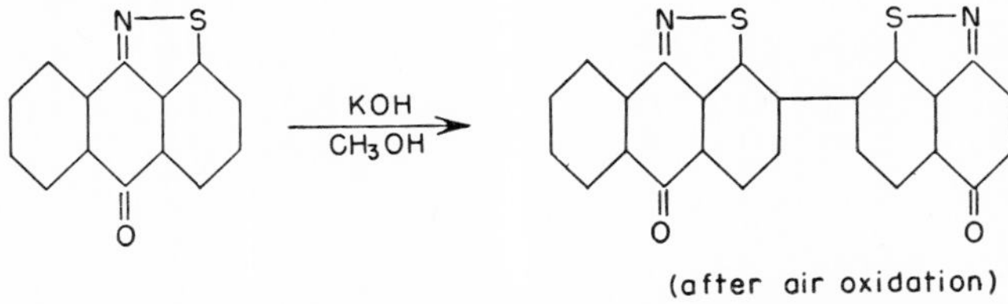

(after air oxidation)

Anthraquinoneimidazoles. The anthraquinoneimidazole group is represented by one (obsolete) type, Algol Orange[5].

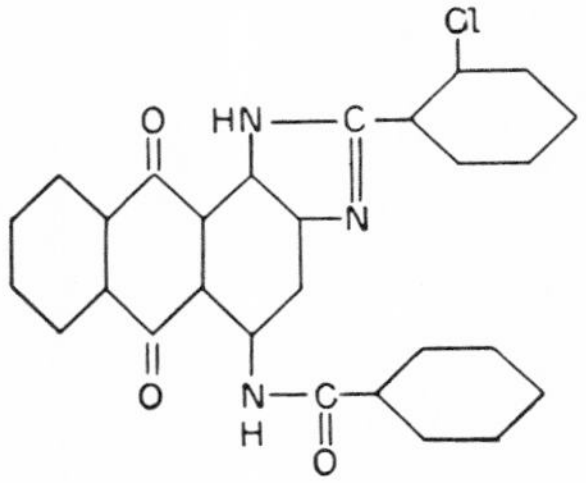

The hydrogen attached to the imidazole nitrogen is, in general, sufficiently acidic to form alkali salts[26]. However, in the above dye this salt formation is prevented, possibly because of the presence of the chlorine in the ortho position of the benzene ring.

The bis-benzimidazodiazapyrenediones are functionally related and have attained some importance because they have such clear shades and because they represent a new type of vat dye. One important product is Indanthrene Brilliant Orange GR, Pr. 287[11], combining extreme thioindigoid brightness with anthraquinone fastness. The *"cis"* isomer is Indanthrene Bordeaux RR[11]. These two products are represented by the following formulas:

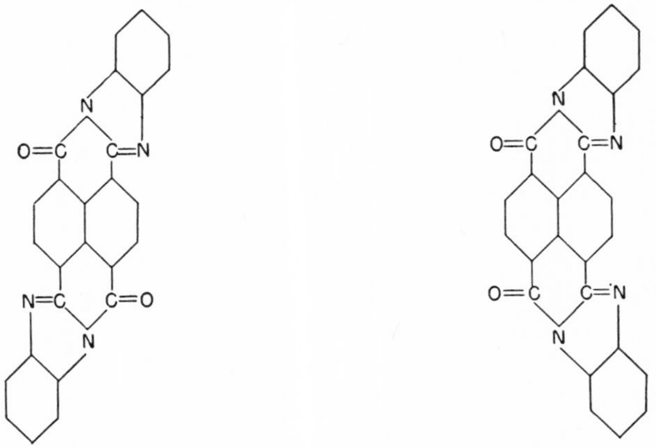

Indanthrene Brilliant
Orange GR, Pr. 287

Indanthrene
Bordeaux RR.

Both of these products are formed when 1,4,5,8-naphthalenetetracarboxylic dianhydride is heated with *o*-phenylenediamine. When pyridine is used as a solvent more of the desirable Indanthrene Brilliant Orange GR is formed. The isomers may be separated by acid crystallization[3] or by a potassium hydroxide/alcohol separation of the rather insoluble alkaline "salt" or addition product[4]. It should be noted that Indanthrene Brilliant Orange GR has the same keto configuration (1,5-dicarbonylnaphthalene) as Indanthrene Golden Yellow GK, Pr. 291.

To avoid the wasteful isomer separation, the I.G. Farbenindustrie studied the following route[16] starting with 1,5-dichloronaphthalene and chloroacetyl chloride:

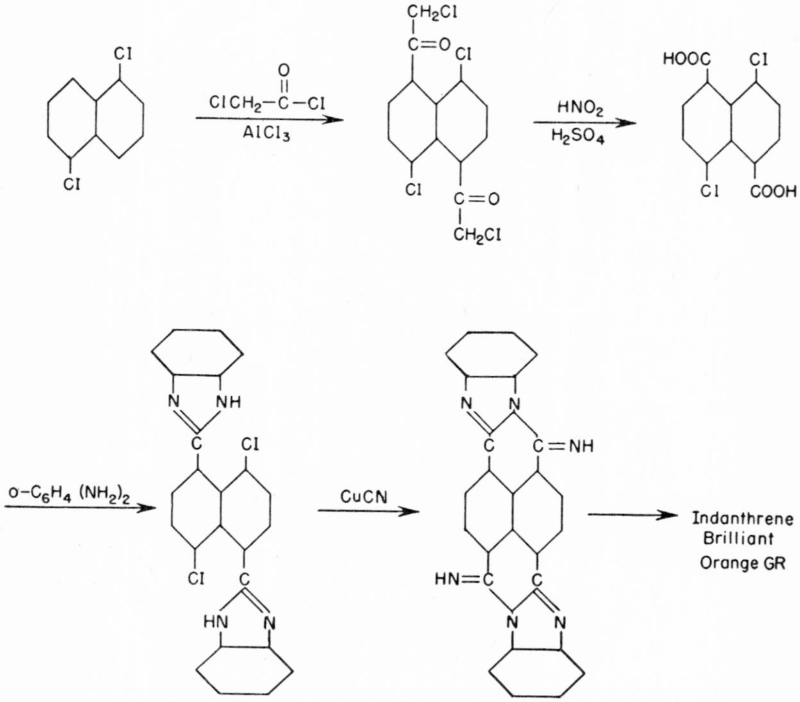

The less desirable *"cis"* isomer has been prepared similarly from 5,8-dibromo-1,4-naphthalenedicarboxylic acid[15].

4-Chloro-*o*-phenylenediamine with naphthalenetetracarboxylic acid similarly yields Indanthrene Red Brown 5R, Pr. 448, while the corresponding ethoxy-*o*-phenylenediamine gives rise to Indanthrene Printing Brown B[7].

Other peri-tetracarboxylic acids have been converted to the mixed imidazoles with *o*-phenylenediamine but none of the following yielded anything of practical importance[12, 19, 28].

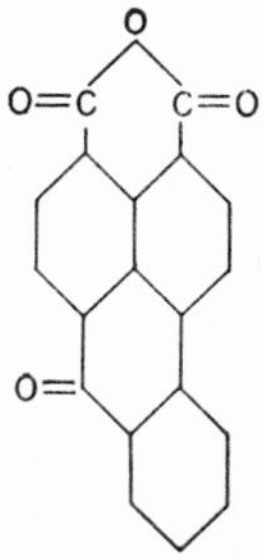

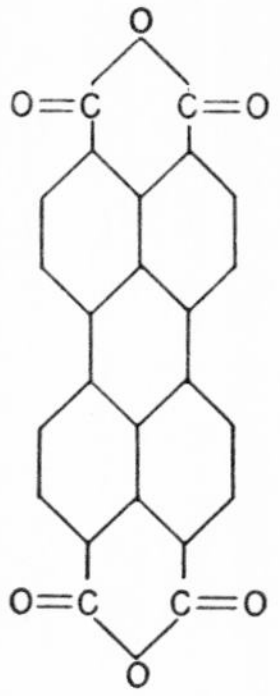

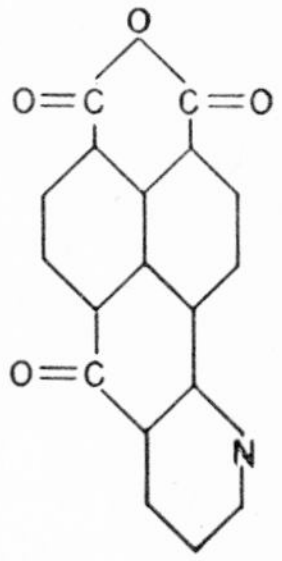

Although bis-benzimidazodiazapyrenedione may be considered a hetero-cyclic benzanthrone, it does not yield dibenzanthrone-like fusion products[13]. However, the following intermediate may be ring-closed by a potassium hydroxide/alcohol fusion analogous to that used on 3-(1-anthraquinonyl-amino)benzanthrone to yield an olive-green vat color[14, 20].

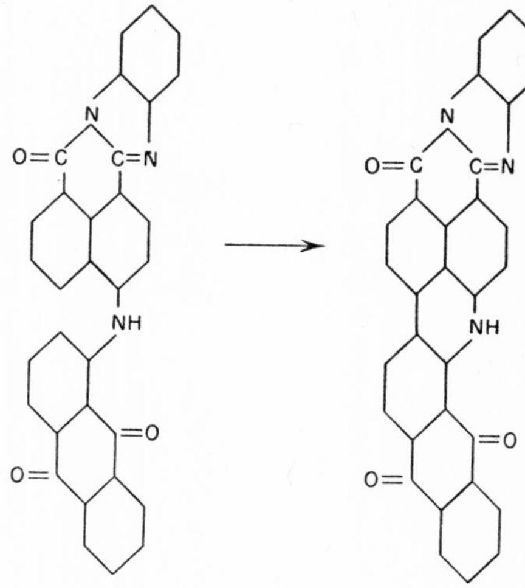

Literature Cited

1. Beard, U.S. Patent 2,028,118 (1936).
2. Bradley and Jadhav, *J. Chem. Soc.*, **1948,** 1622.
3. Eckert, Greune and Eichholz, U.S. Patent 1,888,624 (1932).
4. —— and Sieber, U.S. Patent 1,927,928 (1933).
5. Friedman, U.S. Patent 1,023,248 (1912).
6. German Patent 343,065 (1919).
7. I.G. Farbenindustrie, "Economic Study" (PB 548–561).
8. ——, BIOS 987, pp. 2, 16 (PB 75860).

9. ——, FIAT 1313, Vol. II, pp. 68–73 (PB 85172).
10. ——, *ibid.*, pp. 153–158.
11. ——, *ibid.*, pp. 163–169.
12. ——, PB 70338, frame 9697.
13. ——, *ibid.*, frame 10778.
14. ——, *ibid.*, frame 10780.
15. ——, *ibid.*, frame 10792.
16. ——, PB 76339, frames 10903–10906.
17. ——, PB 82170, frame 3653.
18. Kacer, U.S. Patent 1,095,731 (1914).
19. Kraenzlein, Greune, Corell and Vollmann, U.S. Patent 1,921,360 (1933).
20. Kunz, Rosenberg and Gofferje, U.S. Patent 1,790,102 (1931).
21. Lulek, *Ind. Eng. Chem.*, **23**, 96 (1931).
22. ——, U.S. Patent 1,705,023 (1929).
23. ——, U.S. Patent 1,706,981 (1929).
24. Nawiasky, *Z. angew. Chem.*, **26**-III, 438 (1913).
25. Rintelman and Goodrich, U.S. Patent 1,891,447 (1932).
26. Schaarschmidt and Leu, *Ann.*, **407**, 176 (1915).
27. Schlichenmaier and Berlin, U.S. Patent 2,244,655 (1941).
28. Schmidt and Neugebauer, U.S. Patent 1,808,260 (1931).
29. Ullmann and Junghaus, *Ann.*, **399**, 330 (1913).
30. Unger and Boehner, U.S. Patent 1,927,965 (1933).
31. Wolfrom, Nawiasky, Langbein and Elbs, U.S. Patent 2,069,663 (1937).
32. Wuertz and Rintelman, U.S. Patent 2,097,867 (1937).

MISCELLANEOUS FIVE-MEMBERED HETEROCYCLICS

Frederick B. Stilmar

Anthraquinonethiophenes

Indanthrene Blue Green FFB, CI 1173, a sparingly soluble vat dye of good fastness but of dull shade, is extensively used as a printing color for heavy blue-green shades. It has no value as a dyeing color because of too rapid exhaustion rate. It can be made in poor yield by the sulfur fusion of 4-methylbenzanthrone. The I.G. Farbenindustrie process follows the more clean-cut procedure illustrated by the scheme[2]:

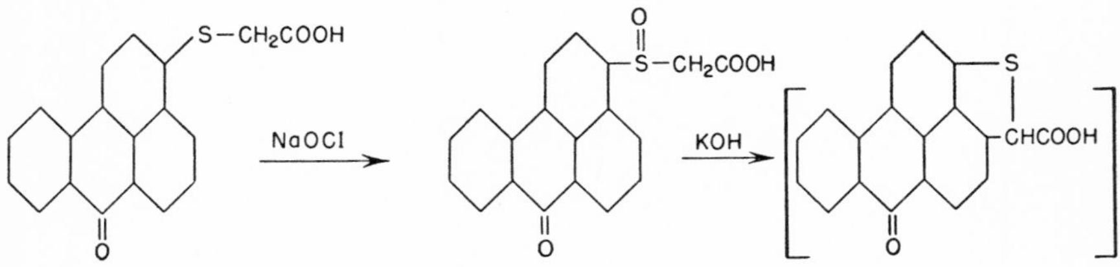

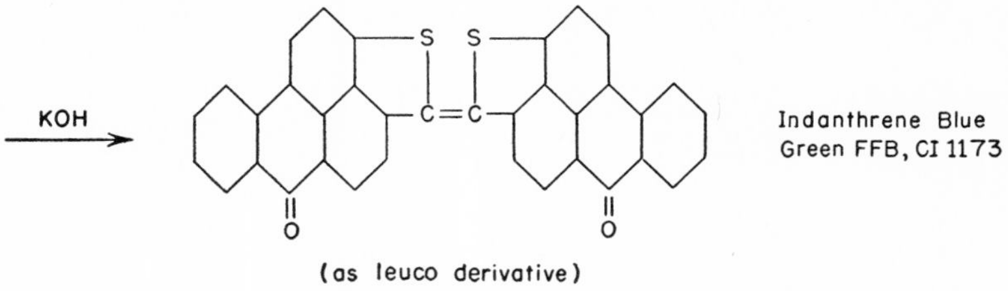

KOH

Indanthrene Blue
Green FFB, CI 1173

(as leuco derivative)

It should be noted that the nucleophilic carbanionoid attack in the 4 position to form the bracketed intermediate requires an oxidizing agent. This is accomplished by the reduction of the sulfoxide to the sulfide, although the mercaptoacetic acid will ring-close directly but in poorer yield. The bracketed intermediate then undergoes "coupling" under the potassium hydroxide/alcohol reaction conditions to yield the leuco form of the dye.

A chemically analogous type of ring-closure is shown by the following naphthalimide derivative, nucleophilic carbanionoid substitution occurring para to the carbonyl, followed by coupling to yield a blue dye[1, 3].

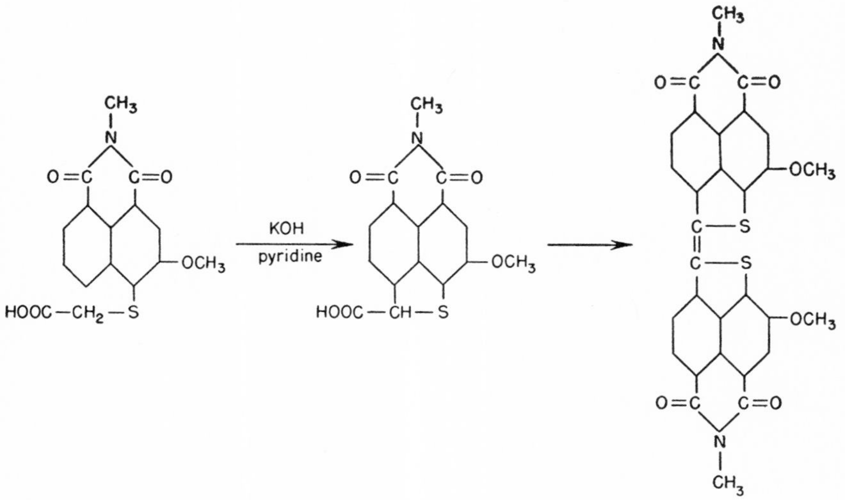

Strangely, the above reaction does not occur in the absence of the methoxy substituent.

6H-Anthra[1,9-bc]thiophenecarboxylic acids have been used to acylate various aminoanthraquinones but the products are of no outstanding technical merit. The acids are obtained as follows[4, 5]:

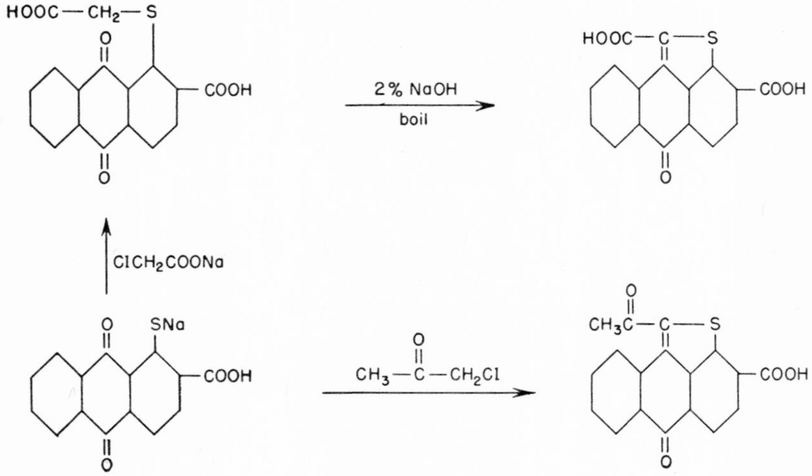

Anthraquinoneoxadiazoles

The oxadiazole ring has been used in the following molecule to give a novel type of vat dye. The amino groups are stabilized by hydrogen bonding and the product is said to be a very fast red[6].

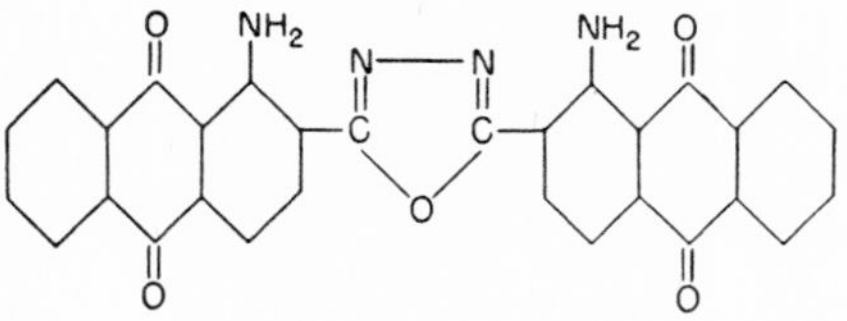

Literature Cited

1. Eckert and Braunsdorf, U.S. Patent 2,231,495 (1941).
2. I. G. Farbenindustrie, BIOS 987, pp. 6, 73–4 (PB 75860).
3. ——, FIAT 1313, Vol. III, p. 37 (PB 85172).
4. Kalischer, Ritter and Baumann, U.S. Patent 1,931,196 (1933).
5. Stilmar, U.S. Patent 2,233,496 (1941).
6. ——, U.S. Patent 2,464,831 (1949).

Six-membered Heterocyclic Vat Dyes

PYRIDINES AND PYRIDONES

Melvin A. Perkins

Historically, vat dyes containing one or more pyridine rings had considerable importance in the period 1904–1910, when a number of products were made from 2-aminoanthraquinone by reaction with glycerol. This resulted in the formation of the so-called "benzanthronequinoline," which is a pyridinobenzanthrone and which, upon further condensation, led to such dyes as dipyridinodibenzanthrone. This dye was referred to in early literature as "cyananthrene" and gave dark blue-violet dyeings. This product gradually lost ground since it had no real advantage over dibenzanthrone itself and was more expensive to produce. Its constitution was the object of a recent scientific study by Pardit, Tilak and Venkataraman[8].

The work of Max Kunz led to revived interest in those pyridino compounds which are vat dyes, since he advanced the theory that such dyes containing pyridino rings could not only overcome the tendering action often encountered in light shade vat colors but also could be so devised as actually to exert protecting action on the fiber[4, 5]. Rigid examination of this theory and testing by synthesis of pyridino derivatives of established vat colors has thrown doubt on this theory[6, 9]. There are no commercial dyes which are pyridino derivatives of the established anthraquinone types. There are, however, two technically important classes of dyes which contain pyridine rings as an integral part of the condensed molecular system. These are the types commonly referred to as (a) benzanthroneacridines and (b) flavanthrones and treated under individual sections below, following "Pyridones."

Pyridones

Although several wool colors containing this ring system have been in use for many years (see section on Acid Dyes, p. 409), there are very few vat colors containing rings of this type. The only ones of practical importance are those derived from 3,4,9,10-perylenetetracarboxylic diimide. This imide is obtained by caustic fusion of naphthalimide in which a condensation involving two molecules of naphthalimide takes place according to the scheme:

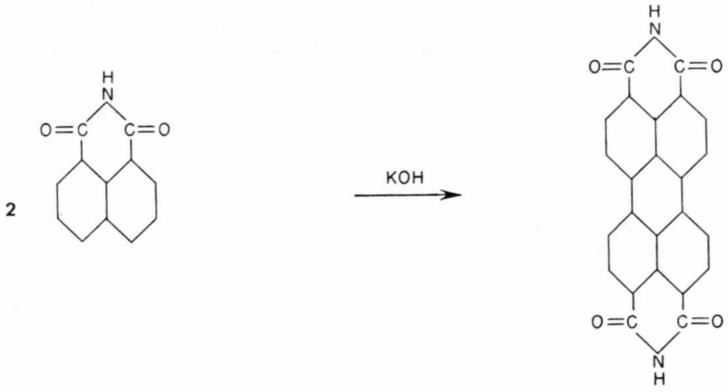

This material can be alkylated to give N-alkyl compounds which are vat dyes of considerable fastness but of rather unattractive dull red shades[1]. Halogenation improves the brightness to some extent but makes the products even more difficult to vat. Products of improved brightness are obtained by different procedures all leading to the same general chemical type, namely, to N-aryl imides. These are best obtained by hydrolysis of the 3,4, 9,10-perylenetetracarboxylic diimide in sulfuric acid[2] to give the tetracarboxylic dianhydride, which is then reacted with aromatic amines to give the brighter shade scarlet or red dyes. The best known of these is Indanthrene Scarlet R, Pr. 449, in which the aromatic amine used is p-anisidine[3, 7]. Indanthrene Red GG is the N,N'-dimethyltetracarboxylic diimide[1, 7].

Literature Cited

1. German Patent 386,057 (1923).
2. German Patent 394,794 (1924).
3. I. G. Farbenindustrie, BIOS 1493, p. 50 (PB 81611) (erroneously called "K" instead of "R").
4. ———, "Economic Study" (PB 555).
5. Kunz, *Angew. Chem.*, **52**, 269 (1939).
6. ———, *Bull. soc. ind. Mulhouse*, **100**, 3 (1933).
7. Landoldt, *Textil-Rundschau*, **5**, 447 (1950).
8. Pardit, Tilak and Venkataraman, *Proc. Indian Acad. Sci.*, **32**, 39–45 (1950).
9. Waly, Preston, Scholefield and Turner, *J. Soc. Dyers Colourists*, **61**, 245 (1945).

BENZANTHRONEACRIDINES

Myron S. Whelen

The benzanthroneacridines are the products obtained by alcoholic caustic alkali fusion of 3-(1-anthraquinonylamino)benzanthrones, the simplest derivative being shown in the following fashion:

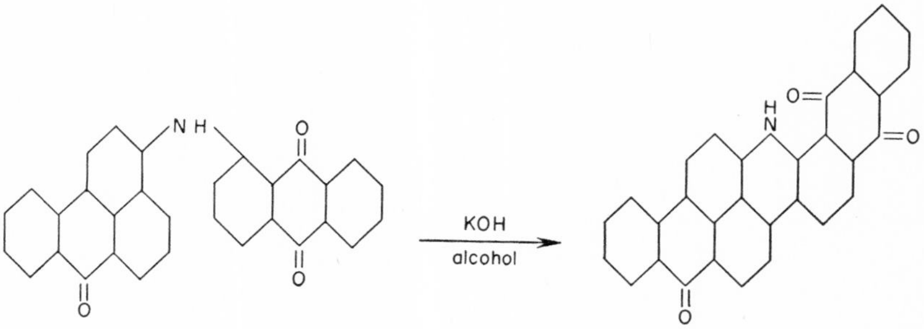

They are vat dyes characterized by very good all-around fastness properties, especially high lightfastness. They have very high affinity for cellulosic fibers and possess excellent vat solubility. They are not good printing colors, their chief application being through dyeing and pigment pad methods. Due to their very good dyeing properties they combine well with other colors and are extensively used. They are obtainable in dull shades from blue-green to green to olive to brown and gray.

The earliest preparation of a benzanthroneacridine as a vat dye is that of the one shown above which was described by Hugo Wolff in 1909[17].

This product is now commercially sold as Indanthrene Olive Green B, Pr. 293. From this original structure a series of dyes has been evolved, which are essentially all of this basic type modified by the addition of groups or additional ring structures.

The benzanthroneacridines are prepared by alcoholic caustic alkali fusion of 3-(1-anthraquinonylamino)benzanthrones at an elevated temperature[17]. The fusion mass is then poured into water and the reduced product is oxidized and separated. Conversion to a proper physical form for application is accomplished by one of the commonly used methods, such as acid pasting or vatting.

Substituted products can be prepared by utilizing substituted α-aminoanthraquinones instead of 1-aminoanthraquinone (as exemplified above), such as 1-amino-5-benzamidoanthraquinone[4], or an aminoanthraquinone to which a heterocyclic system is attached such as 5-amino-1,9-anthrapyrimidine[11]. 3-(1-Anthraquinonylamino)benzanthrones may be halogenated and the halogenated product condensed with α-aminoanthraquinones. These on fusion produce a series of dyes varying in shade from olive to brown[5].

The use of 3,9-dihalobenzanthrone for condensation with two moles of an α-aminoanthraquinone, followed by alcoholic caustic fusion, gives a benzanthroneacridine with an anthraquinonylamino group attached to the 9 position of the benzanthrone portion of the molecule[18]. In this fashion a series of colors dyeing in olive to gray shades can be obtained by utilizing α-aminoanthraquinones to which a heterocyclic or other grouping is attached in various combinations[1, 2, 3, 10, 11].

The condensation of 3-bromobenzanthrone with anthrapyrazolone followed by alcoholic caustic alkali treatment at 90 to 95°C gives rise to a modified type of a benzanthroneacridine[3, 14] which dyes in navy blue shades. It has good lightfastness but is not fast to water spotting. It is shown as follows:

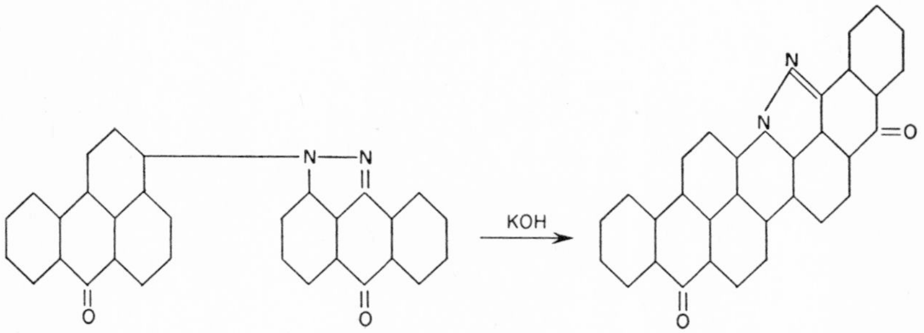

The use of 3-bromo-2-phenylbenzanthrone in a similar manner gives a greenish-blue dye, whose fastness and shade is improved by chlorination[14].

The following summation shows some of the better known commercial products typical of the general class. With the exceptions of the Olive Brown GB and Olive Green GG types which utilize sodium anilide fusion[7, 12], all are benzanthroneacridines prepared by alcoholic caustic alkali fusion of the corresponding anthraquinonylaminobenzanthrones. The component parts are shown. The dyes derived are in some cases mixtures.

Color	Component Intermediates
Indanthrene Olive Green B, Pr. 293[17]	3-Bromobenzanthrone (1 mole) 1-Aminoanthraquinone (1 mole)
Indanthrene Olive Green GG[7]	3-Bromobenzanthrone (1 mole) 1-Amino-5-benzamidoanthraquinone (1 mole) The benzanthroneacridine chlorinated

Color	Component Intermediates
Indanthrene Olive GB[9, 12]	3-Bromobenzanthrone (1 mole) 1,5-Diaminoanthraquinone (1 mole) The benzanthroneacridine benzoylated
Indanthrene Olive G[6]	3,9-Dibromobenzanthrone (1 mole) 1-Aminoanthraquinone (2 moles) The benzanthroneacridine treated with $SOCl_2$ and $AlCl_3$
Indanthrene Olive T[18]	3,9-Dibromobenzanthrone (1 mole) 1-Aminoanthraquinone (2 moles)
Indanthrene Olive Brown GB[12]	3,9-Dibromobenzanthrone (1 mole) 1-Aminoanthraquinone (1 mole) 1-Amino-5-benzamidoanthraquinone (1 mole)
Indanthrene Black Brown NR[3]	3,9-Dibromobenzanthrone (1 mole) 1-Aminoanthraquinone (1 mole) 1,5-Diaminoanthraquinone (1 mole) 1-Amino-2-anthraquinonecarbonyl chloride (1 mole)
Indanthrene Navy Blue R[13, 15]	3-Bromobenzanthrone (1 mole) Anthra[1,9]pyrazol-6(2H)-one (1 mole)
Indanthrene Gray M (MG)[16]	3,9-Dibromobenzanthrone (1 mole) Anthra[1,9]pyrazol-6(2H)-one (1 mole) 1-Aminoanthraquinone (1 mole)

Literature Cited

1. Graham and Frey, U.S. Patent 2,188,537 (1940).
2. ——, U.S. Patent 2,188,538 (1940).
3. Honold, U.S. Patent 2,131,176 (1938).
4. —— and Boehner, U.S. Patent 1,903,181 (1933).
5. —— and Wolff, U.S. Patent 2,014,568 (1935).
6. I. G. Farbenindustrie, BIOS 20, Appendix 45 (PB 31004).
7. ——, BIOS 987, p. 73 (PB 75860).
8. ——, BIOS 1493, p. 26 (PB 81611).
9. ——, *ibid.*, p. 32.
10. Lulek, U.S. Patent 2,212,029 (1940).
11. Lycan, U.S. Patent 2,203,416 (1940).
12. Neresheimer and Honold, U.S. Patent 1,850,562 (1932).
13. —— and Schneider, U.S. Patent 1,846,139 (1932).
14. Wilke, U.S. Patent 1,790,780 (1931).
15. ——, U.S. Patent 1,873,925 (1932).
16. ——, Stock and Schubert, U.S. Patent 1,938,059 (1933).
17. Wolff, U.S. Patent 995,936 (1911).
18. —— and Honold, U.S. Patent 1,845,469 (1932).

FLAVANTHRONE

Myron S. Whelen

Flavanthrone (5,13-didehydro-8,16-flavanthrinedione) was discovered by René Bohn in 1901[1, 2, 3] in conjunction with indanthrone. The caustic alkali fusion of 2-aminoanthraquinone at high temperatures[2] produces flavanthrone together with other impurities. Technically, it is prepared by heating 2-aminoanthraquinone in nitrobenzene with antimony pentachloride[4] and is purified by alkaline bleaching. The course of the reaction is obscure. The yield of flavanthrone is low, from 35 to 40 per cent.

Flavanthrone was synthesized by Scholl[6], who prepared 2,2'-dimethyl-1,1'-bianthraquinone which was oxidized to the dicarboxylic acid; the amide was formed but an attempt to convert the same by Hofmann's reaction to 2,2'-diamino-1,1'-bianthraquinone proved this to be unstable under the conditions employed and it simultaneously lost two molecules of water and formed flavanthrone.

A technical process involving the synthesis of flavanthrone over the 2,2'-diamino-1,1'-bianthraquinone route has been evolved. 1-Chloro-2-phthalimidoanthraquinone is converted to 2,2'-diphthalimido-1,1'-bianthraquinone by heating it in a high-boiling solvent with copper. On alkaline hydrolysis this produces the unstable diamine which, under the alkaline conditions employed, dehydrates and cyclizes to form flavanthrone[5].

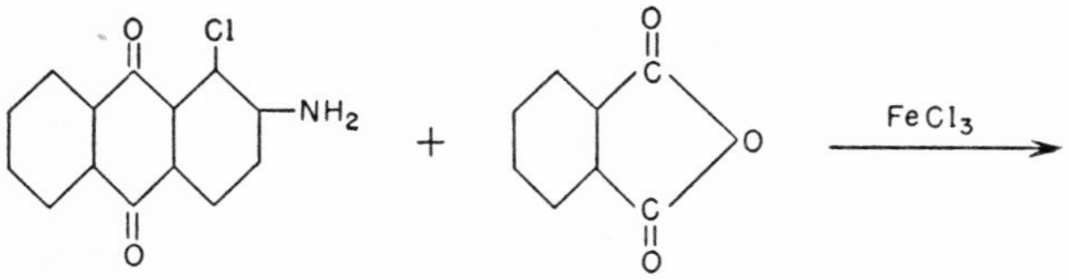

2-Amino-1-chloro-anthraquinone

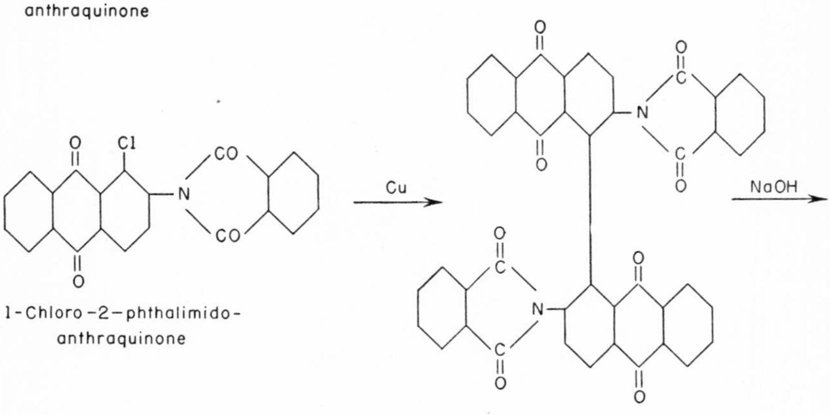

1-Chloro-2-phthalimido-anthraquinone

2,2'-Diphthalimido-1,1'-bianthraquinone

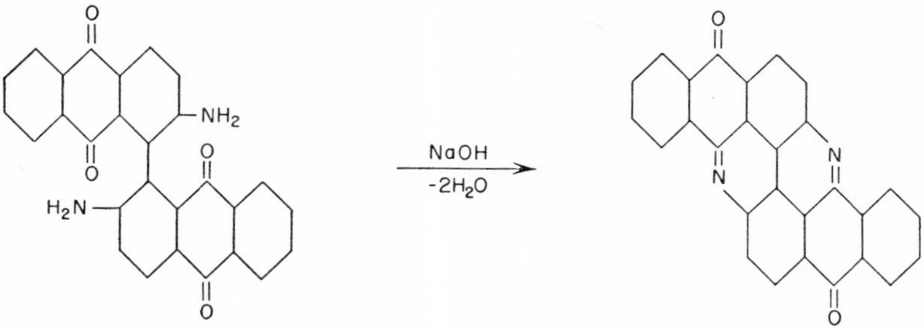

2,2'-Diamino-1,1'-bi-
anthraquinone (not isolated)   NaOH -2H₂O →   Flavanthrone

This synthesis is dependent upon the fact that all the hydrogen atoms attached to the nitrogen atom in the 2 position must be removed, otherwise the bianthraquinone cannot be formed.

Flavanthrone, sold as Indanthrene Yellow G (and related products under similar trade names), CI 1118, is easily reduced and possesses excellent application properties. It is an exceptionally good printing color. It has only fair lightfastness, and suffers from the fact that it is phototropic. When kept in the dark after light exposure it partially recovers from the fade. Despite its poor fastness to light it is used extensively because of its excellent application properties. It has good bleachfastness but is a bleach tenderer; the bleach used must be alkaline and sunlight must be avoided.

Indanthrene Yellow R (now obsolete) is dibromoflavanthrone which is redder and duller than Indanthrene Yellow G.

Literature Cited

1. German Patent 129,845 (1902).
2. German Patent 133,686 (1902).
3. German Patent 136,015 (1901).
4. German Patent 138,119 (1902).
5. I. G. Farbenindustrie, FIAT 1313, Vol. II, p. 174 (PB 85172).
6. Scholl, *Ber.*, **40,** 1691 (1907).

ANTHRAQUINONEACRIDONES

Myron S. Whelen

The phthaloylacridones probably comprise the largest group of vat dyes. This is especially true in respect to the number of patents involved. Almost every possible shade is represented by relatively simple derivatives or by more complex configurations in which the acridone system appears as a vattable unit. The bulk of the literature is concerned with products centered on the phthaloylacridone commonly known as "anthraquinone-2,1(N)-

benzacridone[70]," shown as follows:

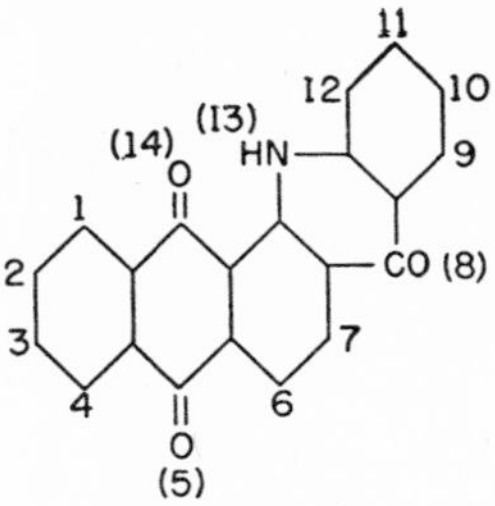

which is naphth[2,3-c]acridine-5,8,14(13H)-trione. There is much confusion as to the nomenclature employed in the literature, at least five systems having been used. A simplified or integrated system of nomenclature will not be attempted in this review and naming will be minimized. However, to assist in integrating the nomenclature of this review with the patent literature, the naming used will be that based on anthraquinone-2',1'(N)-benzacridone, while the numbering system will be that shown in the above formula which will correspond to that of the system used in Chemical Abstracts and which differs from any of the systems commonly used in the patent literature.

There are isomeric but commercially unimportant acridone systems known wherein nitrogen is attached to a β position of the anthraquinone nucleus. The number of phthaloylacridones of the anthraquinone-2',1'(N)-benzacridone type runs into the thousands and no attempt will be made to cover them extensively; rather the various methods known for the preparation of acridones will be shown, as will the various types of acridones which have been prepared. The properties of the acridones as a class will be discussed and the commercially important dyes will be shown.

Methods of Formation of the Acridone Ring. Numerous methods for the formation of the acridone ring are known, and of these the following examples are typical. While a benzene ring is shown in these examples, the acridones may in certain cases be derived from naphthalene, anthraquinone or other aromatic nuclei. The aryl group in some cases may be substituted:

From

By means of

1.

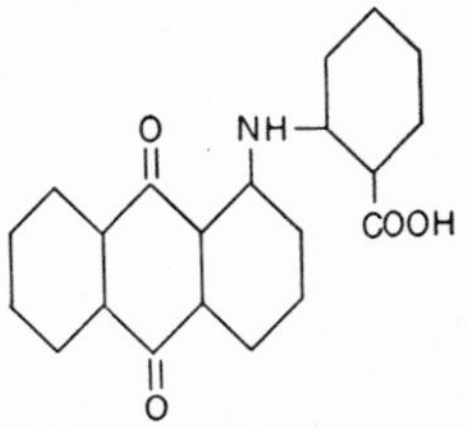

or its substituted products

(a) Sulfuric acid[64, 70]
(b) Chlorosulfonic acid[51, 53]
(c) Benzoyl chloride in solvent[76]
(d) p-Toluenesulfonyl chloride[72]
(e) Phosphorus pentachloride[21, 62]
(f) Thionyl chloride[62]

From By means of

2.

Hydrolysis and cyclization in sulfuric acid[31]

3.

(a) Sodium hydrosulfite, sodium hydroxide (vatting)[64]
(b) Zinc and ammonia[27]

4.

(a) Halogenation and hydrolysis[34, 35]
(b) Oxidation of 2-methyl-1,2'-iminodianthraquinone with lead oxide[20]

5.

Halogenation[40]

6.

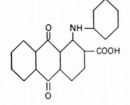

(a) Benzoyl chloride in solvent[7, 56, 76]
(b) Acetyl chloride in solvent[56, 76]
(c) Bromine or chlorine in solvent on ester[47, 60]
(d) Phosphorus pentachloride[59, 75, 77]
(e) Aluminum chloride[24, 70]
(f) Thionyl chloride[16, 24, 25, 75]
(g) Oxalic acid in solvent[37, 77]
(h) Copper, pyridine and sulfur trioxide[43]
(i) Sulfuric or chlorosulfonic acid[56, 59]

From	By means of

7.

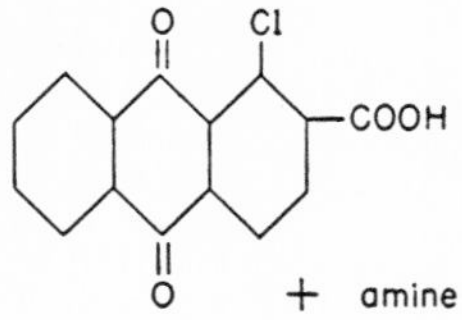

O   Cl
‖
—COOH

O
‖
+ amine

or

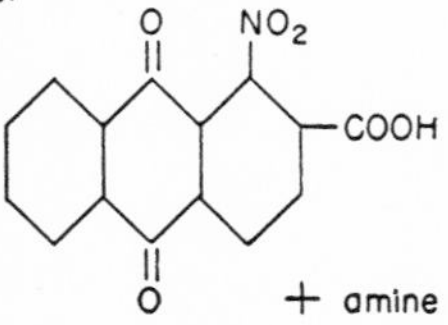

O   NO₂
‖
—COOH

O
‖
+ amine

(a) Boric acid[37, 59]
(b) Oxalic acid[59, 77]
(c) Boric acid[41] (on nitro compound)

8.

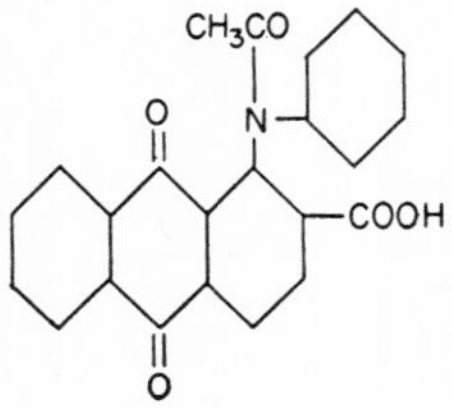

CH₃CO
N—
O
‖
—COOH

O
‖

Acetic anhydride[28] and sulfuric acid (on anilino compound)

9.

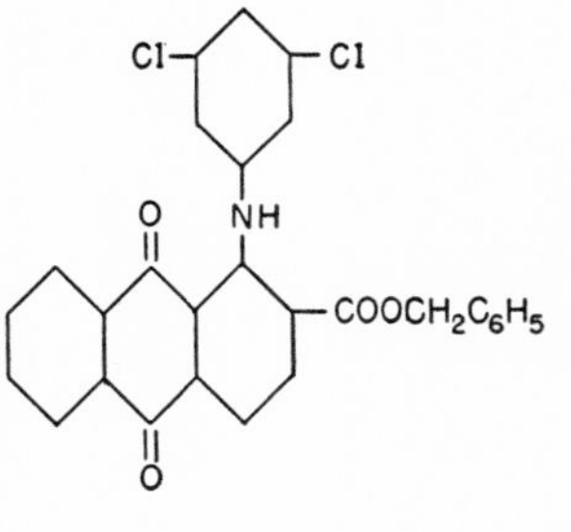

Cl—   —Cl

O   NH
‖
—COOCH₂C₆H₅

O
‖

(a) Acetic anhydride[15] and sulfuric acid in nitrobenzene
(b) Halogens or PCl₅ on similar types[60]

10.

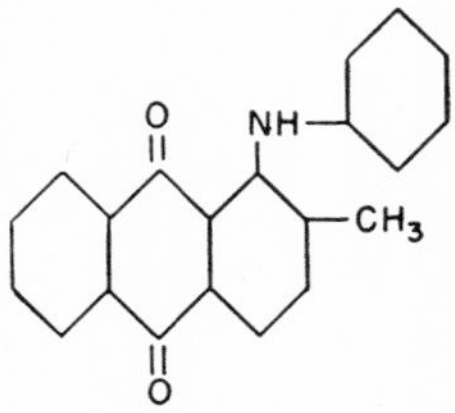

O   NH—
‖
—CH₃

O
‖

Halogenation and hydrolysis[34, 35, 39, 42]

From   By means of

11.

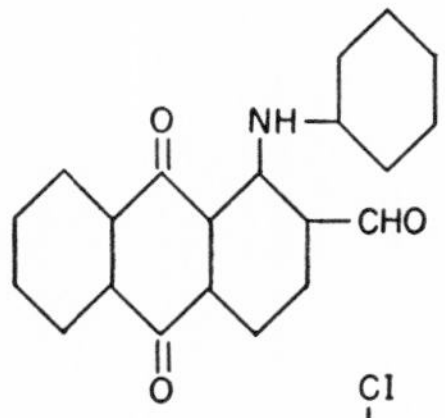

Halogenation[40]

12.

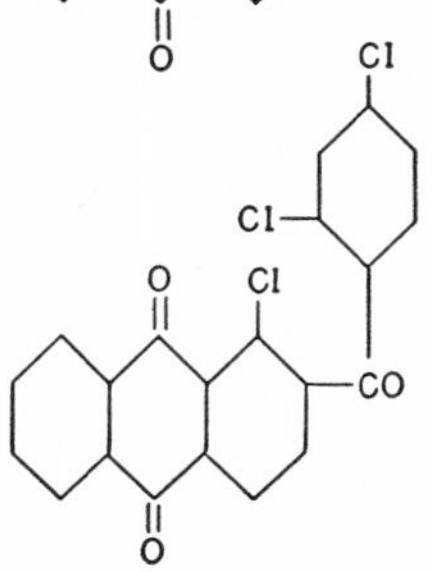

Heating 1-chloro-2-(2,4-dichloroben-zoyl)anthraquinone with *p*-toluenesulfonamide, followed by hydrolysis[33]

13.

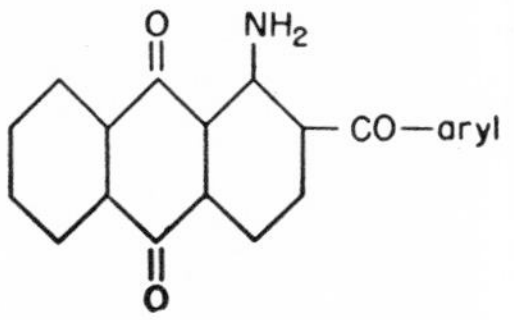

Alkaline condensation[55]

The most satisfactory ring-closure methods are those utilizing chlorosulfonic acid, oxalic acid and acid chlorides.

General Properties. As a class the anthraquinoneacridone dyes exhibit good all-around fastness and application properties. They are particularly fast to light. In general, they are cold-dyeing, but some will dye warm. They vat easily, and show good solubility in the vat. This may account for a general tendency toward poor fastness to soda boil, due to the increased alkali-solubility of the leuco derivative produced by the alkaline reduction associated with Kier boiling. They are not very satisfactory as printing colors. Acridones as a class suffer from poor affinity and do not exhibit good tinctorial value as compared to most other commercial vat dyes. They are subject to change on soaping and some tinctorial value is also lost in this process.

Types of Acridones. The acridones of the anthraquinone-2′,1′(*N*)-benzacridone type may be summarized under the following classes:

(1) Unsubstituted monoacridones.
(2) Anthraquinone-2′,1′(*N*)-benzacridone substituted by halogen only.
(3) Aminoanthraquinone-2′,1′(*N*)-benzacridone derivatives.
    (a) Arylaminoanthraquinone-2′,1′(*N*)-benzacridones.
    (b) Acylaminoanthraquinone-2′,1′(*N*)-benzacridones.

(4) Anthraquinone-2′,1′(N)-benzacridonecarboxamide derivatives.
(5) Unsubstituted di- and triacridones.
(6) Substituted diphthaloylacridones.
(7) Substituted diacridones.
(8) Acridones derived from amines of higher coal tar hydrocarbons.
(9) Acridonecarbazole dyes.

The following discussion and examples show the constitution of a few of the dyes representative of each type. It should be noted that these are merely representative of the several thousand products known, and as such serve to show only the chemical constitution of the various types. The examples chosen are not to be construed as representative commercial types, in fact, few of them are commercially important.

Unsubstituted Monoacridones:

Compound	Method of Preparation
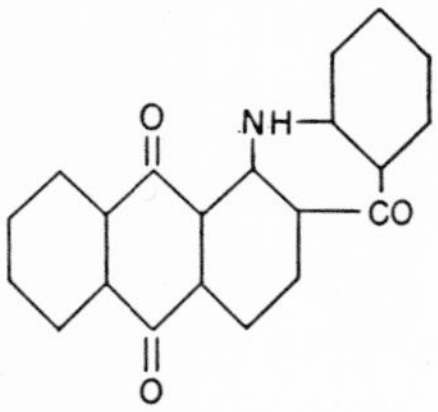	N-(1-Anthraquinonyl)anthranoyl chloride cyclized with aluminum chloride[21] (violet-red)
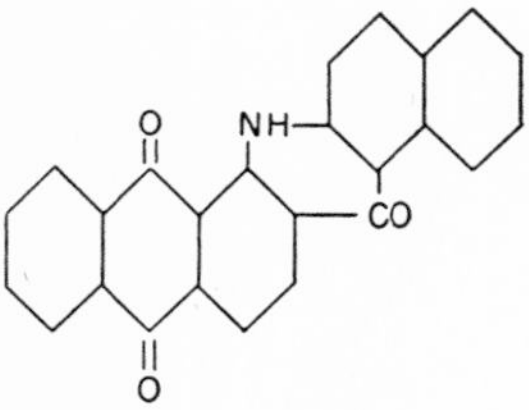	1-(2-Naphthylamino)-2-anthraquinonecarboxylic acid heated with phosphorus pentachloride and aluminum chloride[24, 62] (red)
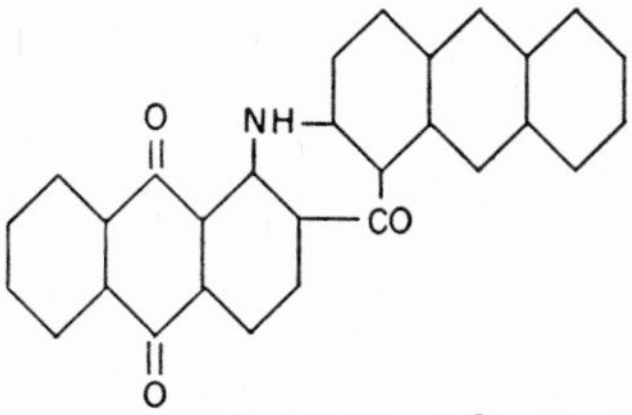	From 1-chloro-2-anthraquinonecarboxylic acid and 2-anthramine and oxalic acid in naphthalene[77] (red-brown)
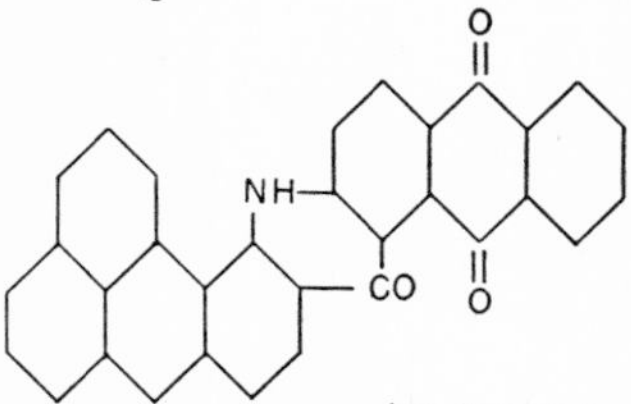 (or isomer)	From 11-chloro-10-benzanthronecarboxylic acid and o-(m-aminobenzoyl)benzoic acid cyclized in sulfuric acid[32] (orange-yellow)

Anthraquinone-2',1'(N)-benzacridone Substituted by Halogen Only. Halogenation of anthraquinone-2',1'(N)-benzacridone takes place easily. Chlorine enters the molecule readily, especially in the 6 position, as well as in the 10 and 12 positions. The final orientation depends on the method employed. Halogenation, dehalogenation and rehalogenation procedures are common. Dehalogenation takes place readily in the 4 , 6 and 9 positions, the first easiest of all. Mono- to hexahalogen compounds are known and with combinations of chlorine and bromine over a hundred different halogen products have been prepared. Halogenation in varying degrees gives rise to a series of dyes ranging from violet through bluish-red, red, orange-red, yellow-red to orange-yellow.

Generalization as to the effect on shade of halogen atoms in different positions in the acridone nucleus is difficult, especially when three or more halogen atoms are present. Halogenation in the "Bz" (positions 9, 10, 11 and 12) ring appears to have more effect on shade than halogenation in the anthraquinone ring. Chlorine in the 11 or 12 positions gives yellower products than when it is in the 9 or 10 positions, but when two chlorine atoms are present in the 11 and 12 positions a bluish-red dye is obtained, while the 9,10; 9,11; 9,12; 10,11 and 10,12-dichloroacridones are yellower in shade.

Derivative	Preparation	Shade
6-Chloro	From 1,4-dichloroanthraquinone and one mole of anthranilic acid	violet[69]
7-Bromo	From N-(3-bromo-1-anthraquinonyl)anthranilic acid	violet[73]
9-Chloro (Mixture with 11-chloro)	From 1-chloro-2-anthraquinonecarboxylic acid and m-chloroaniline	bluish-red[28, 45]
10-Chloro	From 1-p-chloroanilino-2-anthraquinonecarboxylic acid	bluish-red[28, 45]
11-Chloro	From 1-chloroanthraquinone and 4-chloroanthranilic acid	yellowish-red[26, 53]
12-Chloro	From 1-chloro-2-anthraquinonecarboxylic acid and o-chloroaniline	red[44, 59]
9,10-Dichloro or 10,11-Dichloro	From 1-chloro-2-anthraquinonecarboxylic acid and 3,4-dichloroaniline	red[45, 61]
9,11-Dichloro	From benzyl 1-chloro-2-anthraquinonecarboxylate and 3,5-dichloroaniline	red[15, 45]
9,12-Dichloro	From 1-(2,5-dichloroanilino)-2-anthraquinonecarboxylic acid	yellowish-red[59]
10,12-Dichloro	From 1-chloro-2-anthraquinonecarboxylic acid and 2,4-dichloroaniline	red[65]
11,12-Dichloro	From 1-chloro-2-anthraquinonecarboxylic acid and 2,3-dichloroaniline	bluish-red[59]

Aminoanthraquinone-2',1'(N)-benzacridone Derivatives. 1,4,6,7 and 9-aminoanthraquinone-2',1'(N)-benzacridones are known. Of these, 6-aminoanthraquinone-2′,1′(N)-benzacridone, which may be regarded as a substituted 1,4-diaminoanthraquinone, is the most important. It exhibits affinity for cotton (from a "vat"). Halogen derivatives of the various amines are well known and several have been sold commercially. Numerous aminoacridones containing other substituents such as the methyl and methoxy groups have been prepared. 6-Aminoacridones which contain a substituent in the 7 position are not stable to vatting, the group in the 7 position being eliminated. The monoamines and a few of the halogen derivatives typical of the group are shown as follows:

Derivative	Preparation	Shade
1-Amino	From 1-amino-8-chloroanthraquinone and anthranilic acid, cyclized in sulfuric acid	bluish-red[36, 65b]
4-Amino	From N-(5-amino-1-anthraquinonyl)anthranilic acid, in chlorosulfonic acid	bluish-red[36, 65b]
6-Amino	From N-(4-amino-1-anthraquinonyl)anthranilic acid, in chlorosulfonic acid	greenish-blue[51]
6-Amino-7-bromo	From N-(4-amino-3-bromo-1-anthraquinonyl)anthranilic acid, in chlorosulfonic acid	green[30]
6-Amino-9-chloro	From 4-amino-1-bromo-2-anthraquinonesulfonic acid and 6-chloroanthranilic acid	greenish-blue[65a, 66]
6-Amino-10,12-dichloro	From 6,10,12-trichloro compound with p-toluenesulfonamide, followed by hydrolysis	greenish-blue[71]
7-Amino	From 7-bromoanthraquinone-2′,1′(N)-benzacridone and p-toluenesulfonamide, followed by hydrolysis	red[17]
9-Amino-12-chloro	From 9,12-dichloro compound and p-toluenesulfonamide, followed by hydrolysis	corinth[4]

Arylaminoanthraquinone-2′,1′(N)-benzacridones. The most important dyes of this type are those obtained by substitution of the amino group in 6-aminoanthraquinone-2′,1′(N)-benzacridone. Substitution of the amino group by arylamino radicals has a bathochromic effect, the shades varying from bluish-gray, bluish-green, green, greenish-gray to olive and khaki. 6-Anilinoanthraquinone-2′,1′(N)-benzacridones are usually bluish-green or blue, while the naphthylamino and anthraquinonylamino compounds are usually grays or greens depending upon whether the substituent is attached to an α or a β position. The best products are usually found when the attachment is in the α position of the anthraquinone nucleus.

In general, when a component which is definitely yellow is attached to 6-aminoanthraquinone-2′,1′(N)-benzacridone, a duller and more olive shade is obtained, and to approach a green it is best to attach a vattable residue which is essentially devoid of color. Indanthrene Green 4G containing a phthaloylquinazoline residue (formula shown at end of acridone section under commercial dyes, p. 505) is an example of such a combination.

Some typical examples where R = 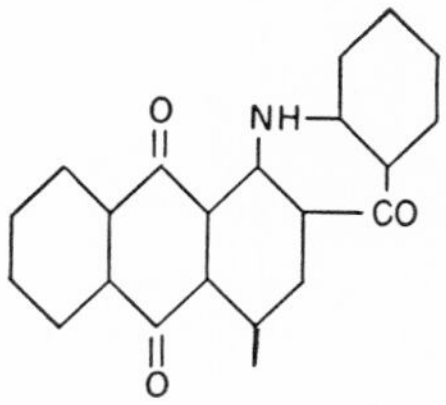 follow:

Example	Preparation	Shade
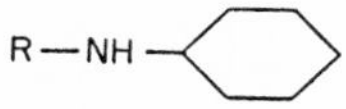 R—NH—⬡	From 6-aminoanthraqui-none-2',1'(N)-benza-cridone and bromobenzene	green[52]
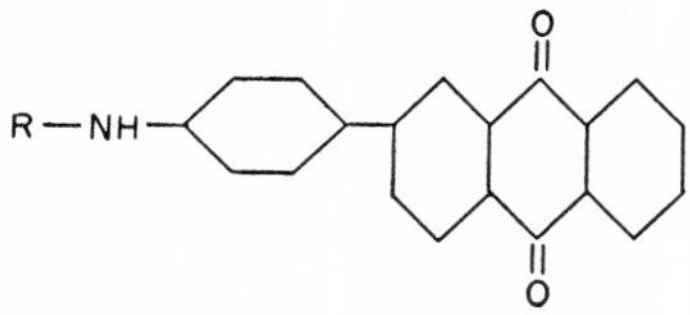 R—NH—⬡—(anthraquinone)	From 2-p-aminophenyl-anthraquinone and 6-chloroanthraquinone-2',1'(N)-benzacridone	olive[57]
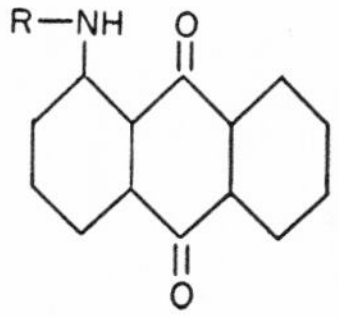 R—NH—(anthraquinone)	From 1-chloroanthraqui-none and 6-aminoan-thraquinone-2',1'(N)-benzacridone	gray[52]
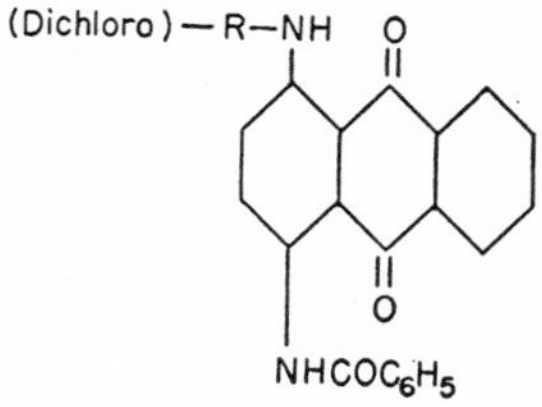 (Dichloro)—R—NH—(anthraquinone) NHCOC₆H₅	From 1-amino-4-benz-amidoanthraquinone and 6,10,12-trichloro-anthraquinone-2',1'(N)-benzacridone	gray[12]
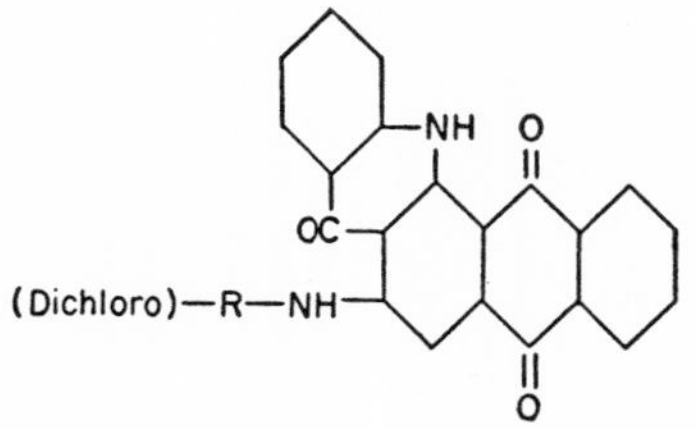 (Dichloro)—R—NH—(anthraquinone with NH/OC)	From 6-amino-10,12-di-chloroanthraquinone-2',1'(N)-benzacridone and 7-bromoanthraqui-none-2',1'(N)-benza-cridone	blue[29a, 38]

<table>
<tr><td>Example</td><td>Preparation</td><td>Shade</td></tr>
</table>

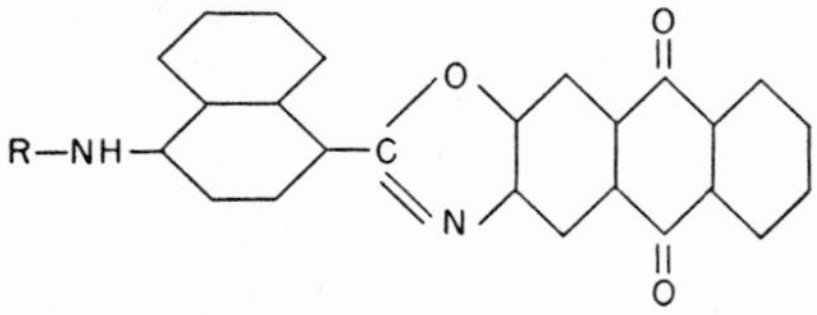	—	yellow-green[14]

Substituted Phthaloylacridones. Many dyes of complex and often indefi-nite structure have been prepared by substitution of the three isomeric phthaloylacridones. The following dark brown dye is an example of such a structure[9, 10].

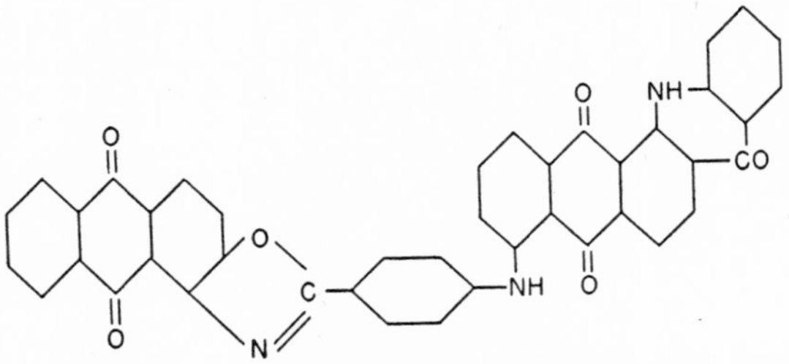

This product dyes cotton in brown shades. When the linkage is in the 6 po-sition of the anthraquinoneacridone nucleus greenish-olive shades are ob-tained. There are no dyes of outstanding interest in this series.

Acylaminoanthraquinone-2′,1′(N)-benzacridones. Acylation of amino-anthraquinone-2′,1′(N)-benzacridones has been carried out with a great variety of acylating agents. The products obtained from 1- and 4-amino-anthraquinone-2′,1′(N)-benzacridones are corinth or bordeaux in shade, while the 6-amino derivatives are grays, olives, greens, blues and violets. The acylated 7-amino and 9-amino derivatives are reddish in shade. As a class the products from 6-aminoanthraquinone-2′,1′(N)-benzacridone are the most important. One member, Indanthrene Printing Blue FG[54], a blue of clear shade which shows good printing properties and is fast to bleach, has had limited use. A few examples follow:

Compound	Preparation	Shade

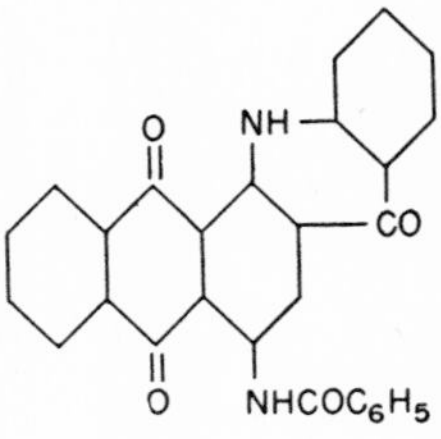

Acylation of 6-am-inoanthraquinone-2′,1′(N)-benzacri-done with benzoyl chloride   reddish-blue[52]

Compound	Preparation	Shade

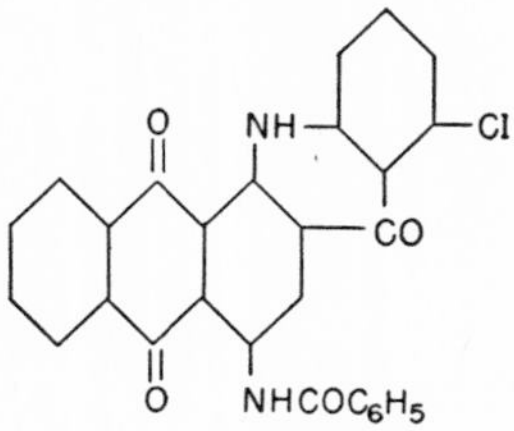

Acylation of 6-amino-9-chloroanthraqui-none-2',1'(N)-benz-acridone with ben-zoyl chloride — red-vio-let[3]

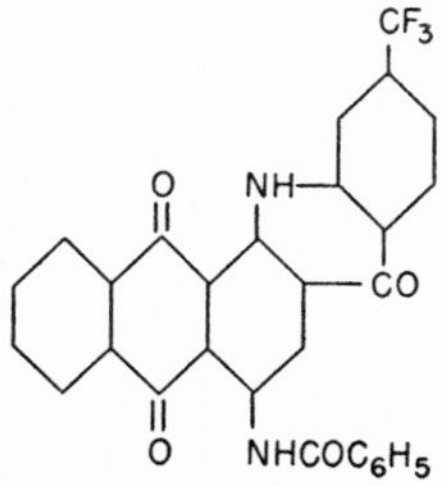

Acylation of 6-amino-11-trifluoromethyl-anthraquinone-2',1'(N)-benzacri-done with benzoyl chloride — blue[67]

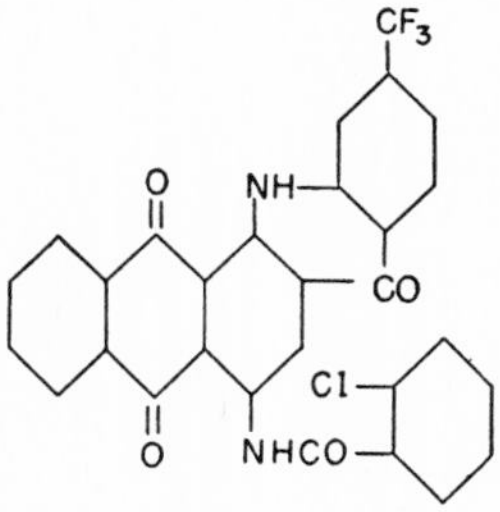

Acylation of 6-amino-11-trifluoromethyl-anthraquinone-2',1'-(N)-benzacridone with o-chloroben-zoyl chloride — violet[67]

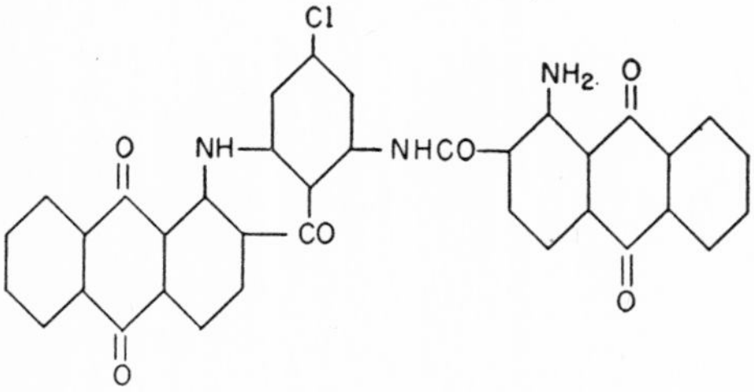

Acylation of 9-amino-11-chloroanthraqui-none-2',1'(N)-benz-acridone with 1-am-ino-2-anthraqui-nonecarbonyl chloride — crimson[4]

Anthraquinone-2',1'(N)-benzacridonecarboxamide Derivatives. These dyes are prepared by the condensation of acridonecarbonyl chlorides with amino compounds and as such contain the —CONH— group. They thus consti-tute products of colored acylating agents and colored amino compounds. The acid chloride group is usually in the 3, 10 or 11 positions and the dyes obtained from them are usually oranges and reds. Alkyl and arylamines have been employed, but to secure products of reasonable tinctorial value, amines of the anthraquinone types are usually used. They often contain heterocyclic systems, such as oxazoles, thiazoles, acridones or carbazoles.

Amine	Carbonyl Chloride from	Shade

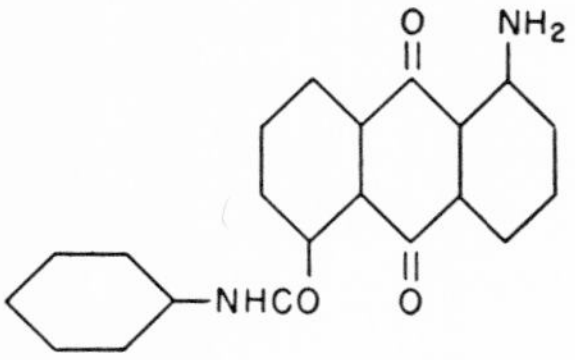

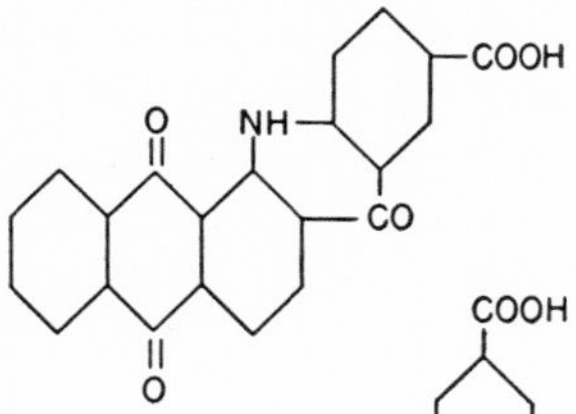

Orange [75]

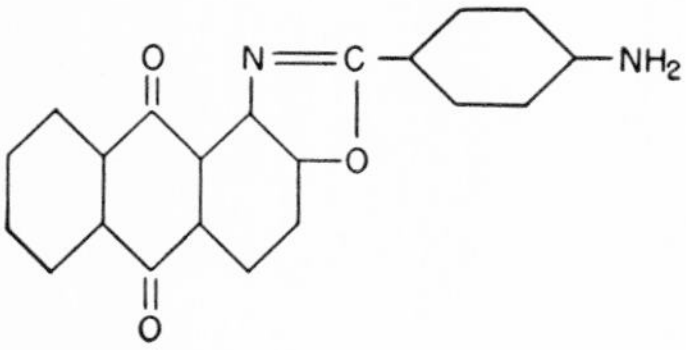

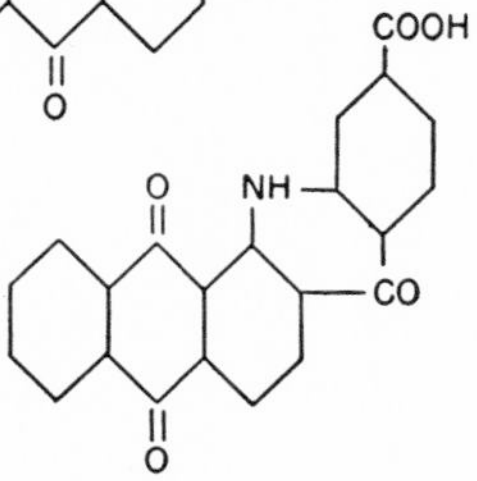

Red-Yellow [68]

Unsubstituted Di- and Triacridones. Di- and triacridones are known. The best known example of a diacridone type is

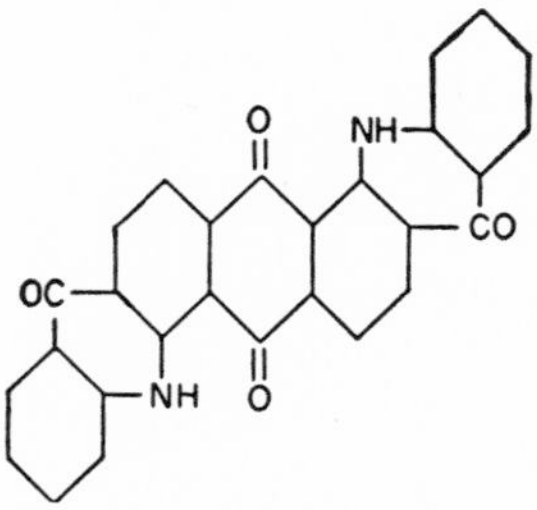

violet[23]

Substituted Diphthaloylacridones. Some diphthaloylacridones show the interesting property of reacting as alpha-gamma diketones; for example, reaction with hydrazine converts them to pyridazino derivatives, some of which are gray dyes of interesting shade, very fast to light but having poor washing fastness. An example of this reaction is the pyridazino derivative, a gray dye, obtained by the reaction of hydrazine on the corresponding acridone[29].

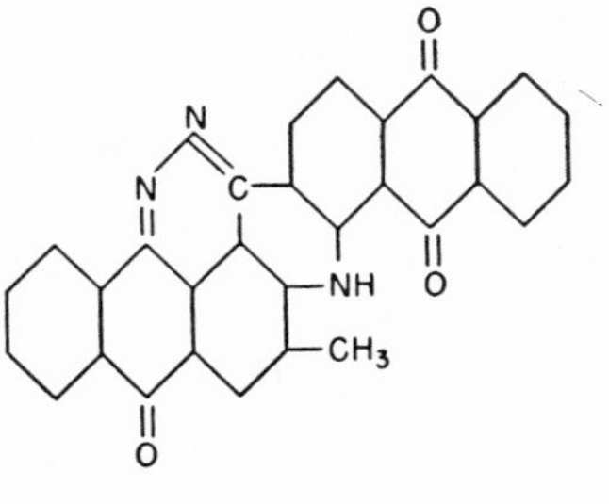

Substituted Diacridones. Diacridones lend themselves to halogenation just as the monoacridones do and numerous halogen derivatives are known in which the positions of the halogen atoms are indefinite[22, 46, 50]. A red-brown dye of complex type is prepared by the condensation of two moles of 1-amino-2-anthraquinonecarboxylic acid ethyl ester with one mole of dibromodibenzopyrenequinone[60], followed by halogenation. It is believed to have the basic nucleus shown below:

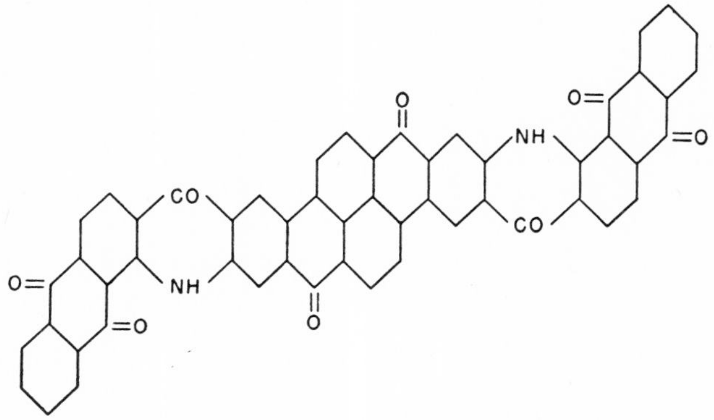

None of the substituted diacridones is of commercial interest.

Acridones Derived from Amines of Higher Coal Tar Hydrocarbons. Pyrene derivatives of acridone types are known. 3-Aminopyrene, when condensed with 1-chloro-2-anthraquinonecarboxylic acid and then cyclized with acetyl chloride in nitrobenzene[56], yields a green dye of the following structure:

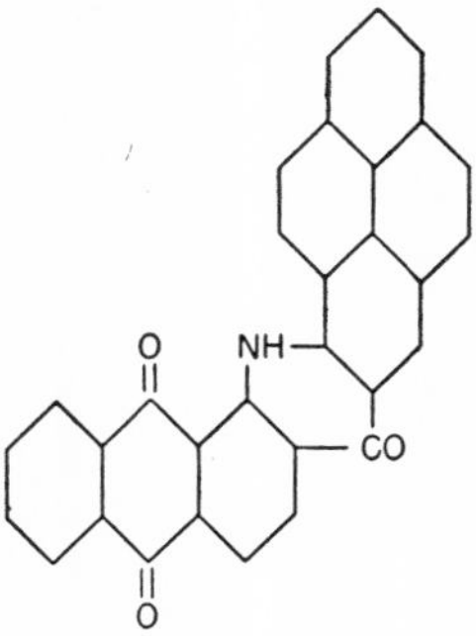

Numerous pyreneacridones are known which contain halogen or alkoxy groups. The shades of the dyes vary from green to olive to brown. Dyes containing perylene, chrysene and other hydrocarbon groups are also known. None of these dyes is of commercial interest.

Acridonecarbazole Dyes. A large number of anthrimidecarbazole type dyes containing a phthaloylacridone unit have been prepared. They are usually brown in shade. The conventional method is to ring-close the anthrimide to the carbazole by fusion with aluminum chloride or by treatment with concentrated sulfuric acid. The dyes are usually of large molecular weight and are of some commercial importance. Many of them contain benzamido groups. The following represent most of the kinds known:

Dye	Anthrimide	Shade

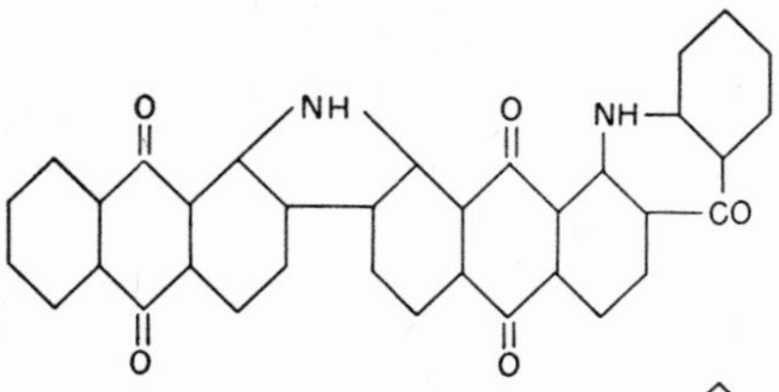

From 1-aminoanthraquinone-2′,1′(N)-benzacridone and 1-chloroanthraquinone

yellow-brown[19]

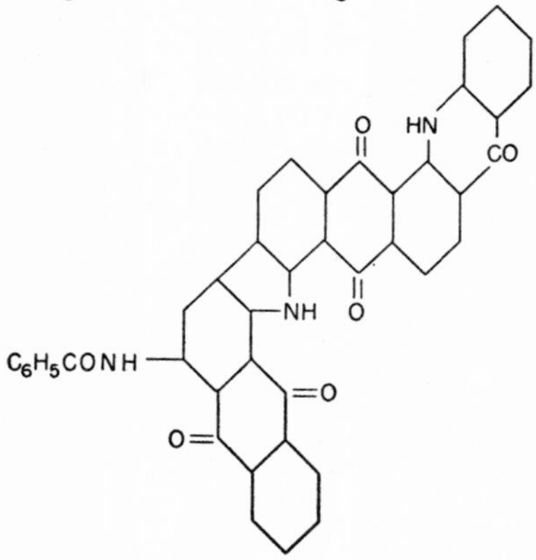

From 4-aminoanthraquinone-2′,1′(N)-benzacridone and 1-benzamido-4-chloroanthraquinone

reddish-brown[18]

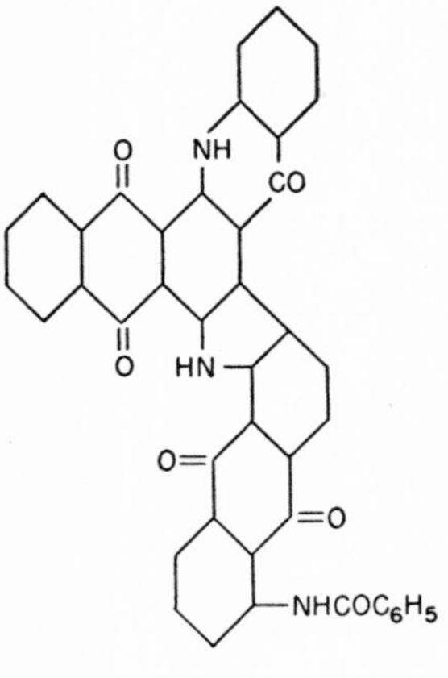

From 6-aminoanthraquinone-2′,1′(N)-benzacridone and 1-benzamido-5-chloroanthraquinone

olive-brown[63]

Dye	Anthrimide	Shade

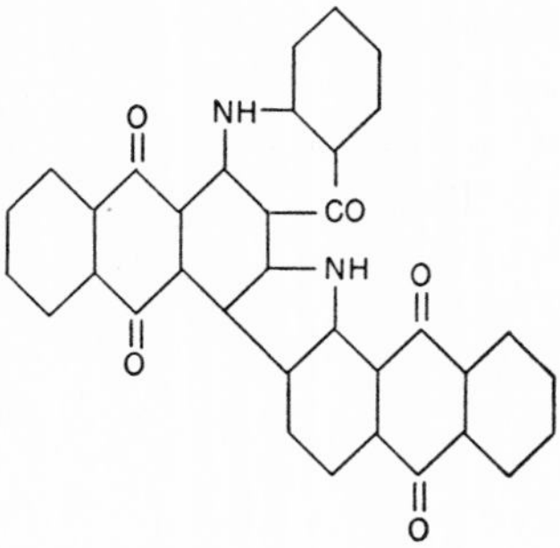

From 7-bromoanthraqui-none-2′,1′(N)-benzacri-done and 1-aminoanthra-quinone   brown[48]

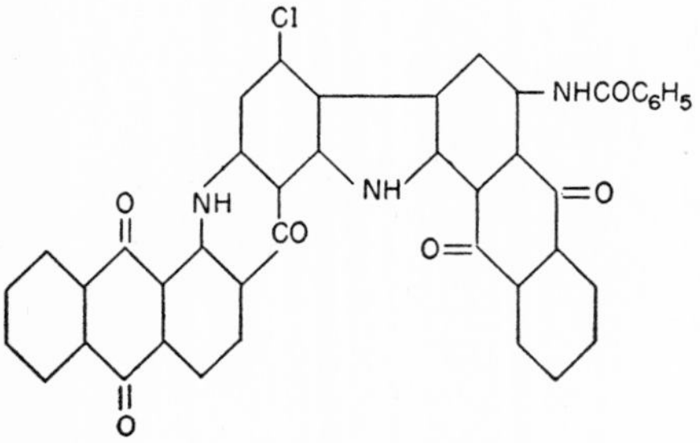

From 9,11-dichloroan-thraquinone-2′,1′(N)-benzacridone and 1-am-ino-4-benzamidoanthra-quinone   brownish-red[1]

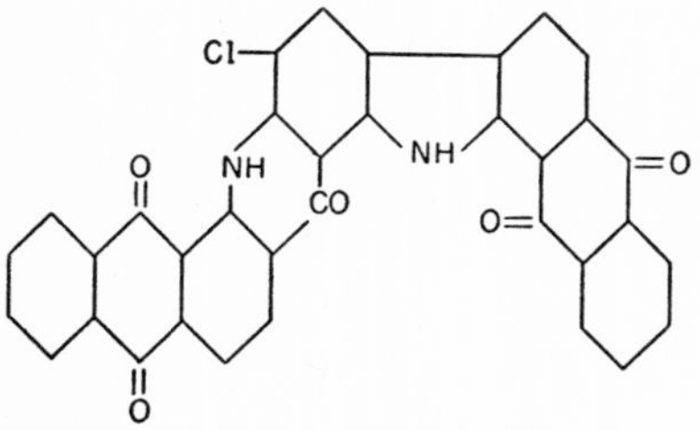

From 9,12-dichloroanthra-quinone-2′,1′(N)-benz-acridone and 1-amino-anthraquinone   red-brown[2]

Acridonecarbazoles from two or more acridone molecules and anthraquinone compounds

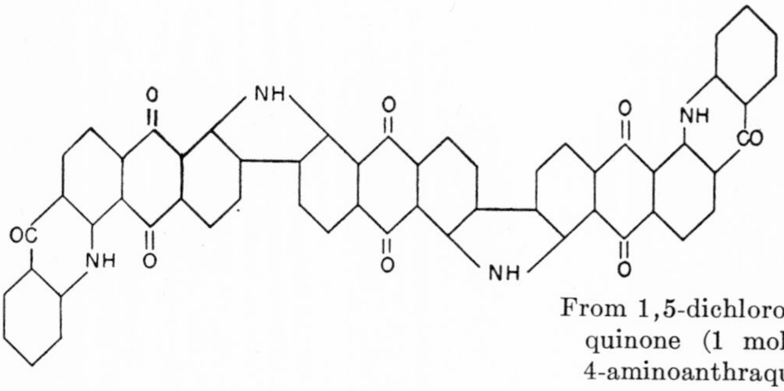

From 1,5-dichloroanthra-quinone (1 mole) and 4-aminoanthraquinone-2′,1′(N)-benzacridone (2 moles)   brown[19, 49]

Dye	Anthrimide	Shade

Acridonecarbazoles from two acridone molecules and an aromatic molecule

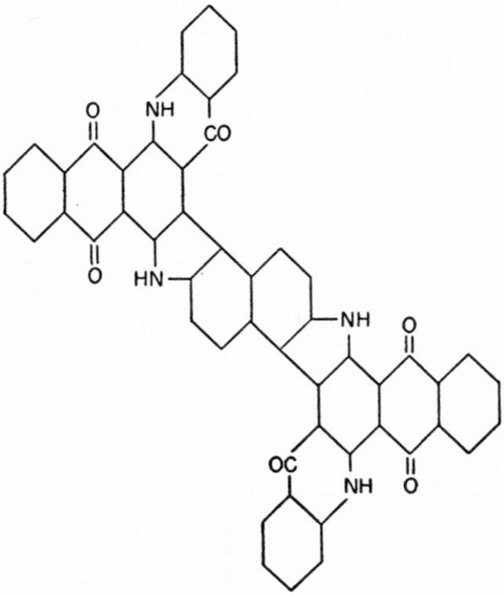

From 2,6-dibromonaph-   gray[13]
thalene (1 mole) and
6-aminoanthraquinone-
2′,1′(N)-benzacridone
(2 moles)

Acridonecarbazoles from diaminophthaloylacridones

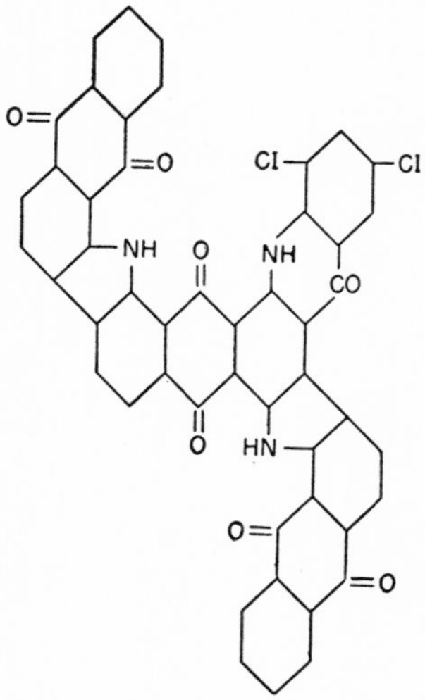

From 1,6-diamino-10,12-   yellow-
dichloroanthraquinone-   brown[11]
2′,1′(N)-benzacridone
(1 mole) and 1-chloro-
anthraquinone (2 moles)

Dye   Anthrimide   Shade

Phthaloylacridone-diphthaloylcarbazoles

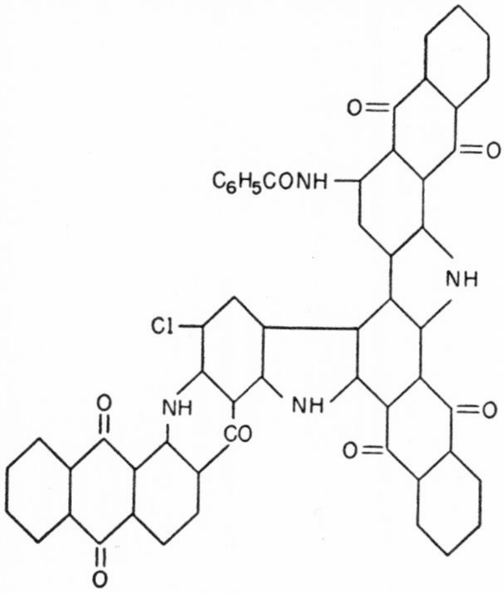

From 9,12-dichloroanthra- corinth[6]
quinone-2′,1′(N)-benz-
acridine, 1,4-diaminoan-
thraquinone and 1-ben-
zamido-4-chloroanthra-
quinone

Commercial Dyes of the Acridone Series.

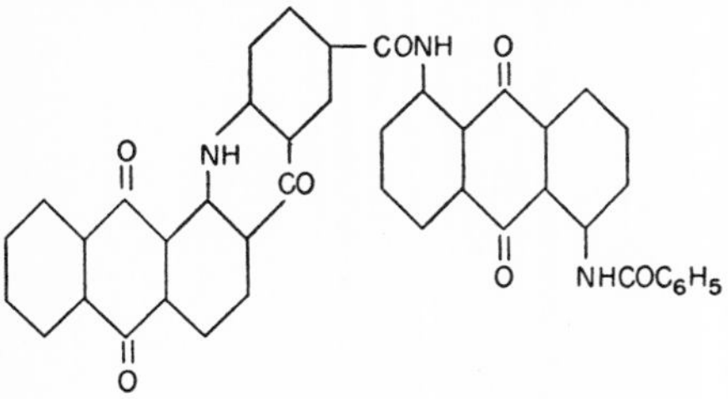

Indanthrene Orange 2R[75]
A light- and wash-fast specialty color

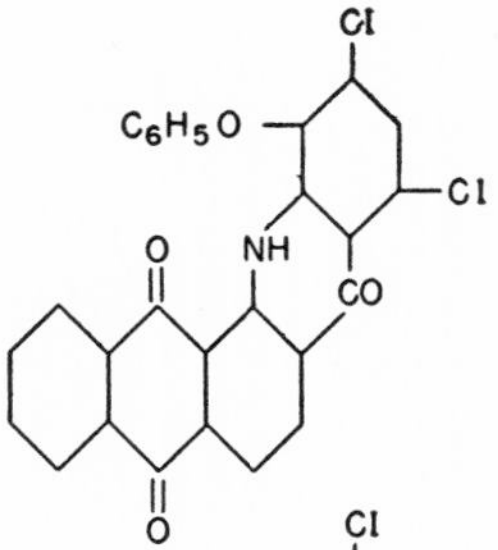

Indanthrene Brilliant Pink BL[7]
A bright, light- and wash-fast color

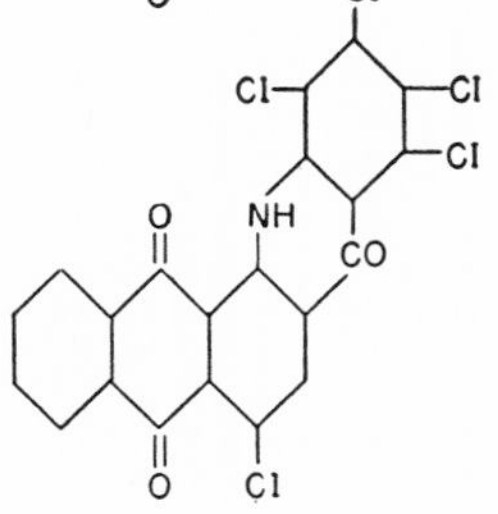

Indanthrene Brilliant Pink BBL[42]
Bluer than Indanthrene Brilliant Pink
   BL

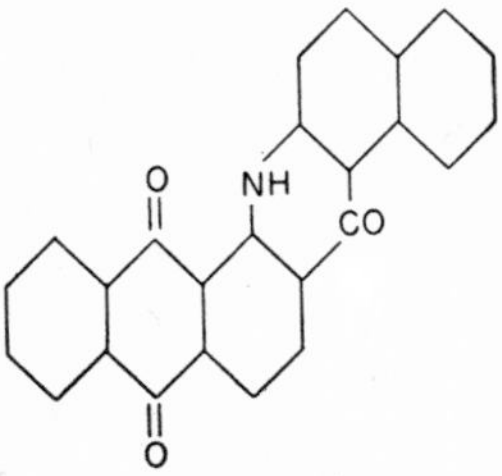

Indanthrene Red RK[25], CI 1162
A dull red of poor tinctorial strength,
very light-fast and widely used

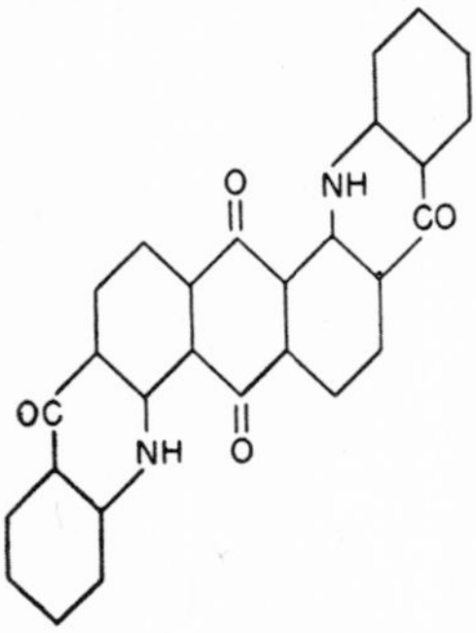

Indanthrene   Violet   BN   (FFBN)[23],
CI 1163
Used extensively as a shading color

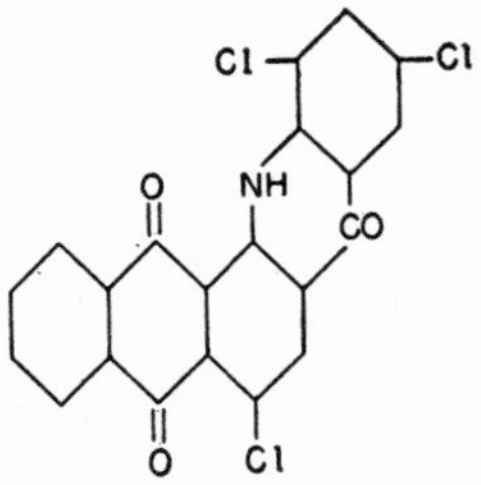

Indanthrene Red Violet RRK[74], CI 1161
A specialty shading color. Has poor
tinctorial strength and changes on
soaping

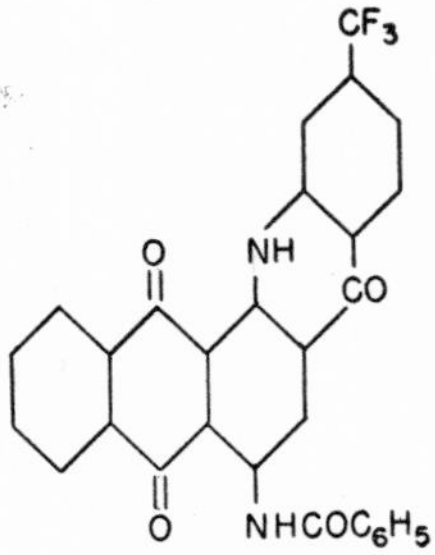

Indanthrene Printing Blue FG[67]
A chlorine-fast printing color of bright
shade. Has very poor dyeing properties

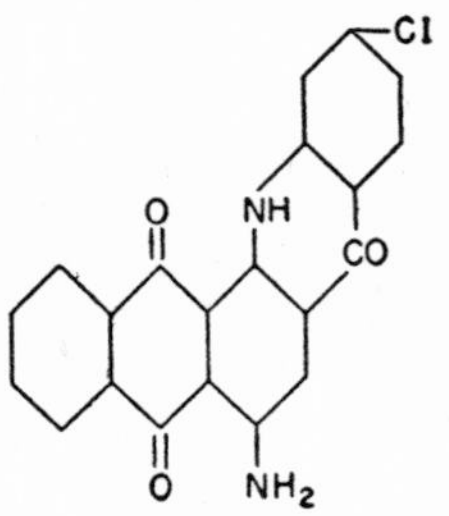

Indanthrene Turquoise Blue GK[8, 58, 71]
A dull and weak specialty color

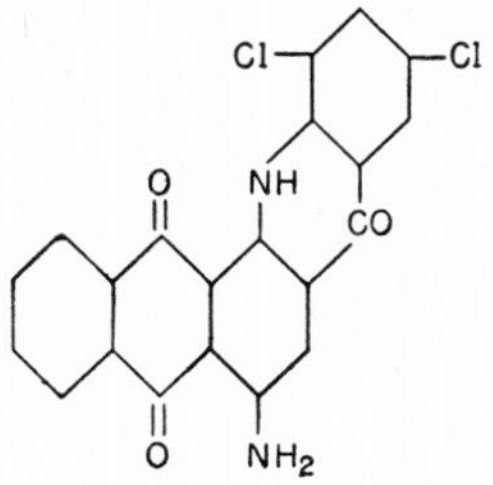

Indanthrene Turquoise Blue 3GK[71]
A dull and weak specialty color

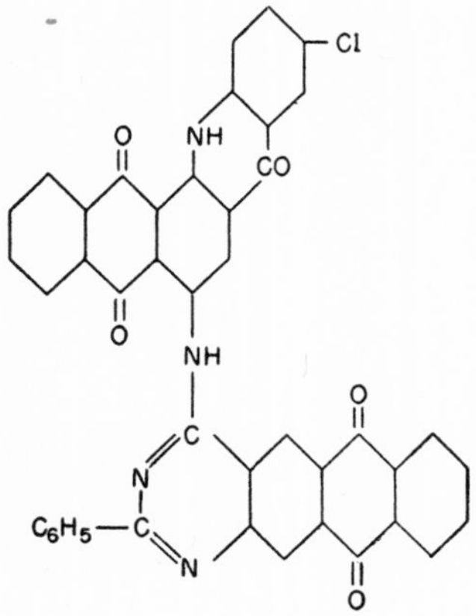

Indanthrene Green 4G[8]
Dyes in a yellowish-green shade which
can be matched with mixtures of vat
yellows and greens

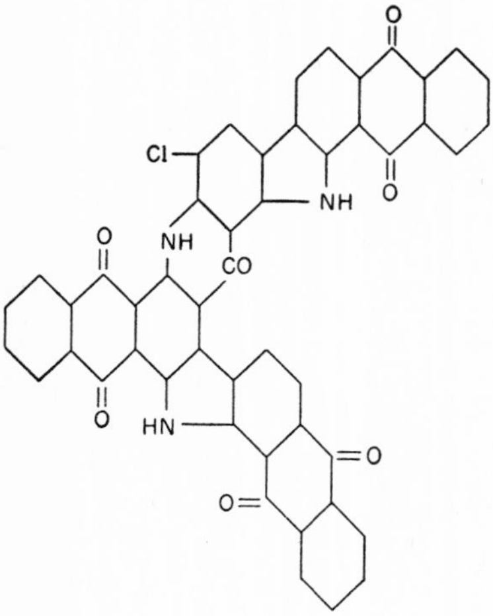

Indanthrene Khaki GR[5]
A specialty color with better dyeing
properties than the cheaper Indanthrene Khaki 2G, Pr. 122

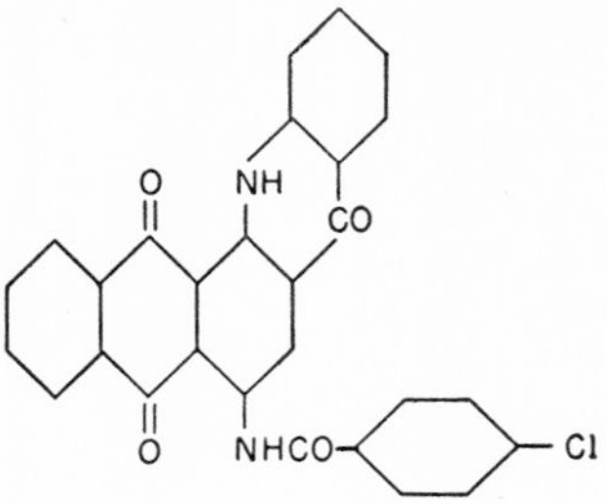

Indanthrene Blue CLN[52]
A specialty color suitable for high-temperature dyeing

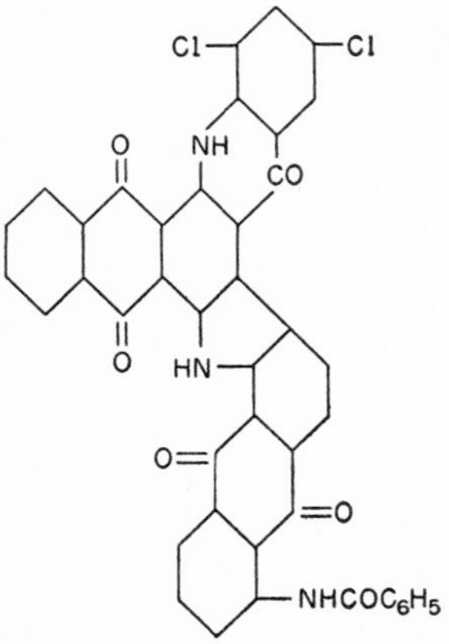

Indanthrene Brown 3GT[12] (anthrimide)
A yellow-brown specialty color

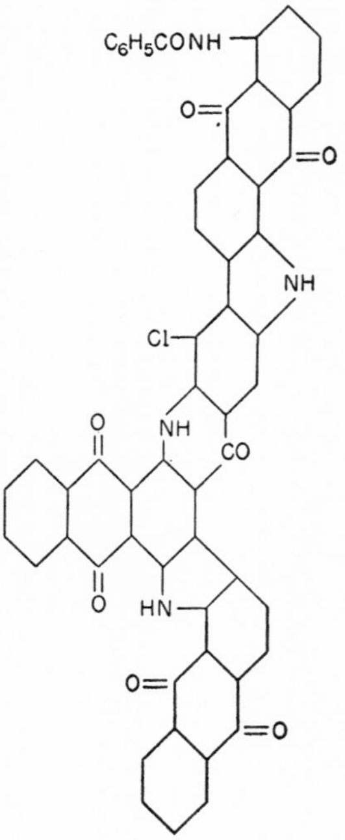

Indanthrene Brown NGR[54a]
A dark brown specialty color. (See Reference 5 for description of general method of preparation)

Literature Cited

1. Bauer, U.S. Patent 2,078,996 (1937).
2. ——, U.S. Patent 2,086,843 (1937).
3. ——, U.S. Patent 2,185,140 (1939).
4. ——, U.S. Patent 2,242,441 (1941).
5. ——, U.S. Patent 2,242,446 (1941).
6. —— and Bollweg, U.S. Patent 2,238,209 (1941).
7. ——, Hoyer and Bollweg, U.S. Patent 2,097,112 (1937).
8. Baumann and Schwechten, U.S. Patent 2,187,813 (1940).
9. —— and ——, U.S. Patent 2,245,520 (1941).
10. —— and ——, U.S. Patent 2,245,521 (1941).
11. Berliner, U.S. Patent 1,857,232 (1932).
12. ——, U.S. Patent 1,994,033 (1935).
13. British Patent 522,657 (1940).
14. British Patent 611,786 (1948).
15. Bruck, U.S. Patent 1,848,073 (1932).
16. Davidson and Shepherdson, U.S. Patent 1,901,288 (1933).
17. Dettwyler, U.S. Patent 2,111,091 (1938).
18. ——, U.S. Patent 2,373,817 (1945).
19. —— and Gubelmann, U.S. Patent 1,969,210 (1934).
20. German Patent 192,436 (1907).
21. German Patent 221,853 (1910).
22. German Patent 233,038 (1911).
23. German Patent 234,977 (1911).
24. German Patent 237,236 (1911).
25. German Patent 237,237 (1911).
26. German Patent 245,875 (1912).
27. German Patent 246,966 (1912).
28. German Patent 248,170 (1912).
29. German Patent 248,582 (1912).
29a. German Patent 254,096 (1912).
30. German Patent 256,626 (1913).
31. German Patent 269,800 (1914).
32. German Patent 269,850 (1914).
33. German Patent 272,297 (1914).
34. German Patent 275,671 (1914).
35. German Patent 283,724 (1915).
36. German Patent 444,984 (1927).
37. German Patent 450,921 (1927).
38. German Patent 485,568 (1929).
39. German Patent 501,746 (1930).
40. German Patent 517,277 (1931).
41. German Patent 523,626 (1931).
42. German Patent 525,666 (1931).
43. German Patent 534,658 (1931).
44. German Patent 551,885 (1932).
45. German Patent 558,489 (1932).
46. German Patent 560,236 (1932).
47. German Patent 572,215 (1933).
48. German Patent 630,788 (1936).

49. Gubelmann and Dettwyler, U.S. Patent 1,969,216 (1934).
50. —— and Goodrich, U.S. Patent 1,972,093 (1934).
51. Hessenland, U.S. Patent 998,772 (1911).
52. ——, U.S. Patent 1,002,270 (1911).
53. ——, U.S. Patent 1,023,847 (1912).
54. I. G. Farbenindustrie, BIOS 1493, p. 34 (PB 81611).
54a. ——, BIOS (Misc.) 20, Appendix 44 (PB 31004).
55. ——, PB 70339, frames 11740–7.
56. Kern, U.S. Patent 2,189,503 (1940).
57. Kramer, U.S. Patent 2,180,419 (1939).
58. Kunz, Berthold and Koeberle, U.S. Patent 2,005,321 (1935).
59. ——, Koeberle and Berthold, U.S. Patent 1,924,445 (1933).
60. ——, —— and ——, U.S. Patent 1,924,446 (1933).
61. Luettringhaus, U.S. Patent 1,010,930 (1911).
62. ——, U.S. Patent 1,011,068 (1911).
63. Mieg and Baumann, U.S. Patent 1,804,538 (1931).
64. Nawiasky, Bauer and Krauch, U.S. Patent Reissue 19,437 (1935).
65. Neresheimer, U.S. Patent 1,052,507 (1913).
65a. ——, U.S. Patent 1,207,981 (1916).
65b. Schetelig, U.S. Patent 1,568,627 (1926).
66. Schlichenmaier and Berlin, U.S. Patent 2,143,717 (1939).
67. —— and ——, U.S. Patent 2,204,232 (1940).
68. Schlichting, U.S. Patent 2,168,174 (1939).
69. Ullmann, *Ber.*, **43,** 536 (1910).
70. ——, U.S. Patent 961,047 (1910).
71. ——, U.S. Patent 1,850,482 (1932).
72. —— and Conzetti, *Ber.*, **53,** 836 (1920).
73. —— and Eiser, *ibid.*, **49,** 2154 (1916).
74. Wolff, U.S. Patent 1,133,081 (1915).
75. Wuertz, U.S. Patent 1,989,904 (1935).
76. —— and Dettwyler, U.S. Patent 2,100,532 (1937).
77. Zerweck, U.S. Patent 1,785,801 (1930).

ANTHRAPYRIMIDINES

Melvin A. Perkins

The only known vat colors of the pyrimidine type are yellows and yellowish-greens. The work of Kunz pointed to the desirability of obtaining vat dyes containing nitrogen 6-membered rings [to avoid "tendering"[5]] and this was instrumental in leading to the discovery of such products in the pyrimidine and quinazoline series. All of these cases deal with a 6-membered ring containing two nitrogen atoms separated by a single carbon atom. A few have achieved some practical importance.

Two well-known yellows were discovered which are derivatives of 1,9-

anthrapyrimidine (7H-dibenzo[de,h]quinazolin-7-one) of the following constitution:

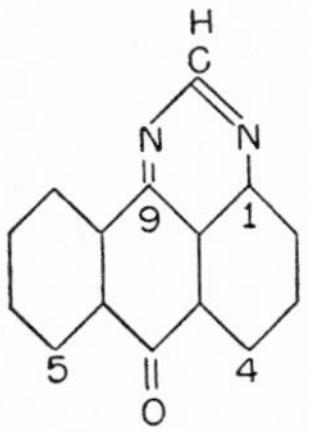

Contrary to the usual nonvattability of 1,9-anthraquinone heterocycles, it was observed that this particular anthrapyrimidine nucleus was vattable with considerable ease and a great deal of work has been done on the different derivatives of this system[5]. Subjects of a high percentage of this work are the amino-1,9-anthrapyrimidines containing the NH_2 group in either the 4 or 5 position as indicated on the above formula. While 4-amino-anthrapyrimidine itself is very difficult to condense with halogen compounds, the 5 isomer condenses readily in the same fashion as 1-aminoanthraquinone and simple derivatives thereof. Both the 4- and the 5-amino compounds are readily acylated, however, and give easily vattable yellow dyes, the 4-acylamino derivatives being very greenish in shade and more so than the 5 isomer. Perhaps the most important single dye of this class is Indanthrene Yellow 4GK which has the following structure[4, 5]:

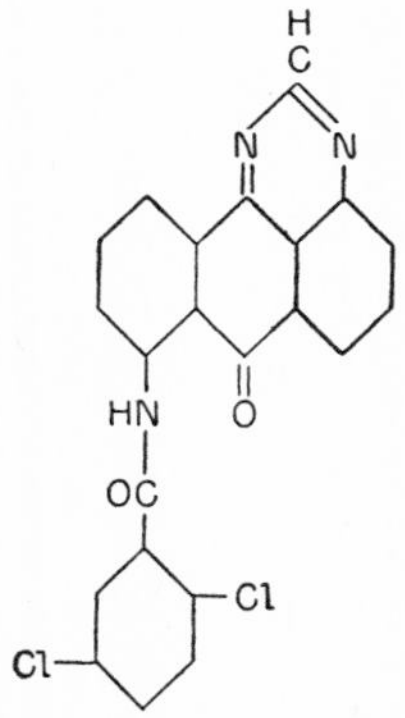

This dye is obtained by acylating 5-amino-1,9-anthrapyrimidine with 2,5-dichlorobenzoyl chloride. The aminoanthrapyrimidine can be obtained by either of two methods: (a) condensing 1,5-diaminoanthraquinone with formamide in nitrobenzene in the presence of copper compounds; this method gives a 50 to 60 per cent of theory yield of pure product, (b) sulfonating 1,5-diaminoanthraquinone to give 1,5-diamino-2-anthraquinonesulfonic acid;

this is heated with formamide in nitrobenzene in the presence of ammonium chloride to give an essentially quantitative yield of 5-amino-1,9-anthrapyrimidine-2-sulfonic acid which is desulfonated by treatment with sodium hydrosulfite[3]. Other isomeric aminoanthrapyrimidines (the 2-, 3-, 6-, 7- and 8-amino compounds) have been prepared in a similar manner but have found no application in vat dye chemistry[7].

4-Amino-1,9-anthrapyrimidine is readily obtained in good yield by condensing 1,4-diaminoanthraquinone with formamide in phenol solution[2, 8]. Acylation of this material with *p*-chlorobenzoyl chloride gives the dye known as Indanthrene Yellow 7GK[2], a very greenish shade of yellow especially adapted for producing chartreuse and other yellowish-green shades when used in combination with vat greens or blues. Both of these anthrapyrimidine yellows are said to be nontendering.

A yellowish-green of the pyrimidine type, having a complex structure not obviously related to the yellow discussed above, is Indanthrene Green 4G, ordinarily referred to as a quinazoline derivative[1, 6]. It is at the same time an acridone (see pages 494 and 505). This product has the following configuration:

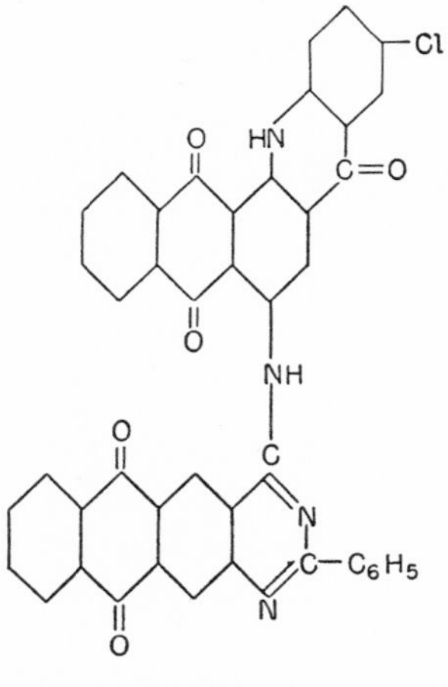

The synthesis of the acridone part of this molecule follows normal methods as discussed under the section on acridones and will not be repeated here. The synthesis of the quinazoline begins with 3-chloro-2-anthraquinonecarboxylic acid, which is obtained by sulfuric acid ring-closure of 2'-chloro-2,4'-carbonyldibenzoic acid. This material is then aminated by 20 per cent NH_3 in the presence of copper power (30 to 40 atm. pressure) to give 3-amino-2-anthraquinonecarboxylic acid, which is benzoylated and ring-closed with benzoic acid in 20 per cent oleum to form the phenyl-*m*-oxazinone. Treatment with ammonia and enolization leads to 4-hydroxy-2-phenylnaphtho[2,3-g]quinazoline-6,11-dione, which is converted to the corresponding 4-chloro compound with phosphorus pentachloride in nitrobenzene. This chloro derivative is then condensed with 6-amino-10-chloroanthraquinone-2′,1′(N)-benzacridone (6-amino-10-chloronaphth-2,3-c]acridine-5,8,14(13H)-trione) to give the final dye, p-toluenesulfonic acid being used as catalyst for the condensation. This product dyes in considerably more yellowish shade than does dimethoxydibenzanthrone and is said to have very good fastness properties including lightfastness.

Literature Cited

1. Baumann and Schwechten, U.S. Patent 2,187,813 (1940).
2. I. G. Farbenindustrie, BIOS 987, pp. 88–93 (PB 75860).
3. ——, *ibid.*, p. 94.
4. ——, *ibid.*, pp. 95–98.
5. ——, *ibid.*, pp. 172–8.
6. ——, BIOS 1493, pp. 19–22 (PB 81611).
7. Kunz and Koeberle, U.S. Patent 2,040,857 (1936).
8. —— and ——, U.S. Patent 2,040,858 (1936).

PYRAZINES

Melvin A. Perkins

In 1938 there was described a class of pyrazinoanthraquinones which led to bright-shade vat dyes upon condensation with simple aromatic amines[3]. The starting material for this class of compounds was 1,2-diaminoanthraquinone, obtainable in 56 per cent yield by amination of 1-amino-2-anthraquinonesulfonic acid under pressure in the presence of a small amount of nitrobenzene and arsenic acid[1]. This material was then condensed with oxalic acid to give a dihydroxy-1,2-pyrazinoanthraquinone (2,3-dihydroxy-naphtho[2,3-f]quinoxaline-7,12-dione) which can be condensed with aromatic amines such as m-toluidine, either directly in the presence of zinc chloride, or after conversion to an intermediate compound containing one atom of chlorine[2]. The entire scheme is illustrated by the following:

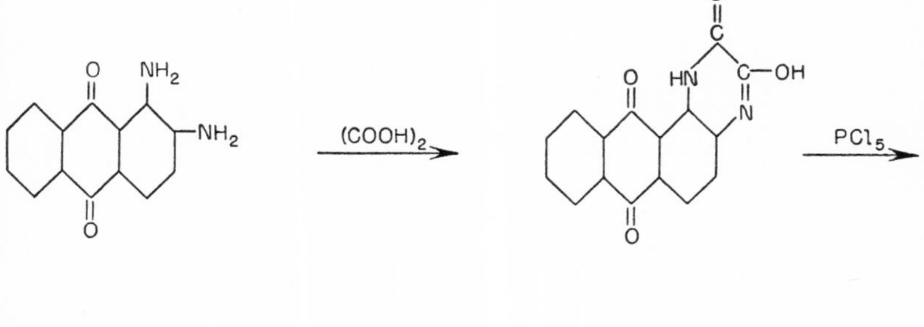

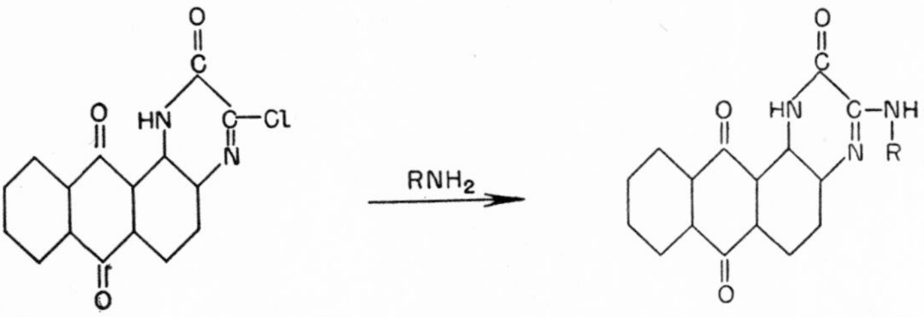

The shades of the resulting dyes vary over a considerable range, being peculiarly sensitive to small changes in the nature of the aromatic amine employed in the final condensation. Still more particularly, substitution in the meta position in the benzene ring of the aromatic amine appears to be a determining factor in achieving good brightness and fastness properties. Even among such products, shades varying all the way from yellow to violet are obtainable. Trifluoromethyl-substituted anilines give the lightest shades while methoxy- and halogen-substituted ones give darker shades.

Perhaps the most important product from a commercial standpoint is the *m*-toluidine product which is known as Indanthrene Brilliant Scarlet RK[2]. This is a dye of unusual brightness when properly developed by soaping, a shade change which is probably connected with growth of crystals or aggregates. This dye is outstanding in that it combines brilliance of shade with high lightfastness and good printing properties. This is believed to be the only important pyrazinoanthraquinone derivative which has been marketed as a vat dye thus far.

Literature Cited

1. I. G. Farbenindustrie, BIOS 987, pp. 78–80 (PB 75860).
2. ——, *ibid.*, pp. 81–85.
3. Neresheimer, Ruppel and Eichholz, U.S. Patent 2,123,251 (1938).

ANTHRAQUINONEAZINES

Myron S. Whelen

The anthraquinoneazines are an important class of vat colors, as it is in this group that some of the most extensively used vat colors are found. There are two main types of interest. The 1,4-diazines, represented by indanthrone, are used in large volume, while the *s*-triazines, cyanuric acid derivatives, are used to a lesser degree. These two types are discussed in order.

Indanthrone

Indanthrone, N,N'-dihydro-1,2:2',1'-anthraquinoneazine, and its derivatives are the most important dyes of the 1,4-diazine type. Discovered by René Bohn in 1901[14], indanthrone, CI 1106, was the first vat dye of the anthraquinone series and stimulated great interest in the development of fast dyes, particularly of the anthraquinone type. Indanthrone is the source of the principal blue vat dyes. Most of the fundamental work relative to the elucidation of its structure and method of formation was carried out in the early part of the century by Roland Scholl[31] and his collaborators. The Bayer Company proved its structure by synthesis by condensing 1-amino-2-bromoanthraquinone with itself[15].

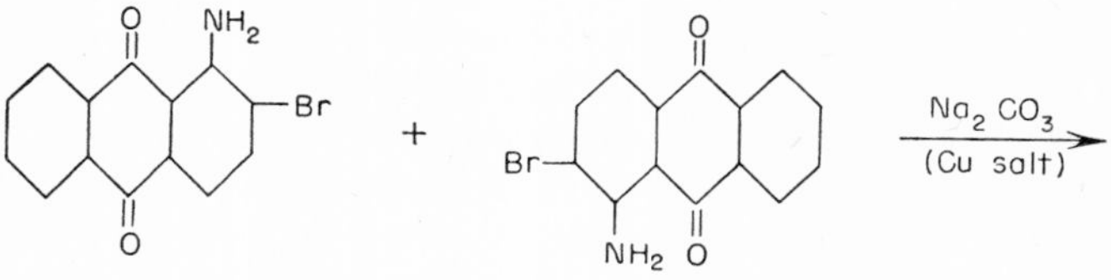

1- Amino-2- bromoanthraquinone

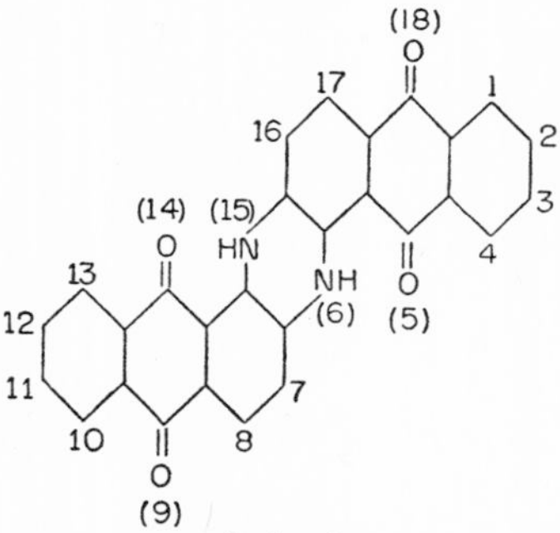

Indanthrone
(6,15-dihydro-5,9,14,18-anthrazinetetrone)

René Bohn, in his original synthesis of indanthrone, prepared it by the caustic potash fusion of 2-aminoanthraquinone. Flavanthrone (5,13-didehydro-8,16-flavanthrinedione) and other impurities were formed with it. If this fusion is carried out in the presence of an oxidizing agent such as potassium chlorate, indanthrone is formed together with indefinite impurities but no flavanthrone is obtained. If the fusion is carried out in the presence of a reducing agent or at high temperatures, flavanthrone is formed. Indanthrone is produced commercially by the fusion of 2-aminoanthraquinone, usually with a mixture of sodium and potassium hydroxides and an oxidizing agent at about 200 to 220°C[5]. Other ingredients are often added to assist the fusion and to increase the yield of indanthrone[4, 43]. The product, obtained in the form of a leuco body, is impure and it may be purified by allowing the leuco sodium salt of the indanthrone to crystallize from the vat of the crude dye, which is then filtered[44]. The leuco body so obtained is oxidized to the dye by air, oxygen or alkaline oxidizing agents. The yield of pure indanthrone under the most favorable conditions is of the order of 55 per cent. The dye at this stage is usually pure enough for most purposes, but further purification can be accomplished by crystallizing it as a sulfate from 85 per cent sulfuric acid[23].

Indanthrone as a vat dye is now much less important commercially than in former years. This is due to its objectionable sensitivity to bleaching, and to overcome this chlorination is used. Indanthrone is either chlorinated directly[18] or a dichloro derivative is prepared by synthesis[22]. Contrary to some early literature statements, chlorination of indanthrone by all practical methods causes the chlorine atoms first to enter the two positions which are adjacent to the azine nitrogen atoms, the 7,16 positions. The synthetic preparation of 7,16-dichloroindanthrone consists either of condensing 2-amino-1,3-dibromoanthraquinone with itself to produce 7,16-dibromoindanthrone whose bromine atoms are then replaced by chlorine[12], or of direct condensation of 2-amino-1-bromo-3-chloro(or 1,3-dichloro)anthraquinone with itself[22, 42], as illustrated:

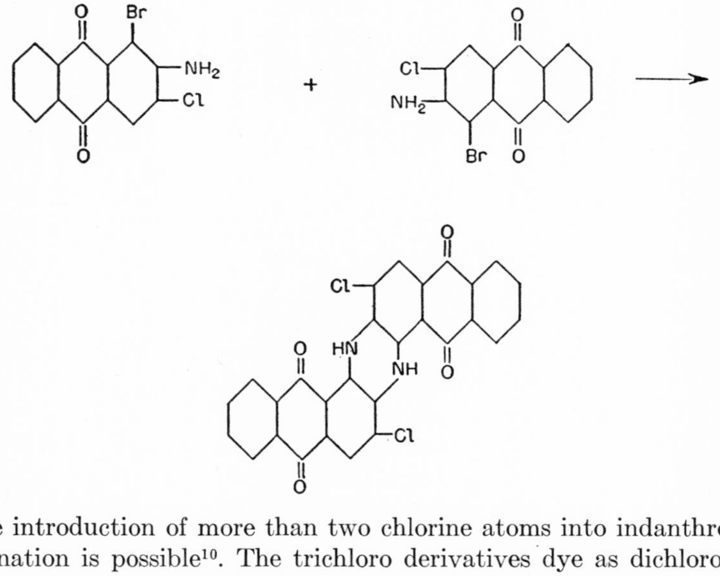

The introduction of more than two chlorine atoms into indanthrone by chlorination is possible[10]. The trichloro derivatives dye as dichloroindanthrone, due to loss (during vatting) of those chlorine atoms not in the 7,16 positions. Monochloroindanthrone is difficult to prepare but it can be obtained by the condensation of 2-amino-1-bromo-3-chloroanthraquinone with

2-amino-1-bromoanthraquinone in molecular proportions followed by exhaustive purification. Chlorination of indanthrone by the usual methods until the product analyzes for one chlorine atom produces a mixture consisting mostly of 7,16-dichloroindanthrone and unchanged indanthrone together with some monochloro- and trichloroindanthrones.

Indanthrone and its halo derivatives dye cotton from a sodium hydroxide-sodium hydrosulfite vat in attractive blue shades. They are very strong tinctorially and the dyeings exhibit excellent light- and washfastness. Bleachfastness of indanthrone is rather poor but its halogen derivatives, particularly the 7,16-dibromo and 7,16-dichloro ones, are improved in this respect. The indanthrone colors are used primarily for dyeing purposes, but some printing of the so-called monochloro derivative is carried out. They are produced at reasonable cost and sold in large volume, as nearly all blues of the anthraquinone series are indanthrones. Some other blue anthraquinone vat dyes have been designed with properties to overcome the moderately poor bleachfastness or lack of printing quality exhibited by them, but these are used in only a limited way, and consumption of the indanthrone colors remains high because of their outstanding brilliance and low cost.

Theories for the Formation of Indanthrone in the Oxidizing Caustic Fusion of 2-Aminoanthraquinone. Several theories have been set forth to explain the formation of indanthrone in the oxidizing caustic alkali fusion of 2-aminoanthraquinone. Scholl and Eberle[34] considered that the reaction passed through an intermediate stage wherein dihydro-2-amino-1,2'-dianthraquinonylamine was formed.

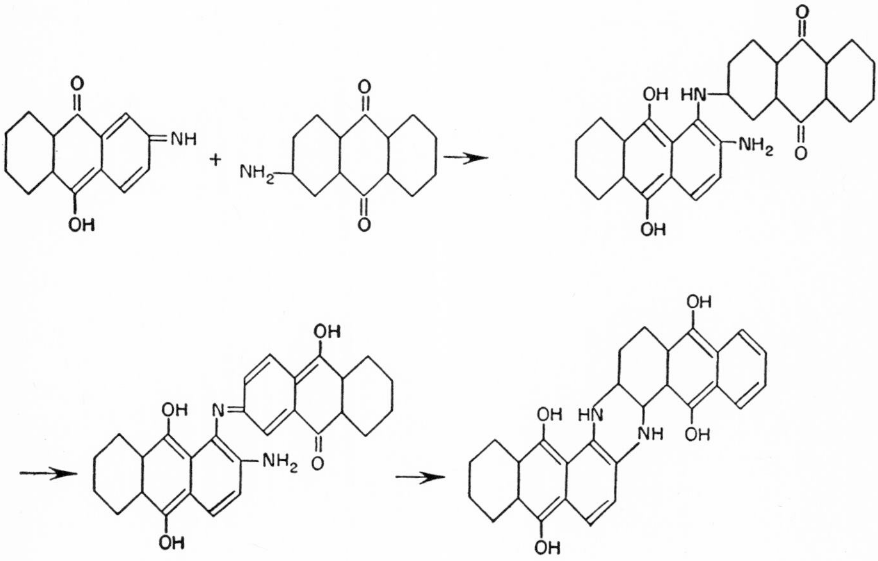

Scholl and Eberle also considered that the formation of indanthrone in the oxidizing fusion might proceed by the formation of 2,2'-hydrazodianthraquinone which would undergo an ortho semidine rearrangement to produce 2-amino-1,2'-iminodianthraquinone which would be oxidized to indanthrone during the course of the reaction. However, Scholl and Eberle[35] were unable to prepare 2,2'-hydrazodianthraquinone to prove this theory. This theory called for a semidine rearrangement under alkaline conditions which in the light of present day knowledge appears extremely improbable.

It was later shown by Lulek[25] that the desired intermediate, 2,2'-hydrazodianthraquinone, could be obtained from 2,2'-azodianthraquinone by reducing the latter with ammonium sulfide in alcohol. This product rearranged in 70 per cent sulfuric acid to a mixture of indanthrone and flavanthrone, a one-sided semidine rearrangement producing indanthrone through 2-amino-1,2'-iminodianthraquinone and the double one producing flavanthrone through 2,2'-diamino-1,1'-bianthraquinone. Lulek further showed that 2,2'-hydrazodianthraquinone in which the 1,1' positions are occupied cannot yield either indanthrone or flavanthrone because the semidine rearrangement is blocked.

The study and review of the mode of formation of indanthrone from 2-aminoanthraquinone and potassium hydroxide has been made more recently by Bradley and Leete[6]. They consider "that 2-aminoanthraquinone yields the 2-anthraquinonylamine anion, which then replaces hydrogen in another molecule of 2-aminoanthraquinone forming 2-amino-1,2'-dianthraquinonylamine (2-amino-1,2'-iminodianthraquinone)." Hydrogen is dissociated from the amino group and two anions condense to indanthrone. These authors consider that the negative ion (A) is resonance stabilized as a result of the effect of the structure (B) which explains why a proton is repulsed from 2-aminoanthraquinone and why the condensation to indanthrone occurs.

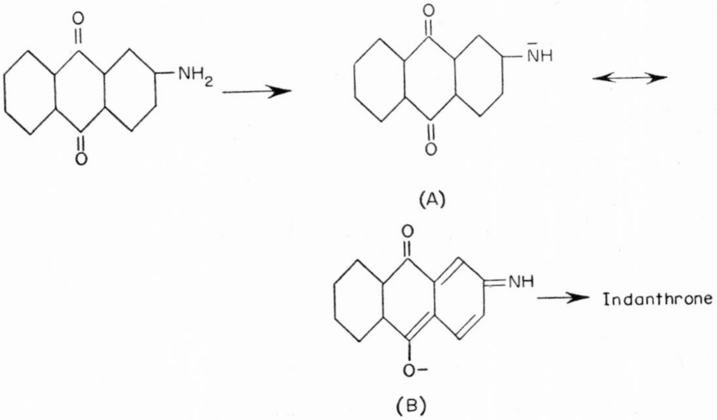

(A)

(B)

Reduction and Oxidation Products of Indanthrone. Indanthrone is the dihydroazine form (blue) which is converted by oxidation, for example, by nitric acid, to the azine form (yellow), which readily reverts to the blue dihydroazine by reduction, e.g., vatting with two equivalents of sodium hydroxide and sodium hydrosulfite. Despite the fact that indanthrone is very stable on the fiber, many changes can occur to the leuco compound during the dyeing process. These are associated with the reduction which must be controlled very carefully. Vatting at temperatures below 60°C produces a blue vat; at more elevated temperatures with an excess of sodium hydroxide and sodium hydrosulfite, a brown vat is obtained. The N-methyl derivative of indanthrone vats at much lower temperature (35°C) and gives a brown vat. These are just two examples of numerous anomalies that require explanation. In considering the reduction products of the indanthrone molecule, it must be borne in mind that it has four keto groups and should, by analogy with other anthraquinone dyes, be readily vattable. Three structures have been postulated to explain the reduction products of indanthrone, none of which is entirely satisfactory.

Scholl[38] originally suggested the following reduction products.

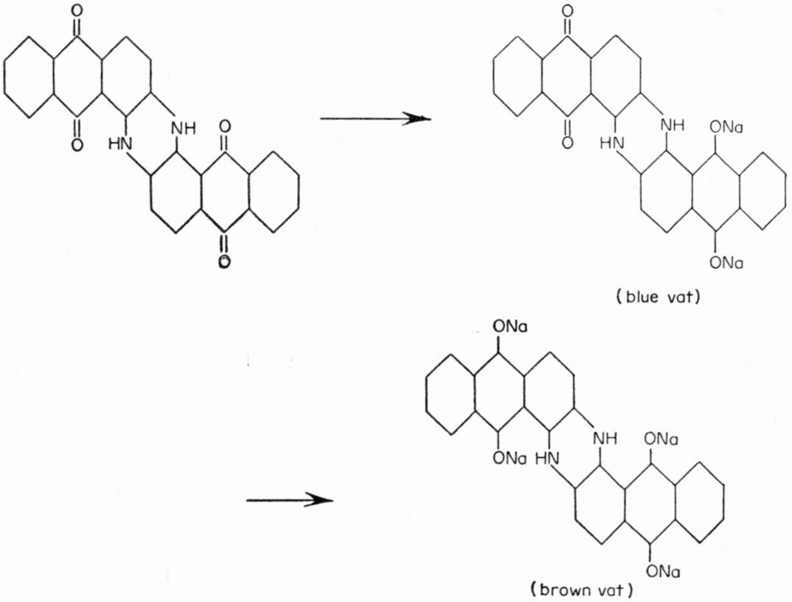

(blue vat)

(brown vat)

This formulation simply shows two keto groups reduced in one case and all four in the other. It does not explain the brown vat of N-methylindanthrone obtained at low temperature.

The reduction of indanthrone beyond the leuco stage is possible and is described by Scholl[32].

A polar formula for indanthrone was suggested by Kuhn[24] and enlarged on by Brassard[7].

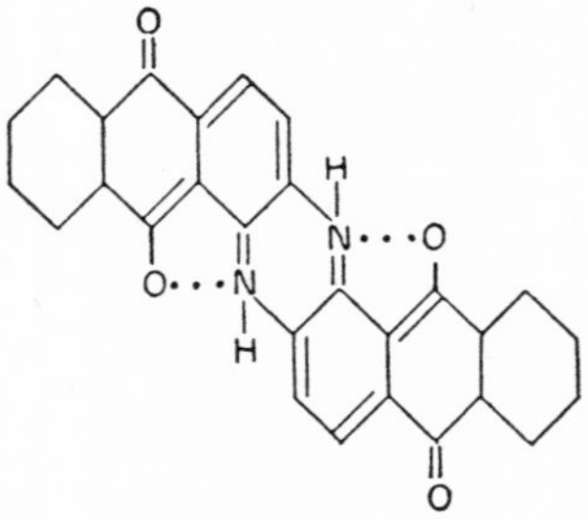

It was devised to explain the fact that only two atoms of hydrogen are required to produce the normal blue vat and consequently two of the four keto groups are unaltered.

Gill and Stonehill[19] prefer a hydrogen-bonded structure acting as a resonance hybrid and consider the blue color of the vat due to this.

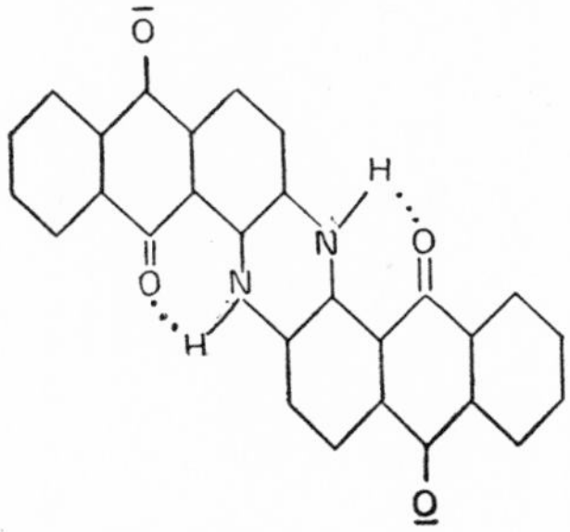

The inner carbonyl groups are regarded as being not truly quinoid in character, being modified by hydrogen bonding, and hence the molecule requires only two equivalents of a reducing agent to give the normal blue vat.

From a study of the leuco sulfuric esters of indanthrone it becomes apparent that the azine form of indanthrone is the stable form and the dihydroazine form the unstable form. By referring the reduction products to the azine form, an explanation of the many anomalies can be made. On this basis the blue vat, which is the result of indanthrone taking up only two hydrogen atoms, is a completely reduced system in respect to the carbonyl groups and the molecule can be considered to be in a state of reduction equivalent to four equivalents of hydrogen with respect to the basic substance diphthaloylphenazine. Hydrogen bonding stabilizes the molecule in the doubly reduced state.

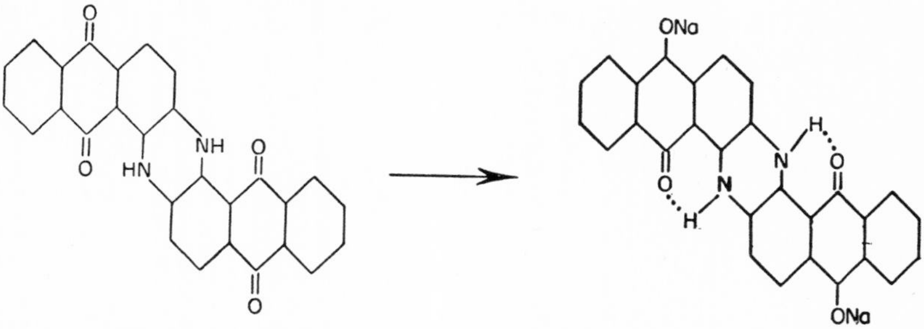

With N,N'-dimethylindanthrone, where hydrogen bonding is not possible, azine formation cannot take place. Here all four carbonyl groups become reduced in normal manner in the following formula and the vat is brown rather than blue:

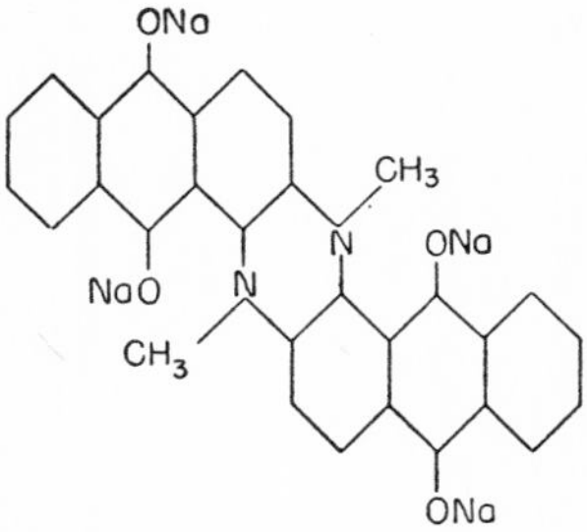

It is evident here that vatting arises in two separate anthraquinone nuclei, while in the previous example vatting takes place through a different type of conjugated system and hence the difference in color of the respective vats.

The subject of the reduction products of indanthrone and its derivatives is admittedly a complex one, a complete portrayal of which is beyond the scope of this discussion. For those further interested the following additional literature will be helpful[2, 3, 7, 9, 19, 20, 24, 26, 27, 29, 33, 36, 37].

Derivatives of Indanthrone. Outside of the previously described chlorine compounds there are few other derivatives of commercial interest. Amino derivatives, such as 8,17-diaminoindanthrone[15], which is a green dye of attractive shade but very fugitive to bleaching, are known. 8,17-Di-p-toluidinoindanthrone[15] is also a blue-green dye but lacks solubility in the vat and is hard to dye. 8,17-Dihydroxyindanthrone[16] is a blue-green dye of attractive shade which vats satisfactorily but is not fast to bleach. 7,16-Dibromoindanthrone has been used commercially but due to its insolubility in the vat and lower tinctorial strength it is not now used extensively.

N-alkyl[11] derivatives are known. N,N'-dimethylindanthrone, prepared by the condensation of 2-bromo-1-methylaminoanthraquinone with itself, was used as a dye at one time[17]. Sulfonic acid derivatives are known[48] which have minor interest as pigments and paper dyes. Formaldehye condensation[8] products have been used in a limited manner, the condensation product of 7,16-dibromoindanthrone being so employed.

The leuco tetrasulfuric ester of 7,16-dichloroindanthrone is commercially important and is sold as Indigosol Blue IBC, CI 1113. It is a soluble form and is discussed more fully in the subsequent section entitled Solubilized Vat Dyes. 7,16-Dichloroindanthrone cannot be solubilized economically by conventional methods involving treatment of the dye with chlorosulfonic acid and pyridine in the presence of copper or iron. Instead it is necessary to resort to oxidation of the leuco disulfuric ester of 2-amino-3-chloroanthraquinone with lead peroxide[13].

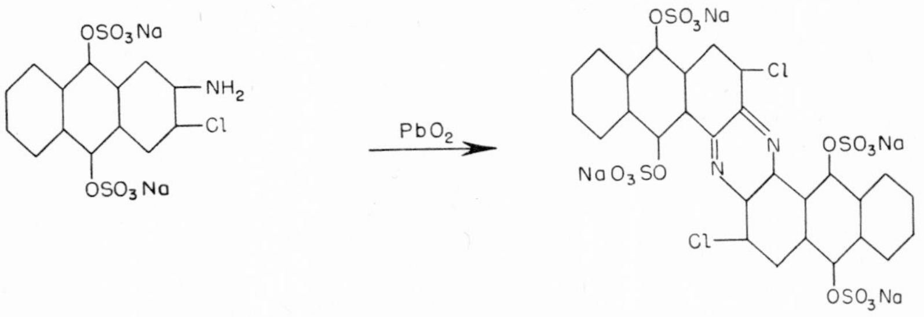

Crystalline Forms of Indanthrone. Organic dyes may change in shade and tinctorial power as they assume different polymorphic forms. The diffraction pattern of an unknown dye may be identified by comparison to a known standard. This principle has not been applied to all vat dyes, but it is known for indanthrone.

Indanthrone exists in four different crystalline forms which can be distinguished by x-ray analysis[41]. The tinctorial value of the different forms varies widely when they are used as pigments. Some of the properties of these forms with their method of formation are as follows:

Alpha Form	Beta Form	Gamma Form	Delta Form
Most stable, with highest tinctorial value	Relatively unstable. On heating above 60°C it converts to the alpha form	Redder than alpha form, somewhat weaker tinctorially	Quite stable. Has practically no color value

Alpha Form	Beta Form	Gamma Form	Delta Form

Made by

1. Oxidation of the leuco form of indanthrone above 60°C	Slowly drowning a sulfuric acid solution of indanthrone in water, avoiding temperature rise	Oxidation of leuco indanthrone below 50°C	Slowly adding water to a sulfuric acid solution of indanthrone or by treating alpha, beta or gamma forms with 80–85% sulfuric acid at room temperature
2. Heating beta, gamma or delta forms in the dry state above 60°C			
3. Recrystallization of alpha, beta or gamma forms from high-boiling solvents, such as nitrobenzene			
4. Vacuum sublimation			

Color and Crystalline Form

Transparent blue needles	Transparent pure blue, crystalline form ill defined	Needlelike crystals which aggregate on drying	Rhombic sheets with transparent olive-green color

X-ray Pattern

Has many lines	Has only a few red lines	A few sharp distinct lines in the violet	Has a very strong band in the red

Commercial Dyes

Indanthrene Blue RS (RSN)[14], CI 1106 Indanthrone	
Indanthrene Brilliant Blue R[23], CI 1106 Indanthrone (purified)	Brighter than Indanthrene Blue RS
Indanthrene Blue BC (BCS)[12], CI 1113 7,16-Dichloroindanthrone	Greener and faster to chlorine than Indanthrene Blue R
Indanthrene Blue GC (GCN)[12] 7,16-Dibromoindanthrone	Has poor dyeing properties
Indanthrene Blue GCD[30], CI 1112 Monochlorinated indanthrone	Greener than Indanthrene Blue RS and has printing properties which others lack
Indanthrone Blue 3GF[8] Indanthrone-formaldehyde condensation product	

Commercial Dyes

Indanthrene Blue 3G, CI 1109 (also called   Green and bright vs. Blue RS
Indanthrene Brilliant Blue 3G)
Indanthrone—partly sulfonated and oxi-
dized
Indanthrene Blue 5G[16], CI 1111   Greenest of the indanthrones. It is
8,17-Dihydroxyindanthrone   cold dyeing but has poor affinity
Indanthrene Blue RK, CI 1108   Obsolete
N,N'-dimethylindanthrone
Indanthrene Blue WBC[39], CI 1093   Paper dye, pigment
Indanthronemonosulfonic acid
Indanthrene Green 2B, CI 1116   Weatherfastness is good
8,17-Diamino-7,16-dichloroindanthrone

s-Triazines—Cyanuric Acid Derivatives

Numerous dyes are known which are prepared by the condensation of
one mole of cyanuric chloride with from one to three moles of an aminoanthraquinone, an aminoanthraquinone derivative or a combination of these
with an aromatic amine[40]. Usually two or three of the chlorine atoms in
cyanuric chloride are involved. The shades vary with the components
used. A typical example, which is a yellow dye, is

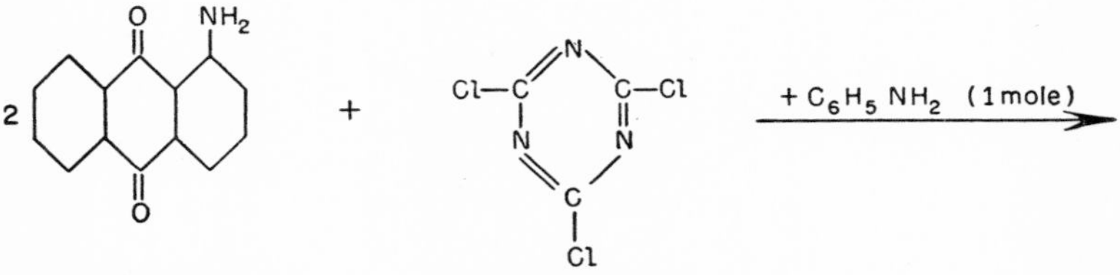

1-Aminoanthraquinone   Cyanuric chloride

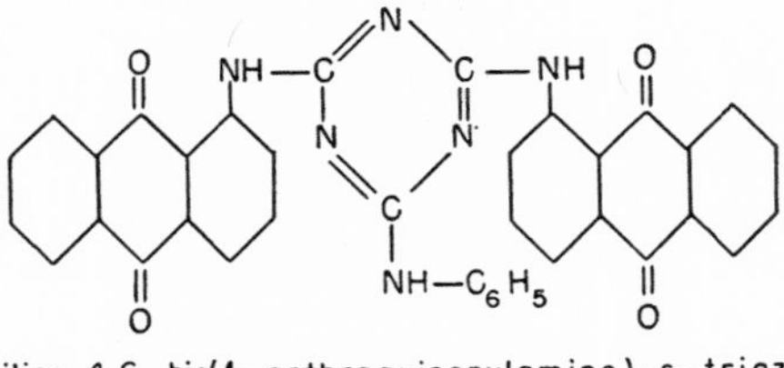

2-Anilino-4,6-bis(1-anthraquinonylamino)-s-triazine

When 1-amino or 1-benzamidoanthraquinones are used the shades are
usually yellow, bordeaux or red. When an aminoanthraquinone-2',1'(N)-
benzacridone is used, violet, bordeaux, brown, green and blue shades may
be obtained[1].

Many of the dyes prepared from cyanuric chloride are cotton tenderers,
but the presence of a benzamido group in the 5 position of the 1-aminoan-
thraquinone nucleus confers nontendering properties. In general, dyes of

this series often possess good but not outstanding fastness and are not outstandingly bright in shade. A few are used commercially[21].

Commercial Types		Probable Constituents
Cibanone Yellow 2GR	1 mole	Cyanuric chloride
	2 moles	2-Aminoanthraquinone
	1 mole	Aniline
Cibanone Orange RN	1 mole	Cyanuric chloride
	1 mole	1-Aminoanthraquinone
	1 mole	1,5-Diaminoanthraquinone
Cibanone Orange 2R	1 mole	Cyanuric chloride
	1½ moles	1-Aminoanthraquinone
	½ mole	1,8-Diaminoanthraquinone
Cibanone Orange 3R	1 mole	Cyanuric chloride
	2 moles	1,4-Diaminoanthraquinone
Cibanone Orange 6R	1 mole	Cyanuric chloride
	1 mole	1-Aminoanthraquinone
	1 mole	1-Amino-4-methoxyanthraquinone
Cibanone Red B	1 mole	Cyanuric chloride
	2 moles	1-Amino-4-benzamidoanthraquinone
	1 mole	1-Amino-4-methoxyanthraquinone
Cibanone Red 4B	1 mole	Cyanuric chloride
	3 moles	1-Amino-4-benzamidoanthraquinone
Cibanone Red G	1 mole	Cyanuric chloride
	2 moles	1-Amino-4-methoxyanthraquinone
	1 mole	Aniline
Cibanone Red 3G	1 mole	Cyanuric chloride
	1 mole	1-Amino-4-benzamidoanthraquinone
	1 mole	1-Amino-4-methoxyanthraquinone

Literature Cited

1. Ackerman and Schetelig, U.S. Patent 1,719,792 (1929).
2. Appleton and Geake, *Trans. Faraday Soc.*, **37**, 45 (1941).
3. Bader, *Chem. Ztg.*, **61**, 741 (1937).
4. Bishop and Perkins, U.S. Patent 1,975,248 (1934).
5. Bohn, U.S. Patent 724,789 (1903).
6. Bradley and Leete, *J. Chem. Soc.*, **1951**, 2129.
7. Brassard, *J. Soc. Dyers Colourists*, **59**, 127 (1943).
8. British Patent 351,032 (1931).
9. Clibbens, *J. Soc. Dyers Colourists*, **59**, 275 (1943).
10. Crowell, U.S. Patent 1,847,329 (1932).

11. Deinet, U.S. Patent 2,091,236 (1937).
12. ——, Goodrich and Stallmann, U.S. Patent 1,862,843 (1932).
13. Fairweather and Thomas, U.S. Patent 1,976,689 (1934).
14. German Patent 129,845 (1902).
15. German Patent 158,287 (1905).
16. German Patent 193,121 (1907).
17. German Patent 234,294 (1911).
18. German Patent 331,283 (1920).
19. Gill and Stonehill, *J. Soc. Dyers Colourists*, **60,** 183 (1944).
20. Houben, "Das Anthracen und die Anthrachinone," p. 722, Leipzig, Georg Thieme, 1929.
21. I. G. Farbenindustrie, PB 74772, frames 3855–3926.
22. Johnson, U.S. Patent 2,030,877 (1936).
23. Kraenzlein, U.S. Patent 1,541,156 (1925).
24. Kuhn, *Naturwissenschaften*, **20,** 618 (1932).
25. Lulek, *J. Soc. Dyers Colourists*, **43,** 370 (1927).
26. Mueller, *Melliand Textilber.*, **28,** 93, 136, 353 (1947).
27. ——, *ibid.*, **31,** 338 (1950).
28. Murch, U.S. Patent 2,044,993 (1936).
29. Robinson, *J. Soc. Dyers Colourists*, **37,** 77 (1921).
30. Sachs, U.S. Patent 1,739,736 (1929).
31. Scholl, *Ber.*, **36,** 3410 (1903).
32. ——, *ibid.*, **36,** 3418 (1903).
33. —— and Berblinger, *ibid.*, **36,** 3427 (1903).
34. —— and Eberle, *Monatsh.*, **32,** 1035 (1911).
35. —— and ——, *ibid.*, **32,** 1038 (1911).
36. —— and Edlbacher, *Ber.*, **44,** 1727 (1911).
37. —— and Stegmueller, *ibid.*, **40,** 924 (1907).
38. ——, Steinkopf and Kabacznik, *ibid.*, **40,** 390 (1907).
39. Schmidt, U.S. Patent 785,122 (1905).
40. Steinbuch, Ackerman and Utzinger, U.S. Patent 1,437,783 (1922).
41. Susich, *Anal. Chem.*, **22,** 425 (1950).
42. Thomas and Drescher, U.S. Patent 1,779,221 (1930).
43. Thompson, U.S. Patent 1,580,700 (1926).
44. ——, U.S. Patent 1,997,610 (1935).

THIAPYRANS AND THIAXANTHONES

MYRON S. WHELEN

The thiapyrans and thiaxanthones are not an important group of vat dyes commercially but they are interesting examples of vat dyes containing sulfur in a 6-membered ring. These dyes are usually of green-to-yellow shade but as a class exhibit poor tinctorial strength.

Anthraquinonethiapyrans

The most interesting thiapyran type is probably that exemplified by 4-thia-4H-benzo[a]naphtho[3,2,1,8-ghij]perylene-7,15-dione[7], prepared by the treatment of 1,2'-dianthraquinonyl sulfide, the condensation product of 2-mercaptoanthraquinone with 1-chloroanthraquinone, with aluminum in sulfuric acid.

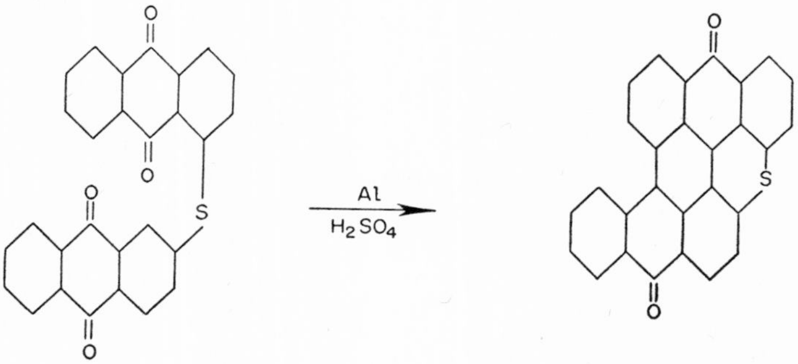

$$\xrightarrow[\text{H}_2\text{SO}_4]{\text{Al}}$$

This product lacks tinctorial strength. On halogenation[2] it yields bottle-green dyes of better strength with improved properties which are of some interest.

Another type of product, exhibiting an interesting type of ring-closure, is obtained by a potassium hydroxide fusion in cyclohexanol in the following manner[6].

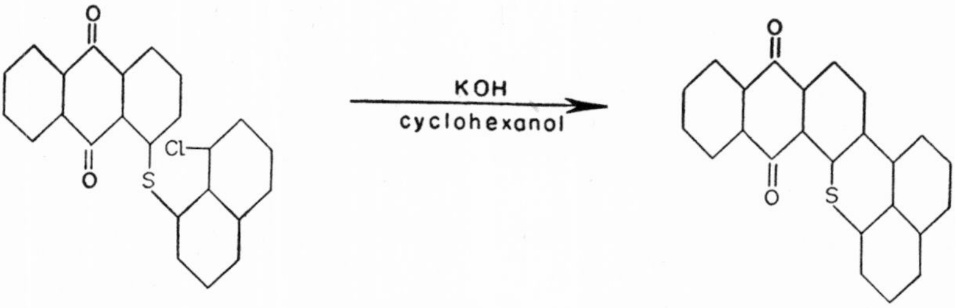

$$\xrightarrow[\text{cyclohexanol}]{\text{KOH}}$$

It dyes cotton violet from a sodium hydroxide-sodium hydrosulfite vat.
Another product of more condensed type is described by Scholl and co-

workers[8]. It was obtained according to the scheme:

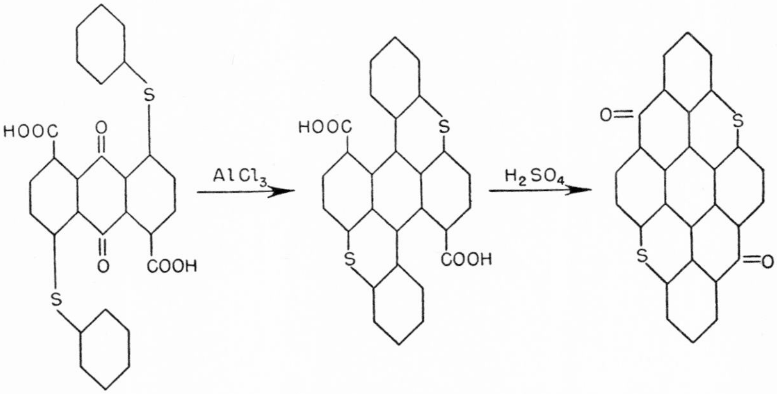

This product vats with difficulty, dyes cotton green but is not fast to bleach.

Anthraquinonethiaxanthones

Four general methods are available for the preparation of thiaxanthones as exemplified by the type,

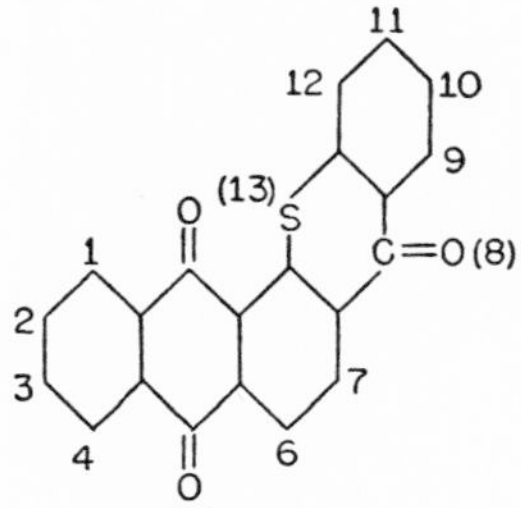

8H-naphtho[2,3-c]thiaxanthene-5,8,14-trione

(1) Condensation of mercaptoanthraquinone with an aromatic *o*-halocarboxylic acid.

(2) Condensation of a haloanthraquinone with an aromatic *o*-mercaptocarboxylic acid.

(3) Condensation of an *o*-mercaptoanthraquinonecarboxylic acid with a haloaromatic compound.

(4) Condensation of an *o*-haloanthraquinonecarboxylic acid with an aromatic thiol.

In each case ring-closure of the condensation product to the thiaxanthone is effected by concentrated sulfuric acid[3] or by heating the acid chloride of the condensation product with aluminum chloride[4, 9]. Various derivatives containing halo, amino and hydroxy groups are known. Of these 4- and 6-aminoanthraquinonethiaxanthones are of interest as they may be used to build up mixed types. A carbazole containing the thiaxanthone nucleus[1] prepared from 4-amino-8H-naphtho[2,3-c]thiaxanthene-5,8,14-trione, which dyes in reddish shades, is shown as follows:

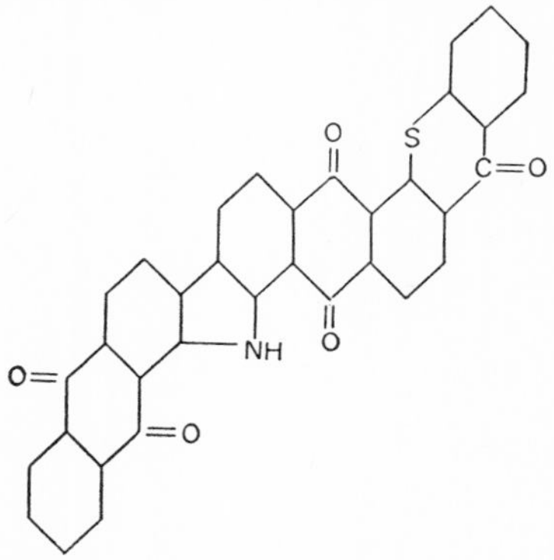

The straight thiaxanthone types dye in orange to red shades but are usually weak tinctorially and have poor fastness properties. The unsubstituted product, for example

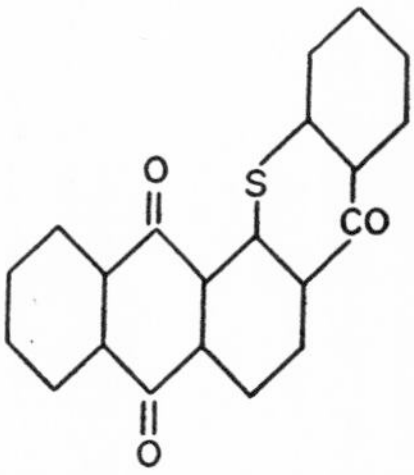

dyes orange compared to the corresponding acridone (where —S— is replaced by —NH—) which dyes red-violet.

The anthraquinonebisthiaxanthone of the following formula

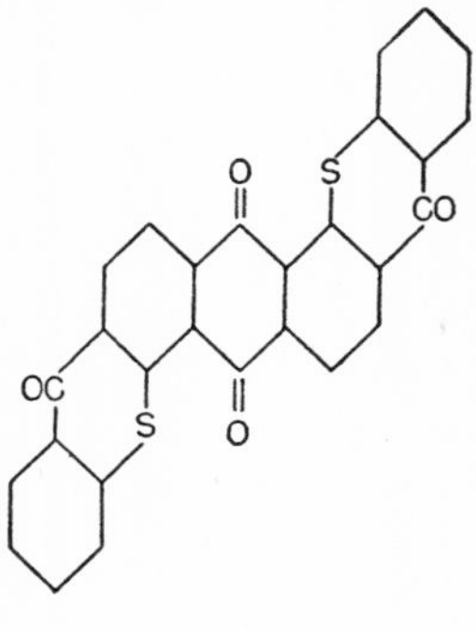

dyes red, while the corresponding acridone dyes violet. None of the thiaxanthones is commercially important, although two dyes (now obsolete) of the following constitution were sold at one time[5].

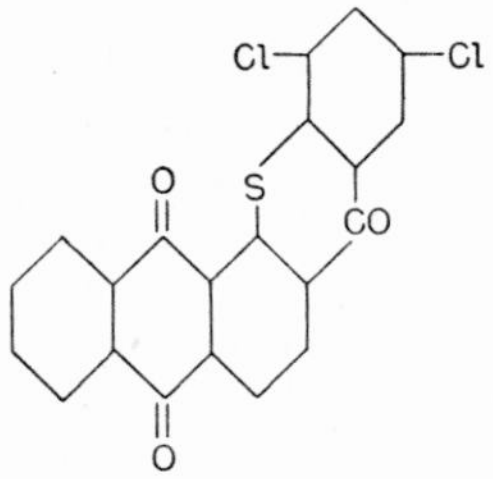

Indanthrene Yellow GN

and

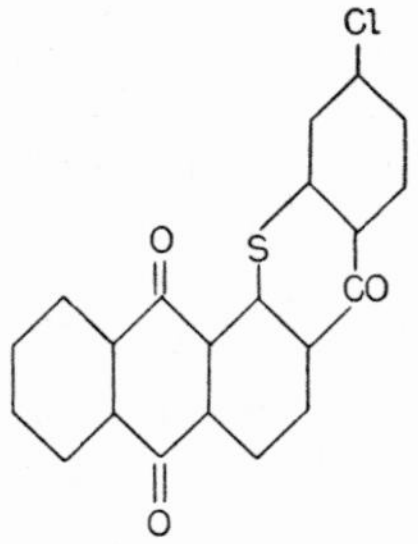

Indanthrene Golden Orange GN

Literature Cited

1. Dettwyler, U.S. Patent 2,344,981 (1944).
2. Eicholz, U.S. Patent 2,144,365 (1939).
3. German Patent 216,480 (1909).
4. German Patent 238,983 (1911).
5. German Patent 243,750 (1912).
6. I. G. Farbenindustrie, PB 70339, frame 11443.
7. Nawiasky and Stein, U.S. Patent 2,025,546 (1935).
8. Scholl, Bottger and Wanka, *Ber.*, **67,** 599 (1934).
9. Ullmann and Knecht, *ibid.*, **44,** 3125 (1911).

MISCELLANEOUS SIX-MEMBERED HETEROCYCLICS

Frederick B. Stilmar

Metoxazones

An intermediate for a vat green falls in this class. 3-Amino-2-anthraquinonecarboxylic acid reacts with benzoic acid in oleum to give a *C*-phenylmetoxazone[3], while the same starting material reacts with 1-nitro-2-anthraquinonecarbonyl chloride in nitrobenzene to give an analogous compound[9].

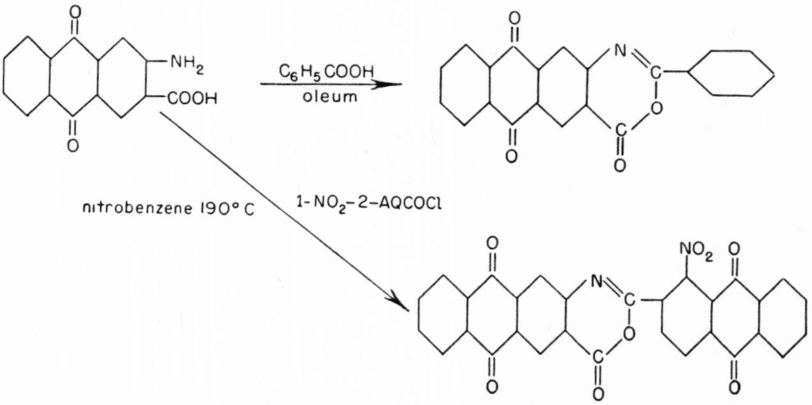

The analogous reaction does not proceed with the isomeric 1-amino-2-anthraquinonecarboxylic acid[14], although a 1,2-metoxazone may be prepared as follows:

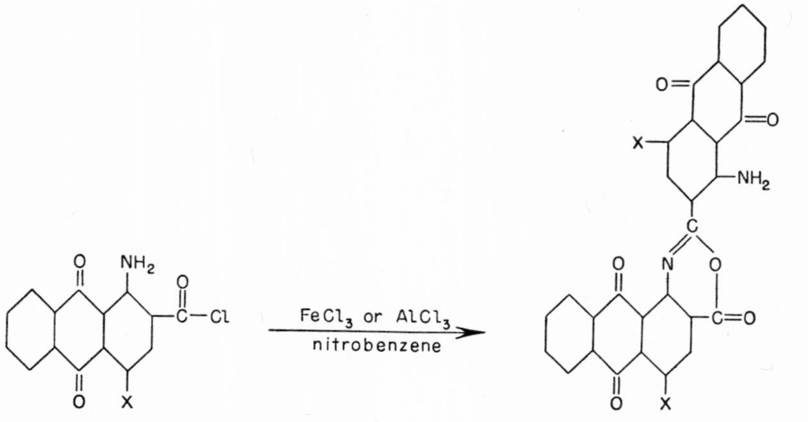

(where X = H, Br, OH)

The metoxazone is also a by-product in the preparation of 1-amino-2-anthraquinonecarbonyl chloride and derivatives unless the temperature is kept low. A small amount of pyridine is reported to avoid this side reaction[2].

Triazines

The following triazine is a yellow compound but it has no affinity for cotton fiber when vatted[7].

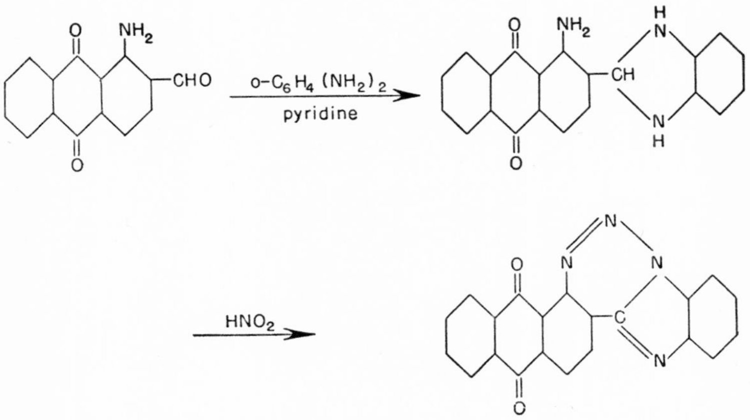

Thiazines

German workers prepared several thiazines by heating *o*-amino-*o'*-nitro-diaryl sulfides in nitrobenzene with a weakly alkaline agent[10]. They pointed out the similarity to the Turpin Reaction for preparing oxazines.

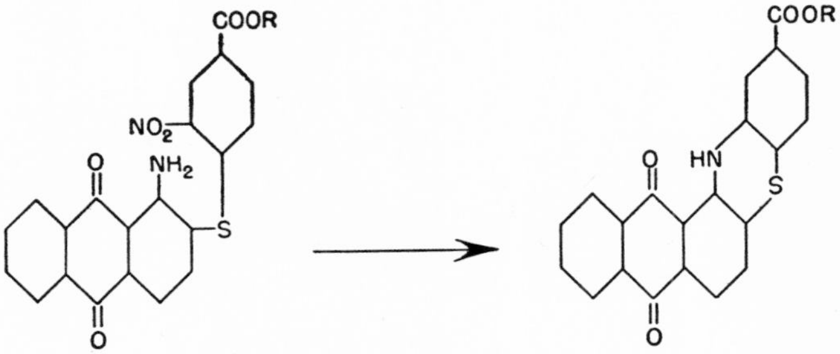

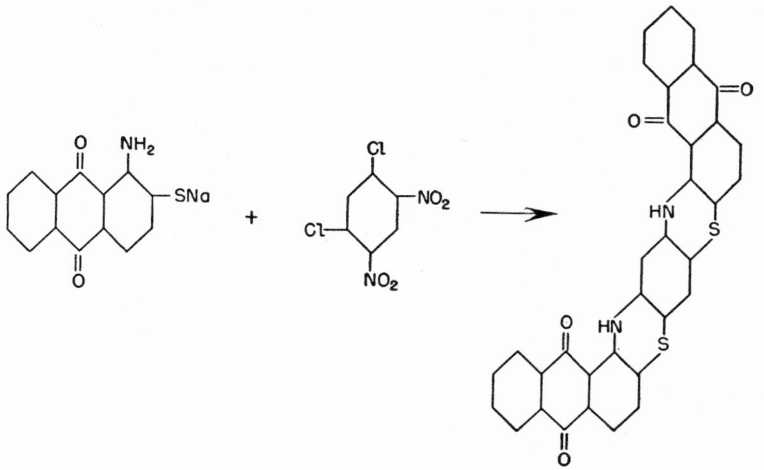

Another new route to thiazines is represented as follows[5]:

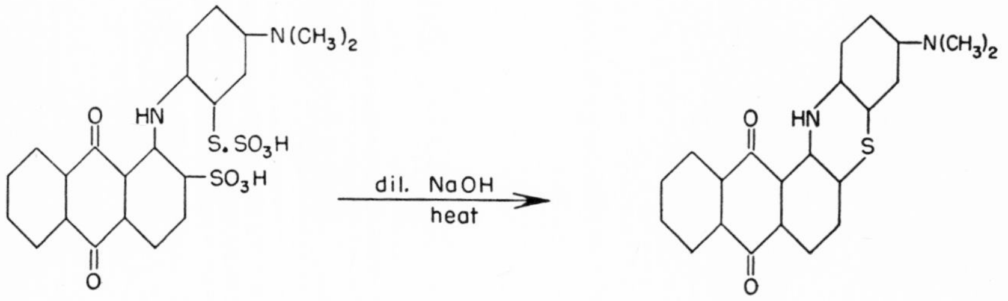

Thiazines generally have poor bleachfastness because of the tendency of the sulfur to oxidize[11].

German chemists have exploited the thiadiazine ring[4, 6].

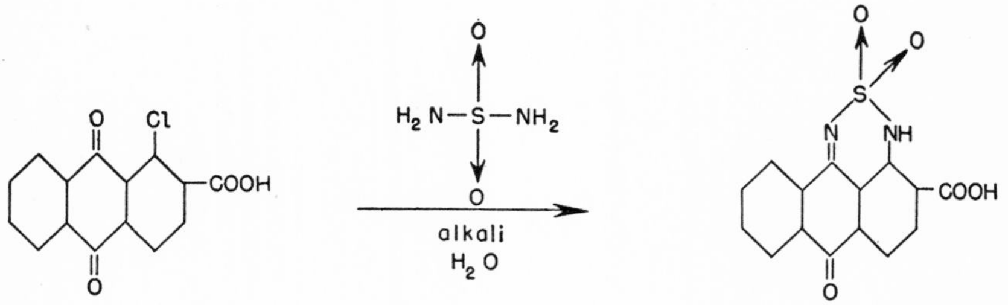

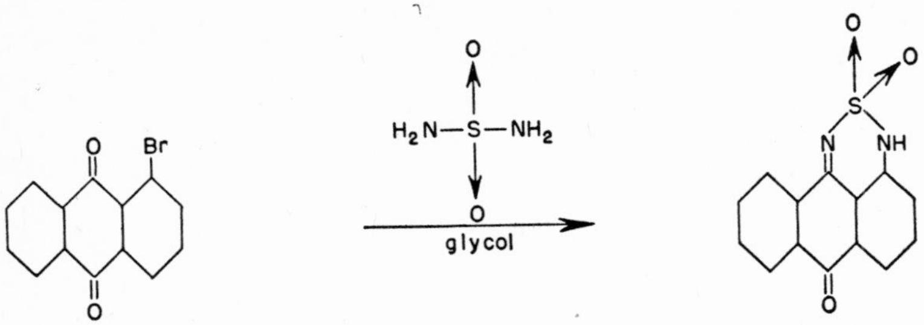

Pyrans

There has been recent academic work in the coeroxonium field[1].

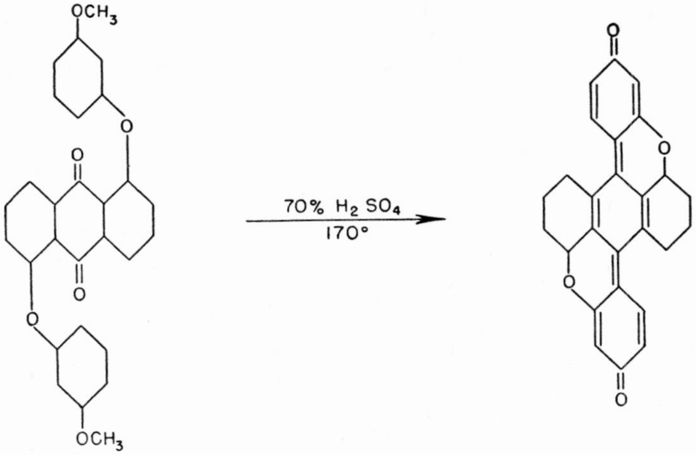

The I.G. Farbenindustrie developed an interesting blue-green vat color. It may be prepared from either anthrone, 10-hydroxyanthrone or 10,10'-bianthrone and p-quinone[4].

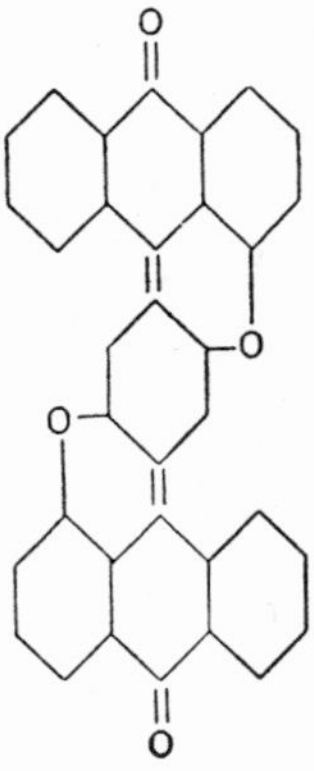

Another interesting type is the green vat color[17] prepared as shown from tetrabromothiophene.

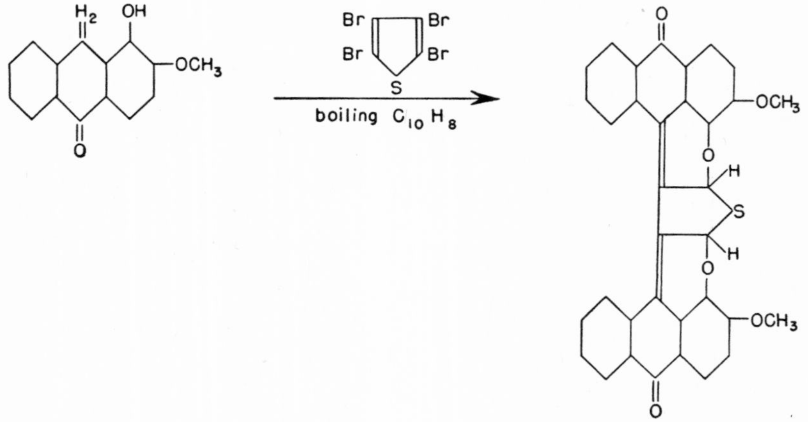

Diacridines

The blue condensation product of 1-aminoanthraquinone and *o*-chlorobenzaldehyde[15, 16] has now been assigned the following structure[13].

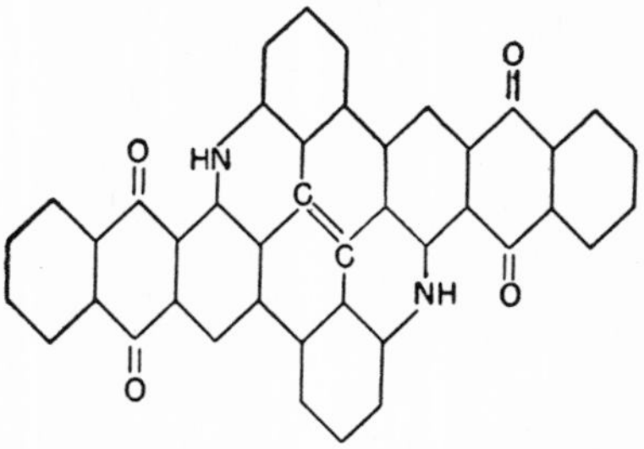

A similar structure is advanced for a barbituric acid condensation product with 1-amino-2-anthraquinonecarboxaldehyde[12], via the intermediate shown on page 534.

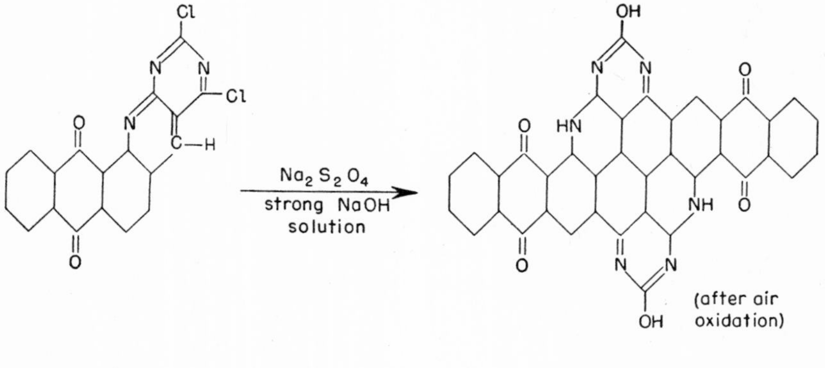

via

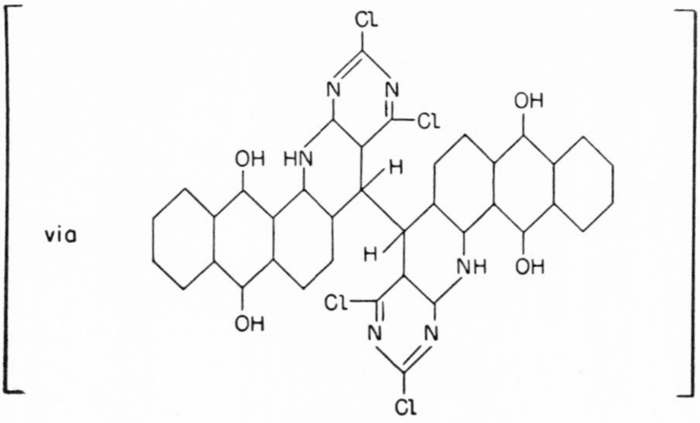

Literature Cited

1. Cook and Waddington, *J. Chem. Soc.*, **1945**, 402.
2. I. G. Farbenindustrie, BIOS 987, p. 17 (PB 75860).
3. ——, BIOS 1493, p. 20 (PB 81611).
4. ——, PB 70338, frames 9920, 9541.
5. ——, *ibid.*, frame 9943.
6. ——, *ibid.*, frame 10059.
7. ——, *ibid.*, frame 10862.
8. ——, PB 70341, frame 13988.
9. ——, *ibid.*, frame 13991.
10. ——, *ibid.*, frame 14046.
11. ——, *ibid.*, frame 14048.
12. ——, PB 70342, frame 14636.
13. ——, *ibid.*, frame 14638.
14. ——, PB 74898, frame 10004.
15. Kalischer and Mayer, *Ber.*, **49**, 1994 (1916).
16. Mayer and Stein, *ibid.*, **50**, 1311 (1917).
17. Perkin, Sheperdson and Haddock, U.S. Patent 1,915,901 (1933).

SOLUBILIZED VAT DYES

Melvin A. Perkins

The greatest disadvantages of vat colors are their uneven dyeing characteristics. To overcome these and obtain uniform dyeings, especially in pale shades and on expensive fabrics, a line of so-called "soluble vat colors" was developed and has enjoyed considerable popularity. Leuco sulfuric acid esters proved to be the best answer.

In 1921, Bader and Sunder discovered that the reduction products of vat dyes could be esterified with chlorosulfonic acid in the presence of a tertiary base to give water-soluble products which were stable enough to prepare and handle but from which the original color could be regenerated by simple treatment with aqueous acidic oxidizing agents[1]. Since indigo and its derivatives were the first objects of this solubilization reaction, the name Indigosol was chosen as the trade name of this class of solubilized vat colors. The work was soon extended to all types of vat colors and the same name was applied even though the products might be entirely nonindigoid.

Bader and Sunder worked for Durand and Huguenin of Basel, Switzerland, who held the earliest patents in this field. Subsequently, other manufacturers have entered the field and have marketed these leuco sulfuric acid esters under other trade names such as Soledon, Anthrasol, Algosol, Coprantine, Leucogene, Solvat and Vat (color name) Soluble. Basically, the solubilization of all quinone dyes, whether vat types or not, is by means of the same general reaction in which the quinone is first reduced to the hydroquinone (or leuco state), and then is reacted with chlorosulfonic acid or some other source of SO_3. The esterifying agent is usually in the form of an addition compound with a tertiary amine, pyridine being the classical tertiary amine which has been most widely employed. Others which have been used or considered are N,N-dimethylaniline[1], 4-alkylmorpholines[16], trialkylamines[15] and N,N-dialkylformamides[2]. The British subsequently made a discovery which gave further emphasis to this class of product when they found that reduction and esterification of the quinone could be carried out in the same mass[19], thus avoiding the necessity of handling leuco compounds which are extremely sensitive to light and air. At the same time the mechanical operation was simplified. Yields were considerably improved as a result and products which were almost impossible to esterify could be solubilized by this combined procedure. In this process the addition compound of SO_3 and the organic base (for example pyridine) was first prepared and to this was gradually added a mixture of the dye and a metal powder, either copper or zinc. Alternatively, the dye could be added directly followed by slow addition of the metal powder. As fast as the dye was reduced, the reduction product was esterified by the SO_3 addition compound to give a complex containing the sulfuric acid ester of the leuco dye in combination with tertiary amine and metal. This complex was then resolved into its component parts by treatment with sodium hydroxide or carbonate, after which the tertiary amine was removed by extraction or distillation and the alkali metal salt of the leuco sulfuric acid ester of the dye was precipitated out by salting. In this way dyes which have almost no solubility whatever in water are converted to soluble products which can be padded or printed on the cloth, then regenerated to the original ketonic dye by treatment, for example, in dilute aqueous sulfuric acid with sodium nitrite. Other oxidizing agents can be used and are preferable for those dyes which are sensitive to nitrite.

It might be supposed that all vat colors could be solubilized satisfactorily by this method, but such is not the case. It appears that all vat colors in strong alkaline hydrosulfite exist in the true enol form, but when the pH is reduced other reduced forms may result. These lead to by-products in the solubilization which either do not give water-soluble, stable esters or give products incapable of regeneration to the original dye. In this latter case the product may have no tinctorial power or it may dye in a shade different from that of the original dye and often may give dyeings of inferior fastness properties.

For the most part indigoid and thioindigoid colors and simple ketonic hydrocarbons such as *p*-quinones, anthraquinone, dibenzopyrenedione, anthanthrone (dibenzo[cd,jk]pyrene-6,12-dione), pyranthrenedione, and dibenzanthrone (violanthrone) give rise to normal solubilization products in yields of from 75 to 99 per cent of theory. The reaction can be illustrated by that for Anthrasol Brilliant Violet I4R, the leuco ester of dichloroisodibenzanthrone. Chlorine atoms are not shown in the formulas below because their actual positions have not been ascertained beyond doubt (but their presence is to be understood):

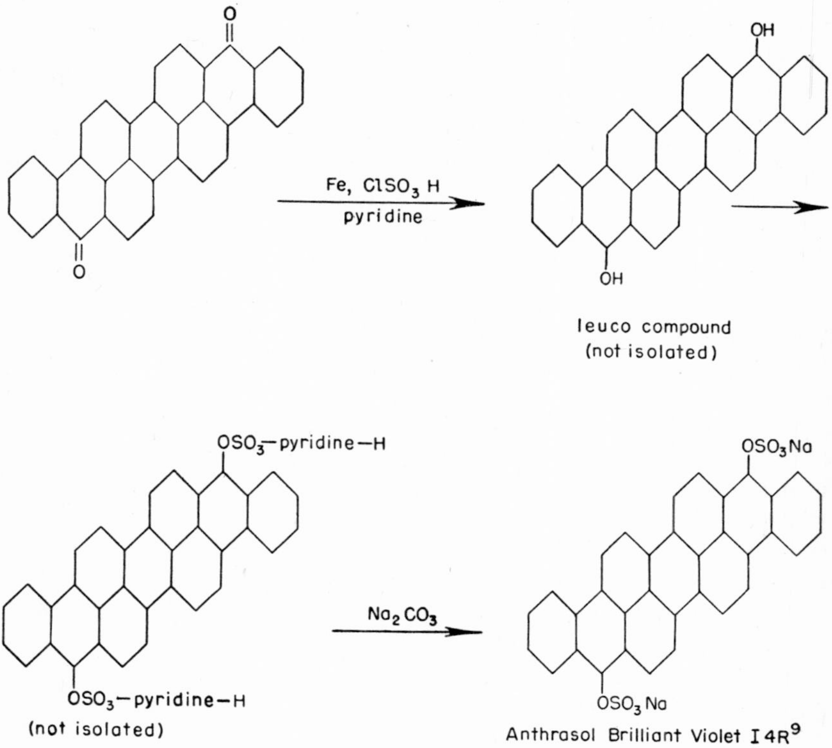

O
O
Fe, ClSO3H
pyridine
OH
OH
leuco compound
(not isolated)
OSO3—pyridine—H
OSO3—pyridine—H
(not isolated)
Na2CO3
OSO3Na
OSO3Na
Anthrasol Brilliant Violet I4R9

Following is a tabulation of Anthrasol dyes which have been listed as of importance[10]. With a single exception, all of these products arise by direct solubilization of the parent ketonic compound which is the original dye. The exception to be noted is that of Anthrasol Blue IBC where solubilization is carried out on the intermediate. This intermediate is then oxidized to give the dye itself in soluble form, according to the scheme[9, 11]:

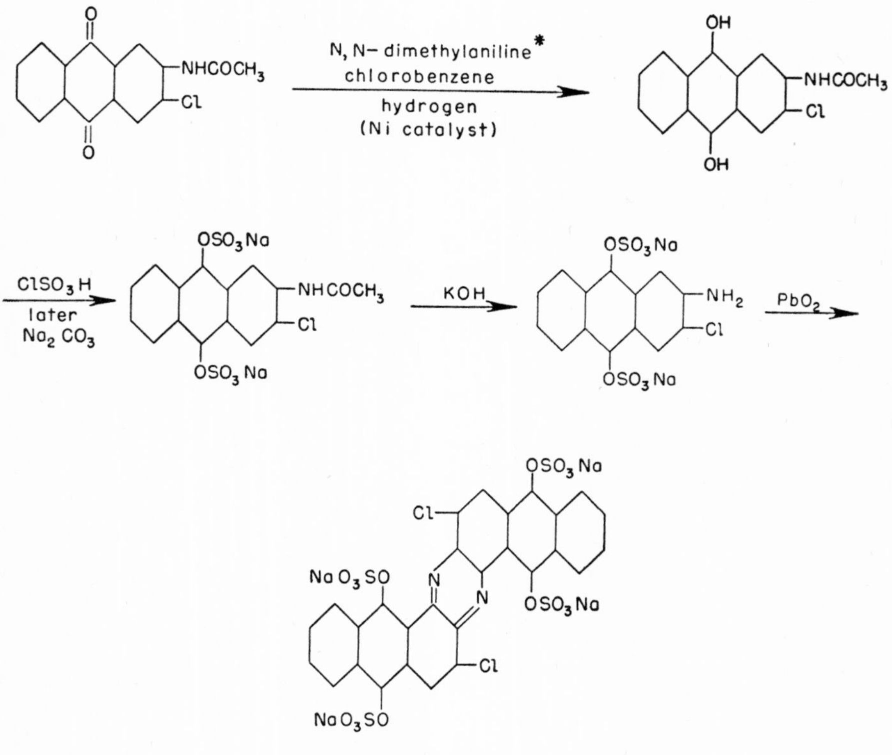

Anthrasol Blue IBC

The general solubilization procedure for all other products listed on pp. 538–546 is the one described above for Anthrasol Brilliant Violet I4R. A typical detailed process is reported[13] to be that for Anthrasol Printing Black IB.

* This is one of two alternative processes used by I.G. Farbenindustrie[8]. In the other process pyridine, iron and chlorosulfonic acid were used as for most other soluble vat dyes and no intermediate anthradiol was isolated[6].

Most Important Soluble Vat Colors[10]:

Name of Product	Name of Parent Dye	Constitution of Parent Dye	Special Comment
Anthrasol O	Indigo, CI 1177	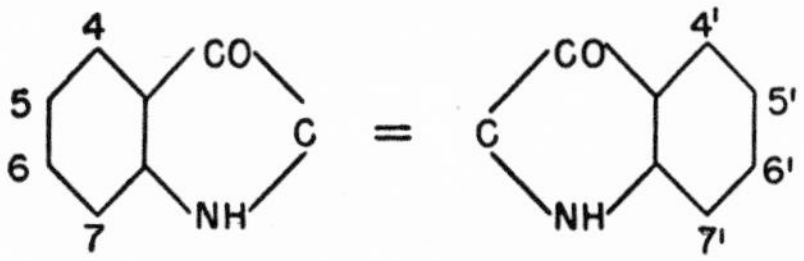	
Anthrasol O4B	Indigo 4B, CI 1184	5,5′,7,7′-tetrabromoindigo	Catalytic hydrogenation can be used for these two colors, prior to esterification
Anthrasol Blue IBC	Indanthrene Blue BC, CI 1113	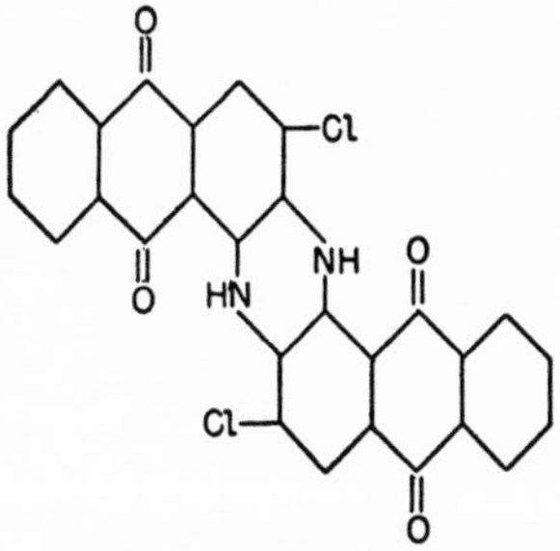	
Anthrasol Blue Black IRD	Indanthrene Printing Black BGL, Pr. 382	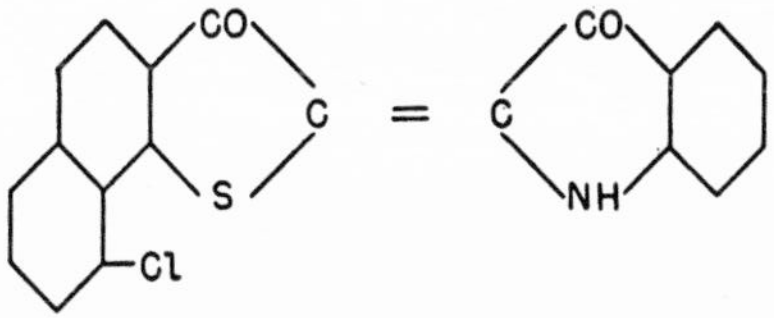	Made from solubilized intermediate only (not from dye)

Anthrasol Brown
IBR

Indanthrene Brown BR,
Pr. 118

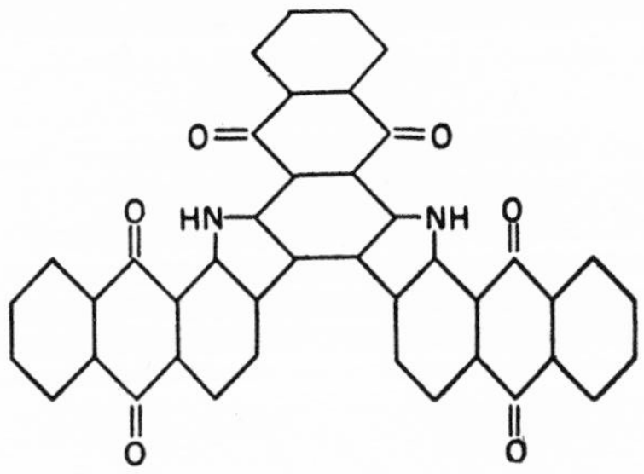

Anthrasol Brown
IRRD

Indanthrene Brown
RRD, Pr. 121

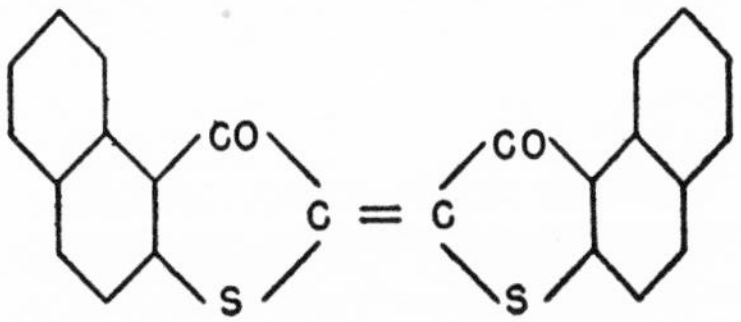

Anthrasol Printing
Black IB

Indanthrene Printing
Black B, Pr. 294

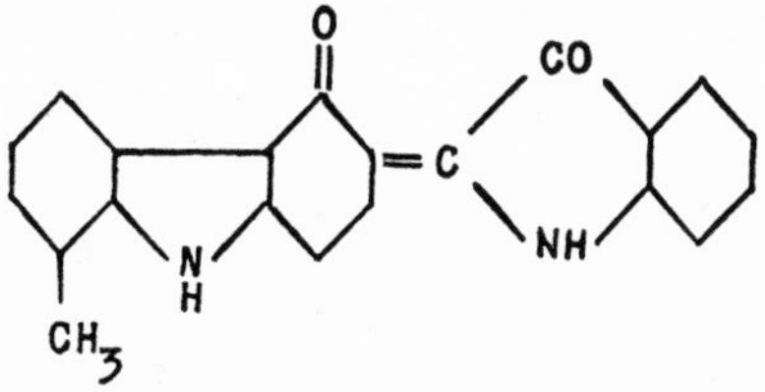

Most Important Soluble Vat Colors[10].—Continued

Name of Product	Name of Parent Dye	Constitution of Parent Dye	Special Comment
Anthrasol Yellow V	—	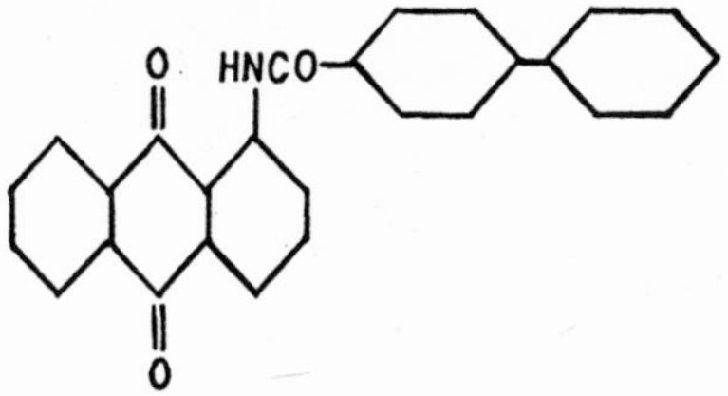	
Anthrasol Golden Yellow IGK	Indanthrene Golden Yellow GK, Pr. 291	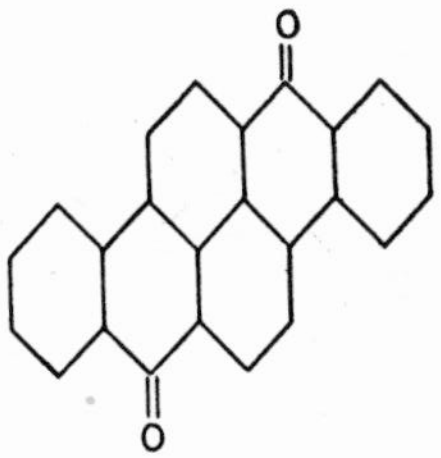	Poor lightfastness
Anthrasol Golden Yellow IRK	Indanthrene Golden Yellow RK, Pr. 292	brominated Golden Yellow GK	Improved lightfastness
Anthrasol Green IB	Indanthrene Brilliant Green FFB, CI 1101	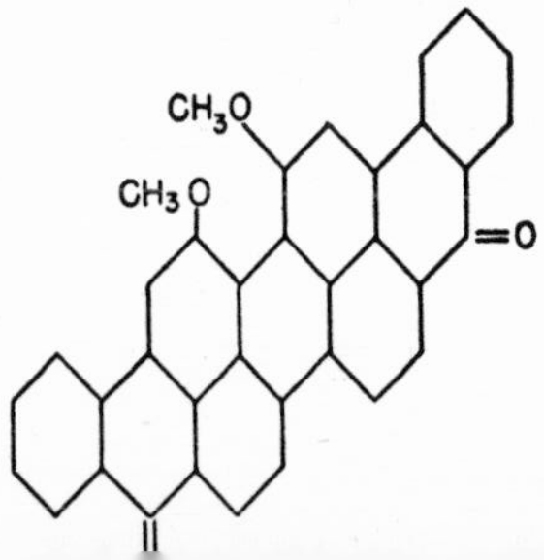	FFB brand is somewhat brighter than Indanthrene Brilliant Green B

Anthrasol Green IGG — Indanthrene Brilliant Green GG — brominated Brilliant Green FFB — Unusually bright, yellowish shade of green

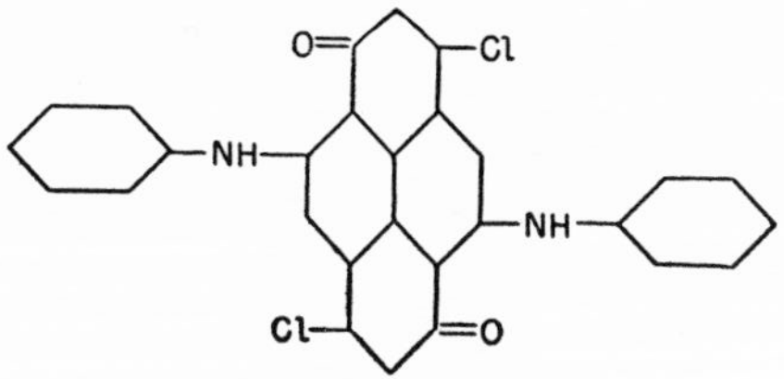

Anthrasol Green I3G — —

Anthrasol Orange HR — Algol Orange RF, CI 1217

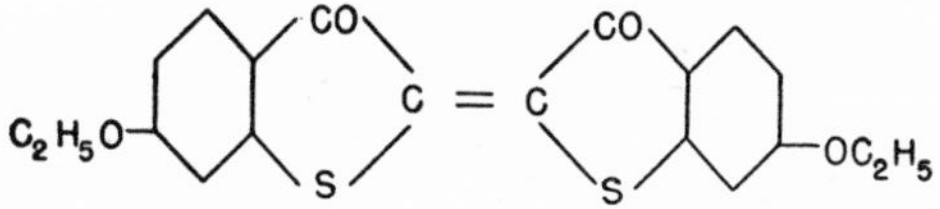

Anthrasol Pink IR Extra — Indanthrene Brilliant Pink R, Pr. 109

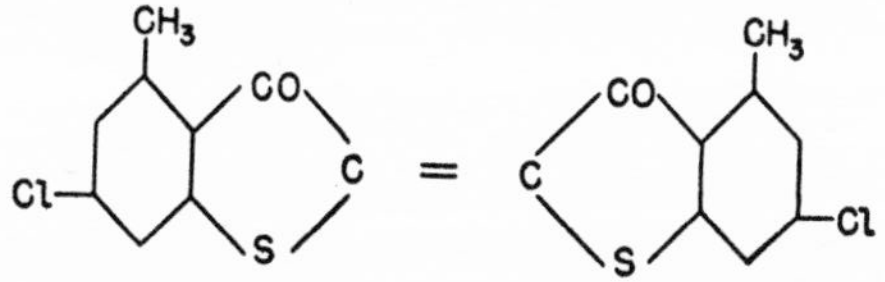

Anthrasol Red IFBB — Indanthrene Red FBB, Pr. 296 — Requires copper (instead of iron) for solubilization

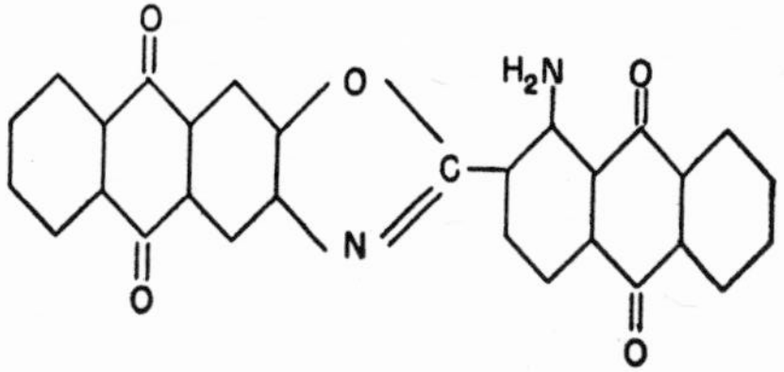

Anthrasol Red Violet IRH — Indanthrene Red Violet RH, CI 1212

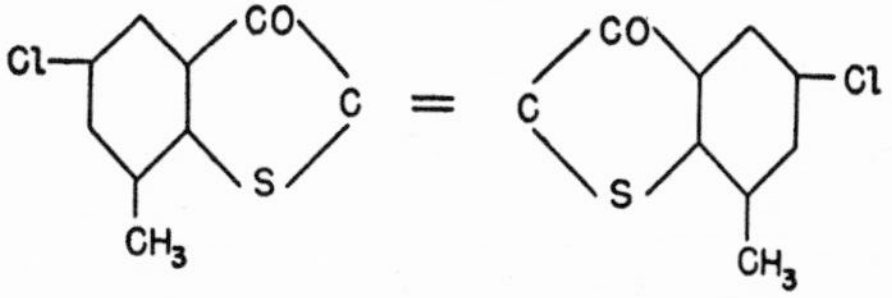

Soluble Vat Colors of Lesser Importance[12]:

Name of Product	Name of Parent Dye	Constitution of Parent Dye	Special Comment
Anthrasol AZG	Alizarin Indigo G, CI 1202	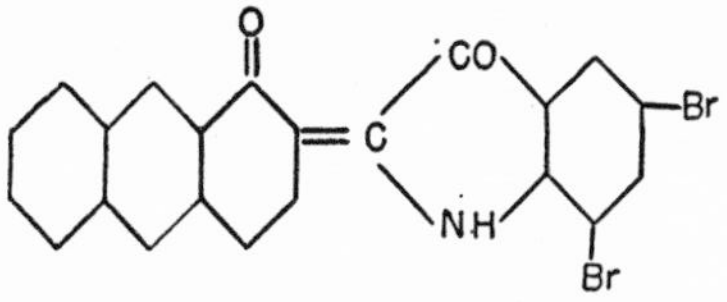	
Anthrasol O4G	Brilliant Indigo 4G, CI 1189	dibromodichloroindigo	Bright turquoise shade
Anthrasol OR	Indigo R, CI 1183	dibromoindigo	
Anthrasol Blue IGC	Indanthrene Blue GC, CI 1115	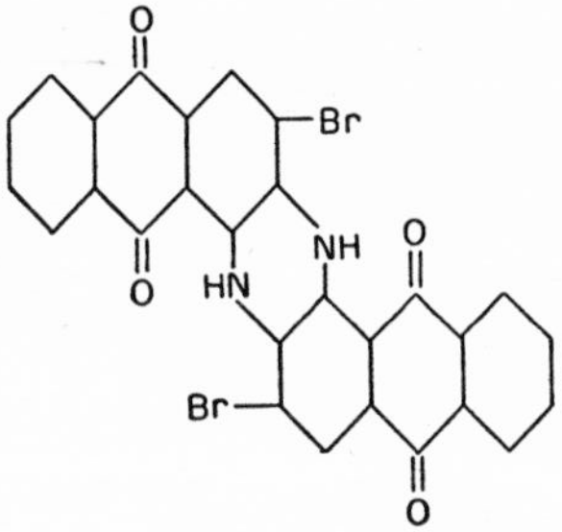	Recommended for printing rayon
Anthrasol Brilliant Orange IRK	Indanthrene Brilliant Orange RK, Pr. 116	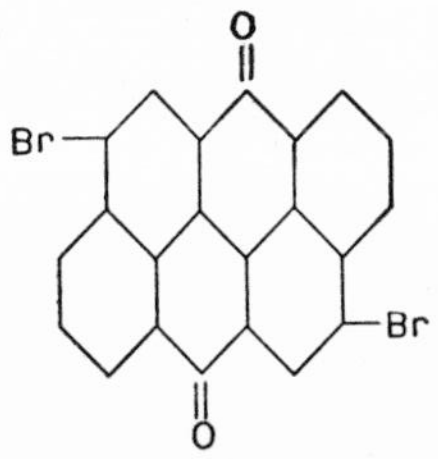	Available only as a paste containing solubilizing agent

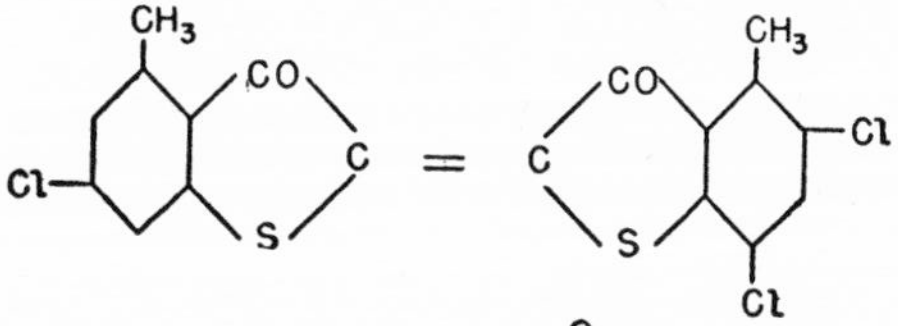

Anthrasol Brilliant Pink I3B	Indanthrene Brilliant Pink 3B		
Anthrasol Brilliant Violet I4R	Indanthrene Brilliant Violet 4R, CI 1104		Position of Cl atoms not ascertained
Anthrasol Gray IBL	Indanthrene Printing Black BL Base, Pr. 295		

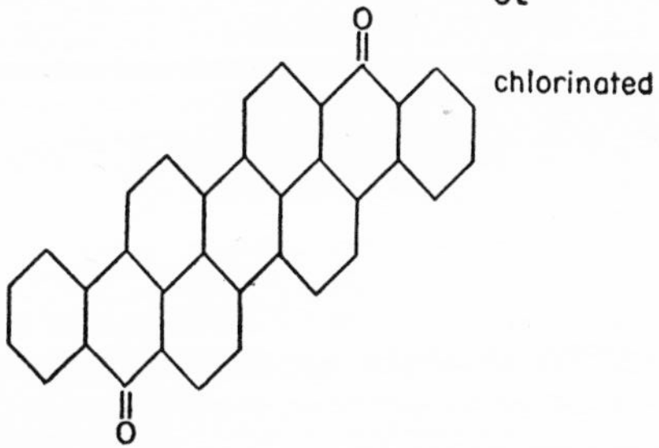

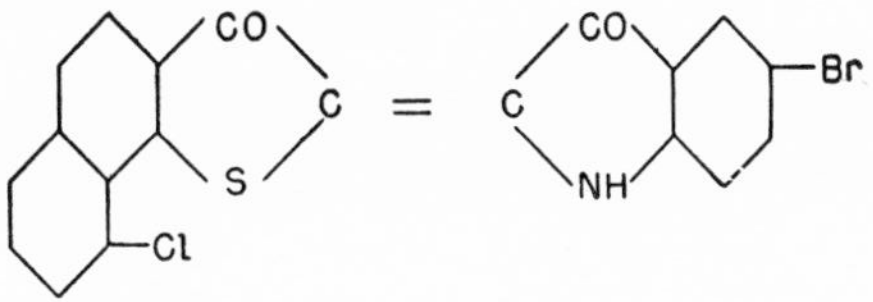

Soluble Vat Colors of Lesser Importance[12].—continued

Name of Product	Name of Parent Dye	Constitution of Parent Dye	Special Comment
Anthrasol Gray IN	Indanthrene Olive T, Pr. 547	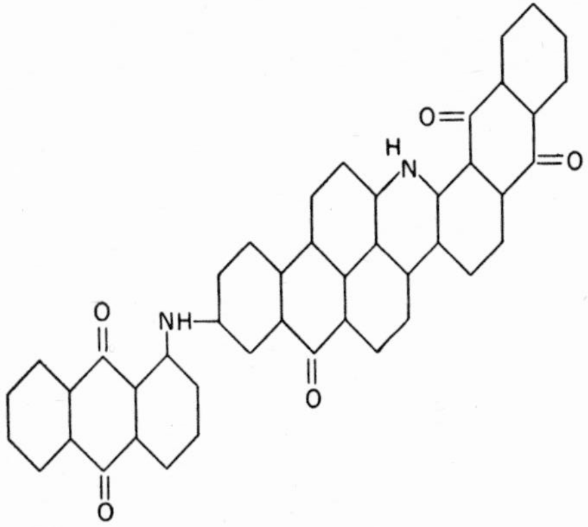	
Anthrasol Green AB	Algol Brilliant Green BK	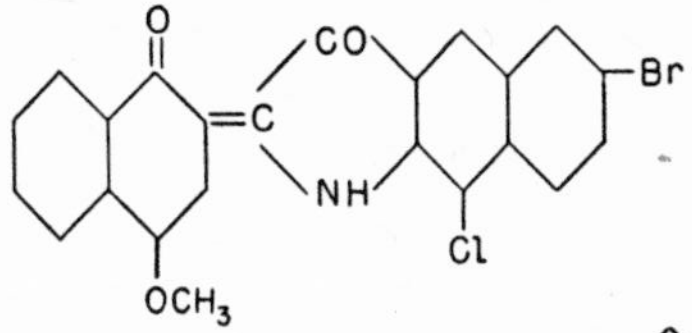	
Anthrasol Olive Green IB	Indanthrene Olive Green B, Pr. 293	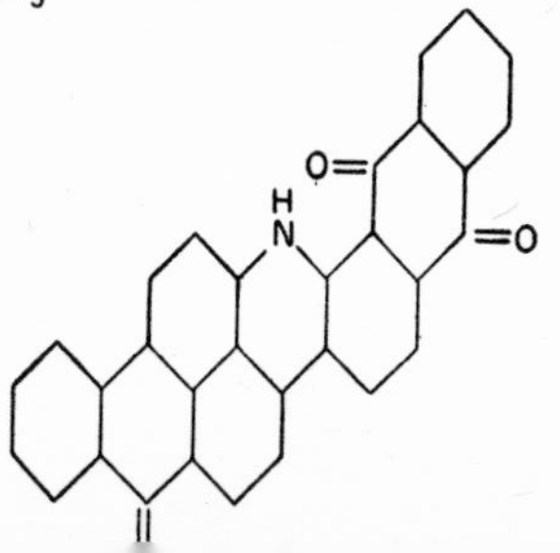	

Anthrasol Printing
Blue IB

Indanthrene Printing
Blue B

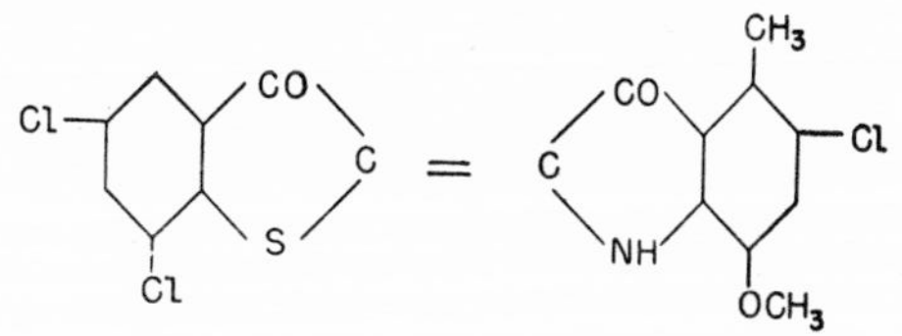

Anthrasol Printing
Blue IGG

Indanthrene Printing
Blue GG

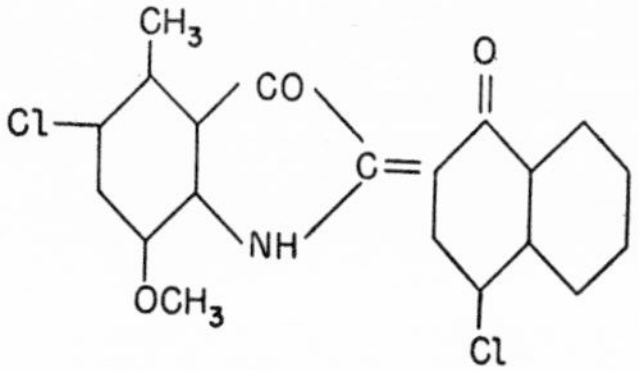

Anthrasol Printing
Purple IR

Indanthrene Printing
Purple R

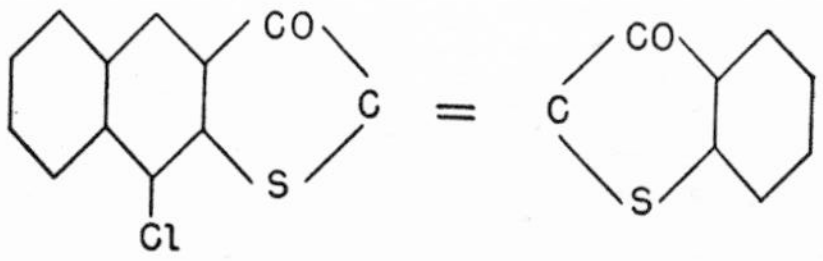

Anthrasol Printing
Violet IBBF

Indanthrene Printing
Violet BBF

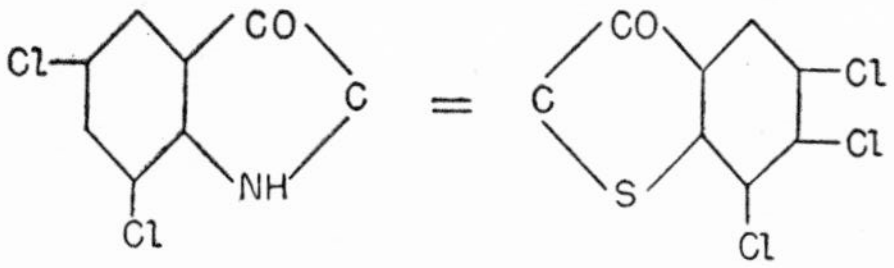

Soluble Vat Colors of Lesser Importance[12].—continued

Name of Product	Name of Parent Dye	Constitution of Parent Dye	Special Comment
Anthrasol Printing Violet IRR	—	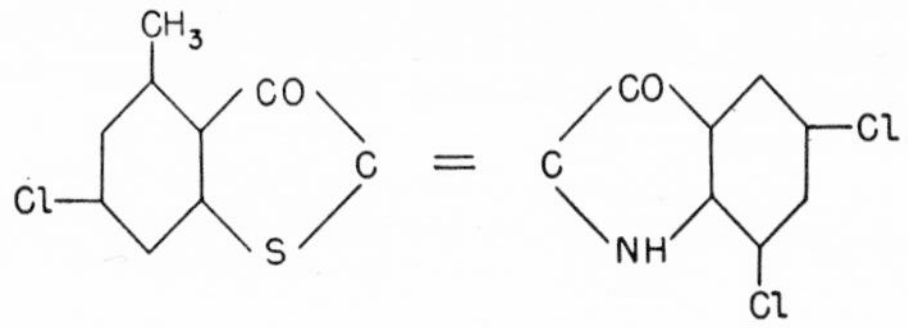	
Anthrasol Scarlet IB	Indanthrene Scarlet B, Pr. 106	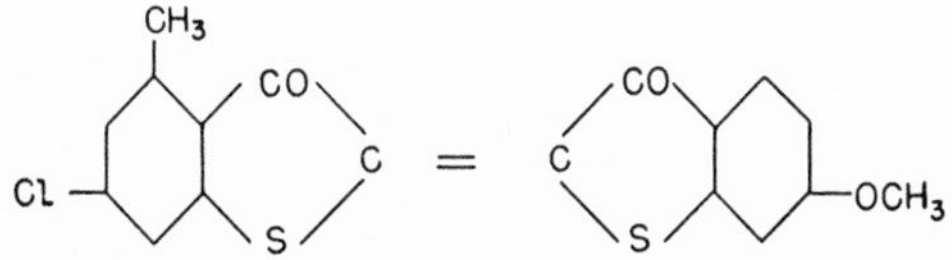	
Anthrasol Scarlet HB, Pr. 107	Mixture of Anthrasol Orange HR and Anthrasol Pink IR Extra		
Anthrasol Yellow HCG	Helindone Yellow CG	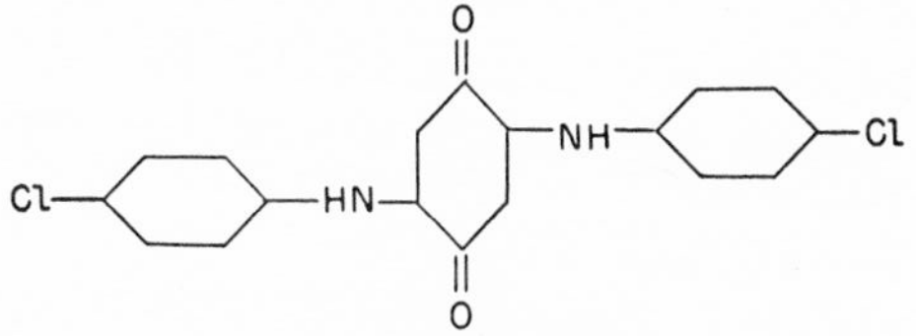	
Indigosol O6B	Indigo MLB/5B, CI 1185		Mixed penta- and hexabromoindigo
Indigosol Brilliant Violet 14B	Indanthrene Brilliant Violet 3B, Pr. 288		Mono- to dibromoisodibenzanthrone

Miscellaneous Solubilization Procedures

A large number of schemes have been proposed and studied for solubilization of vat colors other than by formation of leuco sulfuric acid esters as discussed above. Perhaps the best known of these hoped-for alternatives is the Neocotone process which was made known by The Society of Chemical Industry, Basle in 1938–1941[3, 4, 5]. The Neocotones were obtained by esterification, in the presence of pyridine, of hydroxy or imino groups in vat (or azoic) dyes by acylating agents containing water-soluble groups, e.g., m-(chlorosulfonyl)benzoic acid. These products proved to be too unstable to withstand the storage time necessary for practical use. Acylating agents of this same type condense with leuco vat dyes under certain conditions[17, 18], but the products, while water-soluble, do not regenerate the parent dyes under practical conditions.

Finally a special solubilization of anthraquinoneacridones (naphth[2,3-c]acridone-5,8,14(13H)-triones) has been disclosed in which the acridone is treated with phosphorus oxychloride and this product is reacted with sodium bisulfite to produce a water-soluble product which can be reconverted to the original vat dye upon hydrolysis either by acids or by sodium carbonate or other mild alkalies[7, 14]. This is shown schematically:

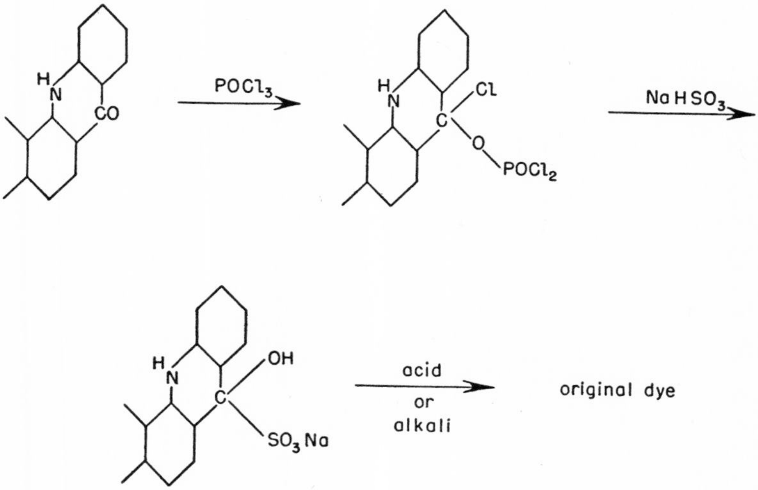

This procedure is said not to apply to other types of dyes but the product from the violet diacridone (CI 1163) of the following formula is satisfactory for use along with the conventional "soluble vat dyes" (as long as acid is used for regeneration):

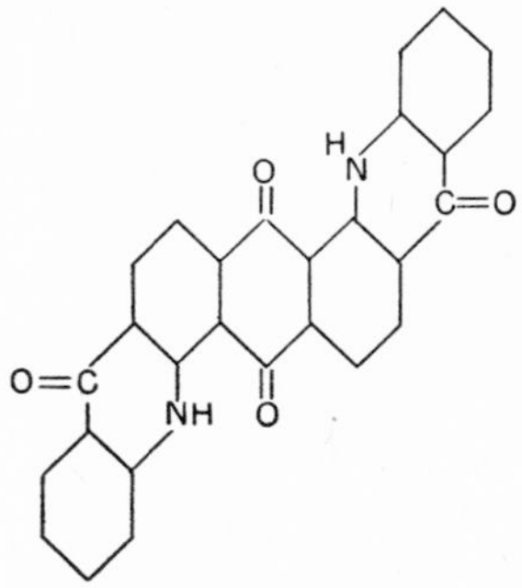

Literature Cited

1. Bader and Sunder, U.S. Patent 1,448,251 (1923).
2. Coffey, Driver and Fairweather, U.S. Patent 2,506,580 (1950).
3. Graenacher, Bruengger and Ackermann, U.S. Patent 2,120,741 (1938).
4. ——, Ackermann and Bruengger, U.S. Patent 2,170,262 (1939).
5. ——, —— and ——, U.S. Patent 2,235,480 (1941).
6. I. G. Farbenindustrie, BIOS 960, pp. 26–31 (PB 65657).
7. ——, BIOS 987, pp. 178–79 (PB 75860).
8. ——, BIOS 1493, pp. 60–61 (PB 81611).
9. ——, *ibid.*, p. 63.
10. ——, FIAT 1313, Vol. II, pp. 188–192 (PB 85172).
11. ——, *ibid.*, p. 192.
12. ——, *ibid.*, pp. 193–6.
13. ——, *ibid.*, pp. 196–8.
14. ——, FIAT 1313, Vol. III, pp. 59–60 (PB 85172).
15. Lecher and Hardy, *J. Am. Chem. Soc.*, **70**, 3789 (1948).
16. ——, Scalera and Lester, U.S. Patent 2,403,226 (1946).
17. Mueller and Muenster, U.S. Patent 2,249,973 (1941).
18. Mieg and Heidenreich, U.S. Patent 1,878,964 (1932).
19. Morton, Jones, Wylam and Harris, U.S. Patent 1,790,759 (1931).

MISCELLANEOUS VAT DYES

Melvin A. Perkins

A new type of vat dye, known as Indanthrene Brilliant Blue 4G, was recently marketed in Europe. This new dye appears to be a partially sulfonated cobalt phthalocyanine[1] and contains no keto groups (which are ordinarily considered to be characteristic of a vat dye). Yet it dissolves in alkaline hydrosulfite to give an olive-colored vat which is at least as stable as that of the average anthraquinone vat dye. No formula for the leuco compound has been given but the metal plays an important role since cobalt appears unique in giving a phthalocyanine which has a stable vat which has affinity for cotton and gives light-fast dyeings. Beautiful blue dyeings are obtained but these are extremely sensitive to oxidizing agents so the product cannot be used on goods which are to be bleached in any way.

Azabenzanthrones with nitrogen in various positions other than "3" and "4" have been used in reactions analogous to those used in building up the well known dibenzanthrone, isodibenzanthrone and benzanthroneacridine dyes from benzanthrone[2, 3, 4]. Although several excellent dyes of violet, blue, olive-green and gray shades are obtainable in this way, none of these dyes shows sufficient advantage over conventional types to merit marketing.

A brown vat dye, CI 1154, now practically obsolete, was produced for many years because of low cost. Its constitution is unknown but it was obtained quite simply by heating 2-aminoanthraquinone with copper powder in sulfuric acid at about 100°C[5].

Two other dyes of uncertain constitution are obtainable by sulfur fusion of 2-methylanthraquinone[10] or of 2-(chloromethyl)anthraquinone[8]. These dyes were obtained only after intensive bleaching of the crude fusion products and were originally known as Cibanone Yellow R, CI 1170, and Cibanone Orange R, CI 1169. The shade was controlled by the temperature employed in the sulfur fusion[6]. The more exact constitution of these products has been the object of a recent scientific study in which it was found that several compounds are present[11].

Hydron Yellow G, CI 1159, although a carbazole derivative, was not discussed under "Anthraquinonecarbazoles" because no anthrimide is involved in its formation. It is a yellow of medium shade and fastness which enjoyed a great deal of popularity until brighter vat yellows appeared. It was synthesized by condensing 9-ethylcarbazole with phthalic anhydride in the presence of sulfuric acid[7, 9] and is represented by the formula

Literature Cited

1. Bienert, U.S. Patent 2,613,128 (1952).
2. British Patent 421,264 (1934).
3. British Patent 444,812 (1936).
4. British Patent 450,244 (1936).

5. Deinet, U.S. Patent 874,743 (1907).
6. Fierz-David, *J. Soc. Dyers Colourists*, **51,** 50 (1935).
7. Luettringhaus, U.S. Patent 1,196,127 (1916).
8. Mayer and Schaarschmidt, U.S. Patent 902,895 (1908).
9. Nissen and Saul, U.S. Patent 1,055,287 (1913).
10. Schaarschmidt, U.S. Patent 899,845 (1908).
11. Shah, Tilak and Venkataraman, *Proc. Indian Acad. Sci.*, **30A,** 1 (1949).

8. INDIGOID DYES

A. J. Johnson

Introduction and Historical Background

The indigoid dyes are vat dyes and, being insoluble in water, are applied to fibers in a reduced or leuco form, or printed with a gum thickener containing alkali and reducing agents. The indigoid dyes include indigo and its substitution products, thioindigo and its substitution products, and unsymmetrical combinations of the general formula:

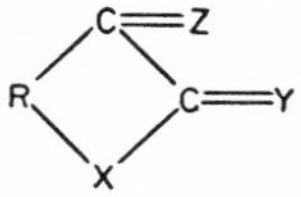

$$R \diagdown \begin{array}{c} C = Z \\ C = Y \end{array}$$

where R is an *o*-arylene radical; X is NH or S; either Y or Z is oxygen and the other represents a substituent having the linkage $=C\diagdown$, this C atom being a member of a ring which bears an adjacent keto group.

The following classes of dyes, which include all important dyes of this type or illustrate the significant chemistry of the group, will be covered in this chapter:

(I)

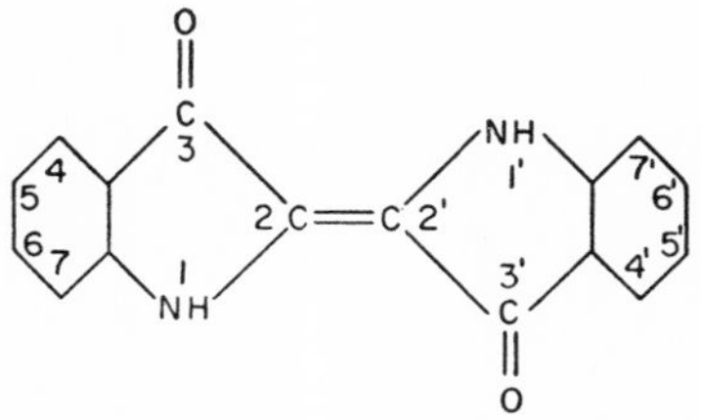

2,2'- Bisindole indigo (Indigotin)

(II)

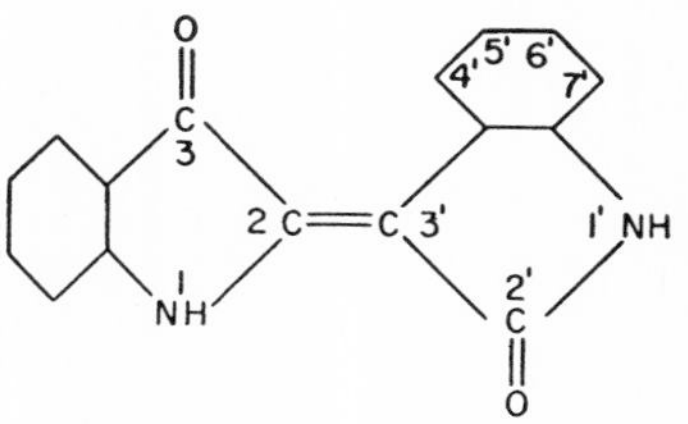

2,3'- Bisindole indigo

551

2,2'- Bisthianophthene indigo

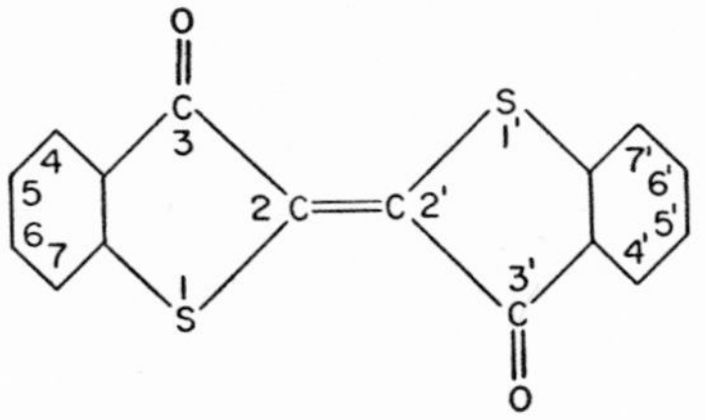

2'- Indole – 2–thianophthene indigo

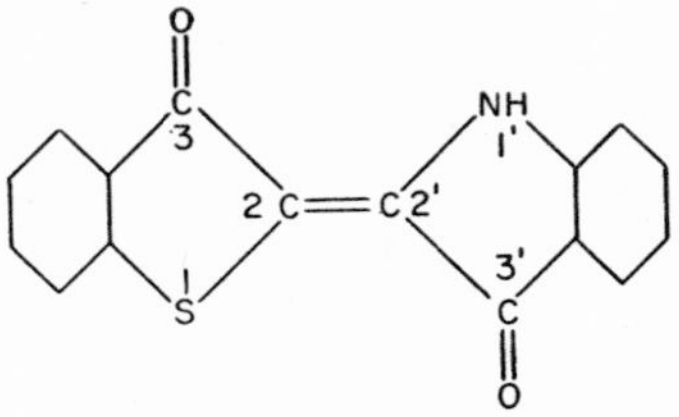

3'- Indole–2– thianophthene indigo

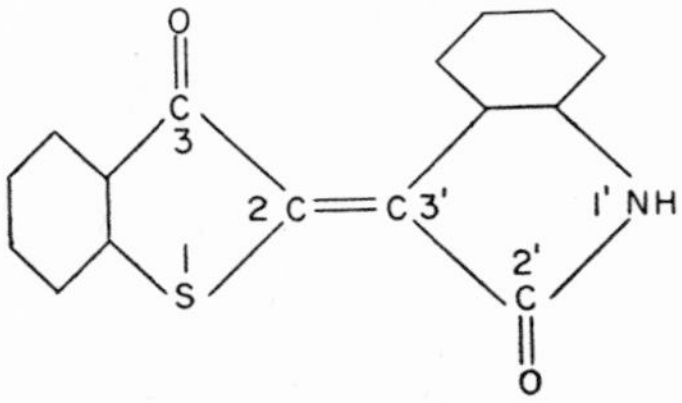

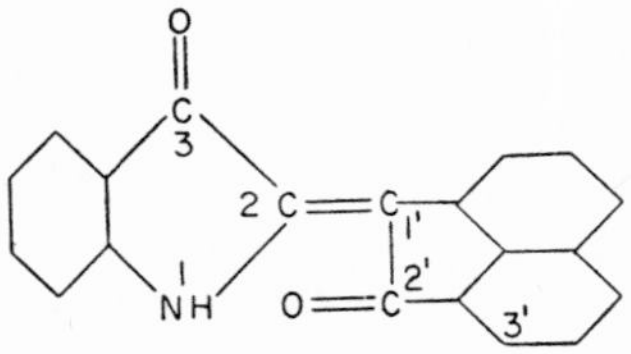

1'- Acenaphthene – 2 – indole indigo

1'-Acenaphthene-2–thianophthene indigo

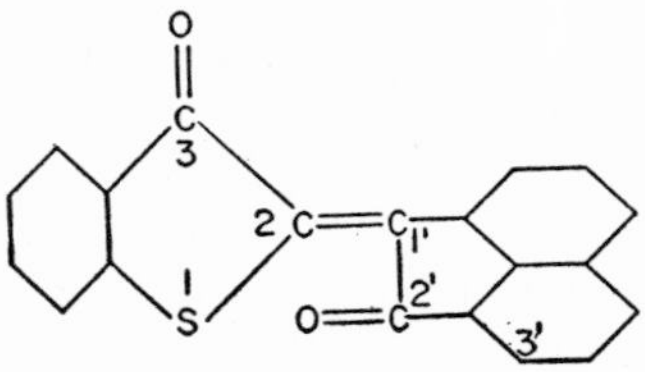

(VIII)

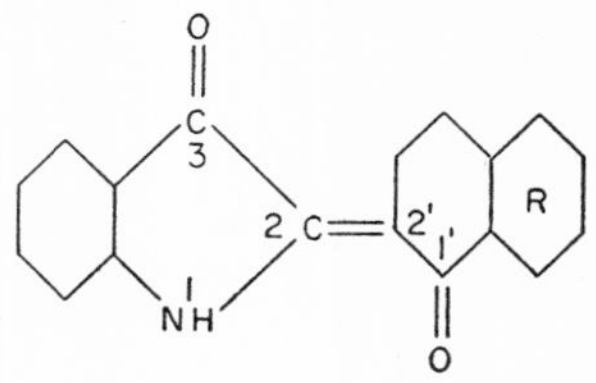

2'– Arene –2– indole indigo

(IX)

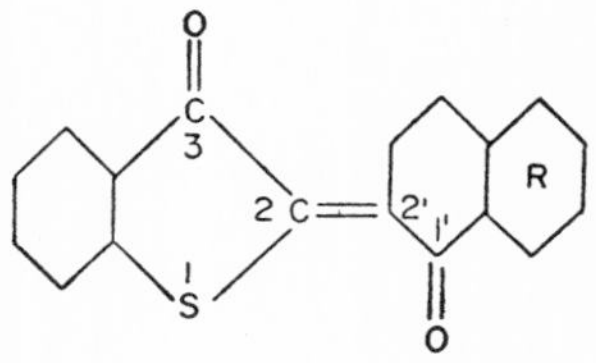

2'-Arene –2- thionophthene indigo

2,2'-Bisindole Indigo

Indigo has been known since ancient times[6, 47, 54] and is still a dye of great commercial importance. It is a derivative of indican, which is a beta-glucoside of indoxyl,

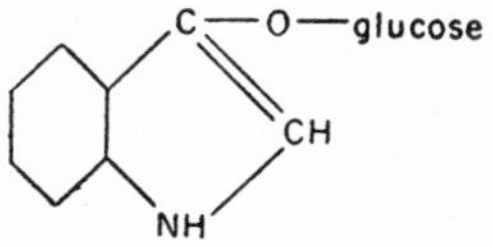

found in the leaves of a number of plants. The chief sources of this substance are various species of the indigo plant (*Indigofera Sumatrana* and *Arrecta*) found in India and Java, and the woad plant (*Isatis tinctoria*) found in Europe. The raising of indigo plants and the extraction of indigo was an important industry in India[50]. In 1897, nearly 1.7 million acres of land was under cultivation for this purpose and a total of close to 17 million pounds of indigo was exported. Following the introduction of synthetic indigo in 1897, the production of natural indigo fell off, and at the present time is of negligible importance.

Early in the nineteenth century indigo was the subject of chemical investigation, and after about fifty years of research[55] by various workers, the following structure of indigo, accepted at the present time, was announced by Baeyer in 1883[3]:

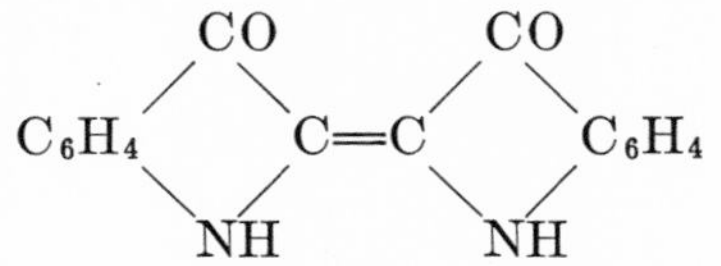

$$C_6H_4 \diagup \begin{array}{c} CO \\ \\ NH \end{array} \diagdown C=C \diagup \begin{array}{c} CO \\ \\ NH \end{array} \diagdown C_6H_4$$

It is now generally recognized that indigo[57] and thioindigo[10] occur in *cis* and *trans* forms, but are usually preponderantly in the *trans* form when in the solid state.

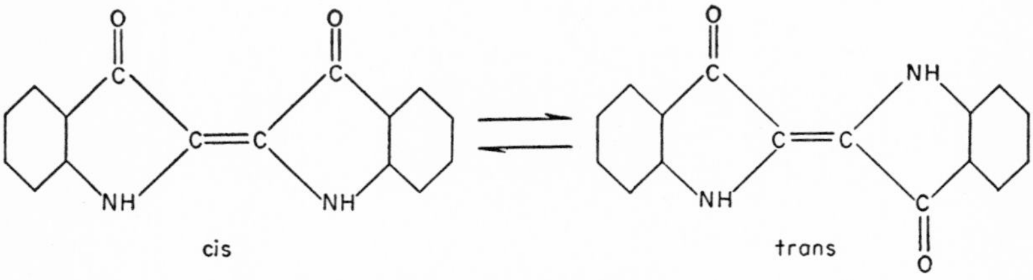

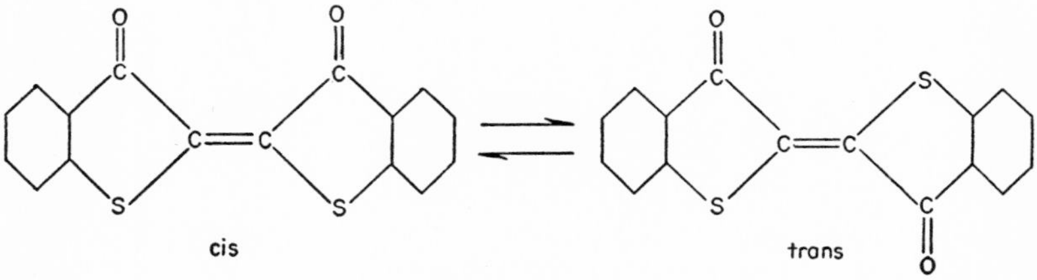

The first commercial process for manufacturing synthetic indigo was developed at the BASF plant at Ludwigshafen by Heumann and others between 1890 and 1897[25]. The process was based on naphthalene as a starting intermediate, oxidizing it to give phthalic anhydride, which was condensed with ammonia to form phthalimide. This was converted to anthranilic acid by the Hofmann reaction[24] and condensed with chloroacetic acid to give N-(carboxymethyl)anthranilic acid, which was fused with sodium hydroxide to give indoxylic acid. The latter was oxidized to give indigo.

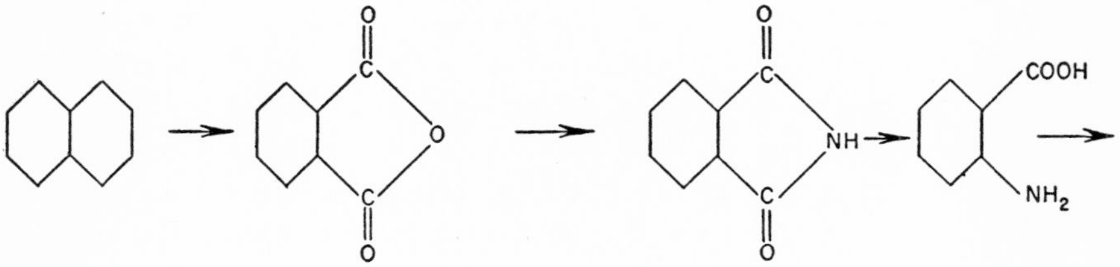

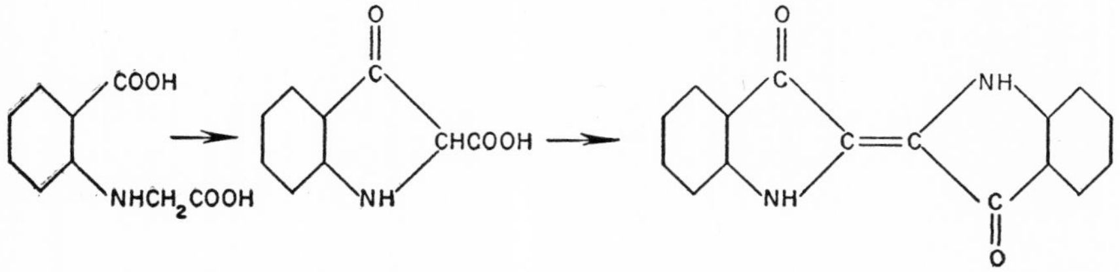

It is reported that 18 million marks was spent over a period of 17 years after Baeyer's determination of the structure of indigo in developing a satisfactory manufacturing process.

A later process, developed at the Meister, Lucius and Bruening (MLB) plant at Hoechst, was based on the discovery by Pfleger[49] of the Deutsche Gold- und Silber-Scheideanstalt that sodium amide could be used to make indoxyl from *N*-phenylglycine. By adding sodium amide to the sodium hydroxide used in the fusion of *N*-phenylglycine, the reaction could be carried out at a lower temperature and good yields were obtained.

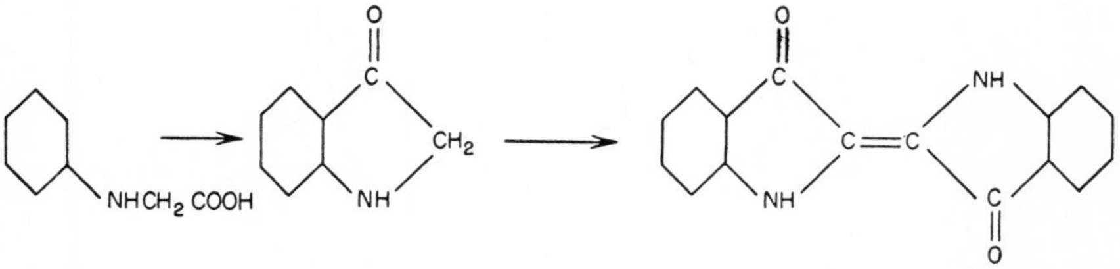

This is the process which is largely used at the present time for the manufacture of indigo, since it is essentially cheaper than the BASF route.

N-phenylglycine was originally made by condensing aniline with chloroacetic acid, but it is also made commercially by the following route:

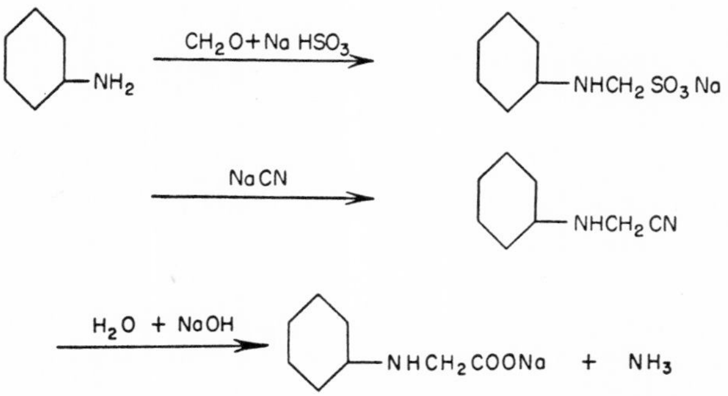

A third commercial process, which was used for some time by Geigy in Switzerland, was based on the work of Sandmeyer[51]. Aniline was reacted with carbon disulfide to give thiocarbanilide, which was treated with basic lead carbonate and sodium cyanide to give α-cyano-*N*,*N*′-diphenylformamidine. This was treated with yellow ammonium sulfide, giving the "thioamide," which on heating with concentrated sulfuric acid gave 2-phenyliminopseudoindoxyl. On boiling this with dilute acid it was split up into isatin and aniline. The isatin was treated with sodium hydrosulfide solution to give 2-thioisatin, which on treatment with dilute alkali formed indigo. The reactions are as follows:

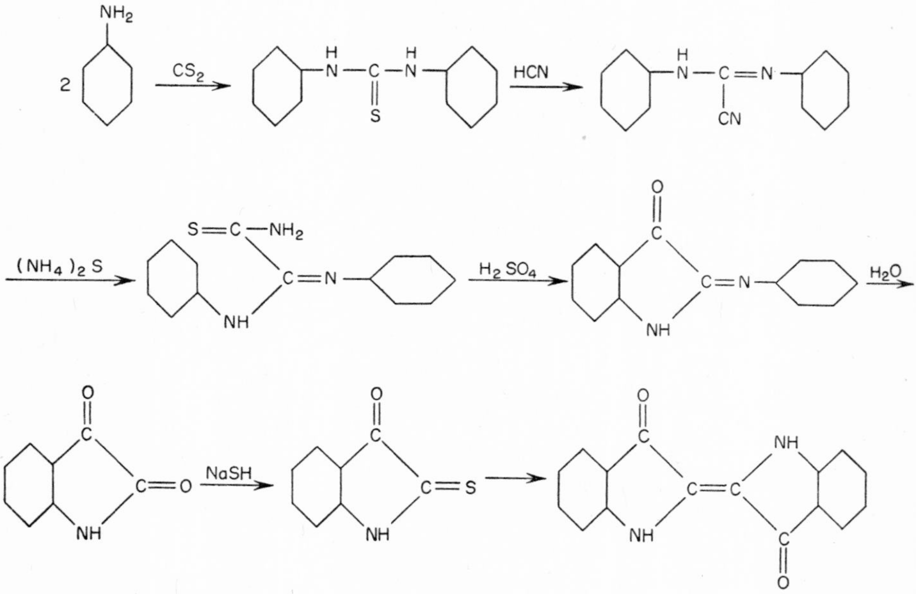

It was claimed that an over-all yield of 80 per cent of theory was obtained, but the process was discontinued because of the use of such large amounts of the obnoxious and toxic hydrogen sulfide gas. It was replaced by the process developed by MLB, which gave yields of 85 per cent of theory.

A large number of methods have been found for synthesizing indigo[15, 55], but only the three methods described above have been used on a commercial scale. Neither of the processes used at present can be readily carried out on a small scale. A method by which indigo can be easily prepared in the laboratory is that of Baeyer and Drewsen[4], in which *o*-nitrobenzaldehyde (or its substitution products, in which case correspondingly substituted indigos are formed) is treated with acetone to form a 4-hydroxy-4-(*o*-nitrophenyl)-2-butanone, which is dehydrated to form 4-(*o*-nitrophenyl)-3-buten-2-one. The latter on treatment with dilute alkali is converted to indigo.

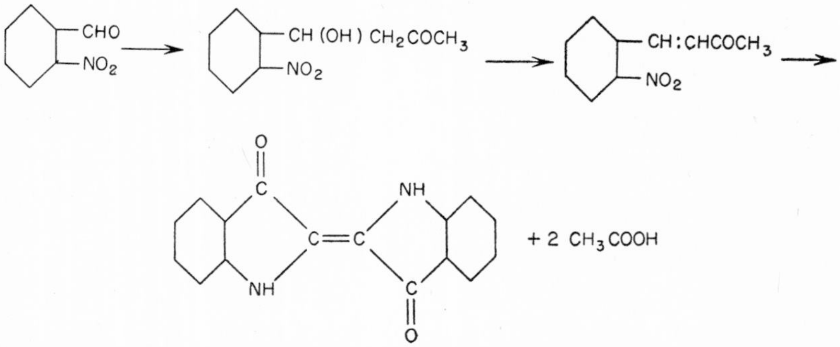

By starting with 4-bromo-2-nitrobenzaldehyde, 6,6′-dibromoindigo is obtained. This dye is identical with Tyrian Purple, CI 1248, or the Purple of the Ancients, which was obtained in very low yield from certain molluscs (*Murex brandaris*) in the Mediterranean area[4].

Another relatively simple laboratory method of preparing indigos is to heat *N*-(carboxymethyl)anthranilic acids with acetic anhydride and anhydrous sodium acetate[53]. The product is oxidized in alkaline solution to give the color.

Still another method of laboratory interest comprises reacting an arylamine with the diethyl ester of bromomalonic acid, ring-closing by heating, hydrolyzing with sodium hydroxide to give the pseudoindoxyl, and finally oxidizing to the color, in this case Helindon Green.

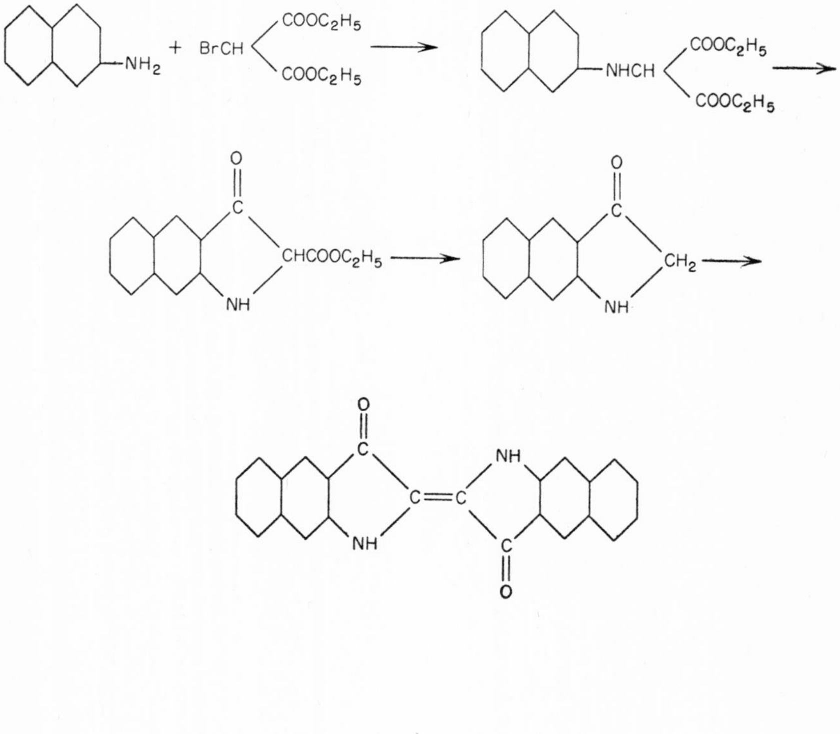

This process was not used commercially because of the unavailability of the bromomalonic ester.

A method of great historical interest[2, 8] is that based on the formation of pseudoindoxyl by the reduction of the reaction product of phosphorus pentachloride and isatin, followed by oxidation to indigo.

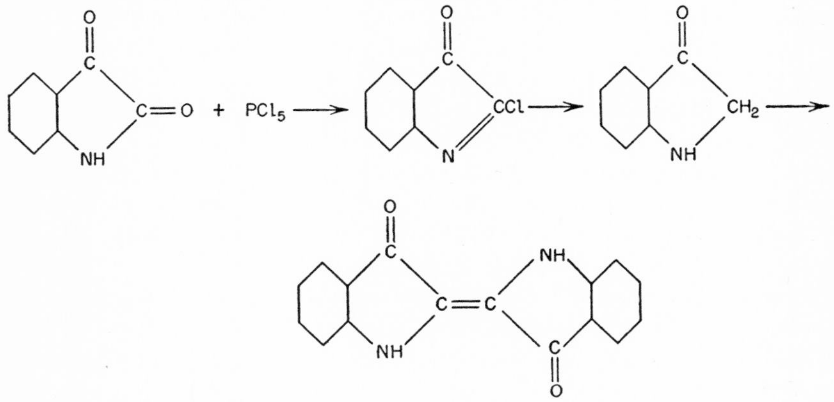

This was the method by which Baeyer[5] prepared the first synthetic indigo in 1870.

The role of isatin and its substitution products has been of considerable importance, since these intermediates have been used in making hundreds of unsymmetrical indigoid dyes as will be shown in syntheses later on. Isatin is readily prepared by the oxidation of indigo with sodium dichromate in dilute sulfuric acid suspension. Yields up to 90 per cent of theory, based on indigo consumed, are obtainable by this method. By monohalogenation of isatin the 5-halo derivatives are obtained, and by further halogenation the 5,7-dihalo products result.

Isatin can be prepared by a Sandmeyer method[37, 52], in which aniline is treated with hydroxylamine and chloral to give α-isonitrosoacetanilide. This is ring-closed by heating with concentrated sulfuric acid to give isatin.

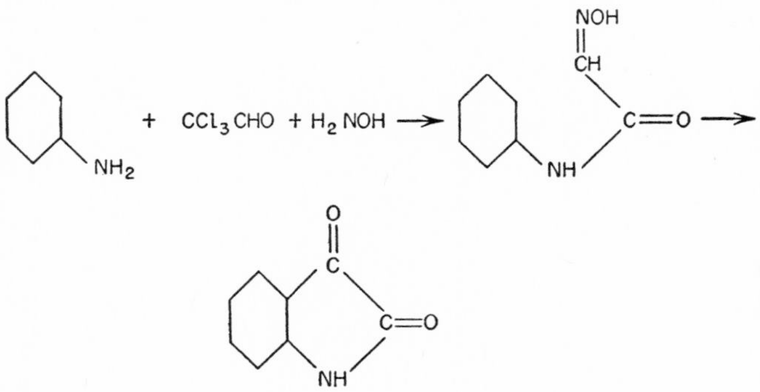

This method is a general one for primary amines of the benzene series. Better yields are obtained from substituted anilines than from aniline itself. This synthesis is not applicable to naphthalene derivatives.

Indigo is still the world's largest volume color and it is also one of the cheapest dyes[56]. In 1951 the total production of indigo in the United States was 20.5 million pounds (on a 20 per cent paste basis), valued at $0.27 per pound. The total production of synthetic organic dyes for the same year was 187 million pounds, with a weighted average value of $1.10 per pound.

The principal use for this large amount of indigo is in the dyeing of cotton for working clothes, such as overalls. A considerable amount of indigo is also used for dyeing wool in heavy shades, as in Navy uniforms. A comparatively small amount is used in pigment form in printing inks.

Of the large number of substituted indigos that have been made and described, especially in issued patents, only a few have been of commercial importance. These have been mostly halogen derivatives, and mainly the bromine substitution products. When indigo is chlorinated or brominated, the 5,5' positions are first occupied, then the 7,7' positions, followed by the 4,4' positions, and finally the remaining 6,6' positions[18]. This holds true whether the halogenation is carried out in nitrobenzene at higher temperatures or in sulfuric acid at lower temperatures. In order to obtain indigo first substituted in other positions, it is necessary to synthesize it from proper halogen-containing intermediates.

A mixture of 5,5'-dibromo- and 5,5',7-tribromoindigo, CI 1183, is known as Brilliant Indigo BR[35]. It is brighter and somewhat greener than indigo and is used for textile printing as well as for vat dyeing.

5,5',7,7'-Tetrabromoindigo, CI 1184, known as Brilliant Indigo 4B, is obtained by brominating indigo in nitrobenzene. It is a color that has attained considerable importance because of its brightness and cheapness. It is used principally in printing rayon and cotton fabrics. The indigosol or leuco sulfuric acid ester of this dye, represented by Algosol Blue O4B, is one of the most important members of this dye class.

A considerable number of the commercial thioindigoid and indigoid dyes have appeared on the market in water-soluble form as leuco sulfuric acid esters, under the names Indigosol (D & H), Algosol (G), Soledon (I.C.I.), Anthrasol (I.G.), etc. The original dye of this type, Indigosol O, is the sodium salt of indigo leuco sulfuric acid ester,

which was discovered by Bader and Sunder in 1921[1]. These dyes are especially suitable for wool dyeing since they are applied from a neutral or slightly acid bath[48]. The dyeings are developed by regenerating the parent vat dye on the fiber by treatment with oxidizing agents in the presence of a mineral acid at comparatively low temperature. They are not used, however, for dyeing in heavy shades, due to their higher cost and the fact that level dyeings are obtainable by conventional vat dyeing. The chief advantage in the use of the Indigosol types is in the production of level dyeings in lighter shades.

The dye sold as Brilliant Indigo 4G, CI 1189, is 5,5'-dibromo-4,4'-dichloroindigo, and is made by the bromination of 4,4'-dichloroindigo, which is known as Janson Indigo. One method of making the latter color is from 2-chloro-6-nitrobenzaldehyde by the Baeyer and Drewsen method[4], which has been described above. The dibromodichloro product is somewhat greener than the tetrabromo, and like the latter, is an important color because of its brightness and greenish-blue shade. It also has the property of retaining its greenish shade in artificial light, whereas other halogenated indigos show a reddening or darkening in shade under these conditions.

More highly halogenated indigos have been prepared, e.g., hexa-, hepta- and octahalogenated indigos, but these products have never been of any commercial interest because of poor dyeing properties due to the lower solubility of the leuco derivatives in the dyeing bath.

The dye 5,5'-indigodisulfonic acid, CI 1180, obtained by the sulfonation of indigo, is called Indigotine I or Indigo Carmine. It was formerly an important blue dye for wool and silk, but has largely been replaced by other dyes of better fastness properties. It is used as a food color, as well as for medicinal purposes and as a stain in microscopic work.

Ciba Lake Red B, CI 1194, is an interesting derivative obtained by the reaction of indigo with phenylacetyl chloride.

It is a bright red compound which is not vattable and hence cannot be used as a vat dye. It has been used as a pigment for paints and lacquers, but is no longer on the market.

Indigo reacts with benzoyl chloride under various conditions to give a number of derivatives, the most important of which is Ciba Yellow 3G, CI 1195, obtained by the reaction with benzoyl chloride in the presence of copper powder. This color on bromination gives Ciba Yellow G, CI 1196, which at one time was of some importance since, in addition to its use for yellow self-shades, it was used in mixtures with indigo to obtain green shades.

The constitution of the benzoylated products of indigo has been a subject of study for many years and a number of structures have been proposed. In a report by de Diesbach, *et al.*, the following condensed ring structure is proposed for Ciba Yellow 3G[11]:

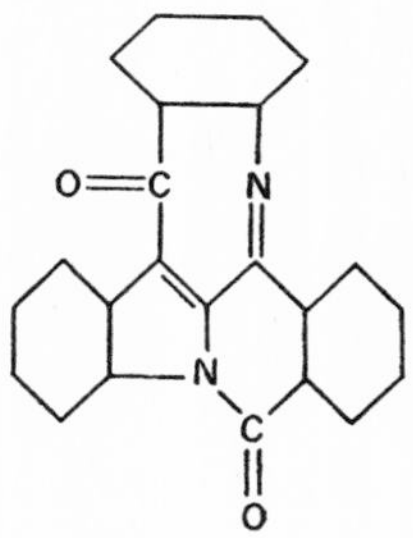

2,3'-Bisindole Indigo

The unsubstituted product, obtained from pseudoindoxyl and isatin,

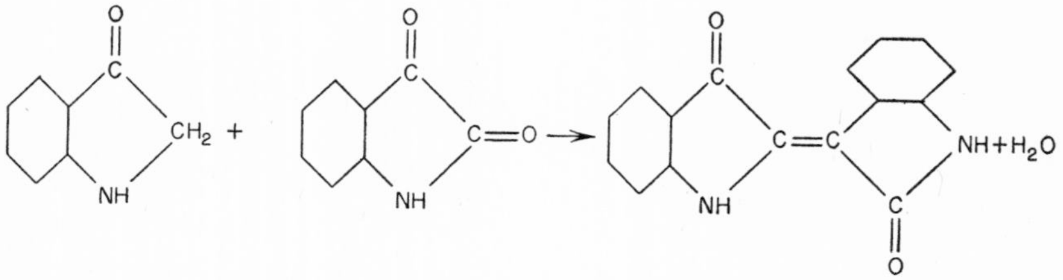

is known as Indirubin, CI 1204. It occurs in natural indigo as an impurity in varying amounts. It cannot be vatted and applied to textiles as such, since it is split by alkaline reducing agents into pseudoindoxyl and oxindole[9]:

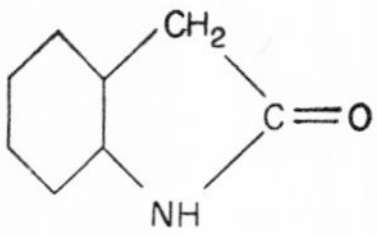

The pseudoindoxyl forms indigo on reoxidation, while the oxindole remains as an insoluble product.

5,5',7,7'-Tetrabromoindirubin, obtainable by the bromination of indirubin[14], was formerly sold as Ciba Heliotrope B, CI 1205. It has been displaced by other dyes, since it possesses only moderate fastness properties.

2,2'-Bisthianaphthene Indigo

The simplest dye of this class is unsubstituted thioindigo, which was first made by Friedlaender in 1905[16]. The most common method for preparing this color is to start with anthranilic acid, diazotizing and reacting with sodium disulfide to give 2,2'-dithiodibenzoic acid, which is reduced to o-mercaptobenzoic acid and condensed with chloroacetic acid to form o-(carboxymethylmercapto)benzoic acid. The latter is converted by heating with sodium hydroxide to thioindoxyl (3(2H)-thianaphthenone), which is oxidized to give the color.

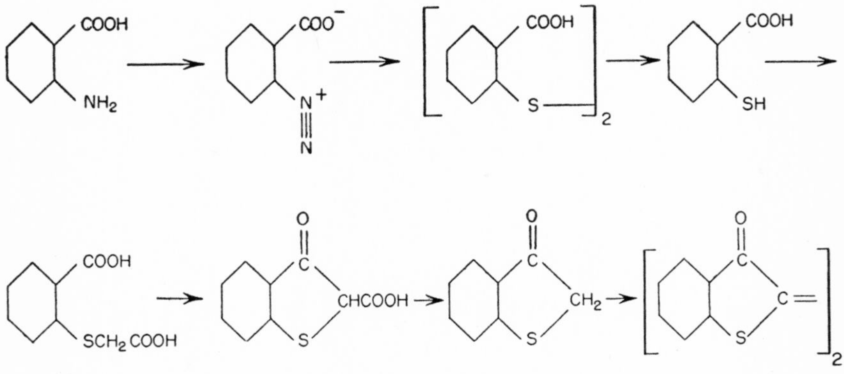

Since the discovery of thioindigo, thousands of substituted products have been made, but of these only a few have attained commercial importance. The thioindigo dyes are of value because of their brightness of shade and generally good fastness properties. Some of them have sufficiently good fastness properties to be rated with the best vat dyes and are sold under the Indanthrene label, which was restricted by I. G. Farbenindustrie to dyes meeting high fastness requirements. The less fast vat dyes of the anthraquinonoid and indigoid types were sold under the Algol label by I. G. Farbenindustrie.

In recent years the greater part of the thioindigo dyes sold has been used in printing rayon or cotton dress goods, draperies, and upholstery materials. A comparatively small use for thioindigoid dyes has been as pigments in paints and for coloring wallpaper. A few thioindigoid dyes have found some outlet in wool dyeing. A selected range of vat dyes, including indigoid dyes, suitable for this purpose is sold under the name of Helindon dyes. The properties which make them suitable for this purpose are their solubility in their leuco forms in comparatively weak alkaline solution and their applicability at comparatively low temperatures.

Although unsubstituted thioindigo, CI 1207 — sold as Thioindigo Red B, possesses very good lightfastness, it does not have as good washfastness as some of the substituted thioindigos. Its use is limited for this reason.

One of the most common chlorine-substituted thioindigos is 6,6'-dichlorothioindigo, CI 1210, Ciba Red B. It is yellower in shade and has better washing fastness than thioindigo. It is no longer sold in the United States and was made in comparatively small amounts in Germany prior to 1940. It was originally made by Engi[13] by heating 2-(carboxymethylmercapto)-4-chlorobenzoic acid in nitrobenzene.

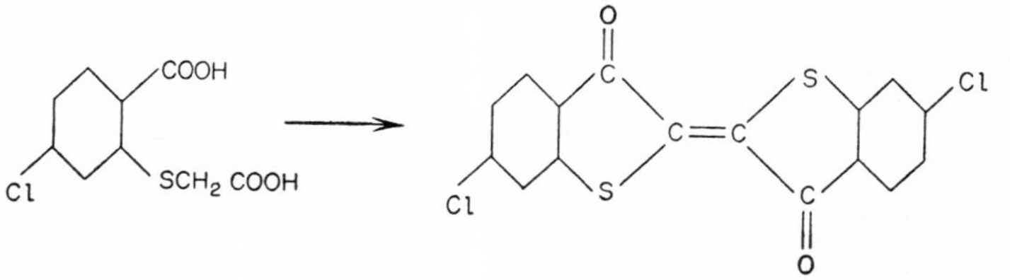

It was later made in Germany by the Herz sulfur chloride method[7, 22]. This unique process, which includes a number of steps, is outlined below:

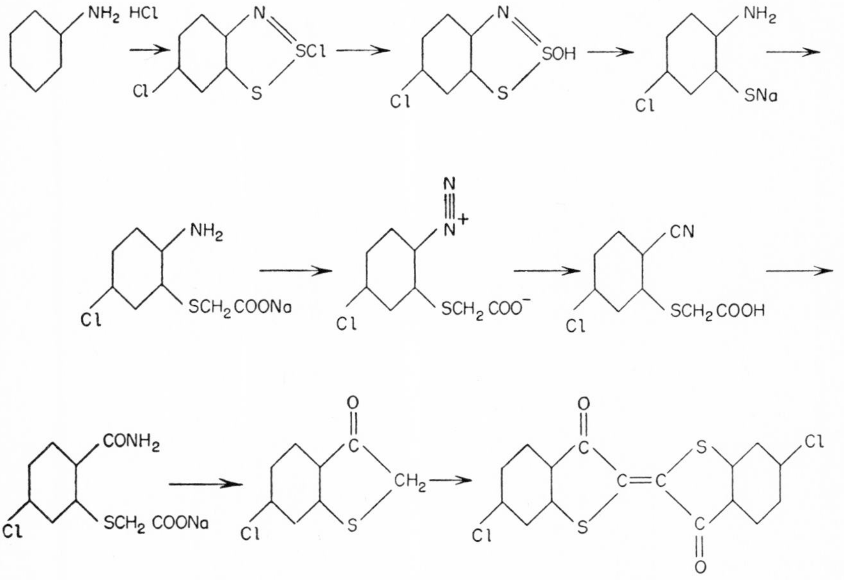

In the Herz sulfur chloride method the hydrochloride of an aromatic amine, such as aniline, is reacted with sulfur chloride to give a benzo-1,3-thiaza-2-thionium chloride as shown above. If the position para to the amino group (position 6) is occupied by hydrogen, chlorination takes place at this point at the same time. This product is hydrolyzed to remove the chlorine attached to the sulfur in the heterocyclic ring. On treatment with alkali this ring is split open and the o-aminothiol results. This is condensed with chloroacetic acid to form the (o-aminophenylmercapto)acetic acid. The amino group is replaced by the cyano group by diazotizing and reacting with sodium cuprocyanide (Sandmeyer reaction). The nitrile is hydrolyzed in alkaline solution to the carboxamide, which on acid hydrolysis ring-closes, splits off ammonia and carbon dioxide and forms the thioindoxyl, which is oxidized to the color.

One of the most important and brilliant thioindigo dyes is 6,6'-dichloro-4,4'-dimethylthioindigo, Pr. 109, which is known as Helindon Pink R. The dye is usually made by the above-outlined Herz method, starting with o-toluidine hydrochloride in place of aniline hydrochloride. In this case, also, chlorine is introduced into the ring in the position para to the amino group. The dye is used as a dyeing or printing color for rayon and cotton. It is also used for dyeing wool, as the Helindon name indicates, and to some extent as a pigment for printing inks. It is also sold in the form of the soluble leuco sulfuric acid ester.

5,5'-Dichloro-7,7'-dimethylthioindigo, which is also prepared from o-toluidine, is sold as Indanthrene Red Violet RH, CI 1212 (incorrectly cited as 5,5'-dichloro-6,6'-dimethylthioindigo).

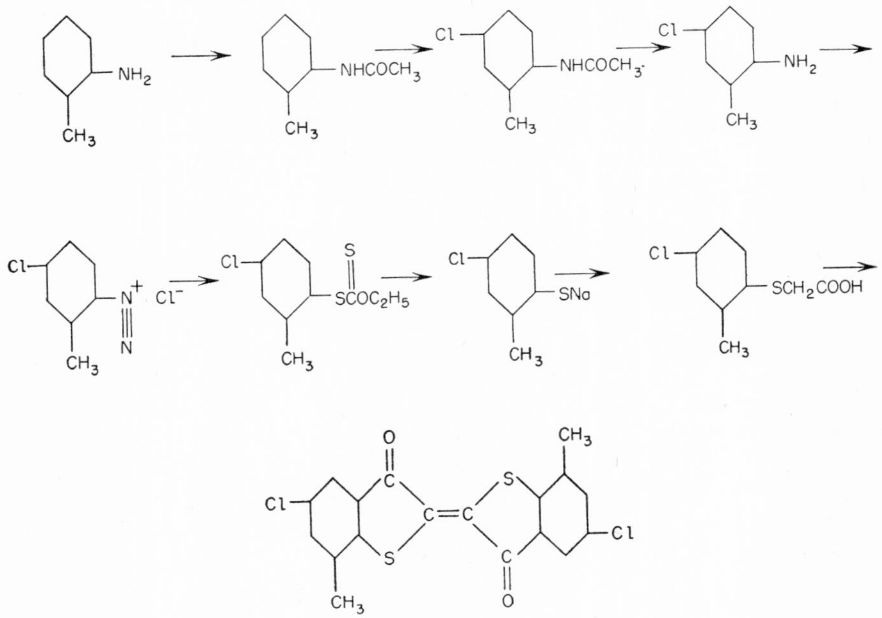

As the above outline indicates, o-toluidine is acetylated, chlorinated, and hydrolyzed to 4-chloro-o-toluidine. This is diazotized and reacted with an alkali ethylxanthate in warm solution, 60 to 70° C. (The addition of diazo solutions to alkali xanthates at room temperature or lower is dangerous, since highly explosive mixtures are formed[45].) The aryl xanthate is hydrolyzed to the thiol, which, without isolation, is reacted with chloroacetic acid to form the (4-chloro-*o*-tolylmercapto)acetic acid. The latter, when dissolved in cold chlorosulfonic acid, first forms the thioindoxyl which soon oxidizes to the final color at slightly elevated temperatures[33].

In a later process developed at Hoechst and used since 1940, the potassium ethylxanthate of the above process is replaced by sodium disulfide[38]. The resulting chlorotolyl disulfide is reduced to thiol and the process from this point on is the same as that outlined above.

A third process[33], developed as a patent-free route by the I. G. Farbenindustrie for use in the United States, started with *m*-toluidine, from which *m*-chlorotoluene was made by the Sandmeyer reaction. The *m*-chlorotoluene was sulfonated, converted to 5-chloro-*m*-toluenesulfonyl chloride, reduced to the thiol and condensed with chloroacetic acid to give the (4-chloro-*o*-tolylmercapto)acetic acid.

The dye is used mostly for printing rayon and cotton and to some extent as a pigment for maroon shades in paints and lacquers. The color is a very bluish red and illustrates the shift toward the blue caused by the introduction of chlorine in the 5,5′ positions[54].

Although it is beyond the scope of this chapter to discuss the effect of substitution on the color of thioindigo dyes, it might be stated here that, in general, substitution in the 5 position gives a bathochromic effect, while substitution in the 4, 6 or 7 positions causes a hypsochromic effect. Thus for the methyl group[21] the order of decreasing depth of shade is 5-CH$_3$ > 4-CH$_3$ > 7-CH$_3$ > 6-CH$_3$.

5,5′-Dichloro-4,4′,7,7′-tetramethylthioindigo, which is sold as Indanthrene Red Violet RRN, Pr. 503, is prepared through the following route[23, 34]:

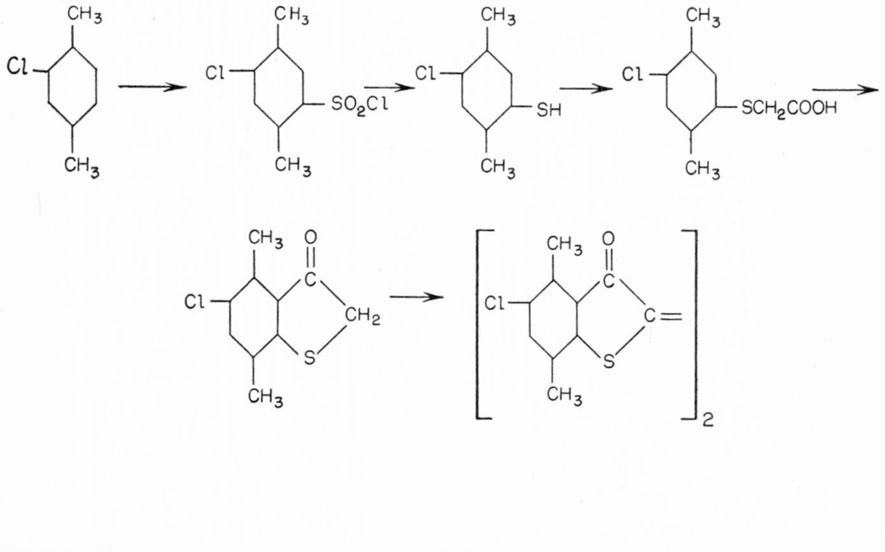

In this process the chloroxylene is converted directly to the sulfonyl chloride by treating with chlorosulfonic acid. This product is reduced to the thiol and condensed with chloroacetic acid to give the (arylmercapto)-acetic acid. By treating the latter with chlorosulfonic acid at low temperatures the thioindoxyl is formed, which is oxidized to the dye in the resulting solution by means of bromine.

A thioindigo color that has been of considerable commercial importance is 6,6'-diethoxythioindigo, Helindon Orange R, CI 1217. It can be prepared by several methods, including the Herz sulfur chloride method, starting with *p*-phenetidine hydrochloride[22]. Another method[46] is through the ethoxymercaptobenzothiazole to (6-amino-*m*-phenetylmercapto)acetic acid, as follows:

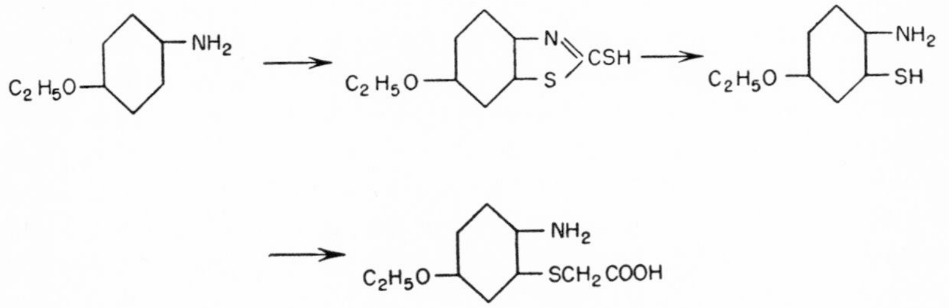

$$C_2H_5O{-}C_6H_4{-}NH_2 \longrightarrow \text{(ethoxymercaptobenzothiazole, } C_2H_5O{-}C_6H_3\text{, ring fused } N{=}C(S){-}CSH) \longrightarrow C_2H_5O{-}C_6H_3(NH_2)(SH)$$

$$\longrightarrow C_2H_5O{-}C_6H_3(NH_2)(SCH_2COOH)$$

The remainder of the process from this intermediate to the color is the same as by the Herz method.

A third method was developed in Germany to produce unique intermediates for export which would not be subject to the high U. S. tariff rates which applied to the intermediates used in the two above methods, since the latter were produced in the United States. This third process was carried out by the following route:

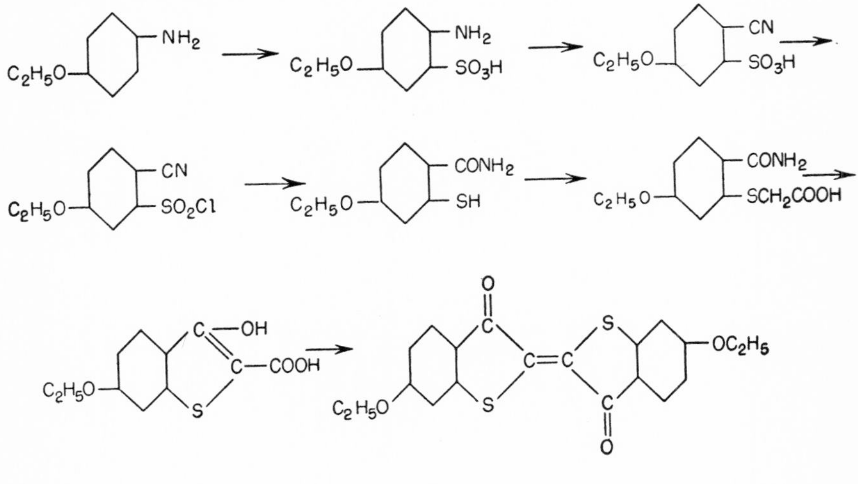

$$C_2H_5O{-}C_6H_4{-}NH_2 \longrightarrow C_2H_5O{-}C_6H_3(NH_2)(SO_3H) \longrightarrow C_2H_5O{-}C_6H_3(CN)(SO_3H) \longrightarrow$$

$$C_2H_5O{-}C_6H_3(CN)(SO_2Cl) \longrightarrow C_2H_5O{-}C_6H_3(CONH_2)(SH) \longrightarrow C_2H_5O{-}C_6H_3(CONH_2)(SCH_2COOH) \longrightarrow$$

$$C_2H_5O{-}C_6H_3\text{(ring: }C{-}OH, C{-}COOH, S) \longrightarrow \text{6,6'-diethoxythioindigo}$$

The "sulfureted phenetol carbonic acid amide," presumably 4-ethoxy-2-mercaptobenzamide,

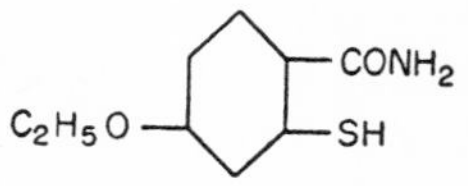

was an export item to the United States.

A corresponding intermediate from 4-chloro-*o*-toluidine (NH_2 = 1), "sulfureted chlorotolyl carbonic acid amide," used in the manufacture of Indanthrene Brilliant Pink R, also was imported into the United States prior to World War II.

The commercial Orange R types are used mostly as printing colors on man-made fibers and cotton, not only for producing orange shades, but also in combination with Indanthrene Brilliant Pink R to produce bright scarlet shades. They are also used for dyeing wool and in the manufacture of a soluble leuco sulfuric acid ester type, such as Algosol Orange HR.

The dye 4,5:4',5'-dibenzothioindigo is known as Indanthrene Brown RRD, Pr. 121. One route[39] for the manufacture of this color is to start with 2-naphthalenesulfonic acid, treat with phosphorus pentachloride to give 2-naphthalenesulfonyl chloride, reduce by tin or zinc and a mineral acid to 2-naphthalenethiol, and condense with chloroacetic acid to give (2-naphthylmercapto)acetic acid. The color is made from this intermediate by forming the acid chloride by treatment with phosphorus trichloride, ring-closing with anhydrous aluminum chloride (Friedel-Crafts reaction) to form naphtho[2,1-b]thiophen-1(2H)-one, and oxidizing this to give the color[29].

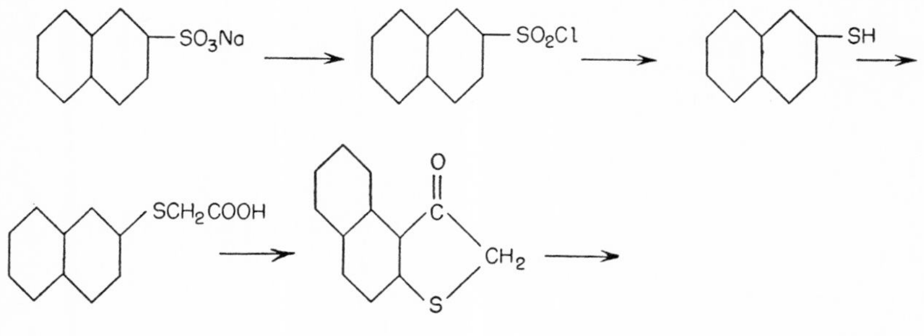

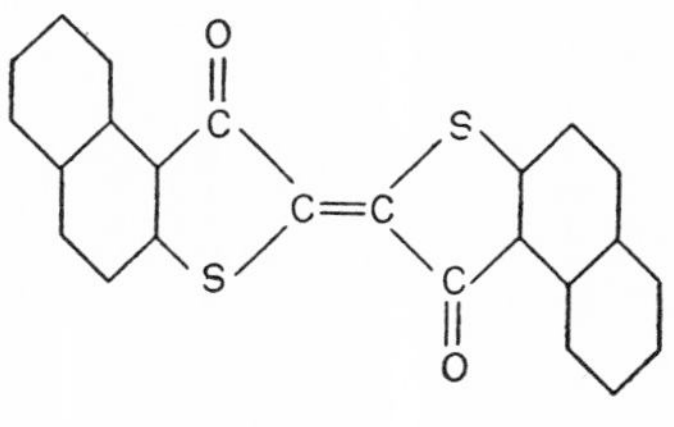

The use of the Friedel-Crafts reaction to form thioindoxyls from (aryl-mercapto)acetic acids, through the acid chloride, is necessary in those cases where sulfonation would take place if the more direct route using chlorosulfonic acid were attempted.

Perhaps the simplest method of preparing a thioindigo dye is that of Dziewonski[12], in which 1-acetonaphthone is heated with sulfur.

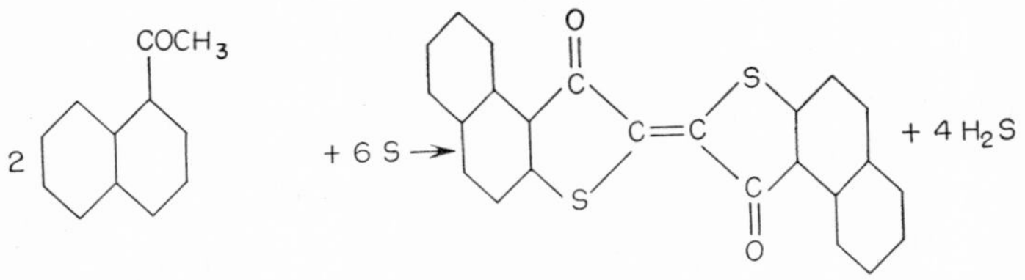

However, due to inherent shortcomings such as high cost of starting intermediate and finishing steps required, this process has not been used commercially.

Indanthrene Brown RRD is used extensively as a printing color on cotton and man-made fibers. It is also used as a wool dye and for dyeing cotton in the form of the soluble leuco sulfuric acid ester, known as Anthrasol Brown IRRD. It has one disadvantage in that the shade of the dye appears considerably redder in artificial light than in daylight.

Another brown vat dye which was quite important in Europe, and was sold only in the form of the soluble leuco ester, was Anthrasol Brown IVD. The parent dye was 6,7-dichloro-5-methoxy-4′,5′-benzothioindigo[28]. The synthesis of this color is outlined below:

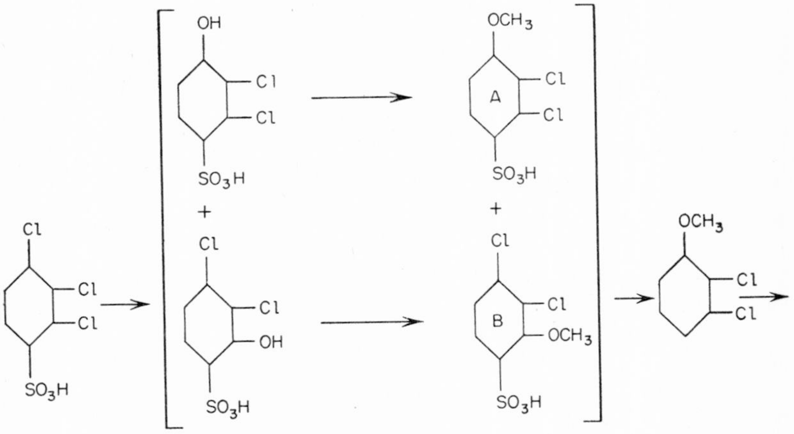

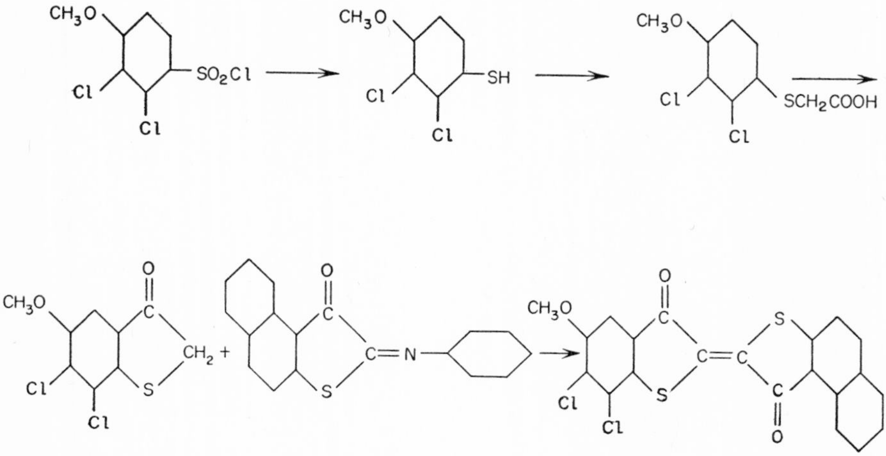

The caustic fusion of 2,3,4-trichlorobenzenesulfonic acid gave a mixture of dichlorophenolsulfonic acids, since either the 2- or the 4-chlorine was hydrolyzed off. Methylation gave a mixture of dichloromethoxybenzene-sulfonic acids, indicated by A and B above, which on desulfonation gave in each case 2,3-dichloroanisole. Treating this with chlorosulfonic acid gave 2,3-dichloro-4-methoxybenzenesulfonyl chloride, which on reduction and condensing with chloroacetic acid gave (2,3-dichloro-4-methoxyphenyl-mercapto)acetic acid. This was converted to the thioindoxyl, which was condensed with 2-phenyliminonaphtho[2,1-b]thiophen-1(2H)-one to form the color.

It is to be noted in this synthesis that there was no suitable method for separating A and B indicated above. These products, if carried through to thioindoxyls, would give a mixture of 6,7-dichloro-5-methoxy- and 5,6-dichloro-7-methoxythioindoxyls. The former of these gives a gray-blue symmetrical thioindigo, while the latter gives a red-violet color. It is evident that such a mixture would be unsatisfactory, especially since it was to be coupled with another component to form an unsymmetrical dye. Thus the synthesis of Anthrasol Brown IVD required the successive desulfonation and chlorosulfonation outlined above.

2'-Indole-2-thianaphthene Indigo

The parent member of this series, the unsubstituted product, was formerly sold as Ciba Violet A. It was first prepared by Friedlaender[17] by condensing 2,2-dibromo-3(2H)-thianaphthenone with pseudoindoxyl in glacial acetic acid.

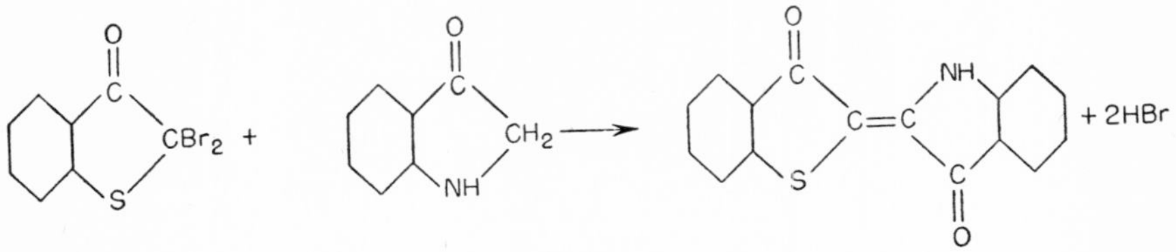

It can also be prepared from 2-phenyliminopseudoindoxyl and the thianaphthenone ("thioindoxyl").

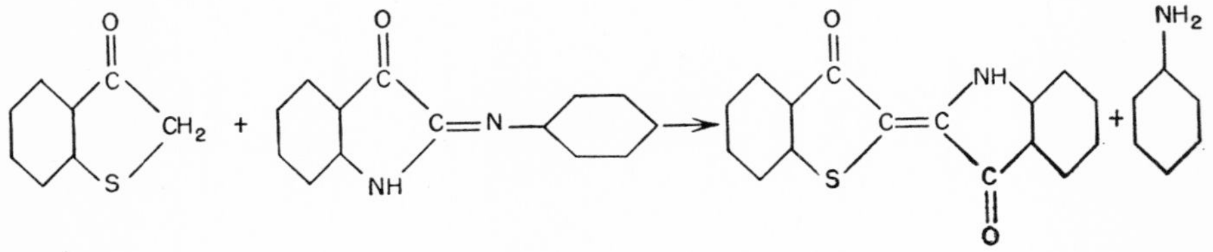

This color was never of much importance since it has relatively poor fastness properties.

Out of a total of 21 indigoid dyes used by the I. G. Farbenindustrie in the manufacture of Anthrasol dyes (Indigosol types or leuco esters), 5 were of the 2'-indole-2-thianaphthene indigo type, and all of these possessed sufficient fastness properties to warrant the Indanthrene label[26].

Indanthrene Printing Violet BBF, used in the manufacture of Anthrasol Violet IBBF, is the 5,5',6,7,7'-pentachloro derivative. It is prepared[27] from 5,6,7-trichloro-3(2H)-thianaphthenone, obtained from 1,2,3-trichlorobenzene through the sulfonyl chloride, reduction, etc., and 2,5,7-trichloro-3-pseudoindolone.

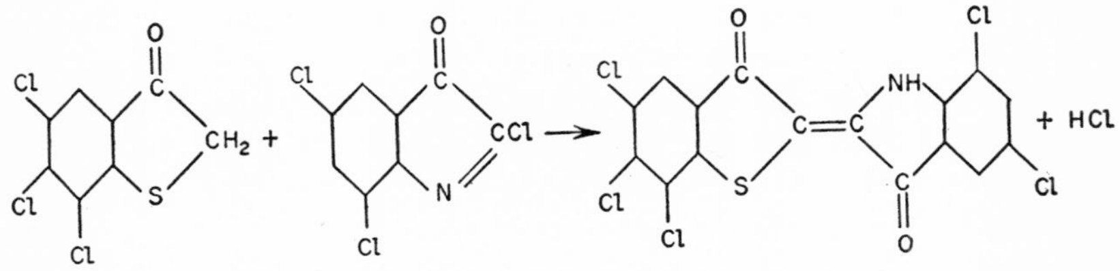

Its lightfastness is superior to that of Indanthrene Red Violet RRN (5,5'-dichloro-4,4',7,7'-tetramethylthioindigo) but its chlorinefastness is inferior.

Indanthrene Printing Violet RR, used in the manufacture of Anthrasol Printing Violet IRR, is the 5',6,7'-trichloro-4-methyl derivative. It is prepared from 6-chloro-4-methyl-3(2H)-thianaphthenone (used for Indanthrene Brilliant Pink R) and the above trichloropseudoindolone.

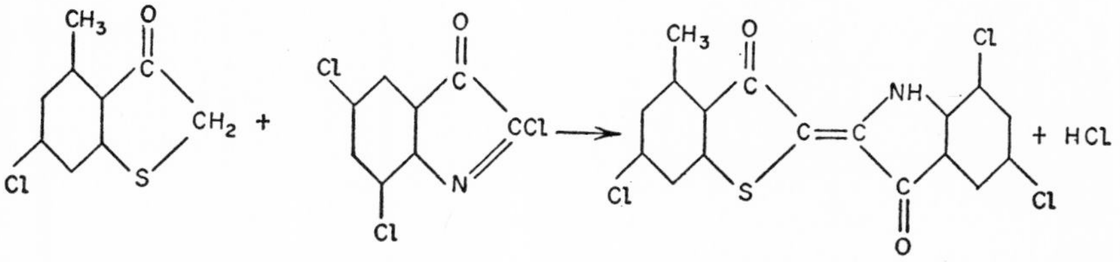

Indanthrene Printing Blue B, used in the manufacture of Anthrasol Printing Blue IB, is the 5,5′,7-trichloro-7′-methoxy-4′-methyl derivative[32].

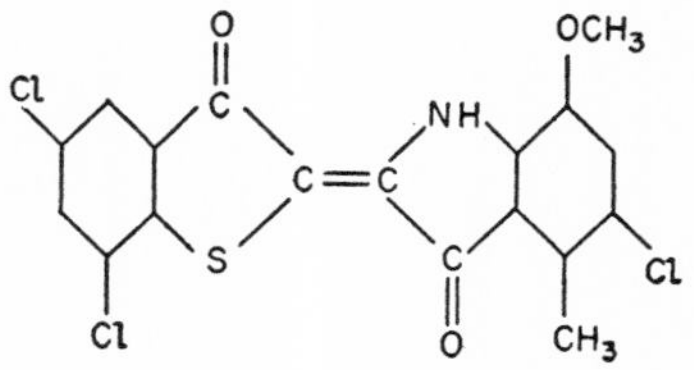

It is made by the condensation of the dichlorothianaphthenone with 2,5-dichloro-7-methoxy-4-methyl-3-pseudoindolone. The 5,7-dichloro-3(2H)-thianaphthenone is obtained by sulfonation of *m*-dichlorobenzene, followed by conversion to sulfonyl chloride, reduction to thiol, reaction with chloroacetic acid and conversion to "thioindoxyl." The indolone is prepared by the Sandmeyer method, starting with 5-methyl-*o*-anisidine ($NH_2 = 1$)[36], treating with chloral and hydroxylamine to give an α-isonitrosoacetanilide derivative, which on ring-closure with 83 per cent sulfuric acid gives 7-methoxy-4-methylisatin. This is dichlorinated with sulfuryl chloride to give the indolone.

Indanthrene Printing Black BGL, used in the manufacture of Anthrasol Blue Black IRD, is a chlorine-substituted 6,7-benzo derivative of the structure[41]:

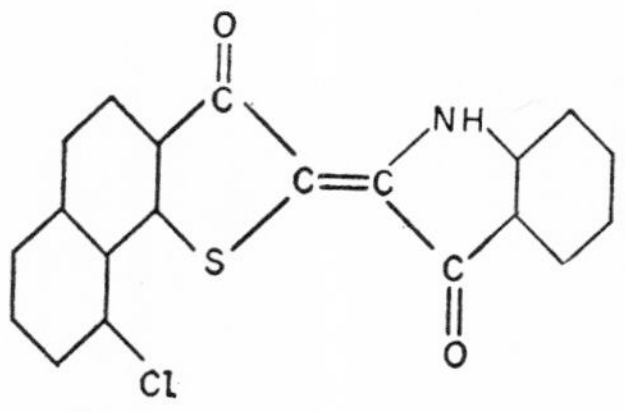

The corresponding 5′-bromo derivative is Indanthrene Printing Black BL[31], which is used in the manufacture of Anthrasol Gray IBL and Suprafix type pastes. The Suprafix pastes, such as Indanthrene Printing Black TL Suprafix Paste, are specially prepared leuco-type pastes containing glycerol and printing assistants. The color is shaded with Indanthrene Golden Yellow to give a better black shade.

3'-Indole-2-thianaphthene Indigo

The unsubstituted product of this class of dyes was sold under the name Thioindigo Scarlet R, CI 1225; the 5',7'-dibromo derivative, CI 1226, was called Thioindigo Scarlet G.

The colors of this type are prepared by reacting thianaphthenones with isatins.

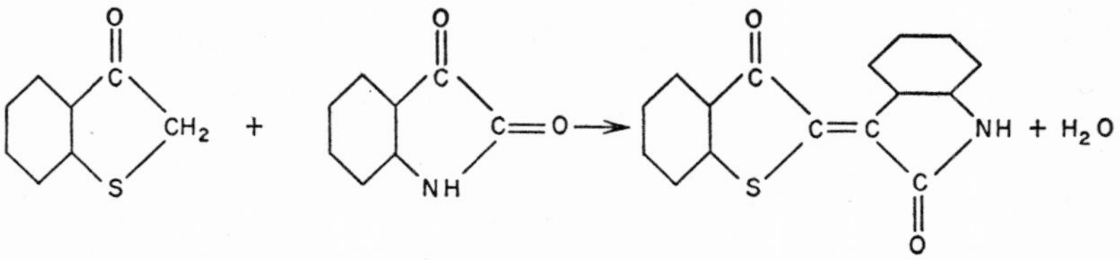

It is to be noted that the 3'-indole part of the dye contributes little tinctorial strength, and this only in the yellow range, so that dyes of this group are generally yellower and tinctorially weaker than the corresponding 2,2'-bisthianaphthene indigos from the thianaphthenone represented on the left in the above formula.

The most important dye of this group, Indanthrene Printing Brown R[44], is the 4,5-benzo-5',7'-dichloro derivative.

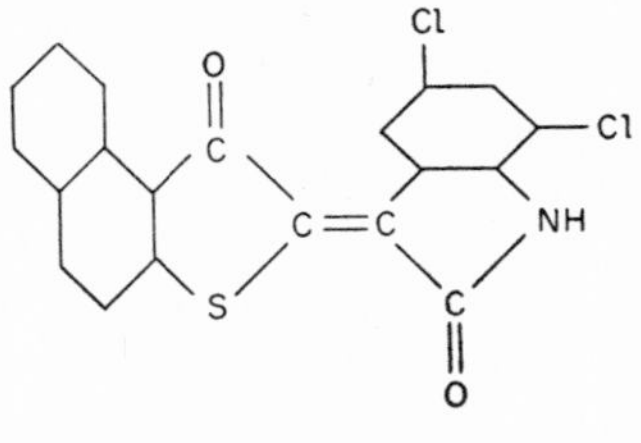

It was the first important vat printing color and was extensively used until it was replaced by 4,5:4',5'-dibenzothioindigo (Indanthrene Brown RRD—see page 567), which possesses better fastness properties.

1'-Acenaphthene-2-indole Indigo

Only a few colors of this type have been prepared and none of them has been of any commercial value. They are usually prepared by reacting pseudoindoxyl with acenaphthenequinone.

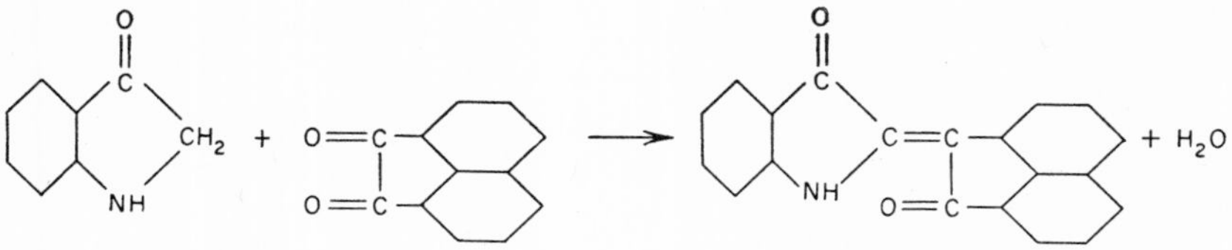

The dye of the above structure is a violet[20] which is of no commercial interest because of inferior fastness properties.

1'-Acenaphthene-2-thianaphthene Indigo

The simplest dye of this type is obtainable by condensing unsubstituted 3(2H)-thianaphthenone with acenaphthenequinone[19].

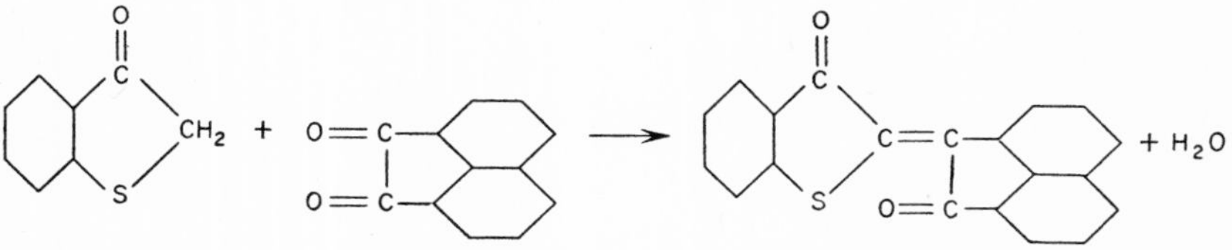

It is a color that has been of considerable interest because of its bright scarlet shade. Sold as Helindon Scarlet GG, CI 1228, it has largely been displaced in the United States by faster dyes. It was used mainly for printing cotton and rayon. It is also used for dyeing wool, as the Helindon name indicates.

Halogenated derivatives are bluer in shade than the parent compound. For instance, the brominated product is Ciba Red, CI 1229.

2'-Arene-2-indole Indigo

This type of dye is obtainable by condensing a 2-chloro- or a 2-phenyliminopseudoindoxyl with polynuclear hydrocarbons containing an alpha hydroxy group and an adjacent replaceable beta hydrogen atom, such as 1-naphthol, 1-anthrol, etc.[42]

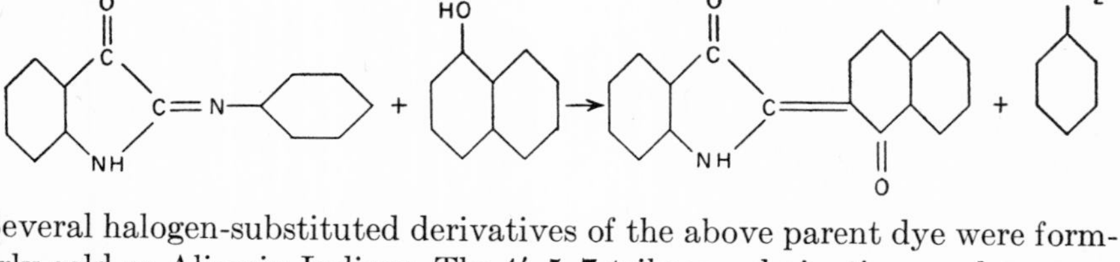

Several halogen-substituted derivatives of the above parent dye were formerly sold as Alizarin Indigos. The 4',5,7-tribromo derivative was known as Alizarin Indigo 3R, CI 1200, the 5,7-dibromo-4'-chloro derivative as

Alizarin Indigo 5R, CI 1200, and the 4′,5,7-trichloro compound as Alizarin Indigo 7R. The letters appended to the names indicate that the replacement of bromine by chlorine has a reddening effect. The substitution of the anthracene ring for the napthalene ring has a yellowing effect. Thus 5,7-dibromo-4′-chloro-2′-anthracene-2-indole indigo is Alizarin Indigo G[43], CI 1202.

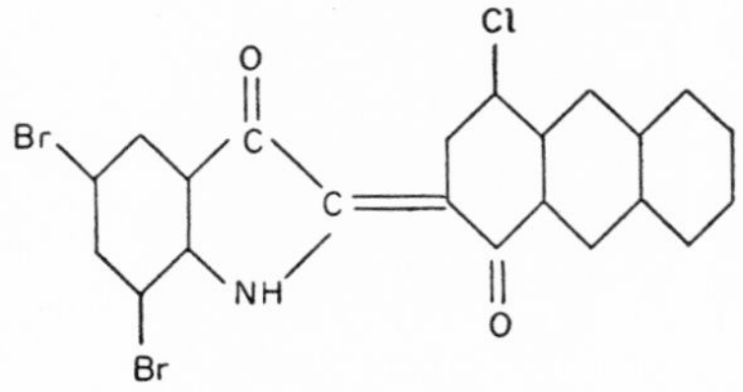

The dye obtained by condensing 6-bromo-2,9-dichloro-3H-benz[f]indol-3(2H)-one with 4-methoxy-1-naphthol has the following structure,

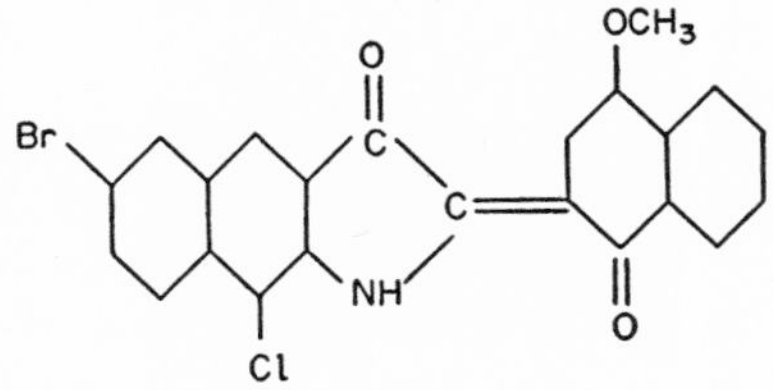

is known as Algol Brilliant Green BK[40], and is used for the manufacture of Anthrasol Green AB. Although this color was apparently never produced in quantity, it had sufficient merit to warrant its manufacture as a specialty color.

Another color of this class is Indanthrene Printing Black B[30], which is made by condensing 2-phenyliminopseudoindoxyl with 10-methyl-11H-benzo[a]carbazol-4-ol (called "Homazol" by the Germans).

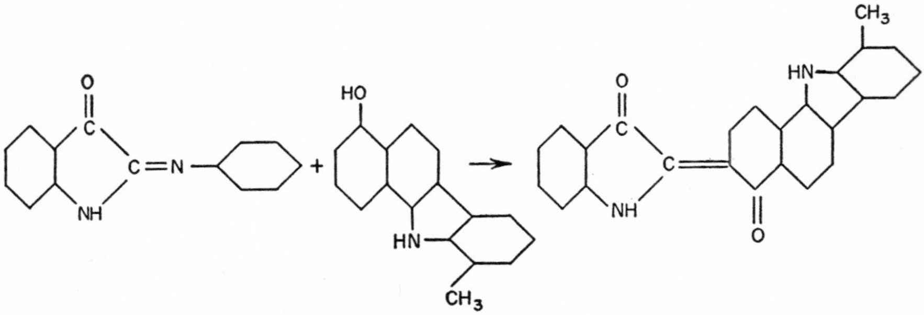

The intermediate "Homazol" was prepared from 1,5-naphthalenediol by treating with sodium bisulfite, condensing with the hydrazine from diazotized and reduced *o*-toluidine, and heating with dilute sulfuric acid.

The dye is a deep-shade black, but has been replaced largely by Indanthrene Printing Blacks BL and TL, which have superior printing properties.

2'-Arene-2-thianaphthene Indigo

A number of these products, obtainable by condensing active forms of 3(2H)-thianaphthenones, such as the 2,2-dibromo or the 2-(*p*-dimethylaminophenylimino) derivatives, with 1-naphthols or 1-anthrols, have been prepared. As an example[19],

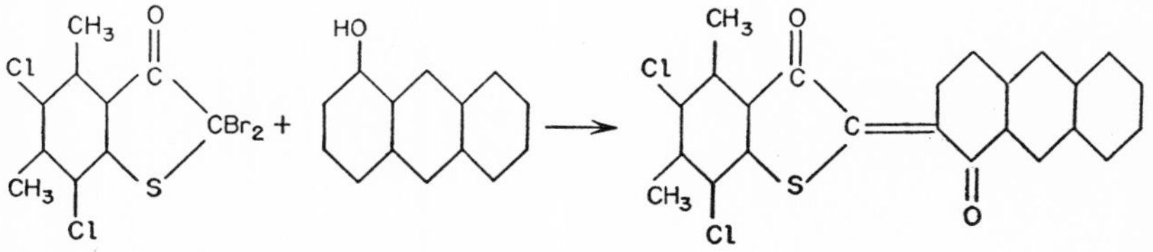

which is a violet dye.

Although the colors obtained range in shade from red, green, and blue to blacks, none of them has been of commercial interest. The class is included to illustrate another case of similarity in the chemistry of "thioindoxyl" and "indoxyl."

Literature Cited

1. Bader, *Am. Dyestuff Reptr.*, **27**, 455–61, 467–71 (1938).
2. Baeyer, *Ber.*, **11**, 1296–7 (1878).
3. ——, *ibid.*, **16**, 2204 (1883).
4. —— and Drewsen, *ibid.*, **15**, 2856 (1882); **16**, 2205 (1883).
5. —— and Emmerling, *ibid.*, **3**, 514–7 (1870).
6. Beilstein, "Handbuch der Organischen Chemie," 4th ed., Berlin, Julius Springer, **24**, 417–29 (1936).
7. Beszubez, *J. Gen. Chem.* (*U. S. S. R.*), **17**, 681–5 (1947).
8. Blank, *Ber.*, **31**, 1812 (1898).
9. Bloxam and Perkin, *J. Chem. Soc.*, **97**, 1460–75 (1910).
10. Brode and Wyman, *J. Research Natl. Bur. Standards*, **47**, 170–8 (1951).
11. de Diesbach, Capponi and Farquet, *Helv. Chim. Acta*, **32**, 1214–27 (1949).
12. Dziewonski, Baraniecki, and Sternbach, *Bull. intern. acad. polon. sci.*, **1930A**, 198; *C. A.*, **25**, 5292 (1931).
13. Engi, U. S. Patent 848,354 (1907).
14. ——, U. S. Patent 876,158 (1908).
15. Fierz-David, "Kuenstliche Organische Farbstoffe," Chap. XVII, pp. 428–76. (Herzog, "Technologie der Textilfasern" Series, Vol. III, Berlin, Julius Springer, 1926).
16. Friedlaender, *Ber.*, **39**, 1060 (1906).

17. ——, *ibid.*, **41**, 776 (1908).
18. Grandmougin, *ibid.*, **42**, 4410 (1909); **43**, 937 (1910).
19. Grob, U. S. Patent 891,690 (1908).
20. ——, U. S. Patent 904,867 (1908).
21. Guha, *J. Indian Chem. Soc.*, **21**, 91–2 (1944).
22. Herz, U. S. Patent 1,243,171 (1917).
23. ——, U. S. Patent 1,832,209 (1931).
24. Hofmann, *Ber.*, **18**, 2734–41 (1885).
25. Holzach, *Melliand Textilber.*, **29**, 24–5 (1948).
26. I. G. Farbenindustrie, BIOS 983 (PB 79226).
27. ——, *ibid.*, pp. 6, 7, 33.
28. ——, *ibid.*, pp. 8–9.
29. ——, *ibid.*, pp. 18–21.
30. ——, *ibid.*, pp. 22–3; BIOS 986, pp. 229–31 (PB 77764).
31. ——, BIOS 983, pp. 24–9 (PB 79226).
32. ——, *ibid.*, pp. 30–1.
33. ——, *ibid.*, pp. 34–5.
34. ——, *ibid.*, p. 36.
35. ——, *ibid.*, p. 37.
36. ——, BIOS 986, pp. 89–91 (PB 77764).
37. ——, *ibid.*, pp. 91–2.
38. ——, *ibid.*, pp. 92–4.
39. ——, *ibid.*, pp. 260–3.
40. ——, BIOS 1482, pp. 12–3 (PB 86136).
41. ——, PB 73377, frames 1862-4; PB 74120, frames 949–57.
42. ——, PB 73719, frames 2602–32.
43. ——, *ibid.*, frames 2626–30.
44. ——, PB 74120, frames 712–15.
45. Leuckart, *J. prakt. Chem.* (2), **41**, 179–224 (1890).
46. Lubs, U. S. Patent 1,954,707 (1934).
47. Mayer, "The Chemistry of Natural Coloring Matters" (translated and revised by Cook), p. 216, New York, Reinhold Publishing Corp., 1943.
48. Peterhauser, *J. Soc. Dyers Colourists*, **42**, 152–4 (1926); **43**, 251–3 (1927).
49. Pfleger, U. S. Patent 680,395 (1901).
50. Rawson, *J. Soc. Chem. Ind. (London)*, **18**, 467–74 (1899).
51. Sandmeyer, *Z. Farben- u. Textil-Chem.*, **2**, 129–37 (1903).
52. ——, *Helv. Chim. Acta*, **2**, 234–42 (1919).
53. Thiess, U. S. Patent 1,792,130 (1931).
54. Thorpe and Whitely, "Thorpe's Dictionary of Applied Chemistry," 4th ed., Vol. VI, pp. 432–57, London, Longmans, Green, 1943.
55. Truttwin, "Enzyklopaedie der Kuepenfarbstoffe," Berlin, Julius Springer, 1920.
56. U. S. Tariff Commission, "Synthetic Organic Chemicals, United States Production and Sales, 1951," Report No. 175.
57. van Alphen, *Ber.*, **72B**, 525–6 (1939).

9. PHTHALOCYANINE PIGMENTS

Newell M. Bigelow and Melvin A. Perkins

The phthalocyanine pigments comprise a class of highly colored synthetic compounds which contain in common the tetrabenzoporphyrazine chromophore indicated below (I):

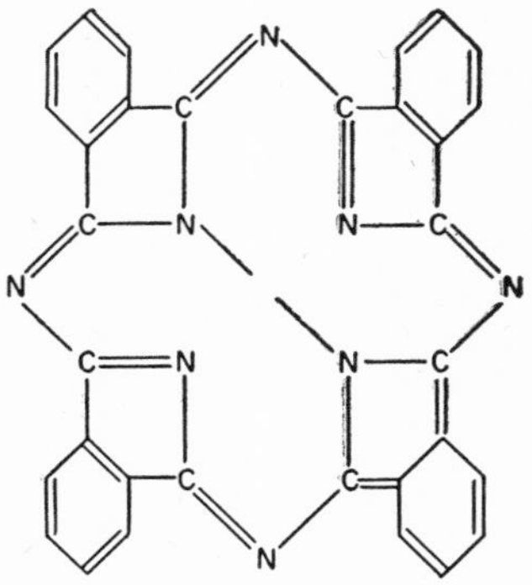

(I)

The name was given to combine their origin (from a phthalic material. e.g., phthalonitrile) and their greenish blue color.

Although this class is relatively new, having been developed since 1928, certain of its members have already attained considerable commercial importance. The commercial phthalocyanine pigments range in shade from blue to green, and are very strong and bright. They are outstandingly resistant to light and to all common chemical reagents, with the exception of strong oxidizing agents.

Arranged in order of increasing greenness or of decreasing redness, commercial types may be listed as follows:

(1) Cobalt phthalocyanine (only as a specially treated product for use as a vat dye).
(2) Copper phthalocyanine (unsubstituted, alpha form).
(3) Copper semichloro- or monochlorophthalocyanine.
(4) Copper phthalocyanine (unsubstituted, beta form).

577

(5) Metal-free phthalocyanine (alpha form; beta form much greener yet).

(6) Copper polychlorophthalocyanine.

A still yellower green is to be found in metal-free polychlorophthalocyanine but this product has not appeared on the market and thus cannot be classed as "commercial."

Metal-free phthalocyanine was unwittingly prepared by Braun and Tcherniac in 1907[12]. These investigators noted that when o-cyanobenzamide was heated above its melting point for a protracted period a blue compound was formed in yields of less than 1 per cent. They did not characterize the compound, nor investigate it further at the time. In 1927, de Diesbach and Van der Weid[47] observed the formation of a deep blue crystalline solid, which was in fact copper phthalocyanine, when o-dibromobenzene, cuprous cyanide and pyridine were heated in a sealed tube. Although they considered it a complex compound of the three ingredients, they noted that its stability was far beyond what would normally be expected from such a complex. Shortly thereafter, chemists of the Scottish Dyes Corporation observed the formation of a blue-green, highly colored impurity when ammonia was passed through molten phthalic anhydride in iron equipment[13]. The compound was iron phthalocyanine. Scottish Dyes recognized the potential value of such a pigment, and undertook commercial development at once[4, 13], Professor R. T. Linstead and his co-workers being entrusted with the elucidation of the structure of these compounds.

This was done as evidenced in a long series of papers beginning in 1934[108]. Professor Linstead characterized the original iron phthalocyanine and discovered a good preparative route from o-cyanobenzamide and later from phthalonitrile. Dent and Linstead[43] quickly found that the copper derivative was of major interest and studied its formation from phthalonitrile. Upon the publication in 1934 of Linstead's original work[108], the I. G. Farbenindustrie in Germany and the Du Pont Company in the United States also undertook the development of phthalocyanine pigments and dyes. These new pigments were received enthusiastically by the trade, not only in Britain and Germany but also in this country[36], and their commercial importance has increased rapidly since that time.

The reflectance spectrum of copper phthalocyanine is very close to that of a true "minus red"[36], and for this reason this pigment is of great value as a blue component in three-color half-tone reproduction. The stability of copper phthalocyanine and of copper polychlorophthalocyanine to light, acids and alkalies makes these colors valuable pigments for printing on paper or textile goods. The phthalocyanine pigments are also used in the coloration of paper, rubber, plastics and linoleum, and their use in paints and lacquers is increasing. While the alpha form of unsubstituted copper phthalocyanine suffers from crystal growth in paint solvents or thinners, a pigmentary beta form stable to such growth can be obtained. In addition, crystal-stable "semi-" or monochloro derivatives can be synthesized which are satisfactory for paint formulations even in the alpha form, giving redder (less greenish) shades than the beta form.

Structure

The structural formula of the phthalocyanine nucleus (I) was deduced from the following considerations:

The phthalocyanines can be prepared from aromatic ortho-dicarboxylic acids, or their amides, imides or nitriles. The carboxy groups may not be separated by a saturated atom or by an extended unsaturated or aromatic grouping. There must be a double bond between the atoms carrying these carboxy or cyano groups, or the possibility for a rearrangement to form such a double bond[44]. Therefore, the phthalocyanine must contain the grouping indicated in (II) below. Molecular weight determinations of a number of phthalocyanine pigments[115, 137] indicate that the molecule contains four of these structural units in every case. The two possible arrangements for these units are the isoindole grouping (III) and the phthalazine ring (IV).

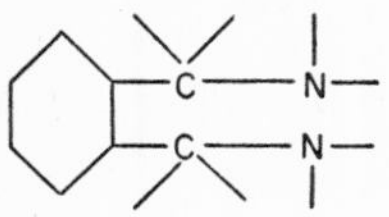

(II) 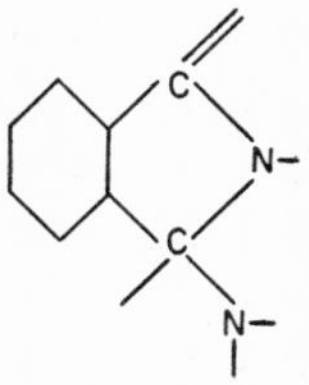   (III) 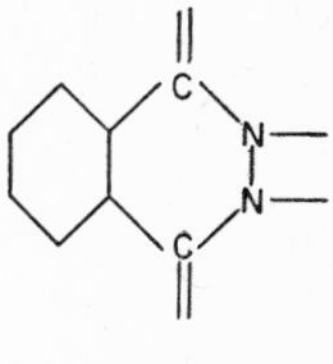   (IV)

Several facts weigh heavily in favor of the former. In the first place, controlled oxidation of one mole of a phthalocyanine with ceric sulfate consumes one atom of oxygen and produces phthalimide quantitatively. The formation of this product strongly suggests the presence of the isoindole grouping in the original molecule. In the second place, it has been proved that 3-iminophthalimidine, containing the isoindole structure, is readily converted to phthalocyanines, while 1(2H)-phthalazone is not[44]. Furthermore, 1,3-diiminoisoindoline can be converted to copper or nickel phthalocyanine in good yield when treated with aqueous salts of these metals in the presence of suitable solvent mixtures[53]. There is also the consideration that if the phthalocyanines were composed of four phthalazine rings, they would necessarily be joined directly to one another; such a molecule would exist in a high state of strain, its ready formation would be unlikely and formation of metal derivatives would be very difficult to explain. The phthalocyanine molecule therefore appears to be composed of four isoindole nuclei. They might conceivably be joined together in an open chain (V) or in closed structures—(VI) and (VII)[44].

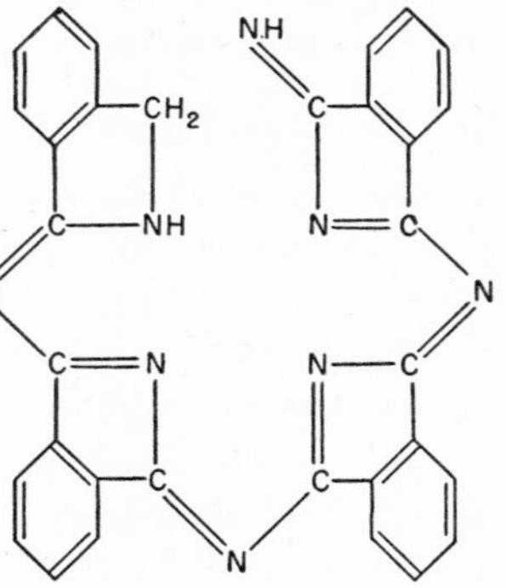

(V)

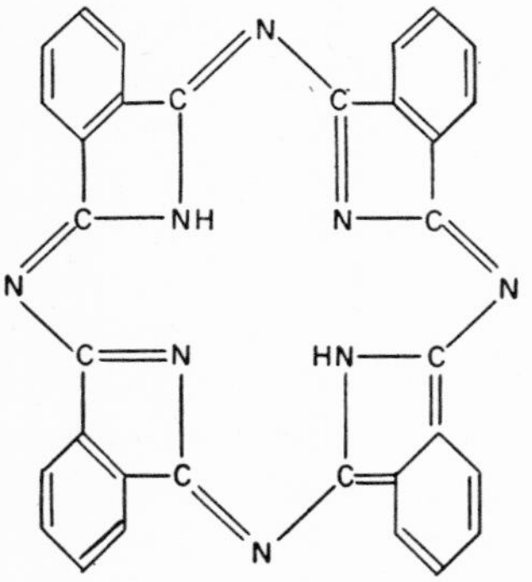

(VI)

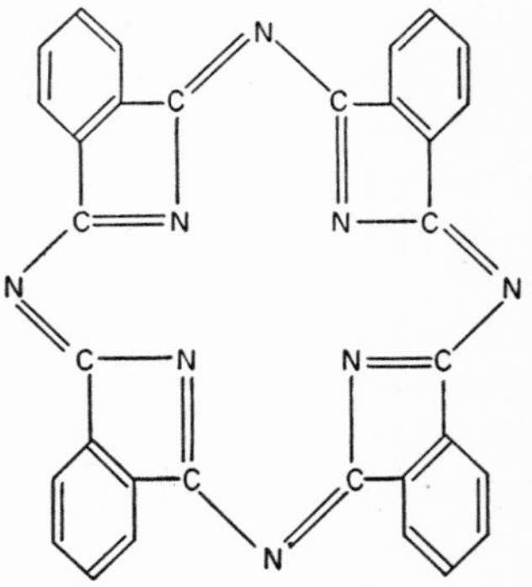

(VII)

The open chain structure is improbable because it does not explain the ready formation of metallic complexes or their remarkable stability. Formula (VI) is more plausible than (VII), both because of the stability of the derived metal complexes, and because of their behavior on oxidation. The fission of a compound of structure (VII) to phthalimide and ammonia requires no oxygen, while the compound of structure (VI) requires an atom of oxygen, in accordance with the observed data.

The cyclic structure of the phthalocyanine molecule is also supported by the results of studies by Robertson and his co-workers[135-139]. Fourier analyses of the x-ray diffraction patterns of single crystals of phthalocyanine and its metal complexes give electron density patterns which agree well with those stipulated by the structure given above. In Barrett, Dent and Linstead's words[4]: "Phthalocyanine is therefore a quadrivalent chelating unit capable of occupying four positions in the coordination sphere of a metal. All four rings thus formed are six-membered and contain one or two double bonds and are hence practically strainless. Primary covalent bonds are not defined, but exist in a state of resonance."

Properties of the Phthalocyanine Pigments

Chemical Properties. The isoindole hydrogen atoms in the center of the phthalocyanine molecule are readily replaced by metals, with the formation of metal phthalocyanines[44, 53, 118]. These metal derivatives may be divided into two classes, electrovalent and covalent[4, 5, 109]. The electrovalent metal phthalocyanines are, in general, complexes of the phthalocyanine molecule with the alkali and alkaline earth metals. They are almost completely insoluble in all common organic solvents and are not volatile. When treated with aqueous mineral acids, and in some cases with aqueous alcohol or even water alone, the metal atoms are removed, with the generation of metal-free phthalocyanine. The phthalocyanine complexes of sodium, potassium, calcium, barium, cadmium and mercury[4] belong to this class. Lithium phthalocyanine is an outstanding exception, being soluble in alcohol and undergoing metal exchange with salts of other metals even at room temperature[5].

The most stable of the covalent phthalocyanine complexes may be sublimed unchanged at temperatures between 400 and 500°C in vacuo or in an inert atmosphere. These most stable ones are not demetallized by prolonged contact with mineral acids. The covalent bond is very firm, giving the whole molecule a pseudo aromatic character. Copper phthalocyanine, for example, although it contains 11 per cent copper, yields in aqueous suspension no detectable trace of cupric ion. It has been certified as a food color in Germany[140] and is widely used in the pigmentation of rubber, although even slight traces of ionic copper are known to cause rapid and far-reaching deterioration of this material[123]. The phthalocyanine complexes of copper, nickel, zinc, cobalt, aluminum, platinum, iron and vanadium are of this relatively stable type.

Much less stable covalent phthalocyanine complexes are found in those of beryllium, lead, manganese, tin and magnesium[4, 5]. Titanium phthalocyanine is intermediate between these two classes in stability. These compounds are volatile and are soluble to a certain extent in organic solvents (especially the magnesium compound), but they are demetallized by mineral acids, with the generation of metal-free phthalocyanine. This behavior is believed to be the result of disparities between the normal atomic radii of the metals in question and the spatial limitations of the phthalocyanine molecule[4]. The radius of the gap in the center of the phthalocyanine molecule measures approximately 1.35 Å, according to x-ray diffraction data. All of the metallic phthalocyanine complexes which resist the attack of mineral acids contain metals whose normal effective radii (as neutral atoms) are of this order of magnitude. Larger or smaller atoms (manganese, 1.18 Å; lead, 1.75 Å) are demetallized by acids.

Many of the trivalent metals form phthalocyanine complexes. In such cases, two of the valence bonds of the metal are linked to the phthalocyanine complex, the third valence remaining ionic and reactive. As an example, ferric chloride reacts with phthalonitrile to form chloro-ferric phthalocyanine; hydrolysis of this compound yields hydroxy-ferric phthalocyanine and hydrochloric acid. Stannous chloride reacts with phthalonitrile to form dichloro-stannic phthalocyanine, which can be hydrolyzed to dihydroxy-stannic phthalocyanine[4].

In general, the phthalocyanine pigments are completely insoluble in water. The electrovalent metal phthalocyanines (except lithium) are also insoluble in organic solvents while the covalent metal types have slight but measurable solubilities. Hot 1-chloronaphthalene has been used as a solvent in the measurement of the absorption spectra of the phthalocyanines and also in the determination of their molecular weights. Phthalocyanine complexes which contain an anion bound to the metal are soluble in amines such as pyridine, quinoline or aniline, as the result of complex formation.

The phthalocyanines are usually readily soluble in concentrated sulfuric acid, ethylsulfuric acid, chlorosulfonic acid and phosphoric acid, and to a much lesser extent in trichloroacetic acid[36]. Solubility is due to the formation of acid salts. Many covalent metal derivatives are stable in sulfuric acid; the electrovalent and a few covalent types are demetallized more or less readily, with formation of metal-free phthalocyanine[4]. The latter compound, though fairly stable, is slowly oxidized by concentrated sulfuric acid[99]. Stable covalent phthalocyanines survive prolonged exposure in aqueous alkali, while some of the electrovalent and less stable covalent types are stable to this reagent and others can be demetallized or destroyed altogether by such treatment.

All of the phthalocyanines are attacked by strong oxidizing agents such as nitric acid or aqueous potassium permanganate[43, 47, 108]. The final oxidation product is phthalimide. Copper phthalocyanine itself is oxidized very rapidly and quantitatively by ceric sulfate in concentrated sulfuric acid[43, 44]. This method has been used for the quantitative estimation of copper phthalocyanine. Sulfuric acid solutions of the phthalocyanines are oxidized fairly rapidly by chlorine. Copper phthalocyanine is attacked by aqueous sodium hypochlorite, but because of the low order of solubility of this pigment the rate of attack is slow[50]. The action of nitric acid in nitrobenzene and of bromine in methanol is notable in that solvent-soluble oxidation products are obtained which can be reduced to the metal phthalocyanine upon suitable treatment[53]. This applies particularly to cobalt and to copper phthalocyanines. Thus, in a sense, a reversible oxidation-reduction phenomenon is met here, even apart from any vatting operation (which decomposes copper phthalocyanine but not the cobalt derivative).

The phthalocyanine pigments vary widely in their fastness to light. Copper, cobalt and nickel phthalocyanines are outstandingly fast in this respect; others are less stable, some much less.

Many phthalocyanine pigments have a definite catalytic activity in promoting oxidation reactions[33, 72, 128-130, 145]. This is not surprising, since they are chemically related to the naturally occurring porphins. Iron phthalocyanine probably has the highest activity for most uses, but cobalt and nickel phthalocyanine are active and the effect is widely observable. The nickel compound is preferred where it can be used because it can be recovered unchanged[130]. Studies have been made of the activity of phthalocyanine complexes in the oxidation of hydriodic acid[33], hydrocarbons[128, 129], ketones and aldehydes[33, 130], unsaturated fatty acids[144] and in the polymerization of butadienes[64]. The use of ferrous phthalocyanine to control the rate of oxidation of vat dyes has been patented[38]. When certain phthalocyanine pigments are shaken with tetrahydronaphthalene which contains peroxides, intense photoluminescence occurs[34, 74].

A number of metal phthalocyanine complexes can be reduced by aqueous sodium hydrosulfite, with the formation of water-soluble reduction products. The phthalocyanine derivatives of cobalt, iron, titanium, chromium, tin and molybdenum[13, 36, 93, 140] show this effect most strikingly. The chemical constitution of these reduction products has not been determined. They are rather unstable; however, under favorable conditions they may be reoxidized to the original pigment. Among these vattable products cobalt phthalocyanine and its derivatives are outstanding. They give stable olive-colored vats from which cotton can be dyed in bright blue shades[6] of good lightfastness, but the dyeings are extremely sensitive to oxidation, being readily destroyed by hypochlorite or peroxide.

Physical Properties. Most of the unsubstituted phthalocyanines can exist in two crystalline modifications[11, 48, 150], which differ from each other in solubility, shade and thermodynamic stability. The metastable form is termed the "alpha" modification, the more stable form is termed the "beta" modification*. The two forms are readily identified by their x-ray diffraction patterns[24]. Infrared absorption spectra can also serve to distinguish these two types with an accuracy approaching that of the x-ray[48]. The x-ray patterns of the alpha form of metal-free phthalocyanine and its covalent

* An exception, where the reverse nomenclature is used, is found in a publication by Kienle[102].

complexes with many metals are similar; the same is true of the corresponding beta modifications[117, 135, 136, 138, 139, 150]. The metastable alpha forms of the phthalocyanine pigments are produced when they are precipitated from polar or salt-forming solvents. This modification is produced, for instance, when a solution of the pigment in sulfuric acid is suddenly diluted with water. This procedure, known as "acid pasting," is the most commonly used method for converting phthalocyanines to pigmentary form.

The more stable beta modifications of the phthalocyanine pigments are produced when they are treated with organic solvents, the rate of phase change being dependent upon the temperature and nature of the solvent. Aromatic hydrocarbons are particularly active in this regard. Most, although not all, of the methods used for preparing crude phthalocyanines produce the pigments in their beta forms. The alpha forms revert spontaneously to the beta modifications when they are heated above 200° C, or when they are exposed, even at room temperature, to many organic solvents, particularly those of aromatic character[94]. The transition from the alpha to the beta modifications is usually accompanied by a marked increase in the size of the individual crystals, and a corresponding decrease in tinctorial strength. This alteration of crystal structure can take place when pigmentary copper phthalocyanine is stored in a vehicle containing aromatic solvents, as for instance in certain paint or lacquer vehicles.

Formation of Phthalocyanines

Metal-free phthalocyanine may be prepared by the treatment of phthalonitrile with amines, phenols, or alcoholates of the alkali metals. It may also be prepared by the demetallization of suitable metal complexes.

Metal phthalocyanines are prepared (1) by the reaction of phthalonitrile or its substitution products with metals or metal salts; (2) by the reaction of phthalic anhydride, phthalimide or their substitution products with urea in the presence of metallic salts; (3) by the reaction of ortho-dihalogenated aromatic compounds with metal cyanides; and (4) by the direct addition of metals to metal-free phthalocyanine or by metal interchange with other metal phthalocyanines under suitable conditions.

None of the mechanisms advanced up to the present time fully satisfies the stoichiometric requirements of the reaction whereby metal-free phthalocyanine is produced. In the formation of disodium phthalocyanine from phthalonitrile and sodium amylate, the fate of the two amylate ions remains unexplained. Metal-free phthalocyanine contains two more hydrogen atoms than the four molecules of phthalonitrile from which it is produced; it is assumed that these are provided by gross decomposition, either of a portion of the phthalonitrile or of any solvents or catalysts which may be present. The fact that the yield is only about 70 per cent of theory lends credence to this hypothesis.

A widely applicable method for the preparation of metal phthalocyanines is through the reaction between a simple or substituted phthalonitrile and metals or metal salts. Linstead and his co-workers[4, 43, 109, 114] prepared a considerable number of metal phthalocyanines by heating massive portions of various metals with a large excess of phthalonitrile, which served both as reagent and reaction medium. This is very useful for the preparation of small samples of metal phthalocyanines but is of no commercial importance since the utilization of phthalonitrile is inefficient. In commercial manufacture, phthalonitrile is mixed intimately with a suitable metal or metal salt in an inert diluent, and the finely powdered mixture is heated to the initiation temperature of the reaction. A vigorous exothermic reaction takes place, and the metal phthalocyanine is formed directly[77, 82]. When a metal chloride is used the chlorine liberated in the reaction may enter the molecule, for instance, the reaction between dry phthalonitrile and cupric chloride yields copper monochlorophthalocyanine[43, 112] when the reaction temperature exceeds 200°C. Use of another metal salt such as copper sulfate avoids this chlorination side reaction but gives low yields unless carried out under carefully controlled conditions in which a large excess of ammonia is used [103, 104].

Several possible mechanisms for the formation of metal phthalocyanines from phthalonitrile have been proposed, for example that of Sander[140], but no rigid proof of the true mechanism exists. Only in the case of cobalt phthalocyanine has an intermediate product been isolated[26].

Metal phthalocyanines can be produced directly from simple or substituted phthalic acids, by reaction with urea and a metal salt in the presence of suitable catalysts. This method is widely applicable, and is used commercially for the manufacture of copper phthalocyanine. The phthalic acid derivative, mixed with a suitable metal salt, urea, catalysts[78, 133, 151] and a high-boiling inert organic solvent, is heated slowly to a final temperature of about 190 to 200°C. The reaction is complicated, and undoubtedly passes through more than one intermediate stage. Pigment formation begins at about 180°C, and is essentially complete after four hours of reaction at 190 to 200°C. The yield amounts to 85 to 98 per cent of theory[81], depending on the reaction conditions employed. The reaction is adapted to wide variation. Phthalic anhydride, phthalamide, phthalimide, or the substitution products of these compounds can be employed. The urea may be replaced by biuret[127], sulfamic acid, ammonium sulfamate[153, 154] or dicyandiamide (cyanoguanidine)[22]. The method has been used in the preparation of a variety of metal phthalocyanines. Under these conditions, metallic halides do not introduce any appreciable amount of halogen into the phthalocyanine nucleus as they do when phthalonitrile is used as starting material. The degradation products of urea probably accept the halogen even more readily than does the phthalocyanine molecule. The presence of a suitable catalyst is necessary for the proper operation of the reaction; among those most commonly used are boric acid[151], salts of molybdic acid[133], arsenic pentoxide[80] and anhydrous ferric chloride[81]. The use of inert solvents in the reaction is advantageous, but not necessary. The urea, which is always used in excess, can act as a flux for the reaction.

The mechanism of this reaction has never been completely explained. At one time it was believed that the precursor of phthalocyanine in this reaction was 3-iminophthalimidine[65, 151]. Sander has disputed this point[140], claiming that phthalonitrile is the precursor of the phthalocyanine. However there is no published record that the presence of phthalonitrile in any stage of the reaction has ever been demonstrated.

Byrne, Linstead and Lowe reported[32] that magnesium phthalocyanine was formed readily by reaction of 3-iminophthalimidine and magnesium oxide. The former arose from isomerization of o-cyanobenzamide just above its melting point[115]. It is known also that 3-iminophthalimidine arises from the reaction of phthalic anhydride, excess urea and ammonium molybdate in o-dichlorobenzene under conditions closely resembling those pertaining in the early stages of the synthesis of the most stable metal phthalocyanines as ordinarily carried out. This might be held to argue that 3-iminophthalimidine is an intermediate in the synthesis of metal phthalocyanines but this is not necessarily so, particularly because the yield of pigment is not nearly so sensitive to experimental conditions as is that of 3-iminophthalimidine. 1,3-Diiminoisoindoline has been mentioned as a possible intermediate in the phthalocyanine synthesis[65] but no proof of this point has ever appeared.

It is possible to prepare metal phthalocyanines (a) by the introduction of a metal atom into the molecule of metal-free phthalocyanine, or (b) by the substitution of the metal atom in a metal phthalocyanine by another metal which forms a more stable complex[4, 43]. The tendency of reaction (a) to take place varies widely, according to the chemical and physical nature of the reactants. When both reactants are in solution, the reaction takes place very readily. An aqueous solution of sulfonated metal-free phthalocyanine will react rapidly with a soluble metal salt at 100°C, yielding a sulfonated metal phthalocyanine identical in every respect with that produced by the direct sulfonation of the corresponding metal phthalocyanine[100]. An aqueous suspension of metal-free phthalocyanine will not react with metal salts; however, the same salts will enter the molecule when the reaction is carried out in boiling quinoline[111]. An unusual physical form of calcium phthalocyanine results from the reaction between phthalonitrile, calcium oxide and formamide[84]; this material can be converted to copper phthalocyanine by digestion with aqueous cupric chloride at temperatures between 100 and 120°C, although the conversion is not quantitative. Beryllium or lithium phthalocyanine will undergo metathesis (reaction b, above) quantitatively with many metal ions in boiling alcohol, producing the corresponding metal phthalocyanine. In fact the dilithium compound will react in this way even at room temperature and is thus unique[5].

Phthalocyanines as Pigments

Particle Size Reduction. Every pigment has an optimum particle size which permits it to yield its maximum tinctorial strength and brightness in a given application. Determinations made by ultracentrifuge methods[95], nitrogen (and other) adsorption techniques[29, 155] and observation under the electron microscope indicate that the optimum particle size for the phthalocyanine pigments lies somewhere in the neighborhood of 0.05 micron (average diameter) for most pigmentary applications. When the individual particles of the pigment exceed about 0.2 micron, either because of unduly large ultimate particle size or as the result of flocculation or agglomeration of the ultimate particles, some of the tinctorial strength and brightness of the pigment is sacrificed. Most methods for the manufacture of the phthalocyanine pigments yield a crude product whose ultimate particles are far too large for pigment application. Before the crude products can be used as pigments, it is necessary to reduce the size of the ultimate particles to acceptable limits. In many cases the crystal form of the pigment must also be transformed from the beta to the alpha modification.

Most methods for reducing the particle size of the phthalocyanine pigments depend on a sudden transformation to the desired crystalline form, under such conditions that no time is afforded for the growth of the primary particles. Practically, these conditions can be realized by drowning in water a solution of the pigment, or by milling the pigment with an inert diluent until it is essentially amorphous and then extracting the diluent. The commercial applications of these methods are known as acid pasting and salt milling.

Acid pasting is the most commonly used method for the development of the tinctorial strength of phthalocyanine pigments. The pigment is dissolved in concentrated sulfuric acid, and the solution is drowned in water. The more rapid the dilution with water, the finer is the (ultimate) particle of the finished product[45]. Slight changes in the conditions of drowning may have profound influences on the working properties of the finished pigment.

The "permutoid swelling" or "acid slurry" process for reducing the particle size of phthalocyanine pigments was first developed in Italy and Germany[20, 21, 86]. In this process the pigment is agitated in sulfuric acid of a concentration not quite sufficient to dissolve the pigment. Under these conditions the pigment is converted to exceedingly fine crystals of its sulfate salt. When the acid suspension of this salt is drowned, hydrolysis occurs and the pigment is set free in a finely divided pigmentary form.

When a phthalocyanine pigment is ground with another crystalline solid (such as sodium sulfate, sodium chloride, calcium chloride, sugar or urea), particle size subdivision of an unusual type takes place. The ultimate particles of the pigment become exceedingly small; under certain circumstances x-ray analysis of the mixture of salt and pigment makes it appear that the pigment has passed into an amorphous state[31, 107]. When this mixture is extracted with water, the pigment is recovered in its alpha modification, with a very small ultimate particle size. By carrying out the grinding in the presence of suitable organic liquids (acetone, tetrachloroethylene, o-dichlorobenzene) subdivision takes place similarly but the pigment is recovered in its beta form, which gives a decidedly greener, clearer shade of blue[63, 106, 119]. The use of oleophilic surface-active agents is of aid in speeding up this process[62].

Finishing. As a final step in the manufacture of a phthalocyanine pigment, it must be processed to a physical form in which it will yield its full tinctorial strength with a minimum of physical work on the part of the ultimate consumer. The phthalocyanine pigments are used under a wide variety of conditions. In some cases the pigment can be ground into its substrate; in other applications vigorous grinding is impossible, and incorporation must be effected by simple mixing methods. Unfortunately, there is no single type of phthalocyanine pigment that can be used successfully in all of these applications. It is therefore necessary to finish the phthalocyanine pigment in several physical forms, each particularly adapted for use under certain conditions. The accepted forms are toners, or dry undiluted powder; "lakes" or diluted dry powders; undispersed press-cakes, dispersed pastes and water-dispersible powders.

A fairly large portion of the phthalocyanine pigments is sold in the form of toners or undiluted pigment powders. These types are used in applications where it is possible to mill or grind the pigment thoroughly into its substrate or vehicle, as in the manufacture of printing inks or paints, and in the pigmentation of plastics or rubber. The conversion of a wet pigment paste into dry powder form is not a straightforward matter. Acid-pasted phthalocyanine pigments tend to agglomerate irreversibly on drying, yielding hard, gritty powders of low tinctorial strength[36]. This tendency to agglomerate may be reduced by treatment of the wet paste with surface-active agents prior to drying. Many inert organic liquids[105, 142, 147, 148], when intimately mixed with the wet pigment, will inhibit its tendency to agglomerate on drying. Treatment of the wet pigment with fatty acids or their salts is said to accomplish the same result[37, 60, 132]. The salt-milling technique, as well as certain modifications of the acid-pasting processes, will produce wet pastes which may be dried directly to powder with little loss of tinctorial strength[85, 107]. Even in these cases, however, treatment with a suitable surface-active agent will produce a further increase in softness and tinctorial strength.

Even when the pigment has been successfully dried, care must be taken that tinctorial strength is not lost during the final pulverization of the product; overgrinding can cause serious loss of tinctorial strength[95].

The phthalocyanine pigments are frequently used in the form of "lakes," or diluted pigment powders, as more fully described in the general chapter on organic pigments. The diluent or substrate is usually formed by precipitation in the presence of the pigment. These "lakes" are usually designed for one particular application, and their range of usefulness is accordingly narrow. "Lakes" of the phthalocyanine pigments with aluminum hydroxide or barium rosinate[141] are used in the manufacture of printing inks. An aluminum benzoate "lake" of copper phthalocyanine is claimed to resist flocculation in paint and lacquer systems[149]. Another method of overcoming flocculation in such systems is by use of a toner containing a copper phthalocyaninesulfonic acid in admixture with unsulfonated material[61]. Both phthalocyanine and monochlorophthalocyanine (copper derivatives) are said to be stabilized against flocculation by admixture of 2 to 12 per cent of tin phthalocyanine[7].

Another commonly used physical form of phthalocyanine pigments is the undispersed presscake. This form is used for the pigmentation of systems containing water, where vigorous mixing is possible. It is also the common starting material for the manufacture of "lakes." The increasingly important procedure known as "flushing" also makes possible the pigmentation of nonaqueous systems with phthalocyanine presscakes. Like many organic pigments, the phthalocyanine pigments are hydrophobic; in other words, they are more readily wetted by organic solvents than by water. When an aqueous presscake of a phthalocyanine pigment is mixed with an organic liquid or vehicle, such as oxidized linseed oil or many synthetic resins, the pigment transfers itself spontaneously to the organic phase, leaving an aqueous phase free of pigment. The greater part of the water can be removed mechanically; the rest is driven off by heating, either as a separate step or incidentally during further processing. The "flushing" procedure thus avoids drying, with its attendant loss of strength and agglomeration of pigment which so frequently accompanies this operation. The "flushing" procedure itself disperses the pigment in the organic medium to a considerable extent, and the development of full tinctorial strength may be accomplished with relatively little further processing.

Dispersed pastes of the phthalocyanine pigments are used when it is desired to incorporate the pigment in an aqueous system with a minimum of physical work. Such pastes are prepared by milling the aqueous presscake with a suitable dispersing agent.

SPECIFIC PHTHALOCYANINE PIGMENTS

Metal-free Phthalocyanine

Metal-free phthalocyanine is most commonly prepared by the demetallization of sodium phthalocyanine. The latter intermediate is readily prepared by heating phthalonitrile with a solution of the sodium salt of a higher alcohol (isoamyl, hexyl, heptyl) in an excess of the alcohol[68, 79]. It may also be prepared by heating phthalonitrile with a variety of organic amines or phenols in an inert solvent[17, 120, 125, 131, 134]. The I. G. Farbenindustrie has produced metal-free phthalocyanine experimentally by reacting phthalonitrile with calcium oxide in the presence of formamide, and demetallizing the resulting calcium phthalocyanine in aqueous suspension[76, 84].

The tinctorial strength of metal-free phthalocyanine may be developed by acid pasting or acid slurrying methods. Metal-free phthalocyanine exists in polymorphic modifications. The crude pigment, when made by solvent processes, is usually isolated in the beta modification. When the crude pigment is acid pasted, acid slurried, or prepared by the alcoholysis of disodium phthalocyanine, the alpha modification is produced. The alpha modification may also be obtained by the permutoid swelling (acid slurry) of the crude pigment in 65 per cent sulfuric acid[87], or by the acid hydrolysis of calcium phthalocyanine which is produced by the reaction between phthalonitrile, calcium oxide and formamide[76, 84]. The alpha modification reverts readily to the beta modification when heated over 200° C or when digested in aromatic solvents.

Metal-free phthalocyanine is a bright greenish-blue pigment, much greener than copper phthalocyanine; in lightfastness, it is slightly inferior to the latter pigment. Like the copper analog, its beta form has a decidedly more greenish shade of blue than the alpha form. Its absorption spectrum in an organic solvent has been reported by Stern[143] and Anderson *et al.*[1]; the reflectance curve of the alpha modification is recorded by Mattiello[122].

Copper Phthalocyanine

Copper phthalocyanine is the most important member of the entire phthalocyanine family from the commercial point of view. It is commonly prepared by the reaction of phthalonitrile with copper or by the reaction of phthalic anhydride with urea in the presence of suitable copper salt and catalyst. Copper phthalocyanine can be prepared by the reaction of ortho-dihalogenated aromatic compounds or ortho-halogenated aromatic nitriles with cuprous cyanide in the presence of organic bases such as pyridine or quinoline[18, 19, 30]. This method is generally applicable, and has been used to great advantage in the preparation of new phthalocyanine derivatives on a laboratory scale. Many of the points connected with this synthesis have already been covered in the foregoing discussions and no attempt will be made here to relate all of the ramifications which have been patented and otherwise published.

Basic work on these syntheses was carried out by Linstead and Dent[110-113], Wyler[151-154], the I. G. Farbenindustrie[81-87, 101] and Du Pont[36]. Process development, on both laboratory and plant scales, has been virtually continuous since 1934, as the multiplicity of references testifies. As a result, a large number of alternatives have been developed for successful manufacture not only of chlorine-free copper phthalocyanine but also of chloro derivatives containing from one to sixteen chlorine atoms. More detail on methods of introducing chlorine is given in a subsequent section of this chapter. Many manufacturers have entered the attractive phthalocyanine field and competition has been particularly keen in the manufacture of unsubstituted copper phthalocyanine itself, of which many brands have been offered for sale.

Copper phthalocyanine exists in the alpha and beta modifications (see Physical Properties, p. 583). The alpha modification is a bright greenish-blue pigment, of excellent lightfastness and of good stability to all external influences save those of strong oxidizing agents, which convert it to phthalimide, and of organic liquids, which convert it to the beta modification. The latter is crystal-stable and is greener, brighter and slightly weaker than the alpha form[63, 106]. The absorption curve of the pigment in 1-chloronaphthalene is reported by Anderson et al.[1]; its reflectance curve by Mattiello[122]. Finishing methods to obtain pigmentary copper phthalocyanine have been discussed in detail in preceding pages. In general, the methods described for developing the tinctorial strength of metal-free phthalocyanine are applicable to the copper complex as well.

Metal-free phthalocyanine and its copper derivative are the only unsubstituted phthalocyanines which have gained commercial acceptance in the United States and even the former has largely disappeared from the market in recent years because of the relatively high cost of manufacture. The metal-free pigment has enjoyed considerable popularity in Europe[96].

Nickel Phthalocyanine

Nickel phthalocyanine resembles copper phthalocyanine more closely than does any other metal derivative, in all respects. Methods of formation and fastness properties (stability) are similar for the two. The only essential difference lies in the shade, the nickel compound being distinctly duller and more greenish and thus less desirable for most purposes.

Almost all of the theoretically possible metal phthalocyanines have been prepared and characterized in the laboratory; almost all have some defect in shade or fastness properties which makes them unsuitable for use as pigments. The tin, iron and cobalt derivatives are typical examples. The first is too unstable, the second too dull for application as a pigment while the third is sensitive toward even mild oxidizing agents. Nevertheless, the chemistry of these compounds merits further consideration for other specific reasons, as explained below.

Tin Phthalocyanines

The phthalocyanine complexes of tin constitute an interesting family of compounds in that the valence of the metal can be altered without destruction of the complex. All of the more probable valence types of tin phthalocyanine complexes have been synthesized in a reasonable state of purity[4]. Stannous phthalocyanine, SnPC, is prepared by the reaction of metallic tin with phthalonitrile, or by the reduction of dichloro-tin phthalocyanine with hydrogen in boiling quinoline[4]. It belongs to the labile covalent class of phthalocyanines; it can be sublimed unchanged, and has a detectable solubility in many organic solvents, but is slowly demetallized by mineral acids. Stannous phthalocyanine is a dark blue pigment, of mediocre lightfastness.

Dichloro-stannic phthalocyanine, Cl_2SnPC, is prepared by the reaction of stannous chloride with phthalonitrile or metal-free phthalocyanine in a suitable solvent[4], by the reaction of stannous chloride with phthalic acid and urea[152] and by treatment of stannous phthalocyanine with chlorine[4]. In the latter reaction some nuclear chlorination also occurs. The two chlorine atoms of dichloro-stannic phthalocyanine are attached to the metal, and are ionic in character. Cautious hydrolysis with aqueous alkali produces dihydroxy-stannic phthalocyanine. More drastic treatment with aqueous alkali causes demetallization and disruption of the molecule; this behavior is exceptional in the field of phthalocyanine complexes. Dichloro-stannic phthalocyanine readily forms complexes with pyridine and other organic bases. The reaction between dichloro-stannic phthalocyanine and disodium phthalocyanine produces stannic phthalocyanine, $Sn(PC)_2$. This is the only case in which a metal atom is considered bound to two phthalocyanine nuclei. The compound is dark blue in shade, can be sublimed unchanged, and is unusually soluble in benzene, xylene and pyridine[4].

Iron Phthalocyanine

Ferrous phthalocyanine is best obtained in the pure state by sublimation from the mixture of iron phthalocyanines which is obtained by the reaction between phthalonitrile and ferric chloride[4, 32]. Anderson *et al.* reported its absorption spectrum[1], and Linstead and Robertson determined its x-ray diffraction pattern[117]. It readily forms crystalline addition products with aniline[5].

Chloro-ferric phthalocyanine is formed, together with chloro-ferric chlorophthalocyanine, by the reaction of phthalonitrile with ferric chloride[4]. It may also be prepared by warming ferrous phthalocyanine with concentrated hydrochloric acid[5], and by replacement when copper phthalocyanine is heated in boiling quinoline with ferric chloride[88]. It is rather difficult to obtain this compound in pure condition.

Much of the work reported in the literature concerns the indeterminate mixture of ferrous phthalocyanine, chloro-ferric phthalocyanine and chloro-ferric chlorophthalocyanine which is obtained by the reaction of iron salts with phthalimide[151], *o*-cyanobenzamide[32, 88], or phthalonitrile[114]. When finished in pigmentary form, "iron phthalocyanine" is a dull yellow-green pigment, stable to mineral acids but fugitive to light[88, 99]. It exhibits chemiluminescence in the presence of organic peroxides[34, 72], can be vatted[93] and has a definite catalytic effect in oxidation reactions[33, 128]. It has been used as a printing assistant to control the rate of oxidation of vat dyes on textile fibers[38].

Cobalt Phthalocyanine

By merely substituting cobaltous chloride for cupric chloride in the ordinary process for synthesis of copper phthalocyanine, the pigment obtained is a more reddish, though somewhat duller, blue. It differs from copper phthalocyanine in several other respects. It possesses strong catalytic activity in oxidation reactions[128] and is itself destroyed by most oxidizing conditions, even by the air oxidation of linseed oil films containing it. Thus, it is not satisfactory for coloration of paints.

It lends itself to reduction better than copper phthalocyanine does and is readily vattable if some hydrophilic group (sulfo, carboxy, etc.) is present even in small proportions[6]. The vat is olive colored and as stable as that of an ordinary vat dye. Indanthrene Brilliant Blue 4G is believed to be partially sulfonated cobalt phthalocyanine. Shade and lightfastness are attractive but fastness toward peroxide or chlorine bleach is poor (see Chapter 10 on Phthalocyanine Dyes).

Specific phthalocyanines are listed alphabetically in the following tabulation which includes a statement of the starting materials or preparative method, type of valency in the metal derivative, pigment behavior and chemical properties as well as the references involved.

Metal Phthalocyanine Complexes

Complex	Preparation	Type	Pigment Properties	Chemical Properties	Ref.
Antimony phthalocyanine	Metallic antimony and o-cyanobenzamide or phthalonitrile	—	—	Abnormal, unstable complex, possibly SbPC—Sb=Sb—SbPC.	5, 32
Barium phthalocyanine	Barium oxide and phthalonitrile; poor yields	Electrovalent	Dull green; unstable		4
Beryllium phthalocyanine	Metallic beryllium and phthalonitrile	Covalent	Unstable	Forms a crystalline dihydrate with water. Fairly readily soluble in anhydrous alcohols; exchanges metal with alcohol-soluble metal salts (other than beryllium)	4, 32, 117, 140
Cadmium phthalocyanine	Metallic cadmium and phthalonitrile	Electrovalent	Unstable	—	4, 69
Calcium phthalocyanine	Calcium oxide or amylate and phthalonitrile; poor yields. Formed, mixed with metal-free phthalocyanine, by reacting calcium oxide, phthalonitrile and formamide	Electrovalent	Dull green	Unstable. Readily demetallized (basis of one process for metal-free pigment)	4, 84, 99, 114
Chloro-aluminum phthalocyanine	Aluminum chloride, phthalic anhydride and urea; metal-free phthalocyanine and aluminum chloride in boiling quinoline	Covalent	Greenish-blue; poor lightfastness	Does not form a hydrate. The chlorine ion may be replaced by an hydroxy group, yielding hydroxy-aluminum phthalocyanine; on vigorous dehydration this compound appears to be transformed to an oxide of the formula $(AlPC)_2O$	1, 4, 16, 99
Chloro-aluminum chlorophthalocyanine	Phthalonitrile and aluminum chloride	Covalent	—	Forms a hydrate, dihydrate and trihydrate	4
Chloro-antimony phthalocyanine	Antimony trichloride and metal-free phthalocyanine in boiling chloronaphthalene	—	—	—	5, 32
Chromium phthalocyanine	Chromous chloride and phthalonitrile or o-cyanobenzamide	Covalent	Dull green; poor lightfastness	Difficult to prepare in a pure condition. Forms complexes with basic dyes; can be vatted	1, 4, 14, 93, 99
Cobalt phthalocyanine	Metallic cobalt and o-cyanobenzamide or phthalonitrile; cobaltous chloride, phthalic anhydride and urea, ammonium molybdate	Covalent	Blue, considerably redder and duller than copper phthalocyanine; good lightfastness	Gives olive-colored, stable vat with alkaline sodium hydrosulfite from which cotton is dyed bright blue. This blue destroyed rapidly by peroxides or hypochlorites. Stable to sulfuric acid	1, 4, 32, 93, 99, 117

Complex	Preparation	Type	Pigment Properties	Chemical Properties	Ref.
Cobalt monochlorophthalocyanine	Cobaltous chloride and phthalonitrile	Covalent	Similar to cobalt phthalocyanine	—	4, 32
Lead phthalocyanine	Metallic lead or litharge and phthalonitrile; metal-free phthalocyanine and lead salts in quinoline	Covalent	Fairly bright green; unstable and fugitive to light	Demetallized by dilute mineral acids	1, 4, 88, 99, 110
(Di) Lithium phthalocyanine (also lithium hydrogen phthalocyanine)	Lithium amylate and phthalonitrile	Electrovalent	Unstable	Rapidly demetallized by mineral acids; undergoes metal exchange readily (even at room temp.)	1. 5
Magnesium phthalocyanine	Metallic magnesium and phthalonitrile or o-cyanobenzamide	Covalent	Blue; unstable	Forms a very stable crystalline dihydrate and amine complexes. Gives a bright red chemiluminescence when suspended in organic liquids containing peroxides	1, 4, 32, 72, 99, 114
Manganese phthalocyanine	Manganese and o-cyanobenzamide; manganese dioxide and phthalonitrile	Covalent	Dull brownish-green	Is demetallized by mineral acids	4, 117
Mercuric phthalocyanine	Lithium phthalocyanine and mercuric chloride in alcohol	—	Bright green; unstable	Readily demetallized by mineral acids	5, 88
Molybdenum phthalocyanine	Molybdenum trioxide and phthalonitrile	Covalent	Dull bluish-green	Vats readily	93, 99, 109
Nickel phthalocyanine	Nickel or nickel oxide with o-cyanobenzamide or phthalonitrile; nickel chloride and phthalic anhydride, urea, ammonium molybdate	Covalent	Greenish-blue; outstandingly fast to light	Stable to sulfuric acid. Resembles copper phthalocyanine in all respects except shade which is greener and duller	1, 4, 32, 99, 114, 135, 138
Palladium phthalocyanine	Hexadecahydro-phthalocyanine plus palladium in boiling o-dichlorobenzene	Covalent	—	Cyclohexene rings aromatized simultaneously with metal coordination	49
Palladium chlorophthalocyanine	Palladium chloride and phthalonitrile	Covalent	—	—	5
Platinum phthalocyanine	Platinous chloride and phthalonitrile. (Metal-free phthalocyanine does not react with platinum or platinous chloride)	Covalent	Stable	—	1, 3, 135, 139
(Di) Potassium phthalocyanine	Potassium amylate and phthalonitrile; yield poor	Electrovalent	Unstable	Less reactive than disodium phthalocyanine; readily demetallized	4, 114
Silver phthalocyanine	Lithium phthalocyanine and silver nitrate in alcohol	—	Unstable	Readily demetallized by mineral acids	1, 5
(Di) Sodium phthalocyanine	Sodium or sodium amylate and phthalonitrile	Electrovalent	Unstable	Demetallized rapidly by mineral acids and anhydrous methanol, more slowly by water	4, 40, 42, 114

Complex	Preparation	Type	Pigment Properties	Chemical Properties	Ref.
Titanium phthalocyanine	Titanium tri- or tetra-chloride and phthalonitrile	Covalent	More stable than tin phthalocya-nine	Reducible by aqueous alkaline sodium hy-drosulfite	93
Vanadium phthalocyanine	Vanadium oxide com-plex and either phthalonitrile or phthalic anhydride	Covalent	Bright greenish-blue	Can be acid pasted. Contains one atom of oxygen combined with vanadium	39
Zinc phthalocya-nine	Metallic zinc and phthalonitrile. The reaction of zinc chlo-ride and phthalo-nitrile yields a mix-ture of zinc phthalo-cyanine and zinc-monochlorophthalo-cyanine	Covalent	Greenish-blue; not stable to light	Forms unusually sta-ble acid salts which can be isolated and purified	1, 4, 88, 99 114

Up to the present time all attempts to prepare phthalocyanine derivatives of thorium, boron, phosphorus and silicon have been unsuccessful[4, 5, 114].

SUBSTITUTED PHTHALOCYANINES

The phthalocyanine nucleus contains two active hydrogen atoms in its central ring system, and sixteen hydrogen atoms attached to its outer benzenoid rings. The two central atoms are not responsive to any reaction except coordination with metal atoms; for instance, all attempts to alkylate or to acylate these hydrogen atoms have failed. The sixteen peripheral hydrogen atoms are considerably more reactive. Except for possible steric effects, the substitution of any or all of these atoms is possible. Substitution may be accomplished directly on the pigment molecule or indirectly by the reaction of suitably substituted intermediates to form the correspondingly substituted phthalocyanine. These two methods, when directed towards the same goal, seldom produce identical products. The difference is apparently the result of the random distribution of substituents which is obtained by direct substitution, as contrasted with the more uniform distribution which is produced by the synthetic method.

Investigations of the substituted phthalocyanines have had two goals: the preparation of substituted phthalocyanine pigments, and the preparation of dyes by the introduction of solubilizing groups into the phthalocyanine nucleus. The latter investigations have been fruitful as seen by the fact that several dyes containing the phthalocyanine chromophore are in commercial use. These compounds are discussed in a separate section of this book under the heading of Phthalocyanine Dyes, p. 607).

The investigation of substituted phthalocyanine pigments has been somewhat disappointing. With a few notable exceptions, the introduction of auxochromic groups into this chromophore merely produces greener and duller pigments.

The most striking exceptions to this generalization are the chlorinated phthalocyanine derivatives, which are greener but usually not duller. To this class belong copper mono(4)chlorophthalocyanine, copper polychlorophthalocyanine and metal-free polychlorophthalocyanine. The phthalocyanines may be readily substituted by halogen, and particularly by chlorine. The spontaneous formation of halogenated phthalocyanines during the reaction between phthalonitrile and anhydrous metal halides has already been mentioned.

Copper Mono(4)chlorophthalocyanine

When an intimate mixture of phthalonitrile and anhydrous cupric chloride is heated above 200°C, a reaction takes place which can be expressed by the following equation[43, 112].

$$4\ C_6H_4(CN)_2\ +\ CuCl_2\ =\ \begin{array}{c} [ClC_6H_3(CN)_2] \\ \diagdown \\ \qquad\qquad Cu\ +\ HCl \\ \diagup \\ [C_6H_4(CN)_2]_3 \end{array}$$

Copper mono(4)chlorophthalocyanine is thus formed in yields approaching 90 per cent of the theory. The same product may also be produced by the reaction between phthalonitrile and anhydrous cupric chloride in an inert solvent. Sander's theory for the formation of phthalocyanines[140] explains this behavior clearly; the first product of the reaction between phthalonitrile and cupric chloride is an unstable intermediate of the type

which then polymerizes with 3 moles of phthalonitrile, eliminating hydrochloric acid and forming copper monochlorophthalocyanine. Oxidation of this compound to monochlorophthalimide indicates clearly that the compound is a true monochloro derivative rather than a statistical mixture of unchlorinated and polychlorinated derivatives.

Copper monochlorophthalocyanine may also be prepared by the condensation of a mixture of 3 moles of phthalic anhydride and 1 mole of 4-chlorophthalic acid with urea and cupric chloride[151]. This pigment has far more resistance than copper phthalocyanine towards crystal growth in the presence of aromatic solvents. While the direct introduction of chlorine into the phthalocyanine molecule will increase its resistance to crystal growth, random distribution within the molecule makes this chlorine less effective. Tinctorially, copper monochlorophthalocyanine is appreciably greener than chlorine-free copper phthalocyanine, and slightly weaker.

In brightness, fastness properties, and working properties, the two pigments are similar[3].

Copper Polychlorophthalocyanine

Copper polychlorophthalocyanine is ordinarily manufactured by the passage of elemental chlorine through a suspension of copper phthalocyanine in a eutectic mixture of aluminum chloride and sodium chloride at about 200°C[51, 83]. The product is insoluble in water, and practically insoluble in most organic solvents. It is stable, but only moderately soluble, in concentrated sulfuric acid. It is much more readily soluble in chlorosulfonic acid, and a mixture of this solvent and sulfuric acid is commonly used in acid pasting the pigment. The absorption spectra of a number of chlorinated derivatives of copper phthalocyanine have been reported by Barrett and his co-workers[3]. Its reflectance spectrum is recorded by Mattiello[122]. Copper polychlorophthalocyanine cannot be sublimed without gross decomposition. All attempts to prepare large crystals of this compound have been unsuccessful; as a result, its detailed molecular structure has not been studied by x-ray diffraction methods similar to those used by Robertson on copper phthalocyanine itself[135-139].

Elemental chlorine reacts readily with the phthalocyanines under proper conditions, yielding highly chlorinated derivatives. Chlorination may be accomplished under a wide variety of conditions: by the addition of elemental halogen either alone or in the presence of inert liquids, such as trichlorobenzene[3], nitrobenzene, carbon tetrachloride, phthaloyl chloride, chloroform[126] or molten aluminum chloride[46, 51]; or by the use of chlorinating agents such as sulfuryl chloride, thionyl chloride[113], phosphorus oxychloride, sulfur monochloride, sulfur dichloride[52], and antimony pentachloride[126]. When elemental halogen is used under mild conditions, the first step is addition. The addition product is broken down by halogen acceptors, leaving the phthalocyanine molecule unchanged[3]. When this addition product is heated, hydrogen halide is eliminated and substitution takes place. Study of the oxidation products of halogenated phthalocyanines indicates that the first entering halogen atoms seek the 4 position, then the 5 position; after this, the two remaining hydrogen atoms in each aromatic ring are substituted. Theoretically, all sixteen hydrogen atoms can be substituted. The phthalocyanine molecule accepts the first eight chlorine atoms readily, the further introduction of chlorine becoming increasingly difficult. The pigment beomes progressively greener as more chlorine is introduced; however, in the case of copper phthalocyanine approximately twelve chlorine atoms must be introduced before a true green pigment is formed[36, 121]. Under drastic conditions, between fourteen and fifteen atoms are introduced, and the commercially valuable copper polychlorophthalocyanine (Heliogen Green G, Pr. 483) is formed. The complete substitution of all sixteen hydrogen atoms by direct halogenation of copper phthalocyanine is not commercially feasible, although Fox[51] states that under "extreme conditions" this can be done in an aluminum chloride-salt melt in the presence of copper chloride.

A novel chlorination method worthy of mention is that of "dry chlorination" of copper or of metal-free phthalocyanine in a fluidized bed[2]. Chlorine gas, alone or diluted, is passed through the pigment which has been conditioned for fluidizing by ball milling with a granular, inert diluent.

Although tetrachlorophthalic anhydride does not react similarly to phthalic anhydride in forming copper hexadecachlorophthalocyanine in the usual condensation with a copper salt, urea and a catalyst, it has been reported recently that high yields of the hexadecachloro compound can be obtained by adding an "ancillary" agent such as zirconium or titanium tetrachloride[124]. Prior to this, a more conventional condensation was described[23] but it would appear from the later reference that the ancillary agent achieves better results.

Other Derivatives

There is little information concerning bromination of copper phthalocyanine but mixed bromo-chloro derivatives have been made by bromination in molten aluminum chloride[51]. Products with up to eleven atoms of bromine and three atoms of chlorine are disclosed.

Copper phthalocyanine cannot be nitrated directly, although copper tetra-(4)nitrophthalocyanine can be prepared by the reaction of 4-nitrophthalimide with urea and suitable metal salts[70]. This compound is a useful intermediate for the manufacture of amino-substituted phthalocyanines, but has no value as a pigment because of its dull and green shade.

Introduction of alkoxy, aroxy, alkylmercapto or arylmercapto groups into the phthalocyanine molecule shifts the shade of the pigment somewhat toward the green[70, 75, 97, 98]. These pigments have no commercial value. Acylated phthalocyanine pigments such as tetrabenzoylphthalocyanines can be prepared by the Friedel-Crafts reaction between phthalocyanines and acyl chlorides[54]. These greenish pigments have good fastness properties, but their dullness has hampered their commercial development[90]. The same is true of the fast olive-green pigment obtained in the usual way from a copper compound and the thiazole-substituted phthalonitrile of the formula

The introduction of alkyl groups into the phthalocyanine molecule has very little effect on the shade or fastness properties of such pigments[89]. Copper tetraphenylphthalocyanine can be manufactured by the reaction of 3,4-biphenyldicarbonitrile with a suitable copper salt[8, 67]. When properly finished, this is a green pigment, somewhat bluer and duller than copper polychlorophthalocyanine.

The reaction of 1,2- and of 2,3-naphthalenedicarbonitrile with suitable metal salts yields naphthalocyanines (VIII) and (IX)[1, 11, 14].

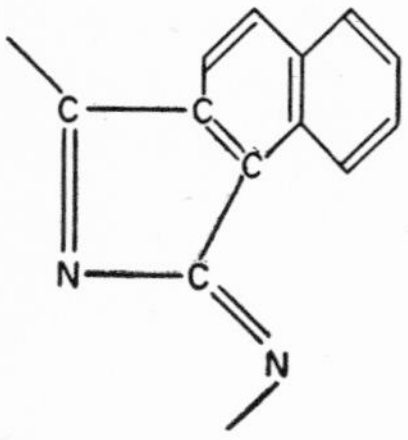

(In these and subsequent representations of tetraazaporphin derivatives, only one quarter of the molecule is shown, to conserve space).

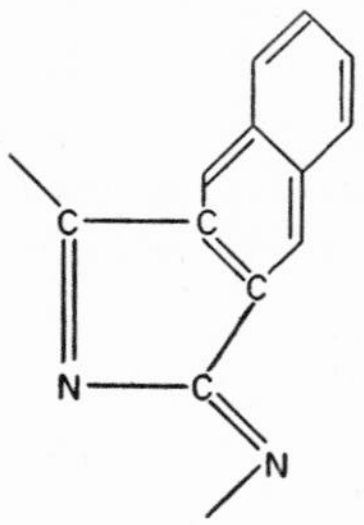

Metal-free naphthalocyanine and its copper, zinc, magnesium, and lead complexes have all been prepared. They are mostly dark greens, of no commercial interest. They do not sublime readily and while they are more soluble than the phthalocyanines in organic solvents, they do not crystallize well. Metal naphthalocyanines resemble the corresponding phthalocyanines in stability; as a class, they are more stable to oxidizing agents. Copper tetra(4)pyridylphthalocyanine

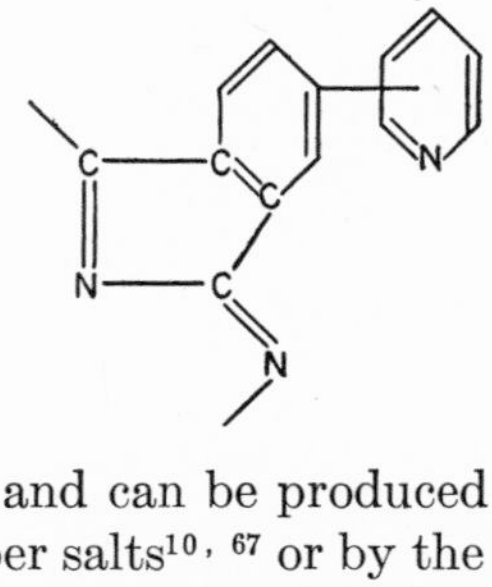

is also a green pigment and can be produced by the reaction of 4-pyridylphthalonitrile with copper salts[10, 67] or by the Gomberg reaction of pyridine with diazotized copper tetraaminophthalocyanine[66]. This compound has no value as a pigment; it can, however, be quaternized to yield interesting direct dyes for animal or vegetable fibers[9].

Structural changes have also been effected in the four phenylene rings in the phthalocyanine molecule. The copper derivative of tetraazaphthalocyanine

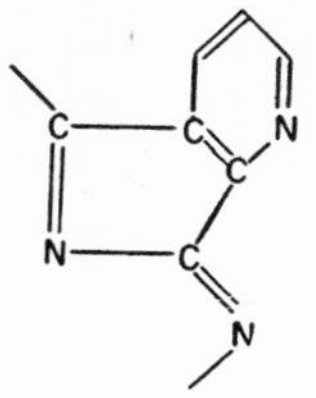

(XI)

(also called tetrapyridinoporphyrazine and tetrapyridinotetraazaporphin) is of marginal interest from the commercial point of view. This compound can be prepared by the reaction of quinolinic acid with urea and copper salts[1, 58, 116] and is probably the reddest known phthalocyanine derivative, being almost as reddish in shade as Ultramarine Blue[91]. It is only slightly inferior to copper phthalocyanine in lightfastness. Copper octaazaphthalocyanine

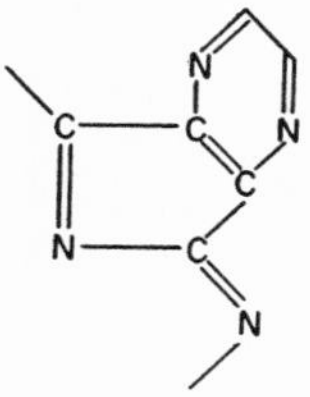

(XII)

also known as copper tetrapyrazinotetraazaporphin, is a dull reddish blue[92]. Tetrathiophenotetraazaporphin

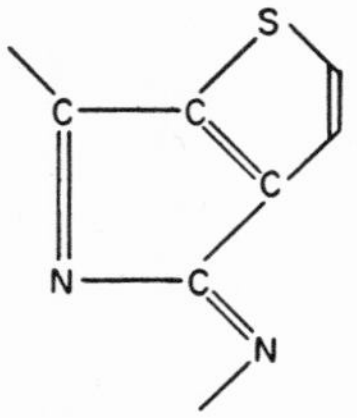

(XIII)

and tetrathianaphthenotetraazaporphin

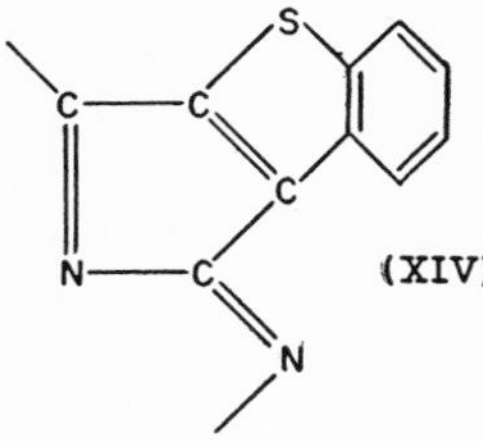

(XIV)

are dull green pigments of academic interest only[1, 116].

The phthalocyanines are themselves substituted derivatives of the parent compound, tetraazaporphin[118]

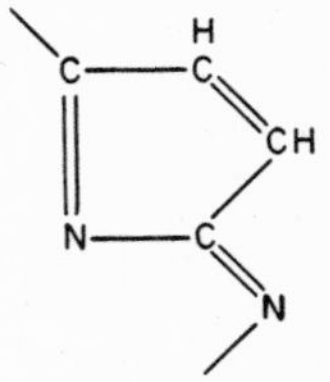

(XV)

For this reason, the consideration of their substitution products must be directed toward simpler analogs as well as toward the more highly substituted derivatives. The substituted azaporphins are of considerable theoretical interest in that they represent bridges between the naturally occurring porphyrins[117] and the synthetic phthalocyanines, and a considerable amount of attention has been devoted to them. So far, all attempts to prepare mono-, di- and triazaporphin have been unsuccessful. Tetraazaporphin has been prepared recently[118] by treating the magnesium derivative with glacial acetic acid. The former, in turn, was obtained by treating maleonitrile with magnesium isopropoxide. Previous to this only the octaphenyl compound was known. Octaphenyltetraazaporphin

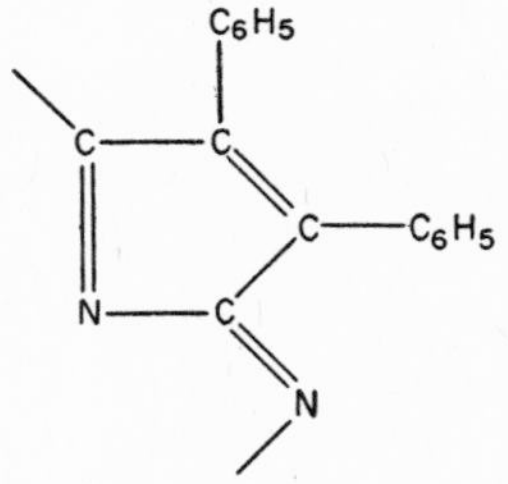

(XVI)

and a number of its metallic complexes have been prepared from diphenylmaleonitrile[1, 35, 57]. The properties of these compounds, and their catalytic effects in particular, have been studied in some detail. They are, however, of no interest as pigments. The successful preparations of tetrabenzoporphin, tetrabenzomonoazaporphin[59, 71, 73], tetrabenzodiazaporphin, tetrabenzotriazaporphin[41] and many of their metal complexes have also been reported. The properties of these compounds, especially as oxidiation catalysts, have been studied in some detail. As pigments, however, they range from dull greenish-blue to olive-green in shade, and have no commercial importance.

Ficken and Linstead[49] reported the preparation of tetracyclohexenotetraazaporphin (hexadecahydrophthalocyanine)

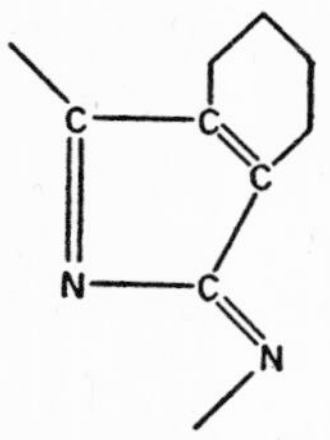

(XVII)

and several of its metal derivatives, of which the nickel and cobalt compounds have been claimed by France and Jones to be reddish blue or violet pigments with good properties[28]. The starting material is Δ^1-tetrahydrophthalonitrile[25]. According to Ficken and Linstead, for example, this material condenses with magnesium in alcohols (in the presence of iodine) to give the magnesium derivative. This is demetallized by acetic acid and the free tetracyclohexenotetraazaporphin is converted to other metal derivatives as desired. A rather complete comparison of properties of the three series is given, i.e., of

1. Copper tetraazaporphin
2. Copper tetracyclohexenotetraazaporphin
3. Copper phthalocyanine[49]

They increase in greenness but also in quality as pigments in the order given. Replacement of the beta pyrrole hydrogens thus causes a bathochromic shift. The cyclohexene compounds, actually hexadecahydropthalocyanines, resemble the unsubstituted tetraazaporphins more closely than they do the phthalocyanines.

Mixtures of dimethyl- or diethylmaleic anhydride or maleonitrile can be used with the Δ^1-tetrahydrophthalic intermediates to give mixed condensations[27, 28]. In fact, phthalonitrile can also be used in such fashion to give shades intermediate between those of phthalocyanine and tetraazaporphin[27]. The presence of methyl or ethyl groups, as in (XVIII)

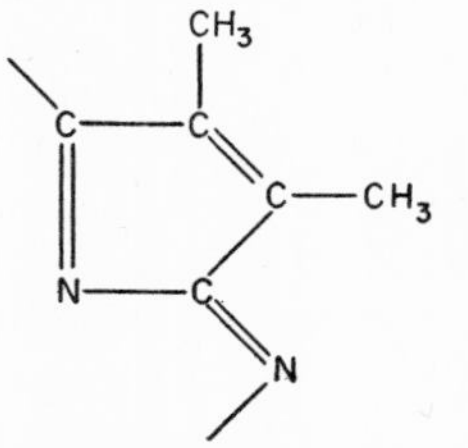

(XVIII)

gives a redder shade pigment than either the corresponding phthalocyanine or the hexadecahydrophthalocyanine, but little is known as to the practical value of any of these new types.

Literature Cited

1. Anderson, Bradbrook, Cook and Linstead, *J. Chem. Soc.*, **1938**, 1151.
2. Barnhart and Grimble, U. S. Patent 2,586,598 (1952).

3. Barrett, Bradbrook, Dent and Linstead, *J. Chem. Soc.*, **1939**, 1820.
4. ——, Dent and Linstead, *ibid.*, **1936,** 1719.
5. ——, Frye and Linstead, *ibid.*, **1938,** 1157.
6. Baumann and Bienert, U. S. Patent 2,613,128 (1952).
7. Beard, U. S. Patents 2,476,950 and 951 (1949).
8. Bienert and Gassner, U. S. Patent 2,213,517 (1940).
9. Bradbrook, Coffey and Haddock, U. S. Patent 2,277,628 (1942).
10. ——, Heilbron, Hey and Haworth, U. S. Patent 2,277,629 (1942).
11. —— and Linstead, *J. Chem. Soc.*, **1936,** 1744.
12. Braun and Tcherniac, *Ber.*, **40,** 2709 (1907).
13. British Patent 322,169 (1929).
14. British Patent 457,526 (1936).
15. British Patent 459,780 (1937).
16. British Patent 464,126 (1939).
17. British Patent 476,168 (1937).
18. British Patent 490,744 (1938).
19. British Patent 490,745 (1938).
20. British Patent 502,623 (1939).
21. British Patent 503,666 (1939).
22. British Patent 506,029 (1939).
23. British Patent 585,727 (1947).
24. British Patent 600,911 (1948).
25. British Patent 686,395 (1953).
26. British Patent 687,655 (1953).
27. British Patent 688,768 (1953).
28. British Patents 689,387, 8 and 9 (1953).
29. Brunauer, Emmett and Teller, *J. Am. Chem. Soc.*, **60,** 309 (1938).
30. Buc, U. S. Patent 2,647,908 (1953).
31. Bucher, U. S. Patent 2,378,283 (1945).
32. Byrne, Linstead and Lowe, *J. Chem. Soc.*, **1934,** 1017.
33. Cook, *ibid.*, **1938,** 1761.
34. ——, *ibid.*, **1938,** 1845.
35. —— and Linstead, *ibid.*, **1937,** 929.
36. Dahlen, *Ind. Eng. Chem.*, **31,** 839 (1939).
37. —— and Detrick, U. S. Patent 2,291,452 (1942).
38. Davidson, Chapman, McQueen and Payman, U. S. Patent 2,327,405 (1943).
39. Davies, Wyler, Barrett and Linstead, U. S. Patent 2,155,038 (1939).
40. Dent, *J. Chem. Soc.*, **1938,** 546.
41. ——, U. S. Patent 2,166,240 (1939).
42. ——, U. S. Patent 2,214,454 (1940).
43. —— and Linstead, *J. Chem. Soc.*, **1934,** 1027.
44. ——, Linstead and Lowe, *ibid.*, **1934,** 1033.
45. Detrick and Brandt, U. S. Patent 2,334,812 (1943).
46. —— and Johnson, U. S. Patent 2,253,560 (1941).
47. Diesbach, de and Van der Weid, *Helv. Chim. Acta*, **10,** 886 (1927).
48. Ebert and Gottlieb, *J. Am. Chem. Soc.*, **74,** 2806 (1952).
49. Ficken and Linstead, *J. Chem. Soc.*, **1952,** 4846.
50. Fleysher and Ogilvie, U. S. Patent 2,276,175 (1942).
51. Fox, U. S. Patent 2,247,752 (1941).
52. —— and Johnson, U. S. Patent 2,377,685 (1945).
53. French Patent 1,023,765 (1953).

54. Gassner and Bienert, U. S. Patent 2,116,196 (1938).
55. —— and ——, U. S. Patent 2,122,137 (1938).
56. —— and ——, U. S. Patent 2,197,860 (1940).
57. German Patent 663,552 (1938).
58. German Patent 696,590 (1940).
59. German Patent 704,927 (1941).
60. Giambalvo, U. S. Patent 2,262,229 (1941).
61. ——, U. S. Patent 2,526,345 (1950).
62. Gottlieb, U. S. Patent 2,645,643 (1953).
63. Graham, U. S. Patents 2,556,728 and 730 (1951).
64. Gumlich and Dennstedt, U. S. Patent 2,234,076 (1941).
65. Haddock, *J. Soc. Dyers Colourists*, **61**, 68 (1945).
66. ——, U. S. Patent 2,277,588 (1942).
67. Haworth, Heilbron, Hey, Wilkinson and Bradbrook, *J. Chem. Soc.*, **1945**, 409.
68. Heilbron, Irving and Linstead, U. S. Patent 2,116,602 (1938).
69. ——, —— and ——, U. S. Patent 2,202,632 (1940).
70. ——, —— and ——, U. S. Patent 2,286,679 (1942).
71. Helberger, *Ann.*, **529**, 205 (1937).
72. ——, *Naturwissenschaften*, **26**, 316 (1938).
73. —— and Rebay, *Ann.*, **531**, 279 (1937).
74. —— and Hever, *Ber.*, **72**, 11 (1939).
75. Holzach and Muehlbauer, U. S. Patent 2,124,299 (1938).
76. I. G. Farbenindustrie, BIOS 960, p. 38 (PB 65657).
77. ——, *ibid.*, p. 40.
78. ——, *ibid.*, p. 47.
79. ——, *ibid.*, p. 48.
80. ——, FIAT 1309, pp. 8–9 (PB 85144).
81. ——, FIAT 1313, Vol. III, p. 276 (PB 85172).
82. ——, *ibid.*, p. 278.
83. ——, *ibid.*, p. 286
84. ——, *ibid.*, p. 292.
85. ——, *ibid.*, p. 295.
86. ——, *ibid.*, p. 298.
87. ——, *ibid.*, p. 300.
88. ——, *ibid.*, p. 310.
89. ——, *ibid.*, p. 323.
90. ——, *ibid.*, p. 325.
91. ——, *ibid.*, p. 334.
92. ——, *ibid.*, p. 337.
93. ——, *ibid.*, p. 344.
94. ——, *ibid.*, p. 346.
95. ——, PB 17892, frames 9060–9073.
96. ——, PB 60946 (Robitschek Report).
97. ——, PB 70339, frames 11340–11353 and 11488.
98. ——, PB 70340, frames 12442–12478.
99. ——, PB 70341, frames 13473–13506.
100. ——, *ibid.*, frames 13507–13522.
101. ——, PB 73754, frames 3003-3014.
102. Kienle, *Offic. Dig. Federation Paint & Varnish Prod. Clubs*, Jan. 1950, p. 48.
103. King, Foote and Felch, U. S. Patent 2,318,783 (1943).
104. Lacey, U. S. Patent 2,318,787 (1943).

105. —— and Lecher, U. S. Patent 2,359,737 (1944).
106. Lane and Stratton, U. S. Patent 2,556,727 (1951).
107. Lang and Detrick, U. S. Patent 2,402,167 (1946).
108. Linstead, *J. Chem. Soc.*, **1934**, 1016.
109. ——, *Ber.*, **72A**, 93 (1939).
110. —— and Dent, U. S. Patent 2,056,944 (1936).
111. —— and ——, U. S. Patent 2,124,742 (1938).
112. —— and ——, U. S. Patent 2,129,013 (1938).
113. —— and ——, U. S. Patent 2,214,469 (1940).
114. —— and Lowe, *J. Chem. Soc.*, **1934**, 1022.
115. —— and ——, *ibid.*, **1934**, 1031.
116. ——, Nobel and Wright, *ibid.*, **1937**, 911.
117. —— and Robertson, *ibid.*, **1936**, 1736.
118. —— and Whalley, *ibid.*, **1952**, 4839.
119. Loukomsky, U. S. Patent 2,486,304 (1949).
120. Lowe, U. S. Patent 2,155,054 (1939).
121. Mattiello, "Protective and Decorative Coatings," Vol. II, p. 258, New York, John Wiley & Sons, Inc., 1942.
122. ——, *ibid.*, Vol. V, pp. 437–9.
123. Morley, *J. Rubber Research*, **16**, 31 (1947).
124. Moser, U. S. Patent 2,549,842 (1951).
125. Muehlbauer, U. S. Patent 2,182,763 (1939).
126. Niemann, Schmidt, Muehlbauer and Wiest, U. S. Patent 2,276,860 (1942).
127. O'Neal, U. S. Patent 2,410,301 (1946).
128. Pacquot, *Compt. rend.*, **209**, 171 (1939).
129. ——, *ibid.*, **214**, 173 (1942).
130. ——, *Bull. soc. chim. France*, **12**, 450 (1945).
131. Palmer and Gross, U. S. Patent 2,413,191 (1946).
132. Park, U. S. Patent 2,047,128 (1936).
133. Riley, U. S. Patent 2,214,477 (1940).
134. Rintelman, U. S. Patents 2,485,167 and 8 (1949).
135. Robertson, *J. Chem. Soc.*, **1935**, 615.
136. ——, *ibid.*, **1936**, 1195.
137. ——, Linstead and Dent, *Nature*, **135**, 506 (1935).
138. —— and Woodward, *J. Chem. Soc.*, **1937**, 219.
139. —— and ——, *ibid.*, **1940**, 36.
140. Sander, *Die Chemie*, **55**, 255 (1942).
141. Siegel, U. S. Patent 2,173,699 (1939).
142. Sloan, U. S. Patent 2,282,006 (1942).
143. Stern and Pruckner, *Z. physik. Chem.*, **178**, 435 (1937).
144. Tamamusi and Tohmatu, *Bull. Chem. Soc. Japan*, **15**, 223 (1940).
145. Thiebert and Pfeiffer, *Ber.*, **71B**, 1399 (1938).
146. Thorpe and Linstead, U. S. Patent 2,000,052 (1935).
147. Vesce, U. S. Patent 2,138,049 (1938).
148. ——, U. S. Patent 2,268,144 (1941).
149. —— and Stalzer, U. S. Patent 2,327,472 (1943).
150. Wiswall, U. S. Patent 2,486,351 (1949).
151. Wyler, U. S. Patent 2,197,458 (1940).
152. ——, U. S. Patent 2,197,459 (1940).
153. ——, U. S. Patent 2,216,761 (1940).
154. ——, U. S. Patent 2,216,867 (1940).
155. Zettlemoyer, *Am. Ink Maker*, **26**, No. 1, p. 25 (1948).

10. PHTHALOCYANINE DYES

W. S. Struve

Introduction and History

This chapter considers the textile dyes and oil- or spirit-soluble colors containing the phthalocyanine nucleus.

The discovery of iron phthalocyanine by chemists of the Imperial Chemical Industries and the elucidation of its structure by R. P. Linstead and co-workers at London precipitated a still-continuing search for methods of adapting the phthalocyanine chromophore to useful dyes. As pigments, the phthalocyanines possess extreme lightfastness, good brilliance and strength, and excellent resistance to chemical reagents. It was hoped that these outstanding properties of the pigments could be carried over to compounds which could be used as dyes for textiles. To be a textile dye a color must be soluble at some point in its application to the fiber, while a pigment is expected to be insoluble in the medium in which it is used.

The general method of attack has been to introduce into the phthalocyanine molecule various groups so that the resulting products have the application properties of direct dyes, sulfur dyes or vat dyes. For instance, to obtain compounds behaving like sulfur dyes, groups such as dithio and mercapto have been introduced. To obtain vat dyes, phthalocyanines containing anthraquinonyl groups have been synthesized. In both of these cases, these are the groups which characterize the particular class of color which is to be duplicated. However, in the case of direct dyes, quaternary systems—a type of solubilizing group new to this color field—have been used.

From all of this research has come a relatively small number of commercial products. The first products to appear were the sulfonated phthalocyanines containing 2–3 sulfo groups per molecule. Such dyes are water-soluble and they have affinity for cellulosic fiber. They are used as direct dyes and as paper beater dyes. Various sulfonic acid derivatives, such as the amide from isohexylamine, have been used as spirit-soluble colors. Sulfonamides from amines such as morpholine have given products which are soluble in the presence of electrolytes and are useful for quick-drying writing inks.

Water-soluble direct dyes are also made by introduction of the chloromethyl group into phthalocyanines, followed by reaction of the —CH$_2$Cl group with compounds such as trimethylamine and thiourea. Alcian Blue 8GS (ICI) is a dye of this type.

Also of commercial importance is a green sulfur dye based on copper phthalocyanine. In this case the brilliance of shade and good lightfastness hoped for from the phthalocyanine nucleus has been obtained and an outstanding sulfur dye is the result.

To these substituted phthalocyanines, there are two main routes. One involves direct substitution of the already-formed phthalocyanine. This method is widely used industrially for economic reasons. A mixture of products is obtained, especially as regards degree of substitution. For instance, sulfonation of copper phthalocyanine, when carried out to give a disulfonic acid, gives a mixture of products containing one, two or three sulfo groups. Further, the position that the entering group takes may not be the desired one. This latter objection may be overcome by the second main route, in which the substituted phthalocyanine is synthesized from the appropriately substituted phthalic acid or phthalic acid derivative. This latter method is preferred when homogeneous products of a definite structure are desired. Substituted phthalocyanines, such as methyl-substituted products, can be made only from the correspondingly substituted phthalic acid derivatives. Since phthalocyanines are not stable to nitric acid, nitro-substituted phthalocyanines are made from the nitro-substituted phthalic acids. If mono-, di-, or trisubstituted phthalocyanines are desired from substituted phthalic acids, recourse is made to "mixed fusions" in which a mixture of the substituted phthalic acid derivative and phthalic anhydride is used. Apparently many substituted phthalic anhydrides enter the phthalocyanine reaction as readily as does phthalic anhydride, and a substituted phthalocyanine containing residues from both the substituted and unsubstituted anhydrides is obtained. The average degree of substitution is, of course, regulated by the ratio of unsubstituted phthalic anhydride to the substituted derivative.

Phthalocyanine Direct Dyes

Direct dyes are water-soluble colors which have affinity for cellulose fibers. To prepare direct dyes from a phthalocyanine it is obvious that water-solubilizing groups will have to be introduced. Three types of solubilizing groups have been studied extensively, sulfo groups, carboxy groups, and derivatives based on chloromethyl groups. Properly substituted derivatives containing any of these groups have some affinity for cotton. These direct dyes vary from blue to yellow-green in shade, depending on the other substituents in the molecule. Commercially, copper is the only metal used to form such a phthalocyanine complex.

Sulfonic Acids. The first phthalocyanine-based dye to reach the commercial market in the middle 1930's was based on sulfonated copper phthalocyanine. While copper phthalocyanine is stable in cold, concentrated sulfuric acid, it is sulfonated with hot oleum. Depending on the concentration of the oleum and the time and temperature of the reaction, up to four sulfo groups can be introduced. The products obtained are greener in shade than the starting material and have good lightfastness, fair affinity for cellulosic fibers, and poor washfastness. Wool dyeings are uneven. By varying the degree of sulfonation an optimum is reached in affinity and washfastness. For cotton dyeing a product averaging two sulfo groups per molecule is used (Heliogen Blue SBL[56], Pr. 278). Higher degrees of sulfonation are used to give material for paper beater dyeing (Heliogen Blue SBP[56]). Imperial Chemical Industries sell sulfonated phthalocyanines under the names Durazol Fast Paper Blue 10GS and Monosol Fast Blue 2GS[23]. Most other metal phthalocyanines give products of inferior lightfastness on sulfonation.

Copper phthalocyanine can be tetra(chlorosulfonylated) in almost theoretical yield by heating in chlorosulfonic acid at 140°C[57]. However, the metal-free phthalocyanine gives only a 60 per cent yield under these conditions. These sulfonyl chlorides can be hydrolyzed to the corresponding tetrasulfonic acids. In all of these direct sulfonations the 3 positions are primarily attacked[48].

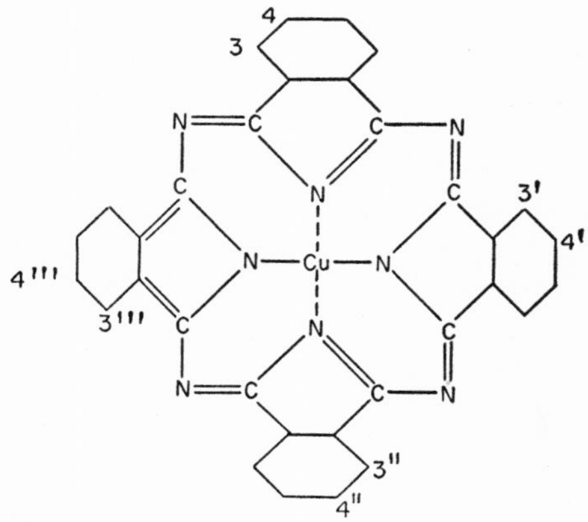

The directly sulfonated products differ in several important respects from those synthesized from 4-sulfophthalic acid. The directly sulfonated products are greener in shade and have better affinity for cellulose fibers while the products made from 4-sulfophthalic acid have better lightfastness and considerably improved fastness to alkali. However, due to their lower cost the directly sulfonated products are the ones most used commercially.

The presence of other groups in the molecule and their position influences sulfonation. Thus it is reported that copper tetra(3)chlorophthalocyanine* can be sulfonated while copper tetra(4)chlorophthalocyanine cannot be sulfonated[48]. However, a large number of other chlorinated derivatives of copper phthalocyanine have been sulfonated in a search for improved properties but many were deficient in affinity. The effect on shade and affinity for cotton is illustrated in Table 1.

TABLE 1.[47] SULFONATED COPPER PHTHALOCYANINES

Phthalocyanine Made From	Probable X in $(SO_3H)_x$	Solubility	Color	Affinity
3 Moles 4-chlorophthalic anhydride + 1 mole phthalic anhydride	1	Scarcely soluble	Too insoluble to test	
2 Moles 4-chlorophthalic anhydride + 2 moles phthalic anhydride	2	Good	Blue-green	Poor
1 Mole 4-chlorophthalic anhydride + 3 moles phthalic anhydride	3	Good	Turquoise blue	Fair
2 Moles 3,6-dichlorophthalic anhydride + 2 moles phthalic anhydride	2	Good	Turquoise blue	Fair
2 Moles 4,5-dichlorophthalic anhydride + 2 moles phthalic anhydride	2	Good	Clear turquoise blue	Good
2 Moles 4-nitrophthalic anhydride + 2 moles phthalic anhydride	2	Good	Redder than chlorinated products	Fair
2 Moles 4-sulfophthalic anhydride + 2 moles 3,4-dichlorophthalic anhydride†	2	Good	Clear turquoise blue	Good

† Not sulfonated after phthalocyanine formation.

Although the more highly chlorinated copper phthalocyanines cannot be sulfonated, the sulfonated phthalocyanines can be chlorinated to give green shade direct dyes of good substantivity. Chlorination of copper phthalocyaninetetra(4)sulfonic acid in an aluminum chloride/sodium chloride melt to introduce about 8 chlorine atoms gives an attractive green shade cotton dye of improved fastness over the starting color[7, 20].

The product obtained by sulfonation of copper tetra(4)methylphthalocyanine has better lightfastness and is greener than the product from copper phthalocyanine. The product obtained by sulfonation of copper octa(4,5)methylphthalocyanine is a dull yellowish green of moderate lightfastness[49]. Sulfonation of copper tetracyanophthalocyanine in oleum gives a highly substantive, alkali-stable product of bright turquoise shade and excellent lightfastness[45]. The high cost of this product has prevented its commercial exploitation.

* In this chapter substituted phthalocyanines which Chemical Abstracts would designate, e. g., 4,4′,4″,4′′′ will be named, e.g., copper tetra(4)chlorophthalocyanine. The nine-ring numbering system (R.I. 3906) given in "The Ring Index" of Patterson and Capell will not be used here.

The yellowest greens of the copper phthalocyaninesulfonic acid type are the copper tetra(5)acylaminophthalocyaninetetra(4)sulfonic acids, which are yellow-green cotton dyes of high lightfastness. These colors were prepared from the correspondingly substituted phthalic acids which were obtained over the following route:

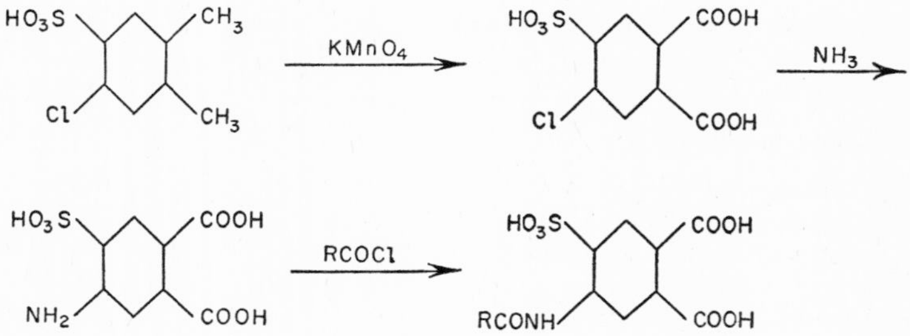

Much attention has been paid to copper tetra(5)benzamidophthalocyaninetetra(4)sulfonic acid and to analogs prepared from substituted benzoyl chlorides. In spite of the yellow-green shades and good fastness to light these colors have not been developed commercially due to their poor affinity for cotton[3, 52, 59].

Sulfonic Acid Derivatives. A number of derivatives of phthalocyaninesulfonic acids are produced commercially for use as spirit- and oil-soluble colors and in quick-drying inks. The most important of these are sulfonamides, produced by reaction of phthalocyaninesulfonyl chlorides with various amines. The reaction of copper phthalocyaninetetrasulfonyl chloride with ammonia or amines in water does not give the tetrasulfonamides. A product corresponding to $CPC(SO_2NHR)_{2-3}(SO_3NH_3R)_{2-1}$ is obtained due to partial hydrolysis of the chlorosulfonyl groups and subsequent salt formation. To obtain the pure tetrasulfonamides it is necessary to start with the properly substituted phthalic acid derivative. However, the copper tetra(4)-butylsulfamylphthalocyanine, prepared from the corresponding phthalic acid (I), was shown to be less soluble in alcohol than the compound pre-

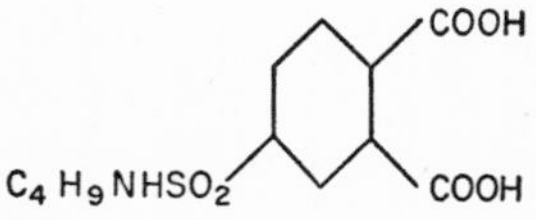

(I)

pared by reacting the tetrasulfonyl chloride with butylamine[57]. Reaction of isohexylamine with copper phthalocyaninetetrasulfonyl chloride gives a product of good solubility in mixed ester solvents (Zapon Fast Blue HFL[54]).

Zapon Fast Blue HL, prepared by reacting N,N-dimethyldodecylamine with copper phthalocyaninetetrasulfonic acid[50], is characterized by good solubility in glycol lacquers but poor solubility in butyl acetate.

By reacting a phthalocyaninesulfonyl chloride with various amines or hydrazines which confer water solubility, products useful in quick-drying writing inks are obtained[16, 17, 63, 64, 66]. These compounds are suitable for this purpose because they are soluble in dilute sodium hydroxide which is used in such inks. Blue, spirit-soluble colors can be made by making salts of phthalocyaninesulfonic acids with quaternary ammonium compounds of the formula $R(CH_3)_3NBr$ where R is an alkyl group containing 8 to 20 carbons[40], or with a diarylguanidine[12], or with a 2-dialkylaminoethanol in which each alkyl group contains 8 carbon atoms[68].

One other type of phthalocyaninesulfonamide derivative studied by German chemists is of interest because of the unique method used to immobilize the dye on the fiber. Condensation of 4-amino-1-butanol with copper phthalocyaninetetrasulfonyl chloride, followed by reaction with chlorosulfonic acid and neutralization with sodium hydroxide, gives a product containing the $-SO_2NHCH_2CH_2CH_2CH_2OSO_3Na$ residue. This derivative has affinity for cellulose fibers. On the fiber it is reported to decompose in the presence of alkali to give the group

$$-SO_2N\begin{array}{c} CH_2-CH_2 \\ | \quad\quad | \\ CH_2-CH_2 \end{array}$$

which no longer confers water solubility[43, 53].

Carboxylic Acids. The phthalocyaninecarboxylic acids have not been as widely studied as the corresponding phthalocyaninesulfonic acids. This has been due partially to their relative inaccessibility. Three methods have been used to prepare phthalocyaninecarboxylic acids: (1) the reaction of copper phthalocyanine with trichloroacetic acid at elevated temperatures, which gives alkali-soluble products[18]; (2) the reaction of phthalocyanines with phosgene in an aluminum chloride/sodium chloride melt to give a mixture of phthalocyaninecarbonyl chlorides which can be hydrolyzed to the alkali-soluble carboxylic acids[6]; and (3) direct synthesis from the appropriately substituted benzenepolycarboxylic acids or their derivatives[69].

Copper phthalocyaninetetra(4)carboxylic acid is insoluble in water but it is soluble in dilute sodium carbonate to give bright blue solutions. The sodium salt has some affinity for cotton but it has no value as a dye because of its sensitivity to alkali and its poor washfastness[45].

When the German chemists sulfonated copper tetra(4)phenylphthalocyanine they found that if up to four sulfo groups were introduced, presumably on the pendant phenyl rings, the resulting alkali-soluble products had practically no affinity for cotton. If, however, more stringent sulfonation conditions were used and more than four sulfo groups were introduced into the molecule, the resulting product had some affinity for cellulose fibers. They believed that the additional sulfo groups were substituted on the phthalocyanine nucleus and not on the pendant phenyl groups, and that this was the reason for the increase in affinity. A study was therefore made of tetraphenylphthalocyanines in which the solubilizing group was on the phthalocyanine nucleus[46]. Their theory seemed correct because the products in which the solubilizing group was on the central nucleus showed greatly enhanced affinity over those in which the solubilizing group was on a pendant ring. Dyes solubilized both by sulfo and by carboxy groups were studied (see Table 2).

Commercially, the most interesting color of this type is copper tetra(4)-phenylphthalocyaninetetra(5)carboxylic acid, a bright green cotton dye of excellent lightfastness which was referred to as Sirius Supra Light Green FFGL[42, 44]. The requisite intermediate, 2,4,5-biphenyltricarboxylic acid, had been prepared earlier by the I. G. Farbenindustrie starting from 2,3-dimethyl-1,3-butadiene and cinnamic acid[60, 61, 62].

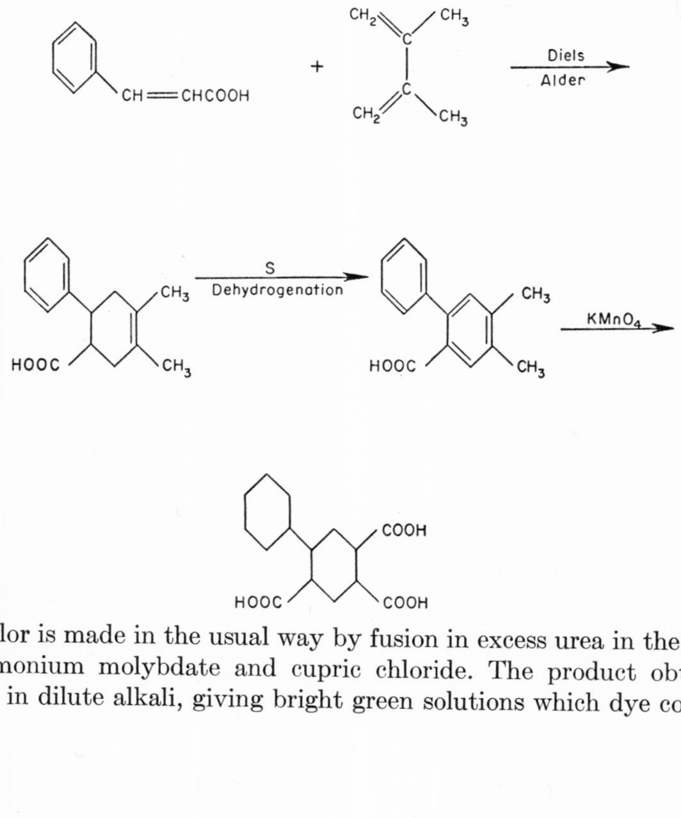

The color is made in the usual way by fusion in excess urea in the presence of ammonium molybdate and cupric chloride. The product obtained is soluble in dilute alkali, giving bright green solutions which dye cotton and

TABLE 2. SUBSTITUTED COPPER PHTHALOCYANINETETRACARBOXYLIC ACIDS

Intermediate	Dyeing Properties	Ref.
Cl〈 〉 COOH / HOOC COOH	Bright green	46
〈 〉 COOH / HOOC COOH	Bluish green	46
Cl / Cl 〈 〉 COOH / HOOC COOH	Weak greenish blue	46
Cl〈 〉 Cl COOH / HOOC COOH	Greenish blue; very poor solubility	46
CH₃O〈 〉 COOH / HOOC COOH	Yellowish green	46
O₂N〈 〉 COOH / HOOC COOH	Weak bluish green	46

614

TABLE 2 (*Continued*)

Intermediate	Dyeing Properties	Ref.
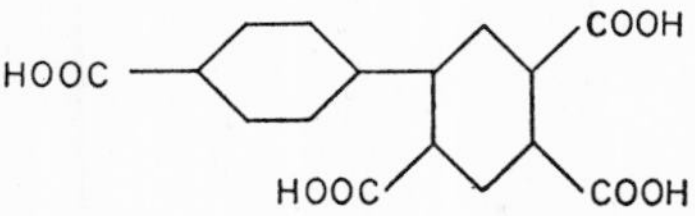	Very poor washfastness	46
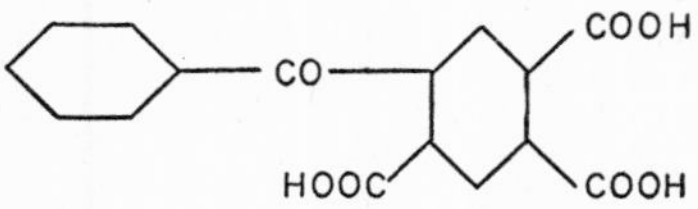	Bright blue	46, 55, 58
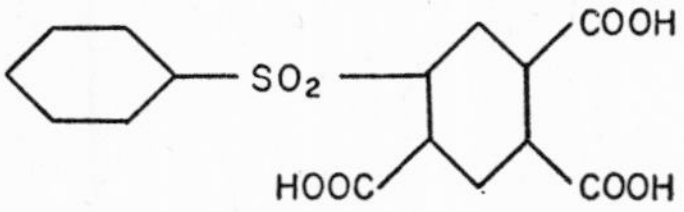	Less green than benzoyl	46, 58
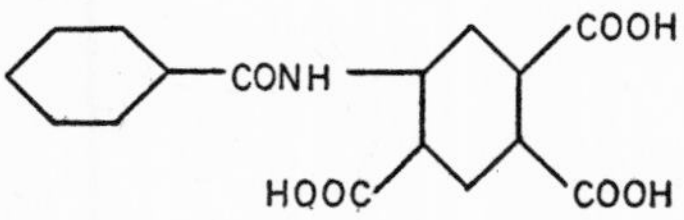	Dull olive green	55

rayon very light-fast green shades. The dyeings have poor washfastness, however. A considerable number of other substituted trimellitic acids were prepared and converted to color. These are summarized in Table 2.

An analogous tetrasulfonic acid made from 6-sulfo-3,4-biphenyldicarboxylic acid gave bluish green dyeings whose shade was inferior to that of Green FFGL[46, 55]. The intermediate was prepared by an interesting method which involves replacement of a carboxy group by a sulfo group[46].

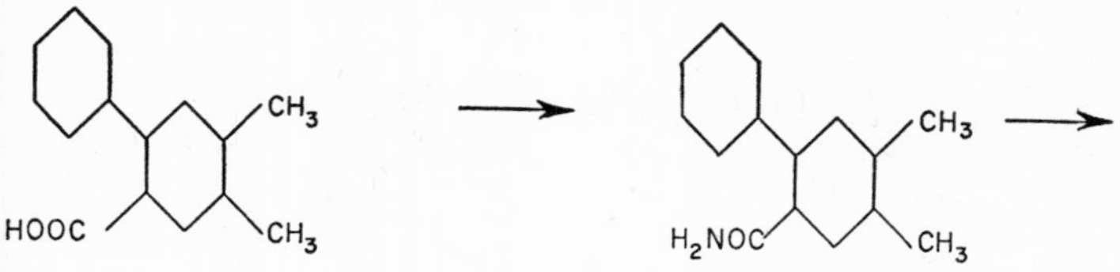

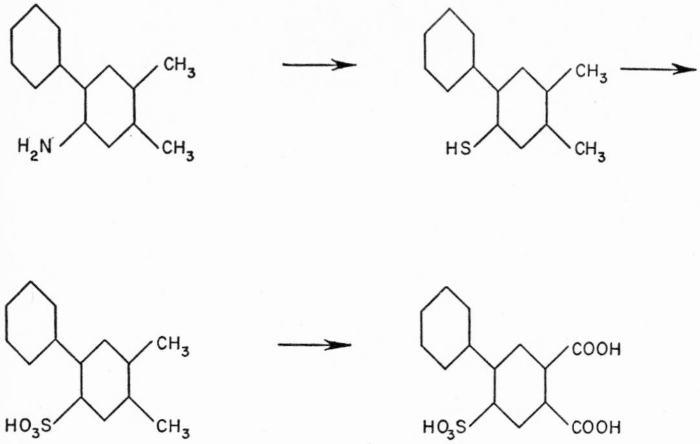

Other Water-soluble Derivatives. The chemists of the Imperial Chemical Industries in England have studied phthalocyanines containing quaternary groups to confer water solubility, a type of structure different from the orthodox classes of dyes[24].

The first type of quaternary compound studied is derived from the pyridylphthalocyanines. The pyridylphthalocyanines can be made either by direct synthesis from a pyridyl-substituted phthalonitrile[5],

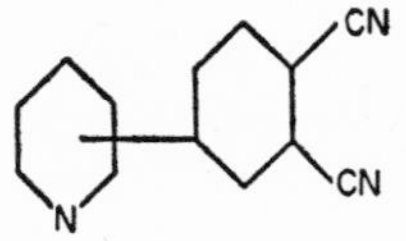

or by reaction of a diazotized aminophthalocyanine with excess pyridine[25]. The pyridylphthalocyanine is converted to a quaternary derivative with methyl sulfate or methyl p-toluenesulfonate[4]. These water-soluble quaternaries have affinity for cotton and rayon, especially when the pH of the dye bath is raised, as by slowly adding sodium carbonate. The resulting green dyeings are fast to washing. It would seem that the pyridinium groups gradually lose their solubilizing action during the alkaline treatment[24]. This discovery led to further work in a search for more suitable dyes.

Related sulfonium salts were also found to have affinity for cotton[13]. These compounds were made by reacting the alkyl- or aralkylmercaptophthalocyanines with alkyl sulfates or sulfites.

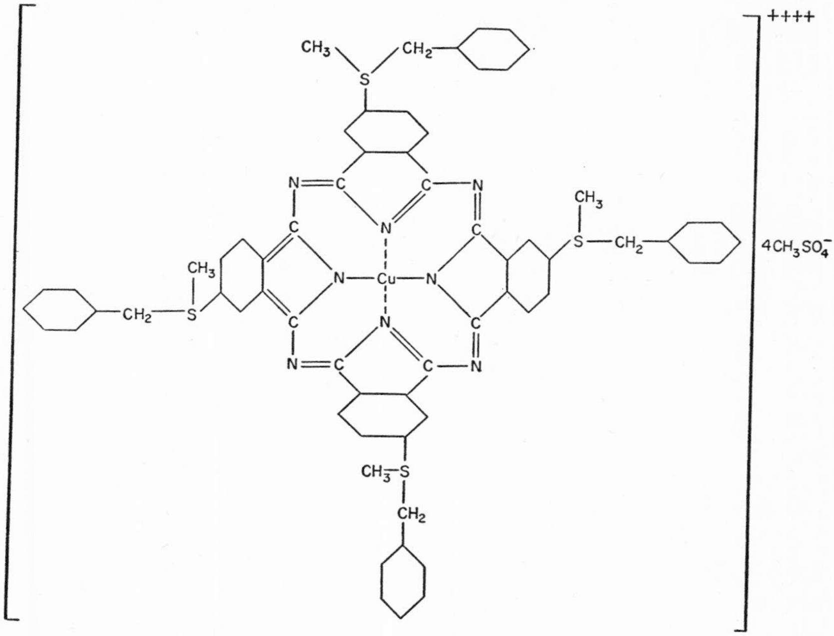

The alkylmercaptophthalocyanines can be made by direct synthesis from the alkylmercaptophthalic acids. These water-soluble sulfonium derivatives are cotton dyes of fair affinity and give blue-green to green shades.

A wide range of stability is observed in these ammonium- and sulfonium-solubilized derivatives. Some are unstable in the dyebath and decompose before dyeing. Others are so stable that they do not regenerate the insoluble color on the fiber when the dyebath is made alkaline.

The I.C.I. chemists found that chloromethyl groups could be readily introduced into the phthalocyanine nucleus by reaction of paraformaldehyde or bis(chloromethyl) ether in a melt of aluminum chloride and a tertiary amine, such as pyridine or triethylamine[36]. Under these conditions the chloromethyl groups do not react further to form the methylene-bisphthalocyanines and the degree of substitution can be controlled by varying the ratio of reactants. The position which the entering CH_2Cl groups take, whether the 3 or 4 position, is not known. The chloromethyl groups can be reacted in a number of ways to form water-soluble derivatives[37, 38]. Amines such as pyridine and trimethylamine give water-soluble quaternary compounds.

$$CPC(CH_2Cl)_x + x(CH_3)_3N \rightarrow CPC[CH_2N(CH_3)_3{}^+Cl^-]_x$$

Thiourea and alkylthioureas give isothiuronium derivatives which also dissolve readily in water.

$$CPC(CH_2Cl)_x + xCS(NH_2)_2 \rightarrow CPC\left[CH_2-S-C\begin{matrix}\nearrow NH_2 \\ \searrow NH_2{}^+Cl^-\end{matrix}\right]_x$$

A further water-soluble type prepared from the chloromethyl derivative is found in the sulfonium salts, which can be prepared by the following series of reactions:

$$CPC(CH_2Cl)_x + xCH_3SNa \rightarrow CPC(CH_2-S-CH_3)_x$$

$$CPC(CH_2-S-CH_3)_x + x(CH_3)_2SO_4 \rightarrow CPC[CH_2-S(CH_3)_2{}^+SO_4CH_3{}^-]_x$$

These various derivatives prepared from chloromethylated copper phthalocyanine have affinity for cellulose fibers, which are dyed blue to greenish-blue shades of fair lightfastness. Similar reactions can be carried out on phthalocyanines containing CH_2Cl groups on pendant phenyl nuclei[39].

Aminophthalocyanines

4-Aminophthalonitrile and 4-aminophthalimide can be converted to phthalocyanines but the products obtained do not contain a free amino group since they cannot be acylated or diazotized[23]. Acylaminophthalocyanines, prepared from the correspondingly substituted phthalic acids or derivatives[2], can be hydrolyzed with sulfuric acid but much decomposition also results.

The aminophthalocyanines are most conveniently prepared by reduction of the corresponding nitrophthalocyanines with sodium sulfide, sodium hydrosulfite or stannous chloride[26]. Copper phthalocyanine cannot be nitrated—nitric acid decomposes it almost quantitatively to phthalimide[14]. Therefore the nitrophthalocyanines must be made from nitrophthalonitrile[41] or a nitrophthalic acid.

Copper tetra(4)aminophthalocyanine is a green compound which turns blue in the presence of strong acids due to salt formation. It shows the usual reactions of amines and can be diazotized in strong hydrochloric acid to give a blue solution of the tetra diazonium salt. This diazo compound undergoes the usual coupling and replacement reactions. It couples to 2-naphthol and pyrazolones to give pigments[29]. The diazo solution also reacts with pyridine to give copper tetrapyridylphthalocyanine, which is a green pigment[25]. Aminophthalocyanines in which the amino group is attached to a pendant phenyl nucleus give more stable diazonium salts than does copper tetra(4)aminophthalocyanine. Consequently, on azo coupling the phenyl-bearing diazonium salts give purer products of greater brilliance of shade than are obtained by diazotizing and coupling the copper tetra(4)amino-phthalocyanine, the diazo derivative of which is reported to decompose slowly even at $0°C$[9, 10, 31, 32, 33]. Among the aminophthalocyanines with the amino groups on pendant phenyl nuclei are copper tetra(4)(p-aminobenzoyl)-phthalocyanine (I), copper tetra(4)(m-aminobenzoyl)phthalocyanine (II), copper tetra(4)(o-aminophenylsulfonyl)phthalocyanine (III), copper tetra-(4)(p-aminophenoxy)phthalocyanine (IV), copper tetra(4)(p-aminoben-zamido)phthalocyanine (V), and copper tetra(4)(p-aminophenylmercapto)-phthalocyanine (VI).

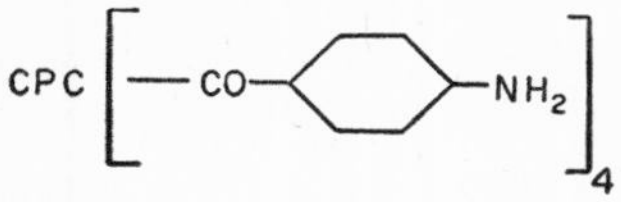

$$CPC \left[-CO-\!\!\!\!\bigcirc\!\!\!\!-NH_2 \right]_4 \quad (I)$$

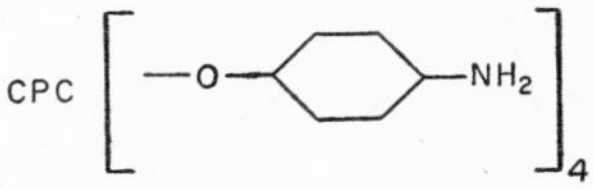

$$CPC \left[-O-\!\!\!\!\bigcirc\!\!\!\!-NH_2 \right]_4 \quad (IV)$$

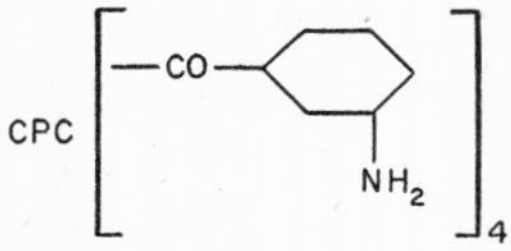

$$CPC \left[-CO-\!\!\!\!\bigcirc\!\!\!\!_{NH_2} \right]_4 \quad (II)$$

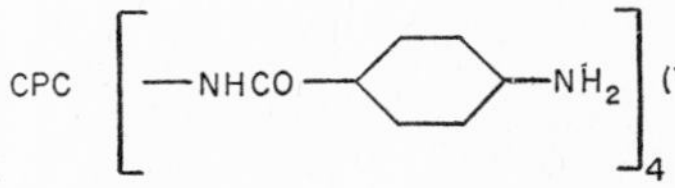

$$CPC \left[-NHCO-\!\!\!\!\bigcirc\!\!\!\!-NH_2 \right]_4 \quad (V)$$

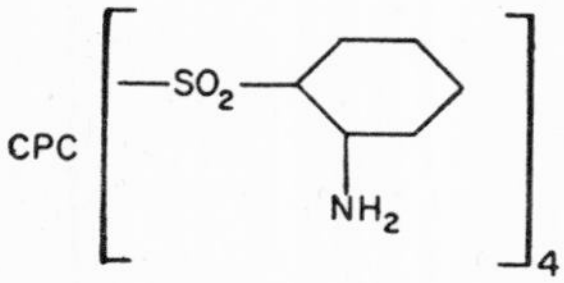

$$CPC \left[-SO_2-\!\!\!\!\bigcirc\!\!\!\!_{NH_2} \right]_4 \quad (III)$$

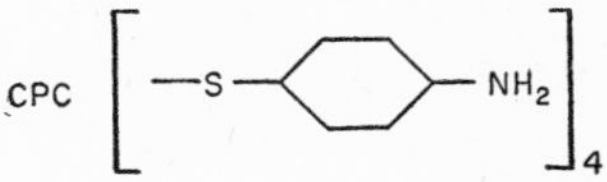

$$CPC \left[-S-\!\!\!\!\bigcirc\!\!\!\!-NH_2 \right]_4 \quad (VI)$$

Phthalocyanine (VI) is made as follows:

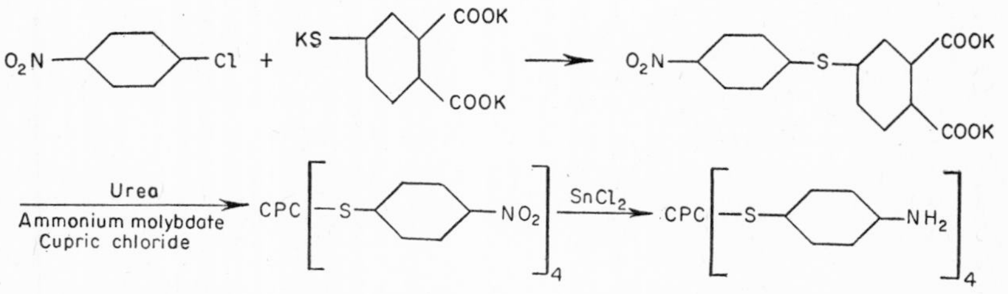

$$O_2N-\!\!\!\!\bigcirc\!\!\!\!-Cl + KS-\!\!\!\!\bigcirc\!\!\!\!\!\!<^{COOK}_{COOK} \longrightarrow O_2N-\!\!\!\!\bigcirc\!\!\!\!-S-\!\!\!\!\bigcirc\!\!\!\!\!\!<^{COOK}_{COOK}$$

$$\xrightarrow[\substack{\text{Ammonium molybdate} \\ \text{Cupric chloride}}]{\text{Urea}} CPC \left[-S-\!\!\!\!\bigcirc\!\!\!\!-NO_2 \right]_4 \xrightarrow{SnCl_2} CPC \left[-S-\!\!\!\!\bigcirc\!\!\!\!-NH_2 \right]_4$$

These phthalocyanines with amino groups on pendant nuclei give soluble blue to green diazonium salts which can be coupled to various coupling components used to prepare azo colors. Second components such as the acetoacetarylamides and the pyrazolones give bright green shades. As yet none of these dyes has attained commercial importance.

Phthalocyanine Vat Dyes

The search for vat colors containing the phthalocyanine nucleus has been directed mainly toward the incorporation of orthodox vattable groups into the molecule. One type of derivative is obtained from 1,2-anthraquinonedicarbonitrile

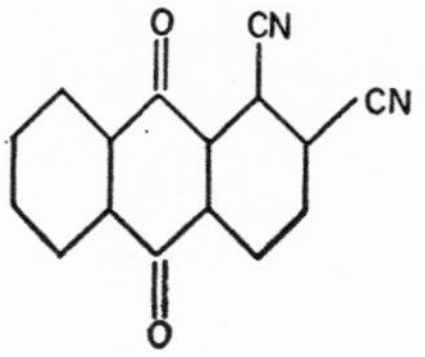

by converting it to the corresponding copper phthalocyanine[45], which gives a vat with sodium hydrosulfite. This vat yields blue-green dyeings on cotton which change to a dull violet on soaping. By heating the 3,4-dibromoanilide of 2-anthraquinonecarboxylic acid with cuprous cyanide in nitrobenzene and pyridine,

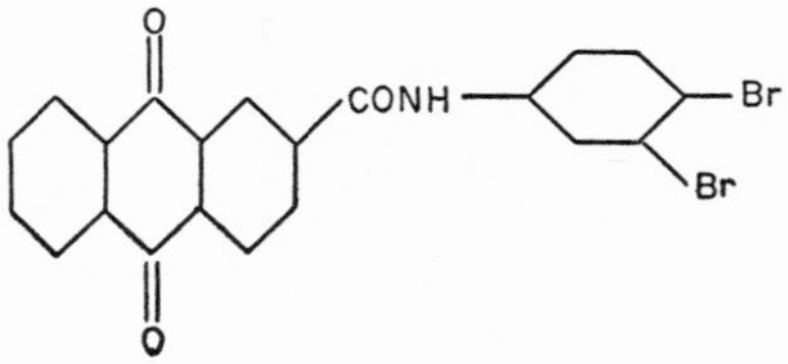

a phthalocyanine containing anthraquinone residues attached by a —CONH— link is obtained[21]. Further, by heating anthraquinonecarbonyl chlorides and copper phthalocyanine with ferric chloride as catalyst in trichlorobenzene, the anthraquinone residues can be attached to the phthalocyanine nucleus to give a vattable compound[19]. Unfortunately all of these derivatives of copper phthalocyanine containing vattable groups give unstable vats on reduction with sodium hydrosulfite. The vats hydrolyze to phthalimide derivatives[24] and thus cannot be used in the normal vat dyeing procedures. To overcome this difficulty, leuco sulfuric acid esters of anthraquinone-substituted phthalocyanine derivatives have been prepared. One method of preparation is the orthodox one with anthraquinone vat dyes, namely reduction with iron and esterification with the pyridine-SO$_3$ complex. Esters of (VII) and (VIII) have been made in this fashion. The first is a dull yellow-green

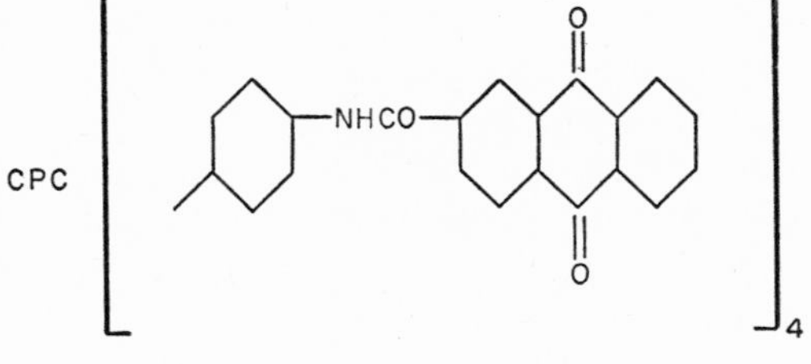

(VII)

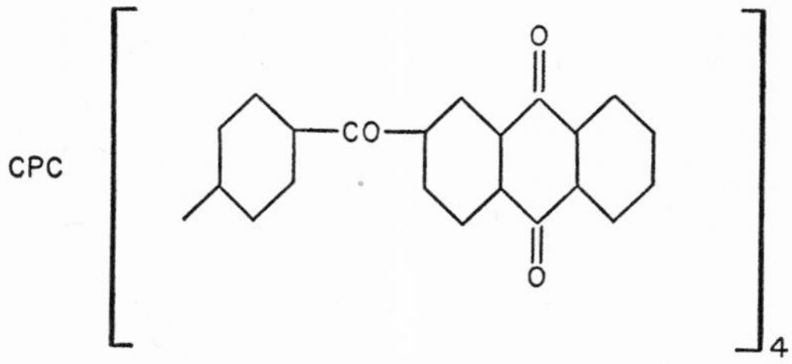

while the second is a brighter green[11, 51]. In addition, esters can be made by reaction of copper phthalocyaninetetrasulfonyl chloride or copper tetraphenylphthalocyaninetetrasulfonyl chloride in aqueous pyridine with aminoanthraquinone esters (IX) and (X) to give the substituted sulfonamides. The products

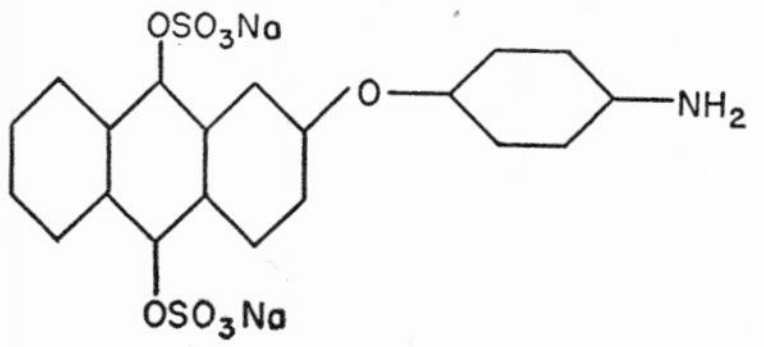

(IX)

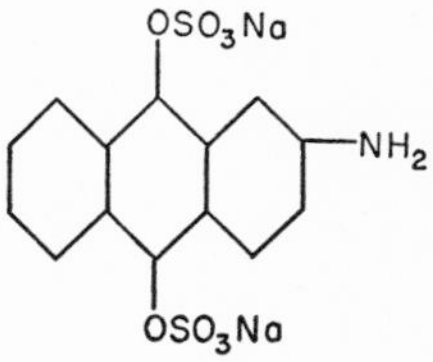

(X)

derived from copper phthalocyaninetetrasulfonyl chloride are blue in shade while those derived from copper tetraphenylphthalocyaninetetrasulfonyl chloride give green shades. These esters do not have good affinity for cotton and their bleachfastness is poorer than that of the vat color standards, so they have never been introduced commercially.

Some metal phthalocyanines can be reduced to give reduction products which have water solubility. These "vat forms" have affinity for cotton and the phthalocyanine can be regenerated on the fiber by oxidation. The structures of the reduction products are not known. Although copper and nickel phthalocyanine cannot be vatted, derivatives such as the sulfonic acids can be reduced. These reduction derivatives are unstable and decompose like the anthraquinone-substituted phthalocyanines described above. Cobalt phthalocyanine is outstanding in that its yellow-brown vat form has good affinity and is stable, even at high temperatures. The ease of reduction and the solubility of the vat form of cobalt phthalocyanine can be increased greatly by incorporation of 15 to 40 per cent of a phthalocyanine which contains hydrophilic groups, such as the phosphonous acid[67], carboxylic acid, or especially the sulfonic acid derivatives[1]. Such a product is Indanthrene Brilliant Blue 4G. Products based on cobalt phthalocyanine show excellent lightfastness and good washfastness, but poor resistance to bleach and to gas fumes.

Phthalocyanine Sulfur Dyes

It was discovered by chemists of the Imperial Chemical Industries in England that phthalocyanine disulfides act like sulfur colors in that they are soluble in sodium sulfide solution by means of reduction to thiols to give a gray-blue vat. These vats, in contrast with the vats prepared from the anthraquinone-substituted phthalocyanines, are stable and have reasonably good affinity for cotton. The reduced color can then be oxidized on the cloth to the original disulfide with, for example, sodium dichromate and acetic acid, giving a bright green shade. Such dyeings are much superior to dyeings of ordinary sulfur colors in brilliance of shade, as well as in fastness to light and washing. There are three known routes to this type of compound. Phthalocyaninesulfonyl chlorides, prepared either by direct chlorosulfonation or from the sulfonic acids by reaction with phosphorus pentachloride or chlorosulfonic acid, can be reduced to the thiols with zinc[28] or iron[65] and hydrochloric acid or with alkyl or aryl thiols[34]. The phthalocyaninethiols are readily oxidized to the disulfides with air. Products of less clearly known structure are obtained by reacting the sulfonyl chlorides with phosphorus pentasulfide[8] or with thioamides, such as thiourea[35]. A second general method of preparing phthalocyaninethiols is the reaction of phthalocyaninediazonium compounds with sodium xanthate, sodium thiocyanate, or sodium thiosulfate, followed by hydrolysis[27]. It has been found that the thiocyano derivatives, thus prepared over the diazo route, are easily hydrolyzed to the thiol with sodium sulfide in the usual sulfur dyeing procedure, and so do not require previous hydrolysis[30]. A third method of converting copper phthalocyanine to a sulfur dye consists in reacting it with a sulfur chloride/aluminum chloride complex. Sulfur and chlorine are introduced into the molecule and the product, which is soluble in sodium sulfide solution, dyes cotton in green shades[15].

Phthalocyanine Formation in the Fiber

None of the above dyes derived from the phthalocyanine nucleus have the combined properties of brilliance of shade, extreme lightfastness, and fastness to wet treatments that are associated with copper phthalocyanine as a pigment. However, dyeings of copper phthalocyanine per se can be obtained by impregnating cotton with an aqueous paste of 1,3-diiminoiso-indoline (XI), a high-boiling solvent such as Carbitol,

(XI)

and a copper salt, followed by heating at 135 to 140°C. In this manner the copper phthalocyanine is formed in the fiber and these dyeings have the brilliance and lightfastness of copper phthalocyanine used as a pigment.

When properly applied these dyeings show definitely improved wash- and crockingfastness compared to pigment prints made with the conventional resin binder.

The 1,3-diiminoisoindoline has been postulated as an intermediate in the formation of phthalocyanines[32]. It can be prepared by reaction at 180 to 200°C of phthalic anhydride and urea in a solvent such as nitrobenzene, using ammonium molybdate as catalyst and ammonium nitrate to form a salt with the product. 1,3-Diiminoisoindoline nitrate precipitates from the reaction. The free base can be formed by careful reaction with alkali[22]. Another method of synthesis is the reaction of phthalonitrile with ammonia at high temperature.

Literature Cited

1. Baumann and Bienert, U.S. Patent 2,613,128 (1952).
2. Bienert, U.S. Patent 2,133,340 (1938).
3. —— and Thielert, U.S. Patent 2,266,404 (1941).
4. Bradbrook, Coffey, and Haddock, U.S. Patent 2,277,628 (1942).
5. ——, Heilbron, Hey and Haworth, U.S. Patent 2,277,629 (1942).
6. British Patent 510,901 (1939).
7. British Patent 514,857 (1939).
8. British Patent 588,696 (1947).
9. British Patent 589,118 (1947).
10. British Patent 603,753 (1948).
11. British Patent 633,478 (1949).
12. Carleton and Woodward, U.S. Patent 2,153,740 (1939).
13. Coffey, Haddock, and Jackson, U.S. Patent 2,290,906 (1942).
14. Dent and Linstead, *J. Chem. Soc.*, **1934,** 1030.
15. Fox, U.S. Patent 2,369,666 (1945).
16. ——, U.S. Patent 2,413,224 (1946).
17. ——, U.S. Patent 2,459,771 (1949).
18. German Patent 677,667 (1939).
19. German Patent 696,592 (1940).
20. German Patent 706,950 (1941).
21. German Patent 721,021 (1942).
22. German Patent Application F-2494 (1950).
23. Haddock, *J. Soc. Dyers Colourists*, **61,** 68 (1945).
24. ——, *Research*, **1,** 685 (1948).
25. ——, U.S. Patent 2,277,588 (1942).
26. ——, U.S. Patent 2,280,072 (1942).
27. ——, U.S. Patent 2,342,662 (1944).
28. ——, U.S. Patent 2,342,663 (1944).
29. ——, U.S. Patent 2,351,119 (1944).
30. ——, U.S. Patent 2,395,117 (1946).
31. —— and Jones, U.S. Patent 2,479,491 (1949).
32. ——, Parkinson, and Rowe, U.S. Patent 2,414,374 (1947).
33. ——, ——, and ——, U.S. Patent 2,430,052 (1947).

34. —— and Wood, U.S. Patent 2,416,386 (1947).
35. —— and ——, U.S. Patent 2,416,387 (1947).
36. —— and ——, U.S. Patent 2,435,307 (1948).
37. —— and ——, U.S. Patent 2,464,806 (1949).
38. —— and ——, U.S. Patent 2,482,172 (1949).
39. —— and ——, U.S. Patents 2,542,327 and 2,542,328 (1951).
40. Harrison and Samuels, U.S. Patent 2,150,741 (1939).
41. Heilbron, Irving, and Linstead, U.S. Patent 2,286,679 (1942).
42. Hoyer, Schroeter, and Rinke, U.S. Patent 2,242,469 (1941).
43. I. G. Farbenindustrie, FIAT 1313, Vol. III, p. 357 (PB 85172).
44. ——, PB 70337, frames 8680–8687.
45. ——, PB 70339, frames 11779–11783.
46. ——, *ibid.*, frames 11996–12005.
47. ——, *ibid.*, frames 12119–12123.
48. ——, *ibid.*, frames 12129–12140.
49. ——, PB 70340, frames 12245–12254.
50. ——, *ibid.*, frames 12256–12262.
51. ——, *ibid.*, frames 12411–12414.
52. ——, *ibid.*, frames 12443–12478; 12546–12558.
53. ——, *ibid.*, frames 12573–12577.
54. ——, *ibid.*, frames 12560–12568.
55. ——, *ibid.*, frames 12636–12640.
56. ——, PB 70341, frames 13507–13522.
57. ——, PB 73754, frames 2591–2611.
58. ——, *ibid.*, frames 3003–3014.
59. ——, PB 74898, frames 9778–9781, 9873.
60. ——, PB 74910, frames 1968–1974.
61. ——, *ibid.*, frames 2022–2035.
62. ——, *ibid.*, frames 1840–1848.
63. Mayhew, U.S. Patent 2,459,773 (1949).
64. ——, U.S. Patent 2,476,991 (1949).
65. ——, U.S. Patent 2,484,300 (1949).
66. ——, U.S. Patent 2,493,724 (1950).
67. McCormack and Stilmar, U.S. Patent 2,613,129 (1952).
68. Paige, U.S. Patent 2,490,704 (1949).
69. Wyler, U.S. Patent 2,213,726 (1940).

11. ORGANIC PIGMENTS

E. R. Allen

INTRODUCTION

Definition

The principal characteristic of a *pigment* which distinguishes it from a *dye* is that it is substantially insoluble in the medium in which it is used. The dominating importance of the physical properties of pigments as contrasted with dyes, which are applied through processes involving solution, is also a distinguishing quality. Numerous instances exist in which the same chemical product serves either as a dye or as a pigment. The distinction in the present case between the two types of colorants is based on usage and physical properties rather than on chemical constitution.

History

The origin of organic pigments, like that of organic dyes, is lost in antiquity. Both sprang from a common origin in that such natural products as Brazilwood, logwood, kermes, lac-dye, cochineal, Persian berries, and madder were "fixed" on the fibers with crude inorganic materials, which markedly increased the intensity and fastness of the dyeings. These highly colored insoluble combinations prepared *in substance* were incorporated into oily and resinous materials or *vehicles* for decorative purposes, hence the word *pigment* from the Latin *pingere*, to paint.

A colorant known to the ancients was *lac-dye*, so named from its source, the insect *Lucifer lacca* (from the Sanskrit laksha, a hundred thousand), which was used with clayey materials for dyeing fibers and for conversion to insoluble bodies *in substance*. Both colorants were called *lakes* (also from laksha).

The dyeing application developed much more rapidly than did the related production of pigments. Both procedures received great impetus in connection with madder and its successor, alizarin, which products occupied a dominant position for a century.

As these methods of dyeing became better understood, the clayey materials were replaced by alum, and the early French workers, believing that the sulfuric acid in alum acted to corrode or open up the fibers, proposed the term "mordant" from *mordere*, to bite or corrode.

The alum (later aluminum sulfate), used as a fixing agent in dyeing or as a precipitant in the production of organic pigments, was partially converted to alumina hydrate in the process, and, in the case of pigments, sometimes served as a *substratum* or *base*. These substrata, originally used as diluents because of the superior color intensity of organic as contrasted with inorganic pigments, are now used to impart desirable physical properties to the finished product.

Terminology

The term "lake" has been so loosely used, both in the pigment and dye fields, that its use has been avoided here except as is necessary to bridge the gap between the old and the new technologies.

Substrata are now used in many different ways to modify and/or control physical properties. In this respect modern pigment colors stand in sharp contrast to the "extended" products of the past, hence the term *distended* pigments is used here.

As the synthetic dye industry progressed it became possible to produce organic pigments without the aid of substrata. Such full strength products were first used, principally in the printing ink industry, to shade or "tone" the weaker colors, hence the use of the term "toner."

The U. S. Tariff Commission[57] now recognizes three groups of organic pigments: toners, lakes and reduced toners. "Lakes and toners are synthetic organic pigments manufactured and sold both as full strength colors (toners), and as extended colors (lakes and reduced toners), the latter having been extended by the addition of a solid diluent." The expression "lakes and toners" is frequently loosely used as synonymous with organic pigments.

Physical Properties

In his discussion of the importance of physical properties to pigments, Pratt[51] points out that particle size and shape, nature of surfaces, refractive indices, and crystal structure are powerful operating variables, any one of which may be influenced by methods of processing out of all proportion to what would be expected with dyes from analogous changes in procedure.

Proper drying of pigments has recently been well reviewed by Glassman[28]. The direct drying of aqueous pigment pastes often produces an undesirable harsh texture which minimizes the useful coloring power of the pigment. A procedure much used to obtain the desirable soft texture is the so-called "transfer" or "flushing" process, in which the watery presscake is kneaded with the vehicle under such conditions that the oily material displaces the water to give a pigment-oil preparation of acceptable properties.

Dispersion of a dry pigment in a vehicle requires displacing a pigment-air interface with a pigment-oil interface, and this involves the complex subject of wetting of surfaces. Closely related are the development of desirable rheological properties of pigment compositions such as body, length, flow consistency, viscosity, and plasticity.

Usage and Requirements

Organic pigments find application in organic coating compositions such as paints and automotive finishes, in printing inks of the graphic arts industry, and in the pigment printing of textiles. They are also used in floor coverings, elastomers, the beater dyeing and coating of paper, and the mass pigmentation of synthetic fibers. As in the case of dyes general fastness to destructive agencies is of course desirable, although the criteria are naturally different for the two industries. The properties particularly desired in organic pigments are (1) insolubility in and compatibility with carriers in which they are applied and (2) desirable physical properties, of which probably texture and dispersibility are of the greatest significance. The elimination of the oil-solubility of organic pigments, i.e., their tendency to "bleed" in vehicles, has been a major research objective in the development of new organic pigments.

The optical properties required of pigment colors for process printing are distinctive. Color reproduction in this art is theoretically possible with only three colors, yellow, greenish blue, and bluish red, each color printing impression requiring a separate passage through the press, hence the expression, process printing. The term *trichromatic* is used to designate those colors which possess (or approach) the theoretical optical requirements of this system of printing. Actually, pigments for meeting this ideal requirement have not been developed on a practical scale, consequently more than three colored inks and therefore more press passes are required in practice. The objective of true trichromatic pigment colors nevertheless does exist, hence the use of the term.*

Table 1 gives the rounded 1951 statistics for these major divisions of organic pigment colors recognized by the U. S. Tariff Commission[57]. The corresponding figures for total synthetic dyes are included for comparison.

THEORETICAL CONSIDERATIONS

While empirical research methods are to be credited with most of the progress in the organic pigment industry from the secret arts of the ancients to present day technology, increasing attention to fundamental concepts

---

* Physical properties, terminology, usage, and requirements of organic pigments have been more fully discussed elsewhere[1, 51].

TABLE 1. 1951 U. S. PRODUCTION AND SALES STATISTICS FOR LAKES, TONERS, REDUCED TONERS, AND DYES

Product	Production 1000 lb	Sales Quantity 1000 lb	Sales Value $1000
Lakes and lake colors..................	10,000	9,000	7,500
Toners................................	25,000	21,000	36,500
Reduced toners.......................	12,000	10,000	8,500
	47,000	40,000	52,500
Coal-tar dyes.........................	187,000	160,000	177,000

has accompanied this growth. Today's theories are still largely qualitative, but it is believed worth-while to mention some of them briefly.

Metallic Linkages

In addition to salt-forming groups, complex-forming (chelating) groups sometimes function in the transformation of colored organic compounds into pigments through reactions with metals[4, 44, 61]. With widening usage, some variations in meaning have become embodied in such pertinent terms as salt formation, chelation, hydrogen bonding, and complex ions.

In the field of organic pigments it is important to recognize the distinction between the essentially nonionic, metallic linkages in chelate derivatives and the electrovalent unions in the orthodox saltlike metallic pigments.

Intramolecular hydrogen bonding and chelation are so intimately related that the two terms are sometimes used interchangeably. However, in the field of organic pigments, it is advantageous to view the very *weak*—5 to 9 kcal per mole—hydrogen bonding as a phenomenon different from chelation in which the metal is held by *strong*—35 to over 100 kcal per mole— covalent linkages.

In formula (1), see p. 630, OH and NO are the reactive functional groups ortho to each other in 1-nitroso-2-naphthol. Formulas (2) to (7) represent the chelate configurations which, from a total of 9 (6 originally proposed by Morgan and Main Smith[50], two added by Lapworth[46] plus the one characteristic of phthalocyanines) in the large number of metallized dyes, are characteristic of products showing properties of interest as pigments.

Chelation as used herein refers to the aromatic configurations designated (2) to (7) in Figure 1. The high resonance associated with conjugation of aromatic rings conceivably magnifies the difference between hydrogen bonding and chelation. In this chapter, as shown in Figure 1, hydrogen bonding is depicted by a dotted line and chelate bonding by an arrow.

The term complex ion is used essentially as defined by Martell and

Calvin[49a], to denote complex formation with simple nonresonating donor groups, as in

$$\left[\begin{array}{c} H_3N \\ H_3N \end{array} \underset{\underset{NH_3}{|}}{\overset{\overset{NH_3}{|}}{Co}} \begin{array}{c} NH_3 \\ NH_3 \end{array} \right]^{+3} , 3\,Cl^- \quad \text{or} \quad 3K^+, \quad \left[\begin{array}{c} Cl \quad Cl \quad Cl \\ Co \\ Cl \quad Cl \quad Cl \end{array} \right]^{-3}$$

Relation of Structure to Properties

The structural chemistry of organic pigments[28] and its relation to the theory of color broadly has much in common with that of dyes (see Chapter 12 on Color and Chemical Constitution of Dyes, p. 662), although added complications, such as surface effects and other physical changes associated with preparing metallic and other derivatives *in substance*, sometimes distort this picture.

In the chemically reactive products (p. 638), both cationic and anionic, the theories of color for dyes apply well since the color changes accompanying salt formation are minor rather than fundamental. However, the increase in color brilliancy accompanying the formation of alkaline earth salts of some of the difficultly soluble azo compounds remains to be explained, as does the change in color accompanying chelation.

The majority of quasi-neutral azo pigments are chemically similar to azoic dyes (see p. 181), with the added factors of stability in vehicles and of tinctorial strength having helped to govern the empirical selection of commercially useful products.

Sulfo groups are substituents of major importance in producing organic pigments from chemically reactive compounds. By formation of their alkaline earth or heavy metal salts they furnish the most direct method of imparting oil-insolubility to an organic molecule, and they may also function as electronegative groups in the diazotizable amines used to make azo pigments.

The discovery in 1899 of Lithol Red R (see p. 649), made from an amino-*mono*sulfonic acid developed specifically for the preparation of azo pigments, was the forerunner of the now dominant group of difficultly soluble products. Sulfonic acid derivatives give the neutral (and thus stable) type of saltlike products desired for pigments. The *degree* of sulfonation has a marked influence on the solubility properties of the resulting pigments.

Monosulfonation frequently produces a slight increase in tinctorial

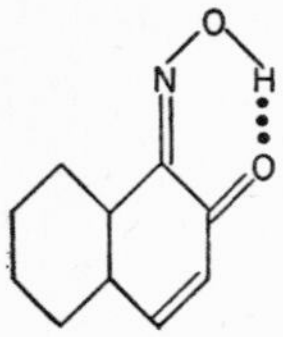

(1)
Intramolecular
hydrogen bonding

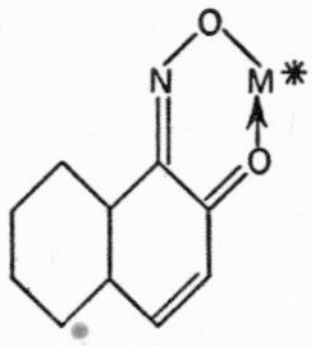

(2)
Chelation

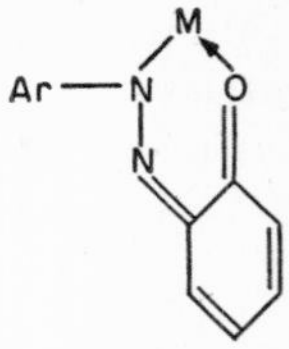

(3)
o–Hydroxy Azo [**]

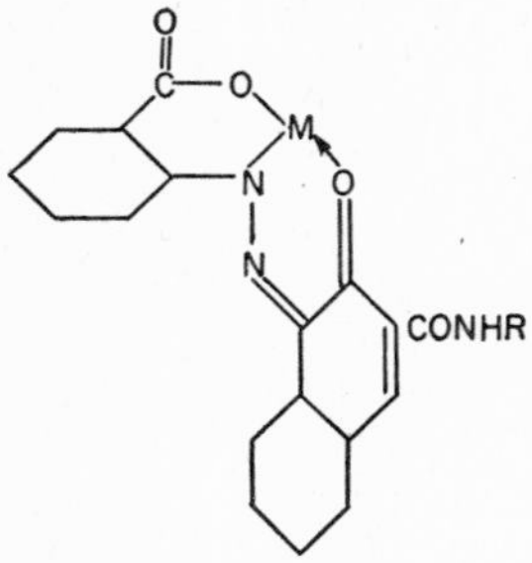

(4)
o–Hydroxy–o′–carboxy Azo [54]

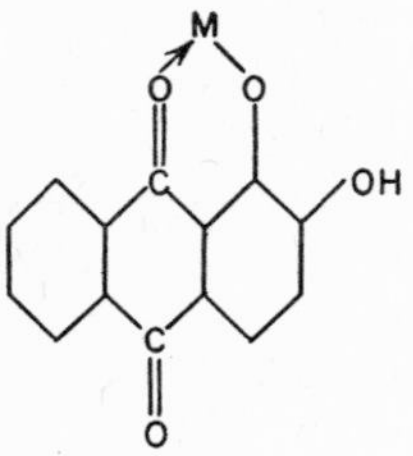

(5)
Anthraquinone'

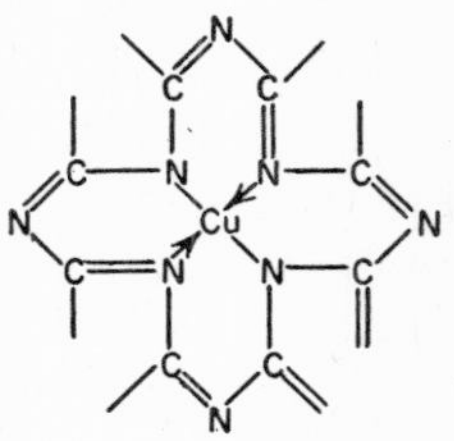

(6)
Copper Phthalocyanines

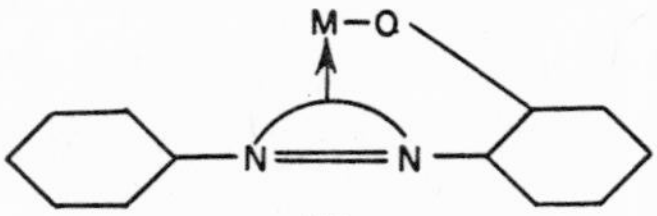

(7)
o–Hydroxy Azo [***]

FIG. 1. Metallic Linkages

[*] In these and all chelate formulas M refers to 1 metal equivalent.

[**] Lapworth gives 6 metallizable azo configurations, 5 of which contain OH ortho to the azo group; the other is the salicylic acid residue.

[***] Bailar[3, 9] depicts the azo group as a resonating center which functions as the donor.

strength, while polysulfonation exerts an opposite effect (see Alkali Blue, p. 653). Sulfo groups usually have little effect on shade.

The lightfastness of a pigment often correlates with that of the related dye, although there are numerous exceptions. The precipitation of cationic dyes with heteropoly acids (see p. 639) is an outstanding case of improvement in resistance to light resulting from insolubilization. Sulfonation tends to decrease lightfastness, an effect that becomes more marked with an increase in the number of sulfo groups.

The stability to light which is generally characteristic of chelate derivatives is visualized as resulting from increased resonance and greater ring stability accompanying the transformation from hydrogen bonding to chelation. More than this is required, however, to account for the extraordinary stability of copper phthalocyanine, even though the chelate derivative is more stable than the hydrogen-bonded metal-free derivative. The stability of copper phthalocyanine is, according to Iler[37], best explained as due to multibonding. That is, all the coordinating or donor groups in a single molecule are associated with a given metal atom, consequently decomposition requires simultaneous rupture of all linkages so involved. Martell and Calvin[49b] attribute this high stability to the fact that the metal is "completely surrounded by the donor atoms, thus rendering attack by other molecules or ions very difficult."

This multibonding of the chelate macromolecule formed from four moles of alizarin (see p. 655) may account for the unusual stability of this pigment, a phenomenon which has been the subject of a large amount of research over a long period of years.

NOMENCLATURE

The system used in naming commercial pigments represents even less consistency in the grouping together of items of common properties, or in relating names to chemical constitution, than that used for dyes. Pigments are often designated by a system of numbers or codes. No attempt is made here to record completely either the trade names or codes.

Organic pigments have been prepared from practically all classes of colored organic compounds. Representative products now in use are discussed in accordance with the outline on p. xiii.

REPRESENTATIVE ORGANIC PIGMENTS

Chemically Quasi-neutral Compounds

The dominating characteristic of this group, which includes the nitro, azo, and polynuclear classes, is that the materials as synthesized possess the substantial insolubility required of pigments. Blumenthal[7], in proposing the appropriate term, *quasi-neutral*, recognized that functional groups exist within the molecules, but that they are chemically latent in pigment technology. Members of this group generally possess high tinctorial strength and good resistance to destructive agencies.

Nitro Compounds. Compounds (8) and (9), made by condensing formaldehyde with an arylamine, are yellows of creditable tinctorial properties, but are inferior to azo yellows in heat stability and in fastness to light, and thus have not attained a major commercial position. Their general physical properties resemble those of the quasi-neutral azo compounds (below).

(8) Pigment Chlorine GG, CI 13

(9) Lithol Fast Yellow GG, CI 14

Azo Compounds. Azo compounds have contributed by far a larger number of products to the pigment industry than has any other chemical class of synthetic organic coloring matters.

These quasi-neutral azo pigments are organophilic, and therefore show a tendency to bleed in commercial vehicles. Elimination of this defect has continually been an important research objective. As a group their texture is good, but they tend to lack heat stability, and thus are not usually suitable for use in tin printing or in baking enamels. Sublimation from printed pages in bound volumes also sometimes occurs with products in this class. They will be discussed in groups based on the coupling components used.

2-Naphthol Derivatives. (1) 2-Naphthol. The first historically, and still foremost in commercial poundage, of the quasi-neutral azo pigments are the monoazo compounds using 2-naphthol as the coupling component (coupling at position 1). One of the earliest of these was *Paranitroaniline Red* (10), CI 44, or *Para Red*, still used, and historically important in that it stemmed from the method of textile dyeing with "ice colors" originated by the British firm of Read, Holliday and Sons in 1880 (Chapter 4).

Two shades of Para Red, bluish (B) and yellowish (Y), have been used both on the fiber and in substance. The bluish shade is obtained by incorporating with the 2-naphthol 5 to 10 per cent of 2-naphthol-7-sulfonic acid (F acid).

Para Reds possess good but not outstanding lightfastness and durability. Despite their decided bleed in commercial vehicles, they still find considerable usage because of their tinctorial value.

The trade reception to Para Red stimulated activity in related compounds. Two important observations were made at almost the same time, relative to overcoming the serious defect of vehicle bleed. In 1905 the Bayer Co. observed that 2-nitro-*p*-toluidine (*m*-nitro-*p*-toluidine, MNPT)[4, 8] gave, when diazotized and coupled to 2-naphthol, a pigment (11), CI 69, suffi-

TABLE 2. QUASI-NEUTRAL AZO PIGMENTS FORMED BY COUPLING WITH 2-NAPHTHOL

Product	Diazotizable Amine
(10) Paranitroaniline Red	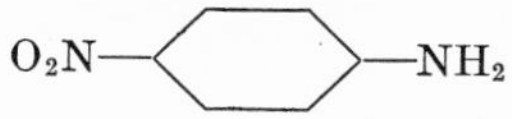 O$_2$N—⟨ ⟩—NH$_2$ *p*-Nitroaniline
(11) Toluidine Red R	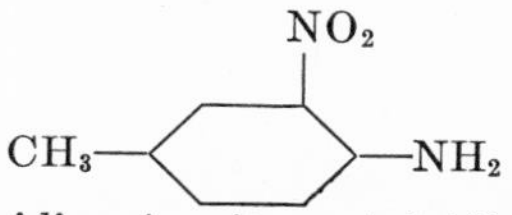 NO$_2$ CH$_3$—⟨ ⟩—NH$_2$ 2-Nitro-*p*-toluidine (*m*-nitro-*p*-toluidine, MNPT)
(12) Fire Red	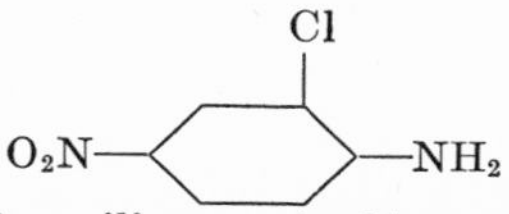 Cl O$_2$N—⟨ ⟩—NH$_2$ 2-Chloro-4-nitroaniline (*o*-chloro-*p*-nitroaniline, OCPNA)
(13) Red Toner	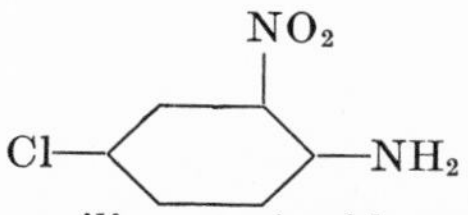 NO$_2$ Cl—⟨ ⟩—NH$_2$ 4-Chloro-2-nitroaniline (*p*-chloro-*o*-nitroaniline, PCONA)
(14) Permatone Orange	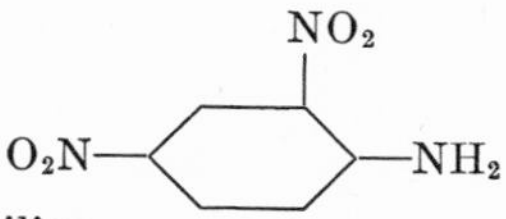 NO$_2$ O$_2$N—⟨ ⟩—NH$_2$ 2,4-Dinitroaniline

ciently fast to vehicles for all but the most severe industrial requirements. Now the most important of this group, it is known in the United States as *Toluidine Red R*, or *Toluidine Toner*.

Almost simultaneously with the Bayer observation, Aktien Gesellschaft für Anilinfabrikation (AGFA) disclosed that replacement of *p*-nitroaniline by 2-chloro-4-nitroaniline (*o*-chloro-*p*-nitroaniline, OCPNA)[15] gave the product (12), *Fire Red*, showing marked improvement in resistance to oil bleed, as well as in lightfastness and brilliance.

Slightly later Badische Anilin- und Soda-Fabrik (BASF) disclosed that the isomeric compound (13) from 4-chloro-2-nitroaniline (*p*-chloro-*o*-nitro-aniline, PCONA)[16] is a brilliant orange-red product of good properties. AGFA contributed the brilliant reddish orange 2,4-dinitroaniline[17, 47] derivative (14), known as *Permatone Orange*.

These five products occupy a dominant commercial position in the United States.

Table 3 gives the 1951 U. S. production statistics for these 2-naphthol derivatives in the toner or full strength form.

TABLE 3. 1951 PRODUCTION STATISTICS FOR AZO PIGMENTS DERIVED FROM 2-NAPHTHOL

Product	Production 1000 lb
Para Red Dark	526
Para Red Light	1,079
Toluidine Red	2,725
o-Chloro-p-nitroaniline Red	617
2,4-Dinitroaniline Orange	187

(2) Arylamides of 3-hydroxy-2-naphthoic acid. An important milestone in the dye industry, which also contributed in a smaller degree to the development of organic pigments, was the introduction in 1912 of the Naphtol AS compounds and their use as azoic coupling components (Chapter 4). The azo coupling with these intermediates takes place in the 4 position in 3-hydroxy-2-naphthoic acid, analogous to that in 2-naphthol. Through selection from a large number of these arylamide derivatives, definite improvements in vehicle fastness over the 2-naphthol counterparts[19, 28, 60] have been realized.

The pigments made from Naphtol AS-BS (15) and from Naphtol AS-D (16), using 2-nitro-p-toluidine as the diazo component, are maroons that have found commercial application in America in automotive finishes, although the fastness of both products varies markedly with the vehicle in which they are used.

(15) Naphtol AS-BS   (16) Naphtol AS-D

The pigment from (15)[53] was the first maroon to meet the American automotive industry's severe requirements of durability in lacquers. Oddly enough, this durability was not realized in synthetic resin enamels. The maroon from (16), however, gives useful enamel life in both vehicles[58].

The I. G. Farbenindustrie produced ten monoazo Naphtol AS derivatives as their F series, each bearing the designation, Permanent[35]. These are summarized in Table 4.

Active Methylene Derivatives. (1) Arylamides of acetoacetic acid. At almost the same time that the arylamides of 3-hydroxy-2-naphthoic acid were announced, it was disclosed that acetoacetanilide gives products of value as yellow pigments. Thus, 2-nitro-p-toluidine (MNPT) diazotized and coupled with acetoacetanilide[20, 59] gave what is now known as Hansa

TABLE 4. NAPHTOL AS DERIVATIVES

		Naphtol AS Component	
Trade Name	Diazotizable Amine	Arylamide	Trade designation
Permanent Red FR extra	o-Chloroaniline	Anilide	AS
Permanent Red FRL extra	2,5-Dichloroaniline	p-Toluidide	—
Permanent Red FRLL	2,5-Dichloroaniline	o-Anisidide	AS-OL
Permanent Red FRR	2,5-Dichloroaniline	Anilide	AS
Permanent Bordeaux FRR	4-Nitro-o-toluidine (5-nitro-2-aminotoluene)	o-Toluidide	AS-D
Permanent Bordeaux F3R	4-Nitro-o-anisidine (5-nitro-2-aminoanisole	1-Naphthylamide	AS-BO
Permanent Red F4R extra	5-Nitro-o-toluidine (4-nitro-2-aminotoluene	p-Chloroanilide	AS-E
Permanent Red F4RH	4-Chloro-o-toluidine (5-chloro-2-aminotoluene)	4-Chloro-o-toluidide	AS-TR
Permanent Rubine FBH	5-Chloro-o-toluidine (4-chloro-2-aminotoluene)	5-Chloro-o-toluidide	—
Permanent Red FGR extra	2,4,5-Trichloroaniline	o-Toluidide	AS-D

Yellow G (17), which is still one of the most important members of this group.

By using 4-chloro-2-nitroaniline and o-nitroaniline as diazotizable amines the greener and weaker *Hansa Yellows 3G and 5G,* respectively, are formed. 4-Chloro-2-nitroaniline diazotized and coupled to o-chloroacetoacetanilide[11] gives *Hansa Yellow 10G* (18). This pigment is greener than the G brand and appreciably weaker, but is valuable because of its superior lightfastness. The 2,4-xylidide counterpart of *Hansa Yellow 10G* is *Hansa Yellow GR.*

Coupling of diazotized 2,5-dichloroaniline (2 moles) to Naphtol AS-G gives *Permanent Yellow NCG*[35, 36] (19), claimed to be fast to overlacquering. *Benzidine Yellow*[18] (20) is used chiefly in the graphic arts where it has partially replaced Hansa Yellow G because of its higher tinctorial strength. It is also used as a rubber color, although the preference in this field is for pigments containing methyl groups in the arylamide. This is illustrated in the German Vulcan Fast pigments listed in Table 5.

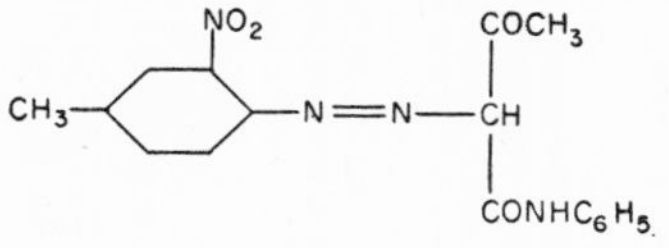

(17) Hansa Yellow G 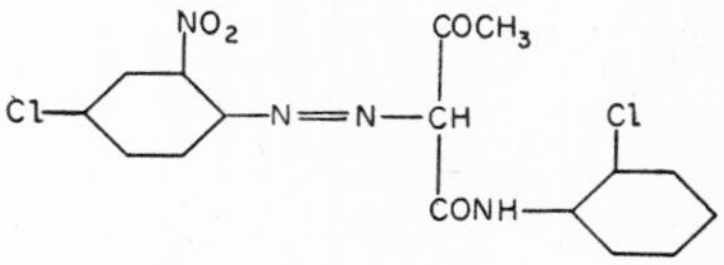   (18) Hansa Yellow 10G

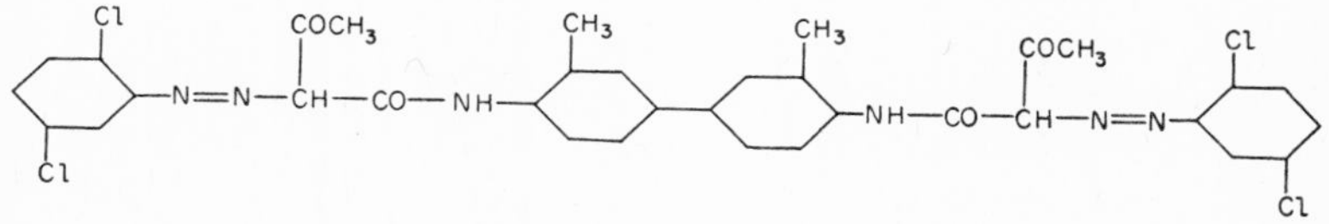

(19) Permanent Yellow NCG

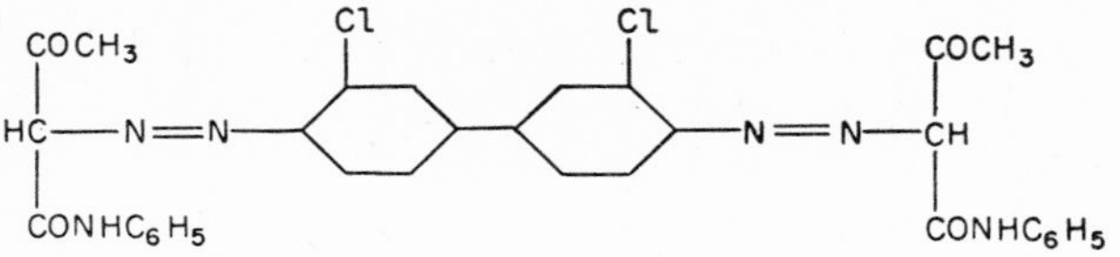

(20) Benzidine Yellow

TABLE 5. VULCAN FAST PIGMENTS

Trade Name	Diazotizable Amine	Arylamide of Acetoacetic Acid*
Orange GG............	3,3'-Dimethoxybenzidine	2,4-Xylidide
Yellow R..............	o-Tolidine	2,4-Xylidide
Yellow GR............	3,3'-Dichlorobenzidine	2,4-Xylidide
Yellow G.............	3,3'-Dichlorobenzidine	o-Toluidide
Yellow 5G............	2,2'-Dichloro-5,5'-dimethoxybenzidine	2,4-Xylidide

* 2 moles in all cases.

(2) Pyrazolones. As azo coupling components, pyrazolones give pigments which are slightly redder than those from acetoacetarylamides but which have the same general fastness properties. The most widely known monoazo pyrazolone pigment is *Hansa Yellow R* (21), obtained from 2,5-dichloroaniline and 3-methyl-1-phenyl-5-pyrazolone. With the same pyrazolone, o-toluidine gives *Pigment Chrome Yellow*, CI 638.

Several disazo pyrazolone pigments have been developed primarily for the coloration of rubber, including *Permanent Orange G*[34, 35] (22), *Vulcan Fast Red B and BF* (23), and *Vulcan Fast Red GF*[36] (24).

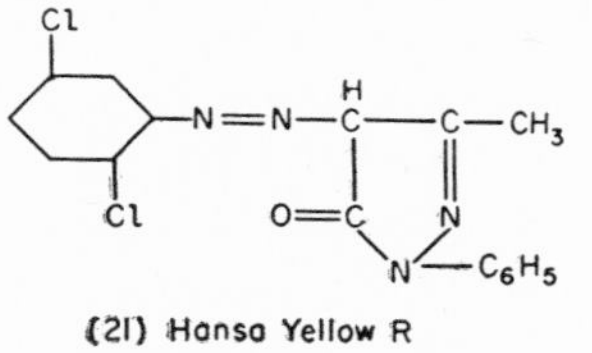

(21) Hansa Yellow R

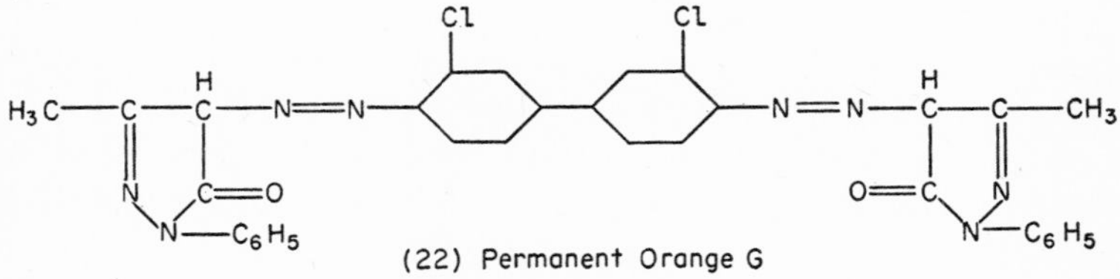

(22) Permanent Orange G

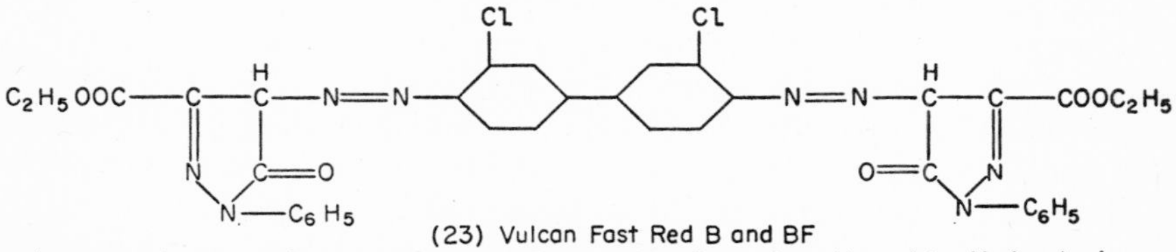

(23) Vulcan Fast Red B and BF

3,3'- dichlorobenzidine ⇄ (5-oxo-1-phenyl-2-pyrazoline-3-carboxylic acid, ethyl ester)₂

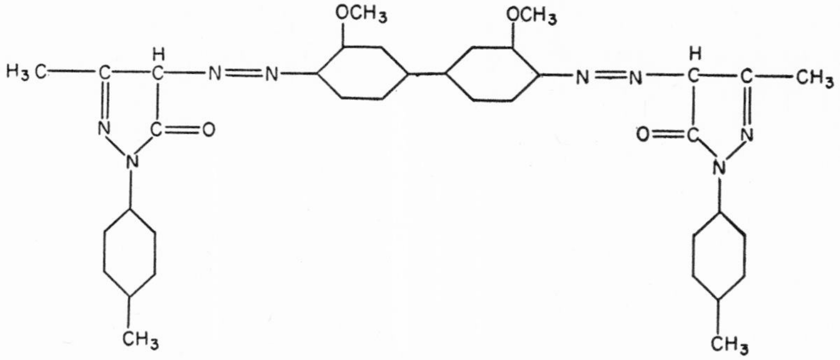

(24) Vulcan Fast Red GF
3, 3'– dimethoxybenzidine $\Longleftrightarrow$ (3– methyl– l–*p*–tolyl– 5– pyrazolone)$_2$

Polynuclear Compounds. Some anthraquinone and indigoid colors possess inherently the insolubility required of pigments. However, they are normally supplied by the dye manufacturer in the paste form, and on drying, they often give materials harsh in texture. This fact, together with their tendency toward lack of brilliance, limits their use in the pigment field despite their desirable properties of fastness to soap, to vehicles, to heat, and to light.

Anthraquinones. Three divisions of this class are represented in the pigment field—the acylamino derivatives, the anthraquinoneazines, and the violanthrones.

The acylamino derivatives do not show the high degree of lightfastness which characterizes the anthraquinoneazines; neither do they, on the other hand, show such harsh textures. *Helio Fast Yellow 6GL* (1-(*o*-hydroxy-benzamido)anthraquinone), CI 1127, and *Algol Pink R* (1-benzamido-4-hydroxyanthraquinone), CI 1128, are examples.

Of the anthraquinoneazines, the important vat dye, *Indanthrene Blue RS*, CI 1106, shows outstanding durability as a pigment in organic coating films.

Representative violanthrones used as specialty pigments are *Indanthrene Dark Blue BO*, CI 1099, and *Caledon Jade Green*, CI 1101.

Indigoid Colors. The members of this group which have found use as pigments are *Indigo* (25), CI 1177, and four derivatives of *Thioindigo Red B* (26), CI 1207.

Indigo has been used for centuries as a pigment, but it has never attained a major position in this field, largely because of its lack of brilliance. It retains a specialty trade position as a soap-fast pigment.

The thioindigo derivatives have found considerable usage as nonbleeding automotive maroons, although their durability here is less than that of the better azo maroon pigments. *Indanthrene Red Violet RH* (27), CI 1212 (incorrectly cited as 5,5'-dichloro-6,6'-dimethylthioindigo), has been used the most in this group. The maroons (28) and (29) have been used in automotive finishes and *Sulfanthrene Pink FF* (30), Pr. 109, has been used to a moderate extent as a pink in the printing ink and paper industries.

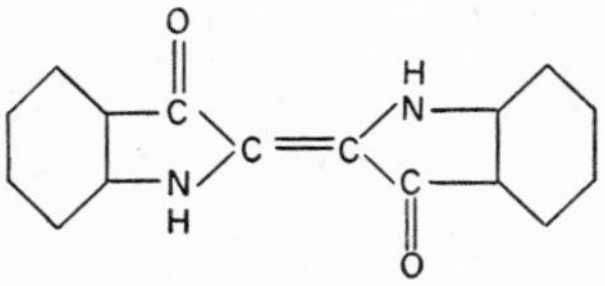

(25) Indigo

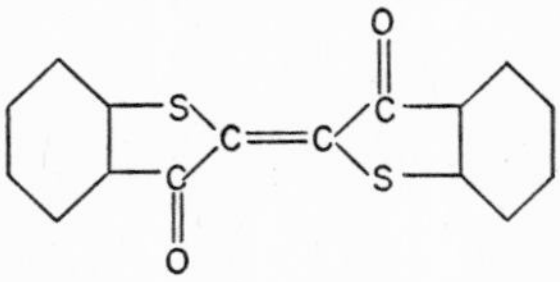

(26) Thioindigo Red B

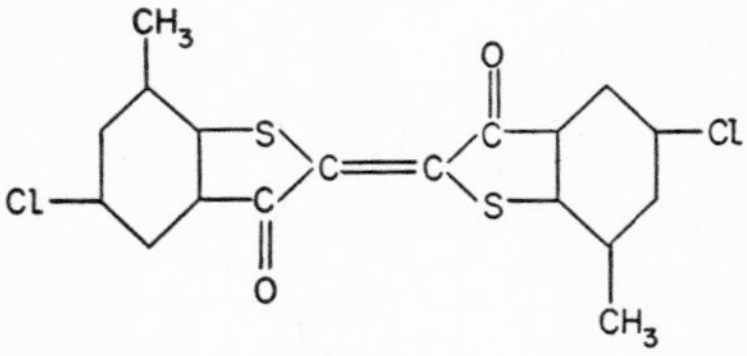

(27) Indanthrene Red Violet R H
5,5'- dichloro- 7,7'- dimethylthioindigo

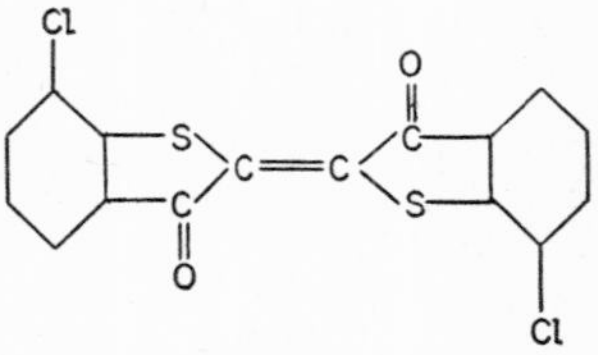

(28) 7, 7'- Dichlorothioindigo

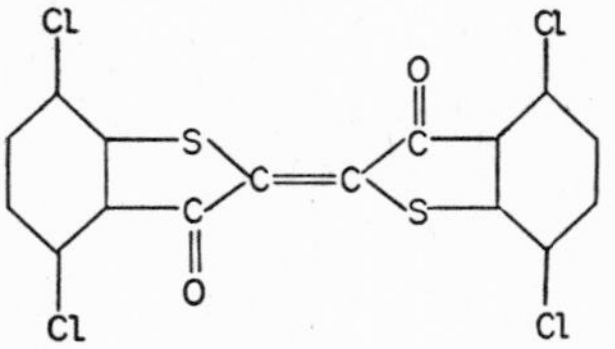

(29) 4, 4', 7, 7'- Tetrachlorothioindigo

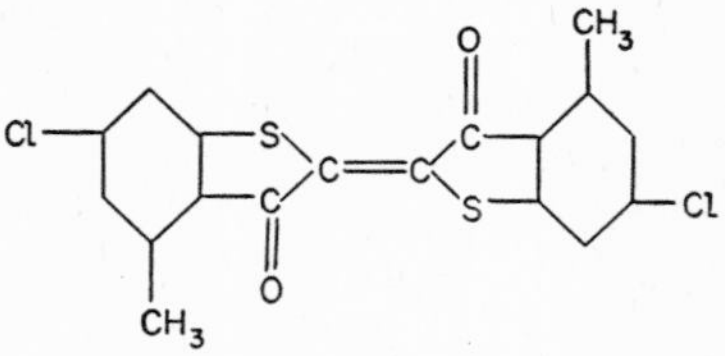

(30) Sulfanthrene Pink FF
6,6'- dichloro- 4, 4'- dimethylthioindigo

Chemically Reactive Compounds

This group includes those colored organic compounds which are chemically reactive and require corresponding processing, most frequently precipitation, to produce the insolubility and other properties required of pigments. Included are products which are either cationic, i.e., basic dyes, or anionic, i.e., acid dyes. In each case the insolubilization typically involves salt formation.

Cationic Derivatives. (See also anionic triarylmethane derivatives, p. 652). Table 6 and Figure 2 give the more important cationic dyes that have found application in the pigment industry.

Although cationic dyes embody a wide range of chemical structures, as shown in Figure 2, they are all characterized by amino or substituted amino

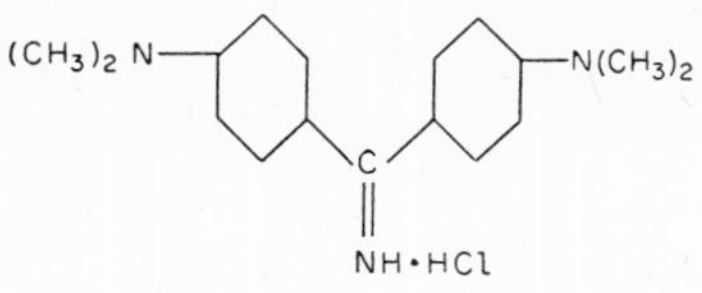

(I) Auramine *

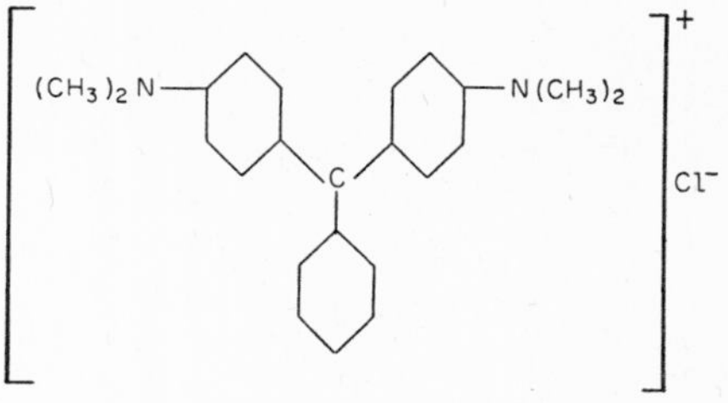

(II) Malachite Green

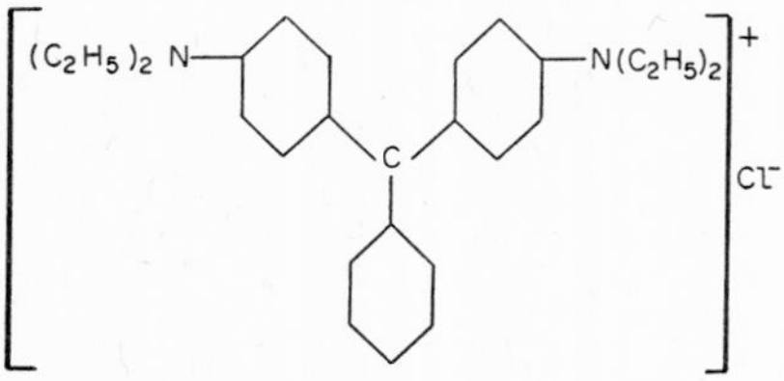

(III) Brilliant Green

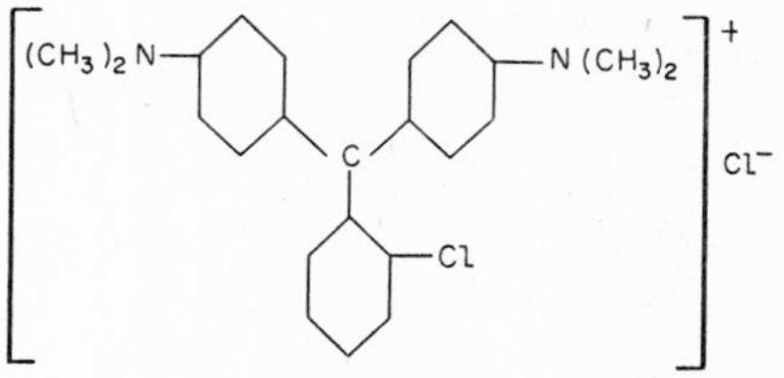

(IV) Rhoduline Blue 6G

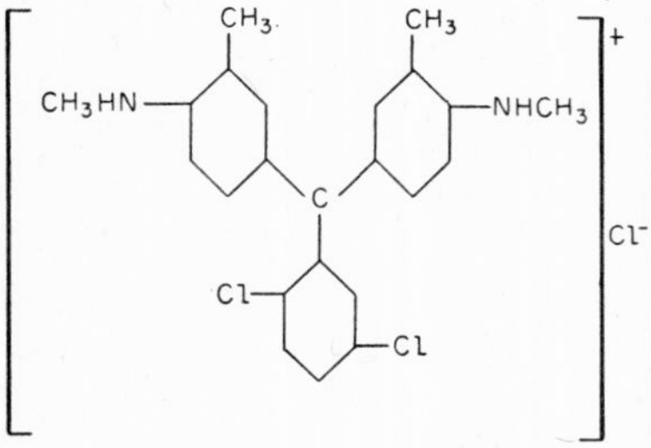

(V) Acronol Brilliant Blue

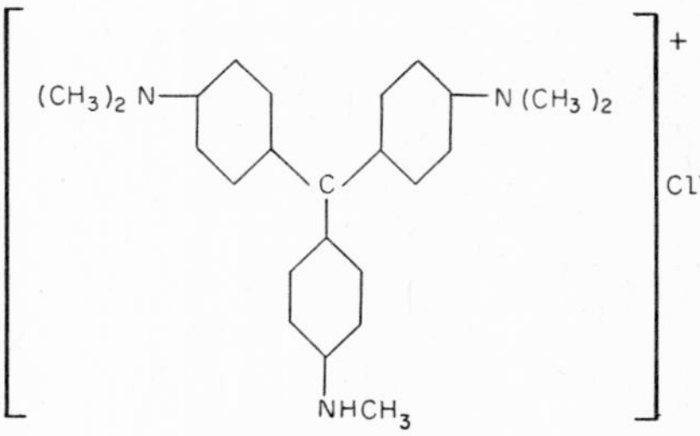

(VI) Methyl Violet B

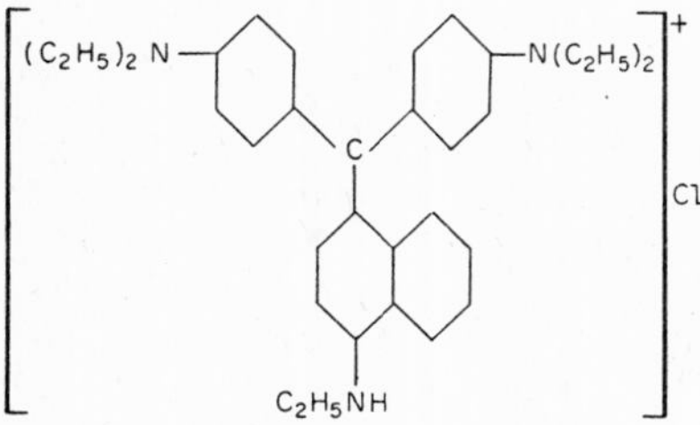

(VII) Victoria Pure Blue BO

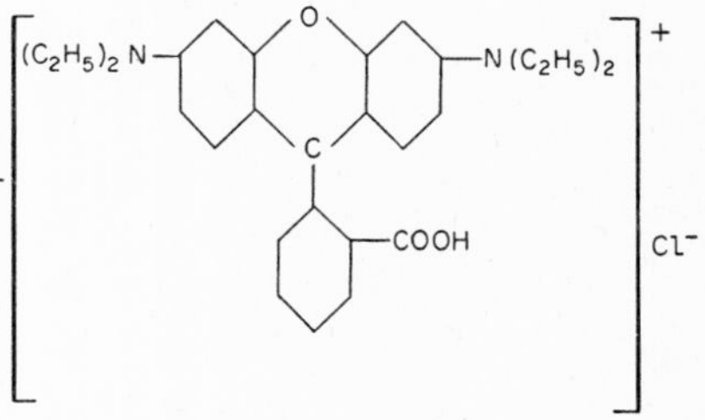

(VIII) Rhodamine B

FIG. 2. Cationic dyes used in the pigment industry

* See Ketone Imine Dyes, p. 245.

(Continued)

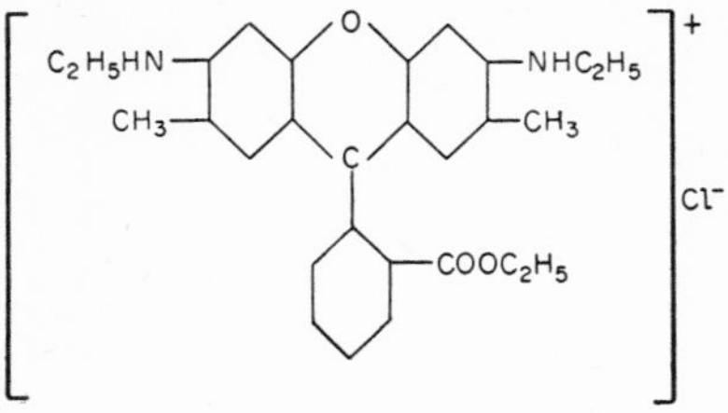

(IX) Rhodamine 6G 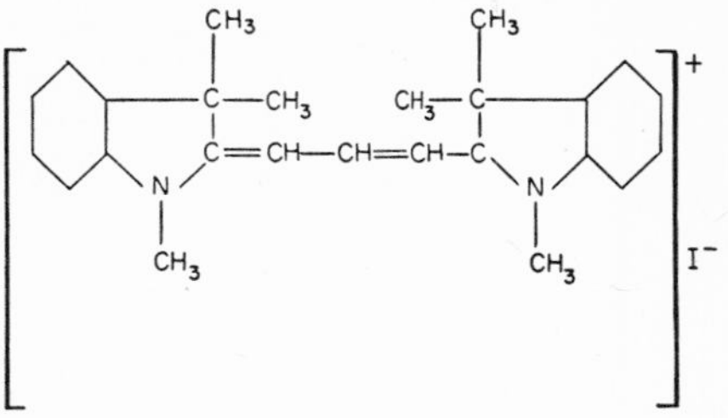   (X) Astraphloxine FF

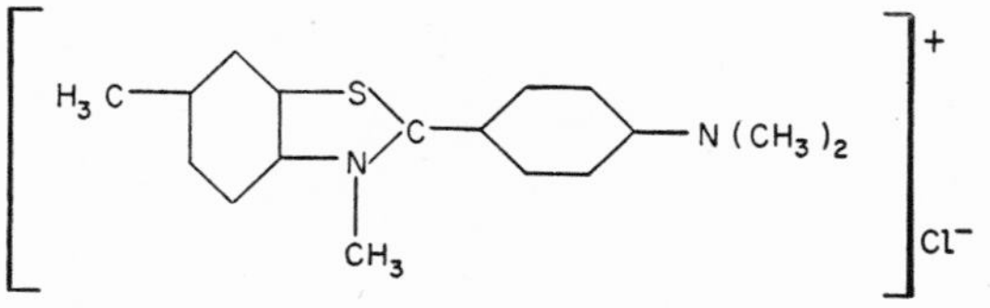

(XI) Thioflavine T

FIG. 2. Cationic dyes used in the pigment industry (continued)

groups. Formation of pigments from them typically involves replacing the simple anions (chlorides and sulfates) of the soluble commercial products with more complex ones. Two groups of pigments, the *permanent* and *nonpermanent*, are so produced.

Permanent. The permanent pigments are produced by the use of the complex heteropoly acids[31, 38, 39, 48], phosphotungstic (PTA), phosphomolybdic (PMA), and phosphotungstomolybdic (PTMA) acids as precipitants[35, 36]. The phosphotungstomolybdate pigments show the best fastness to light, the phosphomolybdates the poorest.

The preparation of these products has been developed on a largely empirical basis. There is no satisfactory explanation for the striking improvement in lightfastness, and the generally used Miolati-Rosenheim heptabasic formula, $H_7P(M_2O_7)_6xH_2O$, is now viewed as a convention rather than as a true chemical formula. The ratio of molybdenum to tungsten, e.g., in the phosphotungstomolybdic acids, varies over a considerable range depending on properties desired, and the optimum for one dye is not necessarily that for another.

The formula for the phosphotungstomolybdate of Methyl Violet B has been reported as follows[35]:

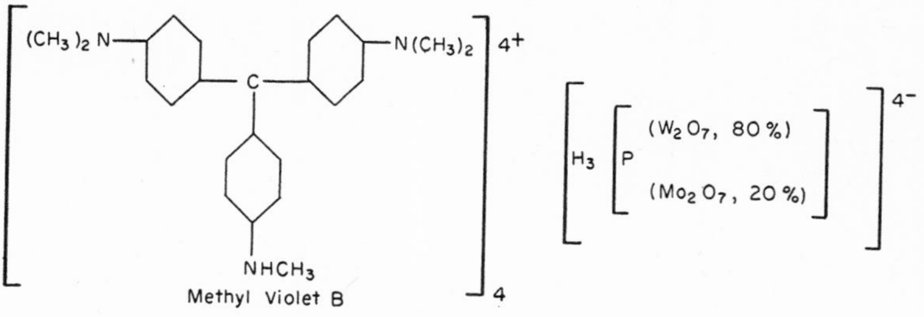

Methyl Violet B

(31) Methyl Violet Pigment

TABLE 6. CATIONIC DYES USED IN THE PIGMENT INDUSTRY

Chemical Class	Dye	CI No.
Diphenylmethane	Auramine	655
Triarylmethane	Malachite Green	657
	Brilliant Green	662
	Rhoduline Blue 6G	658
	Acronol Brilliant Blue	664
	Methyl Violet B	680
	Victoria Pure Blue BO	Pr. 198
Xanthene	Rhodamine B	749
	Rhodamine 6G	—
Polymethine	Astraphloxine FF	—
Thiazole	Thioflavine T	815

Nonpermanent (Fugitive). The nonpermanent pigments based on cationic dyes are usually produced by precipitation with tannic acid and tartar emetic (antimony-potassium tartrate), or with synthetic organic precipitants. Some fatty acids are also used for producing specialties where oil fastness is not required. Arsenious acid and rosin soap precipitations, at one time of importance, have practically fallen into disuse. Pigments obtained through the use of the clay type of precipitants, the clay serving both as a precipitant and as a substratum, find application in the paper coating trade. The glauconitic clays, the "green earths," are the most efficient for this purpose, and give rise to a degree of lightfastness definitely superior to that normally found in the nonpermanent type.

Both the permanent and the nonpermanent types are consumed largely in printing inks, including spirit inks, for the most part in the toner form. A third type of precipitation occurs when cationic dyes are used to assist in the precipitation of anionic dyes in the coloring of paper coatings.

The cationic dye showing the largest consumption in the pigment field is Methyl Violet B (31). See Table 7.

The data for the more important heteropoly acid precipitations grouped in Table 8 as Blue (Victoria Blue B, Victoria Pure Blue B, Rhoduline Blue

6G), Green (Malachite Green, Brilliant Green), and Red (Rhodamine 6G, Rhodamine B) toners, serve to show the magnitude of this branch of the industry.

Similar data for products precipitated on a substratum are given in Table 9.

TABLE 7. 1951 U. S. PRODUCTION AND SALES STATISTICS FOR PIGMENT USES OF METHYL VIOLET B

| | | Sales | |
Type of Toner	Production 1000 lb	Quantity 1000 lb	Value $1000
Phosphomolybdate	292	258	419
Phosphotungstate and phosphotungstomolybdate	105	96	296
Fugitive	342	282	362

TABLE 8. 1951 U. S. SALES STATISTICS FOR HETEROPOLY ACID PRECIPITATIONS OF CATIONIC DYES

| | Sales | |
Group	Quantity, 1000 lb	Value, $1000
Blue Toners	232	902
Green Toners	126	553
Red Toners	135	740
Total	493	2195

TABLE 9. 1951 U. S. SALES STATISTICS FOR REDUCED (DISTENDED) HETEROPOLY ACID PRECIPITATIONS OF CATIONIC DYES

| | Sales | |
Group	Quantity, 1000 lb	Value, $1000
Blues	75	115
Greens	134	108
Reds	128	121
Total	337	344

Anionic Derivatives. Anionic derivatives, as defined and used herein, include organic coloring materials capable of producing metallic derivatives suitable for use as pigments. The chemical reactions involved include both chelation and salt formation, and the two types of reaction are in turn associated with different types of functional groups in the organic molecule. They are advantageously discussed by chemical classes with the following three subheadings:

(1) Chelates. The relatively few metallic derivatives formed from organic compounds containing chelating groups which have attained recognition as pigments are found in the nitroso, azo, anthraquinone, and phthalocyanine classes.

(2) Salts. This class of compounds is made up primarily of metal salts of aromatic sulfonic acids, although carboxylic acids sometimes also function as salt-forming groups. The marked influence of polysulfonation as compared with monosulfonation on the solubility of the resulting pigments is noteworthy.

The *easily soluble* (polysulfonated) compounds, which might be designated as the older type, are typically precipitated by barium chloride, less frequently by aluminum chloride, on a substratum in which alumina hydrate[7] is necessary to assist in the precipitation and to attain satisfactory pigment properties; thus, they are seldom used as full strength or toner products. They lend themselves to coprecipitations in blends to obtain a wide range of effects. Sometimes they are partially precipitated by cationic dyes. These mixed or blended precipitations are frequently used in wall and coated papers and in beater dyeings. Their lowered tinting strengths are usually associated with transparency which may be desirable in some usages. Representative easily soluble salt-forming compounds are found in the nitro, azo, triarylmethane, xanthene, and quinoline chemical classes.

The *difficultly soluble*, or more modern, type of anionic colored organic compounds, typically monosulfonated derivatives, were developed primarily for the pigment industry. They are convertible into various alkaline earth salts to form pigmentary materials without the aid of a substratum. Indeed, in some cases, either the sodium salts or the free acids have been so used. Substrata when used therefore are for distending purposes and not to assist in precipitation. The popularity of this group of pigments rests on the fact that broadly they combine the high tinting strength and desirable working properties of the quasi-neutral products with the superior fastness to heat and the organophobic and nonbleeding properties of the pigments from the easily soluble dyes. The major part of their rise to a position of dominating importance in the industry has been in the azo field. They have been more completely discussed by Pratt[51].

(3) Chelates plus salts. Blangey[4] points out that compounds containing, in addition to strongly acid groups, the "mordanting" or chelating groups—requiring therefore "double laking" to form pigments, are most frequently encountered among the anthraquinone derivatives, and that in some cases the metallic complexes are manufactured and sold to be processed into pigments by the normal methods of precipitation (salt formation). Actually, pigment-producing materials do exist, however, in addition in the nitroso, azo, and phthalocyanine classes, which possess this property of forming the two types of metallic linkages.

Nitroso Compounds. (1) Chelates. One unsulfonated product, 1-nitroso-2-naphthol, or quinone oxime, the iron chelate of which is the familiar *Pigment Green B* (34), Pr. 149, is of commercial importance[27, 40]. Pigment

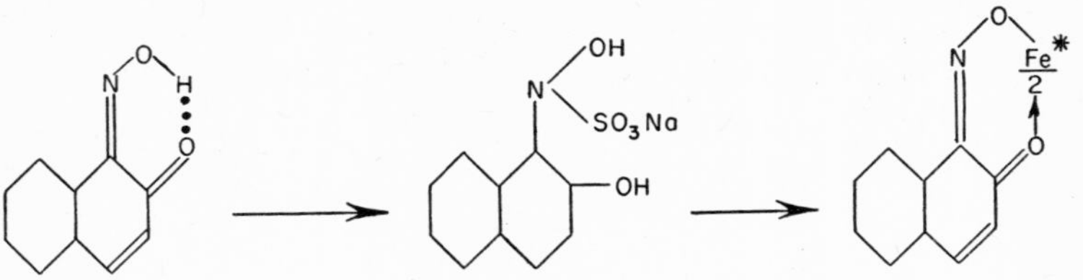

(32) Quinone Oxime   (33) Bisulfite   (34) Pigment Green B
     Gambine Y   Ester

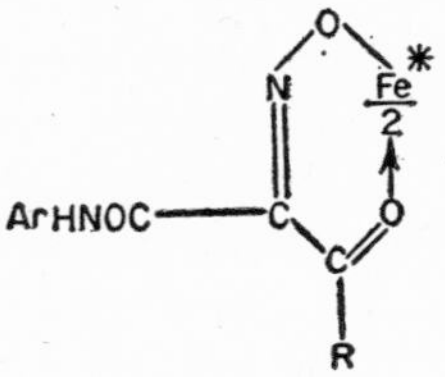

(35)

FIG. 3. Nitroso pigments; chelates

* Fe[II] is used by Fitzner, *Angew. Chem.*, **62**, 242 (1950).

Green B, prepared by the action of alkalies on a solution of the bisulfite ester of the quinone oxime and ferrous sulfate (Figure 3), has practically displaced the sulfonated derivative, *Naphthol Green B* (36). It is fast to light and to alkali, and is therefore used as a limeproof pigment and as a soap-fast pigment. Because of its fastness to most rubber cures it finds considerable use in this industry.

Related nitroso derivatives will also produce pigments of similar properties but no one of them is sufficiently distinctive over Pigment Green B to establish a commercial position. Likewise, the nitroso derivatives of the acylacetarylamides[10] (35 of Figure 3) give blues possessing similar properties, but they have not thus far received commercial adoption.

(2) Chelates plus salts. *Naphthol Green B* (36), CI 5, the sulfo derivative of Pigment Green B, is prepared by nitrosating 2-naphthol-6-sulfonic acid, or Schaeffer's acid, and reacting this product with ferrous sulfate under proper conditions. This iron complex serves as a paper dye, but it also dyes wool from an acid bath, and is therefore usually classified as an acid dye. It is converted into a pigment by precipitation with barium salts in the presence of an adsorbing substratum. The iron complex is, however, so very soluble that it is difficult to precipitate it completely and it has been almost entirely supplanted on the American market by Pigment Green B.

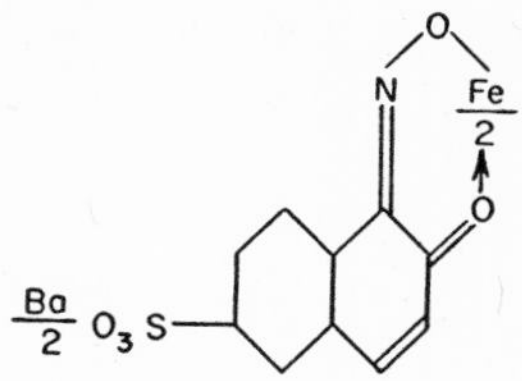

(36) Naphthol Green B

Nitro Compounds. One product, *Naphthol Yellow S* (37), CI 10, of this class has attained prominence in the manufacture of pigments.

The pigment obtained from this dye is a brilliant yellow, widely known as "Indian Yellow," of moderate fastness to light. It is useful in paper coating compositions and in distemper colors.

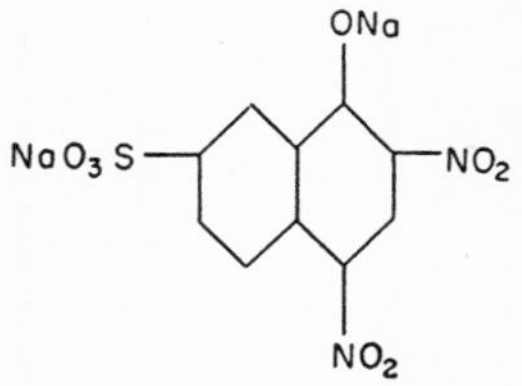

(37) Naphthol Yellow S

Azo Compounds. (1) Chelates. As is well known, many *o*-hydroxyazo compounds form chelate derivatives of the type I[12].

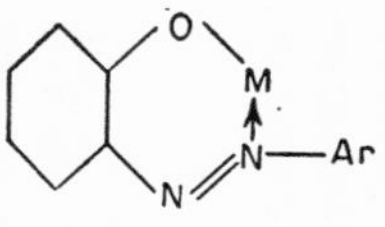

(I)

Paranitroaniline Red (10, above), when boiled with aqueous solutions of copper salts in the presence of weak alkalies, gives a brown pigment (38)[25, 26], which was once used to a minor extent.

An interesting and valuable group of greenish yellow to yellowish brown monoazo chelate pigments has been recently disclosed by Kvalnes and Woodward[45], in which compounds of the 4-hydroxy-2-pyridone series are used as the azo coupling components. An array of diazotizable arylamines, devoid of hydroxy groups ortho to the diazo group, and of sulfo and carboxy groups, is disclosed. Conversion of these azo compounds into chelate derivatives of bivalent metals, in the atomic number range of 25 to 30, gives pigments, some of which possess altogether unexpected and unusual fastness to light, to heat, and to destructive weathering agencies. Although these pigments do not meet the requirement of complete resistance to bleed in the most exacting vehicles, they are sufficiently meritorious in this respect to find commercial application. The yellow (39), in which X is a halogen, is one of the number of products disclosed.

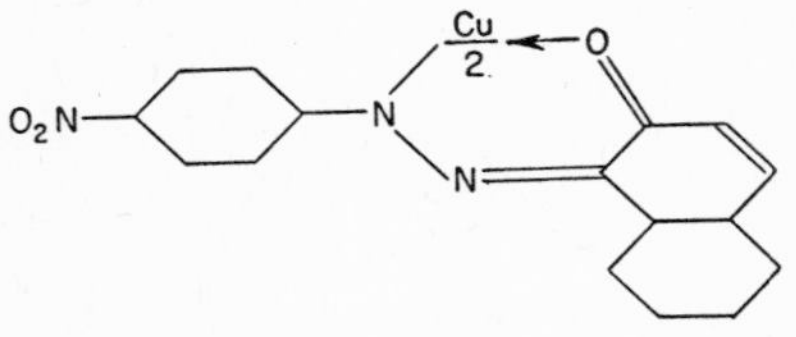

(38) Paranitroaniline Brown 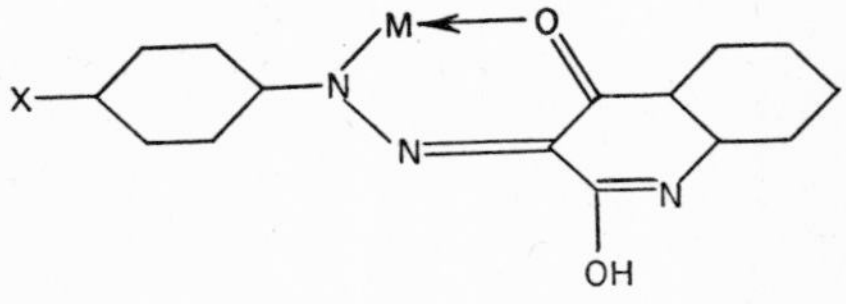   (39) Kvalnes and Woodward Yellow

A red (4), p. 630, involving chelation with an *o*-hydroxy-*o'*-carboxy azo[62] grouping has been disclosed by Woodward.

(2) Salts. A large number of *readily soluble* monoazo dyes have found application over the years in the production of pigments. They are grouped here according to the three types of azo coupling components that have been used: derivatives (a) of naphthols, (b) of pyrazolones, and (c) of aminonaphthols.

(a) Naphthols. The dyes, *Lake Scarlet 2R* (40), CI 79, *Azo Bordeaux B* (41), CI 88, and *Orange II* (42), CI 151, are the three products now remaining of major importance in the American pigment industry.

These three dyes have survived in the pigment industry because of their low costs and desirable shades. Lead precipitations of Lake Scarlet 2R have been used to a limited extent. Orange II is sometimes precipitated with aluminum chloride on an especially prepared alumina hydrate; it may even be precipitated as the barium toner.

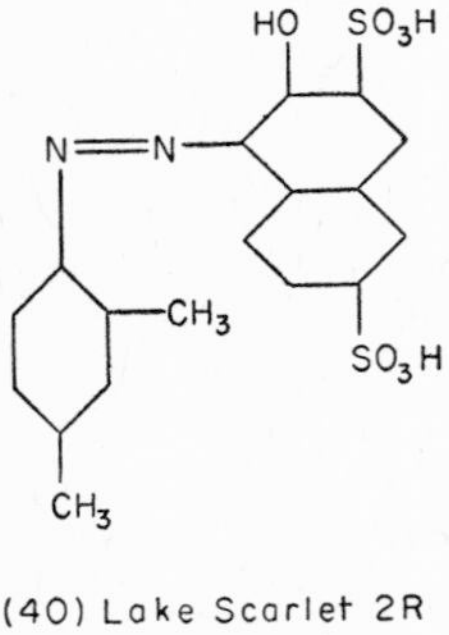

(40) Lake Scarlet 2R 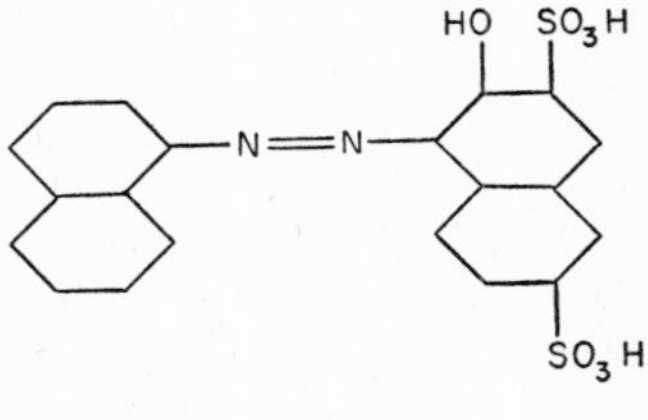   (41) Azo Bordeaux B

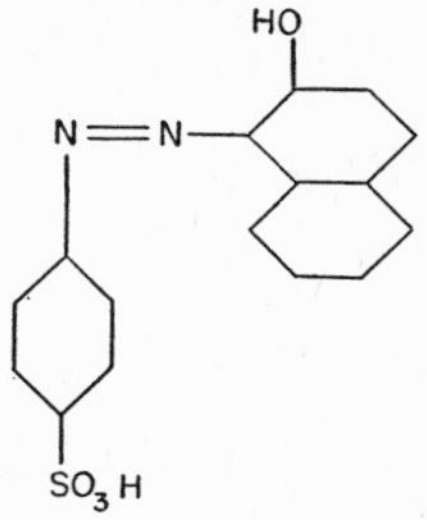

(42) Orange II

(b) Pyrazolones. Two products, *Tartrazine O* (43), CI 640, and *Fast Light Yellow 3G* (44), CI 636, are now the most important members of this group. The pigments formed from these dyes are characterized by a distinctive beauty of tone. Fast Light Yellow 3G shows good fastness to light, and finds use as an important printing ink specialty.

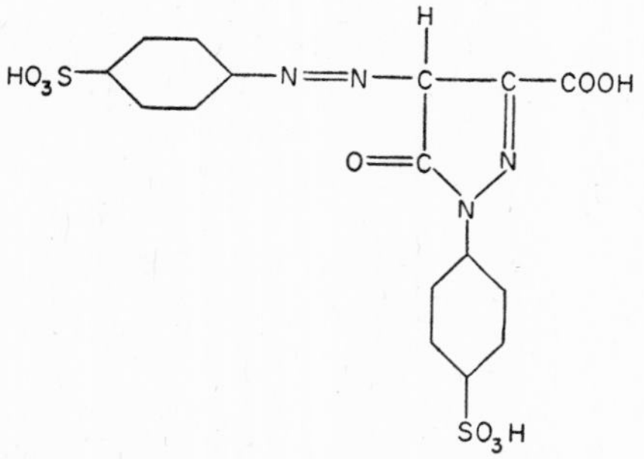

(43) Tartrazine O

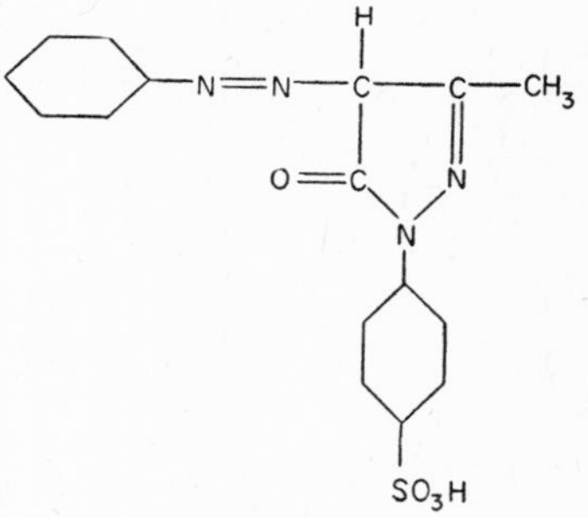

(44) Fast Light Yellow 3G

(c) Aminonaphthols. The group of interesting azo compounds, the *Anthosines*, disclosed in 1912[6, 21, 22, 23, 42, 43], find their principal usage in the preparation of pigments. The distinguishing characteristic of their chemical structure is that they employ derivatives of 8-amino-1-naphthol-3,5-disulfonic acid (K acid) as the azo coupling components. Benzoyl and 2,5-dichlorobenzoyl-K acid have been so used. The barium salts of these azo compounds are brilliant bluish reds and violets, which possess excellent pigment properties, including a high fastness to light.

Anthosine B (45), the most interesting product of the group, approximates a trichromatic red. *Anthosine 3B* (46) is slightly bluer, and greater degrees of blueness, up to and including violet shades, are obtained by the proper choice of related intermediates. Altogether five products have been disclosed, and all are currently manufactured in Germany. *Anthosine BN* is obtained by substituting 2,5-dichlorobenzoyl-K acid in Anthosine B; *Anthosine Violet BB*, by substituting 1-naphthylamine in Anthosine 3B.

The response to these products on the American market thus far has, however, been rather indifferent. The price at which the azo dyes have been available has served as an obstacle to the extensive sale of the derived pigments, with the result that the poundage of the parent K acid, which is without other important application, remains low and its price high.

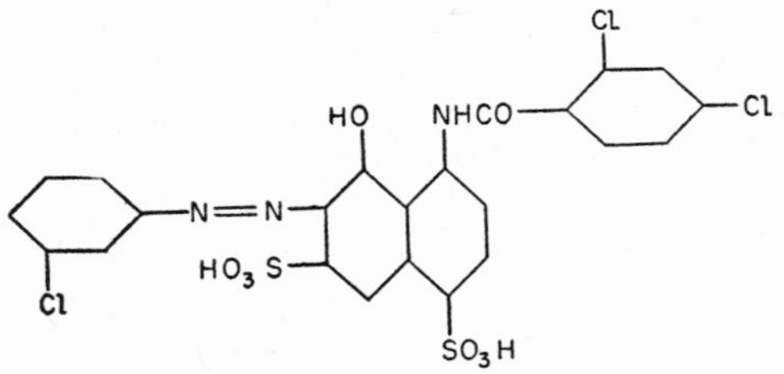

(45) Anthosine B
(*m*-chloroaniline → 2, 4-dichloro-
benzoyl-K acid)

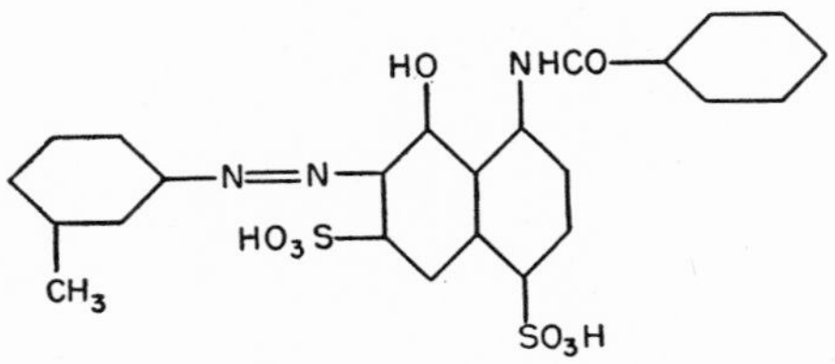

(46) Anthosine 3B
(*m* -toluidine → benzoyl-K acid)

Azo pigments of the *difficultly soluble* type will be described in accordance with three subgroups based on the coupling components (a) 2-naphthol, (b) 3-hydroxy-2-naphthoic acid, and (c) the 1-naphtholsulfonic acids.

In general the manufacture of pigments from difficultly soluble azo derivatives embodies procedures quite distinct from those of the readily soluble dyes. As in the case of the quasi-neutral products the azo synthesis is normally carried out in the pigment industry; moreover, conversion to the desired salt is frequently effected without isolation of the azo compound. In a number of cases a marked increase in brilliance, usually designated as "development," occurs on heating the aqueous suspension to complete the transformation into an alkaline earth salt. The use of metallic rosinates and related materials under proper conditions in connection with these transformations magnifies these desirable effects[2]. Consequently, many of the pigments in this general group have been produced in both the rosinated and nonrosinated forms.

(a) 2-Naphthol. The discovery[14, 41] of the product usually designated as *Lithol Red R* (47), CI 189, the first of the difficultly soluble azo compounds suitable for pigment use, is to be regarded as a milestone in the organic pigment industry. The sodium, calcium, strontium, and barium salts, varying from the orange-red sodium products with increasing depth, blueness, and fastness through the barium, strontium, and calcium salts in the order named, are used as pigments.

These pigments, frequently designated as "Lithols," are now, on a poundage basis, the most important single group of organic pigments. While entering practically every field of pigment application their greatest consumption is in the graphic arts as full strength products.

The barium salt of *Lake Red C* (48), CI 165, is a bright red, the general

TABLE 10. DIFFICULTLY SOLUBLE AZO COMPOUNDS FORMED BY COUPLING WITH 2-NAPHTHOL

Product	Diazotizable amine
(47) Lithol Red R	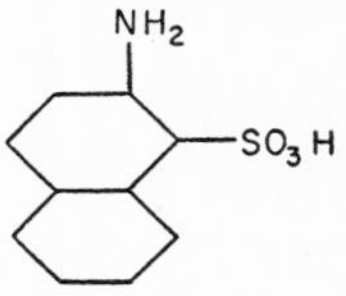 2-Amino-1-naphthalenesulfonic acid
(48) Lake Red C	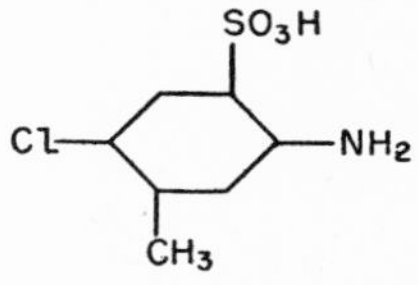 2-Amino-5-chloro-*p*-toluenesulfonic acid (Lake Red C amine)
(49) Lake Red D	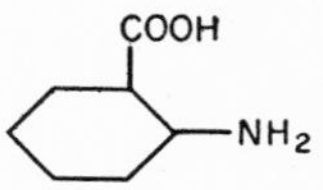 Anthranilic acid
(50) Helio Red RMT	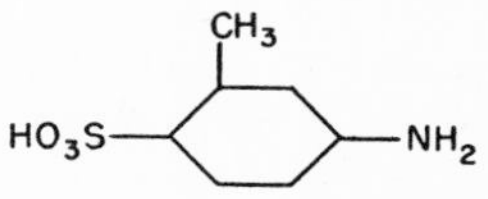 4-Amino-*o*-toluenesulfonic acid

properties of which are similar to slightly superior to those of the "Lithols.' The sodium salt, a reddish bronze orange, is used as a specialty. The barium salt of *Lake Red D* (49), CI 214, possesses creditable properties as a bright red pigment, but has lost a once moderate trade position through competition from "Lithols" and Lake Red C. The barium salt of *Helio Red RMT* (50) is a bright light red, fast to heat and to vehicles, but its lightfastness is not sufficient to overcome its handicap of low tinting strength, hence its consumption is small.

(b) 3-Hydroxy-2-naphthoic acid. Alkaline earth and manganese salts of the four azo compounds shown in Table 11 have found important use as pigments. The 3-hydroxy-2-naphthoic acid derivatives as a group are

TABLE 11. DIFFICULTLY SOLUBLE AZO COMPOUNDS FORMED BY COUPLING WITH
3-HYDROXY-2-NAPHTHOIC ACID

Product	Diazotizable Amine

(51) Lithol Rubine B

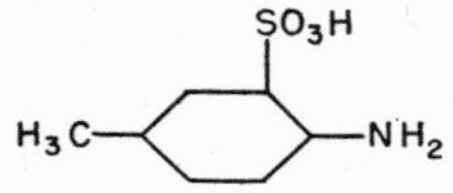

6-Amino-*m*-toluenesulfonic acid
(*p*-toluidine-*m*-sulfonic acid, PTMSA)

(52) Lake Bordeaux B

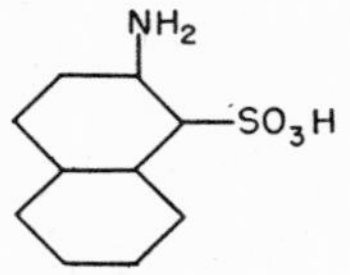

2-Amino-1-naphthalenesulfonic acid
(Tobias acid)

(53) Lithol Red 2G

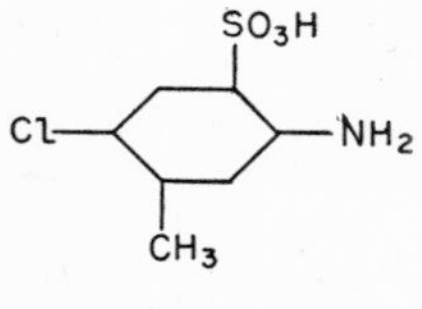

2-Amino-5-chloro-*p*-toluenesulfonic acid
(Lake Red C amine)

(54) Permanent Red 2B

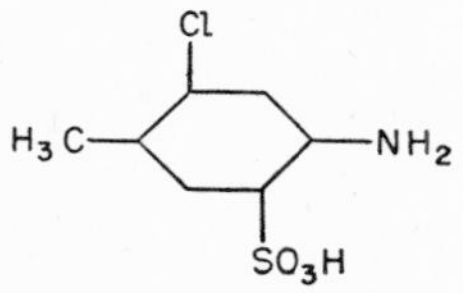

6-Amino-4-chloro-*m*-toluenesulfonic acid

broadly superior to the 2-naphthol counterparts in fastness to heat, to oil, and to light, and their use is on the increase. The calcium salt of *Lithol Rubine B* (51), CI 163, is a deep, brilliant red of pronounced bluish undertone. Various commercial brands are produced, the chief uses of which are in the graphic arts and for the coloring of rubber. The calcium, iron, and manganese salts of *Lake Bordeaux B* (52), CI 190, individually or in combinations, are important automotive maroon pigments. Both the calcium and the manganese salts of *Lithol Red 2G* (53), CI 166, have found use as pigments. The former is the brighter, the latter the more durable.

The calcium salt of *Permanent Red 2B* (54) is used to produce a variety of pigments which are showing increasing trade reception. Their fastness to light is excellent, and their resistance to bleed in commercial vehicles is outstanding, in that they meet both the lacquer and "bake bleed" tests. They are popular as printing-ink pigments, lithograph unusually well, and may be used for tin printing and the coloring of rubber[54] and other elastomers. The manganese toner is a red[55], slightly less brilliant than the calcium derivative, but outstanding in durability in finishes.

In addition the manganese salt of *Pigment Rubine G*, in which 4-chloroaniline-3-sulfonic acid (6-chlorometanilic acid) is the diazotizable amine[55], finds application as a light shade of maroon in organic coating compositions.

(c) 1-Naphtholsulfonic acids. The intermediate, 1-naphthol-5-sulfonic acid, to which is coupled diazotized 1-naphthylamine[52], produces the product generally designated as *Helio Bordeaux BL* (55). Sodium, calcium, and manganese salts have been used, but have shown a rather erratic trade performance on the American market, despite their creditable fastness properties. The isomeric product from 1-naphthol-4-sulfonic acid is slightly inferior and is to be regarded as obsolete.

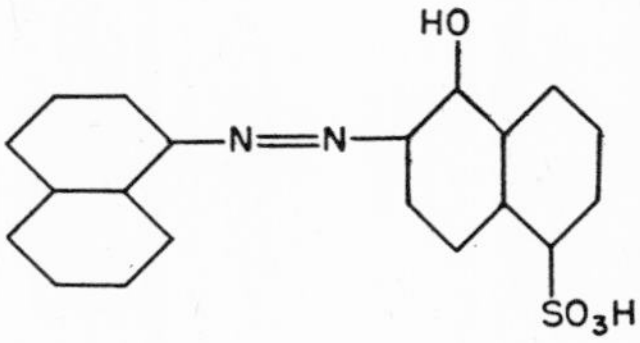

(55) Helio Bordeaux BL

(3) Chelates plus salts. While there are suggestions of chelation in the cases of many of the soluble azo dyes that require the use of substrata containing alumina hydrate for complete precipitation, the only azo compound so classified in this article is *Pigment Scarlet 3B* (56), widely used and well known for the difficulties associated with its conversion to a pigment of

optimum properties. The complications encountered in precipitating this dye, including the use of zinc oxide in addition to the alumina hydrate in the substratum, suggest that both salt formation and chelation are opera-

(56) Pigment Scarlet 3B

tive, possibly supplemented by adsorption by the hydrous alumina. Some chelation through the o-carboxy group could also occur. The configuration (56), in which M is an equivalent of aluminum or zinc, or a mixture of the two, indicates some of these possibilities. When properly precipitated on a substratum, this dye produces a pigment which is valued for high class printing ink work, particularly lithographing on tin, since it is highly resistant to water and to oil. Its resistance to heat is outstanding. It is used to some extent as a trichromatic red, although its bluish undertone does not quite duplicate the brilliancy of the eosins.

Triarylmethane Derivatives. (See also cationic dye derivatives, p. 638).

A small group of anionic triarylmethane dyes, derived from ethylbenzyl-aniline* (*N*-ethyl-*N*-phenylbenzylamine) and characterized by brilliant shades, are historically important in the pigment field. Only one member of the group, *Erioglaucine A* (57), CI 671, is now of importance although some small usage of Acid Green B, CI 666, still continues.

Erioglaucine A is an easily soluble color which is precipitated with diffi-culty, requiring liberal amounts of carefully prepared alumina hydrate as a substratum. The resulting pigment is low in tinting strength, fugitive, and shows a water bleed that is objectionable in lithography. Nevertheless, it retains its trade position because it is a brilliant, transparent, essentially trichromatic blue. The U. S. Tariff Commission reports for 1951 production of 2.6 million lb and sales of 1.7 million lb with a unit value of $0.87 per lb. Appreciable amounts are therefore produced by the consuming plants.†

---

* That sulfonation of ethylbenzylaniline occurs in the meta position, and not, as long supposed, in the para position, has been shown by Blangey, Fierz-David and Stamm[5].

† The manufacture of peacock blue pigments, including a good discussion of the "flushing" process, has been recently reviewed by Hester and Allen[32].

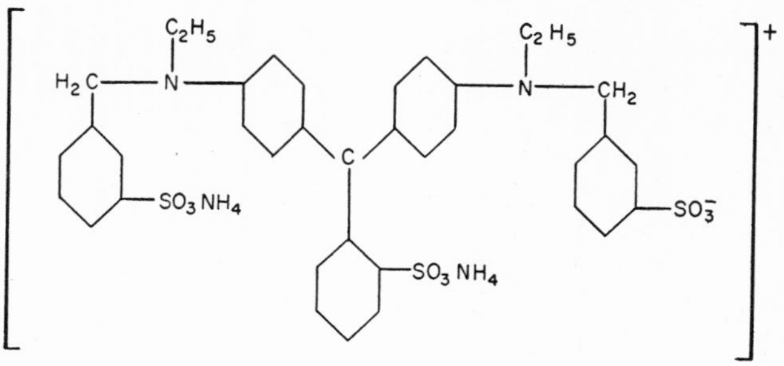

(57) Erioglaucine A

The pigment, *Alkali Blue*, chemically the monosulfonic acid derivative of phenylated rosaniline, is manufactured exclusively for the pigment industry although more highly sulfonated related products are important dyes for wool and for silk. It is difficultly soluble in water. Because of its failure to dry to an acceptable pigment texture it is incorporated into vehicles by the "transfer" or "flushing" process. Its usage is confined to the graphic arts industry where it is used in lithographic and typographic inks in the "toning" of carbon blacks.

Its distinctive bronze lustre, which gives rise to the trade appellative, "Reflex Blue," is probably due to its existence as the free sulfonic acid. Different structural formulas are revealed in the literature. However, formula (59) (compare the recent work of Goldacre and Phillips[29]) is preferred as best representing the symmetry and nonlocalized charge of the excited (colored) dye cation.

The marked influence of sulfonation is well illustrated in this subgroup of derivatives. The unsulfonated product, *Light Blue Superfine, Spirit Soluble* (58), CI 688, triphenylpararosaniline hydrochloride, gives on monosulfonation *Alkali Blue* (59) of increased tinctorial strength, deeper shade, and of sufficiently low solubility in oils to justify its use as a pigment. Polysulfonation reduces the tinctorial strength, lightens the shade, and of course increases the water solubility.

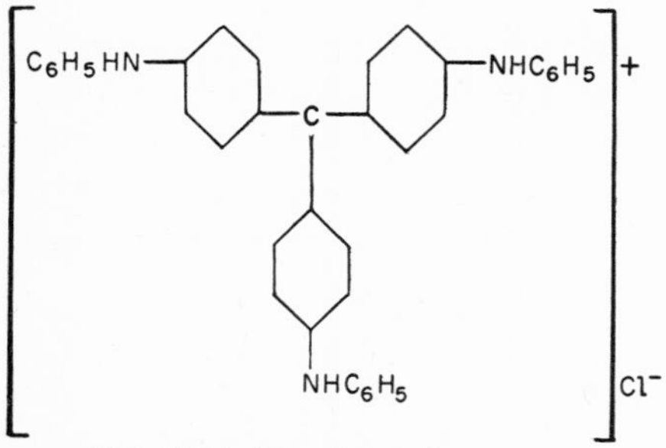

(58) Light Blue Superfine, Spirit Soluble

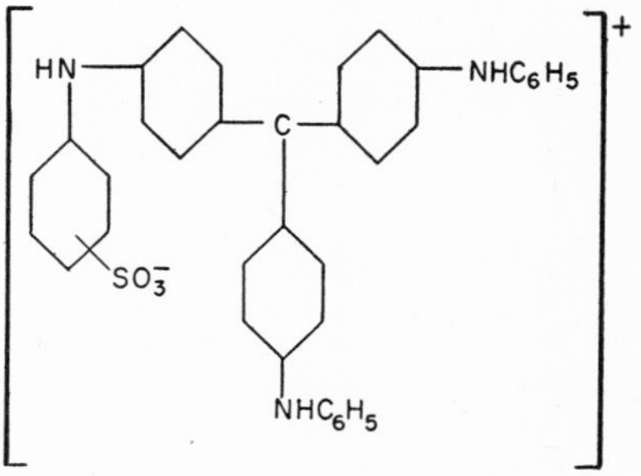

(59) Alkali Blue

Quinoline Derivatives. One dye, *Quinoline Yellow O,* CI 801, prepared by essentially random sulfonation of a mixture of quinophthalones, has long been used for pigment manufacture. Of the various compositions that have been reported it is believed that (60) (see Quinoline Dyes, p. 261) most nearly represents the present product used in pigment manufacture.

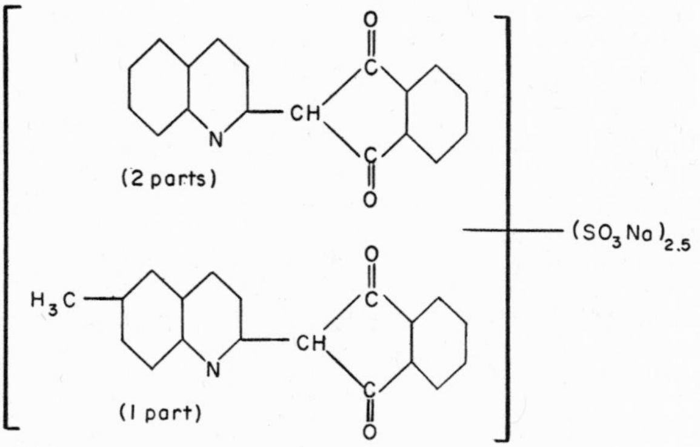

(60) Quinoline Yellow

This dye mixture gives brilliant, greenish-yellow pigments which lack fastness to light, but which find application as self colors and in blends. The sales figures for 1951 of 12,000 pounds, unit value $1.25 per lb, do not include the usage of this product in blends with the other soluble anionic dyes.

Xanthene Derivatives. A small number of anionic derivatives of xanthene which owe their salt-forming property to the presence of the carboxy group in the molecule are of interest as pigments. These products are converted to brilliant reds of a bluish undertone by precipitation with soluble lead salts. While lacking good fastness to light, they find considerable usage in the

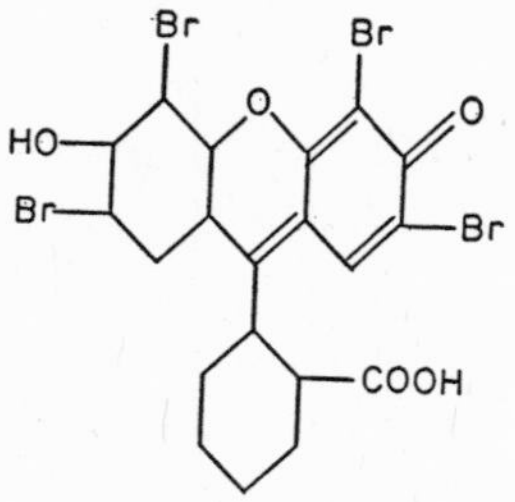

(61) Eosin

graphic arts industry as trichromatic reds. The toners of Eosin (61), prepared by special methods, constitute the "Bronze Reds" of industry, and are sometimes designated by the misleading appellative "Phloxine Toners." The 1951 statistics for these products are given in Table 12.

TABLE 12. 1951 U. S. SALES STATISTICS FOR XANTHENE PIGMENTS

	Production 1000 lb	Sales Quantity 1000 lb	Value $1000	Unit Value $/lb
Eosin (Bromo Acid Toner)......	900	350	550	1.57
Eosin "Lakes".................	49	—	—	—

Anthraquinone Derivatives. As pointed out by Curtis[10] a number of soluble hydroxyanthraquinones give metallic derivatives which are useful pigments. In these insolubilizations, accompanied by color change, alumina hydrate is typically the chief inorganic reactant. The alumina hydrate is, as a general rule, so used that it functions both as a precipitant and as a substratum. Recent work suggests that both salt formation and chelation take place in these metallizations.

Alizarin (62), CI 1027, known and successfully used by the ancients in the form of "madder" as a raw material for pigments, is by far the most widely known pigmentary material of the group and historically is one of the most important of all colored organic compounds. Techniques for its application in dyeing and in pigment manufacture have been known for a long time, and have been difficult to explain. These techniques involve autoclaving or prolonged boiling of the dye with alumina hydrate or phosphate, in the presence of calcium salts and "Turkey Red Oil," a sulfated castor oil.

The voluminous literature on the famous "Turkey Red" dyes and the closely related pigment-producing processes, based on alizarin, has been reviewed by Haller[30] and by Sigfrid Hoffmann[33]. Hoffmann obtained a crystalline pyridine derivative of alizarin by reacting it with calcium oxide and aluminum acetylacetonate in aqueous pyridine. He proposed a macromolecule of 4 alizarin molecules, 2 pyridine molecules, 2 aluminum and 3 calcium atoms.

Fierz-David and Rutishauser[13] also prepared a crystalline metallic derivative of alizarin, in which the complexing with pyridine and the functioning of alumina hydrate as a substratum are both avoided. The structural formula (63) which they proposed is likewise a macromolecule of 4 alizarin molecules, bonded in this case simply to 2 aluminum and 3 calcium atoms. In accordance with the assumption that both saltlike and chelate unions are formed, the calcium is the cation in this remarkably stable complex compound, and the chelate union of 2 moles of alizarin with 1 of aluminum constitutes a complex anion in the terminology of Martell and Calvin[49a] (see p. 629). This formula adequately explains the changes which accompany the formation of metallic derivatives of this dye, and the resemblance to the phthalocyanine formula has been suggested.

The pigment from alizarin, the famous "Turkey Red Lake," is a bright red of deep masstone and yellowish red undertone. Despite its excellent fastness to weathering and to vehicle bleed it has slowly yielded its once dominant trade position to azo pigments because of their ease of manufacture. United States sales of 223,000 pounds of alizarin lake were reported for 1951.

A number of metallized amino, sulfo, and carboxy derivatives of the hydroxyanthraquinones have found application as pigments. In these cases, metallization with alumina takes place with greater ease than in the case of the unmodified hydroxyanthraquinones. Alkaline earth salt formation with the sulfo groups may or may not be involved. The resulting pigments are bright, transparent, and of good fastness to vehicles and to light, although they are usually inferior in lightfastness to the red pigment from alizarin. The pigments from *Alizarin Saphirol* (64), CI 1054, and from *Helio Fast Violet AL* (65), CI 1074, are no longer widely used; those from the quinizarin[24, 35, 56] derivatives, the *Helio Fast Rubines* (66, 67, 68, 69), find usage in the shading of pigments in organic coatings, including limited application in automotive finishes. These rubine pigments are brilliant, transparent, and fast to the influence of vehicles, and they show a high degree of lightfastness, but they do not have the "enamel life" required for high-quality automotive finishes. The 4BL shade is the one most widely used. Chelate ring formation with aluminum probably takes place like that in the case of alizarin (63). This formulation suggests that, provided the 1-hydroxy and the 9-oxo groups are joined in a heterocyclic ring through chelation with aluminum, activation of the 2(or 4)-hydroxy group occurs, and the alkaline earth metals then form saltlike unions with the activated hydroxy groups.

In processes for alizarin pigments prior to those of Hoffmann and of Fierz-David and Rutishauser, the amount of aluminum used is generally far beyond the stoichiometric equivalent of the dye, and in commercial processes the excess alumina hydrate is retained as a substratum. Thus metallized anthraquinone pigments may involve both salt and chelate chemical unions, as well as adsorption of a complex macromolecule by the excess alumina hydrate, which serves as a distending substratum to impart desirable physical and optical properties to the finished pigment.

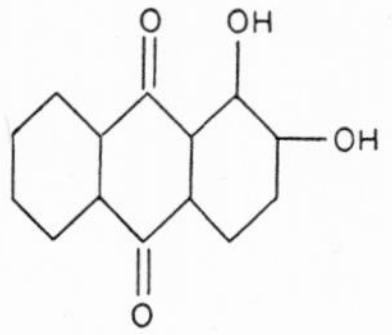

(62) Alizarin

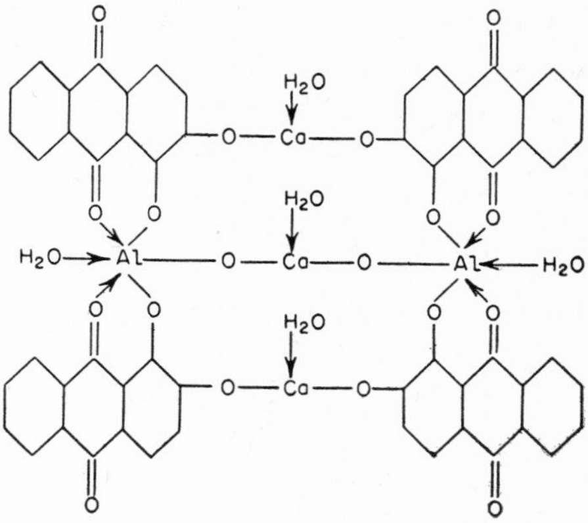

(63) Metallic alizarin derivative

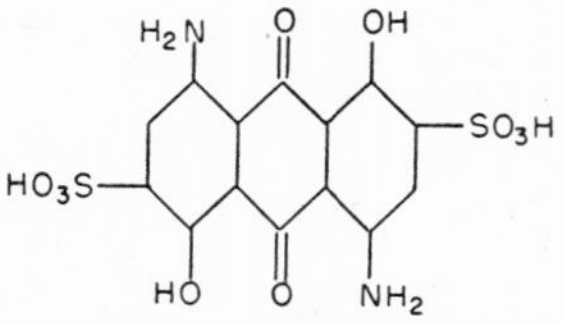

(64) Alizarin Saphirol

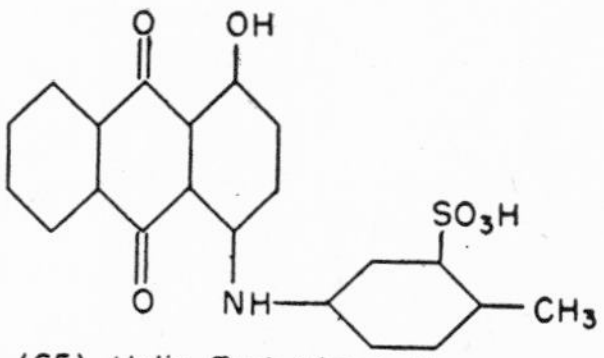

(65) Helio Fast Violet AL

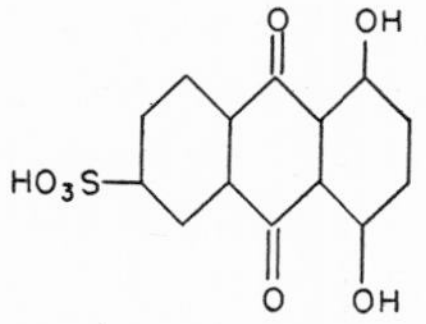

(66) Helio Fast Rubine 3BL

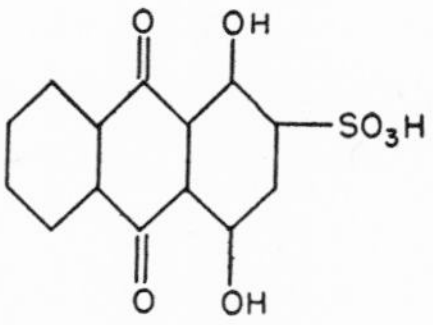

(67) Helio Fast Rubine 4BL

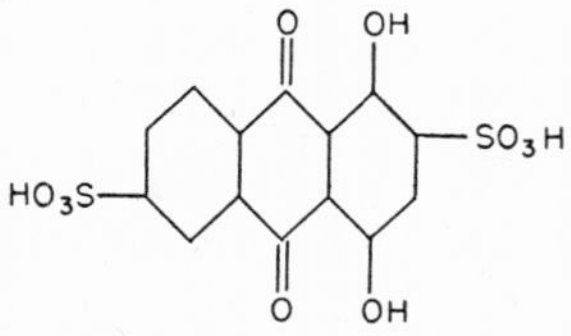

(68) Helio Fast Rubine 6BL

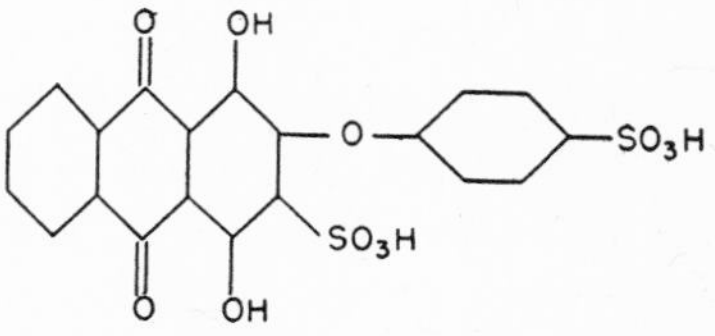

(69) Helio Fast Rubine FF Extra

Phthalocyanines. These products possess such markedly superior general fastness to heat, to light, to general weathering agencies, and to vehicle bleed, together with high tinctorial strength and beauty, that their advent marks a milestone in the pigment industry. They are characterized chemically by a new chromophore, the first of commercial importance in over half a century.

(1) Chelates. Both copper phthalocyanine (71) and copper polychlorophthalocyanine are polydentate chelate derivatives involving in each case linkages of one atom of copper to four pyrrole groups to form four six-membered rings centrally located in a macromolecule. The metal-free product (70), possessing two hydrogen bondings in place of one copper atom, is classed here with the chelate derivatives as a matter of convenience. In harmony with the relative stabilities of hydrogen bondings and chelate linkages, the copper derivatives are superior in fastness to the metal-free product.

A serious problem in the commercial development of the phthalocyanines has been the conversion of the crude, weak, harsh-textured products of synthesis into acceptable pigments. Intensive research work has, however, proven effective in meeting this difficulty. The useful methods, for the most part, involve dissolving the crude product in concentrated sulfuric acid followed by sudden drowning in water. Distending these pigments on various types of substrata also finds considerable application.

Copper phthalocyanine (71), Pr. 481, a brilliant, deep blue pigment, is the most widely used product at the present time and is the most readily synthesized member of the group. It has, however, presented the greatest problems in fabrication of the crude products into acceptable pigments, as well as in the prevention of loss of strength subsequent to dispersion in vehicles. These difficulties have been largely overcome, however, and it has now penetrated essentially all fields of pigment application and represents an approach to the ideal pigment. That it can even be used as a rubber pigment is of special interest in that it confirms the essentially non-ionic nature of the metal linkage involved. The recognition of the alpha and beta crystal forms, the latter of which is solvent stable (see Phthalocyanine Pigments, p. 591), has provided a means of dealing with the above mentioned loss of strength. The greener shade of the beta form can also be used advantageously in applied problems, particularly in the approach to the trichromatic blue shade of the printing ink industry.

Copper polychlorophthalocyanine, Pr. 483, is a brilliant bluish green, equal in stability and general fastness properties to copper phthalocyanine blue. Technically, it has presented greater problems in its synthesis than has the blue unchlorinated product, but less difficulty in the processing to acquire desirable physical properties.

Metal-free phthalocyanine (70), Pr. 482, is appreciably more difficult to synthesize than is the copper derivative since the indirect procedure is employed of preparing certain metallic derivatives and subsequently eliminating the metal by alcoholysis or by acid treatment (see Chapter 9).

Tinctorially, the metal-free product is a slightly greener and an equally bright shade of blue when compared with the copper derivative. In stability and general fastness properties it is slightly but not seriously inferior to the copper derivative. The slightly greater difference in greenness of shade of the metal-free beta form over the alpha, as compared with that in the coppered counterparts, brings the beta form of metal-free phthalocyanine slightly closer to the true trichromatic blue shade. However, cost is an important factor in penetrating this field of application, and as a result the metal-free product is declining in importance.

United States statistics for 1951 show the production of 1.6 million pounds of copper phthalocyanine at a unit sales value of $3.30/lb.

(70) Metal-free phthalocyanine

(71) Copper phthalocyanine

(2) Chelates plus salts. Sulfonated copper phthalocyanine (Chapter 10), a water-soluble product, may be precipitated as a barium salt and used as a pigment. The stability of the copper chelate of the phthalocyanine macromolecule is such that the metallic linkages are not broken under sulfonation conditions stringent enough to introduce up to four sulfo groups. Sulfonation effects a reduction in strength, a greening of shade, and a reduction in lightfastness.

Literature Cited

1. Allen, "Encyclopedia of Chemical Technology," ed. by Kirk and Othmer, New York, Interscience Publishers, Inc., **10,** 660 (1953).
2. —— and Siegel, U.S. Patent 1,772,300 (1930); Reissue 18,590 (1932).
3. Bailar and Callis, *J. Am. Chem. Soc.*, **74,** 6018 (1952).
4. Blangey, "Pigment- und Lackfarbstoffe," in Fierz-David, "Kuenstliche organische Farbstoffe," Vol. III of Herzog, "Technologie der Textilfasern," Berlin, Julius Springer, 1935, Ergaenzungsband, pp. 50–59.

5. ——, Fierz-David, and Stamm, *Helv. Chim. Acta*, **25**, 1162 (1942).
6. —— and Immerheiser, U.S. Patent 1,073,951 (1913).
7. Blumenthal, *Am. Dyestuff Reptr.*, **35**, 529 (1946).
8. British Patent 19,100 (1905).
9. Callis, Nielsen and Bailar, *J. Am. Chem. Soc.*, **74**, 3461 (1952).
10. Curtis, "Artificial Organic Pigments and Their Applications," transl. by Fyleman; London, Pitman, 1930.
11. Desamari, U.S. Patent 1,059,599 (1913).
12. Elkins and Hunter, *J. Chem. Soc.*, **1935**, 1598.
13. Fierz-David and Rutishauser, *Helv. Chim. Acta*, **23**, 1298 (1940).
14. German Patent 112,833 (1899).
15. German Patent 180,301 (1906).
16. German Patent 200,263 (1908).
17. German Patent 217,266 (1909).
18. German Patent 251,479 (1912).
19. German Patent 256,999 (1913).
20. German Patent 257,488 (1913).
21. German Patent 272,862 (1914).
22. German Patent 272,863 (1914).
23. German Patent 272,864 (1914).
24. German Patent 285,614 (1915).
25. German Patent 287,149 (1915).
26. German Patent 295,794 (1916).
27. German Patent 356,973 (1921).
28. Glassman, *J. Oil Colour Chemists' Assoc.*, **33**, 191 (1950).
29. Goldacre and Phillips, *J. Chem. Soc.*, **1949**, 1724.
30. Haller, *Melliand Textilber.*, **19**, 448–52, 504–06, 595–96, 731–34, 796–99 (1938).
31. Hartmann, U.S. Patent 1,653,851 (1927).
32. Hester and Allen, *Ind. Eng. Chem.*, **45**, 1610 (1953).
33. Hoffmann, Sigfrid, Inaugural Dissertation, "Ueber die Konstitution des Turkischrotlacke," Tech. Hochschule, Dresden (1937).
34. I. G. Farbenindustrie, BIOS 961 (PB 60905).
35. ——, BIOS 1661 (PB 91693).
36. ——, FIAT 1313, Vol. III (PB 85172).
37. Iler, *J. Am. Chem. Soc.*, **69**, 724 (1947).
38. Immerheiser, U.S. Patent 1,232,551 (1917).
39. —— and Beyer, U.S. Patent 1,232,552 (1917).
40. —— and Zschimmer, U.S. Patent 1,529,891 (1925).
41. Julius, U.S. Patent 650,757 (1900).
42. —— and Immerheiser, U.S. Patents 1,073,902-3-4 (1913).
43. —— and ——, U.S. Patent 1,073,905 (1913).
44. Kopp, *Bull. soc. ind. Rouen*, **63**, 120 (1935).
45. Kvalnes and Woodward, U.S. Patent 2,396,327 (1946).
46. Lapworth, "Thorpe's Dictionary of Applied Chemistry," 4th ed., Vol. IV, p. 211, London, Longmans, Green, 1940.
47. Lauch, U.S. Patent 912,138 (1909).
48. Linz, U.S. Patent 1,378,882 (1921).
49. Martell and Calvin, "The Chemistry of the Metal Chelate Compounds," New York, Prentice-Hall, Inc., 1952; (a) pp. 7–8; (b) p. 278.
50. Morgan and Main Smith, *J. Soc. Dyers Colourists*, **41**, 233 (1925).

51. Pratt, "The Chemistry and Physics of Organic Pigments," New York, John Wiley & Sons, Inc., 1947.
52. Runkel and Herzberg, U.S. Patent 972,130 (1910).
53. Siegel, U.S. Patent 1,803,657 (1931).
54. ——, U.S. Patent 2,117,860 (1938).
55. ——, U.S. Patent 2,225,665 (1940).
56. Tust, U.S. Patent 1,126,591 (1915).
57. U. S. Tariff Commission, "Synthetic Organic Chemicals, U.S. Production and Sales, 1951," Report No. 175, Second Series.
58. Vesce, "Maroon Organic Pigments," in Mattiello, ed., "Protective and Decorative Coatings," New York, John Wiley & Sons, Inc., **2,** 204 (1942).
59. Wagner, U.S. Patent 1,082,719 (1913).
60. Winther, Laska and Zitscher, U.S. Patent 1,034,853 (1912).
61. Wittenberger, *Melliand Textilber.*, **32,** 454 (1951).
62. Woodward, U.S. Patent 2,416,248 (1947).

12. COLOR AND CHEMICAL CONSTITUTION OF DYES

Donald Graham

Introduction

Dyes owe their color to absorption of visible light. White light comprises an approximately uniform distribution of energy over the visible spectrum. If absorption is similarly uniform, the absorbing object appears to be black or gray, but if selective, the color seen is the complement of that absorbed. Thus absorption of blue light leaves a yellow color. Absorption of both blue and red light leaves green. The color of a dye is therefore the direct result of its visible absorption spectrum, which is in turn closely related to its molecular structure, degree of aggregation, and environment. Although the effects of specific groups are necessarily considered separately, the color is determined by the system acting as a whole.

Basic Concepts

Current theory relating color and constitution is founded upon the following concepts.

Quantization of Light. Light is quantized in units of energy called light quanta, or photons. Light of high frequency (short wavelength) is relatively high in energy. A mole of quanta (6.03×10^{23} quanta), called an "Einstein," varies in energy from 51 kcal for red light of $\lambda = 7000$ Å (λ = wavelength) to 71 kcal for violet light of $\lambda = 4000$ Å. Infrared radiation has less energy per quantum and ultraviolet, more.

Nature of Excitation. Excitation of a molecule by visible (or ultraviolet) light involves, principally, an increase in the electronic energy of the molecule (with some attendant change in the vibrational and rotational energy).

Quantization of Molecular Energy. Molecules are excited to discrete energy levels by the absorption of light. The differences in energy between these levels determine the wavelengths of light which can be absorbed. In the discussion which follows, principal emphasis will be placed upon the wavelength of the peak of the first or longest-wavelength band, symbolized as λ max. (The corresponding extinction coefficient is represented by ϵ max.)

Relative Electron Mobilities. Electrons bonding the atoms of saturated molecules such as ethane or cyclohexane are strongly stabilized and are excited only by high-energy radiation well up in the ultraviolet spectrum. However, more mobile electrons such as the π electrons associated with carbon to carbon double bonds, the nonbonding electrons (lone pairs) of sulfur, oxygen, and nitrogen, and the unpaired electrons of free radicals are excited much more easily.

When a number of mobile electrons interact strongly, as in a conjugated system, the energy requirement for excitation is frequently lowered to a level within the visible spectrum, resulting in color.

The methods of quantum mechanics are employed for the direct application of these basic principles to calculation of the energy levels of a molecule. Exact solutions are not possible for polyatomic systems but approximate, and to some extent empirical methods of increasing effectiveness are being developed. In 1937 Sklar[65] successfully calculated λ max. for several conjugated hydrocarbons. More recently, the "molecular orbital" method has been made usefully applicable to much larger units approaching the complexity of dye molecules[47, 49, 50]. Although it seems probable that, with some further refinement, quantum mechanics will displace less rigorous methods, the synthetic-dye chemist today relies principally on more readily applicable generalizations. These relations, discussed in the pages which follow, are essentially qualitative. Some are firmly supported by theory and others are admittedly empirical. They are particularly useful in predicting spectral changes resulting from substitution or other structural modification of known compounds.

Conjugation of Chromophores

Witt[73] first pointed out that all colored organic molecules contain one or more doubly bonded groups such as $-N=N-$, $>C=C<$, $>C=N-$, $>C=O$, and $-N=O$ which he called "chromophores." In more recent usage, the term is often applied to a complete conjugated unit, a group of atoms bearing a continuous chain or network of interacting mobile electrons which may be excited by a single photon.

The presence of a chromophore, while necessary for color, is not always sufficient. In the absence of extensive conjugation or polar substitution, the absorption may still lie in the ultraviolet, but because such compounds may become colored with substitution, they are called "chromogens."

Polarization with Excitation. In some cases, the absorption of light can raise the energy level of electrons without appreciably affecting their distribution but more often, particularly when absorption is strong, polarization occurs. If we consider the different resonance structures that can be written for a nonionized dye, we see that the polar forms, or those involving a separation of charge, are higher in energy than the others and generally contribute principally to the excited states. A quantitative estimate of the contribution of polar structures to the first excited state of a dye would require an involved calculation. However, a dye of commercial importance is usually a strong absorber so we may assume that polar forms are important. This assumption is supported by the results of calculation, and much information is obtained by consideration of the effects of structure upon the ease of movement of a charge through a conjugated chromophore.

Linear Conjugation. The relation between the color of a dye and the extent of its conjugation varies with structure. The usual effect of increased conjugation is bathochromic (deepening of shade or increase in λ max.) but the reverse (hypsochromic) effect is occasionally observed.

The simplest conjugated structures are those of the polyenes. Their principal resonance forms may be represented as follows:

$$\text{Nonpolar: } R-(CH=CH)_n-CH=CH-R'$$

$$\text{Extreme polar: } R-\overset{\pm}{C}H-(CH=CH)_n-\overset{\mp}{C}H-R'$$

The polar forms also include intermediate structures, their number varying with the length of the chain. Lewis and Calvin[41] have chosen to consider the π electrons of the conjugated chain as oscillators in phase, equivalent to a single oscillator having the force constant of one and the mass of all the individual oscillators. On this basis, the square of the wavelength should vary linearly with the number of units of the polyenic chain, a relation (sometimes called the λ^2 rule) that has been confirmed experimentally with several types of polyenes.

A second class, with principal resonance between two ionic forms of similar energy, is exemplified by the symmetrical cyanines:

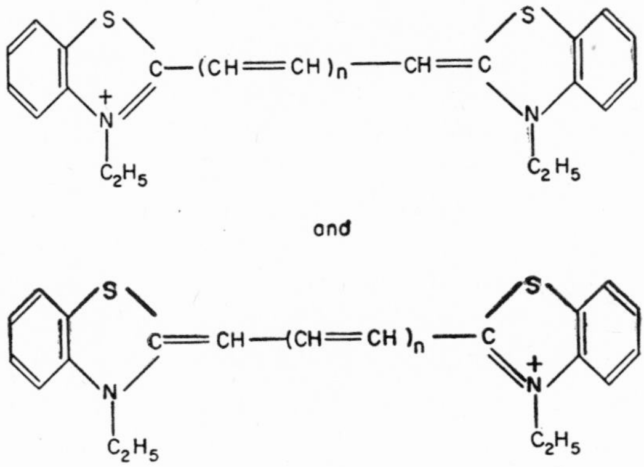

and

In these dyes, λ max. increases in direct proportion to increasing chain length. Herzfeld and Sklar[31] have explained this effect as due to the requirement that the extreme ionic structures interact only through intermediate structures of higher energy. Their calculations indicate that an increase in the number of intermediate interactions decreases the resonance splitting of the ground structures and shifts λ max. toward longer wavelengths.

The two preceding classes are quite well defined both in structure and in behavior of λ max. However, this is not true of all types of linear conjugation. The λ max. values of the *p*-polyphenyls converge more rapidly than indicated by the λ^2 rule and the polyacenes are quite irregular[42].

Molecule	λ max.	Δ λ Difference
Benzene	2600 Å	
		150 Å
Naphthalene	2750	
		950
Anthracene	3700	
		900
Naphthacene	4600	
		1200
Pentacene	5800	

The effect of the condensation of aromatic rings is usually bathochromic. However, the shift is hypsochromic when aromatic rings are added to fulvene or quinone units, exemplified by the following three groups:

(1) Benzofulvenes

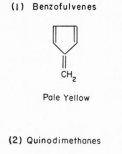

Pale Yellow	Colorless	Colorless

(2) Quinodimethones

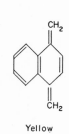
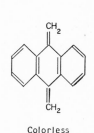

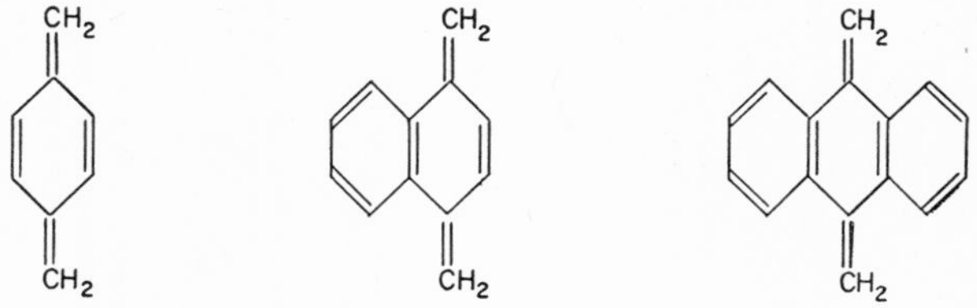

Orange	Yellow	Colorless

(3) Quinones

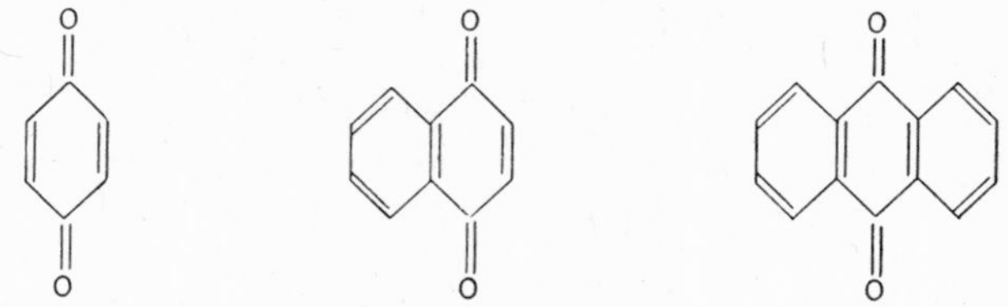

Yellow   Pale Yellow   Almost Colorless

It is also important to note that with further increase in conjugation (above 4 or 5 rings), the aromatic condensation predominates and the effect of additional rings is again bathochromic.

The general hypsochromic effect of an aromatic ring which includes a double bond of a quinone (or fulvene) ring was recognized qualitatively by Izmail'skii[32] who termed it "disperson of the electromeric effect."

Conjugation Involving Linkages Other Than the Carbon-carbon Double Bond. *Triple Bonds.* Although acetylene absorbs at a longer wavelength than ethylene, this effect is not consistently observed in extended conjugation.

The spectra of the α–β dienes and the vinyl acetylenes have been found very similar[29, 30]. A comparison of the effects of ethylene and acetylene linkages upon the colors of the triphenylmethane dyes disclosed some individual differences but, over-all, the effects of the two groups are comparable[21].

Nitrogen Atoms. Of the several atoms, other than carbon, which may participate in conjugation, nitrogen is probably the most important in the dye field and has received the most attention. A comparison of the spectra of butadienes and diphenylbutadienes with derivatives in which one or both ethylene groups were replaced with azomethine groups indicated a hypsochromic shift of approx. 250 Å per nitrogen atom[3].

A much stronger hypsochromic effect was observed when $=$N— replaced $=$CH— in the polyene chain of a cyanine dye[9, 10]. It was concluded that such a molecule could be polarized with a negative charge on the nitrogen atom to give a structure differing but little in energy from an extreme structure and absorbing at shorter wavelengths.

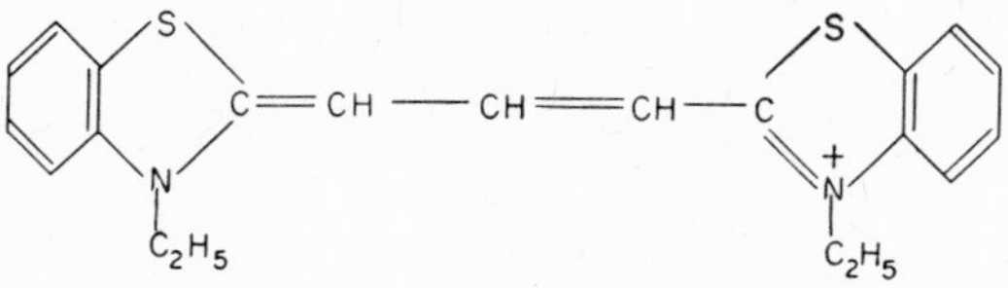

λ max. 5,575 A°
ϵ max. 14.7 x 10^4
(in CH_3OH)

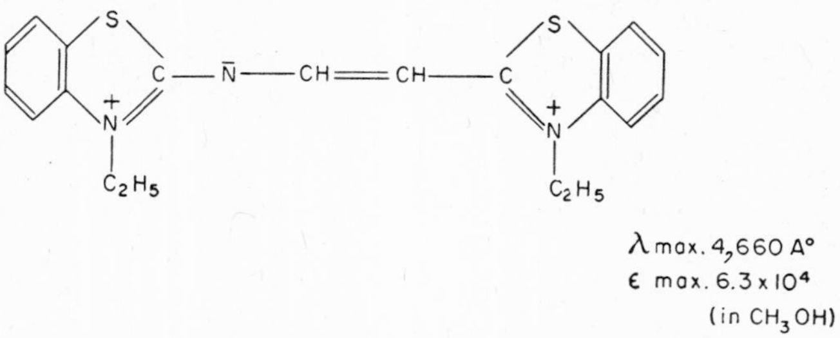

λ max. 4,660 A°
ϵ max. 6.3 x 10⁴
(in CH₃OH)

In accord with the Herzfeld-Sklar treatment of symmetrical cyanines, reduction of the number of high-energy intermediate structures by replacing a =CH— group with =N— should favor interaction of the extreme structures, resonance splitting, and a hypsochromic shift of λ max.

The extent of this shift increases with the basicity of the terminal nuclei[38]. If, on the other hand, the dye structure favors a positive charge on the central nitrogen, the shift is bathochromic. In this case, the effect of basicity is also reversed, dyes with end groups of lower basicity showing the greater shifts on replacement of the =CH— group with =N—.

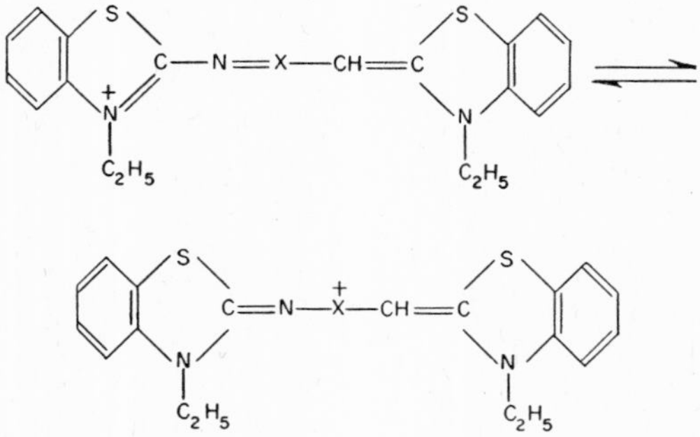

If X = =CH—, λ max. = 4,650 Å
If X = =N—, λ max. = 4,950 Å

Much smaller effects were observed in aromatic systems. Maccoll[42] lists the following λ max. values:

Benzene 2600 Å	Naphthalene 2750 Å	Anthracene 3700 Å
Pyridine 2650 Å	Quinoline 3150 Å	Acridine 3600 A
		Phenazine 3750 Å

These compounds have also been compared (by Barany *et al.*[3]) on the basis of the more intense bands in the 2400–2800 Å region as follows:

Compound	λ	ϵ
Benzene	2550	250
Pyridine	2500	2000
Pyrimidine	2430	3000
Pyrazine	2600	5200

Compounds	λ	ε
Naphthalene...	2760	7900
Quinoline..	2750	4500
Isoquinoline..	2620	3700
Anthracene...	2500	160,000
Acridine...	2500	160,000
Phenazine...	2500	120,000

Although the action of a hetero atom in the body of a conjugated aromatic system may differ negligibly from that of a =CH— unit, this is not true if a cyclic unit containing nitrogen occupies a terminal position. In this case, it may act as an auxochrome with a strong bathochromic effect (as discussed later).

Hyperconjugation. Saturated hydrocarbons (such as ethane) show only very slight π bonding (compared with the strong interaction of the π electrons of a conjugated unit). However, the bond between an alkyl substituent and a conjugated system assumes a significant amount of π character, an effect called hyperconjugation[18]. This effect is principally concentrated in the bond between the conjugated unit and the first aliphatic carbon atom. A methyl substituent is therefore nearly as effective as a higher homolog. The resulting shifts in λ max. are perhaps best classified through consideration of the concept of alternant structures[15]. A conjugated system is termed "alternant" if it is possible to "star" every other carbon atom in such a way that every starred carbon atom is completely surrounded by unstarred carbon atoms and every unstarred, by starred. When this condition is fulfilled, it is assumed that influence upon the electronic character of any starred atom is shared by all starred atoms and vice versa.

Methyl substitution of alternant systems usually produces a bathochromic shift, explained on the basis of preferential resonance stabilization of ionic forms[53]. Molecular-orbital calculations[16] of the absorption frequencies of methyl-substituted ethylenes and benzenes support the conclusion that the observed bathochromic shifts accompanying methyl substitution are largely due to hyperconjugation. The result of the addition of methyl groups to azulene may be either hypsochromic or bathochromic, involving a combination of hyperconjugation and induction[55]. Hypsochromic shifts are also observed in some linear compounds in which the addition of methyl groups provides a shorter conjugation path[51].

Although hyperconjugation must be recognized as a possible factor in determining the color of a dye, it is not often a major one. The λ max. shifts involved are less than 500 Å, usually much less.

Conjugation Involving More Than One Axis. The relation between length of a conjugated path and the corresponding λ max. suggests a directional effect and such is indeed the case. The pleochroism of dye crystals has been well known for some time, but it remained for Lewis and Calvin to relate different bands in the spectrum of a dye with specific orientations of polarization of the molecule. They called the direction of longest conjugation "X" and assumed polarization along this axis to be associated with λ max. The letter "Y" was chosen to represent polarization in another direction (usually perpendicular), and "Z" for electronic interactions in a third direction (as between molecules stacked in a crystal like a deck of cards).

The cation of Michler's hydrol

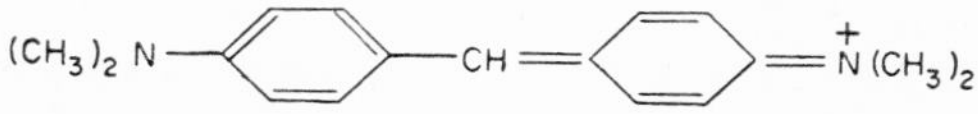

has only a single band in the visible spectrum, which we may call an X band. Crystal Violet

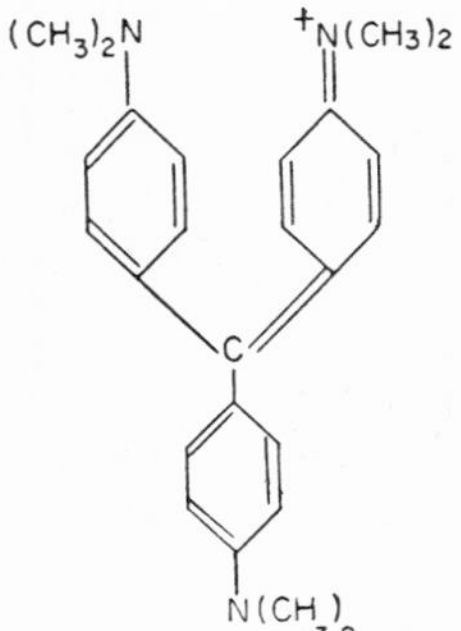

is a two-dimensional molecule but, due to its symmetry, the X and Y bands have the same wavelength and appear as a single band.

Malachite Green, which differs from Crystal Violet only in the absence of one $-N(CH_3)_2$ group, shows an X band of about the same wavelength as that of Crystal Violet but of somewhat lower intensity. In addition, it shows a Y band of shorter wavelength.

Crystalline pseudoisocyanine provides an example of three-dimensional excitation. Its 5730 Å band, observed only in the crystalline state, has been assigned the Z coordinate. Other examples are reported[33, 60, 61].

The validity of this concept was demonstrated by measuring the absorption of polarized light by oriented dye molecules, and by study of the fluorescence resulting from excitation of random-oriented dye molecules by polarized light of different wavelengths[40]. Fluorescence of organic molecules, as far as is known, always involves a nonradiative drop from the higher levels of excitation to a lower level (probably the first excited singlet state) followed by fluorescent emission with the final transition to the ground state. Using Malachite Green, it was observed that absorption of polarized light of the frequency of the X band resulted in fluorescence of the same polarization while absorption at the frequency of the Y band produced fluorescence polarized in a direction perpendicular to that of the incident light.

Although the concept of excitation with polarization in more than one direction through a molecule is well established, the early thought that the longest path is associated with λ max. is not always true. For example, recent calculations[14] indicate that while λ max. of the polyenes is associated with polarization along the axis of the chain, that of the polyacenes relates to the axis across the chain.

Insulation. When the mobile electrons of two conjugated systems within a molecule are prevented from free interaction, they are said to be insulated. Such systems absorb light almost as separate molecules with discrete spectra.

The simplest form of insulation is by an intervening saturated group. If this insulation is not strong (as through a single —CH_2— group) each system may exert a slight bathochromic effect on the other (reviewed by Braude[5]).

Polar insulating groups may influence the spectra of both conjugated fragments, acting as both insulators and auxochromes.

A very strongly polar substituent at an intermediate point in a conjugated system tends to divide the conjugation but bands characteristic of the complete system may also be present.

Another important type of insulation is that resulting from cross conjugation, in which portions of a molecule can conjugate with, but not through, a central group. For example, the *p*-polyphenyls show an increasing λ max. with increasing length but the *m*-polyphenyls show a λ max. very close to

that of biphenyl. Thus, the *m*-phenylene group ⬡ is an effective in-

sulator. In "valence bond" language, we may state that such groups act as insulators because it is not possible to write polar quinonoid structures through the positions of substitution.

Auxochromes

Auxochromes (by classical definition) increase both the tinctorial value and the substantivity of dyes. However, in this chapter, only the effects upon color are considered, permitting inclusion of groups affecting the polarizability but lacking salt-forming or substantive character.

Electronic Character. Displacements of the 2030 Å band of benzene by substitution (measured by Doub and Vandenbelt[19, 20]) show a good correlation with the differential polarizability values calculated by Price[54] from Hammett's $\Delta \sigma$ values[28].

The electron-donating (basic, ortho- and para-directing) groups in order of increasing displacement are CH_3 < Cl < Br < OH < OCH_3 < NH_2 < O— and the electron acceptors (acidic, meta-directing), NH_3^+ < SO_2NH_2 < CO_2^- = CN < COOH < $COCH_3$ < CHO < NO_2. In either case, the most effective auxochromic groups are those capable of participating in the conjugation.

The contribution of monosubstitution of benzene to the intensity of absorption at λ max. has been found proportional to the square of a transition moment or "spectroscopic moment" induced by the substituent[23, 66].

A number of these moments (calculated by Platt[52]) show a "strong but not perfect" correlation with the $\Delta \sigma$ values calculated by Price. Thus, an auxochrome which shifts λ max. toward longer wavelengths may also contribute to the intensity of the absorption.

Orientation. The extent of interaction of two auxochromes depends on their character and on their positions in the molecule. If two complementary groups (capable of interacting with each other) are employed as substituents in an alternant system, their interaction will, in the absence of steric effects, be favored if one is on a starred atom and the other on an unstarred atom.

Under optimum conditions, the combined effect of two interacting, complementary auxochromes may exceed the sum of the effects of the two groups acting individually, as exemplified below from the work of Doub and Vandenbelt[19]. (The polarizations indicated are not assumed to be uniquely associated with the particular bands cited.)

Benzene

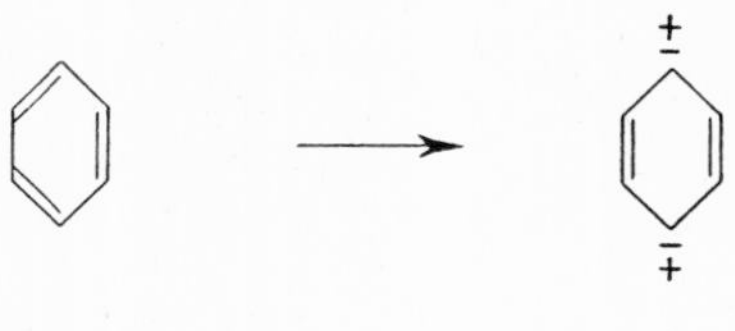

λ max. = 2035 Å
ϵ max. = 7,400

Aniline

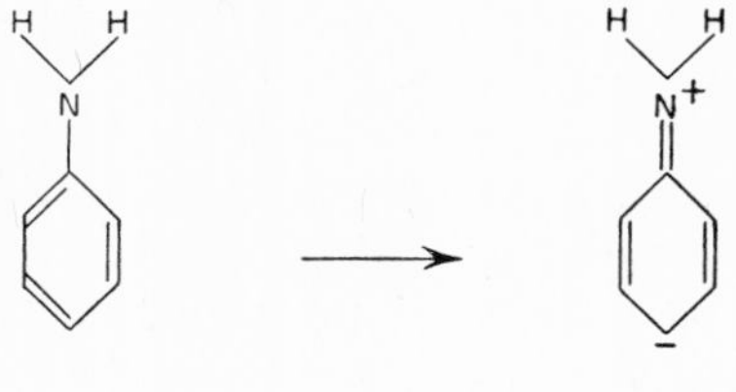

λ max. = 2300 Å
$\Delta\lambda$ = 265 Å
ϵ max. = 8,600

Nitrobenzene

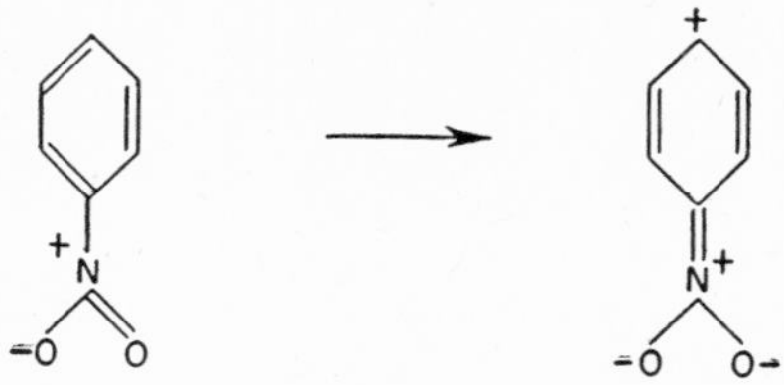

λ max. = 2685 Å
$\Delta\lambda$ = 650 Å
ϵ max. = 7,800

p-Nitroaniline

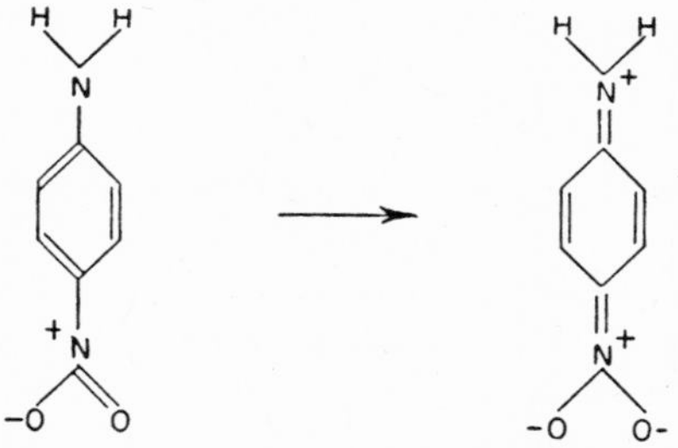

λ max. = 3810 Å
$\Delta\lambda$ = 1775 Å
ϵ max. = 13,500

Displacements resulting from ortho and meta disubstitution with complementary auxochromes were found closely similar and usually somewhat less than those of para disubstitution.

The spectra of isomeric disubstituted benzenes, particularly of the type $X—C_6H_4—NY$ in which $X = CH_3$, CH_3O, COOH, CH_3CO and NO_2 and $NY = NH_2$, $—N(CH_3)_2$, $—NHCOCH_3$, $—NHCOC_6H_5$, and NO_2, show only slight shifts in wavelength with orientation of substituent when $X = CH_3$ but the effect is increased with complementary character of the substitution. Also, the effect of substituent position upon wavelength is less than upon the intensity, the para positions causing the largest effect[25].

The cyanine dyes, characterized by two basic terminal groups (one positively charged) have been extensively studied by Brooker and his co-workers. They have found that for symmetrical cyanines in which the terminal nuclei are of weak or moderate basicity, increasing the basicity tends to deepen the color. However, if the basicity of the terminal groups is very high, the trend is reversed and a further increase in basicity will lighten the color.

If the terminal nuclei of unsymmetrical cyanines differ appreciably in basicity, λ max. will, in general, deviate from the average of the two corresponding symmetrical cyanines toward shorter wavelengths. This deviation increases with increasing difference in basicity, a property expressed in terms of relative stabilization of the positive vs. the uncharged forms of the nuclei using conventional arguments of resonance theory[10].

Lewis[39] developed a method for predicting λ max. for a wide group of dyes represented by the general formula:

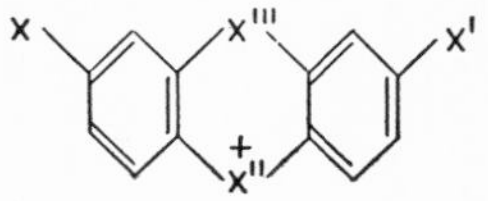

which includes the following six types:

    (1) Diphenylmethane   (X''' absent, X'' = CH)
    (2) Triphenylmethane   (X''' absent, X'' = CR)
    (3) Xanthene   (X''' = O, X'' = CR)
    (4) Acridine   (X''' = NR, X'' = CR)
    (5) Oxazine   (X''' = O, X'' = N)
    (6) Azine   (X''' = NR, X'' = N)

Two assumptions are involved.

(1) λ Max. varies with the fraction of the characteristic charge concentrated at the auxochromes X and X'.

(2) The effects of various groups upon λ max. are additive.

A dye of the Malachite Green type (λ max. = 6200 Å) in which X and X' are dialkylamino groups, X'' = C— 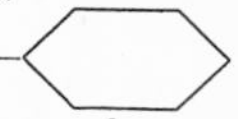 and X''' is absent, was selected as a starting point. The spectra of over seventy individual dyes were studied and a number of additive constants representing the contributions of various groups in different positions were determined. From these constants and λ max. of the standard dye (6200 Å) the values of λ max. of the other dyes were calculated. The agreement was good except in the case of the acridines, a discrepancy explained as possibly due to a difference in orientation of the polarization related to λ max. For the other groups, the average difference between the observed values and those calculated was less than 30 Å suggesting that λ max. of any new compound within these groups (excepting the acridines) could be predicted with the same precision.

With the object of broadening Lewis' first assumption to include all classes of dyes, Knott[37] has offered the following rule:

"The value of λ max. will increase as the contributions by any interauxochromic ionic structures decrease." "Interauxochromic ionic structures" are those in which the charge is on one of the atoms in the conjugated chain between the auxochromes.

This rule eliminates the concept of "characteristic charge" and includes, by implication, the effects of favorable or unfavorable orientation of substituents.

Steric Hindrance

Strain in a dye molecule resulting from steric hindrance may shift the color in either direction but almost always causes a loss in strength. The π orbitals of aromatic systems are normal to the planes of the rings, and interaction of the π electrons (conjugation) of two or more rings is therefore favored by their coplanarity. Any distortion impairs the conjugation and, if large, may effect essentially complete insulation. With increasing distortion, the tendency is for bands related to the complete system to be shifted and weakened, while those corresponding to the separated fragments appear, and become stronger.

The spectra of the arylethylenes, compared by Jones[34], proved similar either to that of *trans*-stilbene

or to that of styrene.

This is assumed to depend on whether or not the configuration allows coplanarity of two benzene rings in trans positions. Triphenylethylene and tetraphenylethylene show spectra similar to that of *trans*-stilbene and Jones explains this by assuming that the additional ring (or rings) are slightly rotated out of plane. *cis*-Stilbene, 1,1-diphenylethylene (unsymmetrical) and α,α'-dimethyl-*trans*-stilbene show styrene-type spectra.

ϵ Max. of N,N-dimethyl-p-nitroaniline is lowered by methyl substitution ortho to the nitro group, particularly in the spectrum of the disubstitution product, and bands appear corresponding to those of the spectrum of unsubstituted N,N-dimethylaniline[57].

The conjugation of biphenyl disazo dyes is at least partially and sometimes completely split by the introduction of two or more methyl groups in the positions ortho to the biphenyl linkage[6, 48, 69].

Brunings and Corwin[13] compared the spectra of pyrromethenes of the following types in the form of their perchlorate salts:

The methyl groups of the second structure make coplanarity impossible with normal bond angles and interatomic distances. The authors assume that the necessary geometric accommodation involves several possible effects, such as:

(1) A slight increase in certain bond angles.
(2) Some penetration of van der Waals' radii.
(3) Some departure from coplanarity.

The observed result is an increased λ max., explained on the basis of a drop in the resonance stabilization of the ground state due to strain. A marked decrease in ε max. was also observed. Brooker and his co-workers[12] have cited additional examples of the "Brunings-Corwin effect" and have also found that in strongly unsymmetrical cyanine dyes, the opposite (hypsochromic) effect (also with reduction in ε max.) occurs. This is believed due to an increase in the energy difference between the extreme ionic structures of the ground state. Inasmuch as interaction between the two extreme ionic structures must pass through intermediate forms of higher energy (excited levels), their contribution to ground state stability is normally small. A further separation of the two ground levels, with excitation principally from the lower level, would tend to increase the energy of excitation and decrease λ max.

When an auxochrome is forced out of coplanarity by ortho substitution, its effect is decreased. λ Max. is shifted to shorter wavelengths and ε max. is decreased[35, 36].

In summary, conjugation is impaired when spatial effects force the atoms of a molecule out of the geometry most favorable to interaction of the mobile electrons. λ Max. may be increased or decreased, as discussed, but ε max. is usually lowered.

Effects of Environment

The colors of most dyes vary to some degree with the type of fiber upon which they are used. An organic molecule can show its complete, unperturbed spectrum only when isolated as in the vapor state at low pressure. The spectrum is altered to some extent by electronic interactions with any other molecules with which it may be closely associated, possibly involving hydrogen bonding, dipole interaction, dielectric effect (particularly with dye ions), steric effect, or crystallization (Z bands, polymorphism). The early work on this subject was reviewed by Sheppard[64], who noted the importance of many factors which have recently been investigated in more detail.

Aggregation. The addition of lyophilic colloids (particularly gelatin) to solutions of cyanine dyes results in absorption spectra closely similar to those of the same dyes in a highly aggregated state, as when adsorbed on solids such as glass. It was therefore concluded that the shifts in λ max. produced by the addition of a lyophilic colloid were related to the tendency of the dyes to polymerize in aqueous solution[67].

Michaelis[46] found that certain ionic dyes such as Methylene Blue, Tolui-dine Blue, Thionine and Pinacyanol chloride are adsorbed on nucleic acid as monomeric cations but are aggregated on agar.

The addition of sodium silicates to such dyes causes a hypsochromic shift of as much as 800 Å, an effect ascribed to interaction of the dye ion with silicate ions and micelles[45].

The aggregation by salt of aqueous solutions of azo dyes such as Benzo-purpurin 4B (measured by the associated spectral change) is inhibited by added pyridine, polyethylene oxide, polyglycols, or even monomeric alco-hols, although the latter require much higher concentrations[43].

Solvent Effects. It is a familiar fact that many dyes show different colors in solvents of different character. This effect is important because of its possible relation to the behavior of dyes when applied to different types of fibers.

The oxyphenazine dye,

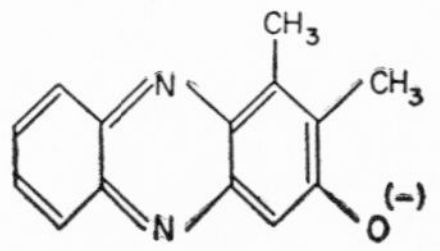

has its first absorption band at 5200 Å and a second, stronger one at 3900 Å. The following results of variation in solvent character were observed[70]:

Solvent	Log ϵ_{5200}	Color observed
Acetic acid	3.5	Dark red
Methanol	2.8	Red
Ethyl acetate	2.2	Light yellow

The λ max. of a strongly polar merocyanine dye shifts to a shorter wave-length with an increase in the polarity of the solvent. The λ max. of a weakly polar merocyanine shifts to longer wavelengths. This effect has been as-cribed to the formation of oriented solvent dipole layers around the polar atoms of the dye molecules. These oriented layers stabilize the contributing dipolar structures which dominate the ground states of the strongly polar dyes, and in contrast they stabilize the excited states of dyes having only slight intrinsic polarity[8].

Two strongly polar merocyanine dyes,

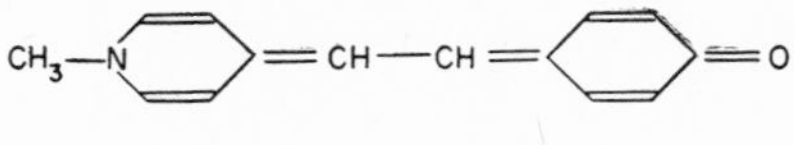

and

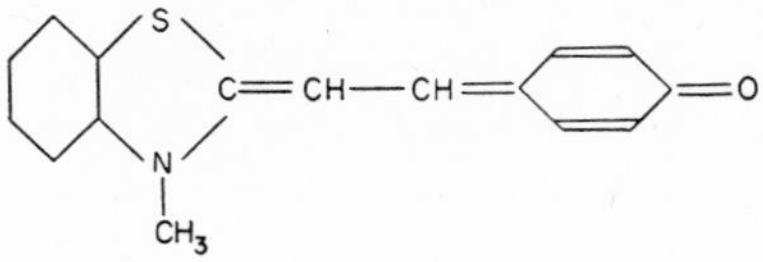

show such a marked hypsochromic shift with increasing polarity of the solvent that they can be used as indicators for the presence of water in pyridine[7].

Adsorption. The effects of adsorption vary considerably with the system studied, and are sometimes appreciable. Colorless triphenylmethyl halides, when adsorbed, sometimes show the color of the corresponding cation[72]. Similarly, some colorless spiropyrans which become intensely colored when their solutions are heated show the same effect when adsorbed from aqueous solution on alumina. This has been ascribed to the formation of a heteropolar structure as shown below for the case of di-β-naphthaspiropyran (3,3'-spirobi[3H-naphtho(2,1-b)pyran]).

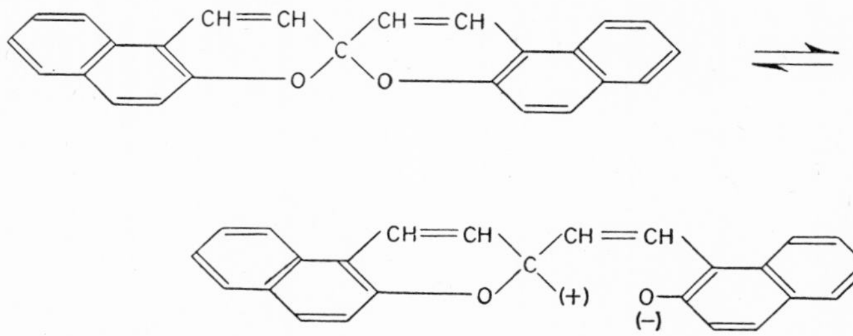

The adsorption of Malachite Green on kaolinite was reported by Vedeneeva[71] to shift λ max. from 5900 to 5500 Å. On drying, it shifts back to 6300 Å. Malachite Green was adsorbed on different varieties of bentonite clays with λ max. varying by as much as 600 Å. In every case, when the dye migrated from one substrate to another (stronger adsorber), the effect was bathochromic. Surprisingly, no such shifts were observed with the homolog, Brilliant Green. She concluded that formation of ionic bonds between clay and dye caused a bathochromic shift, while the effect of intensification of the dipole bond was hypsochromic. More recently, it was observed that *m*-dinitrobenzene is adsorbed on MgO with a blue color. This effect was considered due to the polarizing influence of the MgO dipole upon the nitro group[17].

The Colors of Azo Dyes

The spectral behavior of the azo group differs but little from that of the ethylene group. The nonbonding electrons of the nitrogen atoms do give rise to a weak, long wave band (an n to π transition involving promotion of nonbinding electrons to π states) which is the source of the pale yellow color of azobenzene. However, in the case of dyes whose colors are dominated by the stronger bands (essentially π to π transitions), the visible color differences between azo and ethylene analogs are usually small. The commercial importance of the azo linkage, therefore, lies principally in the wide scope and technical ease of the coupling reaction and its contribution to substantivity rather than in its effect on color.

Application of the principles of conjugation, auxochrome substitution, and insulation to prediction of the colors of azo dyes is facilitated by the fact that they are prepared by coupling two (or more) components. The manner in which the color-giving properties of these units are combined and the general order of the bathochromic effects of a number of diazo and coupling components (applicable to many, but not necessarily all, combinations) has been considered by Reynolds[58]. Such a series is useful in prediction of the color character of new intermediates—or of the color resulting from their use in a dye, by reference to the position of the closest comparable compounds listed. A somewhat similar list (modified to include more commercially important types) follows.

INTERMEDIATES FOR MONOAZO DYES

Diazo Components		Coupling Components
(1) Sulfanilic acid		(1) Acetoacetanilide
(2) Aniline	light shades	(2) Salicylic acid
(3) Anthranilic acid		(3) 3-Methyl-1-phenyl-5-pyrazolone
(4) p-Toluidine		(4) Resorcinol
(5) 6-Amino-2-naphthalenesulfonic acid	intermediate shades	(5) Schaeffer's acid
(6) p-Nitroaniline		(6) 2-Naphthol
(7) Naphthionic acid		(7) R salt
(8) 2-Amino-6-nitro-1-phenol-4-sulfonic acid		(8) N.W. acid
(9) o-Anisidine	deep shades	(9) J acid
(10) 1-Naphthylamine		(10) H acid
(11) H acid		(11) Chicago acid

Reynolds also arranged diamines in order of increasing bathochromic effect (when used as diazo components) as follows:

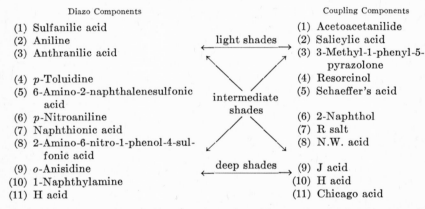

(1) 4,4'-Methylenedianiline

(2) 4,4'-Oxydianiline

(3) 3,3'-Diaminobenzanilide

(4) 3',4-Diaminobenzanilide

(5) 4,4′-Diaminobenzanilide H_2N—⟨ ⟩—CO—NH—⟨ ⟩—NH_2

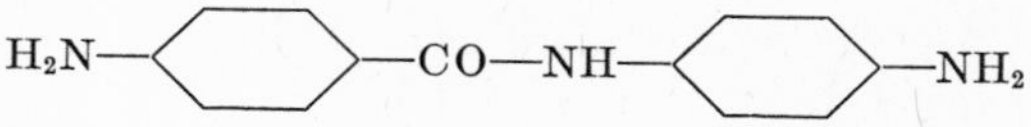

(6) 4,4′-Azoxydianiline H_2N—⟨ ⟩—$\overset{\overset{O}{\uparrow}}{N}$=N—⟨ ⟩—$NH_2$

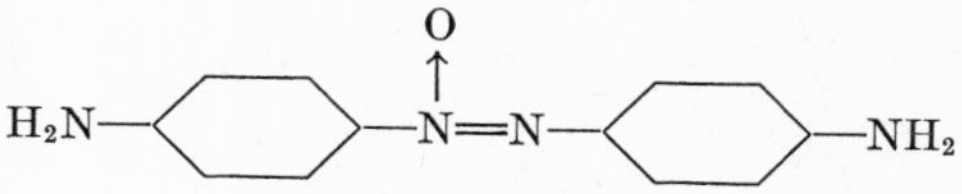

(7) 4,4′-Thiodianiline H_2N—⟨ ⟩—S—⟨ ⟩—NH_2

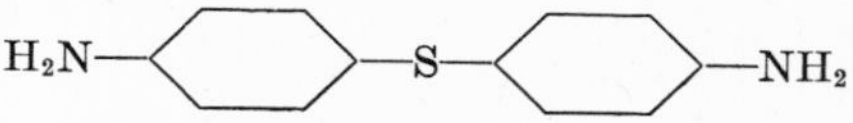

(8) Benzidine H_2N—⟨ ⟩—⟨ ⟩—NH_2

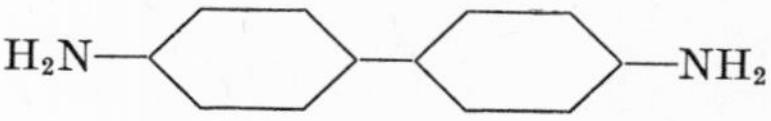

(9) o-Tolidine H_2N—⟨$\overset{CH_3}{|}$ ⟩—⟨$\overset{CH_3}{|}$ ⟩—NH_2

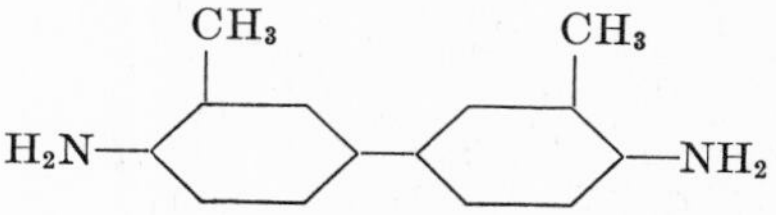

(10) 3,3′-Dimethoxybenzidine H_2N—⟨$\overset{OCH_3}{|}$ ⟩—⟨$\overset{OCH_3}{|}$ ⟩—NH_2

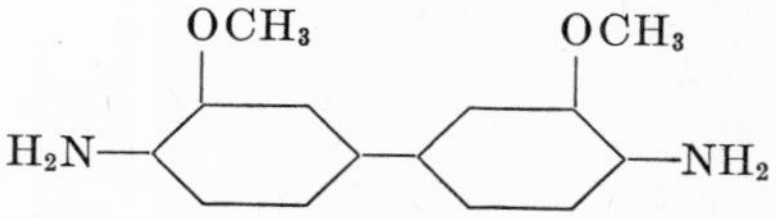

(11) 4,4′-Azodianiline H_2N—⟨ ⟩—N=N—⟨ ⟩—NH_2

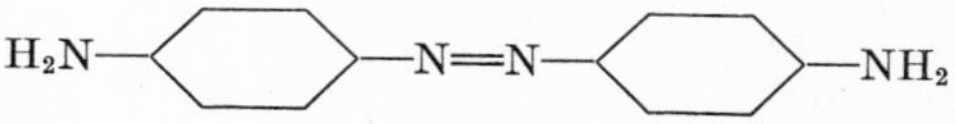

(12) 4,4′-Stilbenediamine H_2N—⟨ ⟩—$\overset{H}{\underset{}{C}}$=$\overset{H}{\underset{}{C}}$—⟨ ⟩—$NH_2$

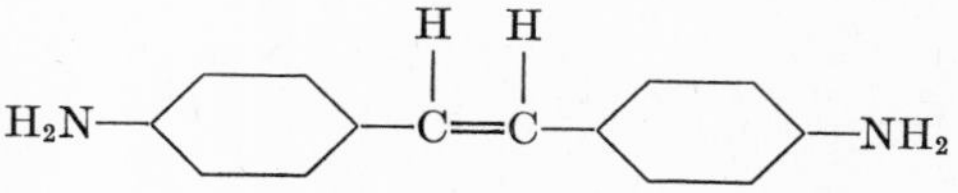

In this list, auxochromes are important but the dominant factor in the gradation of final shade is the degree of insulation between the two benzene rings. In the first example, insulation is almost complete. In the second, there is a very slight conjugation through the oxygen atom. The degree of conjugation increases down the list. Disazo dyes from the bases at the top of the list will be comparable with the monoazo dyes from half the base. Dyes from bases at the bottom of the list may be conjugated throughout (depending on limitations in other parts of the molecule) and show the sum of the bathochromic influences of all three components.

Dyes from 4,4′-diaminodiphenylamine,

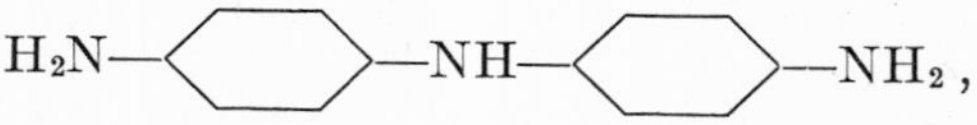

$$H_2N—⟨ ⟩—NH—⟨ ⟩—NH_2,$$

which are usually deeper in shade than those from the above intermediates, may be excited as two separate but highly polarizable units. The central imino groups acts as a powerful auxochrome conjugating with either unit.

The Colors of Quinonoid Dyes

Dyes based on condensed polycyclic hydrocarbons are found in many fields—vat dyes for cotton, anthraquinone colors for wool, and dyes for man-made fibers.

The Role of Quinonoid Structures. A principal factor in determining the colors of these dyes is the electronic interaction of the quinone oxygen atoms with the rest of the molecule. The absorption spectra of many derivatives of anthraquinone are approximated by adding the absorption spectra of the naphthoquinones corresponding to the two halves of the anthraquinone molcule[68].

The accepted mechanism for the polarization of *p*-quinone involves the shift of an electron from the ring to one of the oxygen atoms.

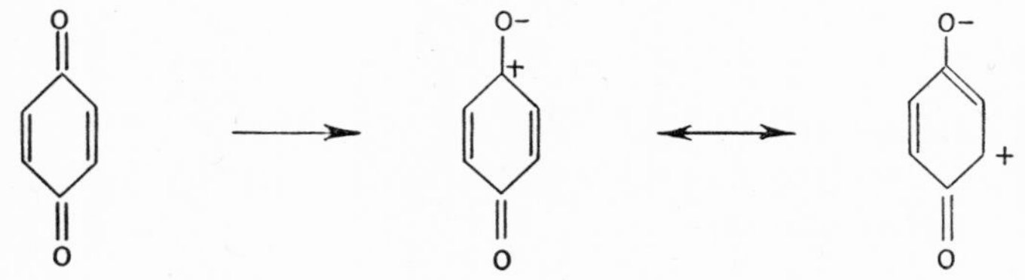

The positive charge is distributed between the 1, 3, (and 5) positions.

In the case of *o*-quinone, the conjugation and resulting resonance between polar structures are somewhat different.

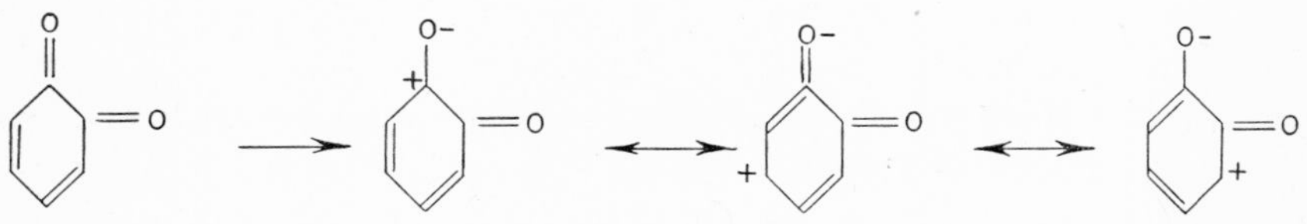

p-Quinone is yellow and *o*-quinone is red. The same is true of the naphthoquinones. This is not surprising since symmetry considerations would suggest more allowed bands for the ortho derivative. The spectra show that this is indeed the case.

The bathochromic influence of the *o*-quinonoid structure (relative to that of the *p*-quinonoid group) results in deeper colors in condensed systems as well as in simpler quinones. An early recognition of this effect is found in the work of Schaarschmidt[59] who ascribed the intense yellow color of 6H-anthr[1,9]isoxazol-6-one to the presence of *o*-quinonoid rings. The isomeric 6H-anthr[9,1]isoxazol-6-one

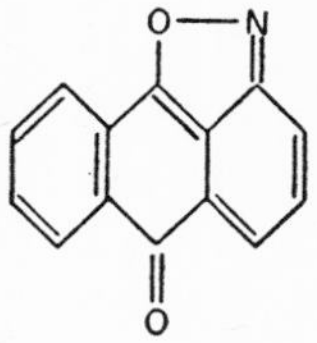

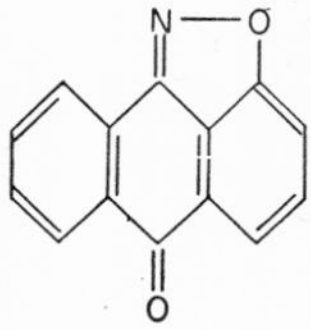

is almost colorless.

Green[26] has reported that the action of thionyl chloride upon quinizarin produces the red compound

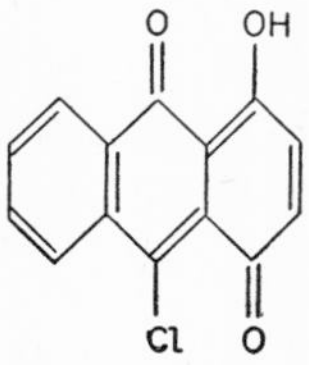

The depth of shade was again credited to the *o*-quinonoid rings. The isomeric *p*-quinonoid compound is yellow.

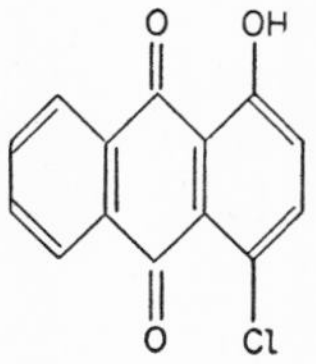

The ionic resonance of the hydroxyanthraquinones has also been considered with emphasis upon the distinction between *o*- and *p*-quinonoid rings[63].

Polynuclear Condensation. The union of condensed rings with simple quinones improves their photochemical stability by blocking the photolabile positions in the same ring with the keto groups. A second, less desirable, result of ring condensation is a tendency toward wide absorption bands (dullness) resulting from the many slightly different conjugated paths.

Application of relations previously discussed to the prediction of colors of polycyclic condensed systems is facilitated by first considering the properties of the individual rings included in the various unpolarized resonance forms that can be written for a given compound as follows:

(a) The influence of an aromatic ring which includes a double bond of a quinone has been shown to be hypsochromic.

(b) A p-quinonoid ring exerts a moderate bathochromic effect.

(c) The o-quinonoid ring is strongly bathochromic.

(d) In addition, information regarding the "diquinonoid" ring is

desirable. No simple compound of this type is known, but this ring is included in one of the resonance structures of phenanthrene which shows a λ max. (3400 Å) slightly below that of anthracene (3700 Å). It is therefore assumed that the effect of the diquinonoid ring is small and may, for the first approximation, be neglected.

An interesting application of this qualitative treatment is afforded by 3,10-perylenequinone, which is yellow, and its isomer, 3,9-perylenequinone, which is a deep violet. Five different structures contribute to the nonpolar resonance of 3,10-perylenequinone while only four can be written for the 3,9 isomer. The individual rings, grouped by ring type for all the nonpolar structures for each isomer, are distributed as follows:

Ring Type	3,10-Perylenequinone (Yellow)	3,9-Perylenequinone (Violet)
Aromatic	10	6
Diquinonoid	5	2
p-Quinonoid	4	2
o-Quinonoid	6	10

The much deeper shade of the 3,9-perylenequinone is thus explained by its predominantly o-quinonoid character, in contrast with the more aromatic character of the 3,10 isomer.

Nonionic Resonance Forms of 3,10-Perylenequinone (Yellow)

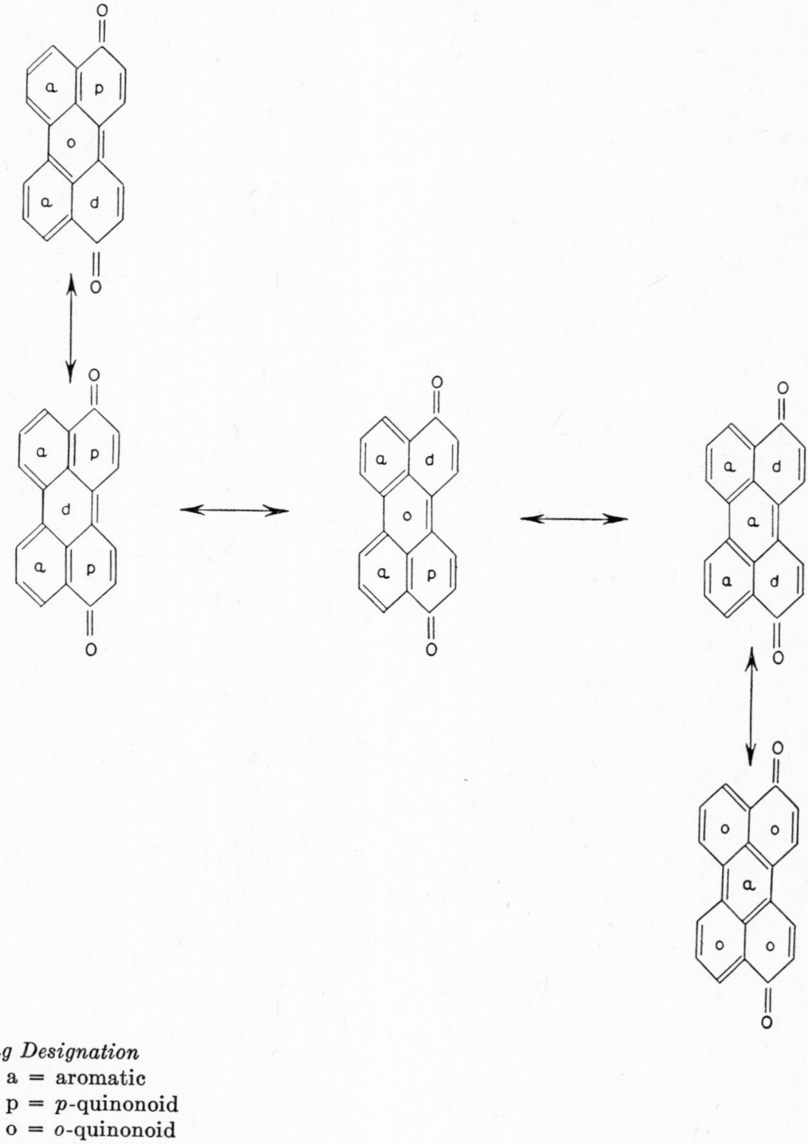

Ring Designation
a = aromatic
p = *p*-quinonoid
o = *o*-quinonoid
d = diquinonoid

Nonionic Resonance Forms of 3,9-Perylenequinone (Dark Violet)

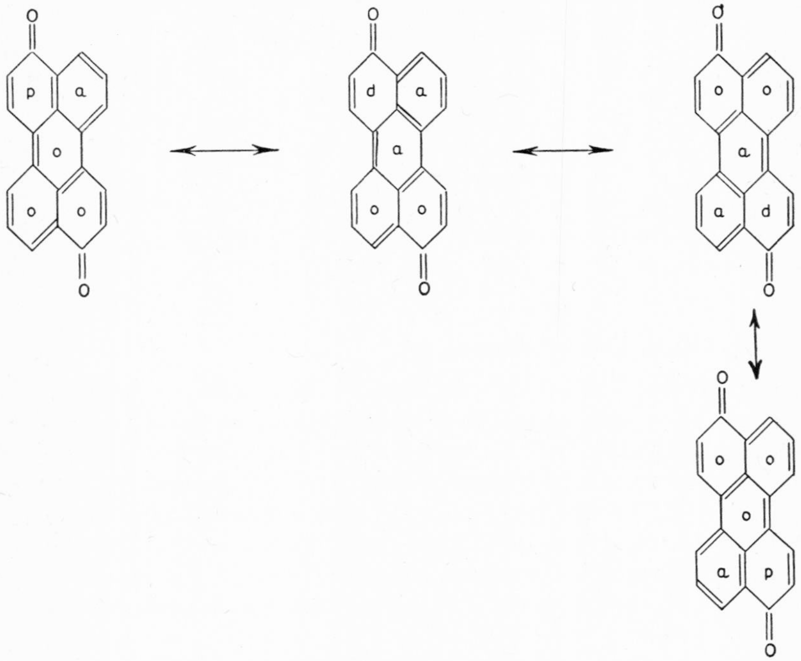

Peri-chelation. The conjugation of auxochromes in condensed quinones is sometimes complicated by interaction of a quinone oxygen atom with an auxochrome in peri position to it. It has been recognized for some time that the carbonyl groups of anthraquinones influence and are influenced by substituents in the α position[26].

A hydrogen bond between the quinone oxygen and hydroxy or amino groups in the α position has been proposed[1]. However, infrared spectra, which support the concept of strong hydrogen bonds in the case of α-hydroxyanthraquinones, fail to show an analogous shift in the N—H valence vibration of α-aminoanthraquinones[24].

These results do not refute the possibility of strong interaction in the polar state. If we can assume that polarization accompanying excitation involves considerable $O-$ and $N+$ character (as suggested by a conventional representation) we must conclude that conditions are ideal for strong hydrogen bonding. This would increase polarizability and offer an explanation for the observed powerful bathochromic influence of an α-amino group on the anthraquinone nucleus.

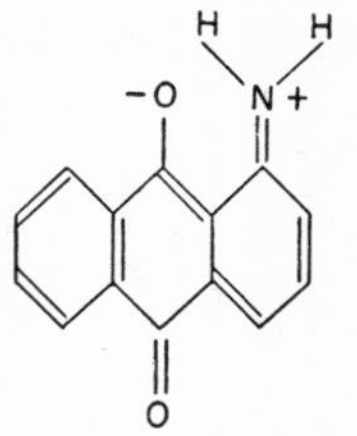

Dyes Containing Metal Atoms

The addition of a metal atom to a dye (usually for improvement of light-fastness) is often accompanied by a marked change in the color. The metal may be linked to the dye by salt formation or by chelation, and the color change is usually greatest when a covalent chelate is formed. In a study of nickel chelates[44], the spectra of paramagnetic complexes (presumably ionic bonded) were found very similar to those of the unmetallized chelating agents. In diamagnetic complexes (covalent bonded), the presence of the nickel atom was usually associated with a broad absorption band of considerable intensity.

An azo dye with a strong donor substituent ortho to the azo linkage is particularly suitable for chelation. Metallization of such a dye usually results in a darker shade, increased dullness, and sometimes a loss of tinctorial strength. The color change is often due more to marked changes in band intensities than to wavelength shifts. This is illustrated in the copper chelation of a series of azo dyes related to 1-phenylazo-2-naphthol[27].

2-Naphthol	Original Dye λ max.	Original Dye ε max.	Copper Chelate λ max.	Copper Chelate ε max.
1-Phenylazo-	5050 Å	1600	4950 Å	10500
1-(o-Tolylazo)-	5050	2000	4950	3650
1-(m-Tolylazo)-	5050	2000	5000	5450
1-(p-Tolylazo)-	5000	1400	5050	10250
1-(o-Chlorophenylazo)-	5000	2200	5050	4400
1-(m-Chlorophenylazo)-	5000	2150	4700	7500
1-(p-Chlorophenylazo)-	5050	2350	5100	9350
1-(o-Methoxyphenylazo)-	5300	1750	5300	4650
1-(m-Methoxyphenylazo)-	5000	2000	5050	6700
1-(p-Methoxyphenylazo)-	5100	2250	5000	9150

	Original Dye		Copper Chelate	
	λ max.	ϵ max.	λ max.	ϵ max.
2-Naphthol				
1-(o-Phenetylazo)-..................	5300	2150	5000	4750
1-(m-Phenetylazo)-..................	5000	2400	5050	6850
1-(p-Phenetylazo)-..................	5150	2300	5100	8650

It is particularly interesting to note that substituents in the phenyl ring limit the increase in ϵ max. with chelation. The effect varies with position, increasing from para to meta to ortho, and is approximately the same for the four groups studied.

Weak bands characteristic of the metal-organic bond have also been reported[22] for the metal chelates of o-hydroxyazo and o-aminoazo dyes. For chelates of nickel, this band was at $\sim$5900 Å, for copper 4900 Å, and for cobalt 4500–5000 Å.

The phthalocyanines constitute an important and, in some respects, a separate group of colored metal chelates. They vary in shade from a reddish blue to a green, with the metal-free compound intermediate in shade. Unlike the metallized azo colors, several of the metal phthalocyanines are very bright, at least equaling the brightness of the parent compound. A study of the spectra[2] has led to a correlation of band shifts (generally to shorter wavelengths) with the atomic number of the central atom, and with the strength of the coordinate bonds linking it to the organic residue.

The observed color differences appear due to variations in intensities of important bands in the long wave region of the visible spectrum and to band shifts in a region of rapidly changing visual acuity.

Summary

(1) Absorption of visible light by a dye molecule involves a displacement of the mobile electrons of the conjugated system.

(2) The effect of extended conjugation is, in general, bathochromic.

(3) A conjugated molecular network may have more than one axis along which it can be polarized by excitation.

(4) Substituent groups which increase the polarizability of a molecule (auxochromes) increase the depth of color. Those groups which partake of the resonance of the conjugated system are most effective.

(5) Deep shades are favored by any condition which tends to favor concentration of charge (with excitation) at the auxochrome.

(6) Two auxochromes so placed that they interact through a conjugated system may produce an effect greater than the sum of their individual effects.

(7) Steric factors which impair the coplanarity of the system may shift λ max. either way but the intensity of absorption is usually lowered.

(8) Interaction of a dye with its environment involving aggregation, solvent effects, or adsorption on a solid may have a strong effect on the color of the dye.

(9) The effects of metallization on the color of a dye are usually most marked when the metal is bound to the dye in a covalent chelate. Azo dyes turn darker and duller with metallization but phthalocyanines are less altered and often retain their brightness.

Literature Cited

1. Allen, Wilson, and Frame, *J. Org. Chem.*, **7**, 169–82 (1942).
2. Anderson, Bradbrook, Cook, and Linstead, *J. Chem. Soc.*, **1938**, 1151–6.
3. Barany, Brande, and Pianka, *ibid.*, **1949**, 1898–1902.
4. Bergmann *et al.*, *Bull. soc. chim. France*, **1951**, 669–81.
5. Braude, *J. Chem. Soc.*, **1949**, 1902–9.
6. Brode and Morris, *J. Org. Chem.*, **13**, 220–7 (1948).
7. Brooker, Keyes, and Heseltine, *J. Am. Chem. Soc.*, **73**, 5350–56 (1951).
8. ——, ——, Van Dyke, Van Lace, Van Zandt, White, Cressman, and Dent, *ibid.*, **73**, 5332–5350 (1951).
9. —— and Simpson, *Ann. Rev. Phys. Chem.*, **2**, 128–129 (1951).
10. ——, White, and Sprague, *J. Am. Chem. Soc.*, **73**, 1087–93 (1951).
12. ——, ——, ——, Dent, and Van Zandt, *Chem. Revs.*, **41**, 325–51 (1947).
13. Brunings and Corwin, *J. Am. Chem. Soc.*, **64**, 593–600 (1942).
14. Coulson, *Proc. Phys. Soc. (London)*, **60**, 257–269 (1948).
15. —— and Rushbrooke, *Proc. Cambridge Phil. Soc.*, **36**, 193–200 (1940).
16. Crawford, *J. Chem. Soc.*, **1953**, 2061–5.
17. Cruse and Mittag, *Z. Elecktrochem.*, **54**, 418–21 (1950).
18. Deasy, *Chem. Revs.*, **36**, 145–55 (1945).
19. Doub and Vandenbelt, *J. Am. Chem. Soc.*, **69**, 2714–23 (1947).
20. —— and ——, *ibid.*, **71**, 2414–20 (1949).
21. Dufraisse, Etienne and Barbieri, *Compt. rend.*, **232**, 1977–80 (1951).
22. Ernsberger and Brode, *J. Org. Chem.*, **6**, 331–40 (1941).
23. Foerster, *Z. Naturforsch.*, **2a**, 149–53 (1947).
24. Flett, *J. Chem. Soc.*, **1948**, 1441–8.
25. Grammaticakis, *Bull. soc. chim. France*, **1951**, 220–6.
26. Green, *J. Chem. Soc.*, **1927**, 2384–85.
27. Haindler and Smith, *J. Am. Chem. Soc.*, **62**, 1669–72 (1941).
28. Hammett, "Physical Organic Chemistry," New York, McGraw-Hill Book Co., Inc., 1940.
29. Heilbron *et al.*, *J. Chem. Soc.*, **1943**, 264–270.
30. ——, *ibid.*, **1944**, 134–147.
31. Herzfeld and Sklar, *Revs. Mod. Phys.*, **14**, 294–302 (1942).
32. Izmail'skii, *Compt. rend. acad. sci. U.R.S.S.*, **29**, 98–102 (1940); *C.A.*, **35**, 3248 (1941).
33. Jelley, *Nature*, **139**, 631–632 (1937).
34. Jones, *J. Am. Chem. Soc.*, **65**, 1818–24 (1943).
35. Kiprianov and Ushenko, *Bull. acad. sci. U.R.S.S. Classe sci. chim.*, **1950**, 492–500, No. 5, Sept.–Oct.; *C.A.*, **45**, 3265 (1951).
36. —— and ——, *J. Gen. Chem. (U.S.S.R.)*, **20** (82), 134–44, 514–17, and 543–6 (1950); *C.A.*, **44**, 5733 and 7837 (1950) and **45**, 3386 (1951).
37. Knott, *J. Chem. Soc.*, **1951**, 1024–8.
38. —— and Williams, *ibid.*, **1951**, 1586–9.
39. Lewis, *J. Am. Chem. Soc.*, **67**, 770–5 (1945).
40. —— and Bigeleison, *ibid.*, **65**, 2102–2106 (1943).

41. —— and Calvin, *Chem. Revs.*, **25**, 273–328 (1939).
42. Maccoll, *Quart. Revs. (London)*, **I**, 16–58 (1947).
43. Martin and Standing, *Shirley Inst. Mem.*, **23**, 127–57 (1949); *J. Textile Inst.*, **40 T**, 671–701 (1949).
44. McKenzie, Mellor, Mills, and Short, *J. Proc. Roy. Soc. N. S. Wales*, **78**, 70–80 (1944).
45. Merrill, Spencer, and Getty, *J. Am. Chem. Soc.*, **70**, 2460–4 (1948).
46. Michaelis, *J. Phys. & Colloid Chem.*, **54**, 1–17 (1950).
47. Moffitt, *Proc. Roy. Soc. (London)*, **A210**, 245–68 (1952).
48. Morris and Brode, *J. Am. Chem. Soc.*, **70**, 2485–8 (1948).
49. Pariser and Parr, *J. Chem. Phys.*, **21**, 466 (1953).
50. —— and ——, *ibid.*, **21**, 767 (1953).
51. Pianka, Barany, and Smith, *Nature*, **167**, 440 (1951).
52. Platt, *J. Chem. Phys.*, **19**, 263–71 (1950).
53. Price, *Chem. Revs.*, **41**, 257–72 (1947).
54. ——, "Mechanisms of Reactions at Carbon-Carbon Double Bonds," New York, Interscience Publishers, Inc., 1946.
55. Pullman, Mayot, and Berthier, *J. Chem. Phys.*, **18**, 257–60 (1950).
56. —— and Pullman, *Discussions Faraday Soc.*, No. 9, pp. 46–52 (1950).
57. Remington, *J. Am. Chem. Soc.*, **67**, 1838–45 (1945).
58. Reynolds, *Am. Dyestuff Reptr.*, **32**, 455–6, 465–7 (1943).
59. Schaarschmidt, *Ber.*, **49**, 1632–8 (1916).
60. Scheibe, *Kolloid-Z.*, **82**, 1–14 (1938).
61. —— and Kandler, *Naturwissenschaften*, **26**, 412–13 (1938).
62. Schoenberg and Asker, *Science*, **113**, 56–7 (1951).
63. Scholl, *Ber.*, **74**, 1129–70 (1941).
64. Sheppard, *Revs. Mod. Phys.*, **14**, 303–40 (1952).
65. Sklar, *J. Chem. Phys.*, **5**, 669–81 (1937).
66. ——, *ibid.*, **10**, 135–44 (1942); *Revs. Mod. Phys.*, **14**, 232 (1942).
67. Soloviev, *J. Gen. Chem. (U.S.S.R.)*, **16**, 1405–15 (1946); *C.A.*, **41**, 4716 (1947).
68. Spruit, *Rec. trav. chim.*, **68**, 325–35 (1949).
69. Standing and Stein, *J. Textile Inst.*, **44**, T244–9 (1953).
70. Suhrmann and Perkampus, *Naturwissenschaften*, **38**, 382 (1951).
71. Vedeneeva, *J. Phys. Chem. (U.S.S.R.)*, **21**, 881–91 (1947); *C.A.*, **42**, 2517 (1948).
72. Weitz *et al.*, *Ber.*, **72**, 2099 (1939); *Z. Elektrochem.*, **46**, 222 (1940).
73. Witt, *Ber.*, **9**, 522–527 (1876).

13. COMMON NAMES OF DYE INTERMEDIATES

C. W. Maynard, Jr.

The vocabulary of dye chemistry is a reflection of the interesting history of the field. The international character of organic chemistry is well illustrated in dye nomenclature, where many common or trivial names of dye intermediates enjoy almost universal use. The more important ones are listed below.

Common names are created for convenience in local and special fields, in contrast to the systematic nomenclature which is so necessary in a large, international, growing science. An inevitable result is the occasional development of several common names for a single intermediate, and of more than one meaning for a single common name. Instances of the latter type have been particularly avoided in compiling the present list. Several of the major published collections of dye intermediate names are cited at the end of this section.

Most commercial aromatic sulfonic acids are isolated and used in the form of alkali metal salts. However, for convenience and uniformity, the acid names will be used here.

1,2,4 acid	1-Amino-2-naphthol-4-sulfonic acid
A acid	3,5-Dihydroxy-2,7-naphthalenedisulfonic acid
m-Aminobenzoyl J acid	6-(m-Aminobenzamido)-1-naphthol-3-sulfonic acid
Amino Epsilon acid	8-Amino-1,6-naphthalenedisulfonic acid
Amino G acid	7-Amino-1,3-naphthalenedisulfonic acid
Amino J acid	6-Amino-1,3-naphthalenedisulfonic acid
Amino R acid	3-Amino-2,7-naphthalenedisulfonic acid
Andresen's acid (Epsilon acid)	1-Naphthol-3,8-disulfonic acid
Anthrimide	An iminodianthraquinone
Armstrong & Wynne's acid	1-Naphthol-3-sulfonic acid
B acid	8-Amino-1-naphthol-4,6-disulfonic acid
Broenner's acid	6-Amino-2-naphthalenesulfonic acid
Bromamine acid	1-Amino-4-bromo-2-anthraquinonesulfonic acid
C acid (Cassella acid)	3-Amino-1,5-naphthalenedisulfonic acid
Chicago acid (SS acid)	8-Amino-1-naphthol-5,7-disulfonic acid

689

Chromotropic acid	4,5-Dihydroxy-2,7-naphthalenedisulfonic acid
1,6 Cleve's acid	5-Amino-2-naphthalenesulfonic acid
1,7 Cleve's acid	8-Amino-2-naphthalenesulfonic acid
Crocein acid	2-Naphthol-8-sulfonic acid
D acid	6-Amino-1-naphthalenesulfonic acid
Dehydrothio-*p*-toluidine	2-(*p*-Aminophenyl)-6-methylbenzothiazole
Dianthrimide	Iminodianthraquinone (The prefix in the common name denotes the total number of anthraquinone nuclei in the molecule)
Dioxy S acid	4,5-Dihydroxy-1-naphthalenesulfonic acid
Diphenyl Epsilon acid	6,8-Dianilino-1-naphthalenesulfonic acid
Epsilon acid (Andresen's acid)	1-Naphthol-3,8-disulfonic acid
Ethyl ketone	4,4'-Bis(diethylamino)benzophenone
F acid	2-Naphthol-7-sulfonic acid
Fast bases	*see* Azoic Dyes, Table 2
Fischer's aldehyde	1,3,3-Trimethyl-$\Delta^{2,\alpha}$-indolineacetaldehyde
Fischer's base	1,3,3-Trimethyl-2-methyleneindoline
Freund's acid	4-Amino-2,7-naphthalenedisulfonic acid
G acid	2-Naphthol-6,8-disulfonic acid
Gamma acid	7-Amino-1-naphthol-3-sulfonic acid
H acid	8-Amino-1-naphthol-3,6-disulfonic acid
Indoxyl	3(2H)-Indolone
J acid	6-Amino-1-naphthol-3-sulfonic acid
J acid urea (Urea J acid)	6,6'-Ureylenebis-1-naphthol-3-sulfonic acid
K acid	8-Amino-1-naphthol-3,5-disulfonic acid
Koch's acid	8-Amino-1,3,6-naphthalenetrisulfonic acid
L acid	1-Naphthol-5-sulfonic acid
Lake Red C base	2-Amino-5-chloro-*p*-toluenesulfonic acid
Laurent's acid	5-Amino-1-naphthalenesulfonic acid
M acid	5-Amino-1-naphthol-3-sulfonic acid
Michler's ketone	4,4'-Bis(dimethylamino)benzophenone
Naphtol AS series	*see* Azoic Dyes, Table 1
Nevile & Winther's acid	1-Naphthol-4-sulfonic acid
m-Nitrobenzoyl J acid	6-(*m*-Nitrobenzamido)-1-naphthol-3-sulfonic acid
Oxy Koch's acid	1-Naphthol-3,6,8-trisulfonic acid
Peri acid	8-Amino-1-naphthalenesulfonic acid
Phenyl Gamma acid	7-Anilino-1-naphthol-3-sulfonic acid
Phenyl J acid	6-Anilino-1-naphthol-3-sulfonic acid
Phenyl Peri acid	8-Anilino-1-naphthalenesulfonic acid
R acid	2-Naphthol-3,6-disulfonic acid
RG acid (Violet acid)	1-Naphthol-3,6-disulfonic acid
Rhoduline acid	6,6'-Iminobis-1-naphthol-3-sulfonic acid
RR acid	7-Amino-1-naphthol-3,6-disulfonic acid
S acid	8-Amino-1-naphthol-5-sulfonic acid
Schaeffer's acid	2-Naphthol-6-sulfonic acid
Silver salt	2-Anthraquinonesulfonic acid, sodium salt
SS acid (Chicago acid)	8-Amino-1-naphthol-5,7-disulfonic acid
Thioindoxyl	3(2H)-Thianaphthenone
Tobias acid	2-Amino-1-naphthalenesulfonic acid
Urea J acid (J acid urea)	6,6'-Ureylenebis-1-naphthol-3-sulfonic acid
Violet acid (RG acid)	1-Naphthol-3,6-disulfonic acid

COMMON NAMES OF DYE INTERMEDIATES

1. Gardner, W., and Cooke, E. I., "Chemical Synonyms and Trade Names," 5th ed., 558 pp., London, Technical Press, 1948.
2. Haynes, W., "Chemical Trade Names and Commercial Synonyms," 279 pp., New York, D. Van Nostrand Company, Inc., 1951.
3. Hodgman, C. D., "Handbook of Chemistry and Physics," 36th ed., pp. 1483–1484, Cleveland, Chemical Rubber Co., 1954.
4. Lange, N. A., "Handbook of Chemistry," 8th ed., pp. 1071–1080, Sandusky, Ohio, Handbook Publishers, 1952.
5. Lange, O., "Die Zwischenprodukte der Teerfarbenfabrikation," 645 pp., Leipzig, O. Spamer, 1920.
6. Rowe, F. M., "Colour Index," 1st ed., pp. 327–336, Bradford, England, Society of Dyers & Colourists, 1924.
7. Schultz, G., ed. by Lehmann, L., "Farbstofftabellen," 7th ed., Vol. 2, pp. 329–408, Leipzig, Akad. Verlag, 1932.
8. Shreve, R. N., "Dyes Classified by Intermediates," 631 pp., New York, Chemical Catalog Co. (Reinhold Publishing Corp.), 1922.
9. U. S. Tariff Commission, "Synthetic Organic Chemicals, U. S. Production and Sales, 1953," Rept. 194, 2nd Ser., pp. 169–180, Washington, Govt. Printing Office, 1954.

14. CRITICAL BIBLIOGRAPHY

C. W. Maynard, Jr.

BIOS and FIAT Reports

An unusual source of dye literature in recent years has been the pre-World War II German dye industry, which was investigated in 1945–1947 by many Allied teams. Most of the resulting information on dyes and dye intermediates was published by the British government in a series of BIOS (British Intelligence Objectives Subcommittee) reports and by the United States government in its FIAT (Field Information Agency, Technical) reports.

A useful organization of these and of many other technical report categories has been achieved by the U. S. Department of Commerce, whose former Office of the Publication Board—now its Office of Technical Services—has assigned a "PB number" to each technical report which it has made available. The information offered by the Office of Technical Services has been listed, abstracted, and partially indexed in its periodical *Bibliography of Scientific and Industrial Reports*, Vol. 1 (1946) to Vol. 11 (1949), continued as the *Bibliography of Technical Reports*, Vol. 12 (1949), and again continued as *U. S. Government Research Reports*, Vol. 22 (1954). Any PB report so listed may be ordered by PB number in microfilm or photostat form from the Library of Congress, Photoduplication Service, Publication Board Project, Washington 25, D.C. Reports available in mimeographed or printed form (e.g., FIAT reports) may be ordered directly from the U. S. Department of Commerce, Office of Technical Services, Washington 25, D.C. BIOS reports available in mimeographed or printed form may be ordered from British Information Services, 30 Rockefeller Plaza, New York 20, N. Y.

The Special Libraries Association has published a "Numerical Index to the Bibliography of Scientific and Industrial Reports, Vols. 1–10, 1946–1948," Ann Arbor, Edwards Bros., 1949. This index correlates BIOS and FIAT (and other) report numbers with PB numbers and with entries in the Bibliography. The Association has also published a companion volume which provides a similar service for PB reports described in Vols. 1 to 17 (January, 1946 to June, 1952) of the Bibliography: "Correlation Index, Document Series and PB Reports," New York, Special Libraries Association, 1953.

Technical Information Service, a private source in Washington, D.C., is compiling a series of twelve subject indexes to the Publication Board reports. Part 6 is to be devoted to dyes, and is expected to cover PB reports listed in Vols. 1 to 17 of the OTS Bibliography.

The most important BIOS and FIAT reports on dyes and dye intermediates are listed below. The corresponding Monograph chapters are cited to permit reference to the selected bibliographies which follow.

BIOS	PB	Chapter
misc. 20	31004	Miscellaneous Dyes
959	63858	Miscellaneous Dyes
960	65657	Miscellaneous Dyes; Anthraquinone Dyes; Phthalocyanine Dyes
961	60905	Azo Dyes
983	79226	Sulfur Dyes; Indigoid Dyes
986	77764	Benzene Intermediates; Naphthalene Intermediates; Azoic Dyes
987	75860	Anthraquinone Dyes and Intermediates
988	60885	Azoic Dyes
1149	80376	Azoic Dyes
1152	81027	Naphthalene Intermediates
1153	85687	Benzene Intermediates
1154	80401	Benzene Intermediates
1155	79309	Sulfur Dyes
1156	80346	Indigoid Dyes
1157	69124	Benzene Intermediates; Naphthalene Intermediates; Azo Dyes; Miscellaneous Dyes
1433	81029	Miscellaneous Dyes
1482	86136	Miscellaneous Dyes
1484	86139	Anthraquinone Dyes and Intermediates
1493	81611	Anthraquinone Dyes and Intermediates
1548	85593	Azo Dyes
1661	91693	Organic Pigments
FIAT		
764	60946	General References
1016	67569	Benzene Intermediates; Naphthalene Intermediates; Anthraquinone Dyes and Intermediates
1313	85172	General References

The references of major importance in the field of this Monograph are collected below in chapter sequence. Important compilations which are broad in coverage and pertinent to several or all chapter topics are designated General References, and are not repeated in the chapter groupings.

Benzene Intermediates

1. Groggins, P. H., ed., "Unit Processes in Organic Synthesis," 4th ed., 937 pp., New York, McGraw-Hill Book Co., 1952.
   Highly regarded reviews of nitration, amination, sulfonation, halogenation, etc.

2. I. G. Farbenindustrie, BIOS 986 (PB 77764). "I. G. Farbenindustrie A. G., Manufacture of Intermediates for Dyestuffs at Griesheim, Hoechst, Ludwigshafen, Mainkur, and Offenbach," Part I, 292 pp.; Part II, 162 pp., 1946.
Extensive compilation of I. G. Farbenindustrie processes for dye intermediates.
3. ——, BIOS 1153 (PB 85687). "I. G. Farbenindustrie, The Manufacture of Miscellaneous Dyestuff Intermediates (Excluding Naphthalene Derivatives)," 376 pp., 1946.
Supplements BIOS 986 and 1157. I. G. Farbenindustrie processes for 252 intermediates, mainly benzene derivatives for small-scale manufacture as specialties.
4. ——, BIOS 1154 (PB 80401). "Some Miscellaneous Organic Intermediates and Products; Manufacture (mainly) by I. G. Farbenindustrie," 47 pp., 1947.
I. G. Farbenindustrie processes for 48 intermediates—indirectly for dyes—at Ludwigshafen, Leverkusen, Uerdingen, and Hoechst. Mainly benzene and aliphatic series.
5. ——, BIOS 1157 (PB 69124). "German Dyestuffs and Intermediates Industry; Dyestuffs and Intermediates at Leverkusen and Uerdingen Factories," 72 pp., ca. 1946.
Equipment and general process condition summaries concerning intermediates for azo and triphenylmethane dyes. Does not include specific processes.
6. ——, FIAT 1016 (PB 67569). "Miscellaneous Dyestuff Intermediates at I. G. Farbenindustrie A. G., Leverkusen," 51 pp., 1947.
I. G. Farbenindustrie processes for 21 benzene, naphthalene, and anthraquinone intermediates.
7. Murphy, W. J., ed., Ind. Eng. Chem., Sept. (1948–49–50–51–52–53), Unit Processes.
Authoritative annual reviews of commercial sulfonation, nitration, halogenation, etc.
8. Suter, C. M., and Weston, A. W., in Adams, R., et al., eds., "Organic Reactions," New York, John Wiley & Sons, Inc., 3, 141–197 (1946).
Complete review of aromatic sulfonation.

Naphthalene Intermediates

1. Groggins, P. H., ed., "Unit Processes in Organic Synthesis," 4th ed., 937 pp., New York, McGraw-Hill Book Co., 1952.
Highly regarded reviews of nitration, amination, sulfonation, halogenation, etc.
2. Huisgen, R., Ann., 559, 101–152 (1948).
Discussion of naphthalene reaction mechanisms.
3. I. G. Farbenindustrie, BIOS 986 (PB 77764). "I. G. Farbenindustrie A. G., Manufacture of Intermediates for Dyestuffs at Griesheim, Hoechst, Ludwigshafen, Mainkur, and Offenbach," Part I, 292 pp.; Part II, 162 pp., 1946.
Extensive compilation of I. G. Farbenindustrie processes for dye intermediates.
4. ——, BIOS 1152 (PB 81027). "I. G. Farbenindustrie, The Manufacture of Miscellaneous Naphthalene Intermediates," 134 pp., 1946.
Supplements BIOS 986 and 1157. I. G. Farbenindustrie processes for 116 naphthalene intermediates, mainly for small-scale manufacture as specialties.
5. ——, BIOS 1157 (PB 69124). "German Dyestuffs and Intermediates Industry; Dyestuffs and Intermediates at Leverkusen and Uerdingen Factories," 72 pp., ca. 1946.
Equipment and general process condition summaries concerning intermediates for azo and triphenylmethane dyes. Does not include specific processes.

6. ——, FIAT 1016 (PB 67569). "Miscellaneous Dyestuff Intermediates at I. G. Farbenindustrie A. G., Leverkusen," 51 pp., 1947.

I. G. Farbenindustrie processes for 21 benzene, naphthalene, and anthraquinone intermediates.

7. Murphy, W. J., ed., *Ind. Eng. Chem.*, Sept. (1948–49–50–51–52–53). Unit Processes.

Authoritative annual reviews of commercial sulfonation, nitration, halogenation, etc.

Azo Dyes

1. Fierz-David, H. E., "Kuenstliche Organische Farbstoffe" in "Technologie der Textilfasern," ed. by Herzog, R. O., Berlin, Julius Springer, **3**, 87–205 (1926).

Synthesis, structure, chemical classification, examples and properties of azo dyes. Authoritative on older work. Ergaenzungsband (1935) pp. 31–50. Newer data, with accent on "new" azoic dyes.

2. I. G. Farbenindustrie, BIOS 961 (PB 60905). "German Dyestuffs and Dyestuffs Intermediates; Azo and Lake Dyestuffs," 171 pp., 1946.

I. G. Farbenindustrie Ludwigshafen, Hoechst, and Mainkur processes for azo dyes and lakes. I. G. Farbenindustrie azo dye research trends.

3. ——, BIOS 1157 (PB 69124). "German Dyestuffs and Intermediates Industry; Dyestuffs and Intermediates at Leverkusen and Uerdingen Factories," 72 pp., *ca.* 1946.

Equipment and general process condition summaries concerning intermediates for azo and triphenylmethane dyes. Does not include processes for specific dyes.

4. ——, BIOS 1548 (PB 85593). "The Manufacture of Azo and Lake Dyestuffs at Hoechst, Ludwigshafen, and Leverkusen," 223 pp., 1947.

Supplements BIOS 961 and 1157. I. G. Farbenindustrie processes.

5. Saunders, K. H., "The Aromatic Diazo-Compounds and their Technical Applications," 2nd ed., 442 pp., London, Edward Arnold & Co., 1949.

The authority on its subject. A thorough monograph which includes diazotization and coupling reactions and types of diazo compounds used in azoic dyes.

6. Thorpe, J. F. and Linstead, R. P., "The Synthetic Dyestuffs," 7th ed. of "Cain and Thorpe," 472 pp., London, Charles Griffin & Co., 1933.

General introductory text on chemistry of dyes and intermediates, with representative laboratory directions. Valuable as background material. Now outdated by 1949 Fierz-David and Blangey and by 1947- Kirk and Othmer (see General References).

Azoic Dyes

1. Adams, D. A. W., *J. Soc. Dyers Colourists*, **67,** 223–235 (1951).

Well-organized, authoritative summary of the development of the azoic dye field. Discusses recent research trends. 105 References.

2. Diserens, L., "The Chemical Technology of Dyeing and Printing," transl. from 2nd German ed. by Wengraf, P., and Baumann, H. P., Vol. 1, pp. 212–409, New York, Reinhold Publishing Corp., 1948. See also 3rd German ed., "Die neuesten Fortschritte in der Anwendung der Farbstoffe," Basel, Birkhaeuser, 1951.

Thorough discussion of azoic colors from the standpoints of their use and of the patent literature.

3. I. G. Farbenindustrie, BIOS 986 (PB 77764). "I. G. Farbenindustrie A. G., Manufacture of Intermediates for Dyestuffs at Griesheim, Hoechst, Ludwigshafen, Mainkur, and Offenbach," Part I, 292 pp.; Part II, 162 pp., 1946.
Extensive compilation of I. G. Farbenindustrie processes for dye intermediates, including many Fast Bases.

4. ——, BIOS 988 (PB 60885). "German Dyestuffs and Dyestuffs Intermediates; Azoic Products, including Napthols, Fast Salts, Nitrosamines, and Rapid Fast Salts, Rapidogens," 45 pp., 1946.
Complete I. G. Farbenindustrie processes for Rapidogens, including manufacture of triazenes.

5. ——, BIOS 1149 (PB 80376). "I. G. Farbenindustrie; The Manufacture of certain Fast Bases and their Intermediates, and of Intermediates for Napthol-AS Products, etc.," 153 pp., 1947.
Complete I. G. Farbenindustrie processes for azoic bases and for Naphtols, excluding final amidation step in Naphtol manufacture. Latter is in film PB 74202.

Miscellaneous Dyes

1. Georgievics, G. v., and Grandmougin, E., "A Textbook of Dye Chemistry," transl. from 4th German ed. by Mason, F. A., 560 pp., London, Scott, Greenwood, 1920.
Well-documented text. Outdated in most sections by several more recent references.

2. I. G. Farbenindustrie, BIOS misc. 20 (PB 31004). "The Development of New Dyes and Color Application Processes in Germany and Italy during World War II," 51 pp. + 87 processes, 1945. Critical summary, including dye processes.

3. ——, BIOS 959 (PB 63858). "I. G. Farbenindustrie, Manufacture of Triphenylmethane Dyestuffs and Intermediates at Ludwigshafen and Hoechst," 102 pp., 1946. I. G. Farbenindustrie processes.

4. ——, BIOS 960 (PB 65657). "German Dyestuffs and Dyestuffs Intermediates, Anthrasols, Heliogens, Sirius Light Blue Dyestuffs," 90 pp., ca. 1946.
I. G. Farbenindustrie processes and development data on dioxazine dyes (Sirius Light Blue Dyes), pp. 70–89.

5. ——, BIOS 1157 (PB 69124). "German Dyestuffs and Intermediates Industry; Dyestuffs and Intermediates at Leverkusen and Uerdingen Factories," 72 pp., ca. 1946.
Equipment and general process condition summaries concerning intermediates for azo and triphenylmethane dyes. Does not include processes for specific dyes.

6. ——, BIOS 1433 (PB 81029). "I. G. Farbenindustrie A.G., The Manufacture of Triphenylmethane Dyestuffs at Hoechst, Ludwigshafen, and Leverkusen," 145 pp., 1946. I. G. Farbenindustrie processes.

7. ——, BIOS 1482 (PB 86136). "The Manufacture of Miscellaneous Dyestuffs (Indigoid, Dioxazine, Auramine, etc.)," 37 pp., 1946.
16 I. G. Farbenindustrie processes, supplementing BIOS 960.

8. Thorpe, J. F., and Linstead, R. P., "The Synthetic Dyestuffs," 7th ed. of "Cain and Thorpe," 472 pp., London, Charles Griffin & Co., 1933.
General introductory text on chemistry of dyes and intermediates, with representative laboratory directions. Valuable as background material. Now outdated by 1949 Fierz-David and Blangey and by 1947- Kirk and Othmer (see General References).

Sulfur Dyes

1. I. G. Farbenindustrie, BIOS 983 (PB 79226). "I. G. Farbenindustrie A.G., Manufacture of Thioindigoid and Sulfur Dyestuffs at Hoechst and Mainkur," 149 pp., *ca.* 1946.
I. G. Farbenindustrie processes.
2. ——, BIOS 1155 (PB 79309). "I. G. Farbenindustrie A.G., The Manufacture of Sulfur Dyestuffs and their Intermediates at Mainkur," 58 pp., *ca.* 1946.
I. G. Farbenindustrie processes.
3. Lange, O., "Die Schwefelfarbstoffe," 2nd ed., 371 pp., Leipzig, O. Spamer, 1925.
History, constitutions, preparative methods, dyeing methods, and patent summary.
4. Zerweck, W., Ritter, H., and Schubert, M., *Angew. Chem.*, **60-A,** 141–147 (1948).
Modern discussion of synthetic routes, structures, and relations between structure and properties.

Anthraquinone Intermediates

1. Houben, J., "Das Anthracen und die Anthrachinone," 890 pp., Leipzig, Thieme, 1929. (Photo-lithoprint by Edwards Bros., Ann Arbor, 1944).
A complete monograph based on published information.
2. I. G. Farbenindustrie, BIOS 987 (PB 75860). "German Dyestuffs and Intermediates Industry; Vat Dyestuffs and Intermediates," 193 pp., *ca.* 1946.
I. G. Farbenindustrie processes.
3. ——, BIOS 1484 (PB 86139). "I. G. Farbenindustrie A. G., Anthraquinone Dyestuffs and Intermediates, including Acid Wool Dyestuffs, Celliton Dyestuffs, and Helio Fast Pigments," 74 pp., 1947.
I. G. Farbenindustrie processes from Hoechst, Ludwigshafen, and Leverkusen.
4. ——, BIOS 1493 (PB 81611). "I. G. Farbenindustrie A.G., Manufacture of Vat Dyestuffs at Hoechst, Mainkur, Leverkusen, and Ludwigshafen," 77 pp., 1947.
I. G. Farbenindustrie processes.
5. ——, FIAT 1016 (PB 67569). "Miscellaneous Dyestuff Intermediates at I. G. Farbenindustrie A.G., Leverkusen," 51 pp., 1947.
I. G. Farbenindustrie processes for 21 benzene, naphthalene, and anthraquinone intermediates.

Anthraquinone Dyes

1. American Association of Textile Chemists & Colorists, "The Application of Vat Dyes," 448 pp., Lowell, Mass., AATCC, 1953. *Its* Monograph No. 2.
Thorough, modern discussion of the theory and practice of applying anthraquinone and indigoid vat dyes to textile fibers. Well-indexed.
2. Houben, J., "Das Anthracen und die Anthrachinone," 890 pp., Leipzig, Thieme, 1929. (Photo-lithoprint by Edwards Bros., Ann Arbor, 1944).
A complete monograph based on published information.
3. I. G. Farbenindustrie, BIOS 960 (PB 65657). "German Dyestuffs and Dyestuffs Intermediates, Anthrasols, Heliogens, Sirius Light Blue Dyestuffs," 90 pp., *ca.* 1946.
I. G. Farbenindustrie (Hoechst) processes and development data on leuco sulfuric acid esters of vat dyes (Anthrasols), pp. 1–31.

4. ——, BIOS 987 (PB 75860). "German Dyestuffs and Intermediates Industry; Vat Dyestuffs and Intermediates," 193 pp., *ca.* 1946.
   I. G. Farbenindustrie processes.
5. ——, BIOS 1484 (PB 86139). "I. G. Farbenindustrie A.G., Anthraquinone Dyestuffs and Intermediates, including Acid Wood Dyestuffs, Celliton Dyestuffs, and Helio Fast Pigments," 74 pp., 1947.
   I. G. Farbenindustrie processes from Hoechst, Ludwigshafen, and Leverkusen.
6. ——, BIOS 1493 (PB 81611). "I. G. Farbenindustrie A.G., Manufacture of Vat Dyestuffs at Hoechst, Mainkur, Leverkusen, and Ludwigshafen," 77 pp., 1947.
   I. G. Farbenindustrie processes.
7. ——, PB 19933. "Eigenschaften und Anwendung der Indanthrenfarbstoffe," 239 pp. + tables.
   Extensive detailed manual on dyeing methods and dye properties of anthraquinone vat colors.
8. Kunz, M. A., *Angew. Chem.*, **52**, 269–82 (1939).
   Comprehensive chemical treatise with many structural formulas and colorfastness diagrams.
9. ——, *Melliand Textilber.* (English ed.), **33**, 60–77 (1952).
   Well-illustrated, authoritative, historical review.
10. Weiss, F., "Die Kuepenfarbstoffe," 371 pp., Vienna, Julius Springer, 1953.
    Treatise on textile dyeing and printing, including trade names and structural formulas of anthraquinone and indigoid vat dyes. Not indexed. Resembles AATCC Monograph No. 2 (above) and Diserens (Azoic Dyes).

Indigoid Dyes

1. American Association of Textile Chemists & Colorists, "The Application of Vat Dyes," 448 pp., Lowell, Mass., AATCC, 1953. *Its* Monograph No. 2.
   Thorough, modern discussion of the theory and practice of applying anthraquinone and indigoid vat dyes to textile fibers. Well-indexed.
2. I. G. Farbenindustrie, BIOS 983 (PB 79226). "I. G. Farbenindustrie A.G., Manufacture of Thioindigoid and Sulfur Dyestuffs at Hoechst and Mainkur," 149 pp., *ca.* 1946.
   I. G. Farbenindustrie processes.
3. ——, BIOS 1156 (PB 80346). "I. G. Farbenindustrie A.G., Manufacture of Thioindigoid Dyestuffs and their Intermediates at Hoechst and Mainkur," 28 pp., *ca.* 1946.
   I. G. Farbenindustrie processes.
4. Martinet, J., "Matières Colorantes; L'Indigo et ses Dérivés," 700 pp., Paris, Baillière et fils, 1926.
   Thorough treatise on chemistry of indigo and its derivatives, including laboratory and industrial preparative details, and natural occurrence.
5. ——, "Matières Colorantes; Les Indigoïds," 484 pp., Paris, Baillière et fils, 1934.
   Chemistry and preparation of thioindigos and other dyes related to indigo.
6. ——, in Grignard, V., ed., "Traité de Chimie Organique," Paris, Massons et Cie., **19**, 465–685 (1942).
   Condensation and revision of references 4 and 5, covering literature to Jan. 1, 1940.
7. Thorpe, J. F., and Ingold, C. K., "Synthetic Colouring Matters; Vat Colours," pp. 1–169, London, Longmans, Green & Co., 1923.
   General historical treatment and summary of chemistry of indigoid dyes.

8. Truttwin, H., "Enzyklopaedie der Kuepenfarbstoffe," pp. 1–202, Berlin, Julius Springer, 1920.

Bibliography, synthesis, structures, properties in substance and on the fiber, of indigoid dyes.

9. Weiss, F., "Die Kuepenfarbstoffe," 371 pp., Vienna, Julius Springer, 1953.

Treatise on textile dyeing and printing, including trade names and structural formulas of indigoid and anthraquinone vat dyes. Not indexed. Resembles AATCC Monograph No. 2 (above) and Diserens (Azoic Dyes).

Phthalocyanine Dyes and Pigments

1. Allen, E. R., in Mattiello, J. J., ed., "Protective and Decorative Coatings," Vol. 2, pp. 249–262, New York, John Wiley & Sons, Inc., 1942.

Simplified discussion of history, structure, manufacturing methods, and commercial uses.

2. Brouillard, R. E., *Am. Ink Maker*, **32**, 32–35, 65 (No. 1, Jan.), 30–33, 65–67 (No. 2, Feb.) (1954).

Thorough, up-to-date review of the history, chemistry, and uses of phthalocyanine pigments and dyes. 78 references.

3. Dahlen, M. A., *Ind. Eng. Chem.*, **31**, 839–847 (1939).

Review of chemical and industrial history.

4. Haddock, N. H., *J. Soc. Dyers Colourists*, **61**, 68–73 (1945).

Well-informed, compact summary of chemistry and uses.

5. I. G. Farbenindustrie, BIOS 960 (PB 65657). "German Dyestuffs and Dyestuffs Intermediates, Anthrasols, Heliogens, Sirius Light Blue Dyestuffs," 90 pp., *ca.* 1946.

I. G. Farbenindustrie processes and development data on phthalocyanines (Heliogens), pp. 32–69.

6. Linstead, R. P., *Ber.*, **72-A**, 93–103 (1939).

Review of synthesis, structures, and properties.

Organic Pigments

1. Curtis, C. A., "Artificial Organic Pigments," transl. from the German by Fyleman, E., 291 pp., London, Isaac Pitman & Sons, 1930.

A descriptive text, marked mainly by patent data and well-organized information on pigment uses.

2. I. G. Farbenindustrie, BIOS 1661 (PB 91693). "German Organic Pigments and Lake Dyestuffs," 187 pp., *ca.* 1946.

I. G. Farbenindustrie processes for azo (mainly), anthraquinone, and basic organic pigments.

3. Mattiello, J. J., ed., "Protective and Decorative Coatings," Vol. 2, 658 pp., New York, John Wiley & Sons, Inc., 1942.

Includes simplified discussions of the history and chemistry of pigments used in the protective and decorative coatings industry. Organized in part by shade groups and in part by chemical classes.

4. Pratt, L. S., "The Chemistry and Physics of Organic Pigments," 359 pp., New York, John Wiley & Sons, Inc., 1947.

A thorough, up-to-date discussion of the chemistry, physical properties, testing, uses, and identification of organic pigments.

Color and Constitution

1. Bowen, E. J., *Quart. Revs.* (*London*), **4**, 236–250 (1950).
   Discussion of light absorption and photochemistry.
2. Brooker, L. G. S., in Burk, R. E., and Grummitt, O., eds., "Advances in Nuclear Chemistry and Theoretical Organic Chemistry," Frontiers in Chemistry Vol. 3, pp. 63–136, New York, Interscience Publishers, Inc., 1945.
   General review.
3. Doub, L., and Vandenbelt, J. M., *J. Am. Chem. Soc.*, **69**, 2714–2723 (1947).
   Ultraviolet absorption spectra of mono- and *p*-disubstituted benzene derivatives.
4. Ferguson, L. N., *Chem. Revs.*, **43**, 385–446 (1948).
   General review.
5. Lewis, G. N., and Calvin, M., *Chem. Revs.*, **25**, 273–328 (1939).
   General review.
6. Maccoll, A., *Quart. Revs.* (*London*), **1**, 16–58 (1947).
   General review.
7. Sheppard, S. E., *Revs. Modern Phys.*, **14**, 303–340 (1942).
   General review.

General References

1. American Association of Textile Chemists & Colorists, "Technical Manual and Year Book," Vol. 30, New York, Howes, 1954.
   An annual compilation of names, application classes, and manufacturers of American-made dyes, organized alphabetically, by CI No., and by Pr. No. American-made dyes which have no Colour Index numbers but which do have recognized foreign or domestic prototypes are assigned "Prototype numbers" which associate them in properties and in structure with the cited prototype.
2. Fierz-David, H. E., and Blangey, L., "Fundamental Processes of Dye Chemistry," transl. by Vittum, P. W., from 5th Austrian ed. of "Grundlegende Operationen der Farbenchemie," 479 pp., New York, Interscience Publishers, Inc., 1949. See also 8th Austrian ed., Vienna, Julius Springer, 1952, which is a partial revision of the 5th Austrian ed., incorporating I. G. Farbenindustrie data from "Allied Reports."
   Essentially a laboratory manual for preparation of dyes and dye intermediates. Excellent for beginning students of dye chemistry. Noteworthy for 21 tables of synthetic routes to dye intermediates.
3. Foerst, W., ed., "Ullmanns Encyklopaedie der technischen Chemie," 3rd ed., Vol. 3–   , Munich-Berlin, Urban & Schwarzenberg, 1953- .
   Similar in concept and form to the Kirk and Othmer Encyclopedia, below.
4. Friedlaender, P., ed., "Fortschritte der Teerfarbenfabrikation. . . ," Vols. 1–25, Berlin, Julius Springer, 1888–1942; Vols. 14–25 ed. by Fierz-David, H. E.
   Valuable historically and as a source of older (1877–1938) German patents on synthetic organic dyes, intermediates, drugs, and perfumes. Each volume contains a discussion of the important advances in the major, chemical dye classes during the period covered, followed by the texts of pertinent, accepted, German patents and the claims of related German patent applications. Corresponding foreign patents are cited by number. Each volume includes indexes to German patent numbers, German patent application numbers, patentees, and subjects. Volumes 4 to 9 have cumulative German patent number indexes. Most volumes (1 to 4, 13, and 14 are exceptions) include indexes to foreign patent numbers.

5. Grimmel, H. W., in Gilman, H., ed., "Organic Chemistry," New York, John Wiley & Sons, Inc., **3,** 243–391 (1953).

A brief, well-organized, accurate survey of organic dye chemistry.

6. I. G. Farbenindustrie, FIAT 764 (PB 60946). "Dyestuffs Manufacturing Processes of I. G. Farbenindustrie A.G.," 375 pp., 1947. (in 4 Vols.).

Two indexes, one alphabetical and one by structural and application groups, to I. G. Farbenindustrie processes for individual dyes. The processes are recorded on the following 12 microfilm reels available from the Office of Technical Services, U. S. Dept. of Commerce, Washington 25, D.C.:

FIAT Reel No.	PB No.
17-G	73561
18-G	70135
21-G	73726
80-CC	74024
81-CC	74025
82-CC	74026
83-CC	74027
92-AA	70276
185-C	25625
186-C	25626
187-C	25627
188-C	25628

7. I. G. Farbenindustrie, FIAT 1313 (PB 85172). "German Dyestuffs and Dyestuff Intermediates, including Manufacturing Processes, Plant Design, and Research Data"; Vol. I. "Dyestuff Intermediate Processes and Analytical Procedures," 529 pp.; Vol. II. "Dyestuff Processes and Engineering Data," 405 pp. + drawings; Vol. III. "Dyestuff Research," 593 pp., 1948.

This is the broadest and the most recent of the numerous Allied reports on the pre-World War II German dye industry. It was written by the last American team to visit Germany for this purpose, and is generally supplementary to earlier, more specific references (see BIOS and FIAT reports).

8. Kirk, R. E., and Othmer, D. F., eds., "Encyclopedia of Chemical Technology," New York, Interscience Publishers, Inc., 1947- .

Accurate, general discussions of synthetic methods, uses, dyeing mechanisms, and the relation of structure to properties of dyes. The articles in the Encyclopedia are alphabetized by chemical dye classes.

9. Rowe, F. M., ed., "Colour Index," 1st ed., 371 pp., Bradford, England, Soc. Dyers Colourists, 1924. 1st Suppl., 55 pp., 1928.

Well-organized but old compilation of data on commercial dyes. Each dye structure has a "CI number." Includes names, structures, syntheses, references, properties, and uses. Organized under Synthetic Organic Dyes, Natural Organic Dyes, Inorganic Dyes, and Indexes. 2nd ed. (1955) in preparation.

10. Schultz, G., ed. by Lehmann, L., "Farbstofftabellen," 7th ed., Vol. 1, 764 pp., Leipzig, Akad. Verlag, 1931. Vol. 2, 445 pp., 1932. 1st Suppl., 182 pp., 1934. 2nd Suppl., 352 pp., 1939.

Similar in concept to the "Colour Index." Includes data on names, structures, syntheses, references, properties, and uses of commercial dyes.

11. Venkataraman, K., "The Chemistry of Synthetic Dyes," Vol. I, 704 pp., New York, Academic Press, 1952.

A scholarly review of the history and chemistry of azo and azoic colors, drawing fully on BIOS, CIOS, and FIAT reports on German chemical industry. Includes discussions of dyeing, color measurement, and relation of color to constitution. Vol. II, 738 pp., 1952. Similar treatment of anthraquinone, indigoid, sulfur, phthalocyanine, and miscellaneous dyes. Includes discussions of lightfastness, fiber affinity and dye identification.

DYE INDEX

A

Acid Alizarin Blue GR, 429
Acid Alizarin Green B, 429
Acid Alizarin Red B, 156
Acid Anthracene Brown PG, 157
Acid Anthracene Brown RH, 158
Acid Anthracene Red 3B, 152
Acid Anthracene Red G, 152
Acid Green B, 652
Acid Leather Brown EGB, 257
Acid Violet 6B, 281
Acridine Orange NO, 233
Acridine Yellow, 232
Acronol Brilliant Blue, 639, 641
Alcian Blue 8GS, 608
Algol Bordeaux 3B, 464
Algol Brilliant Green BK, 544, 574
Algol Orange, 475
Algol Orange RF, 541
Algol Pink R, 637
Algol Red B, 463
Algol Red FF, 438
Algol Red R, 438
Algol Yellow 3G, 437
Algol Yellow GC, 473
Algol Yellow WG, 436
Algosol Blue O4B, 559
Algosol Orange HR, 567
Alizarine Astrol B, 405
Alizarine Black P, 430
Alizarine Black R, 157
Alizarine Blue, 430
Alizarine Blue Black B, 406, 408, 410
Alizarine Bordeaux BA, 428
Alizarine Brilliant Green B, 402
Alizarine Brilliant Pure Blue R, 415
Alizarine Chrome Blue FFG, 415
Alizarine Cyanine AC, 428
Alizarine Cyanine Green G, 400
Alizarine Cyanine Green 5G, 401
Alizarine Direct Blue A, 405
Alizarine Direct Blue A2G, 415
Alizarine Direct Blue ARA, 415

Alizarine Fast Gray BBLW, 410
Alizarine Geranol, 403
Alizarine Green S, 430
Alizarine Indigo G, 542, 574
Alizarine Indigo 3R, 573
Alizarine Indigo 5R, 574
Alizarine Indigo 7R, 574
Alizarine Irisol R, 406
Alizarine Light Brown BL, 411, 412
Alizarine Light Gray RLL, 410, 411
Alizarine Orange G, 428
Alizarine Pure Blue FFB, 415
Alizarine Red S, 429
Alizarine Rubinol R, 409
Alizarine Saphirol, 656
Alizarine Saphirol A, 415
Alizarine Saphirol B, 397
Alizarine Sky Blue B, 404
Alizarine Supra Blue SE, 402
Alizarine Viridine FF, 400
Alizarine Yellow GG, 155
Alizarine Yellow R, 155
Alkali Blue, 630, 653
Amaranth, 145, 179
Amido Naphthol Brown 3G, 256
Amido Naphthol Red 6B, 151
Amido Naphthol Red G, 151
Aniline Black, 243, 244
Aniline Yellow, 113
Anthosine B, 647
Anthosine 3B, 647, 648
Anthosine BN, 647
Anthosine Violet BB, 648
Anthracene Blue SWX, 428
Anthracene Blue WR, 429
Anthracene Brown, 428
Anthracene Chromate Brown EB, 160
Anthracene Chrome Violet B, 157, 162
Anthracene Yellow C, 155
Anthralan Violet 4BF, 403
Anthrasol AZG, 542
Anthrasol O, 538
Anthrasol O4B, 538

703

Anthrasol O4G, 542
Anthrasol OR, 542
Anthrasol Blue IBC, 537, 538
Anthrasol Blue IGC, 542
Anthrasol Blue Black IRD, 538, 571
Anthrasol Brilliant Orange IRK, 542
Anthrasol Brilliant Pink I3B, 543
Anthrasol Brilliant Violet I4R, 536, 543
Anthrasol Brown IBR, 539
Anthrasol Brown IRRD, 539, 568
Anthrasol Brown IVD, 568
Anthrasol Golden Yellow IGK, 540
Anthrasol Golden Yellow IRK, 540
Anthrasol Gray IBL, 543, 571
Anthrasol Gray IN, 544
Anthrasol Green AB, 544, 574
Anthrasol Green IB, 540
Anthrasol Green I3G, 443, 541
Anthrasol Green IGG, 541
Anthrasol Olive Green IB, 544
Anthrasol Orange HR, 541
Anthrasol Pink IR Extra, 541
Anthrasol Printing Black IB, 537, 539
Anthrasol Printing Blue IB, 545, 571
Anthrasol Printing Blue IGG, 545
Anthrasol Printing Purple IR, 545
Anthrasol Printing Violet IBBF, 545
Anthrasol Printing Violet IRR, 546, 570
Anthrasol Red IFBB, 541
Anthrasol Red Violet IRH, 541
Anthrasol Scarlet HB, 546
Anthrasol Scarlet IB, 546
Anthracol Violet IBBF, 570
Anthrasol Yellow HCG, 432, 546
Anthrasol Yellow V, 540
Artisil Direct Violet RRP, 423
Astraphloxine FF, 249, 640, 641
Astrazone Pink FG, 250
Astrazone Yellow 3G, 250
Auramine, 245, 639, 641
Auramine G, 247
Aurine, 285
Azo Acid Carmine, 150
Azo Bordeaux B, 646
Azocarmine G, 237
Azo Flavin FF, 145
Azo Rubine, 146

B

Benzazurin, 116
Benzidine Yellow, 635

Benzo Brown D3G, 117
Benzo Fast Black L, 126
Benzo Fast Blue 8GL, 135
Benzo Fast Copper Blue F3GL, 123
Benzo Fast Copper Rubine RL, 122
Benzo Fast Copper Violet F3BL, 123
Benzo Fast Copper Yellow RLN, 122
Benzo Fast Orange S, 129
Benzo Fast Pink 2BL, 124
Benzo Fast Red 8BL, 131
Benzo Fast Scarlet 4BS, 129
Benzo Fast Scarlet 8BS, 130
Benzo Fast Yellow 4GL, 119
Benzo Fast Yellow 5GL, 119
Benzo Light Blue 4GL, 133
Benzopurpurin 4B, 116, 676
Benzo Sky Blue 5B, 125
Biebrich Scarlet, 147
Bismarck Brown, 114, 143
Blue I, 238
Blue Black B, 147
Bordeaux Extra, 115
Brilliant Benzo Fast Blue BL, 131
Brilliant Benzo Fast Violet 2RL, 131
Brilliant Benzo Fast Yellow GL, 134
Brilliant Green, 276, 639, 641, 677
Brilliant Indigo 4B, 559
Brilliant Indigo BR, 559
Brilliant Indigo 4G, 542, 560
Brilliant Indocyanine 6B, 283
Brilliant Milling Green B, 277
Brilliant Phosphine G, 233
Brilliant Sulfur Green, 326
Brilliant Yellow, 118
Bronze Red, 655

C

Cachou de Laval, 302, 313
Calco Fast Spirit Black R, 177
Caledon Jade Green, 637
Carmoisine, 146, 160
Carmoisine L, 146
Cellitazol B, 172
Cellitazol ST, 172
Celliton Blue Extra, 423
Celliton Blue 3G, 423
Celliton Discharge Blue 5G, 170
Celliton Discharge Pink BRF, 169
Celliton Fast Blue B, 423
Celliton Fast Blue BF, 423
Celliton Fast Blue FFB, 423

Celliton Fast Blue FFG, 423
Celliton Fast Blue FFR, 423
Celliton Fast Blue FW, 423
Celliton Fast Blue Green B, 423
Celliton Fast Brown 3R, 171
Celliton Fast Green 5B, 423
Celliton Fast Pink B, 423
Celliton Fast Pink FF3B, 423
Celliton Fast Pink RF, 423
Celliton Fast Red 2G, 170
Celliton Fast Rubine B, 170
Celliton Fast Violet B, 423
Celliton Fast Violet 6B, 423
Celliton Fast Violet R, 423
Celliton Fast Yellow G, 168
Celliton Fast Yellow 7G, 249
Celliton Orange, 423
Celliton Orange GR, 169, 173
Celliton Orange R, 423
Celliton Scarlet B, 169
Celliton Violet R, 170
Celliton Yellow 5G, 168
Chicago Blue 6B, 125
Chloramine Yellow, 270
Chlorantine Fast Green BLL, 137
Chlorantine Fast Green 5GLL, 137
Chlorantine Fast Red 6BLL, 137
Chlorantine Light Brown BRL, 139
Chlorantine Light Green BL, 137
Chromogen Red B, 299
Chromotrope FB, 160
Chromotrope 2R, 156
Chromoxane Brilliant Red BL, 298
Chromoxane Brilliant Violet 5R, 284
Chrysamine, 116
Chrysoidine, 114, 143
Chrysophenine, 118
Ciba Heliotrope B, 562
Ciba Lake Red B, 560
Ciba Red, 573
Ciba Red B, 563
Ciba Violet A, 569
Ciba Yellow G, 561
Ciba Yellow 3G, 561
Cibanone Orange R, 549
Cibanone Orange 2R, 523
Cibanone Orange 3R, 523
Cibanone Orange 6R, 523
Cibanone Orange RN, 523
Cibanone Red B, 523
Cibanone Red 4B, 523

Cibanone Red G, 523
Cibanone Red 3G, 523
Cibanone Yellow 2GR, 523
Cibanone Yellow R, 549
Citronine, 145
Cochineal Red, 145
Coerulein, 301
Columbia Black FF, 126
Congo Brown R, 118
Congo Corinth, 116
Congo Orange, 116
Congo Red, 115, 117
Congo Violet, 115
Crystal Violet, 229, 277, 280, 669
Cyananthrene, 481
Cyananthrol R, 404
Cyanine, 251

D

Delphine Blue B, 260
Developed Black BH, 125
Diamine Black B, 123, 124
Diamine Blue 2B, 125
Diamine Brown M, 124
Diamine Fast Blue FFB, 132
Diamine Fast Orange EG, 120
Diamine Fast Red F, 124, 155
Diamine Green B, 126
Diamine Violet N, 123, 124
Diamond Black F, 156
Diamond Black PV, 160
Diamond Phosphine GF, 233
Diamond Red 3B, 156
Diazo Brilliant Green 3G, 132
Diazo Brilliant Scarlet 2BL, 130
Diazo Brown, 138
Diazo Fast Bordeaux 2BL, 131
Diazo Green, 139
Diazo Indigo Blue 2RL, 133
Diazo Light Red 7BL, 131
Diazo Orange, 138
Diazo Violet, 138
Diazo Yellow, 138
Diazo Yellow 2GL, 134
Diphenyl Fast Blue Green BL, 136
Direct Black RX, 129
Direct Sulfur Blue, 310, 321
Dispersol Fast Red R, 170
Doebner's Violet, 274
Duranol Blue CB, 423
Duranol Blue G, 423

Duranol Brilliant Blue B, 423
Duranol Brilliant Yellow 6G, 423
Duranol Red B, 423
Duranol Red X3B, 423
Durazol Fast Paper Blue 10GS, 609

E

Eclipse Yellow, 318
Emeraldine, 244
Eosine, 654
Eosine G, 300
Erie Direct Black EW, 128
Erie Direct Green ET, 129
Erika 2GN, 271
Eriochrome Azurole B, 285
Eriochrome Black A, 159
Eriochrome Black T, 159
Eriochrome Blue Black B, 159
Eriochrome Cyanine R, 285
Eriochrome Flavine A, 155
Eriochrome Red B, 159
Eriochrome Verdon A, 160
Erioglaucine, 275, 276
Erioglaucine A, 652
Erythrosine Bluish, 300
Ethyl Violet, 280

F

Fast Light Yellow G, 3G, 148, 647
Fast Red B, 146
Fast Red AV, 145
Fast Red VR, 146
Fast Sulfur Green, 326
Fast Yellow GLF, 169
Fire Red, 633
Flavinduline O, 236
Fluorescein, 291, 299
Fuchsine, 272, 278

G

Gallein, 301
Gallocyanine, 260
Gambine Y, 644
Guinea Fast Red BL, 150
Guinea Green B, 277

H

Hansa Yellow G, 635
Hansa Yellow 3G, 635
Hansa Yellow 5G, 635
Hansa Yellow 10G, 635

Hansa Yellow GR, 635
Hansa Yellow R, 636
Helindon Green, 557
Helindon Orange R, 566
Helindon Pink R, 564
Helindon Scarlet GG, 573
Helindon Yellow CG, 546
Helio Bordeaux BL, 651
Helio Fast Rubine 3BL, 657
Helio Fast Rubine 4BL, 429, 657
Helio Fast Rubine 6BL, 657
Helio Fast Rubine FF Extra, 657
Helio Fast Violet AL, 656
Helio Fast Yellow 6GL, 439, 637
Helio Red RMT, 649
Heliogen Blue SBL, 609
Heliogen Blue SBP, 609
Heliogen Green G, 599
Hydron Blue, 310
Hydron Blue G, 328
Hydron Blue R, 327
Hydron Olive GX, 313
Hydron Yellow G, 549

I

Immedial Black, 303
Immedial Black V Extra, 321
Immedial Black Brown GN, 313
Immedial Bordeaux, 328
Immedial Brown BR Extra, 314
Immedial Dark Brown A, 321
Immedial Green Yellow G, 318
Immedial Olive FF Extra, 316
Immedial Orange C, 316
Immedial Orange FR Base, 318
Immedial Orange FRR, 318
Immedial Orange Brown 3RL, 318
Immedial Pure Blue, 303, 324
Immedial Red Brown CL3R, 330
Immedial Yellow D, 317
Immedial Yellow G Extra, 316
Immedial Yellow GG, 329
Immedial Yellow 3GT, 316
Immedial Yellow RT, 318
Immedial Yellow 4RT, 318
Immedial Yellow 6RT Extra, 318
Immedial Yellow Brown G 26 Base, 318
Immedial Yellow Brown O Base, 318
Immedial Yellow Olive 3GR, 318
Indanthrene Black BA, 456
Indanthrene Black BB, 456

Indanthrene Black BBN, 456
Indanthrene Black BGA, 456
Indanthrene Black Brown NR, 485
Indanthrene Blue BC, 521, 538
Indanthrene Blue CLB, 474
Indanthrene Blue CLG, 474
Indanthrene Blue CLN, 506
Indanthrene Blue 3G, 522
Indanthrene Blue 5G, 522
Indanthrene Blue GC, 521, 542
Indanthrene Blue GCD, 521
Indanthrene Blue 3GF, 521
Indanthrene Blue RK, 522
Indanthrene Blue RS, 521, 637
Indanthrene Blue WBC, 522
Indanthrene Blue Green 3B, 456
Indanthrene Blue Green FFB, 478
Indanthrene Bordeaux R, 464
Indanthrene Bordeaux RR, 475, 476
Indanthrene Brilliant Blue 3G, 522
Indanthrene Brilliant Blue 4G, 548, 593, 621
Indanthrene Brilliant Blue R, 521
Indanthrene Brilliant Green B, 456
Indanthrene Brilliant Green 3B, 456
Indanthrene Brilliant Green FFB, 456, 540
Indanthrene Brilliant Green 2G, 456, 541
Indanthrene Brilliant Orange GK, 445
Indanthrene Brilliant Orange GR, 475, 476
Indanthrene Brilliant Orange RK, 445, 542
Indanthrene Brilliant Pink 3B, 543
Indanthrene Brilliant Pink BL, 503
Indanthrene Brilliant Pink BBL, 503
Indanthrene Brilliant Pink R, 541
Indanthrene Brilliant Scarlet RK, 512
Indanthrene Brilliant Violet 3B, 455, 457, 546
Indanthrene Brilliant Violet 2R, 455, 457
Indanthrene Brilliant Violet 4R, 455, 457, 543
Indanthrene Brilliant Violet RK, 439
Indanthrene Brilliant Violet 4RN, 455
Indanthrene Brown BR, 466, 539
Indanthrene Brown 3GT, 506
Indanthrene Brown NG, 458
Indanthrene Brown NGR, 506
Indanthrene Brown R, 466

Indanthrene Brown RRD, 539, 567, 568, 572
Indanthrene Corinth B, 464
Indanthrene Dark Blue BO, 637
Indanthrene Dark Blue BOA, 453, 456
Indanthrene Direct Black RB, 452
Indanthrene Golden Orange G, 452
Indanthrene Golden Orange 3G, 466
Indanthrene Golden Orange GN, 528
Indanthrene Golden Orange RRT, 452
Indanthrene Golden Yellow GK, 449, 540
Indanthrene Golden Yellow RK, 449, 540
Indanthrene Gray 3B, 456
Indanthrene Gray BG, 446
Indanthrene Gray 3G, 456
Indanthrene Gray M, 470, 485
Indanthrene Green 2B, 522
Indanthrene Green 4G, 494, 505, 510
Indanthrene Khaki 2G, 467
Indanthrene Khaki GR, 505
Indanthrene Navy Blue BF, 457
Indanthrene Navy Blue G, 457
Indanthrene Navy Blue R, 470, 485
Indanthrene Navy Blue RB, 457
Indanthrene Olive G, 485
Indanthrene Olive 3G, 466
Indanthrene Olive GB, 485
Indanthrene Olive R, 464, 466
Indanthrene Olive T, 485, 544
Indanthrene Olive Brown GB, 485
Indanthrene Olive Green B, 483, 484, 544
Indanthrene Olive Green GG, 484
Indanthrene Orange 2R, 503
Indanthrene Orange 4R, 452
Indanthrene Printing Black B, 539, 574
Indanthrene Printing Black BGL, 538, 571
Indanthrene Printing Black BL, 571
Indanthrene Printing Black BL Base, 543
Indanthrene Printing Black TL Suprafix Paste, 571
Indanthrene Printing Blue B, 545, 571
Indanthrene Printing Blue FG, 496, 504
Indanthrene Printing Blue GG, 545
Indanthrene Printing Brown B, 476
Indanthrene Printing Brown R, 572
Indanthrene Printing Brown TM, 449
Indanthrene Printing Purple R, 545
Indanthrene Printing Violet BBF, 545, 570
Indanthrene Printing Violet RR, 570

Indanthrene Red FBB, 472, 541
Indanthrene Red G, 463
Indanthrene Red GG, 482
Indanthrene Red 5GK, 438
Indanthrene Red R, 463
Indanthrene Red RK, 504
Indanthrene Red Brown GR, 466
Indanthrene Red Brown RR, 458
Indanthrene Red Brown 5R, 476
Indanthrene Red Brown 5RF, 466
Indanthrene Red Violet RH, 541, 564, 637
Indanthrene Red Violet RRK, 504
Indanthrene Red Violet RRN, 565, 570
Indanthrene Rubine B, 474
Indanthrene Rubine R, 468
Indanthrene Scarlet B, 546
Indanthrene Scarlet GK, 446
Indanthrene Scarlet R, 482
Indanthrene Scarlet RM, 445, 446
Indanthrene Turquoise Blue GK, 504
Indanthrene Turquoise Blue 3GK, 505
Indanthrene Violet BN, 504
Indanthrene Violet R, 455, 457
Indanthrene Yellow FFRK, 466
Indanthrene Yellow G, 487
Indanthrene Yellow 6GD, 433
Indanthrene Yellow GGF, 441
Indanthrene Yellow GK, 437
Indanthrene Yellow 4GK, 509
Indanthrene Yellow 5GK, 437
Indanthrene Yellow 7GK, 510
Indanthrene Yellow GN, 528
Indanthrene Yellow GOW, 449
Indanthrene Yellow R, 487
Indanthrene Yellow 3R, 466
Indian Yellow, 645
Indigo, 538, 553, 637
Indigo 4B, 538
Indigo MLB/5B, 546
Indigo R, 542
Indigo Carmine, 560
Indigosol O, 559
Indigosol O6B, 546
Indigosol Blue IBC, 520
Indigosol Brilliant Violet I4B, 546
Indigotine I, 560
Indirubin, 561
Indocarbon CL, 320
Indocyanine B, 240
Indophenol Blue, 264

Induline 3B, 241
Induline 6B, 241
Ionamine Yellow MA, 168

J

Jade Green, 456
Janson Indigo, 560

K

Kryogene Brown S, 313
Kvalnes and Woodward Yellow, 646

L

Lake Bordeaux B, 650
Lake Red C, 649
Lake Red D, 649
Lake Scarlet 2R, 646
Lauth's Violet, 266
Light Blue Superfine, Spirit Soluble, 653
Lithol Fast Yellow GG, 632
Lithol Red 2G, 650
Lithol Red R, 629, 649
Lithol Rubine B, 650

M

Malachite Green, 274, 275, 639, 641, 642, 669, 670, 673, 677
Martius Yellow, 255
Mauve, 235
Meldola's Blue, 259
Metachrome Brown B, 157
Metanil Yellow, 144
Methyl Eosine, 178
Methyl Violet B, 277, 278, 639, 641, 642
Methylene Blue, 266, 267, 676
Methylene Green B, 268
Mikado Orange, 119
Mikado Yellow, 119
Monosol Fast Blue 2GS, 609

N

Naphthol Black B, 147
Naphthol Blue Black B, 150
Naphthol Green B, 258, 644
Naphthol Yellow S, 255, 645
Naphtol AS, 182
Neolan Black WA, 163
Neolan Blue 2G, 163
Neolan Bordeaux R, 163
Neolan Orange R, 163
Neolan Yellow BE, 164
Neolan Yellow GR, 163

Nerol 2B, 152
Neutral Red, 237
New Blue R, 260
New Methylene Blue N, 268
Nigrosine, 177, 242
Nile Blue A, 260

O

Oil Orange, 175
Oil Red, 175
Oil Yellow, 175
Orange I, 144, 179
Orange II, 144, 646
Orange III, 144
Orange IV, 144, 145
Orange G, 145, 146
Orange R, 144
Oxydiaminogen OB, 128

P

Palatine Chrome Black 6B, 158
Palatine Fast Green BL, 164
Palatine Fast Pink BN, 164
Palatine Fast Violet 5RN, 164
Paranitroaniline Brown, 646
Paranitroaniline Red, 632, 645
Para Red, 181, 632
Pararosaniline, 273, 278
Patent Blue A, 284
Patent Blue V, 284
Perlon Fast Yellow RS, 248
Pernigraniline, 244
Permanent Bordeaux F3R, 635
Permanent Bordeaux FRR, 635
Permanent Orange G, 636
Permanent Red 2B, 650
Permanent Red FGR Extra, 635
Permanent Red FR Extra, 635
Permanent Red F4R Extra, 635
Permanent Red F4RH, 635
Permanent Red FRL Extra, 635
Permanent Red FRLL, 635
Permanent Red FRR, 635
Permanent Rubine FBH, 635
Permanent Yellow NCG, 635
Permatone Orange, 633
Phloxine Toner, 655
Phosphine, 231
Phosphine E, 234
Pigment Chlorine GG, 632
Pigment Chrome Yellow, 636

Pigment Green B, 643
Pigment Rubine G, 651
Pigment Scarlet 3B, 651
Pinacyanol, 252
Pinacyanol Chloride, 676
Plutoform Black, 127
Polar Brilliant Red 3B, 153
Polar Red G, 153
Polar Yellow 5G, 153
Ponceau 2G, 145
Ponceau R, 146
Primuline, 121, 270
Pyrazol Orange, 134
Pyrogene Green, 314
Pyronine G, 292

Q

Quinoline Yellow, 261, 262
Quinoline Yellow KT, 262
Quinoline Yellow O, 654
Quinophthalone, 261, 262

R

Rapidogen Developer N, 218
Red Toner, 633
Reflex Blue, 653
Resorcin Brown, 147
Resorcin Dark Brown, 148
Rheonine AL, 234
Rhodamine B, 291, 296, 639, 641
Rhodamine 5G, 295
Rhodamine 6G, 298, 640, 641
Rhodamine 12GM, 299
Rhodamine 3GO, 297
Rhodamine S, 294
Rhoduline Blue 6G, 639, 641
Rosanthrene O, 130
Rosanthrene Orange R, 133
Rose Bengale, 300
Rosophenine 10B, 271

S

Saccharein, 294
Safranine T, 238
St. Denis Black, 318
Setoglaucine, 276
Sirius Light Blue F3GL, 289
Sirius Light Green BB, 135
Sirius Red Violet RL, 140
Sirius Supra Green BTL, 140
Sirius Supra Light Green FFGL, 613

Sirius Supra Rubine BBL, 139
Sirius Supra Violet BL, 140
Solacet Fast Scarlet BS, 172
Solantine Fast Red 8BNL, 136
Soluble Blue, 283
Spirit Blue, 178, 281
Spirit Induline, 178
SRA Golden Orange I, 171
SRA Golden Yellow XIII, 171
SRA Green Blue II, 423
Sudan Black B, 176
Sudan Blue GL, 176
Sudan Brown 5B, 176
Sudan Green BB, 176
Sudan Red G, 176
Sudan Violet R, 176
Sudan Yellow 3G, 176
Sudan Yellow 3GN, 176
Sulfanthrene Pink FF, 638
Sulfon Acid Blue R, 150
Sulfon Cyanine Black B, 152
Sulfon Cyanine Blue GR, 151
Sulfur Black T Extra, 314, 315
Sulfur Brilliant Blue, 323
Sulfur Brown R, 316
Sulfur Navy Blue, 323
Sulphaniline Brown 4B, 313
Sulpho Rhodamine B, 295
Sulpho Rhodamine G, 296
Sun Yellow, 119
Supra Light Yellow GGL, 262
Supramine Brown GR, 256
Supra Sky R, 415

T

Tartrazine, 148, 179, 647
Thioflavine T, 271, 640, 641
Thioindigo Red B, 563, 637
Thioindigo Scarlet G, 572
Thioindigo Scarlet R, 572
Thionine, 676
Thionine Blue GO, 267
Thiophore Bronze 5G, 316
Toluidine Blue, 676
Toluidine Red R, 633
Toluidine Toner, 633
Toluylene Blue, 264
Trisulfon Brown BT, 118
Trypaflavine, 231, 232

Turkey Red Lake, 656
Tyrian Purple, 557

U

Ultramarine Blue, 601
Uranine, 299

V

Vat Brown G, 432
Vat Violet RR, 546
Vat Yellow G, 432
Victoria Blue B, 286
Victoria Fast Violet 2R, 150
Victoria Pure Blue BO, 286, 639, 641
Victoria Violet 4BS, 149
Violamine R, 297
Vulcan Fast Orange GG, 636
Vulcan Fast Red B, 636
Vulcan Fast Red BF, 636
Vulcan Fast Red GF, 637
Vulcan Fast Yellow G, 636
Vulcan Fast Yellow 5G, 636
Vulcan Fast Yellow GR, 636
Vulcan Fast Yellow R, 636

W

Wool Fast Blue BL, 240
Wool Fast Blue FBL, 287
Wool Fast Blue FGL, 287
Wool Fast Blue GL, 241
Wool Green S, 286

X

Xylene Light Yellow 2G, 149

Y

Yellow AB, 176

Z

Zambesi Black D, 127
Zambesi Black V, 127
Zapon Black, 178
Zapon Fast Blue G, 178
Zapon Fast Blue HFL, 611
Zapon Fast Blue HL, 612
Zapon Fast Orange GE, 178
Zapon Fast Red RE, 178
Zapon Fast Scarlet CG, 177
Zapon Fast Violet BE, 178
Zapon Fast Yellow G, 247
Zapon Fast Yellow GR, 178

SUBJECT INDEX

The indexing principles of Chemical Abstracts have been used as a guide in the preparation of this index. Most of the text of this book went to the publisher before the August, 1953 issue date of the 1952 Chemical Abstracts subject index, with its numerous, minor nomenclature changes. Thus pre-1952 Chemical Abstracts names are generally used in both text and index.

Aromatic sulfonic acids of indefinite structure are indexed as sulfo derivatives of the parent compounds. Multiple index entries are freely used. Many of the common, nonsystematic names for condensed ring systems are entered, usually with cross references to Chemical Abstracts names.

A

A acid, 689
Aceanthra[2,1-*a*]aceanthrylene-5,13-dione, 457
Acedianthrone, 457
Acenaphthenequinone, 572
Acetamide, α-[N-(p-hydroxyphenyl)-2,4-dinitroanilino]-, 256
Acetanilide, *o*-amino-, 316
—, *p*-amino-, 316
—, 2,4-dinitro-, 316
—, α-isonitroso-, 558
—, α,α'-terephthaloylbis[5-chloro-2,4-dimethoxy-, 188
o-Acetanisidide, α,α'-terephthaloylbis[4-chloro-5-methyl-, 188
Acetate rayon dyes, azo, 167
Acetic acid, (1-amino-4-anilino-2-anthraquinonylsulfonylimino)di-, 406
—, (6-amino-*m*-phenetylmercapto)-, 566
—, (*o*-aminophenylmercapto)-, 564
—, (4-chloro-*o*-tolylmercapto)-, 565
—, (2,3-dichloro-4-methoxyphenylmercapto)-, 569
—, (ethylenediimino)di-, 219
—, (methylamino)-. *See* Sarcosine
—, (2-naphthylmercapto)-, 567
Acetoacetanilide, azo pigments derived from, 635
—, 4-chloro-2,5-dimethoxy-, 187
—, α-nitroso-, iron deriv., 644
1-Acetonaphthone, 568
Acetophenone, 43, 44

—, α,α-difluoro-, 24
—, *p*-phenyl-, 34
—, α,α,α-trifluoro-, 27
Acetyl chloride, phenyl-, 560
1,2,4 Acid, 689
Acid azo dyes, 144
Acid pasting, phthalocyanine pigments, 587
Acid slurry, phthalocyanine pigments, 587
Acridine, absorption spectrum, 667, 668
—, 3-amino-9-(*p*-aminophenyl)-, 231
—, 6,9-diamino-2-ethoxy-, lactate, 232
Acridine dyes, 231, 232, 673
Acridonecarbazole dyes, 500
Acrylophenone, 380
Acyclic intermediates, azo dyes from, 133
Acylacetarylamides, 193
N-Acylation, 435
Adsorption, effect on color, 677
Affinity, of dyes for cotton, 113
After-treated dyes, 121
After-treatment, copper, 122
—, formaldehyde, 123, 127, 129
Aggregation, effect on color, 675
Alcohol-soluble dyes, 177, 281
Algol dyes, 434
Algol dyes, indigoid, 562
Algosol dyes, 535, 559
Alizarin, 337, 368, 369, 419, 428
—, metal derivs., 630, 631, 655, 657
—, 5,8-di-*p*-toluidino-, 362
—, 3-nitro-, 351

Alkoxylation, 31, 32
Alkylation, 30
—, of aromatic amines, 41
—, of leucoquinizarin, 376
—, of sulfur dyes, 311
Aluminum mordant dyes, 427
Amination, of aromatic halides, 38
—, of naphthalene, 76
Amines, aromatic, nitration of, 13
—, diazotizable, azoic, 193, 196
—, sulfonation of, 5
Amino Epsilon acid, 689
Amino G acid, 689
Amino J acid, 689
Amino R acid, 689
m-Aminobenzoyl J acid, 689
Ammonia, reactions of substituted aromatic nucleus with, 38.
Analytical reagents, 259
Andresen's acid, 689
Anhydrides, dicarboxylic, 476, 477
Aniline, 46, 48, 231
—, absorption spectrum, 671
—, oxidation of, 242
—, *N*-butyl-, 41
—, *m*-chloro-, 50, 199
—, *o*-chloro-, 207
—, 5-chloro-2-(*p*-chlorophenoxy)-, 202
—, 4-chloro-2,5-dimethoxy-, 50
—, 5-chloro-2,4-dimethoxy-, 52
—, 2-chloro-4-nitro-, 633
—, 4-chloro-2-nitro-, 39, 203, 633
—, 5-chloro-2-phenoxy-, 202
—, *N*-(2-chloro-3-phenyliminopropenyl)-, 253
—, 2,4-dichloro-, 50
—, 2,5-dichloro-, 205
—, 2,6-dichloro-4-nitro-, 23
—, 2,4-dimethoxy-, 250
—, 2,5-dimethoxy-, 50, 52
—, 2,5-dimethoxy-4-(*p*-nitrophenyl-azo)-, 196
—, *N*,*N*-dimethyl-, 41, 275, 278, 279
—, *N*,*N*-dimethyl-*p*-nitro-, derivs., spectra, 674
—, *N*,*N*-dimethyl-*p*-nitroso-, 237, 259, 260, 264, 321, 324
—, 2,4-dinitro-, 39, 633
—, 2-(ethylsulfonyl)-5-trifluoromethyl-, 29, 200
—, *N*-methyl-*p*-nitro-, 14

—, *N*-methyl-*p*-nitro-*N*-nitroso-, 216
—, *N*,*N*'-methylenebis[4-chloro-2-nitro-, 632
—, 4,4'-methylenebis[*N*,*N*-dimethyl-, 233, 246
—, 4,4'-methylidynebis[*N*,*N*-dimethyl-, cation, 669
—, *m*-nitro-, 201
—, *o*-nitro-, 39, 200
—, *p*-nitro-, 38, 203, 316, 633
—, —, absorption spectrum, 672
—, *p*-phenylazo-, 113, 143, 242
—, *N*-(5-phenylimino-1,3-pentadienyl)-, 253
—, *o*-(phenylsulfonyl)-, 200
—, 4,4'-sulfonyldi-, 50
—, 4,4'-thiodi-, 316
—, 3,4,5-trichloro-, 23
p-Anisamide, *N*,*N*'-(4, 8-dihydroxy-1,5-anthraquinonylene)bis-, 439
p-Anisic acid, 31
—, 3-nitro-, 18
m-Anisidine, 6-(2-chloro-4-nitrophenyl-azo)-4-methyl-, 198
—, *N*-phenyl-, 31
o-Anisidine, 5-(benzylsulfonyl)-, 206
—, 5-chloro-, 50, 204
—, 5-chloro-4-nitro-, 15
—, 5-(ethylsulfonyl)-, 203
—, 5-methyl-, 50
—, 5-methyl-4-nitro-, 220,
—, 5-methyl-4-(2-nitro-*p*-tolylazo)-, 199
—, 4-nitro-, 201
—, 5-nitro-, 206
p-Anisidine, 52
—, 2-nitro-, 15, 198
Anisole, 31, 32
—, 4-chloro-2-nitro-, 32
—, 2,3-dichloro-, 568, 569
—, *m*-methyl-, 32
—, 3-methyl-4-nitro-, 19
—, 4-methyl-2-nitro-, 32
—, *o*-nitro-, 32, 255
—, *p*-nitro-, 32
—, 2,4,6-trinitro-, 256
Anthanthrone, 445
—. See Also Dibenzo[*cd*, *jk*]pyrene-6,12-dione
—, bromoiodo-, 445

—, dibromo-, 445
—, dichloro-, 445
Anthracene, 313, 344
—, absorption spectrum, 665, 667, 668
—, 9,10-dihydro-9,10-dimethylene-, 665
1,10-Anthracenedione, 9-chloro-4-hydroxy-, 681
—, 2(or 3),9-dianilino-4-hydroxy-, 407, 408
Anthragallol, 428
2-Anthramine, 492
Anthranilaldehyde, N-1-anthraquinonyl-, 489
Anthranilic acid, 649
—, N-1-anthraquinonyl-, 488
—, N,N'-1,5-anthraquinonylenedi-, 360
—, N-(carboxymethyl)-, 554, 557
—, N-ethyl-5-sulfo-, 219, 220
—, N-[p-(p-hydroxyanilino)phenyl]-, 324
—, N-isobutyl-, 39
—, N-methyl-5-sulfo-, 220
—, N-phenyl-, 41
—, 4-sulfo-, 220
Anthranilonitrile, N-1-anthraquinonyl-, 489
Anthranoyl chloride, N-1-anthraquinonyl-, 492
Anthrapyrazole ring system, 409
1H-Anthra[1,2-c]pyrazole-6,11-dione, 3-(p-carboxyphenyl)-, 471
2H-Anthra[1,2-c]pyrazole-6,11-dione, 2-(p-carboxyphenyl)-, 471
1H-Anthra[1,2-c]pyrazole-3,6,11(2H)-trione, 1-phenyl-, 471
Anthra[1,9]pyrazol-6(1H)-one, 1-methyl-, 470
Anthra[1,9]pyrazol-6(2H)-one, 468, 484
—, 2-methyl-, 470
Anthrapyridazone ring system, 409
Anthrapyridone ring system, 409
1,9-Anthrapyridone, 422
—. See Also 7H-Dibenz[f, ij]isoquinoline-2,7(3H)-dione
—, 4-(2-anthraquinonylamino)-N-methyl-, 463
—, 4-bromo-N-methyl-, 463
Anthrapyrimidine ring system, 409
1,9-Anthrapyrimidine, 509
—. See Also 7H-Dibenzo[de, h]quinazolin-7-one

—, amino-, 509
—, 5-amino-, 483
—, 5(or 8)-amino-, 422
—, 6-amino-, 375
—, 3-(3-amino-2-hydroxypropyl)-, 422
—, 4-amino-2-methoxy-, 422
—, 4-(p-chlorobenzamido)-, 510
—, 5-(2,5-dichlorobenzamido)-, 509
—, 5-(methylamino)-, 422
1,9-Anthrapyrimidine-2-sulfonic acid, 5-amino-, 510
1,9-Anthrapyrimidone, 422
—. See Also 7H-Dibenzo[de,h]quinazoline-2,7(3H)-dione
Anthraquinone, 337, 355
—, color of, 666
—, diazonium salts of, 366
—, ethers of, 369
—, oxime, 338
—, polarization, 338
—, reduction potential, 338
—, thioethers of, 372
—, 1-acetamido-, 419
—, 1-acetamido-4-amino-, 419
—, 2-acetamido-3-chloro-, 364
—, 2-acylamino-3-mercapto-, 372
—, alkyl-, 356
—, 2-alkyl-1-amino-, 376
—, 1-alkyl-2-hydroxy-, 376
—, 2-alkyl-1-hydroxy-, 376
—, 1-alkyl(or aryl)mercapto-, 372
—, amino-, diazotization, 366
—, 1-amino-, 201, 348, 354, 361, 419
—, —, derivs., spectra, 684
—, 2-amino-, 348, 359, 419
—, —, brown vat dye from, 549
—, —, leuco sulfuric acid ester, 621
—, 1-amino-4-anilino-, 420
—, 1-amino-4-anilino-2-[bis(carboxymethyl)sulfamyl]-, 406
—, 2-amino-1-anilino-3-chloro-, 419
—, 1-amino-4-anilino-2-(2-hydroxyethoxy)-, 420
—, 1-amino-4-anilino-2-methoxy-, 420
—, 1-amino-4-anilino-2-methyl-, 365
—, 1-(p-aminoanilino)-4-methylamino-, 420
—, 4-(p-aminoanilino)-1-methylamino-5-nitro-, 420
—, 1-amino-2-aroyl-, 491
—, 1-amino-4-arylamino-, 356

Anthraquinone—cont'd.
—, 1-amino-4-arylamino-5-hydroxy-, 420
—, 1-amino-4-benzamido-, 364
—, 1-amino-5-benzamido-, 364
—, 1-amino-3-bromo-, 348
—, 2-amino-1-bromo-, 356
—, 1-amino-2-bromo-4-hydroxy-, 349
—, 1-amino-2-bromo-4-(sulfoanilino)-, 395
—, 1-amino-2-bromo-4-(*ar*-sulfo-*p*-toluidino)-, 404
—, 1-amino-2-bromo-4-*p*-toluidino-, 360, 393
—, 1-amino-3-chloro-, 348
—, 1-amino-4-chloro-, 419
—, 1-amino-6-chloro-, 348
—, 2-amino-1-chloro-, 346
—, —, reactions, 348
—, 2-amino-3-chloro-, 339
—, —, leuco sulfuric acid ester, 520
—, 1-amino-5-chloro-4-hydroxy-, 349, 359
—, 1-amino-4-(3-chloro-*x*-sulfoanilino)-2-methyl-, 405
—, 1 amino-2,4-dibromo-, 347, 419
—, 2-amino-1,3-dibromo-, 347
—, 2-amino(dihydro)-1,2'-iminodi-, 515
—, 2-amino-1,4-dihydroxy-, 369
—, 1-amino-4-(*p*-dodecylanilino)-2-(sulfophenoxy)-, 406
—, 1-amino-4-guanidino-, 419
—, 1-amino-2-hydroxy-, 369
—, 1-amino-4-hydroxy-, 349, 362, 374, 419, 423
—, 2-amino-3-hydroxy-, 339
—, 1-amino-4-[*p*-(2-hydroxyethyl)anilino]-, 420
—, 1-amino-4-hydroxy-2-methoxy-, 419, 423
—, 2-amino-1,2'-iminodi-, 516
—, 1-amino-2-(isopropylmercapto)-, 419
—, 1-amino-2-mercapto-, 365
—, 2-amino-1-mercapto-, 372
—, 1-amino-2-methoxy-, 419
—, 1-amino-2-methoxy-4-methylamino-, 420
—, 1-amino-2-methoxy-4-(*p*-tolylsulfonamido)-, 370
—, 1-amino-2-methyl-, 359, 419, 423
—, 1-amino-4-methylamino-, 420
—, 2-amino-1,2'-(methylimino)di-, 365

—, 1-amino-2-methyl-4-(*ar*-sulfo-*p*-toluidino)-, 404
—, 1-amino-2-methyl-4-*p*-toluidino-, 360
—, 2-(*p*-aminophenoxy)-, leuco sulfuric acid ester, 621
—, 1-amino-2-(phenyliminomethyl)-, 358
—, 1-amino-2-(2-sulfatoethoxy)-4-(*ar*-sulfo-2,6-xylidino)-, 406
—, 1-anilino-, 351, 374, 392, 419
—, 2-anilino-1,4-dihydroxy-, 369
—, 1-anilino-4,8-dihydroxy-5-nitro-, 352
—, 4-anilino-1-hydroxy-2-(sulfophenoxy)-, 407
—, 1-anilino-2-methyl-, 490
—, 1-anilino-4-methylamino-, 420
—, 1-anilino-4-(1,2,3,4-tetrahydro-2-naphthylamino)-, 371
—, 1-arylamino-4-hydroxy-, 363
—, 1-arylamino-4-hydroxyalkylamino-, 420
—, 1-benzamido-, 436
—, 1-benzamido-4-chloro-, 346
—, 1-benzamido-5-chloro-, 363
—, 1-benzamido-4-hydroxy-, 363, 438, 637
—, 1-benzylamino-4-(2-sulfatoethylamino)-, 406
—, 1,5-bis(anisoylamino)-4,8-dihydroxy-, 439
—, 1,4-bis(arylamino)-, 399
—, 1,4-bis(4-butyl-*ar*-sulfoanilino)-, 401
—, 1,4-bis(cyclohexylamino)-, 420
—, 1,4-bis(hydroxyalkylamino)-, 420
—, 1,4-bis(*m*-hydroxyanilino)-, 420
—, 1,4-bis(2-hydroxyethylamino)-, 423
—, 1,5-bis[*N*-(2-hydroxyethyl)anilino]-, 419
—, 1,4-bis(methylamino)-, 362, 420, 423
—, 1,8-bis(methylamino)-, 419
—, 2,6-bis(phenyliminomethyl)-, 359
—, 1,4-bis(propionylamino)-, 419
—, 1,4-bis(sulfobenzylamino)-, 394
—, 1,4-bis[2-(sulfobenzyl)cyclohexylamino]-, 402
—, 1,4-bis(*ar*-sulfomesitylamino)-, 401
—, 1,4-bis(sulfo-*p*-phenoxyanilino)-, 402
—, 1,4-bis(*ar*-sulfo-*p*-toluidino)-, 400
—, 1,4-bis(5,6,7,8-tetrahydro-*ar*-sulfo-2-naphthylamino)-, 402
—, bromo-, 346
—, 1-bromo-4-hydroxy-, 347
—, 2-bromo-3-methyl-, 343

—, 1-bromo-4-methylamino-, 347
—, 1-butylamino-4-methylamino-, 420
—, 1-(3-carboxy-2-hydroxy-*x*-sulfoanilino)-4-methylamino-, 406
—, chloro-, reactions, 347
—, 1-chloro-, 345
—, 2-chloro-, 339, 345
—, 1-chloro-2-(2,4-dichlorobenzoyl)-, 491
—, 1-chloro-2-(dichloromethyl)-, 358
—, 1-chloro-4-hydroxy-, 340, 419
—, —, color of, 681
—, 2-(chloromethyl)-, sulfur dye from, 549
—, 1-chloro-2-methyl-, 345, 346
—, 2-chloro-6(and 7)-methyl-, 344
—, 1-(8-chloro-1-naphthylmercapto)-, 525
—, 1-chloro-5-nitro-, 345, 352
—, 1-chloro-2-phthalimido-, 364, 486
—, 1,2-diamino-, 355, 361, 365, 511
—, 1,4-diamino-, 362, 374, 420, 423
—, 1,5-diamino-, 355, 361, 419
—, 1,8-diamino-, 419
—, 2,6-diamino-, 355, 361
—, 1,4-diamino-2,3-bis(sulfophenoxy)-, 394, 403
—, 1,4-diamino-2-butoxy-, 371
—, 1,4-diamino-2,3-dichloro-, 346
—, 2,6-diamino-1,5-dichloro-, 356
—, 1,5-diamino-4,8-dihydroxy-, 420, 438
—, —, alkylated, 420
—, 1,8-diamino-4,5-dihydroxy-, alkylated, 420
—, 1,4-diamino-2,3-dimethoxy-, 371, 420
—, 1,5-diamino-4,8-dinitro-, 351
—, 1,4-diamino-2,3-diphenoxy-, 370
—, 1,5-diamino-2-(2-hydroxyethylmercapto)-, 420
—, 1,4-diamino-2-methoxy-, 419, 423
—, 1,5-diamino-2-methyl-, 420
—, 1,8-diamino-2-methyl-, 420
—, 1,4-diamino-5-nitro-, 420, 423
—, 1,5-diamino-2,4,6,8-tetrachloro-, 346
—, 1,4-dianilino-, 365
—, 1,5-dianilino-, 420
—, 1,4-dianilino-5,8-dichloro-, 375
—, 1,2(and 1,3)-dianilino-4-hydroxy-, 407
—, 1,2-dibenzamido-, 438
—, 1,4-dibenzamido-, 438
—, 1,5-dibenzamido-, 437, 438

—, 1,8-dibenzamido-, 438
—, 2,3-dibenzamido-, 438
—, 2,6-dibenzamido-, 438
—, 1,5-dibenzamido-4-hydroxy-, 438
—, 1,5-dichloro-, 345
—, 1,8-dichloro-, 345
—, 2,6-dichloro-, 345
—, 1,8-dichloro-4-nitro-, 350
—, 1,2-dihydroxy-. *See* Alizarin
—, 1,4-dihydroxy-. *See* Quinizarin
—, 1,5-dihydroxy-, 368, 419
—, 1,8-dihydroxy-, 368
—, 1,4-dihydroxy-5,8-bis(2-hydroxyethylamino)-, 362, 420, 423
—, 1,5-dihydroxy-4,8-bis(methylamino)-, 423
—, 1,2-dihydroxy-5,8-bis(*ar*-sulfo-*p*-toluidino)-, 400
—, 1,4-dihydroxy-5,8-bis(*ar*-sulfo-*p*-toluidino)-, 401
—, 1,5-dihydroxy-4,8-dinitro-, 372
—, 1,2-dihydroxy-4,8-di-*p*-toluidino-, 362
—, 1,4-dihydroxy-2-mercapto-, 369
—, 1,4-dihydroxy-2-phenoxy-, 370
—, 1,5-dimethoxy-, 419
—, 1,5-dinitro-, 350
—, 1,8-dinitro-, 350
—, 1,5-dinitro-4,8-diphenoxy-, 351
—, 1,5-diphenoxy-, 370
—, 1,4-di-*p*-toluidino-, 362, 374
—, 2-ethyl-, 356
—, 1-ethylamino-, 374
—, 1-ethylmercapto-, 419
—, 1-guanidino-4-hydroxy-, 419
—, 1,2,4,5,6,8-hexahydroxy-, 368, 429
—, 1-hydrazino-, 347
—, 2-hydrazino-, 347
—, 2,2'-hydrazodi-, 516
—, hydroxy-, 367
—, 1-hydroxy-, 368
—, —, derivs., spectra, 684
—, —, reactions, 369
—, 1(or 2)-hydroxy-, 354
—, 2-hydroxy-, 368
—, 5-hydroxy-1,4-bis(*p*-hydroxyanilino)-, 420
—, 5-hydroxy-1,4-di-*p*-toluidino-, 362
—, 1-[2-(2-hydroxyethoxy)ethylamino]-4-methylamino-, 423
—, 1-(2-hydroxyethylamino)-, 419

Anthraquinone—cont'd.
—, 1-[p-(2-hydroxyethylamino)anilino]-4-methylamino-, 423
—, 1-(2-hydroxyethylamino)-4-methylamino-, 420, 423
—, 1-[N-(2-hydroxyethyl)anilino]-, 419
—, 1-hydroxy-4-methyl-, 341
—, 1-hydroxy-4-methylamino-, 420
—, 1-hydroxy-4-nitro-, 351
—, 1-hydroxy-4-(ar-sulfo-p-toluidino)-, 407
—, 1-hydroxy-4-m-toluidino-, 420
—, 1-hydroxy-4-p-toluidino, 362, 374, 393
—, iminodi-. *See Also* Dianthrimide
—, 1,1'-iminodi-, 348
—, 1,2'-iminodi-, 348
—, 2-isobutylmercapto-1-methylamino-, 419
—, leuco-1-amino-4-hydroxy-, 373
—, leuco-1,4-diamino-, 373
—, 1-mercapto-, 348
—, 2-mercapto-, 348
—, 1-methoxy-, 347, 351, 354, 370, 371
—, 2-methoxy-, 347
—, 1-methoxy-4-nitro-, 351
—, 2-methyl-, 338, 356
—, —, sulfur dye from, 549
—, 1-methylamino-, 354, 361, 371, 419, 423
—, 2-methylamino-, 419
—, 1-methylamino-4-(sulfo-1-pyrenylamino)-, 405
—, 1-methylamino-4-(ar-sulfo-p-toluidino)-, 394, 405
—, 1-methylamino-4-p-toluidino-, 393
—, 2-methyl-1-nitro-, 350
—, 1-(4-morpholinyl)-, 419
—, 1-nitro-, 350
—, 1,1'-oxalyldi-, 458
—, 1,2,4,5,8-pentahydroxy-, 428
—, 1-phenyl-, 366
—, 2-(phenyliminomethyl)-, 359
—, 1-(sulfoanilino)-, 396
—, 4-(sulfoanisidino)-1,1'-iminodi-, 411
—, 1,4,5,8-tetraamino-, 420, 423
—, 1,4,5,8-tetrachloro-, 345, 346, 352
—, 1,2,5,8-tetrahydroxy-, 367, 428
—, 1,4,5,8-tetrahydroxy-, 355, 377
—, 1,2'-thiodi-, 525
—, 1-o-toluidino-, 489
—, 1-p-toluidino-, 347
—, 1-p-tolylsulfonamido-, 347

—, 1,4,5-triamino-, 420
—, tribenzamido-, 438
—, 2-trifluoromethyl-, 359
—, 1,4,5-triguanidino-, 419
—, 1,2,3-trihydroxy-, 428
—, 1,2,4-trihydroxy-, 367, 369
—, 1,2,5-trihydroxy-, 369
—, 1,4,8-trihydroxy-, 368
—, 1,2,6-trihydroxy-3-nitro-, 428
—, 1,4,5-trimethoxy-, 419
1,2:2',1'-Anthraquinoneazine, N,N'-dihydro-. *See* Indanthrone
Anthraquinone-2',1'(N)-benzacridone, 488, 492
—, anthrimide, 464
—, solubilization, 547
—, acylamino-, 496
—, amino-, 493, 494
—, 4-amino-, 501
—, 6-amino-x-[alkyl(or aryl)sulfonyl]-, 377
—, 6-amino-10-chloro-, 511
—, aminohalo-, 494
—, arylamino-, 494
—, 4-benzamido-6-hydroxy-, 350
—, 7-bromo-, 501
—, chloro-, 493
—, dichloro-, 493
—, 9,11-dichloro-, 501
—, 9,12-dichloro-, 501
—, 6-hydroxy-, 375
Anthraquinone-2',1'(N)-benzacridonecarboxamide dyes, 497
Anthraquinonebisthiaxanthone dyes, 527
Anthraquinonecarbonitrile, 356
1-Anthraquinonecarbonitrile, 348
2-Anthraquinonecarbonitrile, 1-amino-4-methylamino-, 355
—, 1,4-diamino-, 420
2-Anthraquinonecarbonyl chloride, 1-amino-, 438, 485
—, 5-benzamido-, 440
—, 5-nitro-, 440
2-Anthraquinonecarboxaldehyde, 1-amino-, 533
—, 1-anilino-, 491
—, 1-chloro-, 358
2-Anthraquinonecarboxamide, 1-amino-4-cyclohexylamino-, 423
—, 4-amino-1-hydroxy-, 420
—, 1-amino-4-methylamino-, 420, 423

—, 4-anilino-1-(2-hydroxyethylamino)-
N-methyl-, 420
—, *N*,*N*'-1,5-anthraquinonylenebis[1-
amino-, 439
—, 1,4-diamino-, 420
2-Anthraquinonecarboxanilide, 3',4'-
dibromo-, 620
Anthraquinonecarboxylic acid, 356
1-Anthraquinonecarboxylic acid, 357
—, 3-methyl-, 357
2-Anthraquinonecarboxylic acid,
1-amino-, 358, 361
—, 3-amino-, 348, 360
—, 1-amino-4-nitro-, 350
—, 1-anilino-, 489
—, 1-(*p*-carboxyanilino)-, 352, 361
—, 1-chloro-, 356, 490
—, —, reactions, 348
—, 3-chloro-, 358
—, 1-(3,5-dichloroanilino)-, benzyl ester,
490
—, 1,4-dihydroxy-, 357
—, 1-(2-naphthylamino)-, 361, 492
—, 1-nitro-, 357, 490
—, 1-(*N*-phenylacetamido)-, 490
—, 5-(*ar*-sulfo-*p*-toluidino)-8-(5,6,7,8-
tetrahydro-*ar*-sulfo-2-naphthyl-
amino)-, 2-methyl ester, 401
Anthraquinonediacridone dyes, 498
1,2-Anthraquinonedicarbonitrile, 620
2,3-Anthraquinonedicarbonitrile, 1-bu-
tylamino-4-hydroxy-, 366
—, 1,4-dihydroxy-, 355, 366, 368, 369
1,5-Anthraquinonedicarboxylic acid,
4,8-bis(phenylmercapto)-, 526
1,5-Anthraquinonedisulfonic acid, 353
1,8-Anthraquinonedisulfonic acid, 353
2,3-Anthraquinonedisulfonic acid, 1,4-
diamino-, 404
2,6-Anthraquinonedisulfonic acid, 352,
353
—, 3,7-diamino-4,8-dichloro-, 346
—, 4,8-diamino-1,5-dihydroxy-, 359, 397,
657
—, 4,8-diamino-1,3,5,7-tetrahydroxy-,
429
—, 1,4-dihydroxy-, 657
—, 1,5-dihydroxy-, 353, 396
—, 1,5-dihydroxy-4,8-dinitro-, 351
—, 1,3,4,5,7,8-hexahydroxy-, 428
—, 1,3,5,7-tetrahydroxy-4,8-dimer-
capto-, 429,

2,7-Anthraquinonedisulfonic acid, 352
—, 4,5-diamino-1,8-dihydroxy-, 398
Anthraquinoneoxadiazole dyes, 480
1,2-Anthraquinonepyrazoles, 471
Anthraquinonepyridazine dyes, 498
1-Anthraquinonesulfonic acid, 351, 352,
353 .
—, 5,6-dihydroxy-, 429
—, 4,4'-iminodi-, 411
—, 5-nitro-, 350
—, 8-nitro-, 350
2-Anthraquinonesulfonic acid, 337, 339,
352, 353
—, 5-acetamido-1-amino-4-bromo-, 364
—, 4-(*p*-acetamidoanilino)-1-amino-, 415
—, 8-(*p*-acetamidoanilino)-5-cyclohexyl-
amino-, 402
—, 1-amino-, 353
—, 3-amino-, 353
—, 1-amino-4-anilino-, 393, 405, 410, 415
—, 1-amino-4-arylamino-, 354, 360, 410,
412
—, 1-amino-4-bromo-, 347, 412
—, 1-amino-4-(*m*-carboxyanilino)-, 415
—, 1-amino-4-[5-(3-carboxy-4-hydroxy-
phenylsulfonylmethyl)-*o*-anisidino]-,
415
—, 1-amino-4-cyclohexylamino-, 415
—, 1-amino-4-[*p*-(*N*-methylacetamido)-
anilino]-, 415
—, 1-amino-4-methylamino-, 360
—, 1-amino-4-(1-naphthylamino)-, 410
—, 4-(*m*-chloroanilino)-1-hydroxy-, 408
—, 3-cyano-1,4-dihydroxy-, 355
—, 1,4-diamino-, 366, 395, 403
—, 1,5-diamino-, 353
—, 4,8-diamino-1,5-dihydroxy-, 355
—, 1,4-diamino-3-phenoxy-, 354, 403
—, 1,4-dihydroxy-, 353, 369, 429, 657
—, —, reactions, 354
—, 3,4-dihydroxy-, 353, 429
—, 5,8-dihydroxy-, 353, 657
—, 1,4-dihydroxy-3-(*p*-sulfophenoxy)-,
657
—, 4,4'-iminobis[1-amino-, 410
Anthraquinonethiapyran dyes, 525
Anthraquinonethiaxanthone dyes, 526
Anthraquinonethiols, 372
Anthraquinonethiophene dyes, 478
Anthrarufin, 368
Anthrasol dyes, 535, 559

3*H*,7*H*-Anthra[1,9-*cd*][1,2,6]thiadiazine-4-carboxylic acid, 7-oxo-, 2,2-dioxide, 531

3*H*,7*H*-Anthra[1,9-*cd*][1,2,6-thiadiazin-7-one, 2,2-dioxide, 532

Anthra[2,3]thiazole-5,10-dione, 2-(1-amino-2-anthraquinonyl)-, 474

—, 2-(1-amino-4-benzamido-2-anthraquinonyl)-, 474

6*H*-Anthra[1,9-*bc*]thiophenecarboxylic acid, 479

5,9,14,18-Anthrazinetetrone, 6,15-dihydro-. *See* Indanthrone

Anthrimides, 460

Anthrisothiazole ring system, 409

6*H*-Anthr[9,1]isothiazole-3-carboxamide, *N*-1-anthraquinonyl-6-oxo-, 436

6*H*-Anthr[9,1]isothiazole-3-carboxylic acid, 6-oxo-, 474

Anthrisothiazolone dyes, 474

Anthr[1,2-*c*]isoxazole-6,11-dione, 358

6*H*-Anthr[1,9]isoxazol-6-one, 680

6*H*-Anthr[9,1]isoxazol-6-one, 681

1-Anthrol, 573, 575

Anthrone, 10,10'-acetylenedi-, 458

—, 10-hydroxy-, 373

—, 4-hydroxy-3-methoxy-, 533

—, 10-methylene-, 448

—, 2-phenyl-, 342

2-*o*-Anthrotoluidide, 3-hydroxy-, 187

Anthr[2,3]oxazole-5,10-dione, 2-(1-amino-2-anthraquinonyl)-, 541

9-Anthryl acetate, 342

Aposafranines, 237

Arigen dyes, 218

Armstrong & Wynne's acid, 689

Arylation, of aromatic amines, 40

Astrazone dyes, 249

Atabrine, 232

Atcogen dyes, 218

Auramine, acetyl-, 245

Auxochromes, 670

Azabenzanthrone, 549

Azine dyes, 235, 673

Azo coupling reaction, 101

Azo dye intermediates, effect on color, 678

Azo dyes, color of, 677

—, metal derivs., color of, 685

—, steric hindrance in, 674

—, thiazoles, 270

Azo wool dyes, U. S. production, 165

Azoic bases, table, 193, 196

Azoic coupling components, table, 184

Azoic dyes, fastness, 195

—, shade, 194

Azomethine dyes, metallized, 247

Azosol dyes, 177

Azulene, 668

B

B acid, 689

Baking process, 8

Barbituric acid, 533

Béchamp reduction, 49

Benzaldehyde, 275

—, *p*-amino-, 36, 234, 278

—, 4-bromo-2-nitro-, 557

—, *p*-[butyl(2-chloroethyl)amino]-, 249

—, *o*-chloro-, 36, 533

—, *p*-chloro-, 283

—, *p*-[(2-chloroethyl)methylamino]-, 250

—, 2-chloro-6-nitro-, 560

—, *p*-diethylamino-, 36

—, 3,4-dimethoxy-, 31

—, *p*-dimethylamino-, 36

—, *p*-(*N*-methyl-*p*-phenetidino)-, 36

—, *o*-nitro-, 556

Benzamide, 4-ethoxy-2-mercapto-, 567

Benzanilide, 225

—, 4'-amino-2',5'-diethoxy-, 197

—, 4'-amino-2',5'-dimethoxy-, 197

—, 4'-*α*-benzoylacetamido-2',5'-dimethoxy-, 191

m-Benzanisidide, 4'-amino-6'-methyl-, 207

o-Benzanisidide, 4'-amino-5'-chloro-, 199

7*H*-Benz[*de*]anthracene-1-carboxylic acid, 7-oxo-, 357

7*H*-Benz[*de*]anthracene-10-carboxylic acid, 11-chloro-7-oxo-, 492

7*H*-Benz[*de*]anthracene-11-carboxylic acid, 7-oxo-, 380

Benz[*a*]anthracene-7,12-dione, 442

—. *See Also* 1,2-Benzanthraquinone

—, 8,11-diamino-, 421

—, 2(and 3)-methyl-, 343

7*H*-Benz[*de*]anthracene-9-sulfonic acid, 7-oxo-, 382

7*H*-Benz[*de*]anthracen-7-one. *See* Benzanthrone

1,2-Benzanthraquinone. *See Also* Benz-
[*a*]anthracene-7,12-dione
"1,2-Benzanthraquinone," 5,8-di-
amino-, 421
2,3-Benzanthraquinone, 442
Benzanthrone, 377, 454
—, reactions, 381
—, 3-substituted, 454
—, 4-(acylmethyl)-, 383
—, 6-amino-, 381
—, 4-anilino-, 381, 383
—, 3-(4-anilino-1-anthraquinonyl-
amino)-, sulfonated, 411
—, 3-(1-anthraquinonylamino)-, 483
—, 3-benzoyl-, 380
—, 3-bromo-, 382
—, 3-bromo-2-phenyl-, 484
—, 3-chloro-, 454
—, 2-chloro-1-methyl-, 378
—, 3,9-dibromo-, 382, 485
—, 2-hydroxy-, benzoate, 448
—, 4-hydroxy-, 381, 383
—, 1-methoxy-, 380
—, 3-methoxy-, 423
—, 3-methyl-, 378
—, 3-nitro-, 382
—, 3-phenyl-, 379
Benzanthrone-anthrapyrazolone, 470
Benzene, absorption spectrum, 665, 667,
671
—, chlorination of, 21
—, nitration of, 12
—, orientation in, 3
—, substitution of, 1
—, sulfonation of, 3
—, *m*-bis(trifluoromethyl)-, 25
—, 2-chloro-1,4-dimethoxy-, 23
—, 1-chloro-2,4-dimethoxy-5-nitro-, 32
—, chlorodinitro-, 314
—, 1-chloro-2(or 4)-nitro-, 19
—, *m*-dichloro-, 23
—, 1,3-dichloro-4-nitro-, 20
—, 1,4-dichloro-2-nitro-, 20
—, *p*-diethoxy-, 32
—, *o*(or *m* or *p*)-difluoro-, 30
—, *p*-dimethoxy-, 32
—, 1,3-dimethoxy-4-nitro-, 32
—, 1,4-dimethoxy-2-nitro-, 19
—, fluoro-, 30
—, hexafluoro-, 30
—, nitro-, 13

—, —, absorption spectrum, 672
—, (pentafluoroethyl)-, 25
—, 1,2,4-trifluoro-, 30
Benzene aromatic system, 1
m-Benzenedisulfonic acid, 4-amino-, 7
—, 4-formyl-, 295
p-Benzenedisulfonic acid, 2-amino-, 7
—, 2-hydrazino-, 55
Benzenediazotate, *p*-nitro-, 216
Benzenesulfonanilide, 3-(4-amino-3-
methyl-1-anthraquinonylamino)-*N*-
methyl-*x*′-sulfo-, 405
Benzenesulfonic acid, 5-amino-2-anilino-,
240, 256
—, 2-amino-5-chloro-, 10
—, 2-amino-4,5-dichloro-, 6
—, 2-amino-5-ethoxy-, 10
—, 2-amino-5-nitro-, 39
—, *p*-(*p*-aminophenylazo)-, 7
—, amino(trifluoromethyl)-, 28
—, 2-*o*-anisidino-5-nitro-, 41
—, 2-*p*-anisidino-5-nitro-, 41
—, *p*-chloro-, 8
—, 2-(*p*-chloroanilino)-5-nitro-, 41
—, 2-chloro-3,5-dinitro-, 17
—, 3-chloro-4-hydrazino-, 55
—, 2-chloro-5-nitro-, 8
—, 2,5-dichloro-4-hydrazino-, 55
—, 2,4-dihydroxy-, 11
—, *o*-formyl-, 10, 275
—, *p*-hydrazino-, 55
—, *p*-(2-hydroxy-1-naphthylazo)-, 647
—, *p*-(3-methyl-5-oxo-4-phenylazo-2-py-
razolin-1-yl)-, 647
—, *m*-nitro-, 8
—, *m*-(phenylcarbamyl)-, 225
—, 2,3,4-trichloro-, 569
—, 2,4,5-trichloro-3-hydrazino-, 55
Benzenesulfonyl chloride, 3-acetamido-
4-methoxy-, 11
—, 4-chloro-3-nitro-, 11
—, 2,3-dichloro-4-methoxy-, 569
—, *m*-nitro-, 11
1,2,4,5-Benzenetetracarboxylic acid, 44
Benzenethiol, *o*-amino-, 304
—, 2-amino-5-ethoxy-, 566
Benzhydrol, 4,4′-bis(dimethylamino)-,
46, 669
—, —, cation from, 669
Benzidine, 51, 317
—, thionation of, 329

Benzidine—cont'd.
—, 3,3'-dichloro-, 51, 636
—, 2,2'-dichloro-5,5'-dimethoxy, 51
—, 3,3'-dimethoxy-, 48, 51, 196, 637
—, 3,3'-dimethyl-, 51
Benz[f]indolin-3-one, 6-bromo-9-chloro-
2-(4-methoxy-1-oxo-2-naphthylidene)-,
544, 574
3H-Benz[f]indol-3(2H)-one, 6-bromo-2,9-
dichloro-, 574
5H-[1,2]Benzisothiazolo[4,3-ab]phenaz-
ine, 4,4-dioxide, 433
11H-Benzo[a]carbazole-3-carbox-p-anis-
idide, 2-hydroxy-, 190
—, 2-hydroxy-2'-methyl-, 191
11H-Benzo[a]carbazol-4-ol, 10-methyl-,
52, 574
Benzofulvene, 665
Benzoic acid, 43, 44, 45
—, o-(2-acetamido-4,5-dimethylben-
zoyl)-, 341
—, o-acyl-, 342
—, p-amino-, 50
—, 2-amino-4-chloro-, 35
—, 5-amino-2-chloro-, 50
—, 5-amino-2-nitro-, 15
—, m-(4-amino-3-sulfo-1-anthraqui-
nonylamino)-, 415
—, 2-amino-4-trifluoromethyl-, 29
—, o-anthranoyl-, 341
—, o-benzoyl-, 338
—, o-(carboxymethylmercapto)-, 562
—, 2-(carboxymethylmercapto)-4-
chloro-, 563
—, 4-chloro-3,5-dinitro-, 256
—, 2-chloro-4-nitro-, 45, 46
—, 2-chloro-5-nitro-4-sulfo-, 17
—, 2-chloro-4-sulfo-, 46
—, m-(chlorosulfonyl)-, 224, 225, 547
—, 2,4-dichloro-, 35
—, 2,5-dichloro-, 33, 34
—, o-(4-diethylamino-salicyloyl)-, 297
—, 2,2'-dithiodi-, 562
—, 2-ethylamino-5-sulfo-, 219
—, m-[ethyl(phenylazo)amino]-, 217
—, m-hydrazino-, 55
—, p-hydroxy-, 35
—, o-(2-hydroxy-3,6-disulfo-1-naphthyl-
azo)-, metal derivs., 652
—, o-(1-hydroxy-2-naphthoyl)-, 340
—, o-mercapto-, 562

—, nitro-, 45
—, m-[3-(p-nitrophenyl)-5-oxo-2-pyrazo-
lin-1-yl]-, 56
—, m-(phenylazoamino)-, 217
—, o-sulfo-, 8
—, o-(p-toluoyl)-, 338
Benzonitrile, 39, 40
—, 4-amino-2,5-dimethoxy-, 198
Benzophenone, 4,4'-bis(diethylamino)-,
280
—, 4,4'-bis(dimethylamino)-, 234, 245
—, 4,4'-bis(dimethylamino)thio-, 246
—, 4,4'-dichloro-, 287
Benzo[h]quinoline-3,7-diol, 1,2,3,4-
tetrahydro-, 53
Benzo-1,3-thiaza-2-thionium chloride,
6-chloro-, 563
Benzothiazole, 2-α-acetylacetamido-6-
ethoxy-, 189
—, 2-amino-6-ethoxy-, 57
—, 2-(p-aminophenyl)-6-methyl-, 57, 269,
328
—, 6-ethoxy-2-mercapto-, 566
—, 2-methyl-, ethiodide, 253
7-Benzothiazolesulfonic acid, 2-p-amino-
phenyl-6-methyl-, 270
Benzotrifluoride, 3-amino-4-chloro-, 29
—, 4-cyano-3-nitro-, 29
—, 4-ethylsulfonyl-3-nitro-, 28
—, p-pentafluoroethyl-, 25
Benzoxazole, 2-methyl-, 253
2-Benzoxazolinone, 5-nitro-, 15
Benzoyl chloride, 561
Benzoyl fluoride, m-trifluoromethyl-, 25
Benzyl alcohol, 44
Benzylamine, N-ethyl-N-(p-nitroso-
phenyl)-, 238
—, N-ethyl-N-phenyl-, derivs., 652
4,4'-Bi-o-acetoacetotoluidide, 186
[3,3'-Bi-6H-anthra[9,1]isothiazole]-
6,6'-dione, 475
[3,3'-Bianthrapyrazole]dione, 468
[3,3'-Bianthra[1,9]pyrazole]-
6,6'-(1H,1'H)dione, 1,1'-diethyl-, 468
[3,3'-Bianthra[1,9]pyrazole]-
6,6'-(2H,2'H)dione, 2,2'-dimethyl-,
469
1,1'-Bianthraquinone, 2,2'-diamino-, 487
—, 3,3'-dichloro-, 349
—, 2,2'-dimethyl-, 348, 367, 451
—, 2,2'-diphthalimido-, 486

[3,3′-Bi-7H-benz[de]anthracene]-7,7′-dione, 384
[4,4′-Bi-7H-benz[de]anthracene]-7,7′-dione, 382
Bibliography, 692
[1,1′-Binaphthalene]-2,2′-dicarboxylic acid, 444
[1,1′-Binaphthalene]-8,8′-dicarboxylic acid, 444
4′,4‴-Bi-2-naphth-o-anisidide, 3,3″-dihydroxy-, 185
4′,4‴-Bi-2-naphtho-o-toluidide, 3,3″-dihydroxy-, 184
Biological stains, 261, 266, 274
BIOS reports, 692
Biphenyl, 4-nitro-, 18
2-Biphenylamine, 204
4-Biphenylamine, 50
4-Biphenylcarbonyl chloride, 4′,4‴-azobis-, 441
4-Biphenylcarboxamide, 34
—, N-1-anthraquinonyl-, 540
—, 4′,4‴-azobis[N-(5-benzamido-1-anthraquinonyl)-, 441
3-Biphenylcarboxylic acid, 2-hydroxy-, 35
3,3′-Biphenyldicarboxylic acid, 4,4′-diamino-, 51
3,4-Biphenyldicarboxylic acid, 6-sulfo-, 615
2,2′-Biphenyldisulfonic acid, 4,4′-diamino-5,5′-dimethyl-, 51
3,3′-Biphenyldisulfonic acid, 4,4′-diamino-, 51
2,4,5-Biphenyltricarboxylic acid, 613
—, derivs., 614, 615
Bis-benzimidazodiazapyrenedione dyes, 475
Bohn-Schmidt reaction, 427
Bottom chrome dyeing method, 153
Brentogen dyes, 218 .
Broenner's acid, 689
Bromamine acid, 414, 689
—, dyes derived from, 412
Bromination, 268
—, of phthalocyanine, 599
Bucherer reaction, 76
2-Butanone, 4-hydroxy-4-(o-nitrophenyl)-, 556
3-Buten-2-one, 4-(o-nitrophenyl)-, 556
Butter, dyeing, 175

C

C acid, 689
Calconyl dyes, 218
Calco Spirit dyes, 177
Carbanilide, thio-, 556
Carbazole, 1-amino-, 237
—, 3-amino-, 52
—, 3-amino-9-ethyl-, 290
—, 9-ethyl-, 41, 328, 549
3-Carbazolecarboxanilide, 4′-chloro-2-hydroxy-, 187
3-Carbazolecarboxylic acid, 2-hydroxy-, 35
Carbazoles, 52
Carbostyril, 4-hydroxy-1-methyl-, 53
Carboxylation, 33
Cassella acid, 689
Catalysts, oxidation, phthalocyanine, 583
Cellulose, structure, 112
—, sulfur dye intermediate, 313
Cellulose acetate dyes, 249, 256
Cellulose acetate dyes, anthraquinone, 417
Cellulose acetate dyes, azo, 167
Cellulose acetate staining, 135
Chelation, 628
Chicago acid, 689
Chloranil, 289, 304
Chlorination, of benzene nucleus, 21
—, mechanism of, 21
—, of phthalocyanine, 598
—, of phthalocyaninetetrasulfonic acid, copper deriv., 610
Chlorosulfonation, 11
Chromate oxidation, of azo dyes, 160
Chrome dyes, azo, 153
Chrome printing on cotton, 261
Chrome wool dyes, 261, 284
Chromium chelate compounds, 258
Chromium complexes, miscellaneous dyes, 248
Chromium mordant dyes, 426
Chromogens, 663
Chromophores, 663
Chromotropic acid, 689
Chrysaniline 231
Chrysazin, 368
11-Chrysofluorenone, 5-hydroxy-, 379
1,6-Cleve's acid, 689

1,7-Cleve's acid, 690
Cobalt chelate compounds, 258
Cobalt complexes, 248, 311
Cobalt mordant dyes, 427
Coeroxonium dye, 532
Color photography, 264
Complex ions, 628, 656
Conjugation, anisotropic, 669
—, alternant, 668
—, linear, 664
—, nitrogen, 666
—, steric hinderance of, 674
—, triple bond, 666
Copper after-treatment, 122
Copper complexes, 139, 311, 326, 427
Coprantine dyes, 535
Cotton, affinity for dyes, 113
Cotton dyeing, 112
Cotton dyes, indigoid, 559, 562
—, miscellaneous, 245, 271, 289, 292
—, sulfur, 312
—, tannin mordanted, 259, 266, 292
Cotton printing, 261
Coupling components, azo, 101
Coupling reaction, azo, 101
Cresol, 313, 314
m-Cresol, 37
—, 4-chloro-α,α,α-trifluoro-, 27
p-Cresol, 37
—, 2-amino-, 50
—, 3-amino-, 297
—, 3-nitro-, 37
2,3-Cresotic acid, 285
Crocein acid, 690
Crystals, phthalocyanine, 583
2,2'-Cyanine, 1,1'-diethyl-, iodide, 252
Cyanine dyes, 251, 664, 666, 672, 675
Cyanogen bromide, 249
1-Cyclohexene-1,2-dicarbonitrile, 603

D

D acid, 690
Decarboxylation, of anthraquinone compounds, 376
Dehalogenation, of anthraquinone compounds, 376
Dehydrothio-*p*-toluidine, 690
Desulfonation, of anthraquinone compounds, 355, 376
—, of naphthalene compounds, 68, 70
—, of xylene, 4

Developed dyes, 121, 124, 130, 271
Diacridine dyes, anthraquinone, 533, 547
Diagen dyes, 218
Diamines, aromatic, color of azo dyes from, 678
o-Dianisidine, 48, 51, 196
Dianthrimide, 690
1,1'-Dianthrimide, 461
—, 4,4'-diamino-, 462
—, 4,4'-dibenzamido-, 463
—, 4,4'-dinitro-, 462
1,2'-Dianthrimide, 461
—, 4-benzamido-, 464
2,2'-Dianthrimide, 461
Diazo dyes, 121
Diazoamino compounds, 217
Diazosulfites, 221
Diazosulfonates, 221
Diazosulfonic acids, 221
Diazotates, 208, 216, 217
Diazotization, 97
—, of aminoanthraquinones, 366
—, mechanism of, 97
Dibenz[*ah*]anthracene-7,14-dione, 343
Dibenzanthrone, 384, 453
—, derivatives, 456
—, dihydroxy-, 384, 456
—, dimethoxy-, 540
—, —, brominated, 541
—, nitro-, 455
7*H*-Dibenz[*f,ij*]isoquinoline-2,7(3*H*)-dione, 422
—. *See Also* 1,9-Anthrapyridone
3-Dibenzofurancarboxanilide, 2-hydroxy-2',5'-dimethoxy-, 185
Dibenzo[*a,h*]pyrene-7,14-dione, 443, 446, 540
—, brominated, 540
—, dibromo-, 499
—, 2,9-dibromo-, 448, 449
Dibenzo[*a,i*]pyrene-5,8-dione, 447
Dibenzo[*cd,jk*]pyrene-6,12-dione, 444, 445
—. *See Also* Anthanthrone
—, 4,10-dibromo-, 542
7*H*-Dibenzo[*de,h*]quinazoline-2,7(3*H*)-dione, 422
—. *See Also* 1,9-Anthrapyrimidone
7*H*-Dibenzo[*de,h*]quinazolin-7-one. *See Also* 1,9-Anthrapyrimidine
—, derivatives, 422

3,7-Dibenzothiophenediamine, 317
Diels-Alder reaction, 344
Diene reaction, 344
7*H*-Dinaphtho[2,3-*b*,2',3'-*h*]carbazole-5,9,14,17-tetrone, 7-ethyl-, 549
Dioxy S acid, 690
Diphenylamine, 4-amino-4'-(4-amino-6-methyl-*m*-phenetylazo)-, 196
—, 4,4'-diamino-, 196, 679
Diphenylamine dyes, 255
Diphenyl Epsilon acid, 690
Diphenylmethane dyes, 673
Direct azo dyes, U. S. production, 141
Discharge, of azo dyes, 135
Disperse azo dyes, 167
Dow process, 38
Dyeing, by impregnation, azoic, 182

E

Einstein, 662
Elbs reaction, 344
Electron mobility, 663
Electrons, *Pi*, 663, 664
Electrophilic substitution, 1
Environment, effect on color, 675
Epsilon acid, 690
Ethanesulfonic acid, 2-(methylamino)-, 219, 220
Ethanol, 2-anilino-, 41
—, 2-diethylamino-, 218
—, 2-*N*-ethylanilino-, 41
—, 2-(*N*-ethyl-*m*-toluidino)-, 41
—, 2-*o*-hydroxyanilino-, 41
—, 2,2'-iminodi-, 219
—, 2,2'-(phenylimino)di-, 41
Ether, 4-chloro-2-nitrophenyl phenyl, 33
Ethyl ketone, 690
Eurhodines, 237
Excitation by light, 662

F

F acid, 690
Fast bases, 196
Fast salts, 208
Fats, dyeing of, 175, 242
FD&C dyes, 179
FIAT reports, 692
Fischer's aldehyde. *See* $\Delta^{2,\alpha}$-Indolineacet-aldehyde, 1,3,3-trimethyl-
Fischer's base. *See* Indoline, 1,3,3-tri-methyl-2-methylene-

8,16-Flavanthrinedione, 5,13-didehydro-, 486, 513
Flavanthrone, 486, 51
Flavopurpurin, 3-nitro-, 428
Fluoran, 3',6'-dichloro-, 296
Fluorene, 9-methylene-, 665
Fluorescein dichloride, 296
Fluorination, 24
Flushing, of pigments, 589, 626
Food, dyeing of, 174, 178
Food dyes, azo, 179
Formaldehyde after-treatment, 123, 127, 129
Formamidine, α-cyano-*N*,*N*'-diphenyl-, 556
Formylation, 33, 35
Freund's acid, 690
Fries rearrangement, 448
Fuchsin, 231
Fuchsone imine, 272
Fuel, motor, dyeing of, 174
Fulvene, 665
Fur, dyeing of, 244

G

G acid, 690
Gallic acid, 260
Gamma acid, 690
Gasoline, dyeing of, 174
Glucamine, *N*-methyl-, 219
Glycine, *N*-phenyl-, 555
Gomberg reaction, 380
Grignard reaction, 341

H

H acid, 690
Hair, dyeing of, 244
Halogenation, of benzene nucleus, 17
—, of naphthalene, 73
—, of phthalocyanine, 598
Helindon dyes, indigoid, 562
Herz synthesis of indigoid dyes, 563
Heterocyclic intermediates, 52
—, azo dyes from, 133
Heterocyclic nitro dyes, 256
Homazol, 574
Hydrazine, *p*-nitrophenyl-, 55
—, *p*-tolyl-, 55
Hydrogenation, 47
Hydrogen bonding, 628
Hydrogen peroxide, 356

Hydroquinone, 37
Hydroxylamine, N-phenyl-, 49
Hydroxylation, aromatic, 37
—, of naphthalene, 75
Hyperconjugation, 668

I

Ice colors, 181
Indamine, 237, 263
Indanthrene. *See* Indanthrone
Indanthrene dyes, indigoid, 562
Indanthrone, 364, 513, 515, 518
—, crystalline forms of, 520
—, formaldehyde condensation product, 521
—, reduction of, 517
—, 8,17-diamino-, 519
—, 8,17-diamino-7,16-dichloro-, 522
—, 7,16-dibromo-, 515, 519, 521, 542
—, —, formaldehyde condensation product, 520
—, 7,16-dichloro-, 514, 515, 520, 521, 538
—, —, leuco sulfuric acid ester, 520
—, —, solubilization, 537
—, 8,17-dihydroxy-, 519, 522
—, N,N'-dimethyl-, 519, 522
—, N-methyl-, 517
—, 8,17-di-p-toluidino-, 519
—, trichloro-, 514
Indanthronesulfonic acid, 522
Indican, 553
Indicator paper, 115, 118
Indigo, 638
—, *cis* and *trans* forms, 554
—, halogenation, 559
—, syntheses, 554–558
—, dibromo-, 542
—, 5,5'-dibromo-, 559
—, 6,6'-dibromo-, 557
—, dibromo-dichloro-, 542
—, 5,5'-dibromo-4,4'-dichloro-, 560
—, 4,4'-dichloro-, 560
—, pentabromo-, 546
—, 5,5',7,7'-tetrabromo-, 538, 559
—, 5,5',7-tribromo-, 559
5,5'-Indigodisulfonic acid, 560
Indigosol dyes, 535, 559
Indigotin, 551
—. *See Also* Indigo
Indirubin, 561

—, 5,5',7,7'-tetrabromo-, 561
2'-Indole-2-thianaphthene indigo,
5,5',6,7,7'-pentachloro-, 545, 570
—, 5,5',7-trichloro-7'-methoxy-4'-
methyl-, 545, 571
—, 5',6,7'-trichloro-4-methyl-, 570
Indoaniline, 263
Indoline, 1,3,3-trimethyl-2-methylene-, 250
$\Delta^{2,\alpha}$-Indolineacetaldehyde, 1,3,3-tri-
methyl-, 250
Indophenol, 263
—, sulfur dyes from, 321
Indoxyl, 690
—. *See Also* Pseudoindoxyl
Indulines, 241
Ingrain dyes, 121
Ink dyes, 274, 612
Insulation, of conjugated systems, 670, 678
Ionamine dyes, 424
Ions, complex, 628, 656
Iron chelate compounds, 258
Iron complexes, 311
Iron mordant dyes, 427
Isatin, 237, 556, 558
—, 7-methoxy-4-methyl-, 571
—, 2-thio-, 556
Isobenzofuran, 1,3-diphenyl-, 345
Isodiazotates, 216, 217
Isodibenzanthrone, 454
—, bromo-, 455, 546
—, dichloro-, 455
—, —, solubilization, 536
Isoindoline, 1,3-diimino-, 579, 622
$3H$-Isophenothiazin-3-one, 304, 330
—, 2,4,6,8-tetrabromo-7-dimethylam-
ino-, 325
—, 1,2,4-trichloro-7-methyl-, 330
Isophthalamide, N,N'-di-1-anthraquin-
onyl-, 437
Isophthalic acid, 46
Isoquinoline, absorption spectrum, 668
Isoviolanthrone. *See Also* Isodibenzanthrone
—, chlorinated, 543

J

J acid, 690
J acid urea, 690

K

K acid, 690
Kehrmann's synthesis, 267, 268
Ketone chloride process, 246, 280
Ketone imine dyes, 245
Ketones, polycyclic, 458
Koch's acid, 690
Kolbe-Schmitt reaction, 34

L

L acid, 690
Lacquer dyes, 174, 230, 242, 243
Lake Red C base, 690
Lakes, definition, 626
Laundry blue dyes, 274, 278
Laurent's acid, 690
Leather dyes, 114, 147, 174, 231, 242, 243, 255, 257, 259, 312
Lepidine, 251
Leucogene dyes, 535
Leucoquinizarin, 372, 373, 377, 398
—, reactions, 362
Luxol dyes, 177

M

M acid, 690
Malonic acid, bromo-, diethyl ester, 557
—, (2-naphthylamino)-, diethyl ester, 557
Margarine dyeing, 175
Merocyanine dyes, 676
Metachrome dyeing method, 154
Metal chelates of azo dyes, color of, 685
Metallized dyes, miscellaneous, 247
Metanilamide, N^1-butyl-4-methoxy-, 204
—, N^1,N^1-diethyl-4-methoxy-, 203
Metanilic acid, 50
—, 6-chloro-, 6, 651
—, N,N-diethyl-, 41
—, 4-methoxy-, 7
—, 6-methoxy-, 7
Methanediamine, N,N'-bis(4-chloro-2-nitrophenyl)-, 632
Methanesulfonic acid, o-methoxyanilino-, 41
Methine dyes, 248
Metoxazone dyes, 529
Michler's hydrol. *See* Benzhydrol, 4,4'-bis(dimethylamino)-

Michler's ketone, 690
—. *See Also* Benzophenone, 4,4'-bis(dimethylamino)-
Milling dyes, azo, 151
Molecular orbitals, 663, 668
Molecules, excited, 662
Molybdenum complexes, 311
Motor fuel, dyeing of, 174

N

Naccogene dyes, 218
Naphthacene, absorption spectrum, 665
Naphthacenequinone, 442
—, 6,11-diphenyl-, 345
Naphth[2,3-c]acridine-5,8,14(13H)-trione. *See* Anthraquinone-2',1'(N)-benzacridone
Naphthalene, absorption spectrum, 665, 667, 668
—, desulfonation of, 68, 70
—, 1-bromo-, 74
—, 2-bromo-, 74
—, 2-chloro-, 74
—, 1,4-dihydro-1,4-dimethylene-, 665
—, 1,5-dinitro-, 71, 314
—, 1,8-dinitro-, 71, 313
—, 1-nitro-, 71
—, 1,3,6,8-tetranitro-, 71
—, 1,4,5,7-tetranitro-, 71
—, 1,4,5,8-tetranitro-, 71
—, 1,3,8-trinitro-, 71
—, 1,4,5-trinitro-, 71
1,8-Naphthalenediamine, 82
1,4-Naphthalenedicarboxylic acid, 5,8-dibromo-, 476
1,5-Naphthalenedicarboxylic acid, 4,8-dichloro-, 476
1,5-Naphthalenediol, 79
2,6-Naphthalenediol, dibenzoate, 448
1,3-Naphthalenedisulfonic acid, 6-amino-, 85
—, 7-amino-, 85
1,5-Naphthalenedisulfonic acid, 70, 78
—, 3-amino-, 86
—, 4-amino-, 86
1,6-Naphthalenedisulfonic acid, 70
—, 8-amino-, 86
1,7-Naphthalenedisulfonic acid, 70
2,6-Naphthalenedisulfonic acid, 70, 78

2,7-Naphthalenedisulfonic acid, 70, 78
—, 3-amino-, 86
—, 4,5-dihydroxy-, 81
1-Naphthalenesulfonic acid, 68, 77
—, 2-amino-, 83, 649, 650
—, 4-amino-, 83
—, 5-amino-, 83
—, 6-amino-, 84
—, 7-amino-, 84
—, 8-amino-, 83
—, 8-anilino-, 84, 326
—, 8-anilino-5-(p-hydroxyanilino)-, 326
—, 8-cyano-, 444
—, 6,8-dianilino-, 85, 240
—, 4,5-dihydroxy-, 81
—, 8-p-toluidino-, 84
2-Naphthalenesulfonic acid, 68, 77
—, 1-amino-, 84
—, 5-amino-, 84
—, 5(or 8)-amino-, 326
—, 6-amino-, 85
—, 8-amino-, 84
—, 6,7-dihydroxy-, 81
2-Naphthalenesulfonyl chloride, 567
1,4,5,8-Naphthalenetetracarboxylic di-
    anhydride, 476
1,3,5,7-Naphthalenetetrasulfonic acid,
    71
2-Naphthalenethiol, 567
1,3,5-Naphthalenetrisulfonic acid, 71
—, 4-amino-, 88
1,3,6-Naphthalenetrisulfonic acid, 71, 79
—, 8-amino-, 87
1,3,7-Naphthalenetrisulfonic acid, 71
1,2-Naphthalocyanine, 600
2,3-Naphthalocyanine, 600
2-Naphthamide, 3-hydroxy-, derivatives,
    183
—, 3-hydroxy-N-(2-methoxy-3-dibenzo-
    furyl)-, 190
—, 3-hydroxy-N-1-naphthyl-, 185
—, 3-hydroxy-N-2-naphthyl-, 191
—, 5,6,7,8-tetrahydro-3-hydroxy-N-1-
    naphthyl-, 220
2-Naphthanilide, 4'-chloro-3-hydroxy-,
    186
—, 4'-chloro-3-hydroxy-2',5'-dimeth-
    oxy-, 188
—, 5'-chloro-3-hydroxy-2',4'-dimeth-
    oxy-, 187
—, 3-hydroxy-, 91, 184
—, 3-hydroxy-2',5'-dimethoxy-, 184

—, 3-hydroxy-3'-nitro-, 185, 634
2-Naphth-o-anisidide,   7-bromo-3-hy-
    droxy-, 192
—, 3-hydroxy-, 189
2-Naphth-p-anisidide, 3-hydroxy-, 190
—, 3-hydroxy-2'-methyl-, 189
Naphthionic acid, 83
1-Naphthoic acid, 8-amino-, 445
2-Naphthoic acid, 3-hydroxy-, 90
—, —, azo pigments derived from, 650
1-Naphthol, 79, 264, 321, 573, 575
—, 5-amino-, 82
—, 2,4-dinitro-, 255
—, 4-methoxy-, 574
2-Naphthol, 79
—, azo pigments derived from, 633, 649
—, 8-amino-, 82
—, 1-arylazo-, copper derivs., 685
—, 1-(p-nitrophenylazo)-, copper deriv.,
    645
—, 1-nitroso-, 630
—, —, iron deriv., 643
1-Naphthol-2,4-disulfonic acid, 79
1-Naphthol-3,5-disulfonic acid, 8-
    amino-, 647
—, 8-benzamido-2-(m-tolylazo)-, 648
—, 2-(m-chlorophenylazo)-8-(2,4-dichlo-
    robenzamido)-, 648
1-Naphthol-3,6-disulfonic acid, 7-
    amino-, 90
—, 8-amino-, 88
1-Naphthol-3,8-disulfonic acid, 271
1-Naphthol-4,8-disulfonic acid, 81
1-Naphthol-5,7-disulfonic acid, 8-
    amino-, 90
2-Naphthol-3,6-disulfonic acid, 80, 81
—, 1-(1-naphthylazo)-, 646
—, 1-(2,4-xylylazo)-, 646
2-Naphthol-6,8-disulfonic acid, 80, 81
1-Naphthol-2-sulfonic acid, 79
1-Naphthol-3-sulfonic acid, 81
—, 5-amino-, 90
—, 6-amino-, 89
—, 7-amino-, 89
—, 6-(m-aminobenzamido)-, 89
—, 6-(p-aminobenzamido)-, 89
—, 6-(4-amino-m-toluamido)-, 89
—, 6-anilino-, 89
—, 7-anilino-, 89
—, 6,6'-iminobis-, 89
—, 6-(m-nitrobenzamido)-, 89

—, 6-(4-nitro-*m*-toluamido)-, 89
—, 6,6'-ureylenebis-, 89
1-Naphthol-4-sulfonic acid, 79
1-Naphthol-5-sulfonic acid, 81
—, 8-amino-, 90
—, 2-(1-naphthylazo)-, 651
1-Naphthol-7-sulfonic acid, 2,4-dinitro-, 255, 645
1-Naphthol-8-sulfonic acid, 80
2-Naphthol-1-sulfonic acid, 80
2-Naphthol-4-sulfonic acid, 81
—, 1-amino-, 89
2-Naphthol-6-sulfonic acid, 80, 258
—, 1-nitroso-, iron deriv., 644, 645
2-Naphthol-7-sulfonic acid, 81, 632
2-Naphthol-8-sulfonic acid, 80
Naphtholsulfonic acids, amino-, 88
1-Naphthol-2,3,4,6-tetrasulfonic acid, 79
1-Naphthol-2,4,7-trisulfonic acid, 79
2-Naphthol-3,6,8-trisulfonic acid, 80
2-Naphtho-*o*-phenetidide, 3-hydroxy-, 190
14*H*-Naphtho[2,3-*a*]phenothiazine-8,13-dione. *See* Thiazine dyes, anthraquinone
Naphtho[2,3-*f*]quinazoline-7,12-dione, 422
—. *See Also* 1,2-Pyrimidinoanthraquinone
Naphtho[2,3-*g*]quinazoline-6,11-dione, 4-chloro-2-phenyl-, 510
Naphtho[2,3-*f*]quinoline-7,12-dione, 5,6-dihydroxy-, 430
—, 5,6,10-trihydroxy-, 430
Naphtho[2,3-*h*]quinoline-7,12-dione,5,6-dihydroxy-, leuco sulfuric acid ester, 430
1,4-Naphthoquinone, 433
—, color of, 666
—, reduction potential, 338
—, 2,3-dichloro-, 433
1,4-Naphthoquinone imine, 8-amino-5-hydroxy-, 434
Naphtho[2,3-*f*]quinoxaline-7,12-dione. *See* 1,2-Pyrazinoanthraquinone
Naphthostyril, 445
1,8-Naphthosultam, 84
8*H*-Naphtho[2,3-*c*]thiaxanthene-5,8,14-trione, 526
—, 4-amino-, 527

—, 11-chloro-, 528
—, 10,12-dichloro-, 528
Naphtho[2,1-*b*]thiophen-1(2*H*)-one, 567
—, 2-(phenylimino)-, 569
2-Naphtho-*o*-toluidide, 4'-chloro-3-hydroxy-, 191
—, 5'-chloro-3-hydroxy-, 192
—, 3-hydroxy-, 186, 634
2-Naphtho-*p*-toluidide, 3-hydroxy-, 192
Naphth[1,2]oxadiazole-4-sulfonic acid, 90
2-Naphtho-2,4-xylidide, 3-hydroxy-, 189
1-Naphthylamine, 82, 260
—, *N*-phenyl-, 82
—, 4-phenylazo-, 237
2-Naphthylamine, 82
—, *N*-phenyl-, 82, 238
Naphtol AS series 182, 183, 634, 635
—, azo pigments derived from, 635
Neocotone dyes, 224, 225, 547
Neutral-dyeing azo dyes for wool, 151
Nevile & Winther's acid, 690
Nickel chelate compounds, 258
Nickel complexes, 311
Nickel mordant dyes, 427
Nicotinic acid, 45
Nigrosines, 242
Nitration, of aromatic amines, 13
—, of aromatic sulfonic acids, 16
—, of benzene nucleus, 12
—, mechanism of, 12
m-Nitrobenzoyl J acid, 690
Nitrodiphenylamine dyes, 255
Nitro dyes, 254, 255, 256
Nitrosamine, 216
Nitroso dyes, 258
Novagen dyes, 218
Nucleophilic substitution, 2
Nylon dyes, 167, 248, 256, 417, 424

O

Oil-soluble dyes, azo, 174
Orbitals, molecular, 663, 668
Orientation effects in benzene intermediates, 3
Orientation of auxochromes, 671
1,3,4-Oxadiazole, 2,5-bis(1-amino-2-anthraquinonyl)-, 480
Oxadicarbocyanine, 10-chloro-3,3'-diethyl-, iodide, 253
Oxalic acid, 285

Oxanthrones, 373
Oxazine dyes, 259, 673
Oxidation, 42, 231, 232, 242, 243, 263, 264, 268, 270, 272, 275
—, of alkylaromatic compounds, 42
—, of anthracene, 344
—, of azo dyes, chromate, 160
—, by nitric acid, 45
—, of phthalocyanines, 582
—, of polycyclic compounds, 357
—, of sulfur dyes, 308, 310
—, in stilbene dyes, 119
Oxindole, 561
Oxy Koch's acid, 690

P

Paper, indicator, 115, 118
Pararosaniline, N,N'-diphenyl-N''-(sulfophenyl)-, inner salt, 653
—, N,N,N',N',N'',N''-hexamethyl-, cation from, 669
—, N,N',N''-triphenyl-, chloride, 653
Particles, phthalocyanine pigment, 587
PB reports, 692
Pentacene, absorption spectrum, 665
Peri acid, 690
Peri-chelation, effect on color, 684
Perylene, 3,9-dibenzoyl-, 454
3,9-Perylenequinone, 684
3,10-Perylenequinone, 683
3,4,9,10-Perylenetetracarboxylic dianhydride, 482
3,4,9,10-Perylenetetracarboxylic diimide, 481
—, N,N'-bis(p-methoxyphenyl)-, 482
—, N,N'-dimethyl-, 482
Pharmaceuticals, 231, 232
Pharmol dyes, 218
Phenanthrenequinone, 236
Phenazathionium bromide, 268
Phenazathionium chloride, amino derivs., 266
Phenazine, absorption spectrum, 667, 668
—, 3,7-diamino-, hydrochloride, 236
2-Phenazinol, 8-amino-, 328
—, 8-amino-7-methyl-, 328
—, 3,4-dimethyl-, 676
m-Phenetidine, N-(p-tolyl)-, 32
p-Phenetidine, 293
Phenetole, 31
—, β,β-dichloro-α,α-difluoro-, 27

—, o-nitro-, 33
—, p-nitro-, 33
—, $\alpha,\alpha,\beta,\beta$-tetrafluoro-, 27
—, β,β,β-trifluoro-, 27
—, β,β,β-trifluoro-p-nitro-, 26
Phenol, 37, 38, 44, 285, 313
—, p-amino-, 49, 50, 244, 317
—, 2-amino-4,6-dinitro-, 52
—, m-anilino-, 40
—, p-anilino-, 40, 319
—, p-(p-anilinoanilino)-, 323
—, 2-chloro-4,6-dinitro-, 16
—, 4-chloro-2,6-dinitro-, 16
—, 2-chloro-5-nitro-, 23
—, 4-chloro-3-trifluoromethyl-, 27
—, 2,6-dichloro-4-nitro-, 23
—, m-diethylamino-, 293, 295, 296, 297
—, 5-diethylamino-2-nitroso-, 260
—, m-dimethylamino-, 292, 294
—, p-(p-dimethylaminoanilino)-, 303, 324
—, dinitro-, 314
—, 2,4-dinitro-, 38
—, p-(2,4-dinitroanilino)-, 41, 303, 320
—, 4,4'-iminodi-, 323
—, p-(2-naphthylamino)-, 320
—, o-nitro-, 254
—, p-nitro-, 38, 314
—, p-nitroso-, 323
—, o-phenylazo-, metal deriv., 630
—, m-(p-toluidino)-, 40
—, 2,4,6-trinitro-, 315
1-Phenol-4-sulfonamide, 2-nitro-, 38
1-Phenol-2-sulfonic acid, 6-amino-4-nitro-, 247
1-Phenol-4-sulfonic acid, 2-amino-6-nitro-, 16
Phenothiazine, 266, 268, 316
Phenoxazine, 259
Phenoxazonium bromide, 259
m-Phenylenediamine, 233, 234
o-Phenylenediamine, 52
—, 4-chloro-, 476
—, 4-ethoxy-, 476
—, N-phenyl-, 236
p-Phenylenediamine, 50, 244, 266, 316
—, N-[p-(4-amino-6-methyl-m-phenetylazo)phenyl]-, 196
—, N-p-anisidino-, 197
—, 2-chloro-, 50
—, N,N-diethyl-, 240, 264

—, *N*,*N*-dimethyl-, 260, 264, 266
—, 2-methoxy-*N*⁴-phenyl-, 52, 197
—, *N*-(*p*-methoxyphenyl)-, 197
—, *N*-phenyl-, 48, 197, 244
Phenyl Gamma acid, 690
Phenyl J acid, 690
Phenyl Peri acid, 690
Phenylrosinduline, 237
Phosgenation, 119, 125
Phosphazo compounds, 183
Phosphomolybdate pigments, 640
Phosphotungstate pigments, 640
Phosphotungstomolybdate pigments, 640
Photographic sensitizers, 251
Photon, 662
Photorapide dyes, 222
1(2*H*)-Phthalazone, 579
Phthaleins, 299
Phthalic acid, 4-acylamino-5-sulfo-, 611
—, 4-(butylsulfamyl)-, 611
Phthalic anhydride, 43, 296, 316
Phthalidyl sulfate, 3-phenyl-, 340
Phthalimidine, 3-imino-, 579
Phthalocyanine, 590, 658
—, aluminum deriv., 581
—, anthraquinone derivs., 620
—, azo derivs., 618
—, beryllium deriv., 581
—, cobalt deriv., 581, 593, 621
—, —, reduction, 583
—, copper deriv., 581, 590, 630, 631, 658
—, formation in fiber, 622
—, iron deriv., 581, 592
—, lead deriv., 581
—, magnesium deriv., 581
—, manganese deriv., 581
—, metal derivs., color of, 686
—, —, table, 594
—, nickel deriv., 581, 591
—, nomenclature, 610
—, platinum deriv., 581
—, preparation, 584
—, structure, 580
—, tin deriv., 581, 589, 592
—, titanium deriv., 581
—, vanadium deriv., 581
—, zinc deriv., 581
—, alkoxy-, 599
—, alkyl-, 600
—, alkylmercapto-, 599
—, —, sulfonium salts, 616

—, aroxy-, 599
—, arylmercapto-, 599
—, chloro-, copper deriv., 597
—, (chloromethyl)-, isothiuronium salts, 618
—, —, quaternary salts, 617
—, dithiodi-, 622
—, hexadecahydro-, 602
—, (methylmercaptomethyl)-, sulfonium salts, 618
—, polychloro-, copper deriv., 598, 658
—, pyridyl-, quaternary salts, 616
—, tetraamino-, copper deriv., 618
—, tetrabenzoyl-, 599
—, tetrachloro-, copper deriv., 610
—, tetrakis(*p*-aminobenzamido)-, copper deriv., 619
—, tetrakis(*m*-aminobenzoyl)-, copper deriv., 619
—, tetrakis(*p*-aminobenzoyl)-, copper deriv., 619
—, tetrakis(*p*-aminophenoxy)-, copper deriv., 619
—, tetrakis(*p*-aminophenylmercapto)-, copper deriv., 619
—, tetrakis(*o*-aminophenylsulfonyl)-, copper deriv., 619
—, tetrakis(6-methyl-2-benzothiazolyl)-, 599
—, tetranitro-, copper deriv., 599
—, tetraphenyl-, 612
—, —, copper deriv., 600
—, tetrapyridyl-, copper deriv., 600, 618
—, thiocyano-, 622
Phthalocyanine sulfur dyes, 622
Phthalocyaninecarboxylic acid, 612
Phthalocyaninesulfonic acid, cobalt deriv., 548
—, copper deriv., 589, 659
—, quaternary ammonium salts, 612
—, chloro-, copper deriv., 611
Phthalocyaninetetracarboxylic acid, copper deriv., 612
—, tetraphenyl-, copper deriv., 613
Phthalocyaninetetrasulfonamide, *N*,*N*′, *N*″,*N*‴-tetrabutyl-, copper deriv., 611
Phthalocyaninetetrasulfonic acid, copper deriv., 609
—, tetrabenzamido-, copper deriv., 611
Phthalocyaninetetrasulfonyl chloride, copper deriv., 609, 621
—, tetraphenyl-, copper deriv., 621

Phthalocyaninethiol, 622
Phthalonitrile, 39
—, Δ¹-tetrahydro-, 603
Phthaloylacridone dyes, 487
Picolinic acid, 45
Pi electrons, 663, 664
Pigments, temporarily solubilized azoic, 224
Pipecolic acid, 219
Plastic materials, dyeing of, 167, 174
Polarization, 663
—, axis of, 669
Polyacenes, 665
Polyenes, 664
Polyester textile dyes, azo, 167
p-Polyphenyls, 665
Polysulfide bake, 306
Pre-metallized azo dyes, 161
Printing compositions, azoic, 208
Printing-ink pigments, 230, 271, 276
Proflavine, 233
Propiolophenone, 380, 448
Propionamide, *N*,*N*′-1,4-anthraquinonylenebis-, 419
3-Pseudoindolone, 2,5-dichloro-7-methoxy-4-methyl-, 571
—, 2,5,7-trichloro-, 570
Pseudoindoxyl, 558, 561
—, 5-chloro-2-(4-chloro-1-oxo-2-naphthylidene)-7-methoxy-4-methyl-, 545
—, 5,7-dibromo-2-(4-chloro-1-oxo-2-anthrylidene)-, 574
—, 5,7-dibromo-2-(1-oxo-2-anthrylidene)-, 542
—, 2-(10-methyl-4-oxo-11*H*-benzo[*a*]carbazol-3-ylidene)-, 574
—, 2-(2-oxo-1-acenaphthenylidene)-, 573
—, 2-(1-oxo-2-naphthylidene)-, 573
—, 2-(phenylimino)-, 556, 570, 574
Pseudoisocyanine, 669
Purpurin, 367, 369
Pyran dyes, 532
8,16-Pyranthrenedione, 450
—, dibromo-, 452
Pyrazine, absorption spectrum, 667
1,2-Pyrazinoanthraquinone. *See Also*
Naphtho[2,3-*f*]quinoxaline-7,12-dione
—, dihydroxy-, 511
—, hydroxy(*m*-toluidino)-, 512

Pyrazoledihydroazine dye, 469
2-Pyrazoline-3-carboxamide, 5-oxo-1-phenyl-, 55
2-Pyrazoline-3-carboxylic acid, 1-(2-chloro-4-sulfophenyl)-5-oxo-, 56
—, 1-(2,5-dichloro-4-sulfophenyl)-5-oxo-, 56
—, 5-oxo-1-phenyl-, 56
—, —, ethyl ester, 636
—, 5-oxo-1-(*p*-sulfophenyl)-, 56
—, 5-oxo-1-(*p*-sulfophenyl)-4-(*p*-sulfophenylazo)-, 647
—, 5-oxo-1-(4-sulfo-*o*-tolyl)-, 56
—, 5-oxo-1-(2,3,6-trichloro-5-sulfophenyl)-, 56
5-Pyrazolone, azo pigments derived from, 636
—, 1-(3-carboxy-2-hydroxy-5-sulfophenyl)-3-methyl-, 56
—, 1-(*m*-carboxyphenyl)-3-(*p*-nitrophenyl)-, 56
—, 1-(6-chloro-4-sulfo-*o*-tolyl)-3-methyl-, 56
—, 3-methyl-1-(*p*-nitrophenyl)-, 56
—, 3-methyl-1-(3-nitro-5-sulfo-*o*-tolyl)-, 56
—, 3-methyl-1-phenyl-, 56, 636
—, 3-methyl-1-*p*-tolyl-, 56, 637
—, 1-*p*-tolyl-, 3-substituted, 54
Pyrazoles, 54
Pyrene, 3-amino-, 499
—, 1,6-dibenzoyl-, 451
Pyreneacridone dyes, 499
1,6-Pyrenedione, 442
—, 2,7-dianilino-4,9-dichloro-, 541
—, 5,10-dianilino-3,8-dichloro-, 443
1,8-Pyrenedione, 442
Pyridine, 249
—, absorption spectrum, 667
Pyrimidine, absorption spectrum, 667
1,2-Pyrimidinoanthraquinone, 422
—. *See Also* Naphtho[2,3-*f*]quinazoline-7,12-dione
Pyrocatechol, 37
Pyrogallol, 300
Pyromellitic acid, 44
Pyronines, 292
Pyrrolidine, phthalocyaninesulfonyl deriv., 612
Pyrromethene compounds, spectra, 674

Q

Quanta, light, 662
Quantum mechanics, 663
Quinaldine, 54, 252, 261
—, 2-iodo-, 252
Quinalizarin, 367, 428
Quinizarin, 340, 349, 367, 419
—, reactions, 368, 398
—, 2-anilino-, 407
—, 5,8-bis(2-hydroxyethylamino)-, 362
—, 2-bromo-, 347
—, 2,3-dialkyl-, 376
—, 4,8-dianilino-, 375
—, 2,3-dihydro-, 398
—, 2-phenoxy-, 370
2,3-Quinizarindicarbonitrile, 368
p-Quinodimethan, 665
Quinoline, 251
—, absorption spectrum, 667
—, derivatives, 53
—, 4-methyl-, 251
2,4-Quinolinediol, 53
—, 3-(p-halophenylazo)-, metal deriv., 646
Quinoline dyes, 261
2(1H)-Quinolone, 4-hydroxy-1-methyl-, 53
Quinone, oxime, 644
o-Quinone, color of, 680
p-Quinone, 46
—, color of, 666, 680
—, redox cycle, 432
—, reduction potential, 338
—, 2,5-bis(p-chloroanilino)-, 432, 546
—, 2,5-dianilino-, 432
—, 2,5-dianilino-3,6-dichloro-, 288
—, 2,5-dichloro-3,6-bis(2-naphthyla-
mino)-, 288
Quinone diazides, 222
p-Quinone imine, N-3-carbazolyl-, 327
—, N-chloro-, 322
—, N-o-tolyl-, 323
p-Quinone imine dyes, 263
p-Quinone imines, 319
Quinones, polycyclic, 682
Quinonoid dyes, color of, 680
Quinophthalone, derivs., 654
—, 3'-hydroxy-, 262

R

R acid, 690
Rapidazole dyes, 221, 222
Rapid Fast dyes, 208, 216
Rapidogen dyes, 218, 220
Rayon dyeing, 134
Reduction, of anthraquinone, 338
—, of azo dyes, 135
—, of benzene intermediates, 46
—, of phthalocyanines, 583
—, of sulfur dyes, 309
—, in stilbene dyes, 119
Reduction potentials, of quinones, 338
References, general, 700
—, selected, 693
Resorcinol, 37, 299
—, 2,4-dinitro-, 259
RG acid, 690
Rhodoles, 299
Rhoduline acid, 690
Ring-closure, of dianthrimides to carba-
zoles, 464
Rivanol, 232
Rosamines, 294
RR acid, 690
Rubber dyeing, 237

S

S acid, 690
Saccharein dyes, 293
Saccharin, 293
Safranines, 238
Salicylaldehyde, 247
Salicylamide, N-1-anthraquinonyl-, 363,
439, 637
Salicylic acid, 35
—, 5-amino-, 52
—, 5-(p-aminobenzamido)-, 52
—, 3-amino-5-sulfo-, 50
—, 5-[3-(4-amino-3-sulfo-1-anthraquin-
onylamino)-4-methoxybenzylsul-
fonyl]-, 415
—, 5-(chlorosulfonyl)-, 11, 418
—, 3,3'-(4,8-dihydroxy-1,5-anthraquin-
onylenediimino)bis[5-sulfo-, 408
—, 3-hydrazino-5-sulfo-, 55
—, 3-(3-methyl-5-oxo-2-pyrazolin-1-yl)-
5-sulfo-, 56
—, 6-nitro-4-sulfo-, 17
—, 5-sulfo-, 8

Salt milling, phthalocyanine pigments, 587
Sandmeyer reaction, 23
Sarcosine, 219, 220
Schaeffer's acid, 690
Schiemann reaction, 30
Scholl method, 379
Sensitizers, photographic, 251
Shoe polish, dyes for, 175, 177
Silver salt, 690
Smith and Mair stain, 261
Solacet dyes, 424
Soledon dyes, 535, 559
Solvat dyes, 535
Solvents, effect on color, 676
Spectra, prediction of, 672
Spirit-ink dyeing, 177
Spirit-soluble dyes, azo, 177
—, phthalocyanine, 612
Spirit-varnish dyes, 242
3,3'-Spirobi[3H-naphtho(2,1-b)pyran], 677
Spiropyran compounds, 677
SS acid, 690
Stable diazonium salts, table, 208, 209
Stains, bacteriological, 237
—, biological, 238, 261, 266, 274
—, wood, 177, 243
Stilbene, derivs., spectra, 674
2,2'-Stilbenedisulfonic acid, 4-amino-4'-nitro-, 52
Styrene, derivs., spectra, 674
Substantivity of azoic coupling components, 183
Substitution, electrophilic, 1
—, free-radical, 2
—, nucleophilic, 2
Succinamide, N,N'-di-1-anthraquinonyl-, 437
Succineins, 294
Succinic anhydride, 294
Sulfamic acid, m-tolyl-, 10
Sulfanilamide, N^4-phenyl-3-nitro-, 256
Sulfanilic acid, 9
—, N-1-anthraquinonyl-, 396
—, 2,5-dichloro-, 6
—, N,N-dimethyl-, 41
—, N-[p-(p-hydroxyanilino)phenyl]-, 324
—, 2-nitro-, 11
Sulfide reduction, 51

Sulfo group, removal of, 4, 68, 70, 355, 376
—, replacement of, 368
Sulfonation, of triphenylmethane dyes, 282
—, of amines, 5
—, of anthraquinone compounds, 393, 394
—, of benzene intermediates, 3
—, by halogen replacement, 393
—, mechanism of, 5
—, of naphthalene, 67, 69
—, of phthalocyanine derivs., 609, 610
—, of sulfur dyes, 311
Sulfone, bis(p-nitrophenyl), 46
—, ethyl α,α,α-trifluoro-2-nitro-p-tolyl, 28
Sulfonic acids, aromatic, nitration of, 16
Sulfur bake, 305
Sulfur chloride, 563
Suprafix dyes, 571

T

Tannic acid, 641
Tartar emetic, 641
Taurine, N-methyl-, 219, 220
Terephthalic acid, 43, 45
Tetraanthrimide, 462
Tetraazaporphin, 602
—, derivs., 601
—, octaphenyl-, 602
Textile-printing dyes, 244
4-Thia-4H-benzo[a]naphtho[3,2,1,8-$ghij$]perylene-7,15-dione, 525
Thiadiazine dyes, anthraquinone. *See Also* 3H,7H-Anthra[1,9-cd][1,2,6]thiadiazine
3(2H)-Thianaphthenone, 562
—. *See Also* Thioindoxyl
—, 6-chloro-4-methyl-, 570
—, 2,2-dibromo-, 569, 575
—, 5,7-dichloro-, 571
—, 5,7-dichloro-4,6-dimethyl-2-(2-oxo-1-anthrylidene)-, 575
—, 5,6-dichloro-7-methoxy-, 569
—, 6,7-dichloro-5-methoxy-, 569
—, 2-(p-dimethylaminophenylimino)-, 575
—, 2-(2-oxo-1-acenaphthenylidene)-, 573
—, 5,6,7-trichloro-, 570
Thianthrene, 304

Thiatricarbocyanine, 3,3'-diethyl-, iodide, 253
Thiazine dyes, 266, 530
Thiazole dyes, 269, 303
Thiazone. *See* 3*H*-Isophenothiazin-3-one
Thioindigo, 562, 638
—, *cis* and *trans* forms, 554
—, 4',5'-benzo-6,7-dichloro-5-meth-
oxy-, 568
—, 6-chloro-6'-methoxy-4-methyl-, 546
—, 4,5:4',5'-dibenzo-, 567, 572
—, 6,6'-dichloro-, 563
—, 7,7'-dichloro-, 638
—, 5,5'-dichloro-7,7'-dimethyl-, 541,564,
638
—, 6,6'-dichloro-4,4'-dimethyl-, 541,564,
638
—, 5,5'-dichloro-4,4',7,7'-tetramethyl-,
565, 570
—, 6,6'-diethoxy-, 541, 566
—, 4,4',7,7'-tetrachloro-, 638
—, 5,6',7-trichloro-4,4'-dimethyl-, 543
Thioindoxyl, 562, 690
—. *See Also* 3(2*H*)-Thianaphthenone
Thionation, solvent, 307
Thiophene, tetrabromo-, 533
Thiosulfonic acids, organic, 267
Tobias acid, 690
o-Tolidine, 48, 51
o-Toluamide, 4-chloro-6-mercapto-, 567
Toluene, bromo-, rearrangement, 342
—, *m*-chloro-, 565
—, *o*(or *p*)-chloro-, 22
—, *o*(or *m* or *p*)-chloro-α,α,α-trifluoro-,
27
—, 2-chloro-4-nitro-, 22
—, 2-chloro-6-nitro-, 22
—, 4-chloro-2-nitro-, 22
—, 4-chloro-2(or 3)-nitro-, 19
—, 3-chloro-α,α,α-trifluoro-4-nitro-, 29
—, 4-chloro-α,α,α-trifluoro-3-nitro-, 29
—, 2,4-dichloro-, 22
—, 3,4-dichloro-, 22
—, 2,4-dinitro-, 13
—, *p*-nitro-, 278
—, α,α,α,2,4-pentachloro-, 22
—, perfluoro-, 30
—, *o*(or *m* or *p*),α,α,α-tetrachloro-, 23
—, α,α,α-trifluoro-*p*-(pentafluoroethyl)-, 25

Toluene-2,4-diamine, 232, 237, 264, 316,
317
—, N^4-phenyl-, 234
Toluene-3,4-disulfonic acid, 6-hydra-
zino-, 55
p-Toluenesulfonamide, 3-amino-N,N-di-
methyl-, 220
—, N-(4-amino-3-methoxy-1-anthra-
quinonyl)-, 370
Toluenesulfonic acid, *ar*-amino-α,α,α-
trifluoro-, 28
m-Toluenesulfonic acid, 4-amino-, 9
—, 6-amino-, 9, 650
—, 2-amino-5-chloro-, 10
—, 4-amino-5-chloro-, 6
—, 6-amino-4-chloro-, 10, 650
—, 6-(1-anthraquinonylamino)-, 396
—, 5-chloro-4-hydrazino-, 55
—, 5-chloro-4-(3-methyl-5-oxo-2-pyra-
zolin-1-yl)-, 56
—, α-(*N*-ethylanilino)-, 275
o-Toluenesulfonic acid, 4-amino-, 9, 649
—, 5-amino-, 50
—, 5-(4-hydroxy-1-anthraquinonyla-
mino)-, 397, 657
p-Toluenesulfonic acid, 2-amino-5-
chloro-, 649, 650
—, 3-amino-5-nitro-, 52
—, 5-chloro-2-nitro-, 16
—, 3-(3-methyl-5-oxo-2-pyrazolin-1-yl)-
5-nitro-, 56
—, 2-sulfamino-, 10
m-Toluenesulfonyl chloride, 5-chloro-,
565
p-Toluenesulfonyl chloride, 11
o-Toluic acid, α-*p*-biphenylyl-, 342
—, 6-(4-chlorosalicyloyl)-, 343
—, α-phenyl-, 342
p-Toluic acid, 2-amino-α,α,α-trifluoro-,
29
—, 3-nitro-, 18
—, α,α,α-trifluoro-2-nitro-, 29
m-Toluidine, 50
—, 6-chloro-α,α,α-trifluoro-, 29
—, 6-ethylsulfonyl-α,α,α-trifluoro-, 29,
200
o-Toluidine, 41, 239, 316
—, 3-chloro-, 50, 206
—, 4-chloro-, 205, 564
—, 5-chloro-, 204
—, 4-chloro-α,α,α-trifluoro-, 206

o-Toluidine—cont'd
—, *N*,*N*-diethyl-, 41
—, *N*,*N*-dimethyl-, 41
—, *N*-ethyl-, 41
—, *N*,*N*'-methylenebis[4-nitro-, 632
—, 4-nitro-, 205
—, 5-nitro-, 205
—, 4-(*o*-tolylazo)-, 199
—, α,α,α-trifluoro-4,6-dinitro-, 28
—, α,α,α-trifluoro-4-nitro-, 28
—, α,α,α-trifluoro-6-nitro-, 28
p-Toluidine, 231, 269
—, *N*-ethyl-3-nitro-, 14
—, 2-nitro-, 14, 202, 633, 634
—, α,α,α-trifluoro-2-nitro-, 28
p-Tolunitrile, α,α,α-trifluoro-2-nitro-, 29
p-Toluquinone, 257
m-Toluyl chloride, α,α,α-trichloro-, 35
m-Toluyl fluoride, α,α,α-trifluoro-, 25
Toners, definition, 626
Top chrome dyeing method, 154
Transfer, of pigments, 626
Trianthrimides, 462
Triarylmethane dyes, 272
Triazenes, 217
—, hydrolysis of, 219
—, preparation of, 221
s-Triazine, 2-anilino-4,6-bis(1-anthraquinonylamino)-, 522
s-Triazine dyes, anthraquinone, 522
v-Triazine dyes, anthraquinone, 530
1,2,4-Triazole-3-carboxylic acid, 5-amino-, 57
Trichromatic color, blue, 652, 659
Trichromatic colors, 627
Trimellitic acid, derivs., 614, 615
—, 5-hydroxy-, 298
—, 5-sulfo-, 46
Triphenodioxazine dyes, 288
Triphenylmethane dyes, 673, 677
Turkey Red dyes, 655
Turkey Red oil, 655
Tyrer process, 4

U

Ullmann reaction, 380, 391
Urea J acid, 690
Ureasulfonic acid, 3-guanyl-, 219

V

Vat dyes, leuco sulfuric acid esters, 534
—, solubilized, 534
Vat soluble dyes, 535
Veratraldehyde, 31
Violanthrone. *See* Dibenzanthrone
Violet acid, 690

W

Water-tracer dyes, 300
Wax dyeing, 174, 242, 243
Wood dyeing, 177, 243
Wool, structure, 144
Wool dyes, azo, U. S. production, 165
—, natural, 143
Writing inks, dyes for, 274, 278

X

Xanthene, 292
Xanthene dyes, 291, 673
Xanthic acid, ethyl-, 565
Xenylamine, 290
Xylene, desulfonation of, 4
m-Xylene, $\alpha,\alpha,\alpha,\alpha',\alpha',\alpha'$-hexafluoro-, 25
—, $\alpha,\alpha,\alpha,\alpha',\alpha',\alpha'$-hexafluoro-5-nitro-, 29
—, 4-nitro-, 18
p-Xylene, α-chloro-, 23
—, 2-chloro-, 22
—, α,α'-dichloro-, 23
3,5-Xylenesulfonic acid, 2-amino-, 9
3,5-Xylidine, $\alpha,\alpha,\alpha,\alpha',\alpha',\alpha'$-hexafluoro-, 29, 200

Z

Zapon dyes, 177
Zinc reduction, 50